The Human Pulmonary Circulation

ITS FORM AND FUNCTION IN HEALTH AND DISEASE

Peter Harris
M.D., Ph.D., F.R.C.P.
Simon Marks Professor of Cardiology, Cardiothoracic Institute, University of London
Physician, National Heart Hospital

Donald Heath
M.D., Ph.D., F.R.C.P., F.R.C.Path.
George Holt Professor of Pathology, University of Liverpool

Foreword by
Sir Melville Arnott
T.D., LL.D., D.Sc., M.D., F.R.C.P., F.R.C.P.E., F.R.C.P.(C), F.A.C.P., F.R.C.Path., F.R.S.E.
Emeritus Professor of Medicine, University of Birmingham

SECOND EDITION

CHURCHILL LIVINGSTONE
EDINBURGH LONDON AND NEW YORK 1977

LQ MM

CHURCHILL LIVINGSTONE
Medical Division of Longman Group Limited

Distributed in the United States of America by Longman Inc., 19 West 44th Street, New York, N.Y. 10036 and by associated companies, branches and representatives throughout the world.

First Edition 1962
Second Edition 1977

ISBN 0 443 01177 X

British Library Cataloguing in Publication Data

Harris, Peter, b.1923 (May)
The human pulmonary circulation.—2nd ed.
1. Pulmonary circulation
I. Title II. Heath, Donald
612′.2 QP107 77-30003

Printed in Great Britain by T. & A. Constable, Edinburgh

Foreword

I deeply appreciate the honour of being asked once again to introduce this excellent monograph which presents a synoptic view of the pulmonary circulation. The approach to a study of man and his organs has for long been dominated, one might say bedevilled, by single-discipline outlooks, such as the functional or the clinical. In this second edition, even more than the first, the subject is treated comprehensively taking full account of how the pulmonary vasculature is fashioned, what are its physical properties, how it works and how disease by its alteration of these properties modifies function. Much new material has been added particularly in the field of ultrastructure. Electron microscopy in conjunction with histochemistry has revealed that the lung is an elaborate organ discharging many functions additional to gas exchange, some of which show that it plays in the endocrine orchestra. There is an excellent account of the autoregulating mechanism which ensures optimum combinations of ventilatory-perfusion values. The authors' several research expeditions to the high Andes have provided much new data on the effects of chronic hypoxia on man and animals.

Full use is made of the principles of classical physics and applied mathematics which are as essential to the modern physician as they are to the engineer, indeed the whole monograph, quite apart from its practical value in helping the clinician to understand his daily problems, illustrates the fundamental unity of the physical and biological sciences. This is a unity which recognises that biological systems consist of aggregates of complex physical systems.

The style is lucid and very critical of the quality of evidence. The monograph, on almost every page, presents problems which will, I feel sure, start many investigators on happy and fruitful studies.

I would emphasise that the outlook of the authors derives from a way of life which consists of a mixture in approximately equal proportions of research and practice, the one as a physician, the other as a pathologist. This I believe to be the proper basis for the practice of clinical science.

I count among the happiest years of my life those in which the authors were my colleagues in Birmingham. I am deeply indebted to them for their intellectual stimulus and warm friendship.

Birmingham,
1977

W. Melville Arnott

Preface to the Second Edition

Over a decade has passed since the publication of the first edition of this book and, during that time, knowledge of the physiology and pathology of the pulmonary circulation has expanded considerably. In addition to the progressive accumulation of knowledge, totally new concepts have arisen. For instance, the production of a raised pulmonary arterial pressure in experimental animals by feeding them on certain plant alkaloids introduced the concept of dietary pulmonary hypertension. A very short time elapsed before this was thought to be of clinical and epidemiological significance, so that an epidemic of unexplained pulmonary hypertension which began in Western Europe in 1968 was suspected to be due to the ingestion of certain anorexigens. This in turn led to the recognition of a need for the precise clinical and pathological diagnosis of diseases causing clinically unexplained pulmonary hypertension, including recurrent pulmonary thrombo-embolism and the comparatively recently identified pulmonary veno-occlusive disease.

Over the past ten years we have become increasingly aware of the importance and relevance of studies of the pulmonary circulation at high altitude to the effects of the respiratory gases on the lesser circulation and on chemoreceptors. This interest has taken us on four expeditions to the Andes and we wish to take this opportunity of expressing our appreciation for the great kindness and cooperation that we have received from our Peruvian colleagues. Prominent among these have been Professor J. Arias-Stella, Dr. R. Guerra-Garcia, Professor A. Hurtado, Dr. H. Krüger, Professor C. Monge, Dr. D. Peñaloza and Dr. F. Sime. Out of such high altitude studies has arisen the histological distinction of hypoxic pulmonary hypertension affecting patients with pulmonary disease at low altitude. The sections dealing with the effects of hypoxia and of pulmonary disease have, therefore, been much expanded.

In addition to new concepts the subject has been advanced by new techniques. Tissue morphometry has led to a greater understanding of the alterations in the lung parenchyma and capillary bed in emphysema and has aided the distinction between various anatomical types of emphysema. Much also has been learned from the application of new physiological techniques in such patients. There remains, however, a gulf between the anatomical and physiological data which we have attempted to bridge.

New techniques, using radioactive tracers, have shed much light on the problems of the regional distribution of the flow of blood and gas in the lungs. They have been associated with new ideas concerning the mechanical factors which have a local influence on perfusion and ventilation. Such advances have not been entirely academic and techniques of lung scanning have had a wide application in the detection of pulmonary embolisation.

To cover all these new developments and ideas we have had to increase the size of the book and also to depart from the principle of restricting ourselves to data obtained from man. The understanding of the human pulmonary circulation has, however, remained our primary objective.

This book is concerned with the white bones of fact and theory. The names of the many scientists on whose work it is based are seldom more than references. It is a pity that it has to be so. In our writing and our study we have been continually reminded of the rich variety of character of the many workers whom we have been privileged to come to know in so many different countries and situations throughout the world. We are glad to take this opportunity of paying tribute to those many personal qualities which make science a part of human life.

We are grateful for the many happy hours of study and discussion with senior colleagues and would particularly mention Professor André Cournand, Professor and Mrs. C. A. Wagenvoort and Professor D. B. Brewer. We also wish to acknowledge our gratitude to younger co-workers for the stimulating challenge of undertaking with them many investigations on the physiology and pathology of the pulmonary circulation. Here we should like to thank especially Dr. J. M. Kay, Dr. Paul Smith, Dr. P. S. Hasleton and Dr. Peter Hicken. We are indebted to Dr. Jane Somerville and Dr. W. Whitaker for their advice and criticism on clinical aspects.

For the considerable secretarial help we are most grateful to Mrs. Mollie White, Miss Susan Segar, Mrs. Lynn Briscoe and Mrs. Jennifer Lambert. Finally we wish to thank David Williams for his great help in producing the new plates from light and electron microscopy.

London,
Liverpool, 1977

P.H.
D.H.

Acknowledgements

The following have kindly provided us with a number of illustrations and we wish to thank them:

Dr. William A. Briscoe for Table 36.2.

Professor Barros Coelho for Figs. 15.2, 15.3, 15.4.

Dr. Gordon Cumming and Advisory Group for Aerospace Research and Development for Table 9.1.

Dr. R. F. Fletcher for Fig. 29.8.

Dr. Harry W. Fritts Jnr. for Fig. 5.14.

Dr. Ivor Gabe for Fig. 6.8.

Dr. Kathleen Hall for Fig. 3.10.

Professor H. Hecht for Fig. 32.9.

Dr. Michael Kay for Figs. 12.1, 12.2, 12.3, 22.1.

Dr. William R. Milnor for Figs. 10.4, 10.5.

Dr. Navin C. Nanda for Fig. 4.11.

Dr. Jane Somerville for Figs. 21.1, 21.11, 21.12, 28.13, 35.7, 39.1, 39.8, 39.9.

Professor Margaret Turner-Warwick for Figs. 39.2, 39.3, 39.4, 39.5.

Professor C. A. Wagenvoort for Fig. 21.2.

Dr. William Whitaker for Figs. 2.5, 2.6, 21.3, 21.4, 21.6, 21.8.

We are indebted to the editors of the following journals for permission to reproduce the illustrations listed below which were previously published by them:

American Heart Journal, Figs. 2.2, 2.3, 15.1.

British Heart Journal, Figs. 4.3, 4.5, 4.6, 4.7, 4.8, 4.9, 15.8, 18.2, 18.3, 18.4, 18.5, 18.6, 18.7, 18.8, 18.9, 18.10, 32.13, 32.14.

British Journal of Diseases of the Chest, Figs. 31.3, 31.4.

Cardiovascular Research, Figs. 22.9, 23.5, 27.4, 32.3, 32.4, 32.6, 32.7, 32.8, 34.8, 34.9.

Circulation, Figs. 6.8, 28.11, 28.12.

Circulation Research, Figs. 10.5, 26.1.

Experientia, Fig. 27.14.

Journal of Pathology, Figs. 27.5, 27.6, 27.8, 27.12, 29.1, 29.2, 29.3, 29.4, 29.5, 29.6, 29.7, 33.3, 33.6, 33.7, 33.9, 33.10, 33.11, 33.14, 33.16, 33.17, 33.18.

Quarterly Journal of Medicine, Fig. 28.14.

Thorax, Figs. 24.6, 24.7, 27.9, 27.19, 31.6, 31.7, 31.8, 39.6, 39.7.

We acknowledge the permission of the following publishers to reproduce the figures indicated.

Academic Press Inc. London, Fig. 10.4.
Charles C. Thomas, Springfield, Illinois, Figs. 22.6, 27.1, 33.1, 33.2, 33.4, 33.5.
Longmans, Green and Co. Ltd., Fig. 2.1.

Contents

Symbols

We have, in general, followed the symbols recommended by the Royal Society of Medicine.[1] Some exception has, however, been made with regard to S.I. units. At a time when the scientific community is turning towards the new units, the medical community clings to the millimetre of mercury for the measurement of pressure. Since our purpose is to communicate, we have chosen to retain the millimetre of mercury throughout the book, both for blood pressure and for the partial pressure of gases. To convert millimetres of mercury to kilopascals, one multiplies by 0·133.

We have also retained the units of dyn. s. cm^{-5} for vascular resistance. To convert dyn. s. cm^{-5} to the appropriate S.I. units of MN. s. m^{-5} one divides by ten.

Except when otherwise stated, the physiological symbols have followed the system laid down by Pappenheimer *et al.*[2] and more recently confirmed by Bartels *et al.*[3] This system consists of a series of primary symbols, denoting general physical quantities such as volume, pressure, or concentration, which may be modified by one or more secondary symbols denoting location, molecular species or special conditions.

The primary symbols consist of large capital letters. Examples are:

Blood
Q = volume
C = concentration
S = % saturation of haemoglobin with oxygen

Gas
V = volume
F = fractional concentration
P = pressure

The secondary symbols are placed immediately following the primary ones. They consist of small capital letters for localization in the gas phase (e.g. P_A = pressure in alveolar gas) and small lower case letters for localization in the blood phase (e.g. Pa = pressure in arterial blood). Examples of such secondary symbols are:

Blood
a = systemic arterial blood
v = venous blood
c = capillary blood
c′ = end-capillary blood

Gas
I = inspired gas
E = expired gas
A = alveolar gas
D = dead-space gas
B = barometric

Other secondary symbols denote molecular species and consist of the conventional chemical symbol (e.g. O_2 or CO_2) printed in small capital letters. When such a symbol qualifies a primary symbol alone, if follows immediately after the primary one (e.g. P_{CO_2} = pressure of carbon dioxide). When the specification of both localization and molecular species is required, the primary symbol is followed by the localizing letter which is, in turn, followed by the chemical symbol. In this case the chemical symbol is written as a subscript (e.g. Pa_{O_2} = pressure of oxygen in arterial blood).

A dot placed above a letter represents a time derivative (e.g. $\dot{Q}$ = volume flow of blood per unit time) while a dash denotes a mean value (e.g. $\bar{v}$ = mixed venous blood).

Measurements of gas volumes have to be made under specified conditions:

STPD = O°C, 760 mmHg, dry
BTPS = body temperature and pressure, saturated with water vapour

References

1. *Units, Symbols and Abbreviations* (1972). The Royal Society of Medicine, London.
2. Standardization of definitions and symbols in respiratory physiology (1950). *Fed. Proc.*, **9**, 602.
3. Glossary on respiration and gas exchange (1973). *J. appl. Physiol.*, **34**, 549.

1. The Anatomy of the Large Pulmonary Blood Vessels

The pulmonary circulation extends from the pulmonary valve to the orifices of the pulmonary veins in the wall of the left atrium. It includes the pulmonary trunk, the right and left main pulmonary arteries and their lobar branches, the small pulmonary blood vessels (which are considered in detail in the next chapter) and the large pulmonary veins. In this chapter we shall be concerned with the anatomy and radiographic features of the major vessels of the pulmonary circulation.

Pulmonary Trunk

The pulmonary trunk[1] arises from the summit of the infundibulum of the right ventricle through the orifice of the pulmonary valve. The orifice is circular, with a diameter of about 3 cm, and is situated close to the ventricular septum, above and to the left of the tricuspid-valve orifice. The pulmonary trunk is about 5 cm long and 3 cm in diameter. It passes upwards and backwards to be at first in front of, and then to the left of, the ascending aorta. Within the concavity of the aortic arch it divides into the right and left main pulmonary arteries. It lies entirely within the pericardium where it is enclosed in a common tube of visceral pericardium with the ascending aorta. The fibrous layer of the pericardium is gradually lost on the adventitia of the two pulmonary arteries.

Angiocardiography demonstrates its slightly upward but predominantly backward course to a point midway between sternum and spine at the level of the lower part of the sixth thoracic vertebra where it bifurcates (Fig. 1.1).[2] In an anteroposterior view the pulmonary trunk is seen to overlap the left border of the spine (Fig. 1.2). The position of the pulmonary valve and the origin of the pulmonary trunk can be detected by the presence of two dilatations which represent two of the three sinuses situated immediately above the pulmonary valve cusps (Figs 1.1 and 1.2). The second curve of the cardiovascular silhouette on the left side is formed solely by the pulmonary trunk, although occasionally the shadow of the left main pulmonary artery running in a much more posterior position is included in the picture. In both oblique views the pulmonary trunk appears foreshortened.

The Vascular Supply to the Pulmonary Trunk

In large blood vessels like the aorta and the pulmonary trunk the thickness of the media exceeds the distance across which oxygen can diffuse at a sufficient rate from the lumen. In both these vessels vasa vasorum penetrate from the adventitia to supply oxygen for the smooth-muscle cells of the media. The vasa vasorum to the descending thoracic aorta originate from the bases of lateral arterial branches, or from small ostia in the intima.[3] However, the ascending aorta and the pulmonary trunk possess neither lateral branches nor intimal ostia. Parke[3], using a dye-injection method, has shown that the vasa vasorum supplying these vessels have multiple origins. The ascending aorta receives most of its blood from the right coronary artery while the pulmonary trunk gets most of its supply from the left coronary artery. In addition the vasa vasorum to the great vessels arise from the bronchial arteries and from the pericardioaortic artery which originates from the base of the left subclavian artery and passes from the aorta to the pulmonary trunk across the ligamentum arteriosum. A study in rabbits showed that there are also numerous,

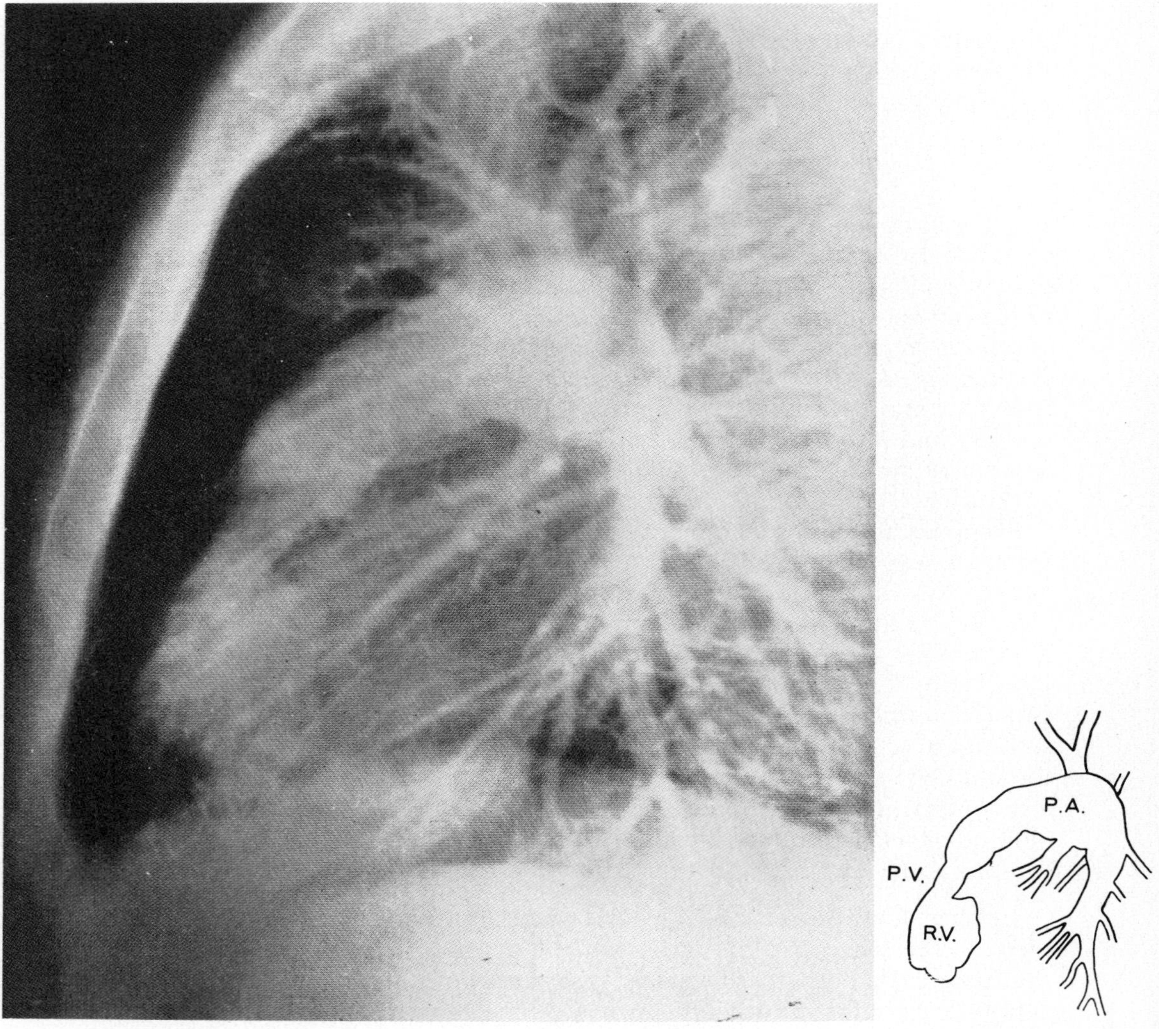

Fig. 1.1 Normal angiocardiogram (lateral view) showing the upward and backward course of the pulmonary artery (PA). The contrast medium can be seen in the right ventricle (RV) and the position of the pulmonary valve (PV) (and the origin of the pulmonary trunk) is indicated by two dilatations which represent two of the three sinuses situated immediately above the pulmonary valve cusps. The lobar and segmental branches to the lungs are demonstrated.

small supplying vessels from the trachea, bronchi and connective tissues of the mediastinum.[4] All these vessels anastomose freely to form a vascular plexus within the adventitia of the aorta and pulmonary trunk, and numerous small branches from this plexus penetrate the media.

Until recently, little was known about the distribution of vasa vasorum within

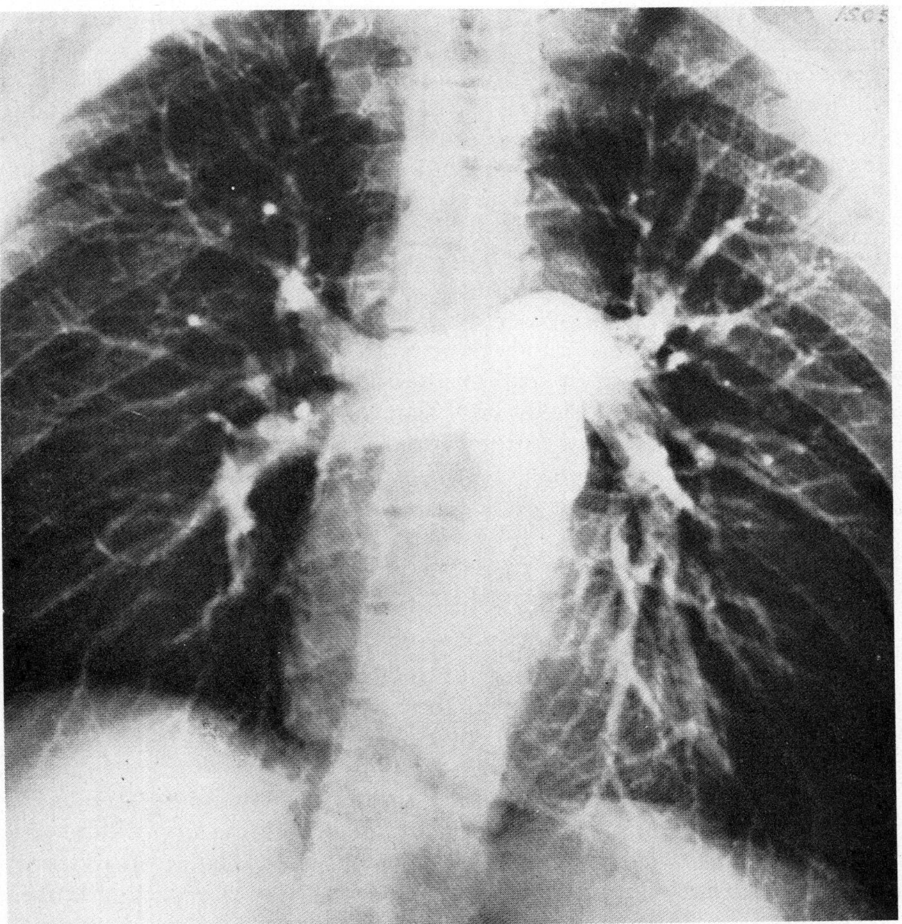

Fig. 1.2 Normal angiocardiogram (anteroposterior view). Some contrast medium is still seen in the right ventricle but most has passed through the pulmonary valve, the position of which is indicated by the dilatations described in Figure 1.1, into the pulmonary trunk, which overlaps the left border of the spine. The bifurcation of the pulmonary trunk into the right and left main pulmonary arteries is seen. The larger and lower branch of the right main artery is seen passing to the right middle and lower lobes. The smaller upper branch which accompanies the eparterial bronchus to the right upper lobe is also seen. The left main pulmonary artery appears foreshortened. The delicate pattern of the branches to the lung parenchyma is visible.

the media of the great vessels. Wolinsky and Glagov[5] studied the vasa vasorum in the aortic media of many species and found that there is a cylindrical zone adjacent to the intima containing no vasa, which they called the 'avascular zone'. This region requires no vascularity since it obtains its oxygen by diffusion from the lumen. The thickness of the avascular zone is roughly constant regardless of species, but is more precisely determined by the number of rings of smooth muscle or 'medial lamellar units'.[6] The avascular zone of the aorta has a constant thickness of 29 medial lamellar units regardless of age or species.[5]

The pulmonary trunk differs from the aorta in that its lumen contains blood with a much lower content of oxygen. As a result the partial pressure gradient down which oxygen can diffuse outwards into the media is small and insufficient to supply the needs of the tissues of the media. Hence one would anticipate that its media would be supplied more richly with vasa vasorum resulting in an 'avascular zone' which is narrower than that found in the aorta. A recent investigation, at the Department of Biophysics of the University of Western Ontario, by Thomson, Smith and Roach (a personal communication) has shown that this is indeed the case. In dogs, vasa vasorum are twice as profuse in the pulmonary trunk as in the aorta. In cats, there are fifteen times more vasa vasorum in the pulmonary trunk than in the aorta, and in this species the avascular zone of the pulmonary trunk is only about a quarter of the thickness of that in the aorta. The concept of medial lamellar units cannot be applied to the pulmonary trunk, since, as we shall see in the next chapter, the elastic laminae of the pulmonary trunk undergo fragmentation during infancy, at least in those born at low altitude.

The Main Pulmonary Arteries

The right main pulmonary artery is slightly larger and longer than the left. Its position and mode of branching at the hilum of the lung show little or no variation. It runs horizontally and to the right in the angle between the azygos vein above and the ascending aorta and superior vena cava in front.[1] It is situated anteriorly to the oesophagus and right main bronchus. It divides into two main branches. The larger and lower branch is distributed to the middle and lower lobes while an upper, smaller branch accompanies the 'eparterial' bronchus to the upper lobe (Fig. 1.2).

The left main pulmonary artery also shows very little variation in its position. It runs horizontally from below the aortic arch to cross the descending aorta. It lies completely above the left main bronchus until it gives off its first branch. Then it runs downwards, behind and laterally to the bronchus. It is connected above to the concavity of the aortic arch by the ligamentum arteriosum which is the remains of the patent ductus arteriosus.

Because of its oblique course, the left pulmonary artery appears foreshortened in the frontal (Fig. 1.2) and lateral views and an accurate estimate of its length can be obtained only in the left anterior oblique view.[2] On angiocardiograms the artery is seen to arch upwards beneath the aortic arch so that its upper point lies on a level with the upper half of the sixth thoracic vertebra, approximately 1 cm higher than the right pulmonary artery.[2] It proceeds in an oblique course posteriorly to the left hilum where it divides into lobar branches described below.

In angiocardiograms, the origin of the right pulmonary artery can be seen at the level of the lower half of the sixth dorsal vertebra at the left border of the spine (Fig. 1.2). It inclines slightly downwards and then passes transversely to the right hilum where it is a little to the right of the spine (Fig. 1.2).[2]

Lobar Branches

In sharp contrast to the main pulmonary arteries, the branches supplying the lobes of the lungs show a great deal of normal variation. The main arrangements of the principal pulmonary arteries in each lobe of the lung are considered below. This shortened account is taken from that of Cory and Valentine[7] who studied the anatomical arrangement of the pulmonary arteries in 524 pneumonectomy and lobectomy specimens resected from 426 patients. The numbers of different vascular patterns they found in each lobe are shown in Table 1.1.

Right upper lobe Only four of the vascular patterns noted in Table 1.1 are common. Usually the lobe is supplied through two vessels, a single high branch which supplies the apical and anterior segments, and a low single branch which supplies the posterior segment.

Less commonly, all three segmental vessels arise from a single trunk situated high and laterally, or anterolaterally, on the main stem. Occasionally the posterior segment receives two separate branches. In others, there is a large upper branch which immediately divides into three and a single branch to the posterior segment.

Right middle lobe Only two arrangements are at all common. In the first, the lobe is supplied by a single vessel and in the second it is supplied by two.

Right lower lobe In most cases there is a single artery to the apical segment. It originates from the pulmonary stem just before this divides into two main terminations which supply the basal segments. In some this arrangement is slightly modified in that there are three terminal branches to the basal segments.

Table 1.1 The degree of variation in the arrangement of the blood vessels in the lobes of the lung[7]

Lobe	Number of specimens examined	Number of different vascular patterns found
Right upper	152	14
Right middle	51	5
Right lower	43	6
Left upper	107	27
Left lower	57	4

Left upper lobe There is virtually no normal arrangement of the pulmonary arteries in the left upper lobe, the branches to it varying in number from two to seven. Usually four arteries supply the lobe with blood. The upper three supply the superior segments and the lowest supplies the lingula.

Left lower lobe The arrangement of the arteries to this lobe is similar to that of the right lower lobe. In the majority of cases there is a single artery to the apical segment which arises posteriorly and just above the point at which the descending pulmonary arterial trunk divides into two terminal divisions. In a few instances two arteries supply the apical segment.

All these lobar pulmonary arteries and their branches can be seen on an angiocardiogram, and in general they closely follow the course of the bronchi and their subdivisions. On the right side the intrapulmonary vessels end in the costophrenic sinus posteriorly, well below the dome of the diaphragm through which they can be seen in anteroposterior view (Fig. 1.2). The left hilum is located considerably more posteriorly than the right and hence both upper and lower branches on this side of the thorax tend to run more vertically than do those on the right.[2]

Branching, Diameter and Length Ratios of the Pulmonary Arterial Tree

Cumming and his colleagues[8] have made measurements of the dimensions and numbers of the branches of the human pulmonary arterial tree from post-mortem casts. Using such data they have attempted to describe the pulmonary arterial system in mathematical terms. Although the obvious way of defining the different generations of the system is to start with the pulmonary artery and number the divisions successively towards the periphery, the irregular and not always dichotomous branching pattern of the pulmonary arterial tree renders this increasingly difficult to apply as one passes toward the smaller vessels. Instead, the authors found it convenient to use an approach devised by geographers to describe the tributary system of rivers.[9] According to this approach, branches (or tributaries) are numbered from the smallest towards the largest. In this way the smallest vessels are designated 'order one'. When two such vessels join to form a larger vessel it is called 'order two'. When two vessels of different order meet, the resultant vessel preserves the order of the higher of the two. Thus, if a vessel of order two joins one of order four the resultant vessel is of order four. It will be seen that the description is a strictly morphological one without reference to the direction of flow.

Expressed in this way, Cumming and his associates found that seventeen orders would describe the human pulmonary arterial system from the alveoli to the main pulmonary artery. The ratio of the number of vessels of one order to that of the order higher ('branching ratio') was roughly constant at 3·4 throughout. Similarly the ratio of the average diameter of one order to that of the preceding order ('diameter ratio') was roughly constant at 1·7. Less constant was the ratio of the average length of one order to that of the preceding order, although this ratio ('length ratio') averaged about 1·8. Thus, in these terms, the pulmonary arterial system could be described as a system of seventeen orders with a 'branching ratio' of 3·4, a 'diameter ratio' of 1·7 and a 'length ratio' of 1·8. The numbers of vessels in each order, their diameter, length and cross-sectional area are shown in Table 9.1, page 127. The physiological implications are discussed in Chapter 9.

Pulmonary Veins

Each lobule of the lung is drained by a single pulmonary vein. These small intrapulmonary veins successively unite with one another so that eventually a single lobar vein emerges from each lobe. The upper and middle lobar veins on the right side usually, but not always, unite so that finally superior and inferior pulmonary veins emerge from each lung.[1] Occasionally there is only one pulmonary vein on the left side.[1] At the hilum of the lung the superior pulmonary vein lies below and in front of the pulmonary artery. The inferior pulmonary vein is situated posterior to the superior one and occupies the lowest part of the hilum of the lung. The left pulmonary veins pass in front of the descending thoracic aorta. On the right side,

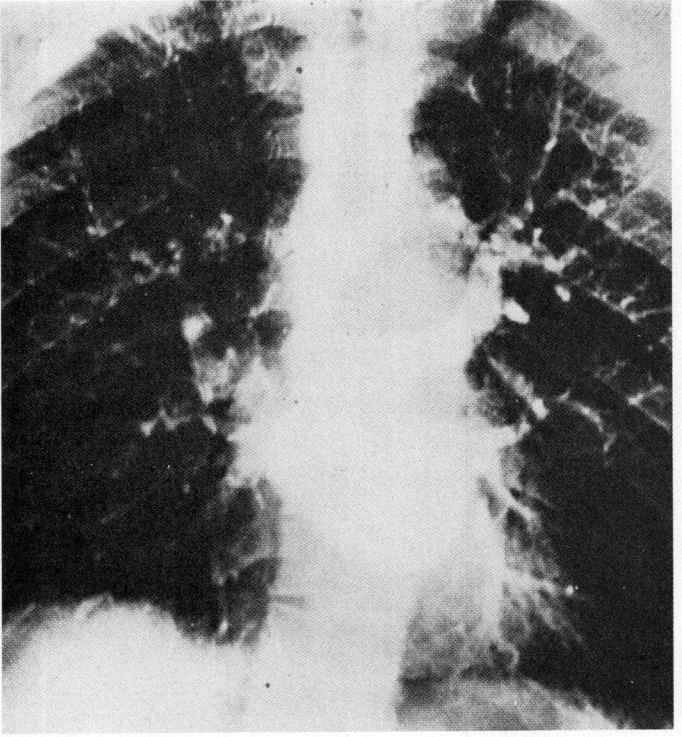

Fig. 1.3 Normal angiocardiogram (anteroposterior view) showing contrast medium in the pulmonary veins which run into the left atrium. The superior veins pass to the left atrium at an angle of 45° to 60°.

the superior vein passes behind the superior vena cava while the inferior vein passes behind the right atrium.

The four pulmonary veins pass through the fibrous layer of the pericardium and their anterior surfaces become covered by the serous pericardium.[1] They enter the upper posterior part of the left atrium. There are no valves either within the pulmonary veins or at their orifices into the left atrium.[1] Frequently the two left pulmonary veins enter the left atrium through a common opening.[1]

On angiocardiography the four main pulmonary veins (Fig. 1.3) are seen to lie anteriorly and inferiorly to their respective arteries.[2] The superior veins pass to the left atrium at an angle of 45° to 60° with the horizontal and are parallel with the superior pulmonary arteries (Fig. 1.3).[2] The inferior veins run at an angle of only 30° to 45° with the horizontal, an appearance in striking contrast to the arterial

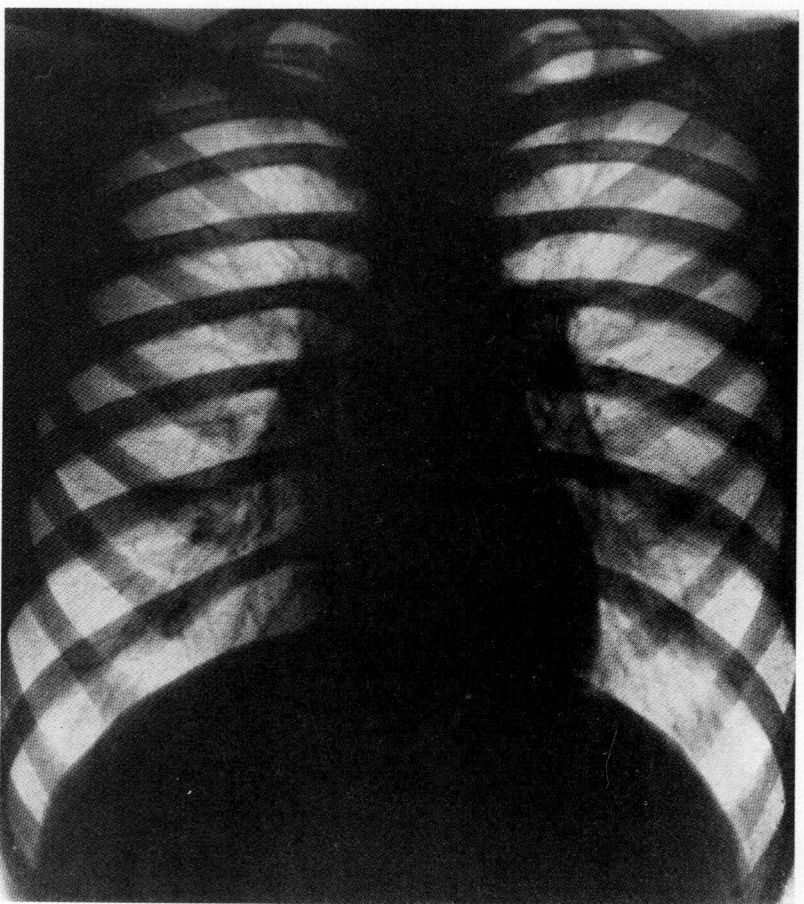

Fig. 1.4 Radiograph of a normal chest.

branches which in this area of lung pursue a predominantly vertical course.[2] On the right side, the superior and inferior pulmonary veins enter the left atrium near the right border of the spine at the level of the lower half of the seventh and eighth dorsal vertebrae, respectively. On the left, both veins are a little higher. The course of the intrapulmonary veins follows closely the arterial pattern already described.

Radiology of the Pulmonary Vessels

In the plain postero-anterior radiograph (Fig. 1.4), the shadow of the right main branch of the pulmonary artery becomes visible as it emerges from the mediastinum. From this point it passes downwards with a lateral convexity becoming gradually smaller and less obvious as it gives off its terminal branches. In the postero-anterior projection the left main branch is less clearly seen since its course is a more oblique one, backwards as well as laterally, and also because a large portion of it lies within the cardiac shadow. The various patterns of the shadows cast by the different arrangements of the smaller arterial branches have been studied by Herrnheiser[10] and Lodge.[11] The observation of their detailed topographical anatomy has not, however, proved of such clinical importance as in other regions of the body because local abnormalities of the pulmonary parenchyma are usually themselves directly visible on radiographs. It is not usually possible to distinguish between venous and arterial shadows in the normal radiograph except in the right lower zone where the shadow of the right inferior pulmonary vein may often be identified by its more horizontal course across the arterial shadows. As will have been gathered from the preceding sections, the use of contrast angiography has provided a clearer picture of the anatomy of the pulmonary vessels and a much clearer distinction between arteries and veins.

Distortions of the Tracheobronchial Tree Associated with Pulmonary Hypertension

Edwards and Burchell[12] have shown that pulmonary hypertension associated with cardiac disease may give rise to distortions and compressions of the tracheobronchial tree. This is because the aorta and the proximal part of the left main pulmonary artery lie in a fixed space between the trachea, to the right, and the left upper lobe bronchus below. When the pulmonary arteries become tense and distended as a result of severe pulmonary hypertension, the left pulmonary artery tends to push the aortic arch upwards and to the right; in this way the aortic indentation on the left side of the trachea may become more accentuated than normal (Fig. 1.5). The displaced aorta may press on the left recurrent laryngeal nerve and lead to hoarseness (Chap. 21). The distended left pulmonary artery may also lead to a distortion downward and to the right of the left main bronchus which thus assumes a broad concave sweep (Fig. 1.5). A localized indentation into the left main bronchus may also occur. The right pulmonary artery lies between the right upper lobe bronchus above the intermediate bronchus (the lower part of the right main bronchus[13])

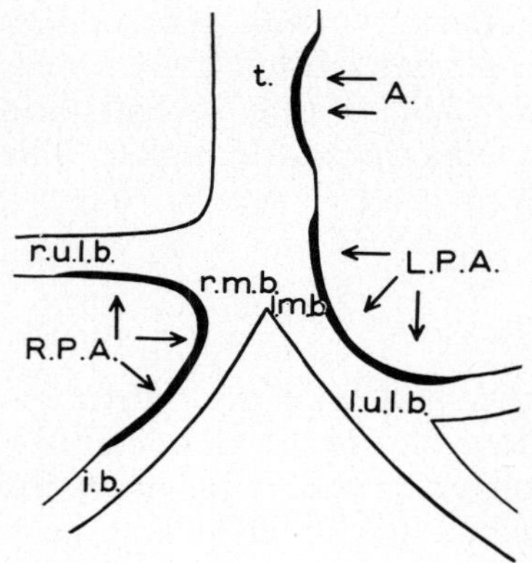

Fig. 1.5 Diagram to show the distortions and compressions of the tracheo-bronchial tree by enlarged pulmonary arteries in pulmonary hypertension. The aorta (A) is pushed upwards and to the right by the dilated left pulmonary artery (LPA) to make an indentation in the left side of the trachea (t). The dilated left pulmonary artery itself distorts and compresses the left main bronchus (lmb) and left upper lobe bronchus (lulb). The right pulmonary artery (RPA) pushes the right upper lobe bronchus (rulb) and the intermediate bronchus (ib) away from each other causing an increase and rounding of the angle between them.

below, and the distal end of the right main bronchus to the left (Fig. 1.5). When the pulmonary artery is tense and distended, it tends to push the bronchi away from each other, causing an increase and rounding of the angle between them (Fig. 1.5) and compressing them, particularly the intermediate bronchus.

When the pulmonary hypertension is associated with enlargement of the left atrium, as in the diseases associated with pulmonary venous hypertension listed in Chapter 15, there will be additional mechanical strains on the tracheobronchial tree. The bifurcation of the trachea into the right and left main bronchi occurs over the left atrium so that as the left atrium enlarges the main bronchi are pushed upwards and the angle of the bifurcation increases (Fig. 1.6). This angle is normally 90° but, when there is aneurysmal dilatation of the left atrium, it may increase to 180° (Fig. 1.6). The enlarged atrium tends to compress the bronchi and lead to collapse of the lung parenchyma. The left main bronchus is compressed because the left atrium tends to push the bronchus up, while the left pulmonary artery, which normally arches down over it, tends to prevent this upward displacement.

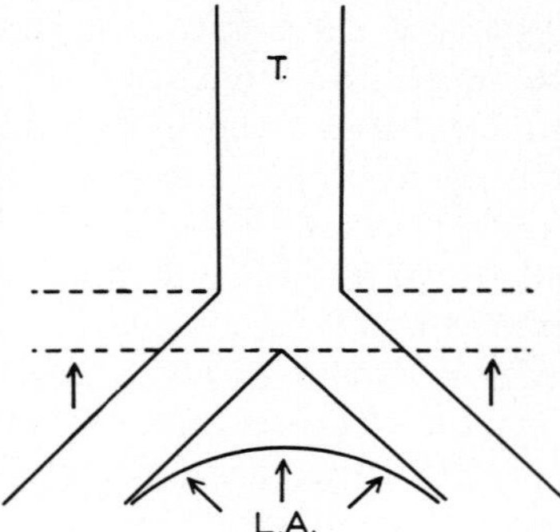

Fig. 1.6 Diagram to show the distortion and compression of the tracheo-bronchial tree by pulmonary hypertension associated with an enlarged left atrium (LA). The bifurcation of the trachea (T) occurs over the left atrium; when this chamber enlarges the main bronchi are pushed upwards and the angle of the bifurcation increases.

REFERENCES

1. Johnson, T. B. & Whillis, J. (Editors) (1942) *Gray's Anatomy—Descriptive and Applied.* 28th edn. London: Longmans.
2. Robb, G. P. (1951) *An Atlas of Angiocardiography,* American Registry of Pathology.
3. Parke, W. W. (1970) *Amer. Heart J.*, **80**, 802.
4. Sobin, S. S., Frasher, W. G. & Tremer, H. M. (1962) *Circulat. Res.*, **11**, 257.
5. Wolinsky, H. & Glagov, S. (1967) *Circulat. Res.*, **20**, 409.
6. Wolinsky, H. & Glagov, S. (1967) *Circulat. Res.*, **20**, 99.
7. Cory, R. A. S. & Valentine, E. J. (1959) *Thorax*, **14**, 267.
8. Cumming, G., Harding, L. K., Horsfield, K., Prowse, K., Singhal, S. S. & Woldenberg, M. (1970) Morphological aspects of the pulmonary circulation and of the airways. In *Advisory Group for Aerospace Research and Development, N.A.T.O.*, Conference proc. No. 65.
9. Strahler, A. N. (1950) *Amer. J. Sci.*, **248**, 673.
10. Herrnheiser, G. (1942) *Amer. J. Radiol.*, **48**, 595.
11. Lodge, T. (1948) *Brit. J. Radiol.*, **19**, 1, 77.
12. Edwards, J. E. & Burchell, H. B. (1960) *Dis. Chest*, **38**, 272.
13. Brock, R. C. (1954) *The Anatomy of the Bronchial Tree.* Page 11. London: Oxford Univ. Press.

2. Developmental Anomalies of the Large Pulmonary Blood Vessels

PULMONARY ARTERIES

Normal Development

The main pulmonary arteries develop from the sixth aortic arches (Fig. 2.1). These arise from the ventral aorta at a stage when it may be termed the truncus arteriosus and terminate in right and left dorsal aortae. A classical review of the aortic arch system was presented by Congdon[1] but the development of the sixth arch in particular has been considered by Pool and co-workers.[2] Like the other aortic arches the sixth is formed by ventral and dorsal buds but it receives an additional component from arteries arising from the dorsal aortae in the vicinity of the primary lung bud. These are termed the 'pulmonary post-branchial plexus'.[3] On the left side the dorsal bud of the sixth arch forms the ductus arteriosus but on the right side it is lost.

The truncus arteriosus divides at this time into the ascending aorta and the pulmonary trunk by the development within it of a spiral septum. Thus communication is effected between the right ventricle and pulmonary arterial tree. Changes occur in the dorsal aortae so that the right is lost distal to the origin of the right subclavian artery to form the innominate artery.

Persistent Truncus Arteriosus

When the spiral (truncoconal) septum fails to develop within the primitive truncus, this vessel remains as a single artery from which arise the aorta, the coronary arteries and, with one exception, the pulmonary arteries. An anatomical

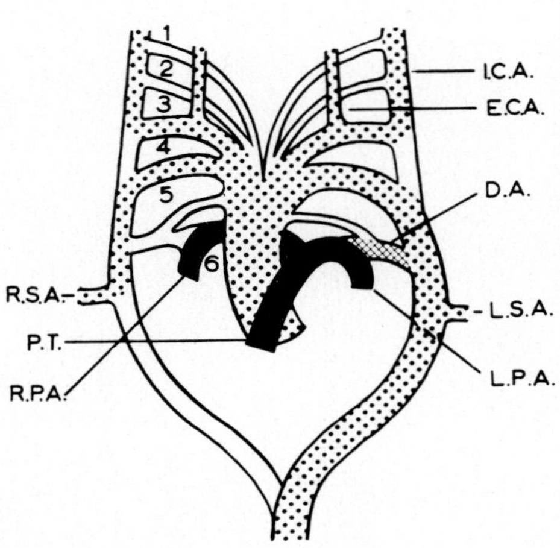

Fig. 2.1 Diagram to show the development of the right and left pulmonary arteries (RPA and LPA) from the sixth aortic arches, the proximal parts of which remain in connexion with the pulmonary trunk (PT) when the truncus arteriosus divides. The persistence of the dorsal part of the sixth arch on the left side as the ductus arteriosus (DA) is shown. The origins of the internal and external carotid arteries (ICA and ECA) and the subclavian arteries (LSA and RSA) are shown. Those parts of the aortic arches remaining as part of the adult systemic vasculature are shown stippled. The adult pulmonary circulation is shown in black. (After Congdon[1])

classification of persistent truncus arteriosus based upon the nature of the arterial supply to the lungs has been given by Collett and Edwards.[4] The functional consequences of a persistent truncus depend on the nature of the blood supply to the lung. In Type I, for example, an incomplete pulmonary trunk and aorta arise from the truncus and the pulmonary arteries arise from the pulmonary trunk. As in all forms of truncus there is a ventricular septal defect. Under these conditions a large left-to-right shunt may occur with the development of pulmonary arterial hypertension and hypertensive pulmonary vascular disease as described in Chapter 16. In contrast, in Type IV there are no pulmonary arteries and the blood supply to the lungs is through the bronchial arteries. Such cases resemble Fallot's tetrad with severe pulmonary stenosis and there will be thrombosis in the pulmonary arterial tree as described in Chapter 37. In Types II and III where the pulmonary arteries arise respectively from the dorsal wall of the aorta, or from either side of the truncus, the haemodynamic and consequent pathological effects on the lungs depend upon the calibre of the pulmonary arteries.

In the condition of aorto-pulmonary septal defect there is an opening between the adjacent walls of the ascending aorta and the pulmonary trunk. This may be regarded as a partial form of persistent truncus arteriosus, the defect representing a focus of absence of the truncoconal septum while elsewhere the septum is formed, yielding its usual derivatives.[5] The functional effects of an aorto-pulmonary septal defect on the pulmonary circulation are those of a post-tricuspid shunt (Chap. 15).

Unilateral Absence of a Pulmonary Artery

One of the main pulmonary arteries may be absent and the blood to the lung on that side is supplied by the aorta.[2] The frequency of involvement of the two lungs is the same. A patent ductus arteriosus tends to be associated with unilateral absence of the right pulmonary artery but not of the left.[5] Pulmonary arterial hypertension has been found in the lung receiving the normal pulmonary arterial supply which is of interest since this complication does not follow pneumonectomy. The difference has been explained on the basis that subjects with unilateral absence of a pulmonary artery are exposed to the entire cardiac output from foetal life when the pulmonary arteries are normally thick-walled[6] (Chap. 14). Pool and his colleagues,[2] in reviewing the literature, estimated that such pulmonary hypertension occurred in about 18 per cent of patients with unilateral absence of the pulmonary artery and no other congenital defect.

Left Pulmonary Artery Arising from Right Pulmonary Artery

Rarely the pulmonary trunk does not bifurcate but is continuous as the right pulmonary artery while the left arises from the proximal segment of the right pulmonary artery.[7] The left pulmonary artery arises on the *right* side and passes over the right bronchus and behind the tracheal bifurcation to reach the left hilum. This condition does not exert deleterious haemodynamic effects on the pulmonary circulation but may compress the right main bronchus.

Localized Pulmonary Arterial Stenosis

There are three types of pulmonary arterial stenosis.[8] In the first, single or multiple stenosis may occur in the pulmonary trunk or one of its main branches or more peripherally in the lung. We consider this condition in Chapter 15. In the second type, stenosis of the bifurcation of the pulmonary trunk leads to what has been termed 'coarctation of the pulmonary artery'.[9] Thirdly, membranous stenosis may occur immediately above the pulmonary valve. In these conditions there is localized narrowing of the affected pulmonary artery and intimal fibrosis. In half the cases of localized pulmonary arterial stenosis there are associated congenital cardiac anomalies which we list elsewhere.[5] The stenosis characteristically gives rise to a systolic murmur. A continuous murmur over the stenotic zone has, however, been described.[10]

Sequestration of Lung

In sequestration of the lung, part of the lung is of abnormal structure resembling a hamartoma. This abnormal pulmonary tissue receives a supply of systemic blood through one or more arteries which are not normal anatomical features. There may or may not be a communication between the systemic arterial supply of the sequestrated lung and the normal pulmonary arterial supply of the surrounding lung. The arterial supply to the area of sequestration is usually from the lower thoracic aorta but may arise from the upper abdominal aorta.[11]

Sequestrations of lung may be intralobar or extralobar. The intralobar form is commoner and usually involves part or the whole of one of the lower lobes of lung. The hamartomatous pulmonary and bronchial elements are not in communication with the bronchial tree and its bronchial components may be cystic. Some authorities regard the anomalous arteries as the primary abnormality leading to the sequestration.[12] Others like Abbey-Smith[13] consider the sequestration primary and the arterial supply secondary. In extralobar sequestration, the hamartoma lies outside the lung surrounded by its own pleura usually between the left lung and the pleura. In one case, personally studied, it formed a diaphragmatic cyst.[14]

It is often very difficult on histological grounds to decide whether the arteries in a sequestration of lung are pulmonary or systemic in nature. Near its origin from the aorta, the anomalous artery is elastic in type but more distally it may be muscular or elastic. Within the sequestration the arteries are usually thick-walled and tortuous. They usually have a distinct internal elastic lamina while the external lamina is incomplete or absent. Such arteries have been termed 'hybrid arteries'. These arteries may show severe fibrosis of the media and intima. In one case of extralobar sequestration that we studied, the vessels showed fibrinoid necrosis.[14]

Pulmonary Artery Communicating with Left Atrium

A rare and specialized form of pulmonary arteriovenous fistula is the malformation in which a branch of a pulmonary artery enters the left atrium without first passing through lung.[15]

Origin of Coronary Arteries from the Pulmonary Trunk

The commonest abnormality of this type is the origin of the left coronary artery from the pulmonary trunk (Fig. 2.2). When this is so, serious ischaemia of the left ventricle usually occurs in infancy[16] (Fig. 2.3). In those patients who survive, most die of left-ventricular ischaemia before middle age. In these patients the right coronary artery becomes considerably enlarged and anastomoses form between the two coronary arteries. In this way the left coronary artery is filled by the right coronary artery and flow is retrograde into the pulmonary artery, causing a small left–right shunt. In order to prevent this 'steal', ligation of the left coronary artery has been carried out.[17] A more effective treatment would appear to be the reconnection of the left coronary artery to the aorta by a vein graft.[18,19]

The origin of the right coronary artery from the pulmonary trunk has been described on only a few occasions. Flow appears also to be retrograde into the pulmonary artery.[20] The abnormality appears to be more benign than the anomalous origin of the left coronary artery. The origin of both coronary arteries from the pulmonary trunk is rapidly fatal.[21]

PULMONARY VEINS

Normal Development

The lungs are derived by division of the foregut and share their blood supply, the splanchnic plexus, with it. This plexus drains into the systemic precardinal and

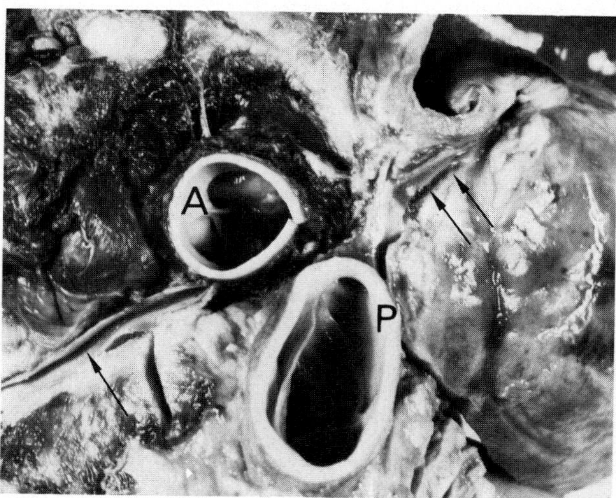

Fig. 2.2 View of cut surface of the great vessels in a boy of 11 years with anomalous origin of the left coronary artery from the pulmonary trunk.[30] The pulmonary trunk, P, is situated anteriorly. It is thickened and dilated and from it arises the left coronary artery (two arrows). The right coronary artery (single arrow) arises normally from the aorta.

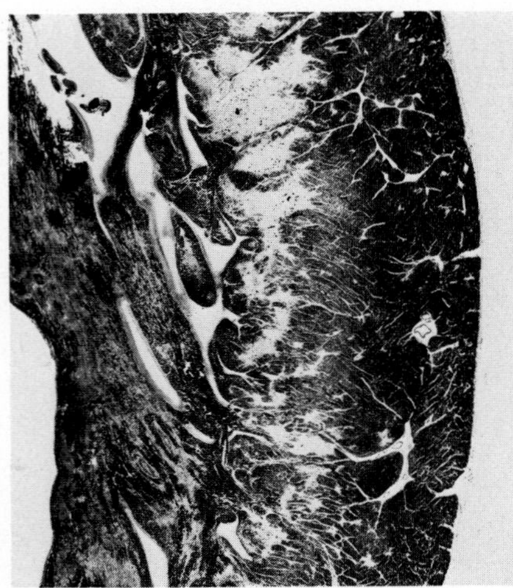

Fig. 2.3 Section of left ventricle and papillary muscle of mitral valve from the same case illustrated in Fig. 2.2 showing myocardial fibrosis. The fibrotic areas appear pale (Masson-trichrome).

postcardinal veins and the visceral veins of the abdomen, the umbilico-vitelline system, with associated hepatic sinusoids.[22] Thus, at this early stage of development the veins of the primordia of the lungs do not drain directly into the heart but into the venous precordia that will form the superior vena cava, the coronary sinus, the innominate veins, the proximal portion of the subclavian veins, the portal vein, gastric veins, ductus venosus and inferior vena cava.[5] Later, an out-pouching from the heart termed the 'common pulmonary vein' extends into that part of the splanchnic plexus related to the lungs. Some of the early connexions between the splanchnic plexus and the cardinal and umbilico-vitelline veins are maintained. This is the basis for the continuity of the portal and pulmonary venous systems which becomes prominent in cases of cirrhosis of the liver as described in Chapter 29.

Stenosis of Pulmonary Veins

Focal narrowing or diminution of calibre over a greater length may involve anomalous or definitive pulmonary veins.[23] The protrusion of the fibrotic lesion into the junction of definitive pulmonary veins and left atrium may cause severe pulmonary venous obstruction and secondary pulmonary arterial hypertension.

Cor Triatriatum

In this congenital anomaly there is an accessory atrial chamber connected to the left atrium by an opening. The pulmonary veins drain into the accessory chamber.[24] One theory is that cor triatriatum is a malformation of the pulmonary venous system brought about by failure of the common pulmonary vein to become absorbed by differential growth into the left atrium. It remains instead as the accessory chamber. The haemodynamic and pathological effects of cor triatriatum, especially if the size of the opening between the left atrium and the accessory chamber is small, are like those of mitral stenosis described in Chapters 22 and 23.

Very rarely atresia of the common pulmonary vein occurs.[25] In this condition the pulmonary veins enter neither the left atrium nor a systemic vein. Collateral connecting veins into the peri-oesophageal venous plexus may be demonstrated. Death occurs in infancy in this condition. The pulmonary veins enter a venous recess looking like the accessory left atrial chamber of cor triatriatum but in this disease there is no connexion with the heart.

Anomalous Pulmonary Venous Drainage

Anomalous pulmonary venous drainage occurs when the pulmonary veins drain into the right atrium or systemic veins. It may be partial when part of the pulmonary venous drainage is into the left atrium and total when none of the drainage is normal. Partial anomalous venous drainage of the right lung tends to be into the right atrium or superior vena cava.[5] That of the left lung tends to be into the left innominate vein.[5] Burroughs and Edwards[26] studied 188 cases of total anomalous pulmonary venous connexion and found major associated cardiac malformations in no fewer than 66 of them. Anatomical sites receiving anomalous pulmonary veins in this series in order of descending frequency were left innominate vein, right atrium, coronary sinus, right superior vena cava, portal vein, ductus venosus, inferior vena cava, and hepatic vein. In total anomalous pulmonary venous drainage the anomalous

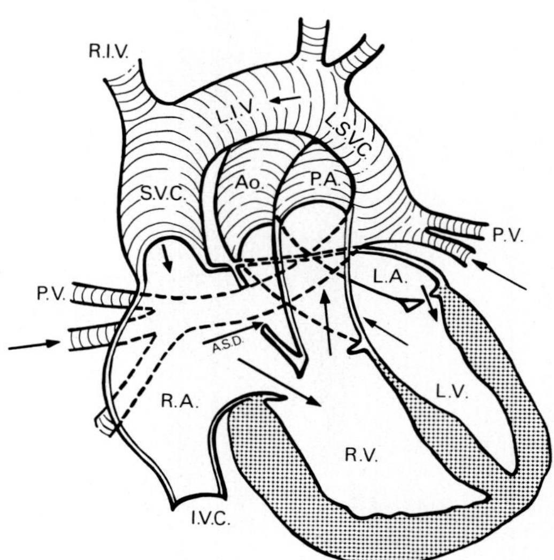

Fig. 2.4 Line diagram to show the flow of blood to and through the heart in total anomalous pulmonary venous drainage.[31]

veins converge in one of two ways. When joining the right atrium, the veins may enter individually or first may form a trunk. When the anomalous pulmonary veins enter a systemic vein, they converge superior to the left atrium in an extrapericardial location to form a vein or a chamber resembling the accessory chamber of cor triatriatum. From the convergence, a vein of varying length leads to the site of systemic venous termination. In rare cases an atretic strand extends from the venous convergence to the left atrium. Edwards[5] believes that such cases lend support to the concept that total anomalous pulmonary venous connexion has close developmental relation to the condition of atresia of the common pulmonary vein referred to above.

In total anomalous pulmonary venous drainage all the blood returning to the heart, in systemic and pulmonary veins, drains into the right atrium (Fig. 2.4). From this chamber it passes in part into the right ventricle and in part through an atrial septal defect into the left atrium and thence into the systemic circulation (Fig. 2.4). The abnormal venous connexion and the increased pulmonary bloodflow may be seen on the chest radiograph (Fig. 2.5). Pulmonary arterial hypertension may be associated with the anomaly as a result of high pulmonary flow or pulmonary venous

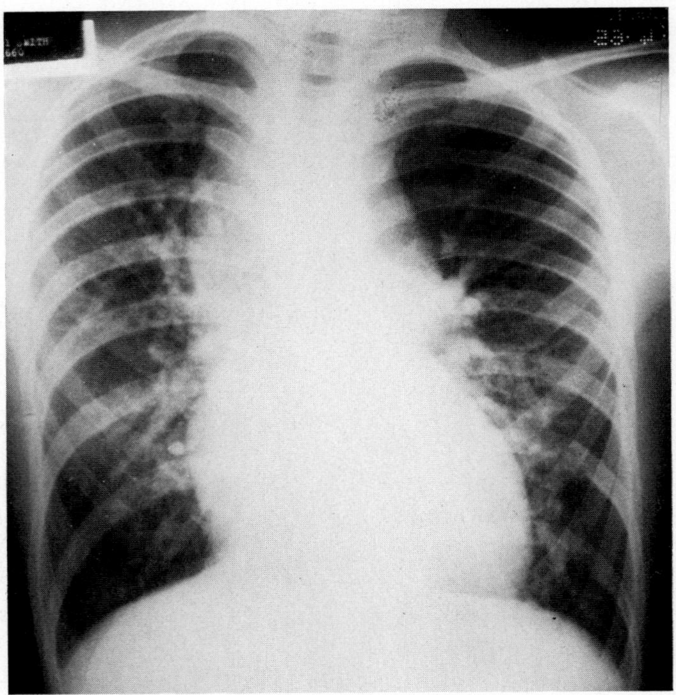

Fig. 2.5 Radiograph of the chest in a boy of 17 years with total anomalous pulmonary venous drainage. Note the shadow in the upper mediastinum formed by the left superior vena cava, left innominate vein and right superior vena cava. The lung fields are plethoric.

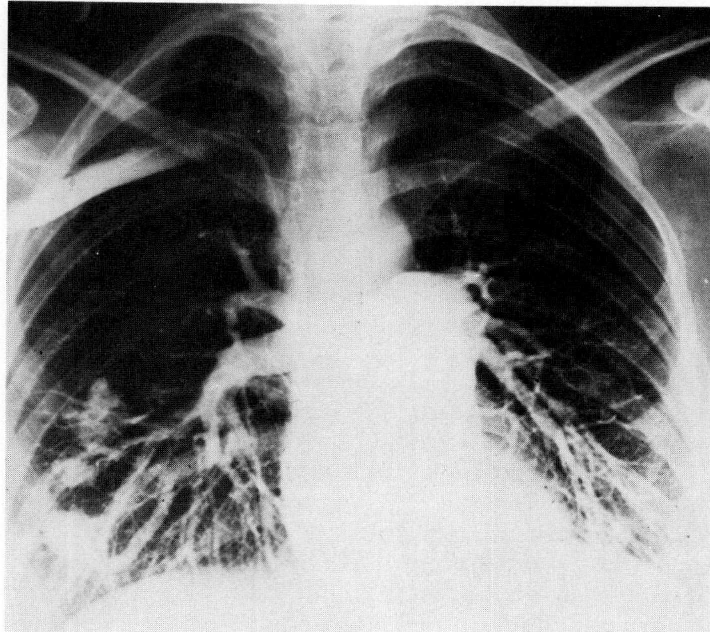

Fig. 2.6 Pulmonary angiogram showing multiple pulmonary arteriovenous fistulae in the lower lobes. The fistulae are more prominent on the right side where the enlargement of the pulmonary arterial and venous vessels may be seen in relation to them.

obstruction. The latter condition may be brought about by the fact that long anomalous veins pursuing an abnormal course may offer a resistance to pulmonary venous flow. It may follow stenotic lesions in the pulmonary veins. Another cause of pulmonary venous obstruction is compression of the anomalous channel by contiguous structures.[5]

Pulmonary Arteriovenous Fistula

Arteriovenous fistula of the lung (Fig. 2.6) mistakenly referred to sometimes as a cavernous haemangioma, is probably the commonest malformation of the pulmonary circulation. The fistulae vary in size from minute collections of dilated vessels, referred to as pulmonary telangiectasia, to large vascular malformations. The majority occur in the lower lobes. When the large fistulae are studied by means of a vinylite-plastic injection technique, they are found to consist of a distended thin-walled afferent artery, distended efferent veins and an intervening labyrinth of distended vessels.[27] Rarely, a whole lobe may be replaced by an arteriovenous fistula and in such cases the pulmonary artery supplying it is abnormally large and both it and the affected lobe pulsate freely.[28]

The arteries forming the fistula are enlarged and may be tortuous. Vessels of more than one bronchopulmonary segment may be involved and there is no regularity in the number and arrangement of these arteries and veins. Two separate aneurysmal loops may be present. The draining veins are larger than the arteries. There is no significant contribution from bronchial arteries.

The histological appearances of pulmonary arteriovenous fistulae consist of cavernous, blood-filled spaces linked to one another. The vascular channels are up to 1·5 cm in diameter. The vessels frequently show severe intimal fibrosis. Some contain organizing thrombi. Structurally the vessels resemble pulmonary veins more than arteries. Rupture of these vessels leads to pulmonary haemosiderosis in the surrounding lung.

Patients with pulmonary arteriovenous fistulae often show vascular naevi elsewhere on the body such as on the lips, face and soft palate. This suggests that in many cases arteriovenous fistulae in the lung are a manifestation of hereditary multiple telangiectasia (Osler-Rendu-Weber's disease).[28] Large arteriovenous fistulae of the lung produce cyanosis as a result of deoxygenated blood shunting directly from the pulmonary arteries into the pulmonary veins without first traversing the pulmonary capillary bed. Finger clubbing and polycythaemia follow hypoxia of the systemic circulation.[28] Systolic murmurs and thrills over the thorax are probably the result of the high flow through the fistula.[29] The fistulae may show up on chest radiographs as circinate shadows or collections of worm-like shadows extending from the hilum. Usually their extent is demonstrated by angiocardiography (Fig. 2.6) but this technique may not show up the small fistulae which constitute pulmonary telangiectasia.

Pulmonary arteriovenous fistulae may be asymptomatic. However, they may be the cause of fatal pulmonary haemorrhage. A fistula may become infected and may lead to a cerebral abscess. Cerebral thrombosis has also been reported.

REFERENCES

1. Congdon, E. D. (1922) *Carnegie Contrib. Embryol.*, **14**, 47.
2. Pool, P. E., Vogel, J. H. K. & Blount, S. G. Jn. (1962) *Amer. J. Cardiol.*, **10**, 706.
3. Huntington, G. S. (1919) *Anat. Rec.*, **17**, 165.
4. Collett, R. W. & Edwards, J. E. (1949) *Surg. Clin. N. Amer.* Page 1245. (Mayo Clinic Number).
5. Wagenvoort, C. A., Heath, D. & Edwards, J. E. (1964) *The Pathology of the Pulmonary Vasculature.* Springfield, Ill.: Thomas.
6. Anderson, R. C., Char, F. & Adams, P. Jn. (1958) *Dis. Chest*, **34**, 73.
7. Niwayama, G. (1960) *Amer. Heart J.*, **59**, 454.
8. Smith, W. G. (1958) *Thorax*, **13**, 194.
9. Søndergaard, T. (1954) *Canad. Med. Bull.*, **i**, 46.
10. Eldridge, F., Selzer, A. & Hultgren, H. (1957) *Circulation*, **15**, 865.
11. Salvioni, D. & Goldin, R. R. (1960) *Dis. Chest*, **37**, 122.
12. Pryce, D. M. (1946) *J. Path. Bact.*, **58**, 457.
13. Abbey-Smith, R. (1956) *Thorax*, **11**, 10.
14. Heath, D. & Watts, G. T. (1957) *Thorax*, **12**, 142.
15. Lucas, R. V. Jn., Lund, G. W. & Edwards, J. E. (1961) *Circulation*, **24**, 1409.
16. Keith, J. D. (1959) *Brit. Heart J.*, **21**, 149.

17. Sabiston, D. C. (1963) *Progr. Cardiovasc. Dis.*, **6**, 299.
18. Cooley, D. A., Hallman, G. L. & Bloodwell, R. D. (1966) *J. Thorac. Vasc. Surg.*, **52**, 798.
19. Somerville, J. & Ross, D. N. (1970) *Thorax*, **25**, 207.
20. Cronk, E. S., Sinclair, J. G. & Rigdon, R. H. (1951) *Amer. Heart J.*, **42**, 906.
21. Alexander, R. W. & Griffith, G. C. (1956) *Circulation*, **14**, 800.
22. Butler, H. (1952) *J. Anat.*, **86**, 95.
23. Edwards, J. E. (1960) *Lab. Invest.*, **9**, 46.
24. Loeffler, E. (1949) *Arch. Path.*, **48**, 371.
25. Lucas, R. V. Jn., Woolfrey, B. F., Anderson, R. C., Lester, R. G. & Edwards, J. E. (1962) *Pediatrics*, **29**, 729.
26. Burroughs, J. T. & Edwards, J. E. (1960) *Amer. Heart J.*, **59**, 913.
27. Lindskog, G. E., Liebow, A. A., Kausel, H. &.Janzen, A. (1950) *Ann. Surg.*, **132**, 591.
28. Whitaker, W. (1947) *Thorax*, **2**, 58.
29. Janes, R. M. (1943) *Brit. J. Surg.*, **31**, 270.
30. Arnott, M., Kearney, M. S. & Heath, D. (1973) *Amer. Heart J.*, **85**, 113.
31. Whitaker, W. (1954) *Brit. Heart J.*, **16**, 177.

3. The Structure of the Normal Pulmonary Blood Vessels After Infancy

The lung receives blood through the bronchial and pulmonary arteries. The bronchial arteries carry blood at systemic pressure and have thick muscular walls. The pulmonary arteries conduct blood at a pressure approximately one-sixth of that in the systemic circulation and after the first six months of post-natal life have thin walls. Such a statement is not true for those who dwell at high altitude (Chap. 32) and the description of the normal pulmonary vasculature which we give in this chapter applies to those who are born and living at low altitude.

HISTOLOGICAL CONSIDERATIONS

Fixation

The first essential for successful histological study of the pulmonary vasculature is to fix the lung properly. The resection of portions of collapsed lung at necropsy and their fixation in this state for subsequent microscopic examination of the pulmonary blood vessels is worthless. It may well mislead the unwary who will spuriously interpret the collapsed state of the pulmonary arteries as medial hypertrophy. The lung should be distended with buffered 10 per cent formol saline until the pleural surfaces are smooth and then left to fix for two or three days. We believe that it is unnecessary to introduce fixative directly into the pulmonary arterial tree at a pressure roughly equal to that which is obtained in the pulmonary circulation in life. When morphometric studies are to be made of the alveolar tissue of the lung with its contained capillary bed we recommend the formalin steam method of Weibel and Vidone[1] in the apparatus described briefly in Chapter 33. This method gives a remarkably good fixation of lung parenchyma in the expanded state suitable for macroscopic and microscopic tissue morphometry. One must, however, bear in mind that fixation and tissue processing lead to contraction of tissues and must be taken into account in assessments of linear dimensions, area and volume of living tissues from histological sections (Chap. 33). Fixation by formalin–steam inflation is not satisfactory for the study of the structure of pulmonary blood vessels in our experience.

An adequate examination of the pulmonary vasculature must include circumferential strips of the pulmonary trunk and aorta cut some 1 cm above the level of the respective valve cusps. This will allow a determination of the ratio of the thickness of the media of the pulmonary trunk to that of the aorta and a study of the elastic tissue pattern of the media as described in Chapter 17. Blocks of lung tissue should be taken from the upper and lower lobes to include the pleural surface. This will provide tissue for examination of the various classes of pulmonary and bronchial arteries and veins, and of pulmonary lymphatics. Blocks from the hilum of the lung should also be taken for the study of elastic pulmonary arteries and 'true' bronchial arteries (Chap. 38).

Studies of the pulmonary capillaries and blood–air barrier will demand electron microscopy and the fixation and tissue processing appropriate to this. We usually employ small blocks of tissue (1 mm^3) which have been fixed in ice-cold glutaraldehyde, post-fixed in osmium tetroxide, stained in uranyl acetate and embedded in araldite. Thin sections (1 μm) are cut on an ultramicrotome, mounted on glass slides and stained with toluidine blue for light microscopy for the selection of suitable areas for electron microscopy. The blocks are then trimmed and ultra thin sections (60 nm) cut, stained with lead citrate, and examined in an electron microscope.

Staining of Sections

Routine staining of lung sections with haematoxylin and eosin is of very limited value in the study of the pulmonary vasculature since it does not stain up the various components of the vascular wall to enable the observer to distinguish the various classes of blood vessel. The most valuable technique is to stain the elastic tissue by Verhoeff's method or one of the many modifications of the Weigert-Sheridan method and to counterstain the muscle and collagen by Van Gieson's reagent. Ferric iron, much in evidence in pulmonary haemosiderosis in states of pulmonary venous hypertension (Chap. 22), may be demonstrated by Perls' method. The presence of fibrin and the 'fibrinoid substances' which sometimes occur in the media of pulmonary arteries exposed to unusually high blood pressure may be suspected after routine staining with haematoxylin and eosin but this may be confirmed by the use of Lendrum's acid picro-Mallory method[2] or Mallory's phosphotungstic acid haematoxylin. The metachromatic substances which sometimes appear in the pulmonary trunk in patients with severe pulmonary hypertension may be apparent on initial staining with Ehrlich's haematoxylin but these acid mucopolysaccharides are better demonstrated by dyes such as toluidine blue, alcian blue, or by Hale's dialysed iron method.

The Definition of Different Classes of Pulmonary Blood Vessel

With experience, the histologist can recognize fairly readily the various classes of pulmonary blood vessels. However, not infrequently the precise identification of a blood vessel under study can be achieved with certainty only by the examination of serial sections. This technique is time-consuming and laborious but it is essential under certain circumstances and is the only way of appreciating the spatial relationships of one blood vessel to another. Serial sections have commonly to be used in the identification of thin-walled vessels whose wall consists of a single elastic lamina. While at first glance they may look like venules they may in fact be revealed as such widely differing classes of blood vessels as thin-walled branches of muscular pulmonary arteries (Chapter 16) or even porta-pulmonary venous anastomoses (Chap. 29).

Clear criteria for the recognition of various classes of pulmonary vessel were laid down in 1935 by Brenner[3] and the system of classification he devised has stood the test of time in being virtually unchallenged and widely used by workers in this field. He terms those pulmonary arteries which lie outside the lung and those exceeding 1000 μm in external diameter 'elastic pulmonary arteries'. Arteries between approximately 100 and 1000 μm in diameter with a distinct muscular media and internal and external limiting elastic laminae he calls 'muscular pulmonary arteries'. Arterial vessels lined by only a single elastic lamina and with no media, arising as a termination of, or as a side branch from, a small muscular pulmonary artery, are 'pulmonary arterioles'. These are usually less than 100 μm in external diameter. Pulmonary venules are of identical structure to pulmonary arterioles and are distinguishable from them only by their connexion with veins. Venous blood vessels exceeding 100 μm in external diameter are called 'pulmonary veins'.

THE STRUCTURE OF PULMONARY VESSELS

The Origin of the Pulmonary Trunk

The pulmonary trunk[3] is inserted into the right ventricle by a short tube or 'annulus' of dense, acellular fibrous tissue. This annulus extends from the level of the pulmonary-valve cusps to the beginning of the musculoelastic media of the pulmonary trunk and is about 6 mm in length. Its collagen fibres are orientated longitudinally and are unaccompanied by muscle, although there are a few elastic fibrils immediately beneath the endothelial lining of the fibrous tube. For 1 mm or so above the point of attachment of the valve cusps, the fibrous tissue in that portion of the annulus immediately beneath the lining endothelium is loosely arranged and is continuous with the similar soft fibrous spongiosa of the pulmonary valve. The media of the pulmonary trunk (M) (Fig. 3.1), which is composed mainly of elastic fibrils and smooth muscle, ends in an apex (A) which is directed downwards. The apex is formed by the inner part of the media and is situated beneath

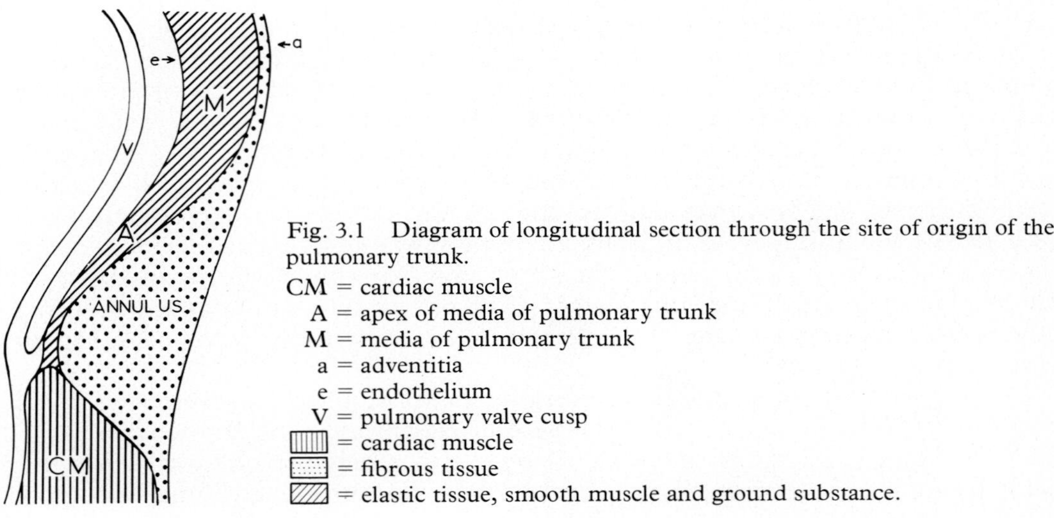

Fig. 3.1 Diagram of longitudinal section through the site of origin of the pulmonary trunk.
CM = cardiac muscle
A = apex of media of pulmonary trunk
M = media of pulmonary trunk
a = adventitia
e = endothelium
V = pulmonary valve cusp
[vertical lines] = cardiac muscle
[dots] = fibrous tissue
[diagonal hatching] = elastic tissue, smooth muscle and ground substance.

the endothelium (e) of the pulmonary trunk. The upper part of the inner surface of the annulus is chamfered away to accept the tapering lower edge of the media of the pulmonary trunk, the relationship between these two tubular structures being analogous to a simple male–female joint. The annulus is continuous above with the fibrous adventitia of the pulmonary trunk (a). The lower half of the fibrous annulus is supported by cardiac muscle (CM). The pulmonary valve commissures, which are areas of dense fibrous tissue, displace outwards the downwardly-projecting apex of the media of the pulmonary trunk. Below the apex of the medial wedge the internal elastic lamina of the pulmonary trunk is thinner and is often replaced by discrete, circularly-orientated elastic fibrils, which may be lost before the root of the pulmonary valve cusps is reached or which may continue into the valve (V). Occasionally the thin internal elastic lamina itself may continue down around the root of the cusp and extend into the arterial aspect of the pulmonary valve.

Elastic Pulmonary Arteries

The pulmonary trunk and the large pulmonary arteries exceeding 1000 μm in external diameter are classified as 'elastic arteries'. The media of these vessels consists predominantly of elastic fibrils with some smooth muscle fibres, collagen and a ground substance, which is generally considered to be an acid mucopolysaccharide related to chondroitins B and C. The elastic tissue in the pulmonary trunk presents in foetal life, in infancy and in the adult different patterns which are characteristic of these different phases of development. The adult pattern is established by the end of the second year, when the thickness of the media of the pulmonary trunk is only 40 to 70 per cent of that of the aorta.[4] The elastic tissue in the media of the adult pulmonary trunk is irregular (Fig. 3.2) and more sparse than in the aorta (Fig. 3.3). The short fibrils which are widely separated by numerous slender wisps of elastin are branched in all directions and end in club-

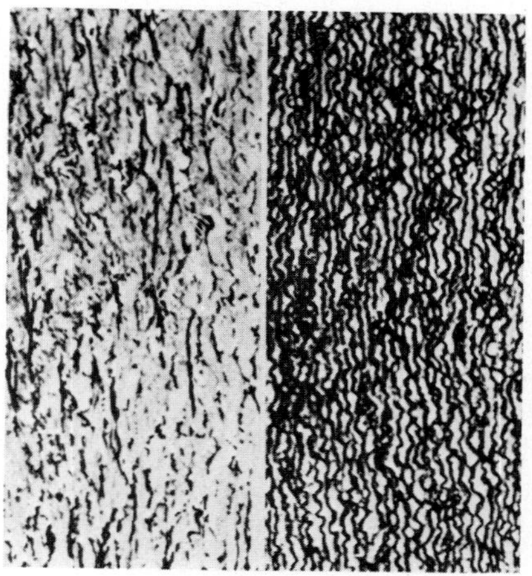

Fig. 3.2 Transverse section of the pulmonary trunk from a boy aged 16 years. The elastic fibrils are short, irregular and branched and form a loosely-arranged network. (Elastic/Van Gieson, × 75)

Fig. 3.3 Transverse section of the aorta from a male foetus aged 7½ months. The elastic fibrils are long, uniform, unbranched and parallel with one another. (Elastic/Van Gieson, × 100)

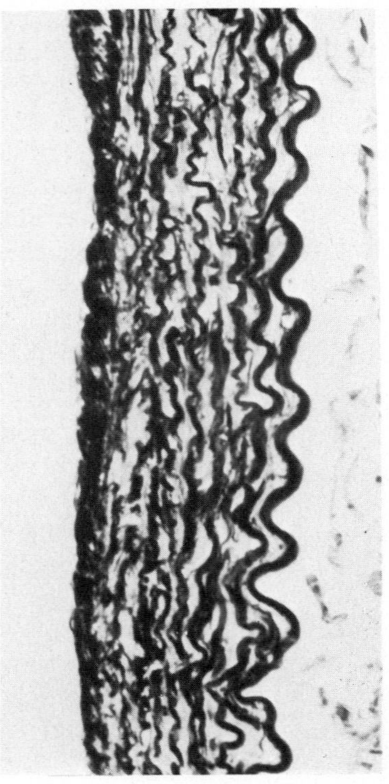

Fig. 3.4 Part of a transverse section of an elastic pulmonary artery showing the concentric elastic laminae. The thick internal elastic lamina is to the right. (Elastic/Van Gieson, × 375)

like expansions (Fig. 3.2). This picture is in marked contrast with the appearance of the elastic tissue in the media of the aorta which shows long, parallel, uniform fibrils (Fig. 3.3). In the media of the pulmonary trunk, individual fibrils show splitting over short distances and clumps of amorphous elastin are found occasionally. A thick internal elastic lamina forms, and there are zones of compressed elastic fibrils in the innermost and outermost parts of the media. The intima of the elastic pulmonary artery comprises fibrous tissue lined by endothelium. The adventitia is composed of acellular fibrous tissue.

In the pulmonary trunk of elderly persons a thick internal elastic lamina is still recognizable but occasionally elastosis causes a fuzziness on staining. Clumping of elastin into amorphous masses is common and frequently there is much fibrosis in the inner media. The vasa vasorum derived from the bronchial circulation are described in Chapter 38, those from the coronary circulation in Chapter 1.

In the smaller elastic arteries there is also an internal elastic lamina but in addition there are laminae within the media. These laminae are arranged concentrically (Fig. 3.4). Their number depends on the size of the artery and ranges from three or four in arteries of 1000 μm external diameter to sixteen to twenty in arteries of 5000 μm in diameter.[3] They are long, regular in thickness, and anastomose with each other. There is less collagen than in the pulmonary trunk, but muscle is more abundant and most of it is arranged circularly. In the smallest elastic pulmonary arteries the elastic laminae within the media are fine but the internal elastic lamina remains prominent. In addition, a distinct external elastic lamina makes its appearance.

Muscular Pulmonary Arteries

As in the systemic circulation the conducting arteries with a predominance of elastic tissue within the media gradually merge into typical muscular arteries. In the muscular arteries the media is composed of circularly orientated smooth muscle fibres and is bounded by internal and external elastic laminae (Figs 3.5 and 3.6). In the systemic circulation this transition occurs in large arteries such as the common iliac which leads from a typical conducting artery, the abdominal aorta, into a typical muscular artery, the femoral.[5] In the pulmonary circulation, the transition occurs in arteries of smaller diameter so that arterial vessels within the range of diameters of 100 to 1000 μm may be regarded as 'muscular pulmonary arteries'.[3] The term 'muscular pulmonary artery' is misleading because to those not very familiar with the classification of Brenner[3] it implies a thick-walled muscular blood vessel. In fact the outstanding characteristic of the normal 'muscular pulmonary artery' is that it is thin-walled.

In order to compare the thickness of the media in arteries of various sizes, we shall use the term 'percentage medial thickness' which indicates the thickness of the

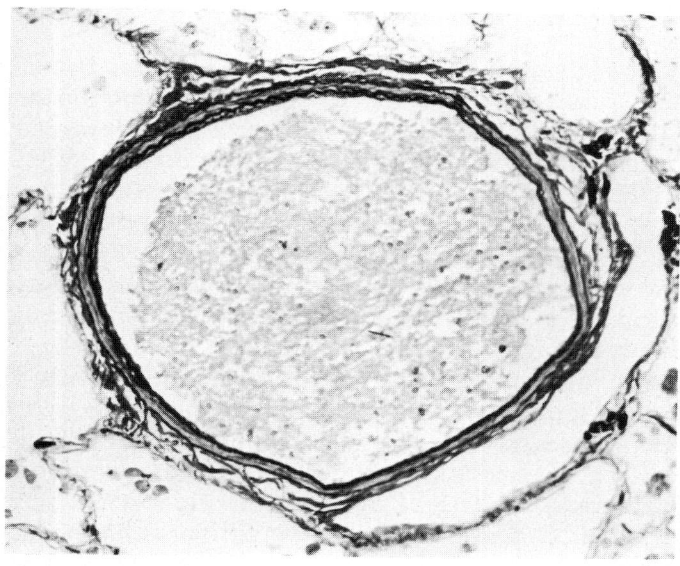

Fig. 3.5 Transverse section of a normal 'muscular pulmonary artery' showing a thin media bounded by internal and external elastic laminae. (Elastic/Van Gieson, × 168)

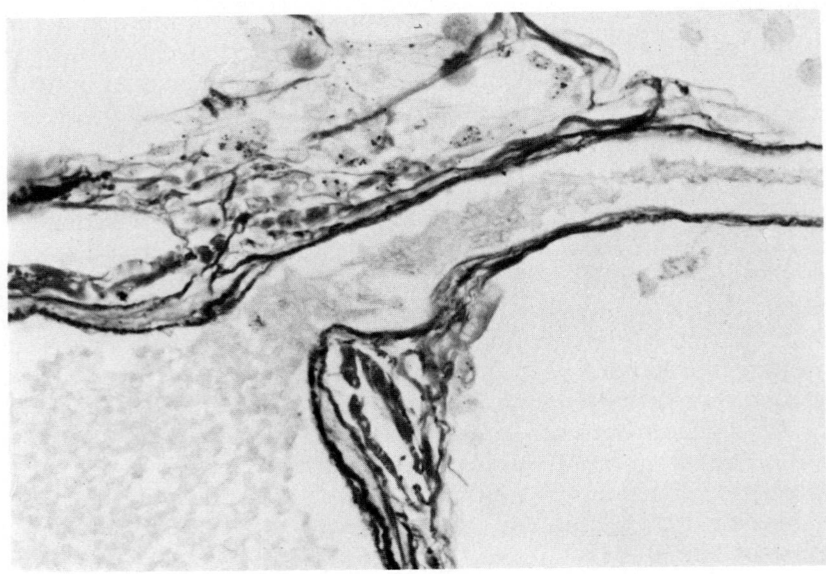

Fig. 3.6 The origin of a pulmonary arteriole. To the lower left is part of a transverse section of a muscular pulmonary artery showing a thin media of circularly orientated smooth muscle bounded by inner and outer elastic laminae. An arteriole arises from this vessel and passes to the right. Its wall is devoid of muscle and consists of only a single elastic lamina. (Elastic/Van Gieson, × 375)

media in terms of the diameter of the external elastic lamina. Brenner,[3] considering the whole range of vessels in this category of 'muscular pulmonary artery' found the medial thickness to vary between 6 and 32 per cent. In the case of the smaller 'muscular pulmonary arteries' below 300 μm in diameter, these values are far too high. Heath and Best[6] found this ratio to be 2·8 to 6·8 per cent for muscular pulmonary arteries with a diameter between 100 and 300 μm and 4·2 to 5·8 per cent for those less than 100 μm. Granston[7] gave an average medial thickness of 4·4 per cent for all muscular pulmonary arteries together, with a range from 3 to 8 per cent. Wagenvoort[8] found the average ratio to be 4·3 per cent with a range of 2·9 to 4·8 per cent for individual lungs.

The muscular pulmonary arteries lie close to the bronchioles, respiratory bronchioles and alveolar ducts. They branch with the bronchial tree. The anatomical structure of these arteries, with a thin media and a wide lumen, suggests a low resistance to flow. The mere presence of muscle in these arteries, however, suggests that they may constrict. In view of the later description of the development of bundles of longitudinal muscle in hypertensive pulmonary vascular disease (Chap. 16), particularly of the form associated with chronic hypoxia (Chap. 33), it may be noted here that longitudinal muscle is not a feature of the structure of the normal muscular pulmonary artery.

Pulmonary Arterioles

Pulmonary arterioles are vessels below 100 μm in diameter. The wall consists of an endothelial lining and a single elastic lamina with no muscular media and virtually no adventitia[2] (Figs 3.6–3.8). The structure is identical with that of a pulmonary venule. The only safe way of identifying an arteriole is to trace its origin from its parent muscular artery by means of serial sections. Arterioles may arise as terminations or side branches of muscular arteries. Those arising as terminal branches do so obliquely to the parent artery and are related to the respective alveolar ducts. The other type originates usually as a branch at right angles to a muscular pulmonary artery more proximal in the pulmonary vascular tree, and is related to a small bronchus.

At their site of origin the pulmonary arterioles have smooth muscle derived from the medial coat of their parent artery (Figs 3.6 and 3.8) and at this point their medial thickness is about ten per cent.[9] This histological feature is of some importance in connexion with the development of thick muscular walls in arterial vessels below 100 μm in diameter and will be discussed later in Chap. 16, dealing with hypertensive changes in pulmonary arteries. In thirteen normal lungs, arterial vessels less than 100 μm in diameter were occasionally found with a distinct muscular media and internal and external elastic laminae, which easily distinguished them from veins.[6] They were infrequent, and only thirty-three such vessels were seen in the sections from all thirteen patients. Twenty-six of them were in the lingula and the remaining seven were in the upper and lower lobes of four cases. We regard these vessels as small muscular pulmonary arteries. Their media is thin.

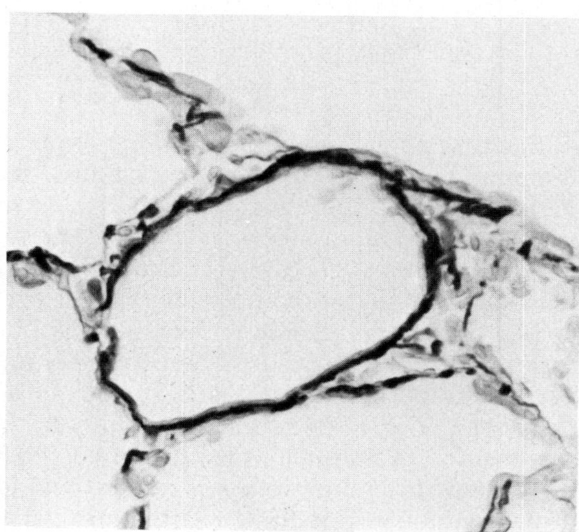

Fig. 3.7 Transverse section of a normal pulmonary arteriole. Its wall is devoid of muscle and consists of a single elastic lamina lined on its inner surface by endothelium. (Elastic/Van Gieson, ×415)

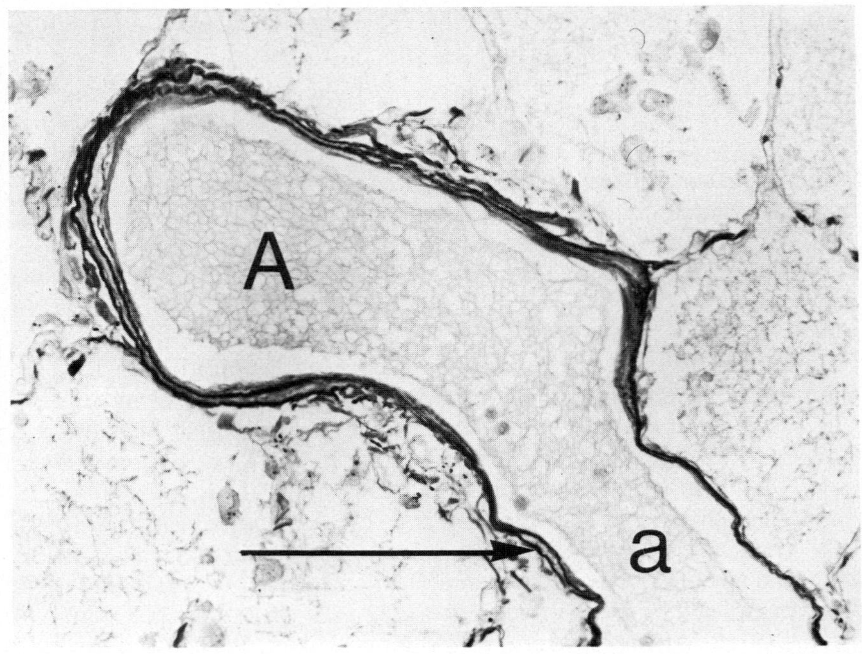

Fig. 3.8 Oblique section through a muscular pulmonary artery, A, showing the characteristic thin media bounded by inner and outer elastic laminae. An arteriolar branch, a, arises from the parent vessel and passes downwards and to the right. Its wall consists of a single elastic lamina except near its origin from its parent artery where the remains of a thin media bounded by two elastic laminae can still be seen (arrow). (Elastic/Van Gieson, × 284)

Pulmonary Capillaries

In a routine paraffin section of lung 5 μm in thickness, it is difficult to distinguish the pulmonary capillaries as separate structures within the thin alveolar walls (Fig. 3.9). When the pulmonary arterial tree is injected with a medium like carmine-gelatin, the rich capillary network in these alveolar walls becomes much more obvious (Fig. 3.10). However, electron microscopy is required to demonstrate the detailed structure of the pulmonary capillaries and blood–air barrier.

The pulmonary capillaries are lined by endothelial cells. For the most part this endothelial lining consists of an extremely thin layer of cytoplasm representing the peripheral portion of the cell spread as a film over the supporting basement membrane (Fig. 3.11). The endothelial cell bulges into the lumen of the capillary at the position of its nucleus (Fig. 3.11). Over much of the alveolar walls there is no interstitial space due to fusion of the basal laminae of the alveolar epithelium and of the pulmonary capillary endothelium (Chap. 24, p. 366).

The major part of normal human alveolar wall is covered by smooth, thin squamous extensions of membranous (type 1) pneumocytes (Fig. 3.11). The nuclei of these cells are commonly situated in the corners and angles of alveoli with scanty small mitochondria and a little endoplasmic reticulum around them.[10]

Interposed between the flat membranous pneumocytes are occasional solitary cells without squamous extension. These are the granular (type 2) pneumocytes which are shaped like demilunes (Fig. 3.12). The flat basal portion of the cell is attached to the underlying basement membrane while the free convex surface of the cell projects into the alveolar space (Fig. 3.12). The free curved surface of the granular pneumocyte is covered by microvilli which are short, straight and fairly regular.[11] Within the abundant cytoplasm are prominent lamellar bodies considered by most to be the source of pulmonary surfactant. Big mitochondria are present and have usually branching and sharply kinked cristae.[11] A well-developed rough endoplasmic reticulum is present.

The function of the membranous pneumocytes appears to be to provide an epithelial covering for the alveolar spaces. The function of the granular pneumocytes is to produce pulmonary surfactant.

The normal human blood–air barrier measures some 200 nm at its thinnest

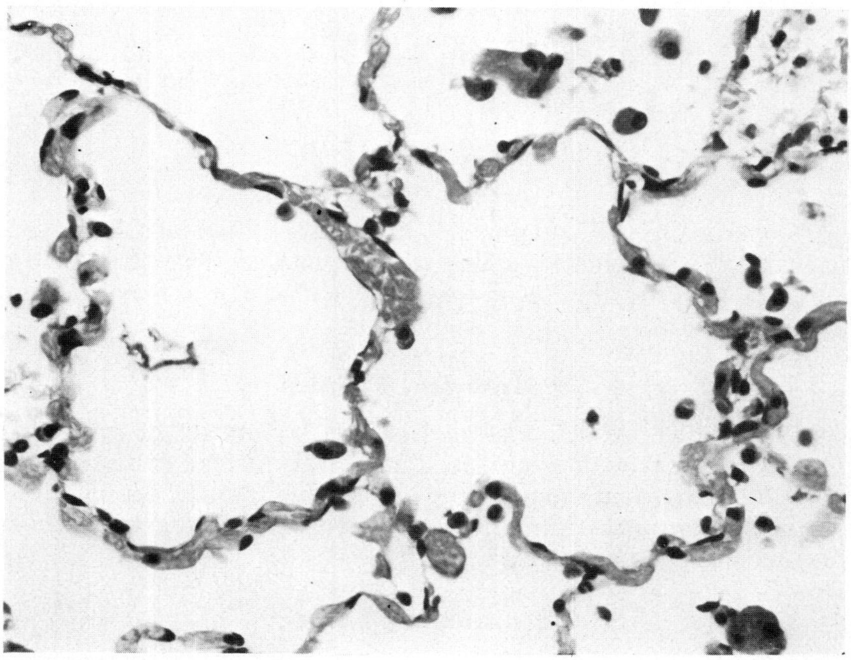

Fig. 3.9 Section of lung showing the thin alveolar walls containing blood capillaries. (Haematoxylin & Eosin, × 375)

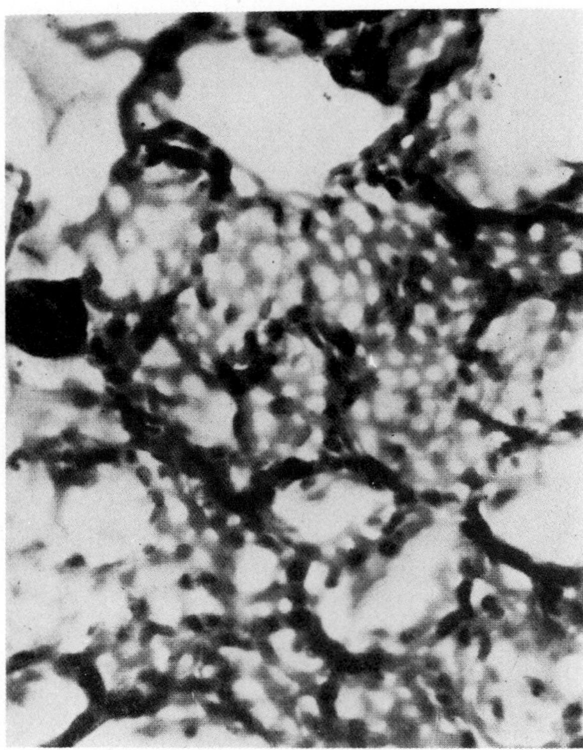

Fig. 3.10 Section of dog's lung injected with carmine-gelatin to show the rich capillary network in the alveolar walls. (×450)

portion and consists of three components (Fig. 3.13). These are an ultra-thin layer of cytoplasm of an endothelial cell lining a pulmonary capillary, the fused basement membrane, and an ultra-thin layer of cytoplasm derived from a membranous pneumocyte (Fig. 3.13).

Pulmonary Venules

These vessels, which we define as vessels with a diameter of less than 100 μm, are identical in structure with arterioles. The wall consists of endothelium and only a single elastic lamina, with virtually no adventitia (Figs 3.14 and 3.15). Formed near bronchioles, they pass into the connective tissue septa between secondary lobules to enter pulmonary veins (Fig. 3.15).

Pulmonary Veins

In contrast to the pulmonary arterial vessels, the pulmonary veins are situated away from the bronchial tree, and the larger veins lie in the interlobular septa. The media is slightly irregular in thickness consisting of bundles of obliquely and circularly arranged smooth muscle fibres and collagen (Figs 3.15 and 3.16). The adventitial coat is thick and fibrous. Fragmented elastic fibrils occur in both the media and the adventitia, the boundary between these two coats being ill-defined (Figs 3.15 and 3.16). The adventitia also contains irregular but chiefly longitudinal elastic fibres and often bundles of longitudinal muscle. Cardiac muscle continues from the left atrium for varying distances along the pulmonary veins separated from the media by a zone of fibro-fatty tissue. Vessels and nerves occur in the adventitia.[3]

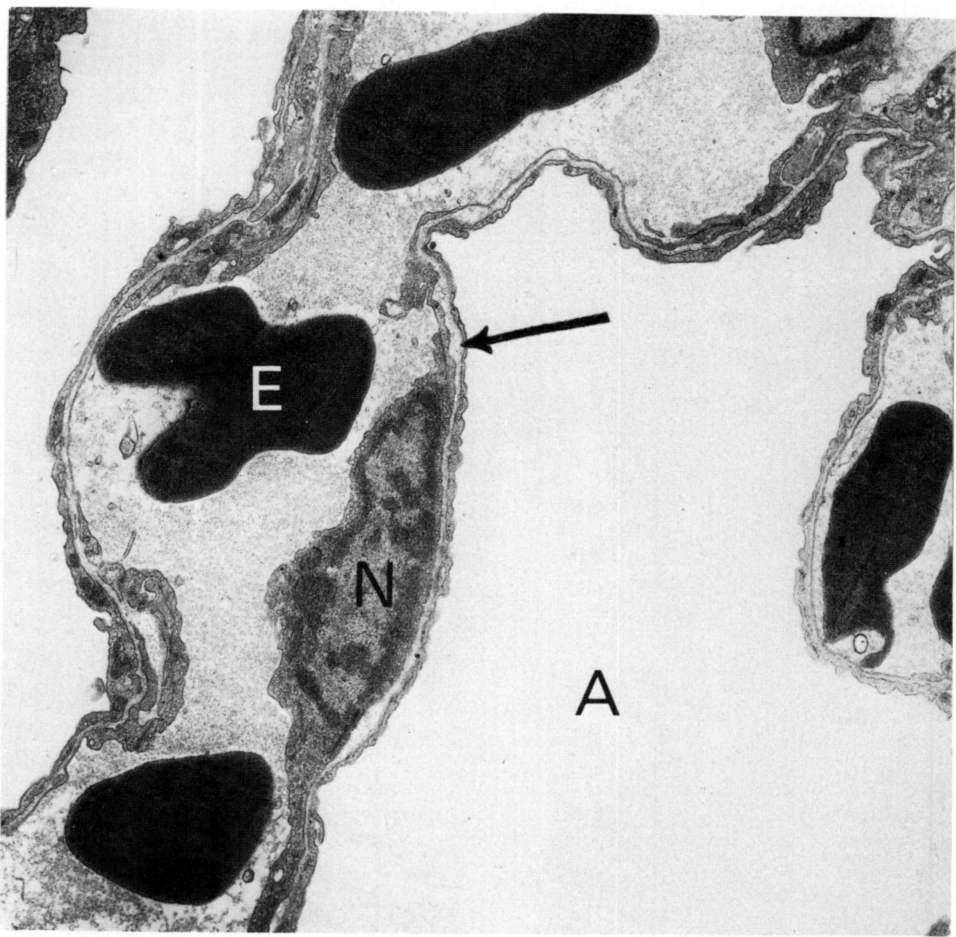

Fig. 3.11 Electron micrograph of a pulmonary capillary from a Wistar albino rat. The capillary contains erythrocytes, E, and is lined by a very thin layer of cytoplasm from endothelial cells which bulge into the lumen at sites occupied by their nuclei, N. The fused basement membrane is indicated by an arrow. The alveolar space, A, is lined by the flattened cytoplasmic extensions of a membranous pneumocyte. ($\times 7500$)

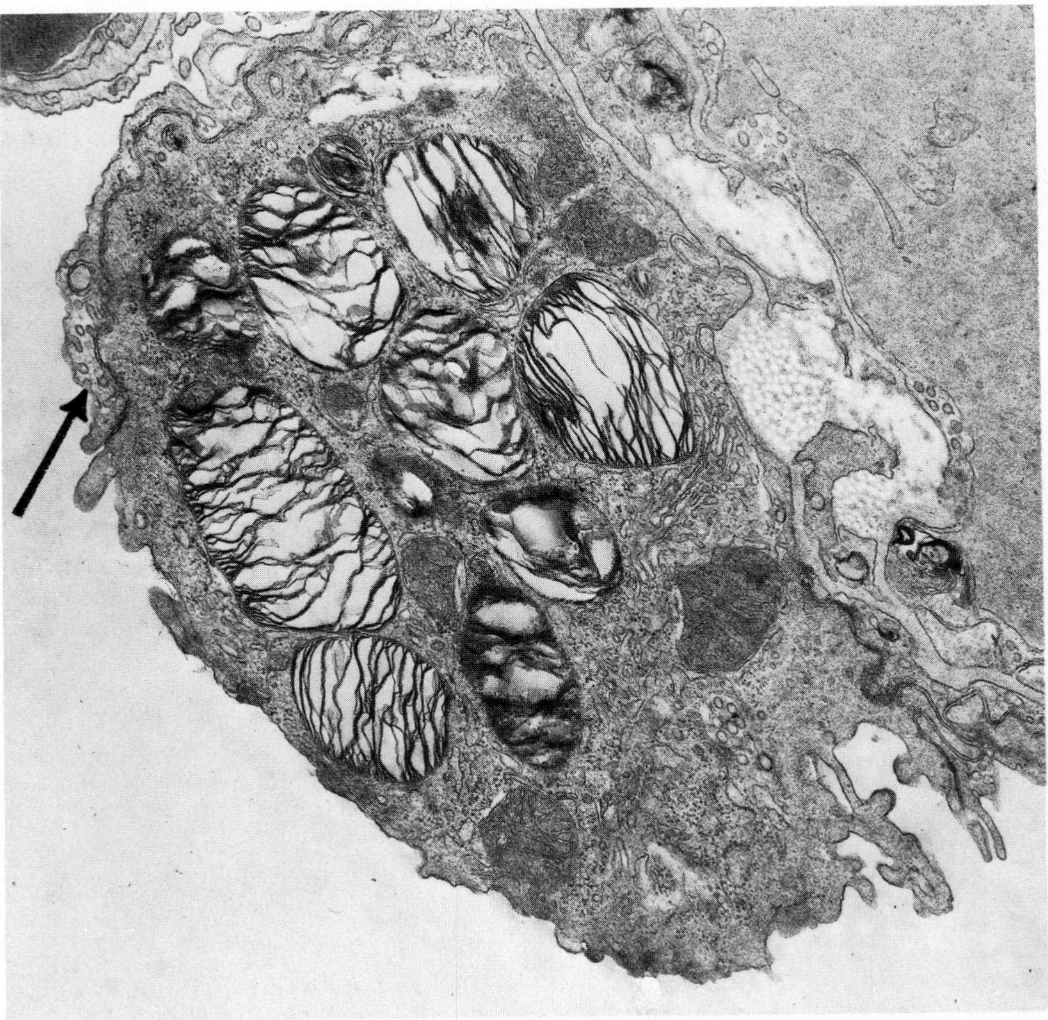

Fig. 3.12 Electron micrograph of part of the lining of an alveolar space in a Wistar albino rat. The cell is a granular pneumocyte. Prominent lamellar bodies are seen within its cytoplasm. The free curved surface of the pneumocyte is partly covered by a cytoplasmic extension from an adjoining membranous pneumocyte (arrow). (× 18 750)

Intimal Fibrosis

Intimal fibrosis is one of the striking histological features of the normal adult pulmonary vasculature (Figs 3.14 and 3.17). It is found almost constantly at necropsy, although it is often slight.[3] It increases in frequency and severity with age and exists without producing any obvious harmful results. The intimal thickening involves the whole or part of the circumference of the pulmonary artery or vein and consists of a very narrow layer of collagen, frequently hyaline in appearance. It is acellular and stains faintly with eosin. There is a striking similarity between these appearances and the concentric and crescentic thrombotic lesions found in the pulmonary blood vessels of patients with cyanotic congenital heart disease without pulmonary hypertension.[12] This suggests that they have a common pathogenesis and that the appearances associated with increasing age may be the result

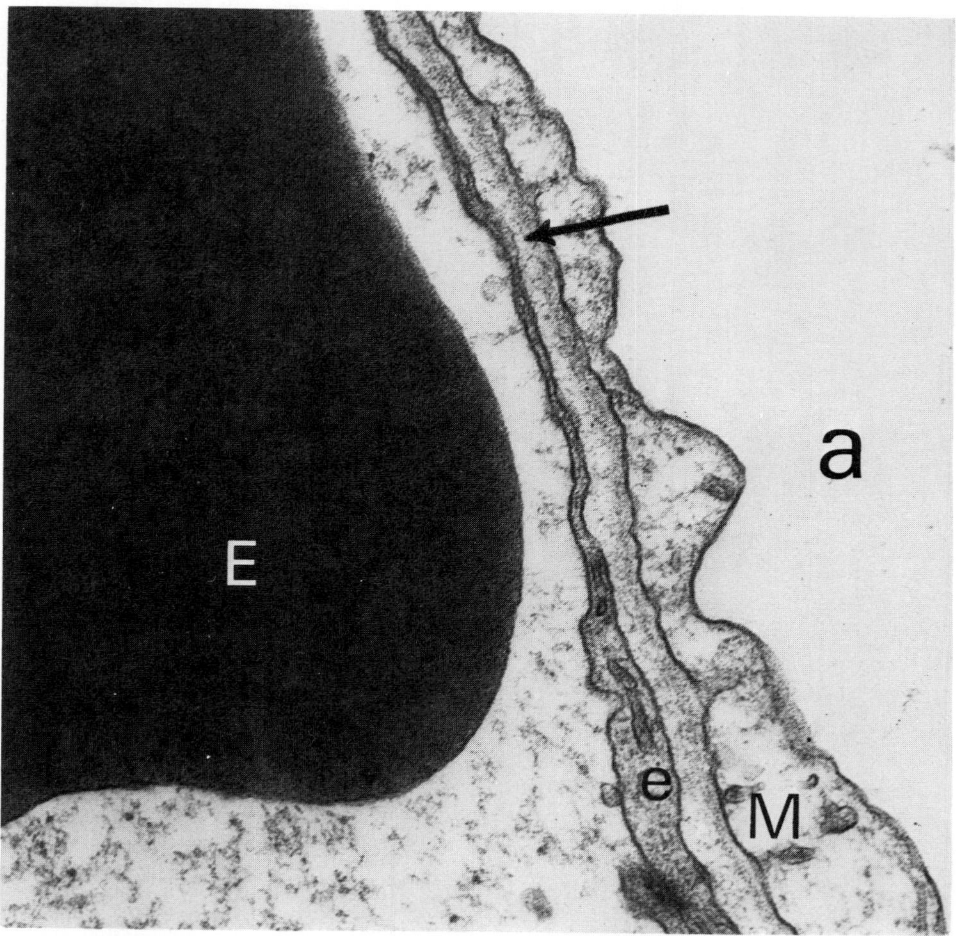

Fig. 3.13 Electron micrograph of alveolar wall in a Wistar albino rat to show the components of the blood–air barrier. The pulmonary capillary contains an erythrocyte, E. The blood–air barrier consists from within outwards of an attenuated layer of cytoplasm of an endothelial cell, e, the fused basement membrane (arrow) and the thin layer of cytoplasm of a membranous pneumocyte, M, lining the alveolar space, a. (× 50 000)

C

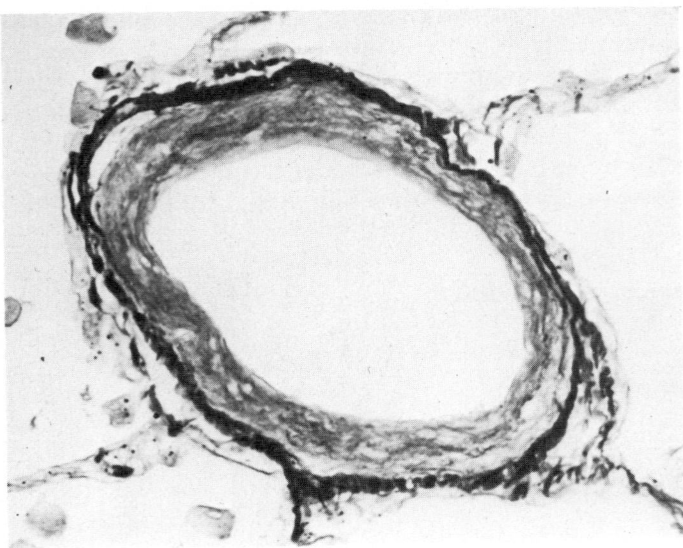

Fig. 3.14 Transverse section of a normal pulmonary venule. The wall consists of a single elastic lamina. There is considerable intimal fibrosis due to age change. (Elastic/Van Gieson, × 375)

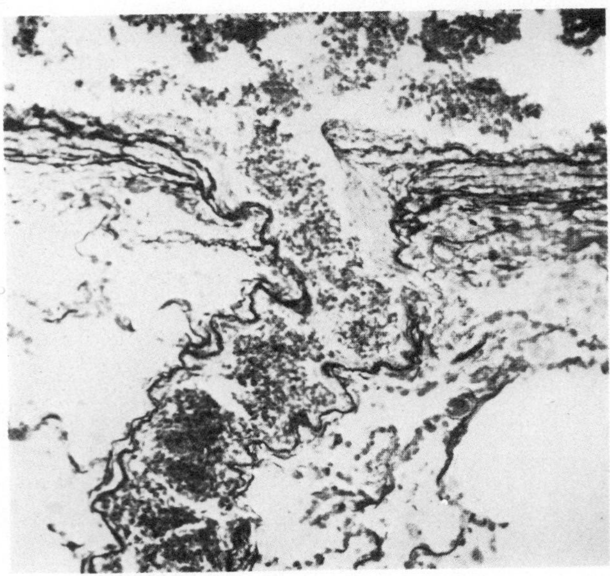

Fig. 3.15 Part of a longitudinal section of a normal pulmonary vein at the point where it receives one of its venular tributaries. The haphazard arrangement of the elastic tissue in the media is seen. The wall of the pulmonary venule consists of a single elastic lamina. (Elastic/Van Gieson, × 150)

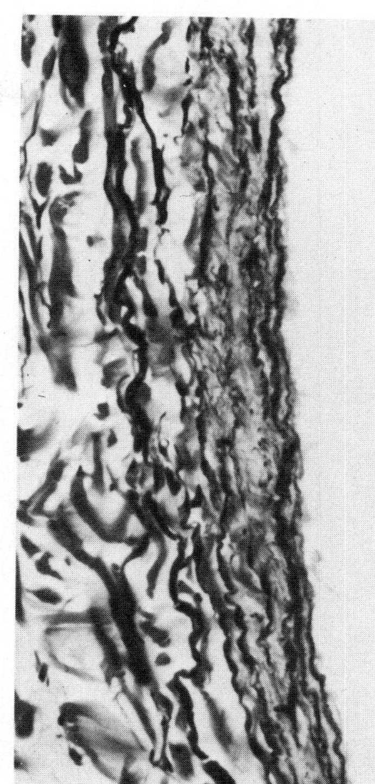

Fig. 3.16 Part of longitudinal section of a normal pulmonary vein. The adventitia is to the left. The haphazard arrangement of collagen, smooth muscle, and elastic tissue in the ill-defined media is in contrast to the structure of the normal muscular pulmonary artery shown in Fig. 3.5. Distinct internal and external elastic laminae are absent. (Elastic/Van Gieson, × 375)

of thrombosis occurring much more slowly and to a lesser degree than in the cases of cyanotic congenital heart disease. A similar conclusion was reached in a study of intimal thickening and organization of mural thrombi in systemic veins, when it was thought that in many instances intimal thickenings were of thrombotic origin.[13]

The Nerve Supply of the Pulmonary Blood Vessels

The following account is based on the description given by Mitchell.[14] The blood vessels of the lung receive a nerve supply of both sympathetic and parasympathetic origin. Afferent and efferent fibres of each system are present.

In the parasympathetic system, the efferent pre-ganglionic fibres arise from cells in the dorsal vagal nuclei while the cell-bodies of the afferent fibres lie in the inferior vagal ganglia. On reaching the root of the lung, each vagus nerve divides into a smaller branch which passes in front of the hilum and a larger branch which passes behind. Below the hilum the two divisions join in the oesophageal plexus. Branches arise from the anterior and posterior divisions of the vagus to form a small anterior and a larger posterior pulmonary plexus on each side. The plexi communicate with the cardiac, aortic and oesophageal plexi, and the left anterior pulmonary plexus communicates with the phrenic nerve.

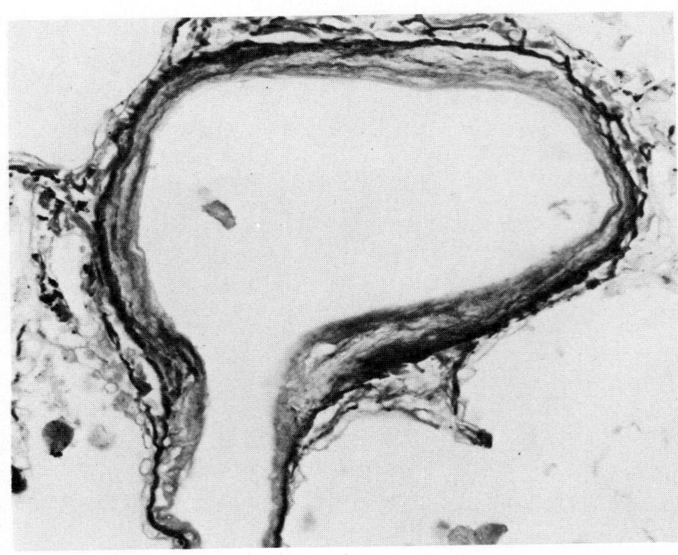

Fig. 3.17 Transverse section of a normal small pulmonary vein at the point of entry of a pulmonary venule, running from below. Both the vein and its tributary show age-change intimal fibrosis. (Elastic/Van Gieson, ×270)

The sympathetic supply to the lungs has its origin in the second to sixth thoracic segments of the spinal cord. The pre-ganglion efferent fibres arise from cells in the lateral horns of these segments. They synapse with the cell-bodies of the post-ganglionic fibres in the second to sixth thoracic ganglia and the stellate ganglia. Afferent sympathetic fibres have their cell-bodies in the posterior root ganglia.

The branches from the sympathetic chain which carry fibres to and from the lung are intimately mixed with cardiac, aortic and oesophageal branches. Most of them pass to the posterior pulmonary plexi.

From the pulmonary plexi, branches accompany the main bronchi and the pulmonary vessels into the lung. The bundles of nerve fibres which travel with the pulmonary arteries are situated between the artery and its accompanying bronchus. The nerve fibres to the bronchial arteries come from the plexi surrounding adjacent bronchi. The bronchial arteries have a more abundant supply than the pulmonary arteries. Few fibres are seen around pulmonary capillaries. The nerve supply to the pulmonary veins is derived from that to the left atrium and becomes more obvious as they approach the heart. The supply to the smaller intrapulmonary veins is very scanty. Sympathetic fibres end in a network or 'ground plexus' which is situated at the junction between the adventitia and media of pulmonary arteries and veins (Chap. 12, p. 174). Groups of nerve cells may be seen close to or within the adventitia of the muscular pulmonary arteries and provide evidence of a parasympathetic supply.

A number of different types of afferent nerve endings, including sub-endothelial arborizations, bulbous nodules and 'grape-endings' have been described in the pulmonary arteries and veins, although these observations have been made mainly in animals.

Pulmonary Lymphatics

The walls of the larger lymphatics consist of collagen, small fragmented elastic fibrils and smooth muscle, and they are lined by endothelium (Fig. 3.18). The muscle fibres are orientated longitudinally and obliquely and are arranged focally so that they do not form a continuous muscular wall as in pulmonary arteries and veins (Fig. 3.18). Hence much of the wall is lined only by endothelium even when the lymphatic vessel exceeds 100 μm in diameter. Pulmonary lymphatics differ from veins in that their diameter varies greatly within short distances, suddenly narrowing and then immediately expanding into wide segments (Fig. 3.19). They do not show the intimal fibrosis which is so characteristic of the small pulmonary blood vessels of the adult human lung. There is less elastic tissue in their walls than in arteries or veins.

The smaller lymphatics comprise a fibro-elastic coat and an endothelial lining, and the lymph capillaries consist solely of endothelium (Fig. 3.20). Valves are common in the pulmonary lymphatics, especially in the pleura (Figs 3.18 and 3.21).

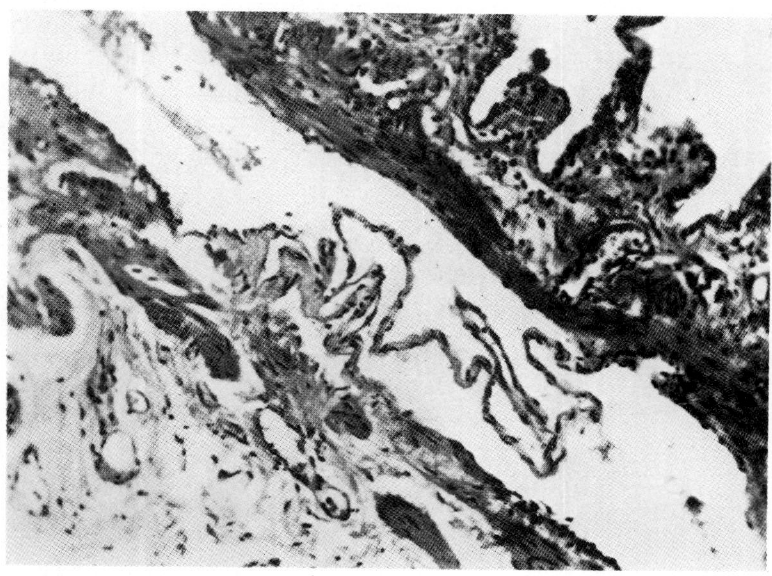

Fig. 3.18 Longitudinal section of a normal large lymphatic trunk in the lung. There are considerable amounts of smooth muscle in its wall. A valve is seen within the lymphatic vessel. (Haematoxylin & Eosin, × 150)

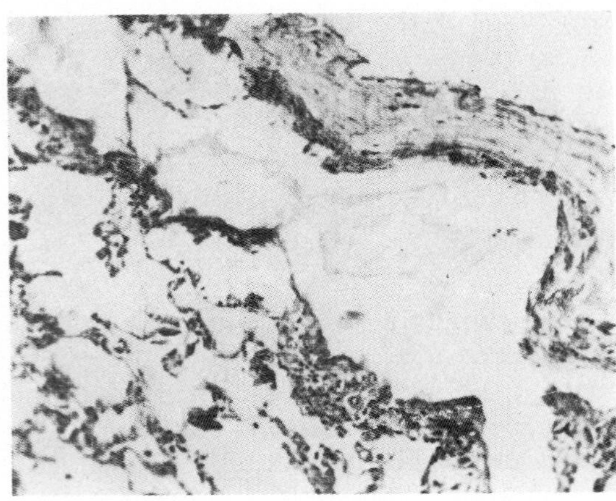

Fig. 3.19 Pleural lymphatic vessel showing great variation in diameter over a short distance. A valve and lymphatic capillaries are present. (Elastic/Van Gieson, × 125)

These are usually arranged in pairs, are formed of intimal folds supported by a minimal amount of fibrous tissue, and aid the ready identification of lymphatics.

The lymphatics of the human lung are arranged in superficial and deep networks. The former occurs in the pleura (Fig. 3.19). The latter is situated around the bronchi, pulmonary arteries (Fig. 22.11) and veins, and in the connective tissue septa between the secondary lobules. The two systems anastomose in the pleura and at the hilum. Miller[15] has demonstrated by injection studies that the superficial lymphatic vessels form a pattern in the pleura of irregular polyhedra which mark out the secondary lobules. Smaller lymphatics, with finger-like projections, delineate smaller zones within the lobular area. He has shown that only one or two lymphatics

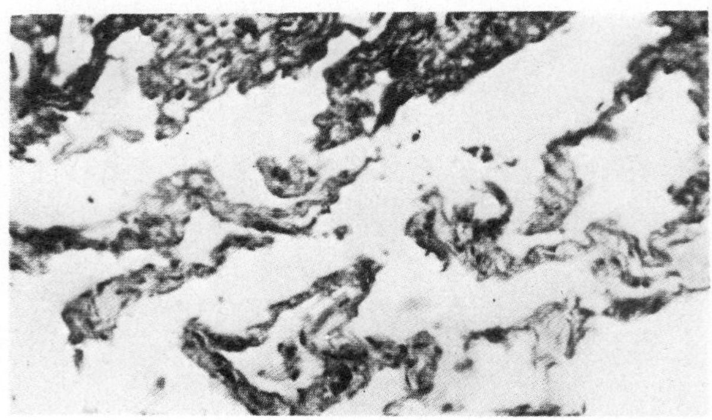

Fig. 3.20 Lymphatic vessels and capillaries in the connective tissue septa between secondary lobules. These have an endothelial lining without muscle in their walls. Contrast with the structure of the larger lymphatic vessels shown in Fig. 3.18. (Elastic/Van Gieson, × 150)

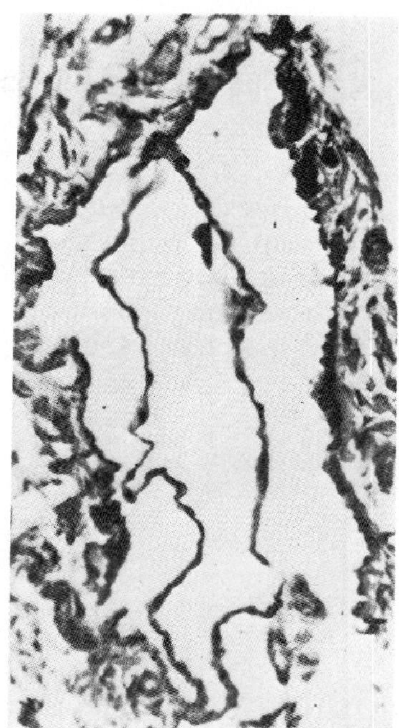

Fig. 3.21 Pleural lymphatic vessels showing a pair of valves. (Elastic/Van Gieson, × 250)

accompany the smaller pulmonary veins but that there is a network around the larger veins; this communicates with the bronchial network at points where pulmonary venous radicles arise from the bronchial tree. Two or three main lymph trunks accompany each pulmonary artery, and loops from these form a network around the vessel; the trunk situated between bronchus and pulmonary artery is common to both networks. Lymphatics can be demonstrated as distal as the lung atria but they are not seen in the alveolar walls. The lymphatics from the pleura, the pulmonary and bronchial blood vessels and the fibrous tissue septa of the lung drain into the tracheobronchial lymph nodes.

Differences in Structure Between Systemic and Pulmonary Arteries

In this chapter we have noted many differences between systemic and pulmonary arteries. We may summarize some of the most striking here. A far greater portion of the pulmonary vasculature is occupied by elastic conducting arteries.[16] In the systemic circulation only the aorta and its major branches are elastic in type but in the pulmonary circulation the transition from elastic to muscular type arteries occurs in arteries as little as 1 mm in diameter.[16] Pulmonary arteries have a much thinner media than their systemic counterparts. In contrast to systemic arteries, which have a thick internal elastic lamina and an absent or much less well developed external lamina, pulmonary arteries have a media sandwiched between well-defined internal and external elastic laminae. The systemic arteriole has a well-defined thick muscular media but the pulmonary arteriole has a wall consisting of a thin, single elastic lamina only.

Human and Animal Pulmonary Arteries

In this second edition we have had occasion to refer to the pulmonary arteries of animals in connexion with various experiments on the pulmonary circulation. Great caution must be applied in evaluating pathological changes in the pulmonary arteries of experimental animals until one is very familiar with the normal features for the species being employed. We have considered this subject in Chapter 26.

REFERENCES

1. Weibel, E. R. & Vidone, R. A. (1961) *Amer. Rev. Resp. Dis.*, **84**, 856.
2. Lendrum, A. C. (1949) *J. Path. Bact.*, **61**, 443.
3. Brenner, O. (1935) *Arch. Intern. Med.*, **56**, 211.
4. Heath, D., Dushane, J. W., Wood, E. H. & Edwards, J. E. (1959) *J. Path. Bact.*, **77**, 443.
5. Heath, D. & Edwards, J. E. (1959) *Amer. Heart J.*, **57**, 29.
6. Heath, D. & Best, P. V. (1958) *J. Path. Bact.*, **76**, 165.
7. Granston, A. S. (1958) *Proc. Inst. Med. Chicago*, **22**, 116.
8. Wagenvoort, C. A. (1960) *Circulation*, **22**, 535.
9. Edwards, J. E. (1957) *Circulation*, **15**, 164.
10. Kay, J. M. & Edwards, F. R. (1973) *J. Path.*, **111**, 239.
11. Brewer, D. B., Heath, D. & Asquith, P. (1969) *J. Path.*, **97**, 317.
12. Best, P. V. & Heath, D. (1958) *J. Path. Bact.*, **75**, 281.
13. Scott, G. B. D. (1956) *J. Path. Bact.*, **72**, 543.
14. Mitchell, G. A. G. (1956) *Cardiovascular Innervation*. Page 229. Edinburgh: Livingstone.
15. Miller, W. S. (1947) *The Lung*, 2nd edn. Springfield, Ill.: Thomas.
16. Wagenvoort, C. A., Heath, D. & Edwards, J. E. (1964) In *The Pathology of the Pulmonary Vasculature*. Springfield, Ill.: Thomas.

4. The Relation Between Structure and Function in Normal Pulmonary Blood Vessels

The previous chapter has described the difference in structure between the various pulmonary blood vessels. The basic materials of which their walls are formed—elastic tissue, collagen, smooth muscle, endothelium and ground substances—are, however, common to most. The present chapter considers the physical properties of these substances and their influence upon the function of the blood vessels. Our understanding of these matters has been clarified by Burton[1] and the following considerations are based largely on his work.

Elasticity and Extensibility

The physicist's definition of elasticity is the force exerted by a substance which opposes any attempt to change its shape. For instance, it is the force exerted by a wire when an attempt is made to extend it. By this definition, a highly elastic wire is one which cannot easily be stretched. Unfortunately this physical definition of elasticity has the opposite sense to the popular use of the word. Thus, to avoid confusion, we shall use the term extensibility to describe changes in length and distensibility to describe changes in volume of a vessel. These terms are reciprocal functions of the physicist's elasticity and have an identical sense in both technical and popular usage.

When a wire is stretched, the relation between the force exerted and the elongation achieved is a linear one up to a certain point. This is Hooke's Law. Eventually the material will start to yield, and beyond this point elongation proceeds

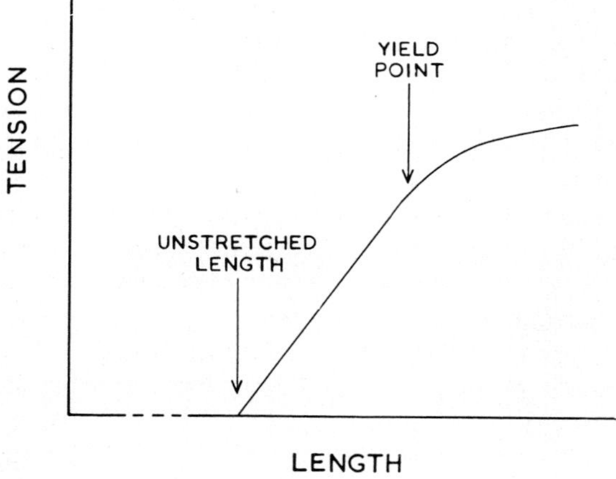

Fig. 4.1 Schematic length–tension diagram of a wire.

with a decreasing rise in tension. A graph plotting tension against length will, therefore, be a straight line until the 'yield point' is reached when it will start to deviate towards the length axis (Fig. 4.1).

Until the 'yield point' is reached, the relation between the force applied (or tension exerted) and the change in length is given by the equation:

$$F = E \cdot \frac{\Delta l}{l_0} \cdot A$$

where F is the force in dynes, Δl is the change in length, l_0 is the unstretched length, A is the cross-sectional area in cm^2 and E is Young's modulus of elasticity. Young's modulus is, therefore, the force per cm^2 cross-sectional area that would theoretically have to be applied in order to double the unstretched length of the material, if it is assumed that Hooke's Law is obeyed up to that point. The modulus is high if the material is inextensible and low if it stretches easily.

The Extensibility of Endothelium, Elastic Tissue, Collagen and Smooth Muscle

The endothelium of blood vessels has very little strength. Elastic tissue has a Young's modulus in the region of 3×10^6 $dyn \cdot cm^{-2}$ and elastic fibres can be extended to two and a half times their unstretched length before they break.[1] Collagen has a Young's modulus in the region of 1×10^9 $dyn \cdot cm^{-2}$ and is so strong that the breaking force has never been measured satisfactorily.[1] Thus elastic tissue is more than 300 times as extensible as collagen. The elasticity of muscle is difficult to measure since the fibres respond to stretch by active contraction. Burton gives a very approximate estimation of 6×10^4 $dyn \cdot cm^{-2}$ for the modulus of relaxed smooth muscle and 1×10^5 for contracted smooth muscle. The order of these figures shows how muscle tissue is considerably more extensible than elastic tissue. For purposes of comparison, the value of Young's modulus[1] for rubber is 4×10^7 and for steel is 2×10^{12} $dyn \cdot cm^{-2}$.

The Extensibility of the Walls of Blood Vessels

Although within limits simple tissues such as elastic tissue or collagen may obey Hooke's Law and show a linear relation between force and length, the composite nature of the walls of blood vessels causes the relation in them to be a curved one.[2] A seemingly universal characteristic of the length–tension diagrams of the walls of blood vessels is that the line of the relation bends toward the tension axis (Fig. 4.2). In other words, the walls of both arteries and veins become less extensible the more they are stretched. This is quite the opposite of a homogeneous material such as metal or rubber which, after a certain point, yields progressively as the tension is increased (Fig. 4.1). Similar observations were made on isolated strips of arterial walls by Roy[3] as long ago as 1880. The explanation has been given by Roach and Burton.[4] These workers studied the distensibility of arteries first in the fresh condition, and then after dissolving the collagen with formic acid or after digesting the elastin with trypsin. In this way the distensibility of the entire vessel could be compared with that remaining when either the collagen or the elastic tissue had been removed from its walls. From these studies it appears that the unstretched

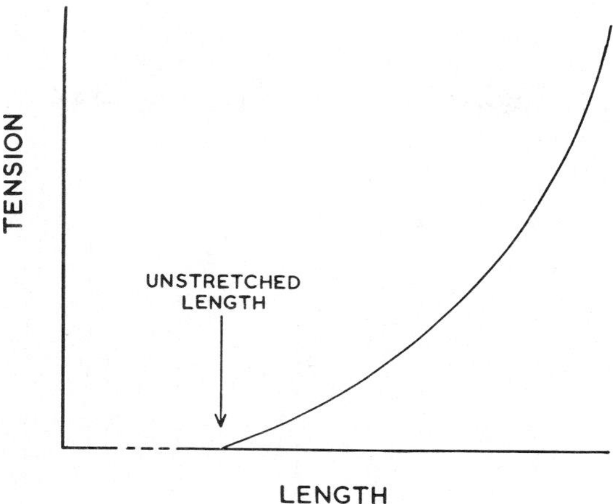

Fig. 4.2 Schematic length–tension diagram of the wall of a blood vessel. (After Burton[2])

length of the elastic tissue in the wall of a vessel is shorter than that of the fibrous tissue. Thus the initial part of the length–tension diagram for an arterial wall is due to the influence of the relatively extensible elastic fibres. With further distension the collagen fibres become more and more involved and thus the arterial wall becomes less and less extensible.

Structure and Function in the Walls of the Large Elastic Pulmonary Arteries

The fibro-elastic structure of the pulmonary arterial trunk and its larger branches (p. 25) is consistent with the function of conduction and storage of blood which this part of the pulmonary circulation fulfils. This function is comparable with that of the aorta, although the lower pressures in the pulmonary artery do not require as strong a wall. Assuming a radius of 1·5 cm for the main pulmonary artery[5] and a mean pulmonary arterial pressure of 15 mmHg, the tension in the wall would be 30 000 $\text{dyn} \cdot \text{cm}^{-1}$.* A comparable figure for the aortic wall would be 200 000 $\text{dyn} \cdot \text{cm}^{-1}$. The different physical properties of the pulmonary artery and aorta are readily apparent in the post-mortem room. If a piece of the wall of the main pulmonary artery is gripped by both hands and pulled, it will be found to be considerably more extensible than a comparable piece of aorta.

In order to determine the extensibility characteristics of the pulmonary trunk we have used the simple mechanical apparatus shown in Figure 4.3 (Ref. 6). A circum-

*TENSION = Pressure × radius (p. 52)
= 15 mmHg × 1·5 cm
= 15 × 1332 $\text{dyn} \cdot \text{cm}^{-2}$ × 1·5 cm
= 30 120 $\text{dyn} \cdot \text{cm}^{-1}$

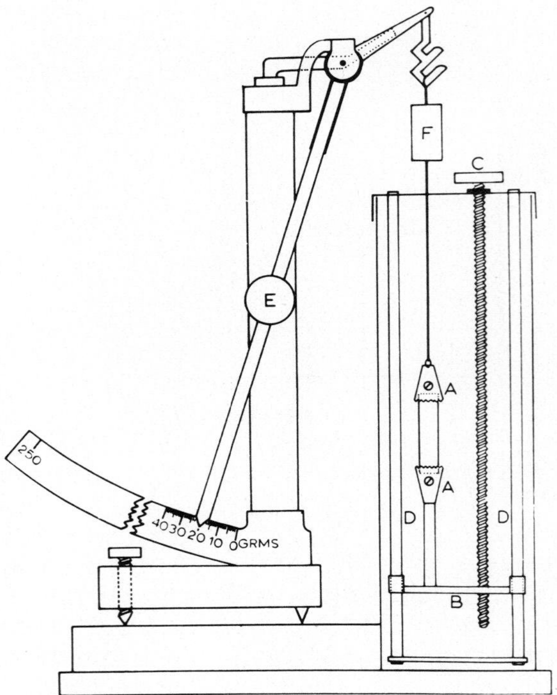

Fig. 4.3 Diagram of extensibility apparatus. The letters are referred to in the text.

ferential strip, 1 cm in width, was cut from the pulmonary trunk 1 cm above the level of the pulmonary valve by means of a rectangular punch operated by means of a simple lever. The loose adventitial connective tissue was stripped off and each end of the strip placed in a serrated clamp (A in Fig. 4.3), tightened by means of a screw. One clamp was fixed to a metallic rod; this was attached to a cross-bar (B) which could be moved by means of a screw (C) and two parallel runners (D) upwards and downwards in a bath filled with physiological saline and maintained at 37°C. The other clamp was suspended vertically above the first by means of a nylon thread attached to one arm of a balance. The opposite arm of the balance acted as a pointer along a circular scale which indicated directly the weight that had been applied to the strip of artery. The scale was calibrated by the application of a series of standard weights for a particular adjustment of the counterweights E and F. Thus, by turning the screw, the strip of artery was subjected to an increasing extensile load, the magnitude of which could be read off on the scale of the balance.

The length of the strip at any load was measured by a telescopic optical system which moved along a vertical scale. A hair-line within the optical system was aligned first with the clamp at one end of the strip of artery and then with the other. The distance between the two clamps could thus be measured along the vertical scale which could be read to 0·01 cm by means of a micrometer adjustment with a Vernier scale. The length of the arterial strip was measured first in the unstretched state and then with extensile loads of 10, 20, 40, 60 and 100 g weight, successively. Five minutes were allowed between the application of an increment in load and the measurement of the degree of extension. During this time a certain amount of slow elongation of the strip occurred while the load was maintained constant by adjusting screw C.

In Figure 4.4 a length–tension diagram for a circumferential strip of the main pulmonary artery is compared with that for the ascending aorta in the same subject. The wall of the pulmonary artery is evidently more extensible than the wall of the aorta, and this is in keeping with both the histological structure and function of these two vessels. It will be observed that the relation between tension and extension is such that the arterial wall becomes increasingly less extensible the more it is stretched.

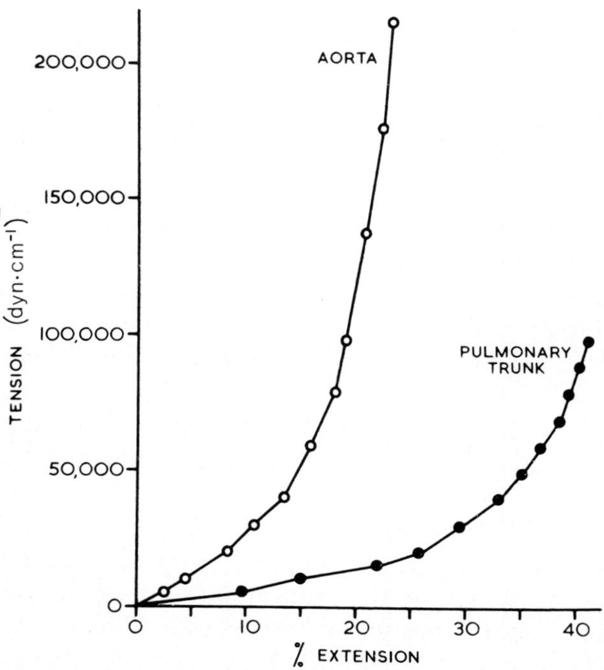

Fig. 4.4 Length–tension diagrams of circumferential strips of the pulmonary trunk and ascending aorta. The length is expressed as the percentage increase of the resting length. The aorta is less extensible than the pulmonary trunk. From a man aged 57 years who died of a cerebral tumour. Systemic blood pressure 135/85 mmHg.

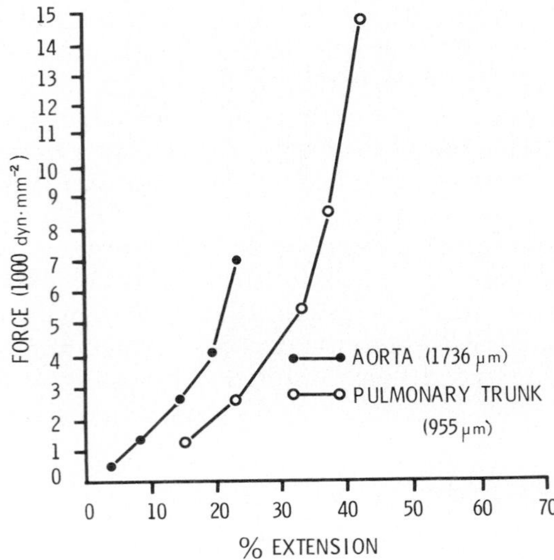

Fig. 4.5 A comparison of the extensibility of the pulmonary trunk and aorta in a woman aged 65 years.

Such a direct comparison between the two vessels is partly dependent on the different thicknesses of their walls. In order to determine whether the material composing the wall has different properties, it is necessary to express the extensile force in terms of the cross-sectional area of tissue through which it is applied.[6] Figure 4.5 compares the media of the human pulmonary trunk and aorta in this way. It is now evident that the material composing the media of the pulmonary trunk is intrinsically more extensible than that of the aorta.

The relation preserves its curvilinear character, so that the first and more horizontal part of the curve may be thought to be due to the extension of elastic tissue alone, while the gradual involvement of the collagenous fibres coincides with the development of the more vertical later part of the curve.[2] It seems unlikely that all similar fibres have the same unstretched length and, with increasing extension, one would expect a progressive recruitment of both elastic and collagenous fibres opposing further stretch. Thus, at a particular length of the arterial strip (l) there will be a number of elastic fibres stretched in varying degrees according to their unstretched length (λ_e) and a number of collagenous fibres stretched according to their unstretched length (λ_c). If E_e and E_c are the coefficients of elasticity of elastic and collagenous fibres respectively, the total extensile force may be represented as:

$$- F = \Sigma\, E_e(l - \lambda_e) + E_c(l - \lambda_c)$$

for all fibres, where $\lambda \leqq l$.

Such a representation is naturally an oversimplification, since not all fibres of one type have the same thickness nor is their orientation homogeneous. It also assumes that each fibre obeys Hooke's Law. It does, nevertheless, give some indication of the probable nature of the relation between the degree of extension and the two groups of 'elastic forces' due respectively to elastin and collagen.

On the basis of this model dF/dl describes the recruitment of new 'elastic forces' (whether these be of elastin or collagen) and d_2F/dl^2 describes the rate of recruitment. Curves for d_2F/dl^2 plotted against the degree of extension in young people give a distinct suggestion of two different populations of elastic forces (Fig. 4.6). Presumably the population arising closer to the unstretched length represents elastic tissue while the second population represents collagen.

The relation between force and extension in the media of the human pulmonary trunk is affected by the age of the subject,[6,7] such that an increasing age is associated with a decreasing extensibility (Fig. 4.7). The relation is also affected by disease, as is discussed in Chapter 18.

To what extent such differences in extensile characteristics can be explained in terms of the proportions of collagen and elastin composing the media is not entirely clear. Histological observations (Chap. 3, p. 25) show more elastic tissue in the aorta than in the pulmonary trunk. Chemical measurements in a number of species have shown more elastin in the aorta than in the pulmonary trunk, while the quantity of collagen is about the same.[8] Such observations might suggest that it is the quantity of elastin in the media which has determined the differences between the pulmonary trunk and the aorta.

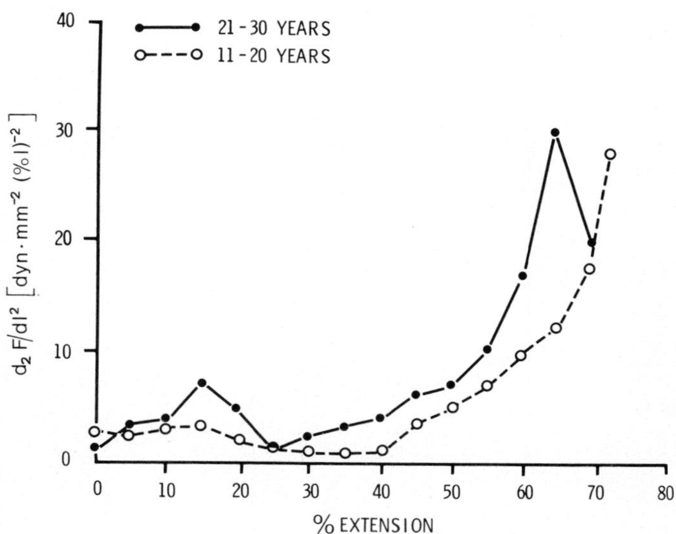

Fig. 4.6 The average relation between d_2F/dl^2 and the degree of extension for the second and third decades.

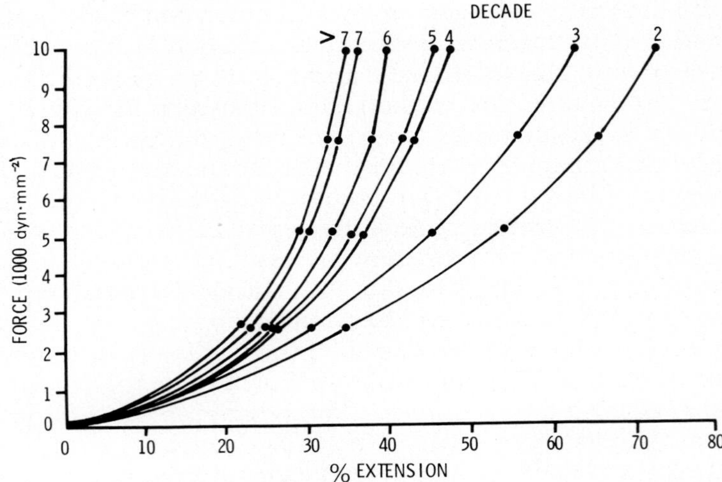

Fig. 4.7 Average values for the extensibility of the pulmonary trunk at different decades.

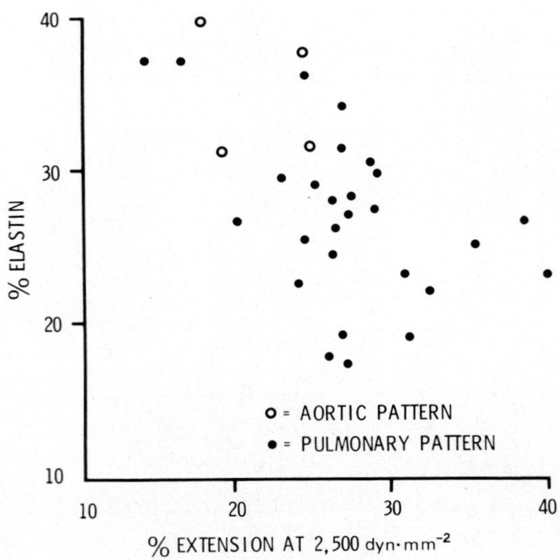

Fig. 4.8 The relation between the degree of extension at 2500 dyn mm^{-2} and the content of elastin (per cent dry weight) in the pulmonary trunk of people with a normal pulmonary circulation from various altitudes in Peru.

With regard to the effects of ageing, there is a discrepancy between the histological observations and the chemical measurements. Histologically, ageing is accompanied by a decrease in the quantity of elastin and an increase in that of collagen in the pulmonary trunk.[6,9] Chemically, an increase in the concentration of elastin is found with increasing age, while the concentration of collagen falls slightly.[7,10]

An increase in the concentration of elastin with age would account for the decreased extensibility of the media of the ageing pulmonary trunk at low degrees of extension. Figure 4.8 shows that there is an inverse relation between the concentration of elastin and extensibility at a low extensile load in pulmonary trunks taken from subjects with diverse ages. However, Figure 4.7 shows that there is a particular increase in the steepness of the force: extension relation at higher extensile loads in the ageing pulmonary trunk. This is consistent with the histological observations of an increased collagen but not with the chemical estimations of collagen.

It is possible that the collagen of the pulmonary trunk changes its tinctorial properties with age. Vascular collagen may also develop an increased Young's modulus with age, although studies on the tendon of the human diaphragm show the opposite.[11] Changes may occur in the unstretched length of the collagenous fibres or there may be alterations in the disposition of the fibres. Both collagenous and elastic fibres form a complex meshwork, the extensile properties of which are likely to depend not only on the simple linear extensibility of the individual fibres

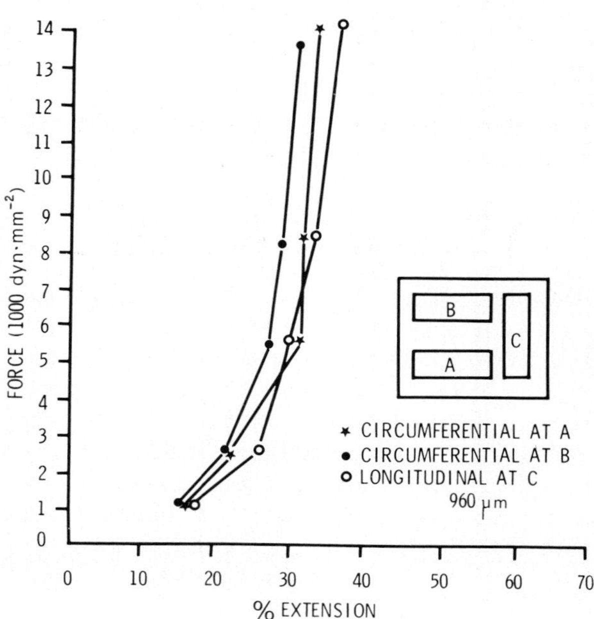

Fig. 4.9 A comparison of the extensibility of circumferential and longitudinal strips of the pulmonary trunk taken from the same subject.

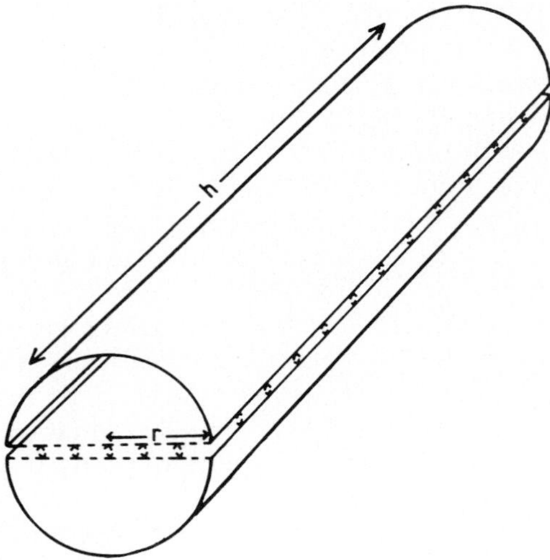

Fig. 4.10 Diagram to illustrate the calculation of Laplace's Law. See text for explanation.

but also on their resistance to lateral deformation and on the geometry of the woven pattern itself. In this context it may be noted that Roach and Burton[4] found that at no time did the extensibility of the wall of the human external iliac artery diminish to the extent that might be expected from a knowledge of Young's modulus for collagen. Whatever rôle the geometric disposition of the fibres may have, measurements of extensibility of the pulmonary trunk taken circumferentially are not substantially different from measurements taken along the long axis of the vessel (Fig. 4.9).

Extensibility and Distensibility

Physiologically, the linear extensibility of the wall of a vessel has usually to be translated into the relation between its diameter and the pressure within it. The mathematical relation between these various factors is given by Laplace's Law. Figure 4.10 represents a blood vessel as a cylinder of radius r and length h. The pressure (P) inside it is thought of as attempting to split the cylinder into two halves. The force exerted on each cut surface which tends to cause the two halves to fly apart is equal to the pressure multiplied by the area of the cut surface:

Force pushing each cut surface away from its opposing surface $= P \times 2rh$.

This force is really exerted along the two cut edges of the cylinder each of length h. The total splitting force (T) at any point in the wall of the cylinder is, therefore, equal to

$$\frac{2Prh}{2h} = Pr$$

Thus Laplace's Law states that the tension in the wall of a cylinder is equal to the distending pressure multiplied by the radius.

It will need to be borne in mind that the distending pressure of a blood vessel is equal to the pressure inside its lumen minus the tissue pressure outside—the 'transmural' pressure. In the lung the tissue pressure is unknown but may be expected to be rather less than atmospheric pressure (Chap. 24, p. 371). The true transmural distending pressure is, therefore, a little more than the conventionally measured intravascular pressure would suggest.

Meyer and Schollmeyer[12] have measured the static volume distensibility of the pulmonary arterial trunk and its two main branches after death. Between a pressure of 10 and 25 mmHg in the pulmonary artery, the volume of these vessels varied between 36·8 and 60·7 ml in the third decade, 44·6 and 61·7 ml in the fifth decade and 67·0 and 85·6 ml in the seventh decade. This represents changes in volume of 65 per cent, 38 per cent, and 28 per cent, respectively, and volume–distensibility coefficients of 1·6, 1·1, and 1·2 ml/mmHg.

Deuchar and Knebel[13] have attempted to estimate the distensibility of the pulmonary arteries in life using a formula derived from Wezler's 'Windkessel' theory (p. 153). They estimated the distensibility at 0·7 ml/mmHg at the age of five years, 1·1 ml/mmHg at ten years and 1·9 ml/mmHg at twenty years.

Patel *et al.*[14] from measurements of radiographs, found that the human right pulmonary artery varied on the average ± 8 per cent around a mean diameter during the cardiac cycle. This would imply an increase of 38 per cent in the volume of this artery during the cardiac cycle, a figure comparable with those of Meyer and Schollmeyer.[12]

The introduction of echocardiography has rendered it possible to record the movements of the pulmonary arterial wall during life. Unfortunately, it is technically very difficult to identify the pulmonary trunk. However, in skilful hands this may be achieved and Figure 4.11 shows such a recording of the root of the pulmonary trunk. The entire trunk moves forward a little during systole. There is an increase in the diameter of the trunk in the region of 10 per cent during systole.

Further confirmation that the distensibility of the pulmonary arteries in life is similar to that found after death may be derived indirectly from studies of the pulse-wave velocity in the pulmonary arteries. From electrokymographic tracings the pulse-wave velocity in the main branches of the pulmonary artery[15] has been found to be 2 $m \cdot s^{-1}$. According to the Hill–Bramwell equation:[16]

$$v = \frac{3{\cdot}57}{\sqrt{E}}$$

where v is the pulse wave velocity ($m \cdot s^{-1}$) and E is the distensibility coefficient of the vessel (percentage change in volume per mmHg). Hence, the distensibility of the larger branches of the pulmonary artery may be estimated as 3·2 per cent change in volume for a 1 mmHg change in pressure. From this one would deduce an approximate increase of 48 per cent in volume during systole.

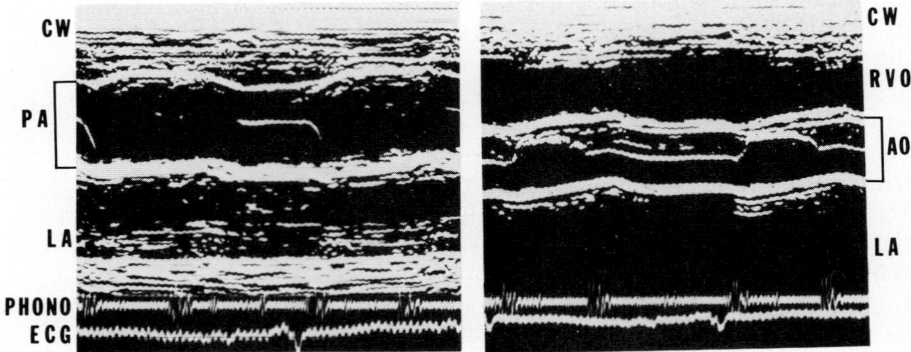

Fig. 4.11 Echocardiographic recording of the great vessels from an adult with non-obstructive cardiomyopathy. The pulmonary artery (PA, left panel) as well as the aortic root (AO, right panel) moves anteriorly (towards the chest wall, CW) in systole and posteriorly in diastole. The valve cusp echoes are visible within the lumen of each vessel. RVO = Right ventricular outflow; LA = left atrium; PHONO = phonocardiogram; ECG = electrocardiogram.

Dubois[17] has made an estimate of the distensibility of the human pulmonary arterial tree during life by measuring instantaneous pulmonary capillary flow (p. 87). During diastole no blood enters the pulmonary artery but a certain volume drains from the arterial tree through the pulmonary capillaries and this volume of blood may be measured. The fall in the volume of the pulmonary arterial tree is compared with the fall in pulmonary arterial pressure which occurs during the same period. Dubois gives figures of 20 ml for the change in volume and 3·5 mmHg for the change in pressure during diastole in a normal subject. The distensibility of the pulmonary arterial system is, therefore, 5·7 ml/mmHg over the volumes studied. This figure is higher than would be expected from the preceding observations but it will be recalled that these observations referred to the whole range of pressure between diastole and systole, whereas those of Dubois refer only to the lowest part of this range. Since distensibility would be expected to increase at lower levels of pressure, this might account for some of the apparent discrepancy.

Viscous Resistance to Stretch

So far the mechanical properties of vessel walls have been considered from a static point of view. Time is not represented in the length–tension diagrams of the preceding pages. When a blood vessel is distended, the various fibres which compose its wall may be thought of as rubbing against each other. In this way they will impose a frictional or 'viscous' resistance to stretch and to contraction. This resistance is dependent on time; the faster the motion, the greater the friction. Under the dynamic conditions of continuously changing length in which the walls of the pulmonary arteries normally exist, such viscous resistance may conceivably have an important function.[18] In animals it has been shown to occur in the aorta[19] but in observations on the pulmonary arteries its magnitude appeared to be very small.[14] We know of no similar observations on human pulmonary arteries.

Structure and Function in the Walls of Muscular Pulmonary arteries

These vessels (p. 27) are distinguished by the presence of a muscular media bounded by internal and external elastic laminae. Normally the thickness of the media is less than 5 per cent of the total diameter of the artery, and the muscular fibres run circularly. The meagreness of the muscle has suggested that these vessels are not capable of active constriction, and the lack of substantial change in pressure following the administration of drugs which alter the calibre of systemic arteries has appeared to confirm this. However, the amount of muscle in the media has to be related to the pressures which it will be required to overcome and these are only one-sixth the magnitude of those in the systemic circulation. Similarly the magnitude of the change in pressure in the pulmonary circulation following the administration of such a drug has to be related to the minute scale of the differences in pressure that normally exist across this circulation. A body of experimental evidence (Chap. 13) suggests that active dilatation and constriction can occur within the pulmonary circulation. It seems likely that it is the muscular pulmonary arteries which constrict since it is in these vessels that the circular muscle fibres are most evident. This belief is also supported by the observation that the muscular coat of these vessels hypertrophies under conditions of pathological pulmonary hypertension (Chap. 16).

Since these vessels appear to be the chief site of resistance in the pulmonary circulation, the physical relations between transmural pressure and calibre existing in them are best elucidated by a consideration of the relations between pressure and flow. This subject is, therefore, deferred until Chapter 9.

Structure and Function in the Walls of the Pulmonary Capillaries

The application of Laplace's Law[1] immediately clarifies the problem of why the main trunk of the pulmonary artery in the adult has walls about 1 mm thick[20] containing much elastic and fibrous tissue to withstand a mean pressure of 15 mmHg, while in the pulmonary capillaries a pressure of 9 mmHg can be withstood by a single layer of endothelium. The radius of the capillary is so much smaller than that of the artery that the tension in the wall of the capillary becomes extremely feeble. If the radius of a capillary were 5 μm and the distending pressure were 9 mmHg, then the tension in the wall would be 6 $\text{dyn} \cdot \text{cm}^{-1}$. By comparison a representative figure for the average tension in the wall of the main pulmonary artery would be 30 000 $\text{dyn} \cdot \text{cm}^{-1}$.

The tension in the wall of the capillary may even be less than the above calculation suggests. It has been suggested that the endothelium of blood vessels possesses a degree of unwettability[21] and, if this is so, forces of surface tension will exist which will oppose the distending force of the blood pressure. The force exerted will depend on the degree of unwettability of the endothelium, which does not have to be very great. If, for instance, the endothelium were completely unwettable and the surface tension of the plasma were 75 dyn · cm^{-1} (Ref. 22) it would require a total pressure of 120 mmHg to maintain the capillary open to a radius of 5 μm.

One further theoretical consideration has to be mentioned only to be dismissed. In any vessel where blood is flowing, the pressure measured with a needle directed against the centre of the stream will be more than the pressure measured at right-angles to this by a needle piercing the wall (Bernoulli's Principle, p. 132). This arises because of the kinetic energy occupied in propelling the blood forward, and the magnitude of the difference in pressure depends on the swiftness with which the blood is flowing. While the difference in lateral and end-pressures may amount to 4 mmHg in the normal pulmonary artery, the velocity of blood in capillaries is so slow that this effect is negligible.

It seems unlikely that the entire capillary bed remains permanently open. Wearn *et al.*[23] made a direct microscopical examination of the small blood vessels of the lung in the living cat and observed that only a small proportion of the capillaries in an alveolus was carrying blood at any one time. Capillaries and arterioles could be seen opening and closing spontaneously, although it was often difficult to say whether this amounted to complete closure or whether the vessel was being perfused only with plasma.

The question whether an increase in the total pulmonary capillary blood volume is achieved by the opening up of previously closed capillaries or by the dilatation of those which are already patent has been raised by Forster[24] in the course of his studies on diffusion (Chap. 42). *A priori*, one would imagine that both these mechanisms play a part. The separate measurement of the pulmonary capillary volume and the diffusing capacity of the membrane (Chap. 42, p. 639) might be expected to throw light on this problem by demonstrating the ratio in which the volume and surface area of the capillaries change. However, the results have not so far been decisive (Chap. 11, p. 162).

REFERENCES

1. Burton, A. C. (1954) *Physiol. Rev.*, **34**, 619.
2. Burton, A. C. (1951) *Amer. J. Physiol.*, **164**, 319.
3. Roy, C. S. (1880) *J. Physiol.*, **3**, 125.
4. Roach, M. R. & Burton, A. C. (1957) *Canad. J. Biochem. Physiol.*, **35**, 681.
5. Krogman, W. M. (1941) *Tabulae Biol. (Hague)*, **20**, 66.
6. Harris, P., Heath, D. & Apostolopoulos, A. (1965) *Brit. Heart J.*, **27**, 651.
7. Castillo, Y., Krüger, H., Arias-Stella, J., Hurtado, A., Harris, P. & Heath, D. (1967) *Brit. Heart J.*, **29**, 120.
8. Heath, D., Harris, P., Castillo, Y. & Arias-Stella, J. (1968) *J. Path. Bact.*, **96**, 161.
9. Heath, D., Wood, E. H., Dushane, J. W. & Edwards, J. E. (1959) *J. Path. Bact.*, **77**, 443.
10. Lansing, A. I., Rosenthal, T. B. & Alex, M. (1950) *J. Geront.*, **5**, 211.
11. Kohn, R. R. & Rollerson, E. (1959) *Arch. Path.*, **68**, 316.
12. Meyer, W. W. & Schollmeyer, P. (1957) *Klin. Wschr.*, **35**, 1070.
13. Deuchar, D. & Knebel, R. (1952) *Brit. Heart J.*, **14**, 225.
14. Patel, D. J., Schilder, D. P. & Mallos, A. J. (1960) *J. Appl. Physiol.*, **15**, 92.
15. Fleischner, F. G., Romano, F. J. & Luisada, A. A. (1948) *Proc. Soc. Exp. Biol. (N.Y.)*, **67**, 535.
16. Bramwell, J. C. & Hill, A. V. (1922) *Proc. Roy. Soc. (B.)*, **93**, 298.

17. Dubois, A. B. (1959) In *Pulmonary Circulation*, ed. Adams, W. R. & Veith, I. Page 36. New York: Grune & Stratton.
18. Hardung, V. (1953) *Helv. Physiol. Acta*, **11**, 194.
19. Remington, J. W. (1955) *Amer. J. Physiol.*, **180**, 83.
20. Krogman, W. M. (1941) *Tabulae Biol. (Hague)*, **20**, 664.
21. Moolten, S. E., Vroman, L., Vroman, G. M. S. & Goodman, B. (1949) *Arch. Int. Med.*, **84**, 667.
22. Zunz, E. (1928) In *Colloid Chemistry*, ed. Alexander, J. Vol. 2, p. 650. New York: Chemical Catalogue Co.
23. Wearn, J. T., Ernstene, A. C., Bromer, A. W., Barr, J. S., German, W. J. & Zschiesche, L. J. (1934) *Amer. J. Physiol.*, **109**, 236.
24. Forster, R. E. (1957) *Physiol. Rev.*, **37**, 391.

5. The Measurement of Pressure

The basic physiological measurements which are required in the study of the haemodynamics of the pulmonary circulation are those of the pulmonary blood flow, the pulmonary blood volume and the pressures in the various blood vessels in the lung. The technical aspects of such measurements will not be given in great detail. Nevertheless, it is thought desirable to describe the theoretical basis for these techniques in order that their limitations may be appraised. This chapter will be devoted to the measurement of pressure.

The Structure of Pulse Waves

The pressure waves which occur in the circulation have various and complex shapes. In order to deal with them in any numerical fashion it is, therefore, necessary to analyse them in terms of simple wave-forms which can be described mathematically. We shall begin by considering a simple sinusoidal wave.

Figure 5.1 represents a point G moving at a constant speed from an initial point A round the circumference of a circle of radius r. As it moves the angle θ gradually increases until, by the time G has returned to A, it has passed through 360°. A line from G runs perpendicularly to the diameter DE, crossing it at a point S. As G moves round the circle so S moves up and down the diameter DE. The

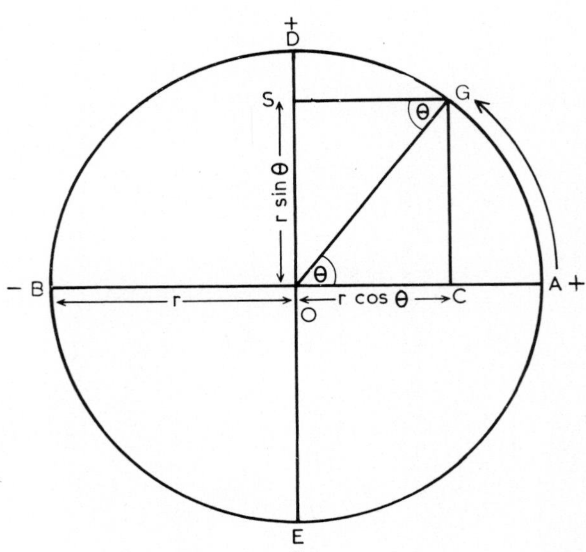

Fig. 5.1 Diagram to illustrate simple harmonic motion. While the point G moves round the circumference, points S and C move to and fro along their respective diameters in simple harmonic motion.

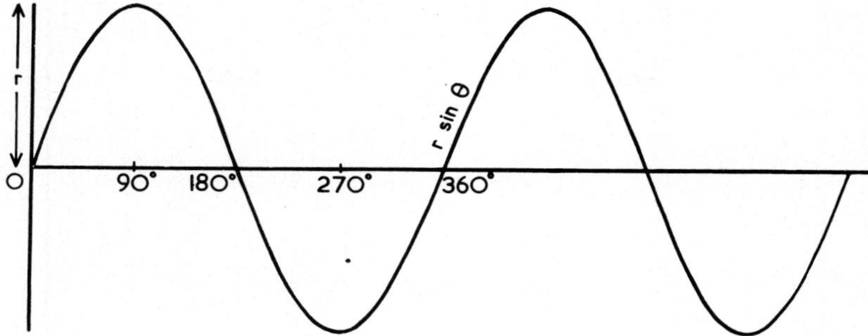

Fig. 5.2 Simple harmonic motion. The motion of S in Figure 5.1 plotted against the angle θ (or against time) describes a sine-wave.

motion of S along the line DE is known as *simple harmonic motion*. It will be seen that the distance of S from its central point of movement (O), is equal to r sin θ. The maximal distance which S moves from O is equal to r which is the *amplitude* of the movement. If we put the central point, O, equal to zero, then S moves between $+$r and $-$r. When the motion of S is plotted against time, a regular undulatory *sine wave* results (Fig. 5.2). The horizontal axis may be marked in degrees instead of time since the rate of increase of θ is constant. In this case the curve will be seen to cross the zero line at 0°, 180°, and 360°. If the horizontal axis were marked in radians rather than degrees, the curve would cross the zero line at O, π, and 2π radians.

The point C moves in a similar fashion to S but along the diameter AB which is at right angles to DE. The distance of the point C from O is always equal to r cos θ. When the motion of C is plotted against time it has the same form as that of S with the same amplitude, r. It occurs, however, later along the time axis. When the horizontal axis is expressed as an angle instead of time the curve of the motion of C is seen to follow that of S by 90° or $\pi/2$ radians (Fig. 5.3). The two curves are thus said to be 90° or $\pi/2$ radians out of phase.

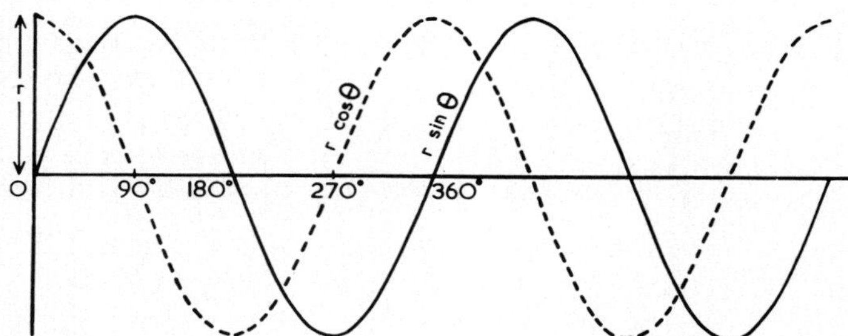

Fig. 5.3 Simple harmonic motion. The curve $y = r \sin \theta$ plots the motion of S in Figure 5.1. The curve $y = r \cos \theta$ plots the motion of C in Figure 5.1. The two curves have the same shape but are 90° out of phase.

D

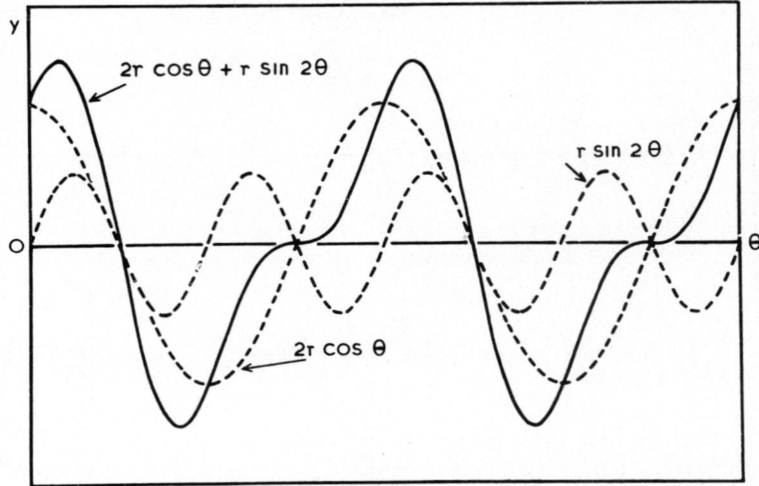

Fig. 5.4 Diagram to illustrate how complex wave-forms may be derived by the addition of simple sinusoidal waves. The two interrupted curves are of $y = 2r\cos\theta$ and $y = r\sin 2\theta$. The continuous line shows the curve of $y = 2r\cos\theta + r\sin 2\theta$.

These two curves represent the functions r sin θ and r cos θ plotted against θ. The curves r sin 2θ and r cos 2θ will have twice the frequency of these curves. Similarly the curves of 2r sin θ and 2r cos θ will have twice the amplitude. Figure 5.4 shows the curves of 2r sin θ and r cos 2θ. The former has twice the amplitude and the latter twice the frequency. Superimposed on Figure 5.4 is the curve obtained by the simultaneous addition of these two curves. This is the curve of 2r sin $\theta +$ r cos 2θ. Two points may be noted about this curve. First, it has a more complex shape than its two component curves; second, it possesses a periodicity with a frequency equal to the slower of its component curves.

The ability to explain complex wave-forms in terms of simple sine and cosine waves may be extended to any periodic curve of whatever complexity by means of *Fourier's Theorem.* The theorem states that any periodic wave-form may be expressed in the form:

$$y = a_0 + a_1 \sin\theta + a_2 \sin 2\theta + a_3 \sin 3\theta + \cdots$$
$$+ b_1 \cos\theta + b_2 \cos 2\theta + b_3 \cos 3\theta + \cdots$$

In this equation, a_0 represents the mean height of the wave. The term $a_1 \sin\theta + b_1 \cos\theta$ contains those components of the lowest frequency and is called the *first harmonic.* This is the basic frequency of the total wave. The term $a_2 \sin 2\theta + b_2 \cos 2\theta$ is called the *second harmonic* and so on.

The above expression can be simplified to

$$y = A_0 + A_1 \sin(\theta + \phi_1) + A_2 \sin(2\theta + \phi_2) + A_3 \sin(3\theta + \phi_3) \ldots$$

where $A_1 = \pm\sqrt{a_1^2 + b_1^2}$ and $\phi_1 = \tan^{-1}(a_1/b_1)$ etc. while A_0 is written instead of a_0 for the sake of uniformity. This allows each harmonic to be described as one sinusoidal wave.

Since any of the intravascular pulse waves in the body are periodic functions, they may be analysed in such a fashion. Figure 5.5, for instance, shows a pulmonary arterial pressure curve analysed into its first six harmonics. In the case of cardiovascular pressure waves, the term a_0 or A_0 represents the mean pressure and the first harmonic has the frequency of the heart beat.

This concept of the structure of pulse-waves will be seen to be helpful in our understanding of some of the problems of manometry and of the concept of impedance in the pulmonary circulation (Chap. 10).

Limitations of Pressure-Recording Instruments[1,2]

The manometer usually used for the measurement of pressure in the pulmonary circulation consists of a small rigid metal chamber, one wall of which is constituted by a flexible metal diaphragm. At the opposite end of the chamber, a rigid opening

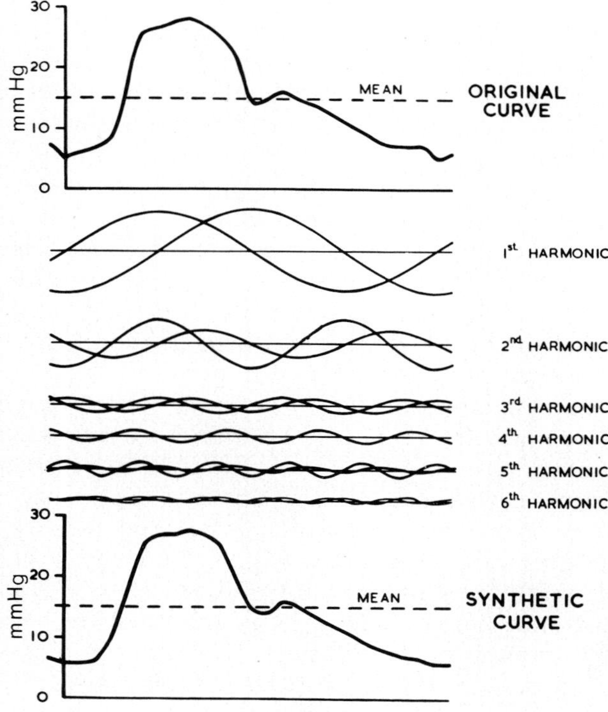

Fig. 5.5 Fourier analysis of a pulmonary arterial pressure tracing. The bottom curve represents the addition of the various sinusoidal wave components.

Fig. 5.6 Mechanical analogue to illustrate resonance and damping. The analogue consists of a weight suspended by a spring from a fixed point.

communicates with the catheter or needle which has been introduced into the blood vessel from which the pressure is to be recorded. The manometric chamber and the catheter or needle are filled with saline. Alterations in pressure in the vessel are transmitted through the saline and give rise to minute movements of the metal diaphragm. These movements are translated into electrical energy which is then amplified sufficiently to drive a recording system. Several systems may be used to convert the mechanical movements into an electrical signal. In one, the diaphragm forms one plate of a condenser, the capacitance of which is altered by the position of the diaphragm. Another, the strain-gauge type, depends on the alteration which occurs in the electrical resistance of a system of wires when they are stretched. In a third, the diaphragm moves a metal core through the centre of a coil and thus varies its electro-magnetic properties.

If any of these manometer-recording systems are tested by means of a series of columns of water or mercury they will be found to give accurate and linearly related measurements of pressure. However, although they respond satisfactorily to a pressure which remains stationary, limitations in their fidelity will develop when they are required to record pressure which is varying rapidly from moment to moment. These limitations have two main origins. The first is the viscous resistance or 'damping' with which the saline and other material in the manometer opposes the small movements necessary to deflect the membrane. The second lies in the fact that the diaphragm, the wall of the chamber, the catheter or needle and the saline contained therein, all possess elastic properties. This causes the whole system to have a certain natural frequency of vibration. Variations in pressure which occur at this frequency will resonate and give rise to a greater amplitude in the response of the instrument than those which occur at other frequencies.

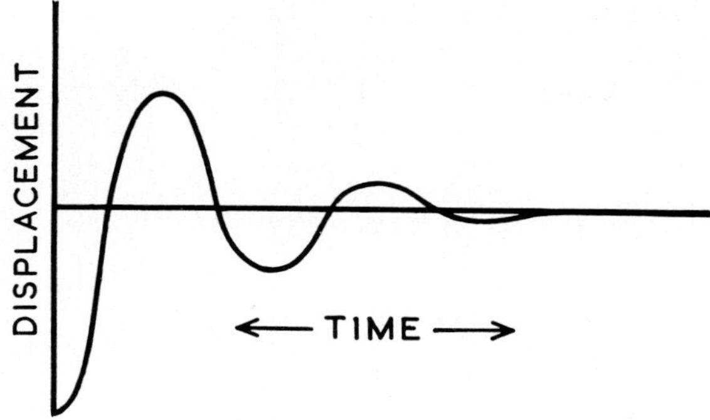

Fig. 5.7 Diagram to illustrate the free motion of the weight in Figure 5.6, after it has been displaced.

The two processes of damping and resonance may be illustrated by a simple mechanical analogue. In Figure 5.6 is drawn a spring from which a weight is suspended. At the position of equilibrium the spring is stretched to such an extent that its force of recoil is exactly balanced by the gravitational force acting on the weight. We shall suppose that the weight is pulled downwards from this point by hand and subsequently suddenly released. It will then undergo an oscillatory movement up and down around the original point of equilibrium. This movement will have the form of harmonic motion. That is to say, it will have the form of a sine wave when plotted against time. If the forces involved were simply due to gravity and the elasticity of the spring, the vibrating movement would continue for ever. In practice the amplitude of the movement will gradually decrease until the weight remains motionless at the point of equilibrium (Fig. 5.7). This is due to the inevitable presence of some viscous resistance to movement or damping which causes the energy of vibration to be wasted in the form of heat.

If the degree of damping becomes very great, it may completely obscure any oscillatory motion. For this purpose we can imagine the spring and weight suspended in a jar of treacle. When the weight is released from the hand under these circumstances it will move gradually upwards towards the point of equilibrium without any oscillation occurring. The movement of the weight upwards will gradually become slower and slower as the difference between the force of recoil of the spring and the gravitational pull diminishes so that, if it were plotted against time, it would describe a curve (Fig. 5.8). If the degree of damping were less, the weight might overshoot a little before settling at the point of equilibrium. A degree of damping just sufficient to prevent this overshoot is called *critical damping*.

The situations just described are equivalent to that which is obtained when a square-fronted wave of pressure, that is, a pressure which is raised immediately from zero to its maximum value, is applied to a manometer. Under these circumstances the rate of change of pressure is infinitely fast. In practice, a manometer is never required to achieve such an impossible task but has to deal with a series

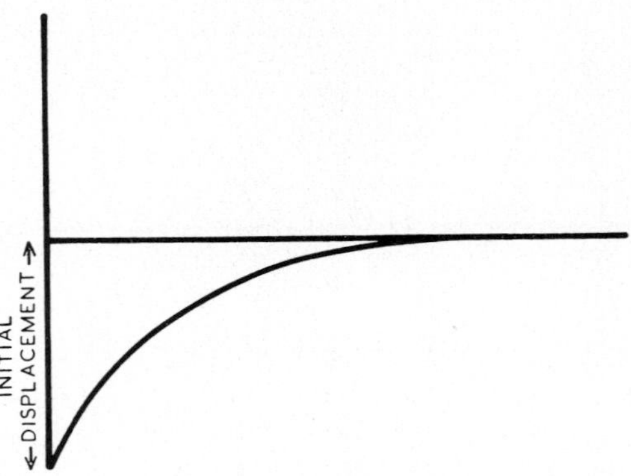

Fig. 5.8 Diagram to illustrate the motion of the weight in Figure 5.6 after displacement, if it were placed in a highly viscous liquid.

of waves of pressure of much lower frequency. The basic frequency of oscillation of cardiovascular pressure waves is that of the heart beat, and for all practical purposes these waves may be adequately described by Fourier analysis as far as the sixth harmonic.[1] For a heart rate of 60 min^{-1} the highest frequency component of practical importance is, therefore, 6 cycles per second (6 Hz). For a heart rate of 150 min^{-1} it will be 15 Hz.

How a manometer system responds to sine waves of various frequencies may

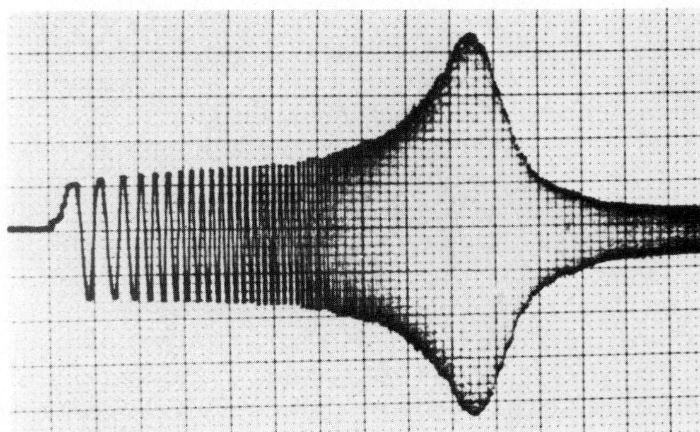

Fig. 5.9 Frequency–response curve of a cardiac catheter–manometer–recorder system. A sinusoidal pressure wave of constant amplitude has been applied at the end of the catheter with a frequency which increases from left to right. The distance between the major vertical lines represents 2·0 s. With an increasing frequency, the recording shows a resonant peak followed by a decline in amplitude. The outline of the recording may be compared with the theoretical frequency–response curves shown in Figure 5.10.

be shown by stimulating it with a mechanical oscillator over a range of frequencies and noting the amplitude of the deflections which are recorded (Fig. 5.9). Such a curve will show that the maximal amplitude occurs at the natural frequency. The curves which the manometer will be required to record are composed of a series of sine waves which extend over a range of frequencies. In order to prevent distortion of the composite curve, it is important that each component should be amplified to the same extent. This means that the frequency–response curve should be approximately horizontal over the appropriate range of frequencies. It will be seen from Figure 5.10 that, the higher the natural frequency of the manometer, the more nearly will this ideal be approached, since the peak of the response curve is removed further away from the operating range.

The formula governing the natural frequency of a manometer was given by Otto Frank:

$$N = \frac{1}{2\pi}\sqrt{\frac{EA}{SL}}$$

where N is the natural frequency, E is the volume elasticity of the system, A is the cross-sectional area of the column of fluid in the system, S is the specific gravity of this fluid, and L is the length of the column. Since a high natural frequency is greatly to be desired, the ideal manometer system has a high coefficient of

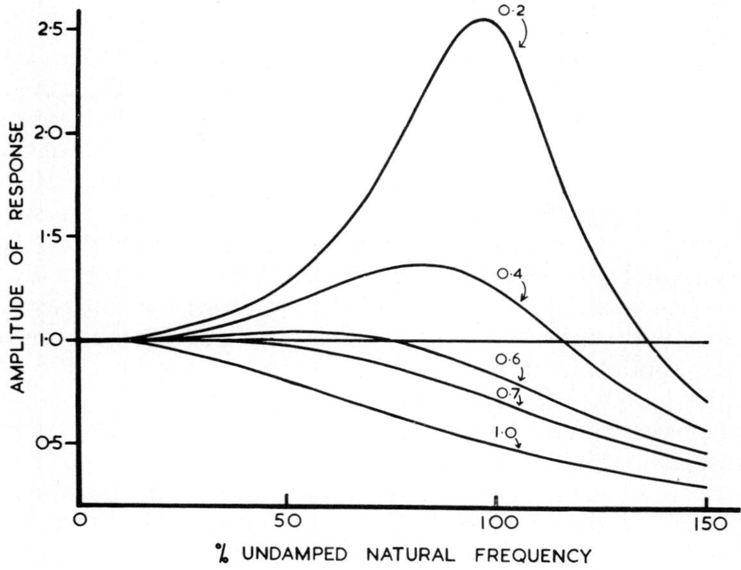

Fig. 5.10 The influence of damping on the frequency–response curve. The degree of damping of each curve is expressed as a fraction of critical damping.

elasticity (*i.e.* rigid walls, p. 43) and a relatively large cross-sectional area and short length. The characteristics imposed by physiological necessity on the design of the cardiac catheter may be seen to be the very opposite of these requirements: it has to be flexible and, therefore, distensible; it has to be thin and it has to be long. These properties of the cardiac catheter severely limit the fidelity of pulse-wave tracings recorded through them.

The natural frequency of a conventional catheter-manometer system has been found[3] to vary between 10 and 59 Hz which would mean that the undamped frequency–response curve would be far from horizontal over the operative range of frequencies. In order to make the frequency–response curve as flat as possible over this range, a certain amount of damping has to be introduced. How much damping to apply is in theory a matter of compromise and in practice not susceptible to a great accuracy of control. Theoretically, a degree of 70 per cent critical damping is the ideal compromise and gives a flat frequency-response curve to 35 per cent of the natural frequency (Fig. 5.10). Such damping may be achieved mechanically or, more conveniently, by electrical means.

The use of damping, however, introduces a new source of infidelity. One of the effects of damping is to cause a phase-shift between the pressure wave and its recording so that the recording is delayed. This occurs because the viscous resistance causing the damping is maximal when the pressure is changing most swiftly (*i.e.* on the upstroke and downslope of a curve) and zero when the pressure reaches its peak or trough. The degree of phase-shift will vary with the frequency of the vibration (Fig. 5.11) and this will cause the different sine wave components of the composite pressure to become delayed to a variable extent. The result of this will be to distort the shape of the recording. Fortunately, with 70 per cent critical damping, the degree of phase-shift increases linearly with the frequency up to the natural frequency (Fig. 5.11). Thus, a vibration at the natural frequency will have a phase-shift of 90° while a vibration of half the natural frequency will have a phase-shift of 45°. Since the cycle length of the former is half that of the latter, the result is that the actual time-delay in the two curves is the same. Hence, with 70 per cent critical damping, all the components of the composite pressure curve are delayed the same fraction of time and the shape of the curve remains undistorted. The entire curve will, however, be delayed. In addition to this there is a mechanical delay of about 0·01 s in the passage of a pulse wave down the catheter.[1]

The above discussion has treated the catheter–manometer system in terms which are only strictly applicable to the simplest vibrating system. The physical and mathematical problems which are involved are considerably more complex than such a treatment suggests and their solution has been most satisfactorily approached by the use of 'transmission line' theory.[1]

Perhaps the most disturbing artefacts in the pressure tracing are those introduced by movements of the catheter by the beating of the heart. These are mainly groups of relatively rapid vibrations occurring chiefly in the region of the first and second heart sounds. The eye can usually recognize these for what they are and a smoothed line may be drawn to represent the undistorted pulse wave. On the other hand,

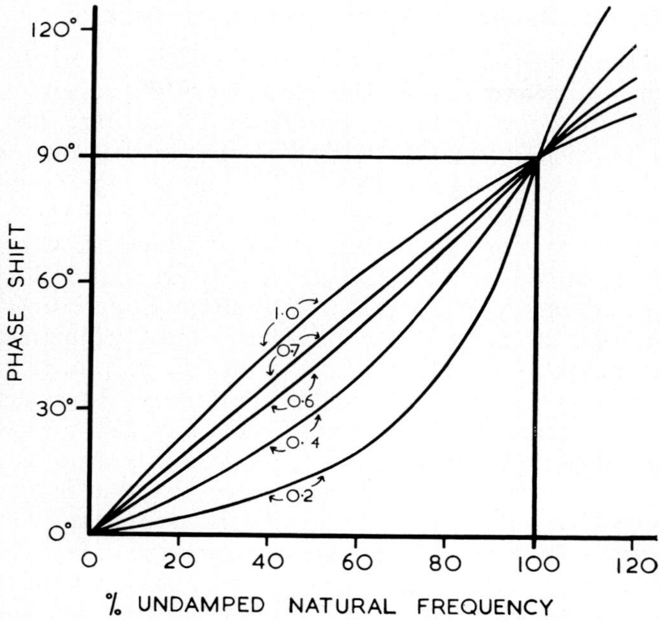

Fig. 5.11 Diagram to show how the relation between phase-shift and frequency varies according to the degree of damping. The degree of damping of each curve is expressed as a fraction of critical damping.

some of the vibrations are of lower frequency and indistinguishable from the waves being recorded.[4]

Even in the absence of instrumental limitations the measurement of pressures in the pulmonary circulation poses a special problem since they vary greatly throughout the respiratory cycle. In order to allow for this, it is customary to average pressures over at least two respiratory cycles. A further technical problem is to decide where to place the level of zero. With the low pressures encountered in the pulmonary circulation, variations in the level of zero can give rise to alterations comparable in magnitude to the pressures actually being recorded. It is usual to take a zero point somewhere near the centre of the heart. Thus, in the recumbent position, a level 10 cm above the surface of the table, or 5 cm below the sternal angle, or half-way between the front and back of the chest may be chosen. In the upright position an adequate anatomical definition of the level of zero becomes very difficult. For this reason, the changes in pulmonary vascular pressures which occur when a subject rises from the laying to the standing position are capable of only a very modified interpretation. Except when otherwise stated, the pressures quoted throughout this book refer to the recumbent, supine position and are taken from a zero point approximating to the centre of the heart.

The Pressure in the Pulmonary Artery

The pressure in the pulmonary artery was first measured by means of the cardiac catheter in man by Cournand *et al.*[5] The mean level of pressure is considerably lower than that in the aorta and averages about 15 mmHg. The shape of the pulse-wave in the pulmonary artery is similar to that in the aorta, with a systolic maximum and a diastolic minimum (Fig. 5.12). The average systolic pressure is about 22 mmHg and the diastolic pressure 10 mmHg (Table 5.1).

Recordings obtained through the cardiac catheter usually show a group of rapid oscillations occurring at the same time as the first heart sound (Fig. 5.12). These oscillations seem to be mainly artefact since they do not appear to any great extent in pressure recordings taken by direct puncture of the pulmonary artery by a needle.[1] They are probably mainly due to the sudden movement of the catheter which occurs at the beginning of ventricular contraction. Immediately following these oscillations the pressure rises to a maximum and then falls towards the incisura. The incisura is usually accompanied by a second group of rapid oscillations which coincide with the second cardiac sound. These are also due in part to artefact.[1] During the portion of the curve so far described, the pulmonary valve is open and there is direct continuity between the right ventricle and the pulmonary trunk. Thus, under normal circumstances, the shape of the pulmonary arterial pressure curve during this part of the cardiac cycle is similar to that in the right ventricle.[6] When the pressure in the pulmonary artery is normal, the systolic peak usually lies nearer to the first sound than to the second. With increasingly raised pressures in the pulmonary artery, the systolic peak becomes rounded and moves towards the second sound.[6] This variation in shape may possibly be explained according to the relative importance of inertia and capacity in the pulmonary arterial tree (Chap. 10).

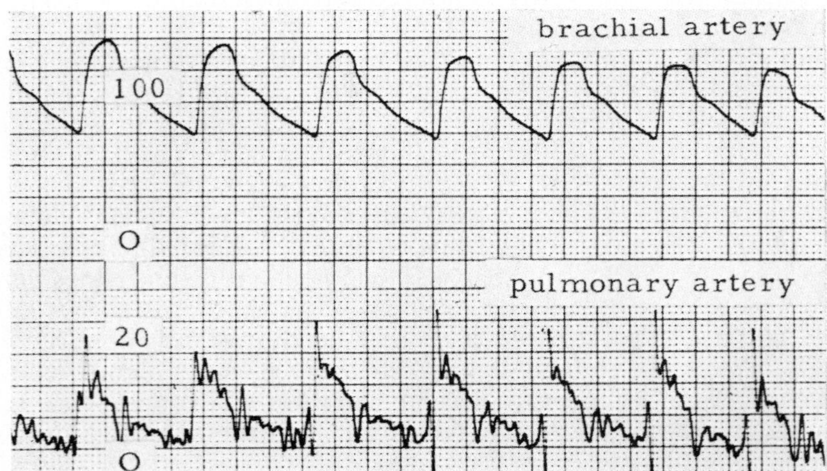

Fig. 5.12 Normal pulmonary arterial pressure tracing recorded via a cardiac catheter. The upper record shows a simultaneous brachial arterial tracing.

Table 5.1 Pressures in the pulmonary circulation in normal adults resting supine

		No. of subjects	Mean	Standard deviation
Pulmonary arterial pressure (mmHg)	Systolic	52	21·5	5·1
	Diastolic	52	9·5	3·0
	Mean	52	14·8	3·5
Pulmonary wedge pressure (mmHg)		33	9·3	3·1

The incisura is followed by a dicrotic wave after which the pressure declines gradually to its diastolic minimum. A small positive wave may occasionally be seen on the pulmonary arterial tracing at the time of auricular systole (Fig. 5.13). It seems to be due to auricular contraction since it has been observed to occur following a P-wave during a period of ventricular asystole.[7] The mechanism involved is obscure, but it may be noted that a similar phenomenon occurs in the systemic arterial pulse.[8]

The pressure in the pulmonary artery varies throughout the respiratory cycle, being higher in expiration than inspiration. These changes in pressure are synchronous with those occurring in the pleural space and usually have an amplitude of about 3 to 6 mmHg. The pulmonary arterial pressure is also influenced by emotion being

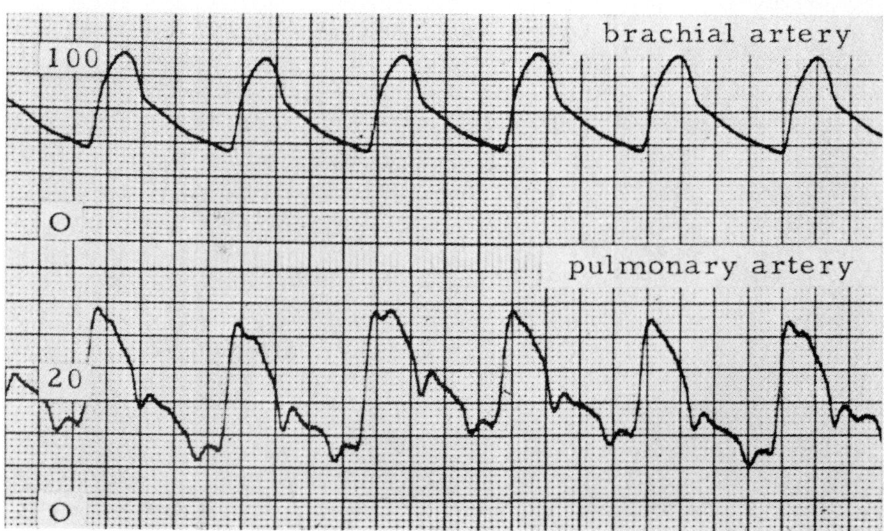

Fig. 5.13 Normal pulmonary arterial pressure tracing to show small *a*-waves. The upper record shows a simultaneous brachial arterial tracing.

noticeably higher when the subject is apprehensive or distressed (Chap. 11, p. 155). During the course of a cardiac catheterization, the pressure in the pulmonary artery often shows a gradual decline and this may lead to difficulties in the interpretation of the effect of drugs on the pulmonary circulation (Chap. 13).

The Pressure in the Left Atrium and Pulmonary Veins

Although, anatomically, the left atrium may not be strictly a part of the pulmonary circulation, the pressure which exists within it has important implications in the haemodynamics of the lungs. In disease, for instance, the pressure in the left atrium distinguishes between pulmonary hypertension due to mitral stenosis and that due

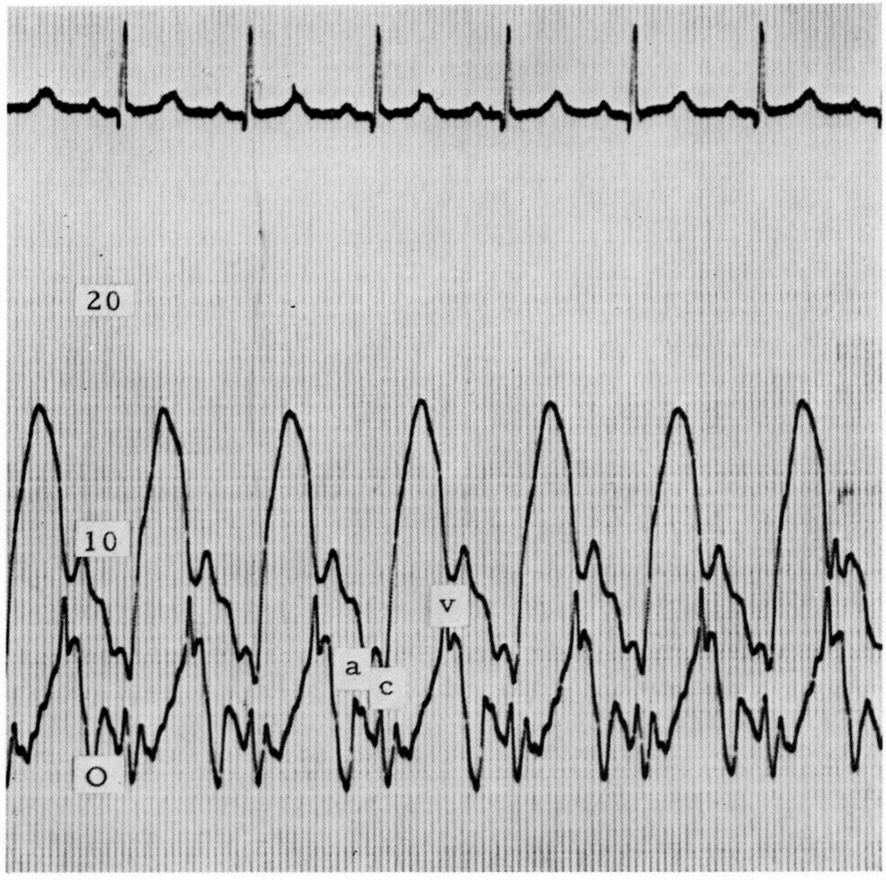

Fig. 5.14 Simultaneous measurements of the left atrial pressure (bottom tracing), pulmonary arterial pressure (middle tracing) and electrocardiogram (top tracing) made during thoracotomy on a patient with a localized tuberculous lesion of the lung.

to intracardiac shunts (Chap. 23). In physiological studies, also, it is often necessary to know the level of left atrial pressure in order to interpret the meaning of changes in the pulmonary arterial pressure (Chap. 11, p. 158, and Chap. 13, p. 183).

The left atrium is even less accessible than the pulmonary artery but several methods are available by which it may be reached. A cardiac catheter may enter the left atrium from the right atrium through the foramen ovale or through an atrial septal defect. The catheter may then be advanced into a pulmonary vein or occasionally it may enter an anomalous pulmonary vein draining into the right atrium. The most commonly used technique for entering the left atrium is that of trans-septal puncture.[9] Direct puncture of the left atrium may be performed by a needle during thoracic operations.[10] A needle may also be introduced directly into this chamber in the conscious patient through the posterior chest wall,[11] a bronchus,[12,13] or the suprasternal notch.[14]

The mean pressure in the left atrium is slightly higher than in the right atrium.[9] The pressure pulses of the two atria are similar in form, although the amplitude of the waves is greater in the left atrium.[9,10] Similar observations were made in dogs[15] where they were attributed to the lesser capacity and distensibility of the left atrium and pulmonary veins compared with the right atrium and systemic veins. The presystolic *a*-wave of the left atrium (Fig. 5.14) follows immediately after that in the right atrium,[16] a finding consistent with the spread of the atrial impulse from right to left. The amplitude of this wave[10] varies between 2 to 8 mmHg. A second small deflection (*c*-wave) may or may not be found at the time of the first heart sound. Following this, the pressure falls sharply early in ventricular systole (*x*-descent) and reaches a level similar to that which exists just before the *a*-wave. Later, in systole, the pressure rises again to form the beginning of the upstroke of the *v*-wave. The *v*-wave reaches its maximum[10] of 1–9 mmHg shortly after the second sound. The left atrial pressure then falls sharply again (*y*-descent) at the moment of opening of the mitral valve. Thereafter it rises slightly before atrial systole gives rise to the *a*-wave. Recordings of pressure from catheters lying freely in pulmonary veins have a similar appearance to that in the left atrium.

The Pulmonary Arterial Wedge Pressure[17]

If a cardiac catheter is advanced through the pulmonary artery far out into the lung field, its end may become impacted in one of the smaller branches. Bearing in mind the size of the cardiac catheter, the internal diameter of the vessel which is occluded lies in the region of 1·5 to 3·0 mm so that it would appear to be one of the smaller arteries of the elastic type (p. 25) Dexter and his colleagues[18] found that the blood withdrawn from the catheter at this point usually had an oxygen saturation within the normal systemic arterial range. This was found to be so even in patients with cyanotic congenital heart disease. It was, therefore, concluded that the blood had been drawn back from the pulmonary capillaries. The conclusion was supported by the observation that the branches of the pulmonary artery are end-arteries.[19]

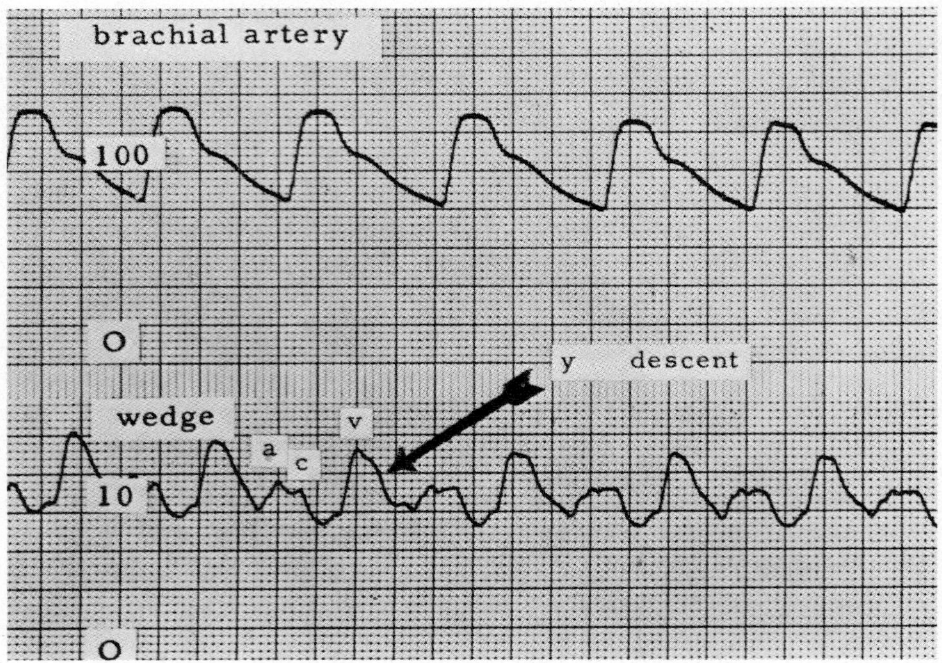

Fig. 5.15 Normal pulmonary arterial-wedge tracing. The upper record shows a simultaneous brachial arterial tracing.

In dogs, the pressure recorded when the catheter was impacted in this position was found to be lower than that in the pulmonary artery[20] and lacking the systolic pulse wave of the pulmonary arterial tracing. Similar observations were made in man, where the mean pressure at this site was found[21] to range between 7 and 15 mmHg. Lagerlöf and Werkö[22] demonstrated that under these conditions a pressure tracing could often be recorded which in man was similar to that in the atria (Fig. 5.15). There were two main pulse-waves to each beat. One started just before the first heart sound, falling again early in ventricular systole. The other started at the end of ventricular systole, just before the second sound, and fell again shortly after the beginning of diastole. In the presence of atrial fibrillation, the first wave was greatly diminished (Fig. 23.2, p. 354) and, in the presence of an atrio-ventricular dissociation, the *a*-waves could be seen separately. In patients with mitral stenosis the pressure at the end of the wedged catheter was found to be higher than normal. From these observations, Lagerlöf and Werkö concluded that the pressure measured was related to the pressures in the venous side of the pulmonary circulation.

The relation between this *pulmonary arterial wedge pressure* and that in the left atrium has been examined by a number of authors by means of direct needle-puncture of the left atrium[11,13,23–25] or during thoracotomy[17,26,27] or at cardiac catheterization in patients with an atrial septal defect.[17,12,22,28–30] In these studies the contour of the pulse wave in the wedge position has, when present, been similar to that in the left atrium. There appears, however, to be a delay of about 0·8 s in the wedge tracing which would suggest a pulse wave velocity of 2–3 $m \cdot s^{-1}$ on the venous side of the pulmonary circulation. The mean wedge pressure was usually comparable with that in the left atrium, although in general a few mmHg higher. The general opinion of these authors has been that the pulmonary arterial wedge pressure tracing is a reflection of events in the left atrium. It has been suggested that the second wave of the wedge tracing is due to a delayed transmission of the main pulmonary arterial wave[31] or to the dicrotic wave of the pulmonary artery.[32] These theories appear unlikely, however, since the occlusion of the corresponding lobar pulmonary artery by means of a rubber balloon does not alter the character of the wedge tracing.[33]

On the basis of the above observations the pulmonary arterial wedge pressure has been widely accepted as an estimate of pulmonary venous or left atrial pressure and it has proved of considerable practical importance. It provides a convenient means of distinguishing pulmonary arterial hypertension secondary to pulmonary venous hypertension from that which arises from other causes and it gives a measure of the severity of the elevation of pulmonary venous pressure. It is also of value in physiological studies since the normal pulmonary arterial pressure is so low that the level of the venous pressure may not be neglected when considering the resistance to the flow of blood through the lungs (p. 130).

The method, however, has not gone without criticism both on the grounds of theory[34,35] and of observation.[36,37] If one supposes that it measures the pressure in the left atrium, this pressure is conveyed to the end of the catheter by a complex network of distensible vessels which may be seen as an extension of the cardiac catheter. This 'extension' has hardly the properties desirable for the faithful transmission of pressure waves (p. 65) and must add even greater distortion to the shape of the tracing than would be imposed by the cardiac catheter alone. Minute analyses of the form of the wedge tracing will, therefore, run the risk of being over-subtle. The use of the wedge tracing in assessing the relative importance of incompetence and stenosis of the mitral valve has, for instance, proved disappointing (Chap. 23, p. 353). The character of the 'extension' to the catheter has also suggested the possibility that all one is measuring is the closing pressure of the small pulmonary arteries.[35] It would certainly seem likely that the pressure measured by the wedged catheter at the apex of the lung in the upright position would be related to the alveolar gas pressure rather than the pulmonary venous pressure (Chap. 7). A clearly pulsatile tracing with two waves to each heart beat is found in only a little over a half of patients with normal pressures in the pulmonary circulation, while it is present in over nine-tenths of patients with a raised pulmonary venous pressure.[17] Distinct pulse waves on the wedge tracing will often be observed to develop in normal people when the left atrial pressure is raised by the effect of drugs. Presumably a high intraluminal pressure renders the left atrium, and the vessels which lie between it and the tip of the catheter, less distensible. This situation will not only magnify the changes in pressure in the left atrium due to alterations in its volume, but will also favour the transmission of pulse waves through the conducting system of distensible vessels.

Even in the absence of a definite 'atrial' form of tracing, the wedge pressure may well give a valid estimate of the mean left atrial pressure,[17] although under these circumstances it can only be accepted with a certain reserve. Certainly no wedge tracing should be accepted which fails to show the customary variation in pressure throughout the respiratory cycle. Sometimes, for instance, on wedging the catheter, the pressure falls gradually to some low fixed level. Sometimes, when the catheter is impacted near the diaphragm, its end appears to be occluded during certain phases of respiration. Sometimes the tracing is clearly a damped version of the pulmonary arterial wave, and a simultaneous recording of the brachial arterial pressure is helpful in defining its timing. On rare occasions one is disturbed to find the wedge pressure higher than that in the pulmonary artery.[38] It should always be possible to flush the catheter freely with saline when it is in the wedge position and this should not disturb the pressure tracing for more than a few seconds. Occasionally the wedge tracing is rendered unacceptable by the fact that it is altered permanently by flushing the catheter. On the other hand, the withdrawal of blood from the wedged catheter is not always possible even when a satisfactory pressure tracing is recorded. Pederson[17] found that even when blood was withdrawn it frequently had an oxygen saturation less than 90 per cent in the presence of pressure tracings which showed distinct 'venous' pulsations, and our experience has been similar.

A particular disease in which the interpretation of the wedge pressure has proved problematic is the rare condition of pulmonary veno-occlusive disease (Chap. 28, p. 433). The disease primarily affects pulmonary veins, reducing their calibre and increasing their resistance. In this way a pulmonary capillary and pulmonary arterial hypertension develops in the absence of any elevation of the left atrial pressure. In some patients the wedge pressure has been found to be elevated while in others it has been normal.

The factors which determine the pressure measured in the wedge position under these circumstances are illustrated in Figure 5.16. The diagram shows three hypothetical situations. In each, a catheter is wedged in one branch of a terminal arterial bifurcation. Each arterial branch supplies a region of the capillary bed which drains into a venule. The two venules from the two capillary regions join to form a common vein. In Figures 5.16A and 5.16B there are stenoses in each of the venules. In Figure 5.16C there is a stenosis in the common vein. In Figure 5.16A the two capillary regions are regarded as separate. In Figure 5.16B there is free communication between the two capillary regions. Where there are multiple stenoses in small venules, the pressure recorded in the wedged position depends on the degree of lateral communication between the two capillary regions. If there is no communication (Fig. 5.16A), the pressure recorded (P) will be that existing in the common vein downstream from the stenoses. In this case the wedge pressure will approximate the left atrial pressure and will not reflect the elevation of capillary

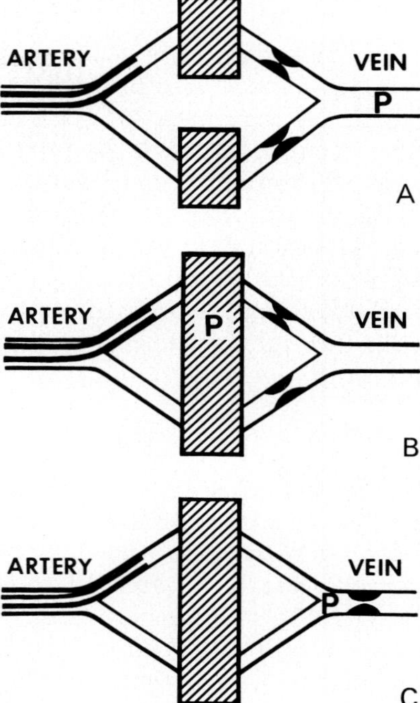

Fig. 5.16 Diagrams illustrating different ways in which the wedge pressure may be affected in pulmonary veno-occlusive disease. Each diagram represents a catheter wedged in one branch of a terminal arterial bifurcation. The capillary bed supplied by each branch of the bifurcation drains into a venule and the two venules join to form a common vein. In A and B there are narrowings in each of the two venules. In A there is no lateral communication between the two capillary beds; in B there is free lateral communication. In C there is a narrowing of the common vein. The effects of these three circumstances are discussed in the text.

pressure which exists when the lung is normally perfused. If there is free lateral communication between the two capillary regions (Fig. 5.16B) the pressure recorded (P) in the wedged position is the pressure in the capillary bed. In this case the wedge pressure will be influenced by the presence of the stenoses and will approximate the pulmonary capillary pressure existing under normal (unwedged) conditions of flow. It will not be identical to such a pressure, because, during wedging, the total arterial flow into the two communicating capillary regions has to pass through only one arterial branch and it may be limited by the resistance imposed by this branch. Where the venous stenosis is beyond the junction of the tributary vessels (Fig. 5.16C) the pressure (P) recorded in the wedged position is that existing in the vein upstream to the stenosis.

Thus, should pulmonary veno-occlusive disease affect only large veins, the wedge pressure will give an adequate indication of the venous obstruction. Should the disease affect primarily the smaller veins, the wedge pressure may not represent the height of the pressure existing generally in the pulmonary capillaries. A more rigorous analysis is given in Appendix A.

While, therefore, the measurement of the pulmonary arterial wedge pressure has in general proved itself of practical value, it is not without its limitations and requires a more critical interpretation than do the other pressure tracings taken at cardiac catheterization.

Pulmonary Venous Wedge Pressures

When a catheter is wedged into a human pulmonary vein the pressure recorded is higher than that in the left atrium. A pulse wave may be observed in this position which has the appearance of a damped and delayed pulmonary arterial tracing.[17,39] The mean pressure of the venous wedge tracing does not, however, ever rise much above 25 mmHg even in patients with severe pulmonary arterial hypertension.[17,39] Thus the pulmonary venous wedge tracing does not bear any direct and uncomplicated relation with the pulmonary arterial pressure and has not the same importance as the arterial wedge tracing.

Since this measurement will not be referred to again, the term 'wedge pressure' will, throughout the rest of this book, refer only to the pulmonary arterial wedge pressure.

Manometers at the Tip of the Catheter

The introduction of very small manometers which can be placed at the intracardiac end of a cardiac catheter[40–43] should avoid many of the problems which have been discussed in this chapter. They have not been widely used up to the present, partly because of the technical difficulties and expense inherent in the design of the manometer itself, partly because the increased accuracy of the recording is not required for practical clinical purposes, and partly because the manometer occupies a lumen through which blood would normally be sampled. They have, however, played an essential part in the study of impedance in the pulmonary circulation discussed in Chapter 10. The most widely used catheter-tip unit is an inductance manometer[40] produced commercially by the Telco Company, France. Recently, excellent results have been reported with a fibre-optic method.[42,43] Light passes up the cardiac catheter along one system of glass fibres. At the tip it is reflected back along another system of fibres by a diaphragm. The diaphragm moves according to the blood pressure and thus the quantity of reflected light varies.

REFERENCES

1. Hansen, A. T. (1949) *Pressure Measurement in the Human Organism.* Copenhagen: Teknisk Forlag.
2. Noble, F. W. (1953) *Electrical Methods of Blood-Pressure Recording*. Springfield, Ill.: Thomas.
3. Fry, D. L., Noble, F. W. & Mallos, A. J. (1957) *Circulat. Res.*, **5**, 40.
4. Wood, E. H., Leusen, I. R., Warner, H. R. & Wright, J. L. (1954) *Circulat. Res.*, **2**, 294.
5. Cournand, A., Bloomfield, R. A. & Lauson, H. D. (1945) *Proc. Soc. Exp. Biol. (N.Y.)*, **60**, 73.
6. Harris, P. (1955) *Brit. Heart J.*, **17**, 173.
7. Harris, P., Fritts, H. W., Jn. & Cournand, A. (1960) *Circulation*, **21**, 1134.
8. Howarth, S. (1954) *Brit. Heart J.*, **16**, 171.
9. Ross, J. (1966) *Circulation*, **34**, 391.
10. Wynn, A., Matthews, M. B., McMillan, I. K. R. & Daley, R. (1952) *Lancet*, **ii**, 216.
11. Björk, V. O., Malmström, G. & Uggla, L. G. (1953) *Ann. Surg.*, **138**, 718.
12. Facquet, J., Lemoine, J. M., Alhomme, P. & Lefelve, J. (1952) *Arch. Mal. Coeur*, **45**, 741.
13. Allison, P. R. & Linden, R. J. (1953) *Circulation*, **7**, 669.
14. Radner, S. (1954) *Acta Med. Scand.*, **148**, 57.

15. Opdyke, D. F., Duomarco, J. L., Dillon, W. H., Schreiber, H., Jn., Little, R. C. & Seely, R. D. (1948) *Amer. J. Physiol.*, **154**, 258.
16. Luisada, A. A. & Liu, C. K. (1954) *Cardiac Pressures and Pulses.* Page 3. New York: Grune & Stratton.
17. Pederson, A. (1956) *The Venous Pressure in the Pulmonary Circulation.* Copenhagen: Nyt Nadisk Forlag, Amold Busk.
18. Dexter, L., Burnell, C. S., Haynes, F. W. & Seibel, R. E. (1946) *J. Clin. Invest.*, **25**, 913.
19. Miller, W. S. (1947) *The Lung.* Springfield, Ill.: Thomas.
20. Hellems, H. K., Haynes, F. W., Dexter, L. & Kinney, T. D. (1948) *Amer. J. Physiol.*, **155**, 98.
21. Hellems, H. K., Haynes, F. W. & Dexter, L. (1949) *J. Appl. Physiol.*, **2**, 24.
22. Lagerlöf, H. & Werkö, L. (1949) *Acta Physiol. Scand.*, **16**, 75.
23. Epps, R. G. & Adler, R. (1953) *Brit. Heart J.*, **15**, 298.
24. Björk, V. D., Malmström, G. & Uggla, L. G. (1954) *Amer. Heart J.*, **47**, 635.
25. Werkö, L., Vernauskas, E., Eliasch, H., Lagerlöf, H., Senning, A. & Thomasson, B. (1953) *Circulat. Res.*, **1**, 337.
26. Connolly, D. C., Kirklin, J. W. & Wood, E. H. (1954) *Circulat. Res.*, **2**, 434.
27. Wilson, R. H., McKenna, W. T., Johnson, F. E., Jenson, N. K., Nazzitello, W. F. & Dempsey, M. E. (1953) *J. Lab. Clin. Med.*, **42**, 408.
28. Calazel, P., Gerard, R., Daley, R., Draper, A., Foster, J. & Bing, R. J. (1951) *Bull. Johns Hopk. Hosp.*, **88**, 20.
29. Walter, H. H., Bayer, O., Loogen, F. & Rippert, R. (1953) *Cardiologia*, **23**, 319.
30. Lenègre, J., Scebat, L., Besson, H., Benchemoul, F. & Damien, J. (1953) *Arch. Mal. Coeur*, **46**, 1.
31. Soulié, P., Carlotti, J., Sicot, J. & Joly, F. (1951) *Bull. Soc. Méd. Hôp. (Paris)*, **67**, 293.
32. Van Bogaert, A., Van Genabeck, A., Nyssens, A., Van Der Henst, H. & Vandael, J. (1952) *Arch. Mal. Coeur*, **45**, 673.
33. Werkö, L., Varnauskas, E., Eliasch, H. & Thomasson, B. (1953) *Circulat. Res.*, **1**, 340.
34. Wiggers, C. J. (1953) *Circulat. Res.*, **1**, 371.
35. Burton, A. C. (1953) *Ann. Rev. Physiol.*, **15**, 213.
36. Ankeney, J. L. (1952) *Amer. J. Physiol.*, **169**, 40.
37. Ankeney, J. L. (1953) *Circulat. Res.*, **1**, 58.
38. Bernstein, W. H., Fierer, E. M., Laszlo, M. H., Samet, P. & Litwak, R. S. (1960) *Brit. Heart J.*, **22**, 37.
39. Weissel, W., Salzmann, F. & Vetter, H. (1952) *Brit. Heart J.*, **14**, 47.
40. Gauer, O. H. & Gienapp, E. (1950) *Science*, **112**, 404.
41. Traite, M., Welkowitz, W. & Downs, R. (1960) *Rev. Sci. Inst.*, **31**, 987.
42. Ramirez, A., Hood, W. B., Jn., Polanyi, M., Wagner, R., Yankopoulos, N. A. & Abelmann, W. H. (1949) *J. Appl. Physiol.*, **26**, 679.
43. Lindström, L. H. (1970) *I.E.E.E. Trans. Bio. Med. Eng.*, *BME*17, 207.

6. The Measurement of Flow

In the pulmonary circulation the flow of blood through all vessels, including the capillaries (p. 87) is pulsatile with the heart beat and undergoes a phasic variation with ventilatory movement. In discussing methods of measuring the flow of blood it is, therefore, necessary to distinguish between those which measure the mean flow over a period of time and those which follow its rapid changes and reversals from instant to instant. Among the former are the direct Fick (p. 79) and dye-dilution (p. 82) methods. Among the latter are the body-plethysmographic method for pulmonary capillary flow (p. 87) and various electromagnetic (p. 91), ultrasonic (p. 93) and thermal (p. 90) devices. Throughout this and all succeeding chapters the term 'pulmonary blood flow' will be used to indicate the time-averaged mean flow through the entire pulmonary circulation to both lungs.

In the absence of any congenital cardiac defect the mean flow through the pulmonary circulation is the same as the cardiac output, with a very small error due to the presence of the bronchial circulation (Chap. 40). In the basal state and in the recumbent position the pulmonary blood flow normally averages about 6 to 7 $l \cdot min^{-1}$ or about 3·5 to 4·0 $l \cdot min^{-1}/m^2$ BSA. Even under these most stable conditions there is a wide variation from person to person and from moment to moment so that the normal range extends from about 2 to 5 $l \cdot min^{-1}/m^2$ BSA. In everyday life the flow must vary considerably from one moment to the next depending on the state both of the body and the mind. Exercise, anxiety and digestion, for instance, all increase the pulmonary blood flow (Chap. 11).

Apart from these momentary variations, there are more sustained differences in the pulmonary blood flow from one person to another which are of constitutional origin. There is a gradual decrease in the cardiac output throughout adult life.[1] There is an increase during pregnancy.[2,3] Flow is also dependent on the temperature of the body and its surroundings, being increased in fever and decreased under hypothermia (Chap. 11). The level of activity of the thyroid has an important influence, the flow being increased in hyperthyroidism and decreased in myxoedema (Chap. 11). Other diseases causing a sustained increase in the cardiac output are anaemia, arterio-venous fistulae in the systemic circulation, Paget's disease of bone, parenchymatous hepatic failure, beri-beri (Chap. 11) and 'alveolar-capillary block' (Chap. 42).

The level of the pulmonary blood flow reaches its most abnormal limits in patients with congenital heart disease. It is not unusual, for instance, for a patient with a large atrial septal defect to have a sustained flow of 20 $l \cdot min^{-1}$ through the lungs (Chap. 19). The increased flow of blood seems to give rise to the intimal fibrosis in the small pulmonary veins which is characteristic of this disease (Chap. 16). At the opposite extreme are patients with Fallot's Tetrad who may have a pulmonary blood flow in the region of 2 $l \cdot min^{-1}$. Here the diminished flow of blood seems to be a major cause of the widespread pulmonary thrombotic lesions which develop in these patients (Chap. 37). In patients with septal defects, the magnitude of the left–right shunt is dependent on the degree of hypertensive vascular disease affecting the vessels of the lungs and the measurement of the pulmonary blood flow is of importance in deciding whether or not the defect should be closed surgically (Chap. 20).

The methods most frequently used to determine the mean pulmonary blood flow will be described below. They all depend on the same principle. A substance enters the circulation at a particular point in a known amount. This may be oxygen or nitrous oxide entering the pulmonary capillaries at a rate which can be measured, or a measured quantity of dye injected into the pulmonary artery. The concentration of the particular substance under consideration is measured in the blood upstream and downstream from its point of entry into the circulation; or, in the case of substances foreign to the body, it may be assumed that the concentration is zero in the blood upstream. It is then argued that, over a certain period of time (t min) each litre of blood collects a certain quantity of the indicator substance (C mol) and thus increases its concentration by C $\text{mol} \cdot \text{l}^{-1}$. If the amount of indicator substance which has entered the circulation during that time is I mol, the rate of flow is given by

$$\frac{I}{C \cdot t} \quad \text{l} \cdot \text{min}^{-1} \qquad \text{(i)}$$

A. The Direct Fick Method

In this method,[4] the indicator substance is oxygen. In a normal person each 100 ml of mixed venous blood which enters the lungs contains a volume of oxygen equal to $C\bar{v}_{O_2}$ ml. As the blood leaves the lungs and passes into the left side of the heart and aorta it contains a volume of oxygen equal to Ca_{O_2} ml. Each 100 ml of blood, therefore, takes up $(Ca_{O_2} - C\bar{v}_{O_2})$ ml of oxygen as it passes from the pulmonary artery to the aorta. If the total volume of oxygen taken up each minute by the lungs ($\dot{V}O_2$ ml) is known, then the flow of blood through the lungs ($\dot{Q}$) is:

$$\frac{\dot{V}O_2}{Ca_{O_2} - C\bar{v}_{O_2}} \times 100 \text{ ml} \cdot \text{min}^{-1}$$

or

$$\dot{Q} = \frac{\dot{V}O_2}{Ca_{O_2} - C\bar{v}_{O_2}} \times \frac{1}{10} \text{ l} \cdot \text{min}^{-1} \qquad \text{(ii)}$$

The estimation of the cardiac output by this method thus requires three measurements: the oxygen content of systemic arterial blood, the oxygen content of the blood in the pulmonary artery (mixed venous blood) and the rate of oxygen uptake by the lungs. The sampling of arterial blood is readily achieved by an arterial needle. The sampling of mixed venous blood had to wait the introduction of the use of the cardiac catheter by the work of Forsmann, Cournand and Richards. The rate of uptake of oxygen by the pulmonary capillaries may be calculated from the collection and analysis of expired air (Appendix B).

This method probably gives the most accurate measure of the pulmonary blood flow. It has, however, a number of limitations which are due both to practical and to theoretical errors associated with the sampling of gas and blood. In the first place, the intermittency of ventilation makes it necessary to collect the expired air for at least one minute and ideally for about three minutes. During this time it is believed that the rate of uptake of oxygen measured at the mouth is the same as that occurring at the alveolar capillaries. There is, however, a large and continuously varying volume of gas interposed between the process which is being measured and the site of the measurement itself, and it has to be assumed (Appendix B) that the volumes of oxygen and nitrogen in the lungs remain unchanged during the period of measurement. Such an assumption becomes temporarily untrue if there is a change in the rate of uptake of oxygen from the alveoli, as for instance at the beginning of exercise. It will also become untrue for a period of time if there is a change in the volume of ventilation per minute or if the composition of the inspired air is altered.[5] Finally, any change in the average total volume of gas held in the lungs will cause oxygen to be stored or lost from them and thus render the oxygen uptake at the mouth different from that in the alveolar–capillary membrane.

Errors will also occur if the mixed venous blood is sampled from the right atrium where the various venous streams fail to mix completely.[6] For this reason it is necessary to obtain mixed venous samples from the pulmonary artery. With high rates of flow the arteriovenous oxygen difference becomes very small and then small analytical errors in measuring the blood gases will cause correspondingly greater inaccuracies in the figure for the cardiac output.

A further error arises out of the nature of sampling.[7–9] The blood flowing past the tip of the catheter or needle does so in a pulsatile fashion. On the other hand, the sample of blood is drawn into the syringe at a steady rate. Let us suppose that the period of sampling is divided into two halves, that the oxygen content and rate of flow of the arterial blood differ between the two halves, but that they remain constant within each half. Let the oxygen content and flow of blood in the artery in the two half-periods be Ca_1, $\dot{Q}_1$, Ca_2 and $\dot{Q}_2$ respectively. Then the average oxygen content of the blood in the artery will be:

$$\frac{\dot{Q}_1 Ca_1 + \dot{Q}_2 Ca_2}{\dot{Q}_1 + \dot{Q}_2} \qquad \text{(iii)}$$

The average oxygen content of the blood in the syringe, on the other hand, will be:

$$\frac{Ca_1 + Ca_2}{2} \qquad \text{(iv)}$$

It is apparent that (iv) will equal (iii) only if the blood flow or the oxygen content of the blood remains constant. Alternatively, the mean oxygen content of the blood in the syringe could be made to equal that of the blood in the artery if the rate of sampling could be varied according to the rate of blood flow.

Similar considerations apply to the sampling of mixed venous blood. Hence, if there is a constant rate of sampling of blood, the Fick calculation will be exact only if the oxygen contents of arterial and mixed venous blood remain constant or if the flow remains constant. Of these two alternatives, the latter is certainly never achieved during life. The flow of blood past the tip of the catheter in the pulmonary artery or past the needle in the brachial artery is highly pulsatile. The situation is complicated ever further by the fact that the rate of flow at any instant is not the same in all parts of the segment of the circulation through which it is being measured. The flow waves through the pulmonary and mitral valves, for example, are 180° out of phase. This lack of uniformity of blood flow is made possible by the distensibility of the system, so that the volume of blood held in various parts is changing from moment to moment. At any one instant, for example, it would be possible for blood to be flowing past the catheter and arterial needle while the blood in the pulmonary capillaries is stationary and the oxygen uptake momentarily zero. Neither is it purely a matter of a change in the distribution of blood within the segment of the circulation between the two sampling points, since the total 'central' blood volume between those points (Chap. 8) is itself varying from moment to moment according to the heart beat and the phase of respiration.

The true relation between the different elements of the Fick equation under these circumstances may be derived by considering the total volume of oxygen passing into and out of the 'central' blood volume during the period of measurement. This is considered in Appendix D where it is concluded that once again the Fick calculation will give a true measure of the average flow only if the flow is constant or if the oxygen contents of mixed venous and arterial blood are constant. Since, as has just been discussed, the former of these two alternatives is physiologically impossible, the accuracy of the Fick method once more depends on the constancy of the oxygen content of the mixed venous and arterial blood.

Since the flow of blood through the pulmonary capillaries may vary with the cardiac and respiratory cycles and since the partial pressure of oxygen in the alveoli will certainly vary throughout the respiratory cycle it is unlikely that the oxygen tension of the blood leaving the pulmonary capillaries is constant. Fortunately, during the breathing of room air and under resting conditions, the variation in the oxygen content of end-capillary blood through the cardiac and respiratory cycles is unlikely to be substantial. This is because any variation in the partial pressure of oxygen in the end-capillary blood will occur on the plateau of the oxygen dissociation curve (Fig. 36.1, p. 568) where large changes in the partial pressure lead to very little change in the oxygen content. Under hypoxic conditions, however, or where there is a severe impairment of the diffusing capacity of the lungs, cyclical variations in the oxygen content of end-capillary blood might conceivably reach more important proportions since the variations in the partial pressure of oxygen in this blood could occur on the steep portion of the oxygen dissociation curve (Chap. 36).

The mixed venous blood in man shows no phasic variations in oxygen saturation with the cardiac cycle,[10] but there are small cyclical changes with the phase of respiration which become more apparent on exercise. It has been estimated that these variations would cause an error in the determination of the cardiac output of about 4 per cent at rest, although during exercise this systematic error may reach more substantial proportions.[10]

Variations in the rate of uptake of oxygen by the capillaries will lead to no discrepancy between the measured and true values for the pulmonary blood flow because they occur in the numerator of the Fick equation.

In the presence of a right–left intracardiac shunt equation (ii) estimates the systemic and not the pulmonary blood flow. In order to calculate the pulmonary blood flow a value for the pulmonary venous oxygen content has to be assumed or special steps taken to sample this blood separately. In the presence of a pure left–right intracardiac shunt the method measures the pulmonary blood flow if the mixed venous blood is sampled at a point after it has been joined by the shunt. When the shunt is directed into the pulmonary artery, as in a patent ductus arteriosus, the incomplete mixing of the streams in this vessel may, however, lead to great error in sampling. The inaccuracies which arise in the presence of broncho-pulmonary anastomoses are described in Chapter 40.

For all its possible errors, the Fick method remains within its limits the most reliable measure that we have of the pulmonary blood flow. There have been numerous reports of the pulmonary blood flow measured in this way[11] the average figure usually lying between 3·5 and 4·0 $l \cdot min^{-1} \cdot m^{-2}$. In our personal series of fifty-five hospital patients with normal hearts and lungs, the average resting value for the pulmonary blood flow measured by this method has been 3·95 $l \cdot min^{-1} \cdot m^{-2}$ with a standard deviation of 0·75.

B. The Dye-Dilution Method

We owe this method to the researches of Hamilton.[12–14] The principle was first suggested by Stewart.[15] Figure 6.1 illustrates how it would apply in the homely instance of a kitchen tap pouring water through a rubber tube into a bucket. We shall consider the rate of flow of water to be $\dot{Q}\ l \cdot min^{-1}$. While the water is flowing, a quantity (I mg) of dye is injected by a syringe into the rubber tubing. Immediately the dye starts to appear at the end of the tube, the outflowing water is collected in a bucket. At the moment, t min later, when the dye ceases to be present in the outflowing water, the bucket is taken away. Since $\dot{Q}\ l \cdot min^{-1}$ of water have poured into the bucket for t min, the volume of water collected is $\dot{Q}t$ litres. This quantity contains all the I mg of injected dye. The mean concentration of the dye in the bucket ($\dot{C}$) is, therefore,

$$\frac{I}{\dot{Q}t} \quad mg \cdot l^{-1}$$

Hence:

$$\dot{Q} = \frac{I}{\bar{C}t} \quad l \cdot min^{-1} \qquad (v)$$

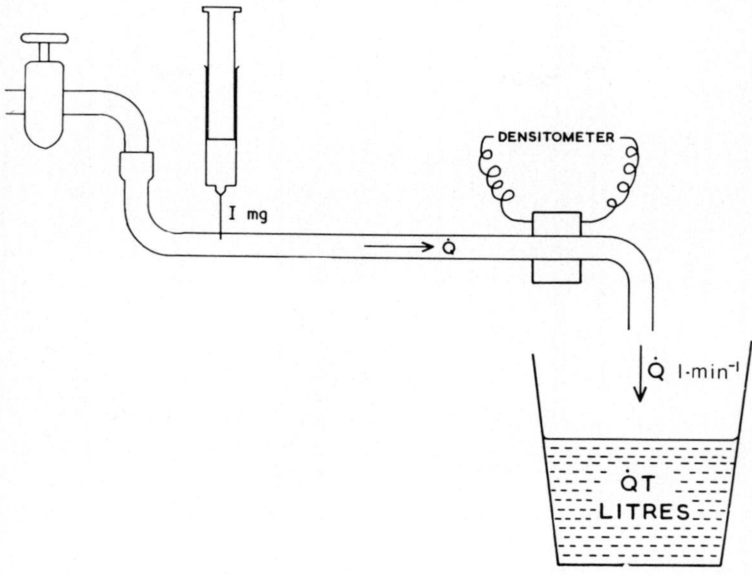

Fig. 6.1 Diagram to illustrate the measurement of the flow of water through a tube by the dye-dilution method.

This is the fundamental relation on which the dye-dilution method is based and it will be seen to be the same as equation (i). Instead of collecting the water in the bucket, the concentration of the dye in the water could be recorded from instant to instant by means of a photoelectric densitometer (Fig. 6.2). The mean concentration of dye ($\bar{C}$) during the inscription of the curve could then be calculated by dividing the area under the curve by the baseline, t.

In clinical practice the dye is best injected into the venae cavae, right atrium or pulmonary artery by means of a catheter. Blood is sampled continuously from a brachial artery and drawn through a photoelectric densitometer or pours into a sequence of containers for subsequent analysis. Unfortunately, under these circumstances, the dye begins to reappear in the systemic arterial blood by recirculation before the initial 'primary' curve is completed (Fig. 6.3). Since it is the primary curve from which the mean concentration of dye ($\bar{C}$ $mg \cdot l^{-1}$) has to be calculated, the problem is how to predict the termination of the primary curve from that part of it which is recorded before recirculation occurs. Kinsman *et al.*[13] showed in a model that, if the fluid passes at some point through a mixing chamber, the downslope of the primary dilution curve becomes logarithmic. They argued that, in the body, the ventricles would act as such mixing chambers and demonstrated that the downslope of the primary arterial dilution curve was in fact logarithmic. Whether the presence of a mixing chamber in the ventricles is the real cause for this observation has been debated. However, the observation need only be accepted empirically to provide a way of completing the primary arterial curve. Thus, when

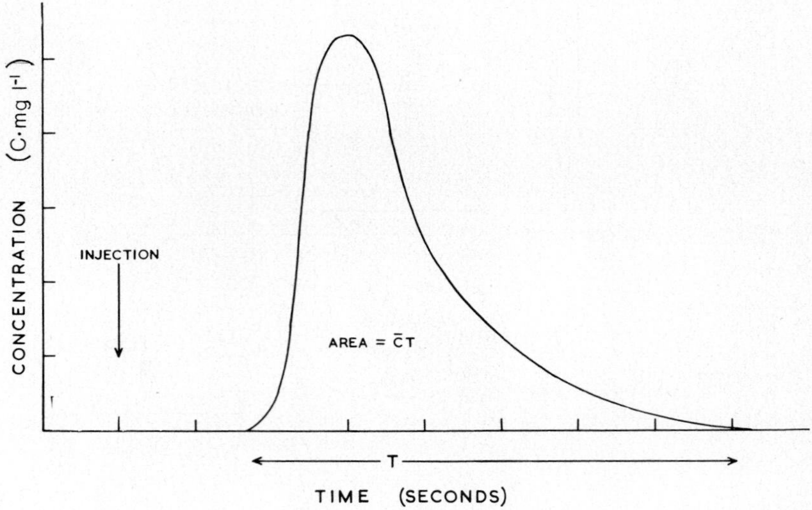

Fig. 6.2 Schematic dye-dilution curve recorded by the densitometer in Figure 6.1.

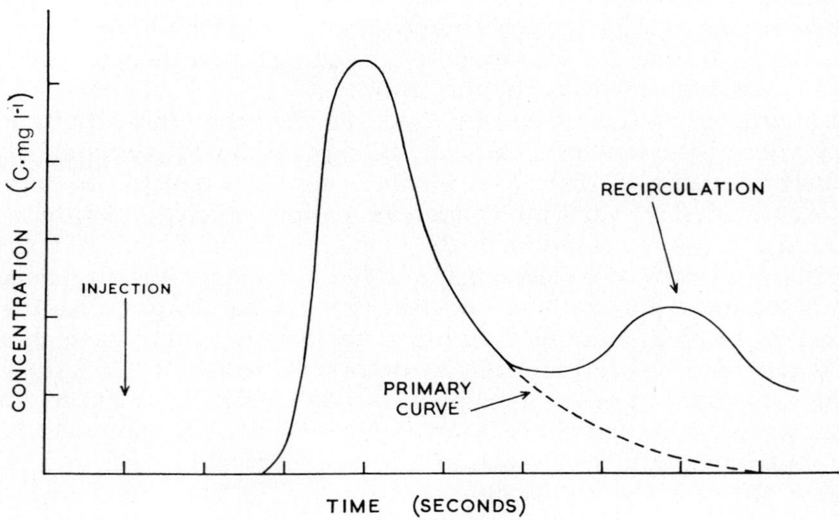

Fig. 6.3 Schematic dye-dilution curve recorded from the brachial artery after the injection of dye into the pulmonary artery.

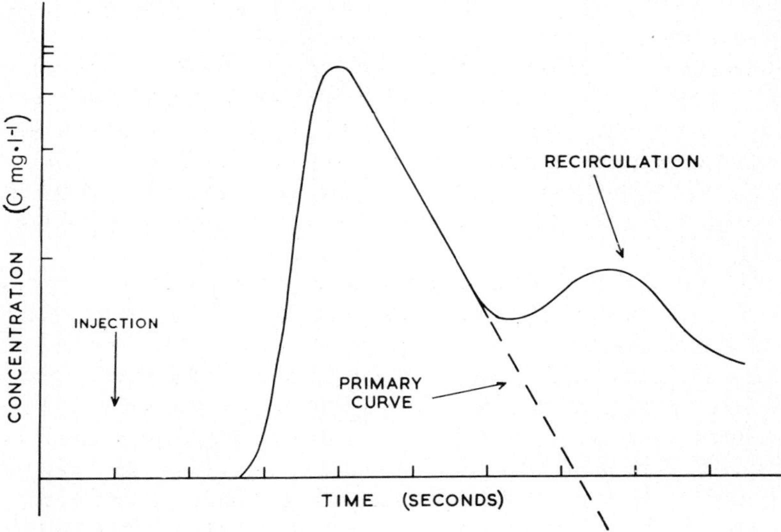

Fig. 6.4 Semi-logarithmic plot of Figure 6.3.

the logarithm of the concentration of dye is plotted against time (Fig. 6.4) the initial, uncontaminated part of the downslope of the primary curve appears as a straight line. The continuation of this straight line predicts the remainder of the primary curve.

The method has been found to give results which correspond with those obtained by the Fick method.[16,17] It has, indeed, certain advantages over the Fick method. Since it measures the cardiac output over a shorter period of time, it is not so dependent on maintaining a steady state. It can be completely independent of the composition of the respiratory gases, provided that the measurement of the dye in the blood is not interfered with by variations in the arterial oxygen saturation. It avoids the necessity to catheterize the pulmonary artery. It allows a measurement of the 'central blood volume' (p. 107). The many published normal values have been reviewed by Wade and Bishop.[11]

The method has, however, certain limitations. Its accuracy is certainly no better than the Fick method and may be less. Two measurements of the cardiac output made by drawing two simultaneous curves from both brachial arteries during a single injection may show differences as high as 15 per cent.[18] The accuracy of the method becomes increasingly in question the higher up the downslope recirculation occurs. This shortcoming is most evident in cardiac failure where it may make the method impossible to apply.

The presence of pulsatile arterial flow leads to sampling errors of the same nature as those described in equations (iii) and (iv) for oxygen. On the other hand, the theoretical difficulties described in Appendix D for the Fick method are obviated by the instantaneous injection of the total quantity of dye and by the lack of necessity to consider the concentration of dye in the mixed venous blood during the operative part of the curve (Appendix E).

The sampling error introduced by the presence of a rapidly pulsatile flow is probably very small. The error introduced by slower changes in the cardiac output might reasonably be expected to be more serious since the extrapolation of the downslope of the primary curve could be inaccurate. Experiments on models, however, seemed to show that the dye method gave a reasonably accurate measurement of the average flow during the inscription of the curve even when the rate of flow was being varied.[19]

A practical limitation of the dye-dilution method lies in the undesirable effects of the indicators themselves. With the original dye, Evans' blue, the number of estimations of the cardiac output was limited to three or four by the occurrence of cyanosis. The use of indocyanine green[20] overcame this difficulty. There are obvious limitations to the number of injections of radioactive indicators.

Several workers have considered the possibility of injecting radioactive material into a peripheral vein and recording its arrival in the heart by means of a precordial counter. Provided that the counting system is able to distinguish adequately between the dilution curves of each side of the heart (*i.e.* can show two distinct peaks) a mathematically valid measurement of the cardiac output can be made.[21] The chief value of this method has been in the assessment of the pulmonary blood volume (Chap. 8, p. 108).

Instead of dye it is possible to use the injection of cold saline or another physiologically acceptable liquid and measure its effect on the temperature downstream from the injection by means of a thermocouple or thermistor.[22] The principles are similar to those for dye particles involving a knowledge of temperature and specific heat. The great advantage of the thermodilution method is that the loss of heat becomes dissipated during passage through the systemic capillaries, so that recirculation does not occur. In this way only a primary curve is registered and the area enclosed by it may be used immediately in the calculation of flow. The precise shape of the primary curve is immaterial provided the cold injection passes through a mixing chamber to prevent streaming.

The cold injection may be given as a bolus or continuously. Probably the most convenient method is to inject into the right atrium or right ventricle and sample from the pulmonary artery.[23–25] Alternatively, the injection may be made into the left side of the heart and the temperature recorded in the aorta.[26]

Another method,[27] based on the dye-dilution principle, utilizes radioactive krypton (^{85}Kr) as the indicator substance. This gas has a low solubility in blood and, when injected on the systemic venous side, it is almost all removed into the alveolar gas as it passes through the lungs. A solution of ^{85}Kr is given into the right atrium at a constant rate and samples of blood are taken from the pulmonary artery for estimation of radioactivity. The radioactivity of mixed venous blood upstream from the point of infusion is estimated from that of systemic arterial blood. The method has been found applicable to rapid changes of cardiac output such as those which occur at the beginning of exercise.

C. Body-Plethysmograph Method for Pulmonary Capillary Blood Flow

This method was introduced by Lee and Dubois.[28] The subject sits in an air-tight box, the body plethysmograph, the pressure within which is measured by a sensitive manometer and recorded graphically. If air is injected from a syringe into the box, the manometer will record an increase in pressure. If air is withdrawn from the box, there will be a decrease in pressure. Changes in pressure may, therefore, be used to measure the volume of gas entering or leaving the plethysmograph.

If the subject holds his breath with his glottis open at the end of a normal expiration, there will be a gradual decrease in the pressure in the plethysmograph because the uptake of oxygen by the lungs exceeds the output of carbon dioxide. If, prior to holding his breath, the subject has taken a deep inhalation of nitrous oxide, the net rate of uptake of gas by the lungs will be much greater because the highly soluble nitrous oxide is also being absorbed into the blood flowing through the pulmonary capillaries. The slope of the manometric recording is, therefore, steeper and the increased steepness of the slope is a measure of the rate of uptake of nitrous oxide ($\dot{V}N_2O$ ml · min^{-1}). In a more recent development of the technique[29,30] the pressure inside the plethysmograph is maintained constant by a sensitive control mechanism which can pump air into or out of the chamber. The uptake of gas by the lungs is then directly related to the rate at which air is pumped into the plethysmograph. A similar device was reported by Wasserman *et al.*[31]

The pulmonary capillary blood flow is calculated by assuming that there is no nitrous oxide in the mixed venous blood during the period of measurement and that the partial pressure of nitrous oxide in the blood leaving the capillaries is the same as that in the alveoli. The content of nitrous oxide in the blood leaving the capillaries may then be calculated by multiplying the partial pressure of the gas in the alveoli (PA_{N_2O} mmHg) by its solubility constant in blood (α ml gas per ml blood per mmHg partial pressure) at 37°C. Since it is assumed that there is no nitrous oxide in the mixed venous blood, the nitrous oxide content of the blood leaving the pulmonary capillaries (αPA_{N_2O} ml · ml^{-1}) also represents the arterio-venous difference. PA_{N_2O} is estimated from expired 'alveolar' samples of air and the pulmonary capillary blood flow ($\dot{Q}c$) is given by the formula:

$$\dot{Q}c = \frac{\dot{V}N_2O}{\alpha PA_{N_2O}} \quad \text{ml} \cdot \text{min}^{-1} \qquad \text{(vi)}$$

which is a re-statement of the Fick formula.

The method suffers from errors associated with the unequal distribution of nitrous oxide in the lung and the necessity to take 'alveolar' samples. The interruption of respiration may also affect the cardiac output and it seems unlikely that this technique will ever achieve the accuracy or convenience of the direct Fick or dye-dilution methods for the measurement of mean flow.

The great interest of the method is its ability to demonstrate the presence of pulsatile blood flow in the pulmonary capillaries.[28–34] The recording of pressure inside the plethysmograph after inhaling nitrous oxide shows distinct pulse waves synchronous with the beat of the heart which represent a pulsatile uptake of nitrous oxide by the capillaries due to a variation in the rate of flow of blood through them. Since it is not the absolute level of pressure but its rate of change which is related to the flow of gas into the pulmonary capillaries, the pressure tracing has to be differentiated with respect to time in order to record instantaneous flow. This may be achieved conveniently and instantaneously by means of an electrical circuit. Alternatively the use of a flow-meter system[29–31] gives a direct measurement of flow.

The body plethysmograph method for measuring the pulsatility of pulmonary capillary flow gives an indication at any instant of the total rate of flow through the capillary bed. Each capillary contributes its individual quantity to the total. Doubtless at any one instant there will be differences in the quantity of flow through different capillaries but what is measured is the sum of flow through all capillaries.

A pressure wave synchronous with the heart beat occurs in the body plethysmograph in the absence of nitrous oxide. It consists mainly in a positive deflection starting very shortly after the QRS-complex of the electrocardiogram. It is greater when the glottis is shut. It is associated with an indrawing of the thoracic cage, a negative deflection of the oesophageal pressure tracing, a diminution in pressure in the closed mouth if the glottis is kept open, a movement of air into the chest if the mouth is open and a diminution in abdominal girth[35–37] (Fig. 6.5). The explanation of the phenomenon appears to lie in pulsatile variations in the volume of blood in the chest. During ventricular systole the rate of flow of blood through the aorta and out of the chest is greater than the rate of venous return. This decreases the volume of blood in the chest and lowers the intra-pleural pressure. The lowered pressure causes the air in the lungs to expand (giving rise to an increase in plethysmograph pressure) and at the same time it draws the thoracic cage inwards and the diaphragm upwards. As might be expected, the amplitude of the plethysmographic systolic pressure wave is increased in patients with aortic incompetence and tricuspid incompetence. It is not, however, affected by diseases of the mitral or pulmonary valve, which disturb the distribution of blood volume within the thorax rather than its total magnitude.[37]

In the estimation of instantaneous pulmonary capillary blood flow these mechanical effects of the heart beat have to be subtracted from the total record in order to obtain the effects due to the uptake of nitrous oxide.

Other Methods Using Soluble Foreign Gases

Since the early experiments of Krogh and Lindhard[38] several methods for measuring the pulmonary blood flow have been introduced which are based on the uptake of a soluble foreign gas by the lungs. At the moment, these have largely been discarded in favour of the direct Fick and dye-dilution techniques. Cander and Forster[39] have, however, more recently revived interest in this approach and their method also provides a measurement of the pulmonary parenchymal tissue volume (Chap. 24).

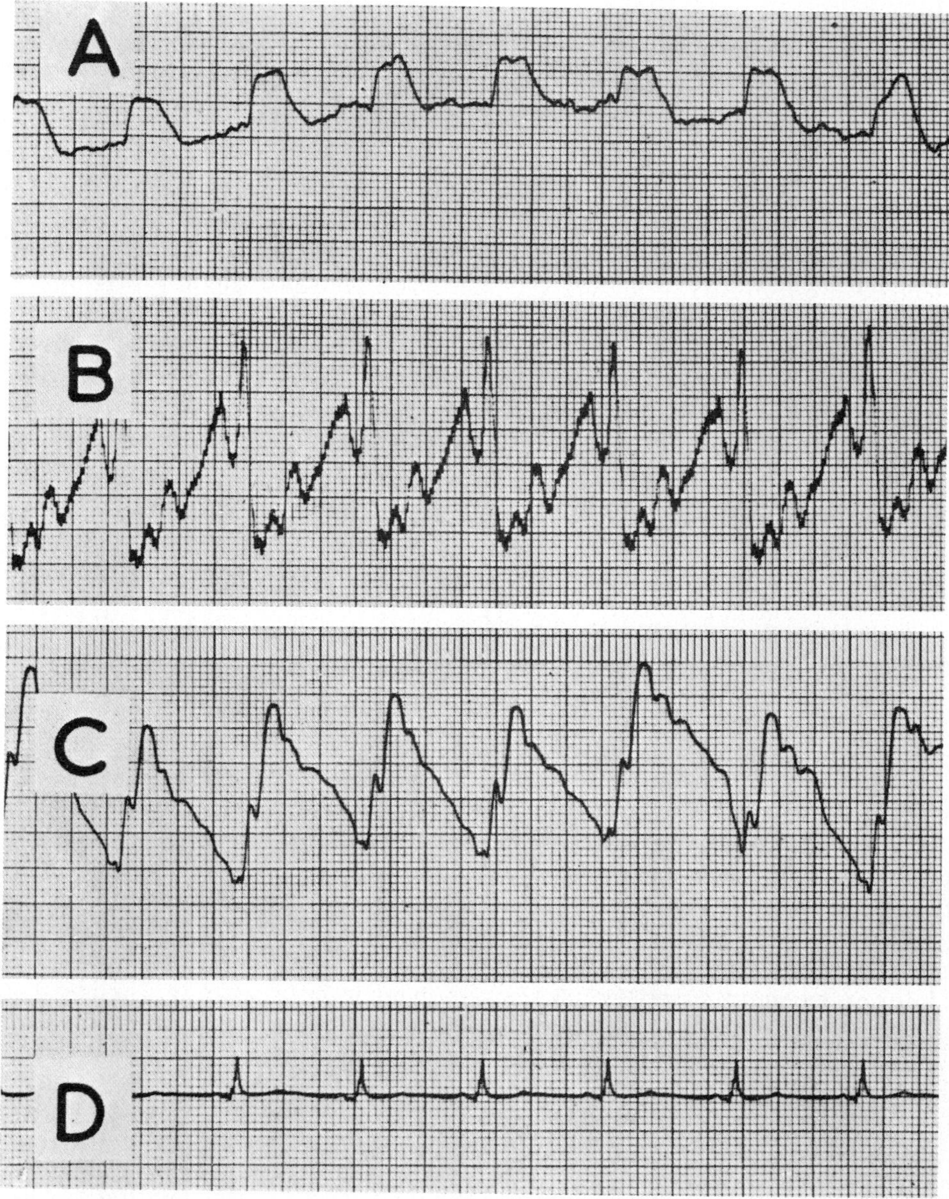

Fig. 6.5 Pulsatile variations in the body plethysmograph pressure in a normal subject with closed glottis and a lung volume of 2·4 l. The tracings are from above downwards:

A. Plethysmograph pressure. C. Thoracic girth.
B. Oesophageal pressure. D. The electrocardiogram.

An upward deflection in A and B means an increase in pressure. An upward deflection in C means a decreased girth. During ventricular systole there is an increase in plethysmograph pressure, a decrease in oesophageal pressure, and a decrease in girth.

D. Measurement of Pulsatile Flow and Velocity

The flow of blood is pulsatile throughout the pulmonary circulation. At any point in the circulation, therefore, it may be analysed[40] in terms of a series of sinusoidal waves in the same way as has been described for pressure. In such an analysis the sinusoidal waves will become alternately positive and negative with respect to the mean level of forward flow. In addition, however, the direction of the flow may at certain phases of the cycle become reversed in absolute terms.

The measurement of instantaneous flow in a blood vessel is of particular importance in studies of impedance (Chap. 10). Three main physical properties have been used in instruments designed for this purpose—electromagnetic induction, ultrasonic reflection and thermally sensitive electrical resistance. It should be appreciated that all these methods measure primarily the velocity of movement of particles of blood and not directly the volume flow of blood. Volume flow can be calculated from the product of the velocity and the cross-sectional area of the vessel.

Thermal Methods

When a heated element is placed in flowing blood, the rate of loss of heat from it by convection will depend on the velocity of the blood flowing past it. In its simplest form such an element would be a wire which is heated to a temperature a little above blood heat by the passage of an electric current through it. If a constant current is passed through the wire its temperature will depend on the velocity of the blood flow. The lower the temperature the lower the resistance of the wire. Since the resistance of the wire can be easily measured by a bridge system, the velocity of the blood flow around the wire can be found. The rate of response of such a system to rapid changes in velocity is limited by the thermal time-constant of the wire and in practice it is better to maintain the wire at a constant temperature by a sensitive feed-back system and measure the power required to keep it constant. The larger the surface area of the wire relative to its volume the more rapidly will it respond and the various instruments which have been described have all used a thin film of metal[41–43] which has usually been maintained 5°C higher than the temperature of the blood. The film is not able to distinguish between forward and backward flow but temperature sensors upstream and downstream from the heated film can be used to determine the direction of flow. Such devices have been incorporated into needles which can pierce the wall of a blood vessel and record the instantaneous velocity of the blood flowing through it.

Thermistors may be used instead of thin films of metal in which case resistance increases as the temperature decreases. Such a device, together with directionally sensitive mechanisms, has been incorporated in the end of a cardiac catheter.[44]

In the case of large vessels such as the pulmonary trunk or aorta the use of thin-film velocity probes incorporated into needles has demonstrated that the velocity is not uniform across the diameter of the vessel.[41,45,46] The nature of this lack of uniformity has important theoretical implications. In the case of a constant

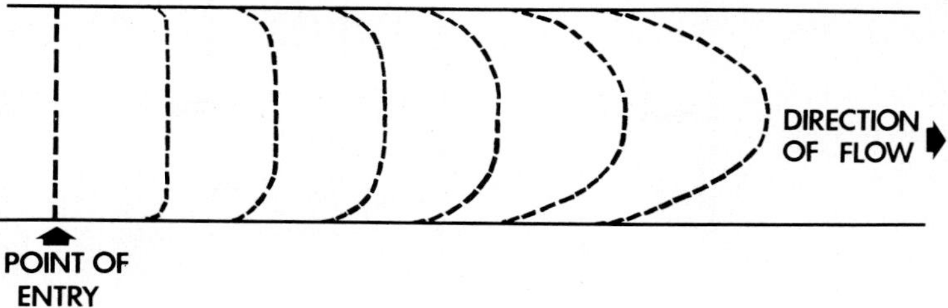

Fig. 6.6 Diagram to show the development of a parabolic velocity profile in liquid as it flows down a tube from the point of entry.

laminar flow of a viscous fluid through a long tube, the velocity of the axial stream is greater than that at the periphery (p. 113). The relation between velocity (v) and distance (x) from the axis for a vessel of radius, r, is given by the equation:

$$v = \frac{\Delta P}{4l\eta}(r^2 - x^2) \qquad \text{(vii)}$$

which is derived in Appendix F. This is the equation of a parabola with velocity reaching a maximum in mid-stream and zero at the vessel wall.

However, in the case of a pipe leading out of a large reservoir, such a parabolic 'velocity profile' would not develop immediately. At the point where the pipe joins the reservoir the velocity will be the same all across its diameter ('flat velocity profile'). As flow proceeds down the tube, the viscous drag of the peripheral layers will become increasingly evident and spread inwards towards the centre of the tube until eventually the parabolic profile will emerge (Fig. 6.6). The distance before the parabolic profile is established is called the 'inlet length'. The inlet length for steady flow in the aorta has been calculated[47] to be in the region of 60 cm. That for the pulmonary trunk would be similar, so that a developed parabolic velocity profile would not be expected in the pulmonary trunk and its main divisions even if the flow were steady. Measurements of the mean velocity at various points across the human pulmonary trunk have been made using a thin-film probe[45] and show a rather flat though asymmetrical profile with a sudden decrease in velocity adjacent to the wall (Fig. 6.7). In the human aorta a parabolic velocity profile begins to emerge in the descending aorta but never completely develops.[46]

Electromagnetic Induction

In this method a magnetic field is created across the path of flowing blood. The motion of blood across the field generates a potential difference at right angles to the flow. The magnitude of the potential difference depends on the velocity of the blood flow and may, therefore, be used to measure velocity. In the simplest form of instrument, blood is made to pass through a rigid cannula across which a magnetic field is induced. Electrodes placed at right-angles to the flow and the field will pick up a potential difference which is related to the velocity of flow. The rate of volume flow is then obtained by multiplying velocity by cross-sectional area. In such a

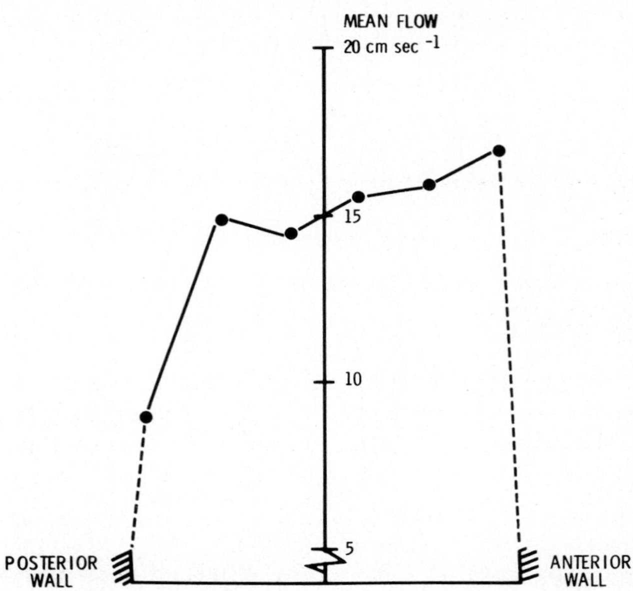

Fig. 6.7 Mean velocity profile across the human pulmonary artery. Re-drawn from Schultz *et al.*[45]

cannula there may well be differences in the magnitude of the velocity across the diameter (see above). With such a geometrical arrangement, however, the instrument will give the average velocity over the cross-section of the cannula provided that the velocity profile is axially symmetrical. For the calculation of volume flow it is the average velocity which is required. In practice, for various reasons, a pulsed magnetic field is found more convenient than a continuous one and a square-wave shaped pulse is usually used.

In physiological investigations the use of a cannula is limited and, to measure flow through a blood vessel, a device in the shape of a cuff which can be placed round the vessel is more often used. The electrodes then make contact with the wall of the vessel. Once again, instantaneous volume flow is derived by multiplying the average velocity across the vessel by its cross-sectional area. During the passage of a pulse wave the cross-sectional area of the blood vessel may be expected to vary but in practice such variation is usually too small to create important difficulties. In such an arrangement it is important to appreciate that asymmetric flow may give false results.

A third device based on the principle of electromagnetic induction can be incorporated in the end of a cardiac catheter.[48–52] Here the instrument is affected only by the motion of blood in its close vicinity so that the calculation of instantaneous cross-sectional volume flow depends on the presence of a flat velocity profile.

Electromagnetic flow-meters have been frequently used to study pulsatile blood flow in the canine pulmonary artery[53–58] and pulmonary veins.[56,59,60] An electromagnetic catheter-tip probe has been used to study the instantaneous velocity in the human pulmonary artery.[61] Such observations have shown a major peak of forward velocity during cardiac systole with a small period of reversed velocity immediately after the pulmonary second sound (Fig. 6.8). One technical problem is the sudden longitudinal motion which the heart beat imposes on the tip of the catheter.

Ultrasonic Reflection

In these instruments an ultrasonic beam is directed into the flowing blood. Two principles are used. In the transit-time technique two crystals capable of transmitting and receiving an ultrasonic beam are placed upstream and downstream in relation to the flowing blood. Their location may be outside the vessel wall[62] or in the blood flow at the end of a cardiac catheter.[63] Pulses of ultra-sound are emitted by the crystals and the time taken to travel between the two crystals compared in the upstream and downstream direction. The difference is an indication of the velocity of blood flow. Instead of the time difference the phase difference may be used.

The difference in transit times is related to the average of the blood velocities through which the beam passes. Where the crystals are located outside the blood vessel this may give rise to inaccuracies. Provided that the crystals are wide enough they will embrace the whole cross-sectional area of the vessel. If, however, the beam is a narrow one it may be influenced by a pathway across which there may not be the same average velocity as across the entire cross-section. The catheter-tip instrument based on this principle[63] has been used to study pulsatile flow in the canine pulmonary artery.

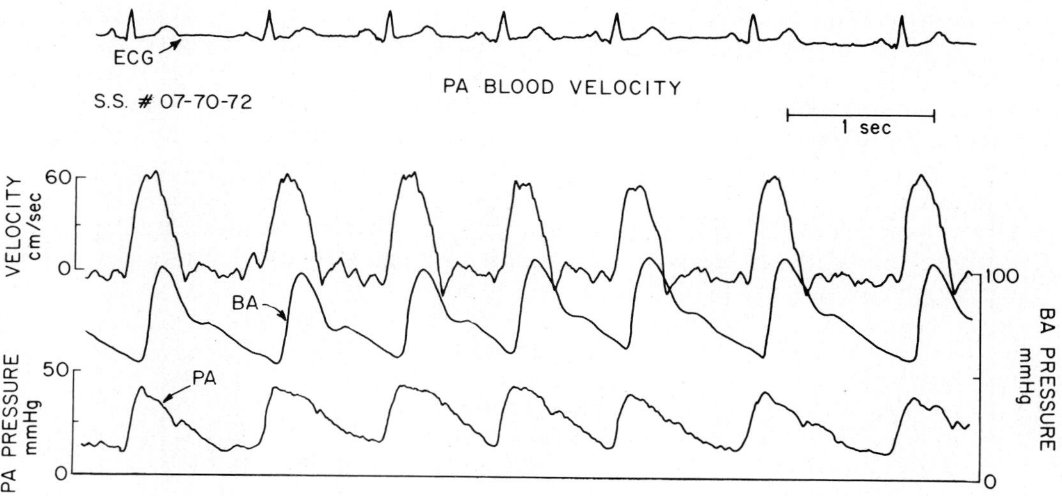

Fig. 6.8 Recording of instantaneous velocity in the human pulmonary artery.[61]

The more popular ultrasonic technique is based on the Doppler effect in which the frequency of the ultrasound reflected from red cells in the blood depends on their velocity relative to the receiver. The general popularity of the technique has largely rested on its ability to sense pulsatile blood flow through the skin but this has not been applicable to the pulmonary circulation. Technical difficulties of the method are discussed by Mills.[40] Probably the most promising system is the one developed by Peronneau *et al.*[64] A catheter-tip system has been used in the human heart and great vessels.[65]

Measurement of Pulsatile Flow and Velocity in the Human Pulmonary Circulation

The observations of Schultz and his colleagues[45] show that the time-mean velocity profile across the pulmonary trunk is flat (p. 91, Fig. 6.7). Those of Gabe and his colleagues[61] show that there is a major forward wave during systole with a minor period of reversed flow early in diastole. As far as the pulmonary trunk is concerned, therefore, one can imagine the bulk of the blood moving backwards and forwards in an oscillatory fashion as a cylindrical plug. One would expect a similar motion to occur in the two main branches and that this motion would gradually be modified as one passed down the pulmonary arterial tree. In addition, the magnitude of the instantaneous and mean forward velocity would become gradually reduced owing to the progressive increase in the cross-sectional area with branching (p. 127).

Measurements in the pulmonary trunk are primarily those of velocity, volume flow being derived from a knowledge of the cross-sectional area. The measurements in the pulmonary capillary bed by the body plethysmograph method are those of instantaneous volume flow. The pulmonary capillary blood flow in normal subjects shows a major systolic wave followed by a dicrotic notch and a dicrotic wave.[31,33] Flow remains positive all the time although the effect of a reversal of capillary flow on the uptake of nitrous oxide must be complex and unlikely to give rise to an output of nitrous oxide into the alveoli unless of a sizeable quantity. Kaplan and Kimbel[33] found that in normal persons the peak flow averaged $14{\cdot}7\ \mathrm{l \cdot min^{-1}}$ while the mean capillary blood flow was $6{\cdot}0\ \mathrm{l \cdot min^{-1}}$. Fragmentation of the pulmonary capillary systolic flow wave was found in patients with a raised pulmonary vascular resistance.[33]

For measurements of instantaneous flow in the pulmonary veins we are dependent entirely on experiments on dogs. The nature and origin of the pulmonary venous flow waves is discussed in Chapter 10, page 150.

REFERENCES

1. Brandfonbrener, M., Landowne, M. & Shock, N. W. (1955) *Circulation*, **12**, 557.
2. Adams, J. Q. (1954) *Amer. J. Obstet. Gynec.*, **67**, 741.
3. Bader, R. A., Bader, M. E., Rose, D. J. & Braunwald, E. (1955) *J. Clin. Invest.*, **34**, 1524.
4. Cournand, A., Riley, R. L., Breed, E. S., Baldwin, E. de F. & Richards, D. W., Jn. (1945) *J. Clin. Invest.*, **24**, 106.
5. Fishman, A. P., McClement, J., Himmelstein, A. & Cournand, A. (1952) *J. Clin. Invest.*, **31**, 770.
6. Barret-Boyes, B. G. & Wood, E. H. (1958) *J. Lab. Clin. Med.*, **51**, 72.

7. Visscher, M. B. & Johnson, J. A. (1953) *J. Appl. Physiol.*, **5**, 635.
8. Stow, R. W. (1954) *Minn. Med.*, **37**, 30.
9. Fritts, H. W., Jn. & Cournand, A. (1959) *Abstracts of IIIrd World Congress of Cardiology*, p. 46.
10. Wood, E. H., Bowers, D., Shepherd, J. T. & Fox, I. J. (1955) *J. Appl. Physiol.*, 7, 621.
11. Wade, O. L. & Bishop, J. M. (1962) *Cardiac Output and Regional Blood Flow*. Blackwell.
12. Hamilton, W. F., Moore, J. W., Kinsman, J. M. & Spurling, R. G. (1928) *Amer. J. Physiol.*, **85**, 337.
13. Kinsman, J. M., Moore, J. W. & Hamilton, W. F. (1929) *Amer. J. Physiol.*, **89**, 322.
14. Hamilton, W. F., Moore, J. W., Kinsman, J. M. & Spurling, R. G. (1930) *Amer. J. Physiol.*, **93**, 654.
15. Stewart, G. N. (1897) *J. Physiol.*, **22**, 159.
16. Hamilton, W. F., Riley, R. L., Attyah, A. M., Cournand, A., Fowell, D. M., Himmelstein, A., Noble, R. P., Remington, J. W., Richards, D. W., Jn., Wheeler, N. C. & Witham, A. D. (1948) *Amer. J. Physiol.*, **153**, 309.
17. Werkö, L., Lagerlöf, H., Bucht, J., Wehle, B. & Holmgren, A. (1949) *Scand. J. Clin. Lab. Invest.*, **1**, 109.
18. Fritts, H. W., Jn., Chidsey, C. A., III, Harris, P. & Cournand, A. Unpublished observations.
19. Chidsey, C. A., III, Fritts, H. W., Jn., Harris, P. & Cournand, A. (1958) *Fed. Proc.*, **17**, 25.
20. Fox, I. J., Brooker, L. G. S., Heseltine, D. W., Essex, H. E. & Wood, E. H. (1957) *Proc. Mayo Clin.*, **32**, 478.
21. Lammerant, J. (1957) *Le Volume Sanguin des Poumons chez l'Homme*. Bruxelles: Editions Arscia.
22. Fegler, G. (1954) *Quart. J. Exper. Physiol.*, **39**, 153.
23. Branthwaite, M. A. & Bradley, R. D. (1968) *J. Appl. Physiol.*, **24**, 434.
24. Spiller, P., Bostroem, B., Kreuzer, H. & Loogen, F. (1966) *Z. Kreisl. Forsch.*, **55**, 665.
25. Balcon, R. & Oram, S. (1968) *Brit. Heart J.*, **30**, 690.
26. Rolett, E. L., Sherman, H. & Gorlin, R. (1964) *J. Appl. Physiol.*, **19**, 1164.
27. Rochester, D. F., Durand, J., Parker, J. O., Fritts, H. W., Jn. & Harvey, R. M. (1961) *J. Clin. Invest.*, **40**, 643.
28. Lee, G. de J. & Dubois, A. B. (1955) *J. Clin. Invest.*, **34**, 1380.
29. Bosman, A. R., Honour, A. J., Lee, G. de J., Marshall, R. & Stott, F. D. (1964) *Clin. Sci.*, **26**, 247.
30. Karatzas, N. B., Lee, G. de J. & Stott, F. D. (1967) *J. Appl. Physiol.*, **23**, 276.
31. Wasserman, K., Butler, J. & Van Kessel, A. (1966) *J. Appl. Physiol.*, **21**, 890.
32. Linderholm, H., Kimbel, P., Lewis, D. & Dubois, A. B. (1962) *J. Appl. Physiol.*, **17**, 135.
33. Kaplan, A. S. & Kimbel, P. (1970) *J. Appl. Physiol.*, **28**, 793.
34. Karatzas, N. B. & Lee, G. de J. (1970) *Cardiovasc. Res.*, **4**, 265.
35. Blair, H. A. & Wedd, A. M. (1939) *Amer. Heart J.*, **17**, 536.
36. Blair, H. A. & Wedd, A. M. (1946) *Amer. J. Physiol.*, **145**, 528.
37. Mills, R. J. & Harris, P. (1965) *Brit. Heart J.*, **27**, 527.
38. Krogh, A. & Lindhard, J. (1912) *Skand. Arch. Physiol.*, **27**, 100.
39. Cander, L. & Forster, R. E. (1959) *J. Appl. Physiol.*, **14**, 451.
40. Mills, C. J. (1972) *Cardiovascular fluid dynamics*, ed. Bergel, D. H. Vol. 1., p. 51. Academic Press.
41. Ling, S. C., Atabeck, H. B., Fry, D. L., Patel, D. J. & Janicki, J. S. (1968) *Circulat. Res.*, **23**, 789.
42. Bellhouse, B. J. & Bellhouse, F. H. (1968) *J. Sci. Inst.*, **1**, 1211.
43. Seed, W. A. & Wood, N. B. (1970) *Cardiovasc. Res.*, **4**, 253.
44. Grahn, A. R., Paul, M. H. & Wessel, H. U. (1969) *J. Appl. Physiol.*, **27**, 407.
45. Schultz, D. L., Tunstall-Pedoe, D. S., Lee, G. de J., Gunning, A. J. & Bellhouse, B. J. (1969) *Circulatory and Respiratory Mass Transport*, ed. Wolstenholme, G. E. W. & Knight, J. Ciba Foundation Symposium. P. 172. Churchill.
46. Schultz, D. L. (1972) *Cardiovascular Fluid Mechanics*, ed. Bergel, D. H. P. 287. Academic Press.

47. McDonald, D. A. (1962) *Blood Flow in Arteries*. London: Arnold.
48. Mills, C. J. (1966) *Phys. Med. Biol.*, **11**, 323.
49. Bond, R. F. & Barefoot, C. A. (1967) *J. Appl. Physiol.*, **23**, 403.
50. Mills, C. J. & Shillingford, J. P. (1967) *Cardiovasc. Res.*, **1**, 263.
51. Mills, C. J., Gabe, I. T., Gault, J. H., Mason, D. T., Ross, J., Jn., Braunwald, E. & Shillingford, J. P. (1970) *Cardiovasc. Res.*, **4**, 405.
52. Warbasse, J. R., Hellman, B. H., Gillilan, R. E., Hawley, R. R. & Babitt, H. I. (1969) *Amer. J. Cardiol.*, **23**, 424.
53. Patel, D. J., de Freitas, F. M. & Fry, D. L. (1963) *J. Appl. Physiol.*, **18**, 134.
54. Elliott, S. E., Hoffman, J. I. E. & Guz, A. (1963) *Med. Electron. Biol. Eng.*, **1**, 323.
55. Bergel, D. H. & Milnor, W. R. (1965) *Circulat. Res.*, **16**, 401.
56. Morgan, B. C., Abel, F. L., Mullins, G. L. & Guntheroth, W. G. (1966) *Amer. J. Physiol.*, **210**, 903.
57. Karatzas, N. B., Noble, M. I. M., Saunders, K. B. & McIlroy, M. B. (1970) *Circulat. Res.*, **27**, 1.
58. Reuben, S. R., Swadling, J. P., Gersh, B. J. & Lee, G. de J. (1971) *Cardiovasc. Res.*, **5**, 1.
59. Morgan, B. C., Dillard, D. H. & Guntheroth, W. G. (1966) *J. Appl. Physiol.*, **21**, 1276.
60. Morkin, E., Collins, J. A., Goldman, H. S. & Fishman, A. P. (1965) *J. Appl. Physiol.*, **20**, 1118.
61. Gabe, I. T., Gault, J. H., Ross, J., Jn., Mason, D. T., Mills, C. J., Shillingford, J. P. & Braunwald, E. (1969) *Circulation*, **40**, 603.
62. Baker, D. W. (1966) In *Methods in Medical Research*, ed. Rusher, R. F. Vol. 2. Chicago, Ill.: Year Book Medical Publishers.
63. Fricke, G., Studer, U. & Scheu, H. (1970) *Cardiovasc. Res.*, **4**, 371.
64. Peronneau, P., Deloche, A., Bui-Mong-Hung & Hinglais, J. (1969) *Europ. Surg. Res.*, **1**, 147.
65. Kalmanson, D., Toutain, G., Novikoff, N., Derai, C., Chiche, P. & Cabrol, C. (1969) *Arm. Med. Interne.*, **11**, 685.

7. The Regional Distribution of Pulmonary Blood Flow

During the last decade several new methods for estimating the regional distribution of pulmonary blood flow were devised. They have been the source of a great deal of activity and interest both in physiological studies and in their application to disease. In addition, they have led to a number of advances in our understanding of the factors which control the flow of blood within the lung.

The newer methods have depended on the ability to measure the gamma emissions of radioactive material in the lungs by means of collimated counters applied to the chest wall. The radioactive materials used have been carbon dioxide ($C^{15}O_2$) introduced by inhalation, xenon (^{133}Xe) introduced by injection intravenously and various radioactive particles also introduced intravenously.

Inhalation of $C^{15}O_2$

This method was developed by West and Dollery.[1] The subject inhaled radioactive carbon dioxide ($C^{15}O_2$) and a series of external counters placed up and down the chest wall recorded the local disappearances of radioactivity as the $C^{15}O_2$ was taken up and carried away by the blood. Carbon dioxide is so highly diffusible (Chap. 42, p. 635) that there is virtually complete equilibration between the alveolar and capillary $P\textsc{c}^{15}O_2$. Thus the uptake of $C^{15}O_2$ is related to its partial pressure, the volume of blood flow and the dissociation curve of blood for carbon dioxide. The relation, which is derived in Appendix G, p. 663, is given by:

$$V(t) = V(o) \exp\left[-(\dot{Q}c/V\textsc{a}) \cdot k(P\textsc{b} - 47)t\right]$$

where $V(t)$ is the quantity of $C^{15}O_2$ remaining in the alveoli at time, t; $V(o)$ is the quantity of $C^{15}O_2$ in the alveoli at zero time; $\dot{Q}c$ is the capillary blood flow; $V\textsc{a}$ is the alveolar gas volume; k is a dissociation curve constant; $P\textsc{b}$ is the barometric pressure; and 47 is the vapour pressure of water at 37°C.

The fractional rate of disappearance of $C^{15}O_2$ is used to calculate $V(t)/V(o)$ from which the ratio $\dot{Q}c/V\textsc{a}$ can be derived. Thus, it will be seen that the method measures the ratio of blood flow to alveolar gas volume in the 'core' of lung which is 'seen' by the counting system.

The technique was the first to explore the regional distribution of pulmonary blood flow. It suffered, however, from the great practical disadvantage that the radioactive isotope of oxygen, $^{15}O_2$, has a half-life in the region of two minutes so that the studies had to be carried out in close proximity to a cyclotron. For this reason it has largely been superseded by the xenon method.

Injection of ^{133} Xe

In this method[2] radioactive xenon gas (^{133}Xe) is dissolved in saline and injected intravenously. The gas is so insoluble in blood that, when it reaches the lung, virtually all of it passes out into the alveoli. Thus, if the breath is held, or in the presence of a slow inspiration, the degree of radioactivity recorded by a surface counter is proportional to the quantity of ^{133}Xe brought to the portion of lung being counted which is in turn proportional to the distribution of blood flow.

The method does not give a measurement of the blood flow per unit lung volume such as is given by the carbon dioxide technique. Hence the distribution of flow recorded will be influenced by the varying amount of lung present under the counter. In order to equate the activity registered by the counter (c.p.m.) with the regional fractional concentration of ^{133}Xe in the alveolar gas (F_r) the subject is made to re-breathe in a closed circuit either following the intravenous injection of ^{133}Xe or following a separate inhalation of ^{133}Xe. When equilibration has occurred, the fractional concentration, F_{eq}, of ^{133}Xe is equal throughout the system, including the lungs, and can be measured by sampling gas from the spirometer. If the activity registered by the surface counter during equilibration is c.p.m.$_{eq}$, then:

$$F_r = F_{eq} \times \frac{\text{c.p.m.}}{\text{c.p.m.}_{eq}}$$

provided the lung volume at equilibration counting (c.p.m.$_{eq}$) is the same as that existing during the first counting (c.p.m.).

If the regional volume of alveolar gas being counted is V_r, the quantity of ^{133}Xe brought to the region will be F_rV_r. If the total quantity of ^{133}Xe injected and arriving in the lungs is I_{Xe}, the percentage of this brought to the region is:

$$\frac{F_rV_r}{I_{Xe}} \times 100\ (\%) = \frac{\dot{Q}_r}{\dot{Q}} \times 100\ (\%)$$

where $\dot{Q}_r$ is the regional blood flow. Thus the ratio of regional blood flow to regional alveolar volume is given by:

$$\frac{\dot{Q}_r}{V_r} = \frac{\dot{Q} \cdot F_r}{I_{Xe}} \qquad \text{(i)}$$

If the ratio of blood flow to pulmonary gas volume ($\dot{Q}_r/V_r$) were constant throughout the lung, F_r would be equal to I_{Xe}/V, where V is the total volume of gas in the lungs. The expression,

$$\dot{Q}_I = \frac{F_r}{I_{Xe}/V} \times 100\ (\%) \qquad \text{(ii)}$$

thus gives the observed regional flow as a percentage of that which would be expected should flow be distributed equally according to gas volume.[2,3] It will be seen by substituting from equation (i) that:

$$\dot{Q}_I = \frac{\dot{Q}_r/V_r}{\dot{Q}/V} \times 100\ (\%) \qquad \text{(iii)}$$

$\dot{Q}_I$ is called the 'regional perfusion index'.

The isotope has a half-life of 5·27 days and the method has proved widely applicable for physiological and clinical studies, especially as it may be combined with measurements of regional ventilation.

'Scintigraphy'

In this method radioactive particles are injected into a systemic vein or the right side of the heart. The particles, in the range of 10–50 μm in diameter, are retained in pulmonary arterioles and capillaries and distributed proportionately to the distribution of the flow of blood. For human use it is necessary that the particles should be subsequently removed by biological processes. The most commonly used particles are composed of human serum albumin in the form of macroaggregates[4,5] or microspheres.[6] Macroaggregates of human serum albumin are removed from the human lung with a half-life ranging from 7 to 31 hours.[7] Clearly also it is important that the deposition of particles in the pulmonary circulation should have no substantial haemodynamic effect. Widimsky[8] found that the injection of macroaggregated albumin had no effect on the pulmonary arterial pressure when this was normal or only slightly elevated. It could, however, cause an increase in the pulmonary arterial pressure in patients with pulmonary hypertension.

The particles are labelled with a radioisotope the gamma emissions of which can be counted with a scintillation counter outside the chest. Radionuclides most commonly used are isotopes of iodine (^{131}I) technecium (^{99m}Tc) or indium (^{113m}In). In order to provide a map of the distribution of the flow of blood the lungs have to be scanned by a single crystal,[9] or multiple crystals[10] or a gamma camera.[11,12]

The method makes no allowance for the regional variations in the quantity of pulmonary tissue being scanned. Although it has been used to demonstrate the physiological effects of gravity on the distribution of the pulmonary blood flow[13] its main application has been a clinical one and it is of particular value in the diagnosis and assessment of pulmonary embolic disease (Chap. 35, p. 555, 562).

The Effects of Posture on the Distribution of Blood Flow

The distance between the apex of the lung and the hilum is such that, in the upright position, the difference in hydrostatic pressure in the blood vessels at these two points must be approximately the same as the mean pulmonary arterial pressure measured at the hilum. Hence there are theoretical reasons for believing that the normal pulmonary arterial pressure is often insufficient to provide adequate perfusion of the apices of the lungs. The degree of patency of the veins at the apices must be even less, since the pressure in the left atrium is lower than that in the pulmonary artery.

A number of indirect observations suggested that the apices of the lungs were poorly perfused in the upright position. Mattson and Carlens[14] studied the regional distribution of ventilation and oxygen uptake in the lungs by means of bronchial catheterisation. In seven normal men they found that, on standing, the right upper lobe showed an average fall of 18·6 per cent of its share of the total oxygen uptake of the right lung. The distribution of ventilation within the lung was very little affected, the right upper lobe showing an average fall of 1·6 per cent of its share of the total ventilation. Similar observations were made during the change from the supine to the lateral position.[15] In this case the proportion of total oxygen uptake occurring in the upper lung became diminished, while the distribution of ventilation between the lungs was very little affected.

Other studies using small non-occlusive bronchial catheters[16] showed that the respiratory exchange ratio in the upper and lower lobes was the same while lying down but that, on standing, the ratio became higher in the upper lobe than in the lower lobe. The results indicated that the ventilation : perfusion ratio becomes increased in the upper lobes in the erect position.

In seven normal men, Riley *et al.*[17] found that the physiological dead space increased by an average of 83 ml on standing. Most of this change appeared to have occurred in the alveolar dead space. It was calculated from this data that approximately one-seventh of the total number of alveoli ceased to be perfused on standing up.

West and Dollery,[1] using the $C^{15}O_2$ method, were the first to show directly that in normal people, sitting up, the rate of perfusion relative to alveolar gas volume is considerably less at the apex of the lung than at the base. A progressive increase in the rate of clearance was demonstrated from 2 per cent per second in the first intercostal space to some 20 per cent per second at the base of the lung. Similar findings were reported for the value of $\dot{Q}_I$ measured by the ^{133}Xe technique.[2]

Studies with ^{133}Xe on the isolated dog's lung showed the same phenomenon and allowed the pulmonary arterial and venous and alveolar pressures to be varied independently.[18] Vascular pressures were equated to atmospheric pressure (see p. 165). No blood flow occurred above the level at which the alveolar pressure equalled the arterial pressure. There was a progressive increase in flow below this level provided the venous pressure was held at a low value. Raising the venous pressure tended to decrease this effect. West and his colleagues explained the observations in terms of the relations between the alveolar pressure and the arterial and venous pressures which had been explored by Riley[19] and Permutt *et al.*[20] The lung could be described in three zones. In the uppermost zone (zone 1) the alveolar pressure exceeded both the arterial and the venous pressure and no flow occurred. In the zone below this (zone 2) the alveolar pressure was less than the arterial but greater than the venous pressure. In this zone the flow of blood was determined by the difference between the arterial and alveolar pressures ('waterfall mechanism') and not by the difference between the arterial and venous pressures. In the lowest zone (zone 3) both the arterial and venous pressures exceeded the alveolar and flow was determined by the difference between the arterial and the venous pressure.

The concept was modified slightly by Bruderman *et al.*[21] who showed that, in gas-filled lungs, a flow of blood would occur when the pulmonary arterial pressure was slightly lower than alveolar. If the alveoli were filled with watery solutions no flow occurred until the arterial pressure exceeded the alveolar. The difference demonstrated the role of surface tension in the liquid lining the alveoli.

In the earlier work on man, the regional blood flow had been related to regional gas volume. This ratio was intrinsic to the equation used with the inhalation of $C^{15}O_2$ (p. 97) and to the calculation of $\dot{Q}_I$ following the injection of ^{133}Xe (p. 98). Milic-Emili and his colleagues[22] found evidence in man that, at lung volumes less than the total capacity, the alveoli at the apex of the lung are larger than those at the base in the upright position. At total lung capacity the alveolar size seemed the same throughout the lung. These physiological observations were to receive anatomical confirmation in the dog.[23] Anthonisen and Milic-Emili[3] pointed out that, if the pulmonary blood flow were distributed so that each alveolus received the same amount, and if the alveolar size were greater at the apex than at the base, the expression of regional flow in terms of regional gas volume would inevitably magnify the gradient of regional blood flow down the lung. Since the number of alveoli per unit of regional gas volume is approximately the same throughout the lung at total lung capacity, equations (ii) and (iii) could be modified so that:

$$\frac{\dot{Q}_r/TLC_r}{\dot{Q}/TLC} \times 100\ (\%) = \frac{F_r \text{ at TLC}}{I_{Xe}/TLC} \times 100\ (\%) = \dot{Q}_{Ialv}$$

In this equation, TLC is the total lung capacity, TLC_r is the regional volume of gas counted at total lung capacity and $\dot{Q}_{Ialv.}$ is the regional perfusion index per alveolus. Expressed in this fashion the perfusion index per alveolus in normal upright man at functional residual capacity increased from the apex of the lung to a level about a third of the way up from the base, below which it showed very little change.[3] At total lung capacity (where $\dot{Q}_I = \dot{Q}_{Ialv.}$) there was a more uniform increase in perfusion index down the lung. At residual volume there was no difference between the apex and the base. Hughes *et al.*[24] have made similar observations at the same three degrees of inflation of the lung with the exception that these authors found that there was some diminution in the perfusion index per alveolus towards the base of the lung at functional residual capacity and at residual volume.

Since such a diminution in perfusion per alveolus at the base of the lung cannot be explained in terms of the relation between alveolar gas pressure and vascular pressures discussed above (p. 100) it has been suggested that, at functional residual capacity or residual volume, there is a distortion of pulmonary blood vessels which are not susceptible to compression by alveolar pressure. The anatomical location of resistance in such vessels remains quite conjectural. There is, in any case, no *a priori* reason why the anatomical distribution of resistances in the pulmonary circulation should, in the absence of 'extrinsic' factors such as alveolar pressure and gravity, be intrinsically equal throughout the lung. It has also to be borne in mind that, if there were an increased resistance affecting the whole lower lobe, the effect in the antero-posterior projection would be a gradation of flow from above downwards owing to the oblique position of the major fissure of the lung.

The maintenance of the lungs in full inflation not only tends to equalise the size of the alveoli throughout the lung but also lowers the intrapleural pressure. This in turn will have the effect of lowering the pulmonary vascular pressures relative to the alveolar pressure (p. 165) provided the glottis is held open. In this way the three zones described by West *et al.*[18] will tend to shift down the lung towards the base, which may have the effect of accentuating the gradient of blood flow from the top to the bottom of the lung.

The distribution of regional pulmonary blood flow per alveolus ($\dot{Q}_{Ialv.}$) in the supine position is virtually constant from top to bottom of the lung,[25] from which it would seem that under these circumstances the alveolar gas pressure is lower than the pulmonary arterial and venous pressures throughout the lung. Such a conclusion together with a relative indistensibility of resistance vessels is consistent with the rectilinear relation between pressure and flow found in the pulmonary circulation in this posture (Chap. 9, p. 128). The difference in regional distribution between the upright and the supine position has little to do with the shape of the lung, the antero-posterior dimension of which is not far short of its vertical height. The difference lies more probably in the relative elevation of the pulmonary vascular pressures consequent on the change in centre of gravity of the total vascular system which occurs on lying down.

Discussions of the factors affecting the regional distribution of the flow of blood in the lungs have customarily been based on the effects of a distribution of peripheral resistances. While this is doubtless the major factor, it is also necessary to bear in mind that the distribution of flow may to some extent be determined by the far from simple shape and branching characteristics of the pulmonary arterial tree. Such considerations are made the more important by the relatively high proportion of the total energy of the pulmonary arterial blood which is present in a kinetic form (p. 152).

Distribution of Pulmonary Blood Flow in Disease

Abnormalities of distribution of the pulmonary blood flow are predictably found in patients with pulmonary embolism (Chap. 35, pp. 555, 562) and it is here that scintigraphy has had its greatest application. Regional deficiencies in perfusion will, however, occur in almost any localized pulmonary lesion. Discrete variations in flow are found also in patients with emphysema (Chap. 34, p. 542). Localized alveolar hypoxia causes a localized reduction in perfusion (Chap. 30, p. 454). In patients with an increased pulmonary blood flow due to a left-right shunt, the gradient of increasing perfusion from the apex to the base of the lung found normally in the upright position tends to disappear, while in patients with mitral stenosis or left ventricular failure, it becomes reversed (Chap. 23, p. 359).

REFERENCES

1. West, J. B. & Dollery, C. T. (1960) *J. Appl. Physiol.*, **15**, 405.
2. Ball, W. C., Stewart, P. B., Newsham, L. G. S. & Bates, D. V. (1962) *J. Clin. Invest.*, **41**, 519.
3. Anthonisen, N. R. & Milic-Emili, J. (1966) *J. Appl. Physiol.*, **21**, 760.
4. Taplin, G. V., Johnson, D. E., Dove, E. K. & Kaplan, H. (1964) *J. Nuc. Med.*, **5**, 259.
5. Wagner, H. N., Jn., Sabiston, D. C., Jn., Masahiro, I., Afee, J. G., Meyer, J. K. & Langan, J. K. (1964) *J. Amer. Med. Ass.*, **187**, 601.
6. Rhodes, B. A., Zolle, Z., Buchanan, J. W. & Wagner, H. N., Jn. (1969) *Radiology*, **92**, 1953.
7. Spencer, R. P. (1972) *Thorax*, **27**, 332.
8. Widimsky, J. (1970) *Prog. Resp. Res.*, **5**, 224.
9. McAfee, J. G. & Mozley, J. M. (1967) *J. Nuc. Med.*, **8**, 371.
10. Hindell, R. & Gilson, A. J. (1967) *Nucleonics*, **25**, 52.
11. Quinlan, M. F. & Wagner, H. N., Jn. (1968) *J. Nuc. Med.*, **9**, 497.
12. Bischof-Delaloye, A., Hedinger, W. & Delaloye, B. (1971) *J. Nucl. Biol. Med.*, **15**, 13.
13. Tauxe, W. N., Burchell, H. B., Chappel, D. W. & Sprau, A. (1966) *J. Appl. Physiol.*, **21**, 1381.
14. Mattson, S. B. & Carlens, E. (1955) *J. Thorac. Surg.*, **30**, 676.
15. Rothstein, E., Landis, F. B. & Narodick, G. B. (1950) *J. Thorac. Surg.*, **19**, 821.
16. Martin, C. J., Cline, F. & Marshall, H. (1953) *J. Clin. Invest.*, **32**, 617.
17. Riley, R. L., Permutt, S., Said, S., Godfrey, M. P. W., Cheng, T. O., Howell, J. B. L. & Shepard, R. H. (1959) *J. Appl. Physiol.*, **14**, 339.
18. West, J. B., Dollery, C. T. & Naimark, A. (1964) *J. Appl. Physiol.*, **19**, 713.
19. Riley, R. L. (1962) In *Pulmonary Structure and Function*. P. 261. Churchill.
20. Permutt, S., Bromberger-Barnea, B. & Bane, H. N. (1962) *Med. Thorac.*, **19**, 239.
21. Bruderman, I., Somers, K., Hamilton, W. K., Tooley, W. H. & Butler, J. (1964) *J. Appl. Physiol.*, **19**, 707.
22. Milic-Emili, J., Henderson, J. A. M., Dolovich, D. T. & Kaneko, K. (1966) *J. Appl. Physiol.*, **21**, 749.
23. Glazier, J. B., Hughes, J. M. B., Maloney, J. E. & West, J. B. (1967) *J. Appl. Physiol.*, **23**, 694.
24. Hughes, J. M. B., Glazier, J. B., Maloney, J. E. & West, J. B. (1968) *Resp. Physiol.*, **4**, 58.
25. Kaneko, K., Milic-Emili, J., Dolovich, M. B., Dawson, A. & Bates, D. V. (1966) *J. Appl. Physiol.*, **21**, 767.

8. The Measurement of Blood Volume in the Lungs

The volume of blood in the lungs and left atrium is about ten to twenty per cent of the total blood volume. Lying as it does directly between the two ventricles, this relatively small volume will be extremely susceptible to the smallest differences in their output. If the stroke output of the left ventricle were persistently to exceed that of the right ventricle by 0·1 ml, the lungs would become exsanguinated within two hours. In the present state of our knowledge the homeostatic mechanism which prevents this happening appears to lie within the properties of the myocardium itself. We do not know how exact the mechanism is or how much variation occurs in the size of the pulmonary blood volume from minute to minute under basal conditions. The volume is presumably greater in systole than diastole since blood passes into the pulmonary artery during systole but leaves the left atrium during diastole. It will presumably also vary throughout the respiratory cycle owing to the variation in intrathoracic pressure and volume and their effects upon the filling of the right and left ventricles. There is evidence of a diminution in the pulmonary blood volume during positive pressure breathing.[1,2]

The precision required of the homeostatic mechanism will become greater the higher the cardiac output, and under conditions such as exercise, where the cardiac output is rapidly changing from minute to minute, it would be surprising if substantial changes in the pulmonary blood volume did not occur. Unfortunately, while the methods available to us agree that during exercise this is so, they do not agree on whether the volume gets bigger or smaller (Chap. 11, p. 159).

It seems also likely that the volume of blood in the lungs is controlled to some extent by the degree of tone in the vessels of the systemic circulation. Noradrenaline (Chap. 13, p. 185) and angiotensin (Chap. 13, p. 196), for instance, cause widespread constriction in the systemic circulation and appear to squeeze blood from the systemic compartment of the circulation into the pulmonary. The opposite probably occurs with hexamethonium salts which cause systemic dilatation (Chap. 13, p. 191).

The relation between pressure and volume in the systemic circulation may equally be altered by purely mechanical means. The inflation of an antigravity suit or immersion of the body in water (Chap. 11, p. 162) both appear to compress blood from the systemic to the pulmonary compartment. Venous tourniquets to the limbs have the opposite effect (Chap. 11, p. 162). The volume of blood in the lungs is less in the upright than in the recumbent position (Chap. 11, p. 163).

Apart from these short-term physiological alterations, it might be expected that a persistent pathological elevation of the left atrial pressure, such as occurs in mitral stenosis, would cause a more permanent increase in the pulmonary blood volume. While the evidence on this point is not unanimous (Table 8.1), it would seem that the pulmonary blood volume is a little higher in mitral valve disease (Chap. 23, p. 358).

Although the amount of blood in the lungs is a quantity of considerable

Table 8.1 Measurements of the pulmonary blood volume (ml/m² BSA) by the dye-dilution technique. Numbers in brackets indicate the numbers of observations.

Injection sites	Sampling sites	Reference	Normals	Mitral valve disease
Pulmonary artery + left atrium	Systemic artery	14	—	365 (19)
Pulmonary artery + left atrium	Systemic artery	15	246 (4)	331 (28)
Pulmonary artery + left atrium	Systemic artery	16	230 (5)	334 (34)
Pulmonary artery + left atrium	Systemic artery	17	211 (15)	400 (33)
Pulmonary artery + left atrium	Systemic artery	18	231 (32)	—
Pulmonary artery + left atrium	Systemic artery	19	271 (12)	238 (6)
Pulmonary artery	Left atrium	20	—	311 (10)
Inferior vena cava	Left atrium + Pulmonary artery	21	310 (12)	373 (11)

conceptual importance in our understanding of pulmonary haemodynamics, it has proved in practice a most elusive quantity to measure. In man and in complete animals such measurements have necessarily to be indirect and, despite a remarkable degree of ingenuity, often suffer from large systematic and observational errors.

Throughout the rest of this chapter the various volumes discussed will refer to both lungs unless otherwise specified.

Direct measurements of the volume of blood in the lungs at necropsy have been made by Backmann and Hartung[3] from estimations of the haemoglobin content. These measurements provided an average figure of 508 ± 120 ml in normal adult lungs. The ratio between the upper and lower lobes was 47 : 53. The ratio between the left and right lungs was 40 : 60 and corresponded to the ratio of the lung volumes. Using an oily liquid which would not enter capillaries, an estimate could be made of the separate volumes of blood in the pulmonary arterial and venous systems. Average values of 115 ml for the pulmonary arterial system and 120 ml for the pulmonary venous system were found. These left a volume of about 270 ml attributed to the pulmonary capillaries, although the precise extent to which the oil flowed into the arterioles and venules was uncertain. Measurements were made of the volume of blood in a single lung in patients with cardiac disease. In a patient with acute left ventricular failure, a single lung contained 452 ml blood. In a patient with mitral stenosis but without pulmonary induration, the volume in a single lung was 633 ml. In two patients with a chronic elevation of pulmonary venous pressure and induration of the lung, the blood volume was normal.

The Pulmonary Blood Volume by the Stewart–Hamilton Dye-Dilution Technique

This has been the measurement most commonly used to give some indication of the pulmonary blood volume. It derives from the dye-dilution method for the cardiac output (Chap. 6, p. 82) and can be calculated from the data obtained in carrying out this procedure. The principle of the calculation[4–6] may be illustrated by reference to the model shown in Figure 6.1 page 83. If the dye is injected very rapidly into this model it will pass down the length of tubing as a discrete bolus. In passing from the point of injection to the end of the tube it will push ahead of it all the water contained in the tube between the point of injection and the collecting end of the tube. If the time taken for the bolus to reach the end of the tube is t minutes and the rate of flow of water from the end of the tube is $\dot{Q}\ l \cdot min^{-1}$, then, between the time of injection and the time of arrival of the dye at the end of the tube, a volume of $\dot{Q}t$ litres of water will flow from the tube. This will be equal to the volume of water contained in the tube between the point of injection and the point of collection which is the end of the tube.

In practice, although the injection can be made very rapidly, the dye disperses to a considerable extent during its passage down-stream and the time interval that has to be calculated is the mean time of arrival of dye particles at the point of collection (t). How this is done is shown in Figure 8.1. Here the same dilution curve is shown as in Figure 6.2, page 84. In this case, the curve is divided into a number of columns, the base of each of which represents a small period of time and the height the average concentration of dye during that time. The time interval between the moment of injection and the middle of the base of each column is designated t_1, t_2, t_3, etc., and the corresponding concentrations of dye are C_1, C_2, C_3, etc. The mean arrival time of the dye is then calculated from:

$$\bar{t} = \frac{C_1 t_1 + C_2 t_2 + C_3 t_3 + \ldots + C_n t_n}{C_1 + C_2 + C_3 + \ldots + C_n}$$

The logic of this calculation may best be understood by considering the dye not in terms of concentration but as a corresponding number of particles. What has to be

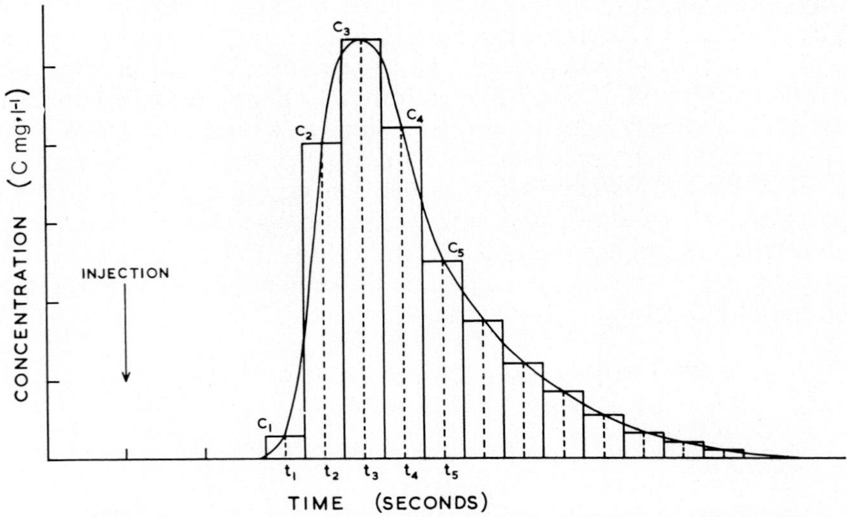

Fig. 8.1 The calculation of the mean circulation time of dye. See text for explanation.

determined is the average time taken by a particle. If two particles take two seconds and four particles take three seconds, the average time taken by a particle is $(2 \times 2)+(4 \times 3)/(2+4) = 2{\cdot}7$ seconds. It will be seen that it is only possible to convert concentrations strictly into numbers of particles if the volume of water passing the collecting point is the same during each small period of time. That is to say, the calculation of mean transit time is dependent on the assumption of a constant rate of flow.

The use of the mean circulation time for the calculation of volume may be seen intuitively to be correct. Appendix H gives a more formal proof that this is so in a branching system. It may also be seen intuitively that the volume of unperfused regions of the lung will not be measured. In fact the calculations shown in Appendix H establish that, in a branching system, the blood volume will be measured correctly only if the distribution of indicator through the various pathways of the system is proportional to the distribution of blood flow through them. For this to be so, it is essential that complete mixing of the indicator occurs at the beginning of the system. For this reason the injection of indicator into the pulmonary trunk, where streaming is known to occur, is likely to lead to erroneous results.

In the application of the method to human physiology, both the rate of flow and the mean circulation time are calculated from the primary dye-dilution curve. Since the volume is calculated by multiplying the mean circulation time by the flow, the measurement of volume is not independent of that of flow either in its final calculation or in its experimental origin. We would, therefore, caution most strongly against the wide-spread publication of correlations between these highly dependent variates. In earlier studies the dye was injected into a peripheral vein or into the right atrium or pulmonary artery while the point of sampling was a peripheral systemic artery. The volume of blood measured in this way was called the 'central blood volume'—a name the studied vagueness of which gives adequate warning of a lack of anatomical precision. If the injection is given into the pulmonary artery, the volume measured consists of the volume of blood in the lungs modified in accordance with the principles discussed above and in Appendix H plus that in the left atrium and ventricle plus a volume of aortic and systemic arterial blood extending as far peripherally as all those points which have the same mean circulation time from the heart as the point of sampling. The value obtained for this volume in normal adults[7–12] was around 1200 ml or 650 ml/m^2. If the injection is given into a peripheral vein a further volume of blood is included in the 'central blood volume'. This consists of the blood in the right atrium and ventricle plus a volume of venous blood extending as far into the peripheral veins as all those points which have the same mean circulation time to the heart as the point of injection. It amounts to an additional volume of about a litre.[13]

The introduction of techniques of puncturing the left atrium has enabled more precise measurements of the pulmonary blood volume to be made by the Stewart–Hamilton principle. In most of the studies which have been published, separate injections have been made into the pulmonary artery and left atrium with sampling of dye taken in each case from a systemic artery.[14–19] In other studies, injections have been made into the pulmonary artery with sampling from the left atrium[20] or injections have been made into the inferior vena cava with simultaneous sampling from the pulmonary artery and left atrium.[21]

Each of these different methods of injection and sampling carries its own mixture of theoretical and practical advantages and disadvantages. Injection into the pulmonary artery should, theoretically, lead to errors, since, as discussed above and in Appendix H, streaming in the pulmonary artery will mean that the distribution of dye in the lungs is not necessarily proportional to the distribution of flow. On the other hand, sampling from the pulmonary artery or left atrium involves the use of long catheters which cause delay and distortion of the dye curve.[22] This becomes proportionately the more important the shorter the mean transit time under investigation, and is thus of great significance where the pulmonary blood volume is concerned. Injection into the pulmonary artery and sampling from the left atrium would seem to be the system most liable to error and our own experience[23] is that dilution curves drawn from pulmonary veins after the injection of dye into the main pulmonary artery do not have an exponential downslope in man. Samet and his colleagues[24] compared the various methods of injection and sampling in 96 patients with various diseases excluding shunts. They found an average value for the pulmonary blood volume of 262 ml/m^2 when consecutive injections were made into the pulmonary artery and left atrium with sampling from the brachial artery. When the injection was made into the superior vena cava with simultaneous sampling from the pulmonary artery and left atrium, the volume measured was similar, with an average of 271 ml/m^2. When, however, the injection was made into the pulmonary artery with sampling from the left atrium, the volume measured was considerably larger, with an average of 427 ml/m^2. On the other hand, Nakhjavan and his colleagues[25] found in 12 patients that, when the left atrial sampling was corrected for delay and distortion,[22] the pulmonary blood volume measured by injection into the pulmonary artery and sampling from the left atrium (average 602 ml) was similar to that measured by injections into the pulmonary artery and left atrium with sampling from the brachial artery (average 558 ml).

The values obtained in subjects with an apparently normal pulmonary circulation by various authors using different methods are summarized in Table 8.1. The values found for the pulmonary blood volume by injection into the pulmonary artery and left atrium with sampling from a systemic artery are rather consistent, with an average of about 250 ml/m^2. That obtained by injection into the inferior vena cava and sampling from the left atrium and pulmonary artery is possibly somewhat larger (310 ml/m^2). The values found in mitral valve disease are also given in the Table and show no evidence of any substantial difference between the different methods. The pulmonary blood volume in mitral valve disease is considered separately in Chapter 23, page 358.

Measurement of the Pulmonary Blood Volume by Radiocardiography

This method was introduced by Lammerant.[13] A radioactive substance (usually albumin tagged with ^{131}I) is injected intravenously and its arrival in the right and left sides of the heart recorded by a precordial counter. With an adequate system for counting the radioactivity, the composite indicator-dilution curve may present two peaks from which separate primary curves may be drawn representing the dilution curves of the right and left sides of the heart successively. The difference in the mean circulation time of these two curves gives the mean circulation time between the two sides of the heart. When this is multiplied by the simultaneously determined cardiac output, a value for the pulmonary blood volume is obtained.

Once more, the volume of blood measured is not precisely that which lies in the pulmonary circulation. In this case, an unknown proportion of the blood in the right and left sides of the heart is included in the estimate, and the method, which might be expected to provide a more refined measurement of the pulmonary blood volume, originally gave values which were similar to those for the central blood volume. Lammerant[13] gave an average figure of 1240 ml (658 ml/m^2) for this volume in forty-six normal adults in the basal state.

A possible weakness in the method lies in its assumption that no substantial recirculation of indicator occurs into the right side of the heart during the time that the upstroke and first part of the downslope of the 'left-heart' curve is being recorded. There is evidence that this assumption is not entirely valid.[28] The early recirculation of indicator will delay the fall of the downslope of the curve from the left side of the heart. This will lead to an erroneously high figure for the mean pulmonary circulation time and thus for the pulmonary blood volume.

Following refinements in the technique and theoretical analysis of radiocardiography,[26] Giuntini and his colleagues[27] introduced a technique of calculation of the pulmonary blood volume which may avoid such errors and which certainly provides a more realistic figure for the pulmonary blood volume. The authors first considered a model in which the blood flows directly from the right ventricle into the left ventricle without any intervening pulmonary circulation. If it were assumed that the volume of the two ventricles was the same, it could be shown theoretically that the peak concentration of dye in the left ventricle after an instantaneous injection into the right ventricle would occur at a time when the volume of blood which had flowed through the right ventricle was equal to the volume of blood in the ventricle (Appendix I). This is the 'turnover time' of the ventricle,

$$T = V/\dot{Q}$$

where V is the ventricular volume and $\dot{Q}$ is the flow of blood. At the turnover time the concentration of dye in the right ventricle will be 37 per cent of its theoretical initial value.

If we introduce a pulmonary circulation between the two ventricles, the peak of the left ventricular dye curve becomes separated from the point when the right ventricular concentration reaches 37 per cent of its theoretical initial value. The degree of separation is a measure of the mean transit time in the pulmonary circulation.

The method avoids an analysis of the downslope of the left ventricular dye curve which is often difficult to define accurately. It provides a measure of the pulmonary blood volume which largely excludes the blood contained in the heart and which compares with measurements made at post-mortem (p. 105) and with the figure given by the injection of a second indicator into the left atrium.[29] The method makes a number of assumptions: the equality of the ventricular volumes, a continuous wash-out curve, single mixing chambers on the right and left sides and lack of modification of the shape of the left ventricular curve by the dispersion of dye in the lungs. From a number of considerations,[30] however, these assumptions do not appear greatly to influence the calculation.

Using this technique the average value of the pulmonary blood volume in 17 normal men was found to be 519 ml.[27] In five normal men there was virtually no change during exercise. In seven men with chronic bronchitis and emphysema the average value was 454 ml. In one patient with mitral stenosis the value was 471 ml. In other patients with various lesions and enlarged hearts the value was elevated to as much as 1037 ml.

An alternative method of analysing the radiocardiographic signal by an analogue computer has been described by Heiskanen and Peräsalo.[31,32] These authors found an average of 341 ml (204 ml/m^2) in 15 normal subjects and 360 ml (211 ml/m^2) in ten patients with mitral stenosis.

The Central Blood Volume by the Bradley Technique

This method[33] also involves the rapid injection of an indicator into a peripheral systemic vein or the right atrium. In this case, dilution curves are measured in the blood drawn from the pulmonary artery through a cardiac catheter as well as from a peripheral systemic artery. From each of these curves the pulmonary blood flow may be calculated (Chap. 6, p. 82). If the two dilution curves are inscribed on the same graph, the curve from the pulmonary artery will start before that from the brachial artery and the two curves will intertwine during the period before complete mixing of the dye occurs in the circulation and they fuse into one line (Fig. 8.2). The calculation proceeds in the following way:

The amount of dye present in the central blood volume at the point of equilibrium is equal to the amount of dye which has entered this volume minus the amount of dye which has left it during the time (TE) preceding the point of equilibrium. The amount of dye which has entered the central volume is equal to the mean concentration of the dye in the pulmonary artery ($\bar{C}p$) during TE multiplied by the volume of blood which has flowed through the pulmonary artery during this time. Thus:

$$\text{Quantity of dye entering the central blood volume} = \bar{C}p \times \dot{Q} \times T_E$$

assuming the pulmonary blood flow ($\dot{Q}$) remains constant. Similarly, the amount of dye leaving the central blood volume during the time TE is equal to:

$$\bar{C}a \times \dot{Q} \times T_E$$

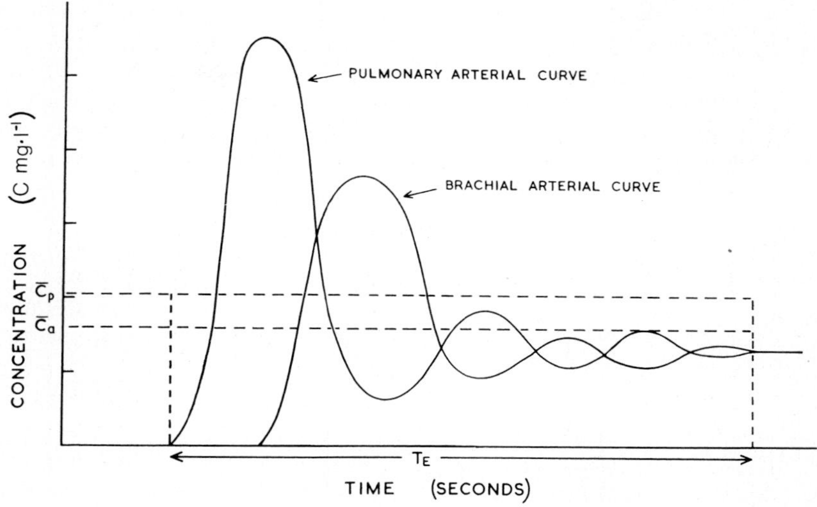

Fig. 8.2 Schematic dilution curves of blood from the pulmonary and brachial arteries following an injection of dye into a peripheral vein.

where $\bar{C}a$ is the mean concentration of dye in the systemic artery. The net gain in dye by the central volume is, therefore, equal to:

$$\bar{C}p\,\dot{Q}\,T_E - \bar{C}a\,\dot{Q}\,T_E$$

The concentration of dye at equilibrium (CE) is equal to this amount of dye diluted in a volume equal to the central blood volume. The magnitude of the central blood volume is thus given by:

$$\frac{\dot{Q}\,T_E(\bar{C}p - \bar{C}a)}{C_E}$$

If the cardiac output is not assumed to be constant, the appropriate formula would be

$$\frac{1}{C_E}\int_{\text{arrival}}^{\text{equilibrium}} \dot{Q}\,(Cp - Ca)\,dt$$

In practice, however, this assumption has to be made, the cardiac output being measured by the analysis of one of the two dye-dilution curves.

The space measured is the same as that defined by the Stewart–Hamilton technique and suffers from the same limitations. Experiments on model circulatory systems have suggested that the Bradley technique is best suited to systems such as the splanchnic bed where the ratio of flow to volume is low and that it loses accuracy when this ratio reaches the higher order found in the lungs.[34] Nevertheless, the method has been used in patients with mitral stenosis[35] where it gave values for the 'central' blood volume comparable with those obtained by the Stewart–Hamilton calculation.

A similar calculation has been applied to the dilution curves resulting from a continuous infusion of dye into the pulmonary artery.[36] The values obtained in normal subjects and patients with various forms of heart disease were again comparable with those obtained by the Stewart–Hamilton method.

The Newman Method

If the blood passes through a mixing chamber between the point of injection of the dye and the point of sampling, the downslope of the dilution curve has an exponential character (p. 83). Theoretically, the steepness of this slope is related to the ratio of the blood flow to the volume of the chamber. Newman and his colleagues suggested that, when blood passes successively through a series of mixing chambers, the downslope of the final dilution curve is influenced by the volume of the largest chamber.[37] They considered that the pulmonary circulation would itself constitute a mixing chamber and would normally have a volume larger than that of the ventricles. Thus, if dye is injected into a peripheral vein or right side of the heart and sampled from a systemic artery, an analysis of the downslope of the arterial dilution curve should provide a measurement of the volume of blood in the lungs. It seems unlikely that the pulmonary circulation does act as a mixing chamber and our experience is that dilution curves drawn from pulmonary veins after the injection of dye into the main pulmonary artery do not have an exponential downslope in man.[23] In addition, the method was found to give very much greater values for the pulmonary blood volume if the injection was made into a peripheral systemic vein than if it was made into the pulmonary artery.[8]

Frequency Function of Transit Times in the Pulmonary Circulation

Much of the difficulty in computing the mean circulation time in the lung has arisen from the recirculation of indicator. To avoid this, it has been usual to extrapolate the downslope of the indicator dilution curve along an exponential line (p. 83). Such an extrapolation is empirical. Provided that recirculation does not occur too early and that the downslope is relatively steep, errors in the estimation of the area under the primary curve and thus of the blood flow are not likely to be great. Errors in the calculation of the mean transit time and thus of the blood volume may, however, be more considerable. This is because the mean transit time may be affected importantly by only a few particles of indicator which have an extremely long transit time.

Stephenson[38] pointed out an alternative approach in which, instead of trying to eliminate recirculation, one takes it into account. According to the principle, indicator-dilution curves drawn downstream from two injection points in the circulation may be unravelled mathematically throughout the initial curve and its subsequent circulations. The technique allows not only a calculation of the mean transit time but also a graphical description of the frequency function of transit times. Maseri and his colleagues[39] have applied this principle of 'deconvolution' to the pulmonary circulation of the dog. Different indicators were injected simultaneously into the pulmonary trunk and the left atrium and dilution curves drawn from the aorta. Analysis by the deconvolution technique revealed a distribution of transit times in the pulmonary circulation which was skewed markedly to the right.

Methods for Assessing Changes in the Pulmonary Blood Volume

Since the methods for measuring the pulmonary blood volume so often include unknown quantities of blood elsewhere in the circulation, the meaning of the changes which they record under varying conditions is often obscure. There are two methods which can measure relative changes in the volume of the blood in small sections of the lungs. One method measures changes in the radiographic density of a portion of the lung.[40,41] The other records the radioactivity of an area of lung after a radioactive indicator has been injected into the bloodstream and allowed to equilibrate.[41,42] These techniques give no indication of the absolute quantities involved but provide information on the presence of a change in the pulmonary blood volume. They have been valuable in following rapid changes in pulmonary blood volume such as accompany changes in posture, the application of tourniquets to the limbs, or the Valsalva manoeuvre. The plethysmographic method of Sjöstrand[43,44] has also given information on the change in the volume of blood in the thorax.

The Volume of Blood in the Pulmonary Capillaries

The volume of blood in the pulmonary capillaries has been calculated from measurements of the diffusing capacity of the lungs for carbon monoxide taken at different concentrations of inspired oxygen.[45,46] The technique is described and discussed in Chapter 42 (p. 639). The average value for the pulmonary capillary blood volume by this method is about 100 ml.[47–49] Assuming a cardiac output of $6\ l \cdot min^{-1}$, the average time spent by a red cell in the pulmonary capillaries may be calculated to be

$$\frac{100 \times 60}{6000} = 1\ s$$

The Pulmonary Vascular Haematocrit

When a viscous liquid flows in a stream-line fashion through a tube, its most peripheral layer tends to cling to the wall of the tube, and the velocity of the flow of the liquid increases as the centre of the tube is approached. This phenomenon is implicit in the Poiseuille equation of flow (Chap. 9, p. 119, and Appendix F). In the case of blood, the faster moving axial stream tends to draw the red blood cells into itself and causes the peripheral layer of blood which is in contact with the wall of the vessel to consist largely of plasma. The theoretical basis for this may

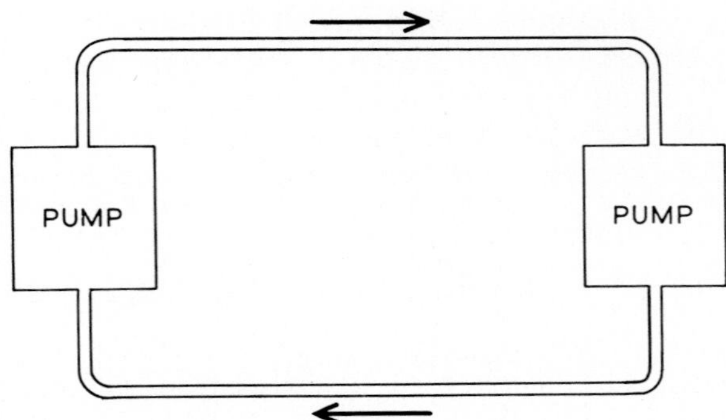

Fig. 8.3 Simple model in which the haematocrit of the blood contained in small tubes would diminish when flow commenced.

be derived from Bernoulli's principle (p. 132). The degree to which the axial streaming of the red cells occurs depends in a complex fashion on the size of the vessel and on the velocity of flow through it. It might be expected to be most evident in the small arteries. It is unlikely to occur in capillaries since the velocity of flow is low and the diameter of the vessel will in any case admit only one red cell at a time.

The effect of these phenomena is to cause the haematocrit to vary throughout the body and this may best be described by reference to a model. Figure 8.3 is a drawing of a model circulation consisting of two large 'ventricles' sending blood around a circle of narrow tubing. The ventricles act both as circulating pumps and as mixing chambers. We shall consider the model first in the motionless state, at which time it is assumed that no settling of blood has occurred and the haematocrit throughout the system is the same.

When flow starts, the velocity of movement inside the tubes is greatest in the axial stream. Hence, the blood leaving each tube will contain a greater contribution from the axial stream than from the peripheral zone. Since, at the same time, the red cells will crowd towards the axis of the tubes there will be a proportionately greater loss of red cells than of plasma from the tubes. Clearly, the haematocrit of the blood leaving the tubes cannot continue indefinitely to exceed that of the blood entering them. The continual loss of red cells relative to plasma will gradually lower the haematocrit of the blood within the tubes and this itself will eventually reduce the haematocrit of the outgoing blood until it equals that of the blood entering. The dilution of the blood inside the tubes must be accompanied by some increased concentration of the blood in the 'ventricles' depending on the ratio of the capacity of tubes and 'ventricles', and this will also tend to equalize the composition of the blood entering and leaving the tubes.

When a final state of equilibrium is reached, there is a lower haematocrit within the tubes than within the 'ventricles'.[50] On the other hand, since there is complete mixing of the blood in the 'ventricles' the haematocrit of the blood entering the tubes and, therefore, of that leaving the tubes is the same as that of the 'ventricles'.

Thus, if one of the tubes is cut across, the haematocrit of the blood which pours out will be that of the 'ventricular' blood. The haematocrit of the blood withdrawn from a tube is higher than the haematocrit of the blood actually in the tube since the haematocrit of shed blood is dependent on the ratio of red cell flow to plasma flow and not on the ratio of red cell volume to plasma volume.[51]

The behaviour of the model may, in general, be applied to the human circulation but the situation is complicated by the fact that it is possible for arterial branches to 'skim' plasma from the peripheral layers of blood within the parent artery.[52]

The passage of red cells preferentially in the axial stream should cause them to travel more swiftly through the lungs than does the plasma. Several observations have confirmed this, showing that the mean circulation time for labelled cells is less than that for plasma in dogs[53–56] and in patients with mitral stenosis.[29] In normal adults, the magnitude of the difference has not been found to be impressive.[8] By multiplying the mean circulation time for plasma by the pulmonary plasma flow the central plasma volume may be calculated. Similarly, if labelled red cells are injected into the pulmonary artery, a measurement of the red cell flow and red cell mean circulation time may be made from which the central red cell volume may be calculated. In this way a value for the 'central' haematocrit may thus be derived. The ratio of the central haematocrit to the haematocrit of blood drawn from a systemic artery has been found to average 0·93 to 0·94 in the dog,[54,55] 0·98 in normal man[8] and 0·97 in patients with mitral stenosis.[29] In normal people this figure did not differ statistically from unity. The reason may lie in the fact that the central blood volume contains a large proportion of blood in the chambers of the heart and in large systemic vessels so that the haematocrit of the pulmonary circulation is over-estimated. Alternatively, there may be little axial accumulation of red cells in the pulmonary vessels because of pulsatility of flow.

The only direct measurements of the haematocrit of small pulmonary blood vessels from specimens of tissue have been carried out on animals.[57–59] In the mouse, the pulmonary tissue haematocrit was found to be 47·9 per cent while the venous blood haematocrit was 48·4 per cent.[59] This very small difference supports the view that there is in fact very little axial accumulation of red cells in the pulmonary vessels.

It has been pointed out that the standard method of measurement of the central blood volume by the injection of a plasma dye is subject to a systematic error because the value for the haematocrit which is used is that of the circulating arterial blood and not that of the central blood space.[51] In view of the above considerations this error must be very small.

REFERENCES

1. Fenn, W. O., Otis, A. B., Rahn, H., Chadwick, L. E. & Hegnauer, A. H. (1947) *Amer. J. Physiol.*, **151**, 258.
2. Braunwald, E., Binion, J. T., Morgan, W. L., Jn. & Sarnoff, S. J. (1957) *Circulat. Res.*, **5**, 670.
3. Backmann, R. & Hartung, W. (1969) *Prog. Resp. Res.*, **5**, 327.
4. Stewart, G. N. (1921) *Amer. J. Physiol.*, **58**, 20.

5. Hamilton, W. F., Moore, J. W., Kinsman, J. M. & Spurling, R. G. (1928) *Amer. J. Physiol.*, **85**, 377.
6. Hamilton, W. F., Moore, J. W., Kinsman, J. M. & Spurling, R. G. (1930) *Amer. J. Physiol.*, **93**, 654.
7. Ebert, R. V., Borden, C. W., Wells, H. S. & Wilson, R. H. (1949) *J. Clin. Invest.*, **28**, 1134.
8. Lilienfield, L. S., Kovach, R. D., Marks, P. A., Hershenson, L. M., Rodnan, G. P., Ebaugh, F. G. & Freis, E. D. (1956) *J. Clin. Invest.*, **35**, 1385.
9. Doyle, J. T., Wilson, J. S., Estes, E. H. & Warren, J. V. (1951) *J. Clin. Invest.*, **30**, 345.
10. Kopelman, H. & Lee, G. de J. (1951) *Clin. Sci.*, **10**, 383.
11. Doyle, J. T., Wilson, J. S. & Warren, J. V. (1952) *Circulation*, **5**, 263.
12. Doyle, J. T., Wilson, J. S., Lepine, C. & Warren, J. V. (1953) *J. Lab. Clin. Med.*, **41**, 29.
13. Lammerant, J. (1957) *Le Volume Sanguin des Poumons chez l'Homme*. Bruxelles: Editions Arscia.
14. Milnor, W. R., Jose, A. D. & McGaff, C. J. (1960) *Circulation*, **22**, 130.
15. Dock, D. S., Kraus, W. L., McQuire, L. B., Hyland, J. W., Haynes, F. W. & Dexter, L. (1961) *J. Clin. Invest.*, **40**, 317.
16. McGaff, C. J., Roveti, G. C., Glassman, E. & Milnor, W. R. (1963) *Circulation*, **27**, 77.
17. Roy, S. B., Bhardwaj, P. & Bhatia, M. L. (1965) *Brit. Med. J.*, **ii**, 1466.
18. Samet, P., Bernstein, W. H., Medow, A. & Levine, S. (1965) *Dis. Chest*, **47**, 632.
19. Schreiner, B. F., Jn., Murphy, G. W. & Yu, P. N. (1966) *Circulation*, **34**, 249.
20. Levinson, G. E., Frank, M. J. & Hellems, H. K. (1964) *Amer. Heart J.*, **67**, 734.
21. de Freitas, F. M., Faraco, E. Z., Nedel, N., de Azevedo, D. F. & Zaduchliver, J. (1964) *Circulation*, **30**, 370.
22. Milnor, W. R. & Jose, A. D. (1960) *J. Appl. Physiol.*, **15**, 177.
23. Fritts, H. W., Jn., Harris, P. & Cournand, A. Unpublished observations.
24. Samet, P., Bernstein, W. H., Lopez, A. & Levine, S. (1966) *Circulation*, **33**, 847.
25. Nakhjavan, F. K., Maranhao, V., Son, R. & Goldberg, H. (1967) *Brit. Heart J.*, **29**, 602.
26. Donato, L., Giuntini, C., Lewis, M. L., Durand, J., Rochester, D. F., Harvey, R. M. & Cournand, A. (1962) *Circulation*, **26**, 174.
27. Giuntini, C., Lewis, M. L., Salesluis, A. & Harvey, R. M. (1963) *J. Clin. Invest.*, **42**, 1589.
28. Fritts, H. W., Jn., Harris, P., Chidsey, C. A., III, Claus, R. H. & Cournand, A. (1957) *J. Appl. Physiol.*, **11**, 362.
29. Lewis, M. L., Gnoj, J., Fisher, V. J. & Christianson, L. C. (1970) *J. Clin. Invest.*, **49**, 170.
30. Giuntini, C. (1971) *Bull. Physio-Path. Resp.*, **7**, 1125.
31. Heiskanen, T. (1971) *Cardiovasc. Res.*, **5**, 268.
32. Peräsalo, J. & Heiskanen, T. (1971) *Cardiovasc. Res.*, **5**, 260.
33. Bradley, S. E., Marks, P. A., Reynell, P. C. & Meltzer, J. (1953) *Trans. Ass. Amer. Phycns.*, **66**, 294.
34. Braunwald, E., Cournand, A. & Fishman, A. P. (1958) *J. Appl. Physiol.*, **12**, 445.
35. Rapaport, E., Kuida, H., Haynes, F. & Dexter, L. (1956) *J. Clin. Invest.*, **35**, 1393.
36. Bowers, D., Shepherd, J. T. & Wood, E. H. (1955) *Canad. J. Biochem.*, **33**, 340.
37. Newman, E. V., Merrell, M., Genein, A., Mange, C., Milnar, W. R. & McKeever, W. P. (1951) *Circulation*, **4**, 735.
38. Stephenson, J. L. (1960) *Bull. Math. Biophys.*, **22**, 1.
39. Maseri, A., Caldini, P., Permutt, S. & Zierler, K. L. (1970) *Circulat. Res.*, **26**, 527.
40. Kjellberg, S. R., Rudhe, U. & Sjöstrand, T. (1950) *Acta Physiol. Scand.*, **20**, 166.
41. Bondurant, S., Hickam, J. B. & Isley, J. K. (1957) *J. Clin. Invest.*, **36**, 59.
42. Weissler, A. M., McCraw, B. H. & Warren, J. V. (1959) *J. Appl. Physiol.*, **14**, 531.
43. Sjöstrand, T. (1951) *Acta Physiol. Scand.*, **22**, 114.
44. Sjöstrand, T. (1952) *Acta Physiol. Scand.*, **26**, 312.
45. Roughton, F. J. W. (1945) *Amer. J. Physiol.*, **143**, 621.
46. Roughton, F. J. W. & Forster, R. E. (1957) *J. Appl. Physiol.*, **11**, 290.
47. Bates, D. V., Varis, C. J., Donovan, R. E. & Christie, R. V. (1960) *J. Clin. Invest.*, **39**, 1401.

48. Forster, R. E. (1959) In *Pulmonary Circulation*, ed. Adams, W. R. & Veith, I. Page 45. Grune & Stratton.
49. Lewis, B. M., Tai-Hon Lin, Noe, F. E. & Komisaruk, R. (1958) *J. Clin. Invest.*, **37**, 1061.
50. Fahraeus, R. (1929) *Physiol. Rev.*, **9**, 241.
51. Meier, P. & Zierler, K. L. (1954) *J. Appl. Physiol.*, **6**, 731.
52. Papenheimer, J. R. & Kinter, W. B. (1956) *Amer. J. Physiol.*, **185**, 377.
53. Dorr, P., Hahn, P. F. & Hamilton, W. F. (1946) *Amer. J. Physiol.*, **147**, 493.
54. Lawson, H. C., Cantrell, W. F., Shaw, J. E., Blackburn, D. L. & Adams, S. (1952) *Amer. J. Physiol.*, **170**, 277.
55. Chinard, F. P. & Enns, T. (1954) *Amer. J. Physiol.*, **178**, 197.
56. Rapaport, E., Kuida, H., Haynes, F. & Dexter, L. (1956) *Amer. J. Physiol.*, **185**, 127.
57. Gibson, J. G., Seligman, A. M., Peacock, W. C., Aub, J. C., Fine, J. & Evans, R. D. (1946) *J. Clin. Invest.*, **25**, 848.
58. Everett, N. B., Simmons, B. & Lasher, E. P. (1956) *Circulat. Res.*, **4**, 419.
59. Friedman, J. J. (1959) *Amer. J. Physiol.*, **196**, 420.

9. Resistance

The preceding three chapters have described methods of measuring pressure, flow and volume in the pulmonary circulation and discussed some of the concepts necessary to the understanding of these physical quantities. We have now to examine the relation which exists between them in the pulmonary circulation. In particular it is necessary to consider the confines within which it is possible to interpret changes in pressure and flow in terms of alterations in the calibre of blood vessels.

It has been usual to relate pressure and flow in the pulmonary circulation in terms of resistance. In any segment of the circulation at any instant this quantity is defined as the drop in pressure across the segment divided by the rate of the volume of flow through it. This is the mechanical equivalent of Ohm's law. In itself it has an unequivocal simplicity. It is, however, capable at best of describing only a limited aspect of haemodynamic events and its application to physiological studies may lead to errors in interpretation.

If pressure were constant and flow were constant the calculation (but not necessarily the interpretation) of resistance would be simple. Since both these quantities are pulsatile it is necessary to obtain the time-average of each before calculating their ratio. In this way the system is treated as though pressure and flow were constant. The reasons why physiologists, pharmacologists and clinicians have so extensively relied on measurements of resistance are largely historical, since measurements of instantaneous flow have only recently become available. Nevertheless it is arguable that, even if measurements of instantaneous flow had been available, the simple measurement of resistance would still have proved of practical value since the input impedance modulus at zero frequency which it represents contributes the major part of the impedance spectrum (Chap. 10, p. 143).

In considering the overall relation between pressure and flow in the pulmonary circulation we shall start by a detailed consideration of resistance in this chapter and continue with a more general consideration of pulsatile flow and pressure in the following chapter. In order to evaluate the physical factors which influence resistance it is convenient to start by examining a simple hydrodynamic example.

The Relation of Pressure to Flow in Rigid Tubes

In the example shown in Figure 9.1 water is flowing through a rigid metal tube in a streamlined fashion at a rate of $\dot{Q}$ ml · s^{-1}. The drop in pressure along the tube is ΔP mmHg. The resistance is, therefore, $R = \Delta P/\dot{Q}$ mmHg ml^{-1} · s. If it is desired to express the drop in pressure in the units of dyn · cm^{-2}, this expression has to be multiplied by 1330 and then has the dimensions: dyn · s · cm^{-5}.

If the flow of water through the tube is increased, the drop in pressure will increase proportionately provided that the character of the flow remains streamlined. Hence when these two measurements are plotted against each other the result is a straight line (Fig. 9.2). In this way the ratio of ΔP to $\dot{Q}$ remains unchanged so that the value of the resistance is constant at all rates of flow (Fig. 9.3). Thus one

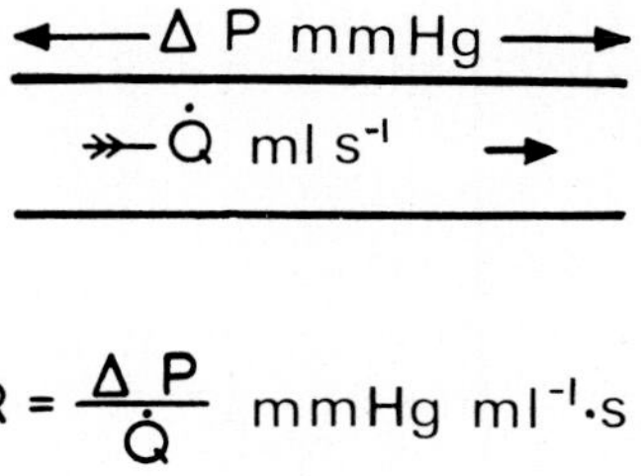

$\leftarrow \Delta P$ mmHg $\rightarrow$

$\dot{Q}$ ml s^{-1} $\rightarrow$

$R = \frac{\Delta P}{\dot{Q}}$ mmHg ml$^{-1}\cdot$s

Fig. 9.1 Diagram to illustrate the relation of resistance (R) to flow ($\dot{Q}$) and drop in pressure (ΔP) when water flows through a rigid tube.

may characterize this system by a single value of the resistance which will hold good under all possible conditions associated with the streamlined flow of water.

Poiseuille's Law

The difference in pressure required to propel a liquid through a rigid tube at a certain steady rate will depend not only on the dimensions of the tube but on the viscosity of the liquid. The equation which relates pressure, flow, dimensions of the tube, and viscosity of the liquid under streamline conditions is:

$$\Delta P = \frac{8\eta l \dot{Q}}{\pi r^4}$$

where: ΔP is expressed in dyn $\cdot$ cm^{-2}; l is the length of the tube in cm; r is the radius in cm; $\dot{Q}$ is the flow in ml $\cdot$ s^{-1}; and η is the coefficient of viscosity of the liquid in poises. This equation was first enunciated by Poiseuille, an early nineteenth-century French physician. Its mathematical derivation is given in Appendix F. It will be seen that the pressure required to produce a certain volume of flow depends directly on the volume of flow, the viscosity of the liquid, and the length of the tube. It is inversely proportional to the magnitude of the fourth power of the radius.

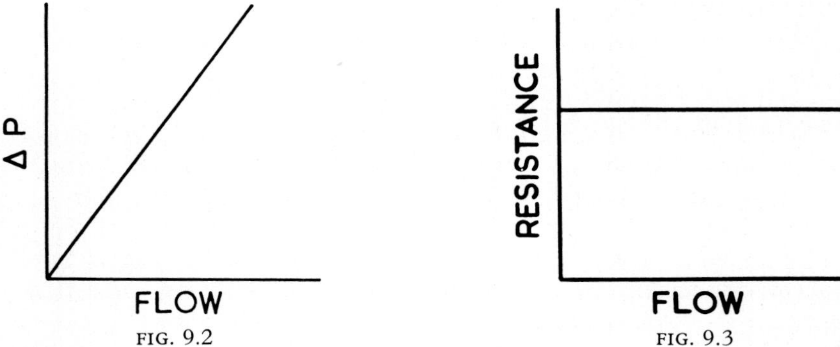

Fig. 9.2 The relation between ΔP and flow which would occur in the example shown in Fig. 9.1 provided flow remained streamlined.

Fig. 9.3 The relation between resistance and flow in the example shown in Fig. 9.1 provided flow remained streamlined.

Thus, small changes in the radius or circumference of the tube have a disproportionately great influence on the resistance.

Turbulence

If the flow through the tube were increased gradually there would come a moment when the particles of fluid would cease to move in streamlines and would appear to move randomly in all directions across the tube. This is the condition of turbulence. When it occurs the ratio of pressure difference to volume flow increases so that the resistance increases. The critical point above which turbulence is likely to occur depends on the diameter of the tube, the mean velocity of flow and the viscosity and density of the fluid. This is expressed as the Reynolds' number which, for a cylindrical tube, is:

$$\mathrm{Re} = \frac{\bar{v}d\rho}{\eta}$$

where $\bar{v}$ is the mean velocity, d is the diameter, ρ is the density of the liquid and η is its viscosity. Turbulence is unlikely to develop when the Reynolds' number is less than 2000. The likelihood of turbulence developing increases progressively as the Reynolds' number exceeds this figure. Calculations made by Cumming and his colleagues[1], assuming a figure of 3 centipoises for viscosity, give a Reynolds' number of 1100 for the mean flow in the pulmonary trunk under normal conditions. Figures for successive branches decrease rapidly, that for the two main branches being 200. Milnor and his colleagues[2] quote Reynolds' numbers ranging from 1200 to 3400 at peak velocity in the human pulmonary trunk.

Such figures are in accordance with clinical experience. Flow through the pulmonary trunk is usually silent throughout the cardiac cycle, indicating an absence of turbulence. In some people, however, a murmur is heard during mid-systole ('pulmonary ejection systolic murmur') when velocity is maximal and presumably the Reynolds' number exceeds 2000 and turbulence has occurred. In persons with a normal heart, such murmurs are more likely to be heard where there is a high pulmonary blood flow due to anxiety, exercise, fever, anaemia or thyrotoxicosis. Systolic murmurs over the pulmonary trunk are found in patients with atrial or ventricular septal defects in whom there is an increased pulmonary blood flow due to a shunt. In such patients the enlargement of the pulmonary trunk will also increase the value of the Reynolds' number and make turbulence more likely. This appears also to be operative in patients with an idiopathic dilation of the pulmonary trunk who have systolic murmurs. Turbulence is known to occur at a stenosed pulmonary valve where a systolic murmur is classically heard and the narrowed orifice causes a high velocity axial stream.[3] It seems unlikely that turbulence occurs beyond the pulmonary trunk except in the rare condition of a pulmonary arterial branch stenosis (p. 239) where a murmur may occur. Thus, under normal conditions, the flow of blood throughout the pulmonary circulation appears to be in streamlines and silent except in some people and under certain circumstances when there is a period of turbulence during peak velocity in the pulmonary trunk.

The Relation of Pressure to Flow in Distensible Tubes

If the tube shown in Figure 9.1 were made of distensible rubber instead of rigid metal, an increase in the flow of water through it would cause it to dilate by increasing the transmural pressure. The increase in calibre which resulted would diminish the resistance which it offered to the flow of water. Thus, under these circumstances, the value for resistance is no longer constant but varies with the volume of flow (Fig. 9.4) and it is no longer possible to describe the system by a single value for resistance. Similarly, the relation between ΔP and flow is no longer linear but bends away from the pressure axis (Fig. 9.5).

The precise relation between pressure and flow will depend on the distensibility characteristics of the tube. It will be recalled from Chapter 4, page 47, that the nature of the relation between tension and circumferential length which is found in the elastic pulmonary arteries is a curved one, and that this property appears to be common to all blood vessels, whether venous or arterial. If a similar curved relation extends down to the muscular pulmonary arteries and arterioles a number of haemodynamic consequences will follow.

To analyse this, Figure 9.6 shows at its top left hand quadrant the relation between circumferential wall tension and radius in a hypothetical small arterial vessel. The shape of the relation is similar to that shown for the pulmonary trunk in Figure 4.5, page 48. According to the law of Laplace (p. 52).

$$P = T/r$$

where T is circumferential tension, P is the transmural pressure and r is the radius. The ratio T/r is equal to the tangent of the angle subtended by the series of radiating lines shown arising from the intersection of the tension and radius axis. In this way, an arbitrary scale of transmural pressure may also be added to the

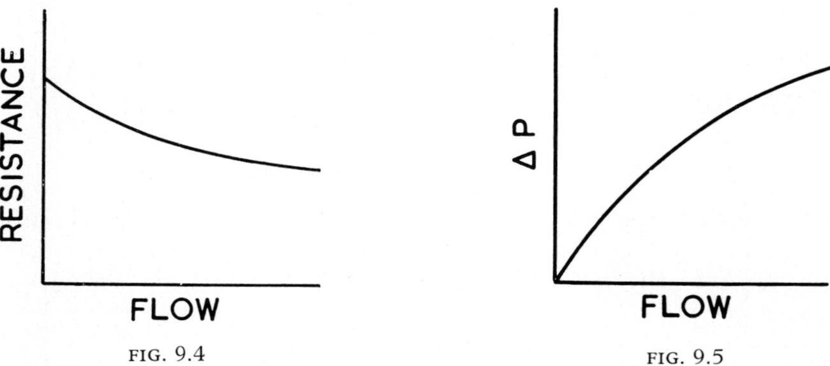

Fig. 9.4 The relation between resistance and flow in a distensible tube.
Fig. 9.5 The relation between ΔP and flow in a distensible tube.

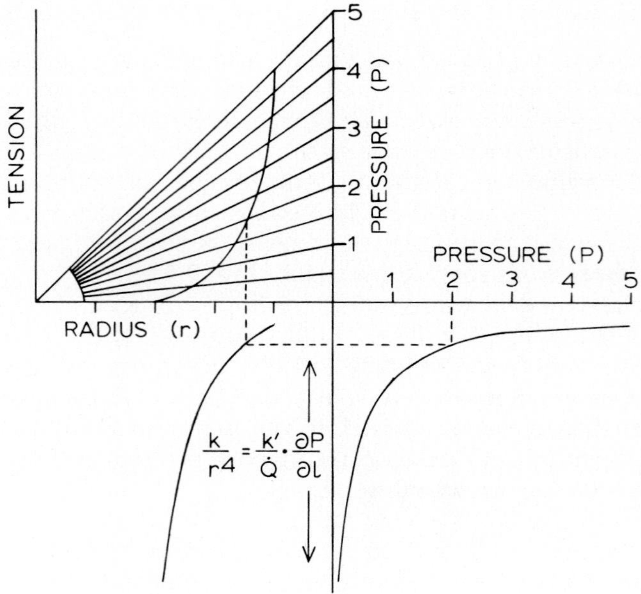

Fig. 9.6 Graphical calculation of the relation between pressure (P) and longitudinal pressure gradient ($\partial P/\partial l$) for a given flow (Q) from the circumferential length–tension diagram of a vessel wall.

graph so that the upper left-hand quadrant of the diagram shows the inter-relation between radius, wall tension and transmural pressure.

According to the Poiseuille equation (p. 119):

$$\Delta P = \frac{8\eta l\dot{Q}}{\pi r^4}$$

so that we may write:

$$\frac{K}{r^4} = \frac{k'}{\dot{Q}} \cdot \frac{\Delta P}{\Delta l}$$

where Δl is a small longitudinal distance along the axis of the vessel and K and k' are constants. The bottom left hand quadrant of Figure 9.6 relates r to K/r^4 where K is arbitrary. Thus, the ordinate of this quadrant reveals (in arbitrary units)

$$\frac{k'}{\dot{Q}} \cdot \frac{\Delta P}{\Delta l}$$

In this way one can relate, for a given flow, the longitudinal gradient in pressure along a small segment of artery of given physical characteristics at a point where its

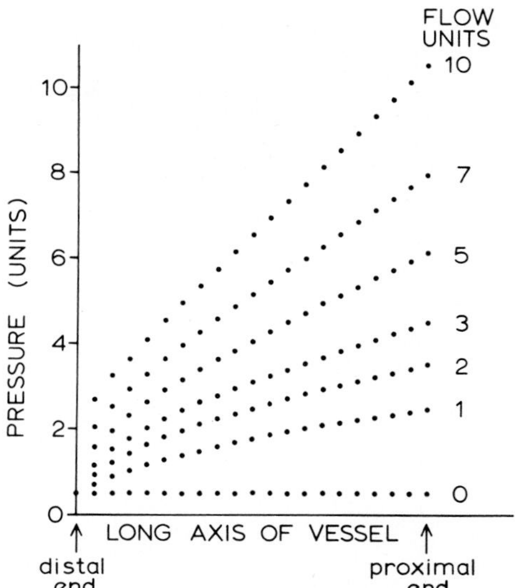

Fig. 9.7 Distribution of pressure along long axis of distensible vessel at different rates of flow.

transmural pressure is known. This is shown in the bottom right-hand quadrant of the diagram.

Using such a nomogram one can demonstrate graphically the distribution of pressure along the long axis of such a vessel. This is effected by dividing the length of the vessel into a large number of small distances (Fig. 9.7 demonstrates 20 such divisions). Starting at the distal end where a given distal transmural pressure occurs, the increase in pressure (ΔP) over the small distance (Δl) is derived from the nomogram in Figure 9.6. This gives a new transmural pressure for the next small distance for which a new value of ΔP is derived. In this way, the distribution of pressure along the long axis of the vessel may be calculated for a given flow. Figure 9.7 illustrates the process for a number of arbitrary values of flow.

It will be seen from Figure 9.7 that the distribution is not linear, especially at high values of flow and, as one passes upstream, the pressure increases at a greater rate initially, gradually decreasing as the proximal end of the vessel is reached. This distribution is particularly influenced by the curved nature of the length–tension relation in the wall of the vessel. A linear relation gives a more uniform rise in pressure on passing upstream. As may be seen from Figure 9.8 this means that for a given total pressure difference the curved length–tension relation in the wall of the vessels allows an increase in the length of the vessel—a property which may have physiological importance.

Returning to the top left-hand quadrant of Figure 9.6, one may derive the radius of the vessel for any value of transmural pressure and thus plot the radius of the vessel along its longitudinal axis. Figure 9.9 shows how the curved length–tension relation in the wall of a vessel permits it to maintain a wide lumen until it gets near to its distal end. This becomes particularly evident at a high level of flow.

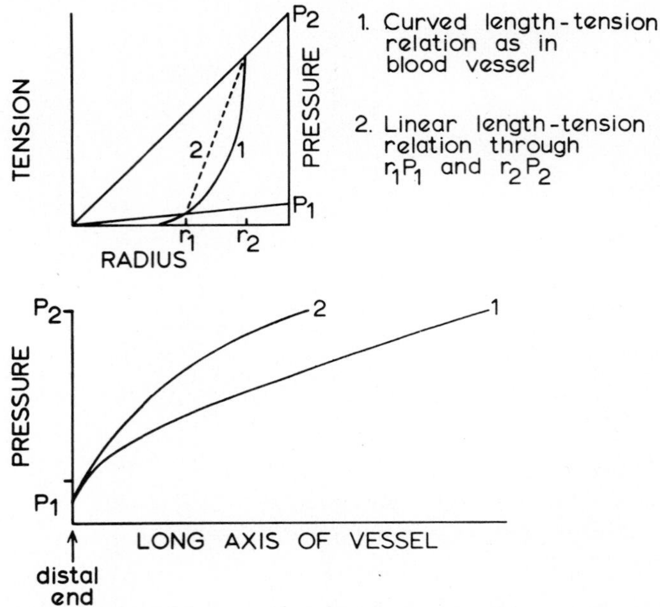

Fig. 9.8 Effect of shape of length–tension diagram of wall of vessel on the distribution of pressure along its long axis.

From Figure 9.7 the relation between the proximal pressure and flow along a vessel can be derived for a given distal pressure. This relation, as is shown in Figure 9.10, is not a simple one. Initially it is curved, but, as pressure and flow increase, it becomes rectilinear. The initial curved portion is due to the particular distensibility of the wall of the vessel at low degrees of stretch. The final rectilinear portion develops when the collagenous coat of the vessel takes the strain and renders the wall virtually inextensible. The linear portion thus represents the situation when the calibre of the vessel has become constant.

Changes in the distal pressure may have important effects not only on the general level of pressure throughout the vessel but also on the distribution of pressure

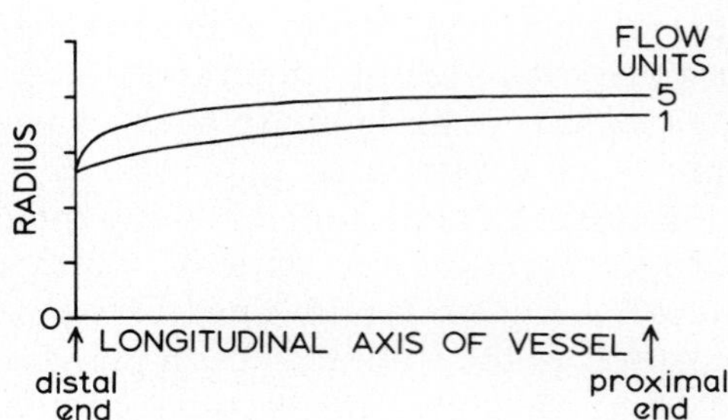

Fig. 9.9 Distribution of radius along distensible vessel.

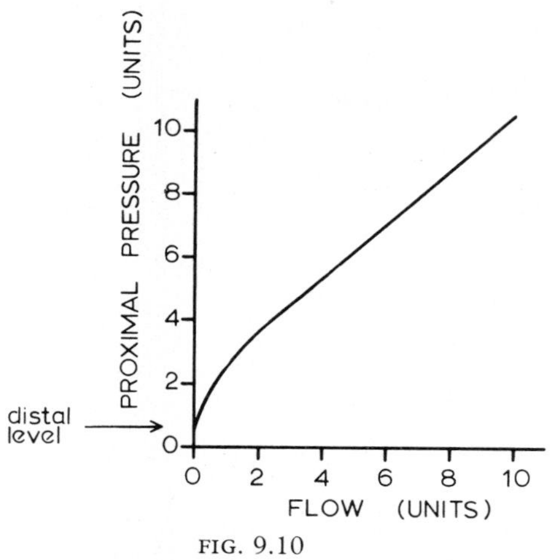

FIG. 9.10

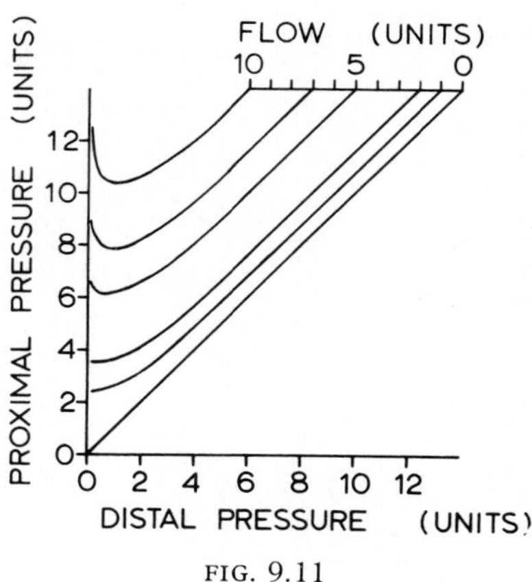

FIG. 9.11

Fig. 9.10 Relation between proximal pressure and flow in a distensible vessel.

Fig. 9.11 Relation between distal and proximal pressure in a distensible vessel at a given rate of flow.

along it. Thus, the relation between the distal and proximal pressures is not a simple one even in the presence of a constant flow. Figure 9.11 is constructed from a series of graphical calculations such as is shown in Figure 9.7. It relates the proximal and distal pressures in a vessel for different rates of flow. As the flow increases the relation between the two pressures becomes progressively less rectilinear. This loss of linearity may, at least theoretically, lead to an increase in proximal pressure following a decrease in distal pressure, as is shown in Figure 9.12.

The Effects of Branching and the Spatial Distribution of Resistance

Consider an artery (a) dividing into two equal branches (b). Let r = radius, v = velocity, $\Delta P/\Delta l$ = pressure gradient, and $\dot{Q}$ = volume flow. The subscripts a and b will refer to the main vessel or its branches respectively.

The flow into the main vessel must equal the flow out of its two branches:

$$\dot{Q}_a = 2\dot{Q}_b$$

Since flow = velocity × cross-sectional area

$$\dot{Q}_a = v_a \cdot \pi r_a^2 = 2v_b \cdot \pi r_b^2$$

Therefore,

$$\frac{v_a}{v_b} = \frac{2r_b^2}{r_a^2} \qquad \text{(i)}$$

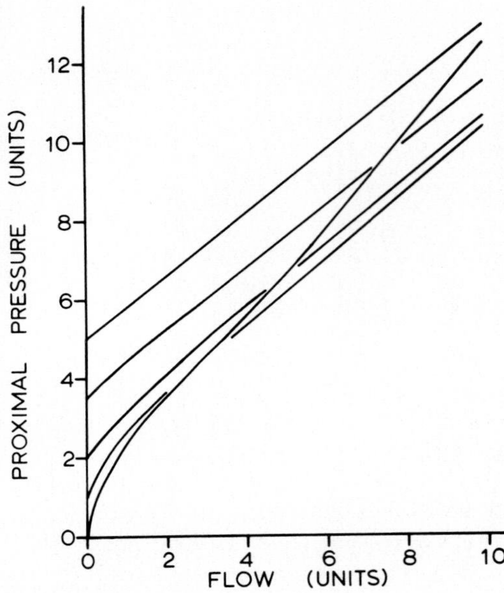

Fig. 9.12 Relation between proximal pressure and flow in a distensible vessel at different levels of distal pressure.

Let A = ratio of the total cross-sectional areas of the daughter vessels (b) to the cross-sectional area of the parent (a). Then,

$$A = \frac{2\pi r_b^2}{\pi r_a^2} = \frac{2r_b^2}{r_a^2} \qquad \text{(ii)}$$

Thus, from (i)

$$\frac{v_a}{v_b} = A$$

which means that the ratio of the velocity of the flow of blood in the parent vessel to that in the daughter vessels is given by the ratio of the total cross-sectional areas of the daughter vessels to that of the parent vessel. From Poiseuille's equation:

$$\dot{Q}_a = \frac{\pi r_a^4}{8\eta} \cdot \left(\frac{\Delta P}{\Delta l}\right)_a = 2\dot{Q}_b = \frac{2\pi r_b^4}{8\eta} \cdot \left(\frac{\Delta P}{\Delta l}\right)_b$$

Therefore,

$$\frac{(\Delta P/\Delta l)_a}{(\Delta P/\Delta l)_b} = \frac{2r_b^4}{r_a^4}$$

Substituting from (ii),

$$\frac{(\Delta P/\Delta l)_a}{(\Delta P/\Delta l)_b} = \frac{A^2}{2}$$

In the case of n equal branches it can similarly be shown that

$$\frac{v_a}{v_b} = A$$

and

$$\frac{(\Delta P/\Delta l)_a}{(\Delta P/\Delta l)_b} = \frac{A^2}{n}$$

From this last result it follows that the pressure gradient remains the same throughout the system if A^2 equals n. If A^2 is less than n the pressure gradient increases in the branches.

The quantity 'n' defines the 'branching ratio' between one order of branching and its parent order. Cumming and his colleagues[4] found that, throughout the human pulmonary circulation, the branching ratio was constant at approximately 3·4 (p. 6). The diameter ratio was 1·63 which gives a value of $A = 1{\cdot}26$ and $A^2 = 1{\cdot}59$ so that, for laminar flow, the pressure gradient would be expected to increase progressively down the pulmonary arterial tree. A gives the ratio of linear velocities as may be seen from Table 9.1.

In order to establish the drop in pressure at each order of branching it is necessary to know the length of each order. Cumming *et al.*[4] found a fairly constant ratio of 1·8 between the length of one order and the length of its daughter

Table 9.1 Dimensions of the human pulmonary arterial vasculature. Data from Cumming *et al.*[4]

Order	Number per order	Diameter (cm)	Length (cm)	Cross-section area (cm^2)	Total cross-section (cm^2)	Linear velocity[a] ($cm \cdot s^{-1}$)
17	1	1·86	12·2	2·71	2·71	29·5
16	3	1·15	6·78	1·03	3·09	25·9
15	12	0·71	3·77	0·395	4·74	16·9
14	39	0·44	2·09	0·151	5·88	13·6
13	132	0·27	1·16	0·0575	7·58	10·5
12	447	0·167	0·65	0·0219	9·80	8·15
11	$1{\cdot}517 \cdot 10^3$	0·103	0·36	$8{\cdot}37 \cdot 10^{-3}$	12·7	6·30
10	$5{\cdot}143 \cdot 10^3$	0·064	0·199	$3{\cdot}19 \cdot 10^{-3}$	16·4	4·88
9	$1{\cdot}743 \cdot 10^4$	0·039	0·111	$1{\cdot}25 \cdot 10^{-3}$	21·1	3·79
8	$5{\cdot}909 \cdot 10^4$	0·024	0·062	$4{\cdot}65 \cdot 10^{-4}$	27·2	2·94
7	$2{\cdot}003 \cdot 10^5$	0·0150	0·034	$1{\cdot}76 \cdot 10^{-4}$	35·2	2·27
6	$6{\cdot}790 \cdot 10^5$	0·0092	0·019	$6{\cdot}71 \cdot 10^{-5}$	45·5	1·76
5	$2{\cdot}303 \cdot 10^6$	0·0057	0·011	$2{\cdot}55 \cdot 10^{-5}$	58·8	1·36
4	$7{\cdot}803 \cdot 10^6$	0·0035	0·0059	$9{\cdot}72 \cdot 10^{-6}$	76·0	1·05
3	$2{\cdot}645 \cdot 10^7$	0·0022	0·0033	$3{\cdot}70 \cdot 10^{-6}$	98·0	0·815
2	$8{\cdot}966 \cdot 10^7$	0·0013	0·00181	$1{\cdot}41 \cdot 10^{-6}$	126·0	0·635
1	$3{\cdot}039 \cdot 10^8$	0·00083	0·00101	$5{\cdot}39 \cdot 10^{-7}$	164·0	0·435

[a] Based on cardiac output of 80 $ml \cdot s^{-1}$.

order in the human pulmonary circulation. Thus the ratio of the total drop in pressure along one order to the total drop in pressure along its parent order.

$$\frac{\Delta P_b}{\Delta P_a} = \frac{l_b}{l_a} \cdot \frac{n}{A^2} = \frac{1}{1 \cdot 8} \times \frac{3 \cdot 4}{1 \cdot 59} = 1 \cdot 2$$

In their anatomical analysis of the human pulmonary arterial tree Cumming *et al.*[4] recognised 17 orders of branching, from vessels with an average diameter of about 8 μm to the main pulmonary trunk. They calculate that with laminar flow the total pressure drop along this system would be 4·5 mmHg. The total pressure drop between the pulmonary valve and branches with an internal diameter of 0·8 mm was calculated to be 0·6 mmHg.[1] Although, as Cumming himself points out, such calculations depend on a number of simplifications and assumptions, they are consistent with the major site of resistance recurring in the muscular pulmonary arteries (external diameter 100–1000 μm) and arterioles (external diameter <100 μm). Thus, in general, they support the equation of changes in pulmonary arterial resistance mainly with changes in the calibre of the muscular pulmonary arteries and arterioles under physiological conditions. Under pathological conditions, also, it is noteworthy that these are the vessels which show the major morphological changes consistent with changes in resistance. It should be noted, however, that in infants a substantial resistance may occur in larger pulmonary arteries. Danilowicz and colleagues[5] found differences of 6–45 mmHg in pressure between the main trunk and its first division in 37 out of 242 infants. They ascribe this to the small size and angulation of the branches.

The Relation of Mean Pressure to Flow in the Normal Pulmonary Circulation

As will be seen in Chapter 12, the pulmonary circulation does not possess such a complex and sensitive system of nervous control which exists in the systemic. Neither, apart from hypoxia, does direct chemical control of the vessels in the pulmonary circulation appear commonly to have much influence of importance under physiological circumstances (Chap. 13). For most of the time, therefore, the factors which control the flow of blood through the lungs are mechanical ones. From this point of view it would be desirable to know what is the passive relation between pressure and flow in the circuit.

Such information becomes doubly important in the interpretation of pharmacological studies on the pulmonary circulation. If the relation between pressure and flow is not linear, then the magnitude of the resistance is not constant, but varies according to the flow through the system. Thus the system cannot be characterized by one figure for the resistance. This means that a change in resistance, in circumstances when flow is changing, does not necessarily imply any active change in the tone of the resistance vessels. Since many drugs, the effects of which are to be tested on the pulmonary circulation, will affect the pulmonary blood flow, a knowledge of the passive relation between pressure and flow in the system is necessary before their action can be interpreted.

It is well known that patients with intracardiac shunts, particularly those of the pre-tricuspid group (Chapter 19) may have a considerable and permanent elevation of the pulmonary blood flow with a pulmonary arterial pressure within the normal range. Similarly, the pulmonary arterial pressure has been measured in patients before and some months after pneumonectomy and it was found that the operation caused no substantial increase in pressure.[6] Such observations have led to the belief that the pulmonary circulation is a remarkably distensible system in which a two-fold or greater increase in flow may be accommodated with no increase in pressure. The distensibility of the pulmonary vessels which underlies these observations is, however, one which had had months or years in which to develop and the situation is not applicable to the immediate effects which a change in flow has on the drop in pressure across the pulmonary circulation.

Our most direct information concerning the immediate physiological relation between pressure and flow in the human pulmonary circulation comes from the effects of occluding one main branch of the pulmonary artery by means of a distensible balloon situated on the end of a cardiac catheter.[7] In practice, it is preferable to occlude the right main branch. In this way the flow of blood through the left lung is suddenly approximately doubled while the left atrial pressure remains constant. Hence, one can plot the flow of blood through the left lung against the pressure in the pulmonary artery before and after occlusion of the blood supply to the right lung. This gives two points on the relation between pressure and flow through the left half of the pulmonary circulation. Three points are necessary to disclose curvilinearity and a third point may be derived by assuming that, at zero flow, the pressure in the pulmonary artery would be the wedge pressure.[8]

Figure 9.13 shows a series of such pressure: flow curves obtained in normal people lying down. Pressure is expressed in terms of the difference between the pulmonary arterial and the wedge pressure so that the relation always passes through the origin. It is clear that the overall pattern is not significantly different from a straight line. This would indicate that, contrary to what has generally been believed, the muscular pulmonary arteries in the normal person lying down do not distend greatly or at all in response to a two-fold increase in flow. Similar observations have been published by Widimsky[9] and Even *et al.*[10] The relation between pressure and flow in the pulmonary circulation may well not be rectilinear in the upright position where there are reasons to believe that the blood vessels in the upper parts of the lungs are normally in a partly collapsed state because the hydrostatic pressure inside them is insufficient to keep them fully open (Chap. 11, p. 163).

The Influence of the Pressure in the Left Atrium

It might be expected that an increase in left atrial pressure would tend to distend the vessels of the lung and thus lower their resistance to the flow of blood. No direct information on this point is available in man. However, the indirect effects of the intravenous infusion of saline or dextran solutions or the application of an

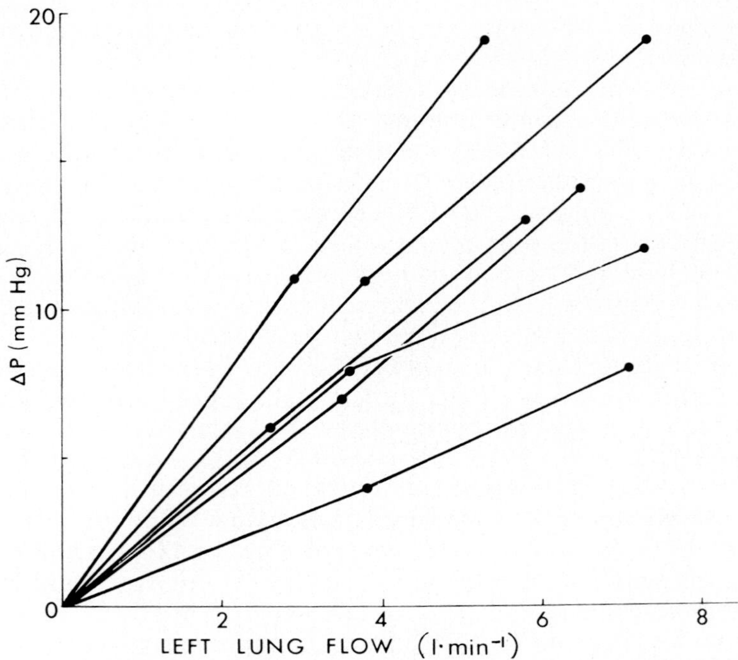

Fig. 9.13 Relation between pressure and flow in the normal human pulmonary circulation in the recumbent position. Each line represents a study on one subject. The point at higher lung flow represents the values obtained during occlusion of the right main branch of the pulmonary artery. ΔP = Pulmonary artery minus wedge pressure.

anti-gravity suit (Chap. 11, p. 162) suggest that, within the physiological range, changes in left atrial pressure have little effect on the pulmonary vascular resistance of the recumbent person. In isolated cats' lungs an increase in left atrial pressure has been shown to cause a diminution in the pulmonary vascular resistance while the rate of flow remains constant.[11] Similar observations were made on dogs' lungs *in situ.*[12] As discussed above (p. 125) it is theoretically possible for an increase in left atrial pressure to lower the pulmonary arterial pressure, but this has not been observed experimentally. The results of such acute experiments are in no way comparable with the effects of a prolonged elevation of left atrial pressure which causes pathological alterations in the structure of the pulmonary vessels and increases the pulmonary vascular resistance (Chaps 22 and 23).

While changes in the left atrial pressure may have little influence on the pulmonary vascular resistance, the magnitude of the left atrial pressure is such that it cannot be ignored in the calculation of the resistance. In the systemic circuit the venous pressure is negligible compared with the arterial. In the pulmonary circuit, however, the magnitude of the venous pressure, using the customary zero level (p. 67), is as much as two thirds that of the arterial pressure.

Failure to take this into account has been partly responsible for the widespread opinion that the pulmonary vascular resistance decreases readily with an acute increase in flow (Fig. 9.14). Similarly variations in the level of the pulmonary venous pressure can give rise to misconceptions where the actions of drugs are concerned. Drugs which cause constriction in the systemic circuit will, for instance, tend to squeeze blood out of the systemic into the pulmonary circuit. Thus, the pulmonary venous and pulmonary arterial pressure will both increase and by about the same amount (Chap. 13). A lack of consideration of the pulmonary venous pressure may lead to the erroneous conclusion that the increase in pulmonary arterial pressure is evidence of pulmonary vasoconstriction.

The Anomalous Viscosity of Blood

The Poiseuille equation assumes that the viscosity of the flowing liquid remains constant under varying conditions of flow, pressure and size of tube. The assumption is true for water and for most homogeneous liquids. It is not true for blood. This is due to the tendency for the red cells to concentrate in the axial stream (p. 113), a tendency which becomes greater with a decreasing calibre of vessel.

The most peripheral layer of blood in a vessel will tend to cling to the wall and, at its extreme boundary, will remain motionless. The layer of blood next to the most peripheral layer will have a certain forward velocity but will be retarded by the viscous drag imposed by the outer layer. A third layer, lying just nearer to the axis of the vessel, will have a slightly greater forward velocity since it is retarded only by the layer surrounding it which has itself a certain forward motion. Thus the velocity of movement increases the nearer the axial stream is approached. The relation between velocity and distance from the centre of the vessel ('velocity profile') has a shape which approximates to a parabola provided that the flow is steady and in streamlines. The equation for a liquid of normal viscosity flowing through a cylindrical tube is given in Appendix F.

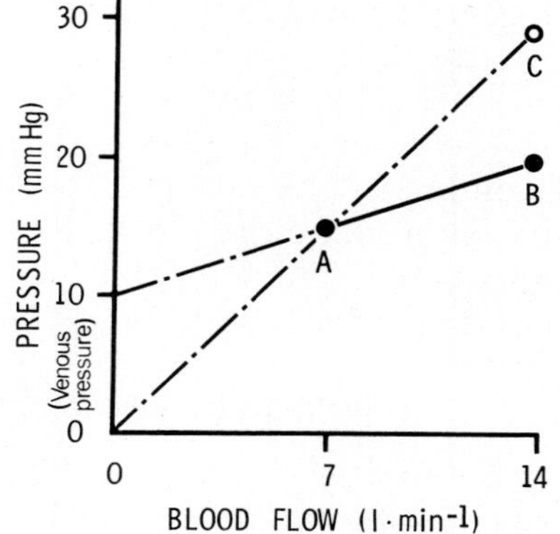

Fig. 9.14 The diagram supposes a mean pulmonary arterial pressure of 15 mmHg and a mean pulmonary blood flow of 7 l · min $^{-1}$ represented by point A. When the blood flow is doubled the pulmonary arterial pressure increases to 20 mmHg (point B). If resistance is calculated, ignoring the level of venous pressure, one would expect the arterial pressure to double if the resistance remained unchanged (point C). The fact that the arterial pressure was not increased to this extent would lead to the conclusion that the resistance has fallen. If a venous pressure of 10 mmHg is taken into account the increase in the pulmonary arterial pressure is what would be expected with a fixed resistance.

How the increased axial velocity causes the red cells to be drawn into the central stream may be seen by applying Bernoulli's principle. This principle is essentially a statement of the conservation of energy in a flowing liquid:

$$P + (\rho v^2)/2 + \rho g h = \text{constant}$$

where P is the lateral pressure, ρ is the density of the liquid, v is the velocity, g is the acceleration due to gravity, and h is the depth of the liquid from its highest point. The expression $(\rho v^2)/2$ represents the kinetic energy of the liquid and the expression $\rho g h$ represents the potential energy due to gravity. Since, in the case of a liquid flowing through a small tube, the gravitational energy is approximately constant, it follows that the sum of the lateral pressure energy and the kinetic energy is constant. As the velocity increases, so the quantity of kinetic energy increases and thus the lateral pressure has to decrease. The lateral pressure exerted by the axial stream is, therefore, less than that exerted by the peripheral layers of fluid, and this creates a force which propels the denser red cells towards the centre.

The effect of the accumulation of red cells in the centre of the vessel is to diminish the viscosity. The viscosity of blood passing through rigid tubes of varying diameters is substantially reduced[13] when the diameter is less than about 300 μm, and this diminution in viscosity continues down to tubes of 14 μm diameter.[14] (The muscular pulmonary arteries are 100–1000 μm in external diameter, p. 27.)

The diminution in the viscosity of blood caused in this fashion will become more evident with an increasing mean velocity of flow since the gradient of velocity between the periphery and the axis will become steeper.[14] Thus, in contrast to the simple example given in Figures 9.1–9.3, the relation between pressure and flow for blood passing through a small rigid tube is theoretically curvilinear and the resistance of the system varies with the rate of flow.

The influence of these factors on the pulmonary circulation remains unknown but, when territories of the systemic circulation have been perfused with blood, the estimated viscosity of the blood has been considerably less than would have been expected.[15] On the other hand, there is evidence that the axial accumulation of red cells reaches its maximum at a relatively low rate of flow.[16] In addition, the shape of the relation between pressure and flow in a vascular bed has been found to be similar irrespective of whether the perfusing fluid were blood or Ringer's solution.[17]

Such experiments have been concerned only with a steady flow of blood and in the pulmonary circulation the flow of blood appears to be pulsatile even as far as the capillaries (Chap. 6, p. 87). The effect of pulsatile flow is to 'flatten' the velocity profile of the blood[18] which will diminish the axial accumulation of red cells. This may help explain why the values for the pulmonary haematocrit have not been so low in normal man as might be expected (Chap. 8, p. 113).

Variation in Resistance During the Cardiac Cycle

If the flow of blood through the vessels which are the main site of resistance is pulsatile, these vessels will undergo variations in calibre throughout the cardiac cycle, and this will cause their resistance to fluctuate with the heart beat. Thus, even in terms of purely laminar flow, the true average resistance would be the mean of an infinite number of instantaneous values for resistance[19]:

$$R_{\text{true}} = \frac{1}{n}\left[\frac{\Delta P_1}{\dot{Q}_1} + \frac{\Delta P_2}{\dot{Q}_2} + \ldots + \frac{\Delta P_n}{\dot{Q}_n}\right] \tag{iii}$$

or

$$R_{\text{true}} = \frac{1}{T}\int_0^T \frac{\Delta P}{\dot{Q}}\,dt \tag{iii a}$$

where T is the length of time over which the observations are made. What is usually measured, however, is an average value for pressure divided by an average value for flow:

$$R_{\text{measured}} = \frac{\frac{1}{n}[\Delta P_1 + \Delta P_2 + \ldots + \Delta P_n]}{\frac{1}{n}[\dot{Q}_1 + \dot{Q}_2 + \ldots + \dot{Q}_n]} \tag{iv}$$

or

$$R_{\text{measured}} = \frac{\frac{1}{T}\int_0^T \Delta P\,dt}{\frac{1}{T}\int_0^T \dot{Q}\,dt} \tag{iv a}$$

Equations (iii) and (iv) are not identical and the measured average resistance will equal the true average resistance only if flow remains constant or if resistance remains constant.

In fact equation (iv) is an over-simplification, since, with the methods usually available, the measurement of average flow is itself a miscalculation (Chap. 6).

If flow is measured by the direct Fick method, then:

$$R_{\text{true}} = \frac{1}{n}\left[\Delta P_1 \frac{(AVo_2)_1}{(\dot{V}o_2)_1} + \Delta P_2 \frac{(AVo_2)_2}{(\dot{V}o_2)_2} + \ldots + \Delta P_n \frac{(AVo_2)_n}{(\dot{V}o_2)_n}\right] \tag{v}$$

or

$$R_{\text{true}} = \frac{1}{T}\int_0^T \Delta P \frac{AVo_2}{\dot{V}o_2}\,dt \tag{v a}$$

where AVo_2 is the instantaneous arterio-venous difference in oxygen content and $\dot{V}o_2$ is the instantaneous oxygen uptake. The actual calculation used is, however:

$$R_{calculated} = \frac{1}{n}[\Delta P_1 + \Delta P_2 + \ldots \Delta P_n] \cdot \frac{\frac{1}{n}[(AVo_2)_1 + (AVo_2)_2 + \ldots + (AVo_2)_n]}{\frac{1}{n}[(\dot{V}o_2)_1 + (\dot{V}o_2)_2 + \ldots + (\dot{V}o_2)_n]} \qquad \text{(vi)}$$

or

$$R_{calculated} = \frac{1}{T}\int_0^T \Delta P\, dt \cdot \frac{\frac{1}{T}\int_0^T (AVo_2)\, dt}{\frac{1}{T}\int_0^T (\dot{V}o_2)\, dt} \qquad \text{(vi a)}$$

It is evident that equations (v) and (vi) are not identical, but how great an error is attributable to this calculation of resistance under varying conditions is not certain. Some indication may be deduced from calculation of the pulmonary vascular resistance at different heart rates obtained during cardiac pacing.[20] Figure 9.15 shows that, under such circumstances, the pulmonary vascular resistance calculated in the conventional way changes very little over a wide range of cardiac rate.

The Practical Value of the Measurement of Resistance

The limitations in the concept of resistance which have been discussed in this chapter arise because we are considering a large volume of liquid with an anomalous viscosity flowing at a low pressure gradient in a pulsatile fashion through a system of highly distensible vessels suspended in a thorax which is itself undergoing

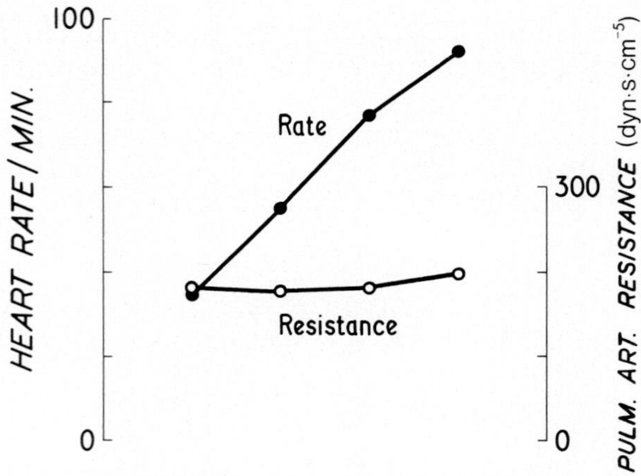

Fig. 9.15 Effects of varying the cardiac frequency by pacemaking on the pulmonary vascular resistance. Mean of 14 patients.[20]

rhythmic changes in size and internal pressure. Such limitations are most severe in the normal circulation where the pulmonary arterial pressure is only a few mmHg higher than the venous pressure.

By contrast, in many diseases the level of the pulmonary arterial pressure may rise so far as to equal or even exceed that in the aorta. In the interpretation of such extreme changes in pressure, the details which have just been considered become minutiae and the calculation of vascular resistance has a practical value. It has been found of use, for instance, in the assessment of the degree of hypertensive pulmonary vascular disease in patients with septal defects (Chap. 20) since in these patients there is a wide variety of pressure and flow in the pulmonary circulation.

The standard calculation of resistance in the pulmonary circulation is:

$$R = \frac{\text{Pulmonary arterial pressure} - \text{Wedge pressure (mmHg)}}{\text{Pulmonary blood flow } (\text{l} \cdot \text{min}^{-1})} \times 80 \text{ dyn} \cdot \text{s} \cdot \text{cm}^{-5}$$

Expressed in this way the normal resistance is about 100 dyn · s · cm^{-5}. In patients with the severest grades of hypertensive pulmonary vascular disease, this figure may be more than twenty times higher. Many clinicians prefer to express resistance simply as mmHg pressure difference per l · min^{-1} blood flow, which gives a normal value approximating unity. There is a great deal to be said for such units which have a magnitude more appropriate to the accuracy of the measurement and the purposes in hand.

The resistance calculated in this way is that which is offered by the pulmonary arterial tree, since the pressure measured in the wedge position is primarily that in the capillaries. It may be referred to as the 'pulmonary arterial resistance'. The difference between the wedge pressure and the left atrial pressure appears to be very small (Chap. 5, p. 73) and the resistance offered by the pulmonary veins is, therefore, minute. Nevertheless, in the presence of an obstruction to flow through the pulmonary veins such as in pulmonary veno-occlusive disease (p. 433), the wedge pressure may sometimes substantially exceed the pressure in the left atrium (Chap. 5, p. 74). Under these circumstances, the above calculation will underestimate the total resistance of the pulmonary circuit.

REFERENCES

1. Cumming, G., Henderson, R., Horsfield, K. & Singhal, S. S. (1969) *The Pulmonary Circulation and Interstitial Space*, ed. Fishman, A. P. & Hecht, H. H. p. 237. Univ. of Chicago Press.
2. Milnor, W. R., Conti, C. R., Lewis, K. B. & O'Rourke, M. F. (1969) *Circulat. Res.*, **25**, 637.
3. Schulz, D. L., Tunstall-Pedoe, D. S., Lee, G. de J., Gunning, A. J. & Bellhouse, B. J. (1969) *Circulatory and Respiratory Mass Transport*, ed. Wolstenholme, G. E. W. & Knight, J. P. 172. Ciba Symposium.
4. Cumming, G., Harding, L. K., Horsfield, K., Prowse, K., Singhal, S. S. & Woldenberg, M. (1970) *NATO Advisory Group for Aerospace Research and Development*. Conference proceedings, **No. 65**, 23.
5. Danilowicz, D. A., Rudolph, A. M., Hoffman, J. I. E. & Heymann, M. (1972) *Circulation*, **45**, 410.
6. Cournand, A., Riley, R. L., Himmelstein, A. & Austrian, R. (1950) *J. Thorac. Surg.*, **19**, 80.

7. Carlens, E., Hanson, H. E. & Nordenström, B. (1951) *J. Thorac. Surg.*, **22**, 527.
8. Harris, P., Segel, N. & Bishop, J. M. (1968) *Cardiovasc. Res.*, **2**, 73.
9. Widimsky, J. (1970) *Prog. Resp. Res.*, **5**, 224.
10. Even, P., Duroux, P., Ruff, F., Caubarrere, I., de Vernejoul, P. & Brouet, G. (1971) *Scand. J. Resp. Dis. Suppl.*, 77, 72.
11. Carlill, S. D., Duke, H. N. & Jones, M. (1957) *J. Physiol.*, **136**, 112.
12. Borst, H. G., McGregor, M., Whittenberger, J. L. & Berglund, E. (1956) *Circulat. Res.*, **4**, 393.
13. Fahraeus, R. & Lindquist, T. (1931) *Amer. J. Physiol.*, **96**, 562.
14. Bayliss, L. E. (1952) In *Deformation and Flow in Biological Systems*, ed. Frey-Wyssling, A. Ch. 6. Amsterdam: North Holland.
15. Whittaker, S. R. F. & Winton, F. R. (1933) *J. Physiol.*, **78**, 339.
16. Haynes, R. H. & Burton, A. C. (1959) *Amer. J. Physiol.*, **197**, 943.
17. Burton, A. C. (1959) In *Pulmonary Circulation*, ed. Adams, W. R. & Veith, I. P. 27. New York: Grune & Stratton.
18. Hale, J. F., McDonald, D. A. & Womersley, J. R. (1955) *J. Physiol.*, **128**, 629.
19. Fritts, H. W., Jn. (1959) In *Pulmonary Circulation*, ed. Adams, W. R. & Veith, I. P. 62. Chicago.
20. Segel, N., Hudson, W. A., Harris, P. & Bishop, J. M. (1964) *J. Clin. Invest.*, **43**, 1541.

10. Distensibility, Inertia and Impedance

The waves which occur in the circulation are either pressure waves or flow waves. In each case they may be thought of as consisting of an oscillatory component and a steady component (p. 61). The steady component is the net forward flow in the case of the flow wave and the mean pressure in the case of the pressure wave. The relation between mean pressure and flow has been considered in the previous chapter. Here, we shall be concerned only with the forces which are involved during the oscillatory motion of the blood in the pulmonary circulation. The energy involved in such motion is not negligible, amounting to some 30 per cent of the magnitude of the energy required for mean forward flow (p. 152) in normal people and likely to be more so in disease. The flow and pressure waves may be regarded as being positive and negative with respect to the steady component or, in other words, they have an oscillatory movement about the steady component. This oscillatory movement can always be analysed in terms of a number of simple sinusoidal waves (Chap. 5, p. 58), which will form the basis of the following discussion. For a more detailed treatment of the subject the reader is referred to the excellent monograph edited by Bergel[1] and especially the contributions on impedance by Gessner[2] and on pulmonary haemodynamics by Milnor.[3]

Distensibility

The expansion which occurs in the pulmonary trunk and its main branches during ventricular systole is obvious when the heart is exposed on the operating table. It is not usually visible on fluoroscopy in normal people but becomes so in patients in whom there is a great increase in the volume of blood ejected into the pulmonary artery at each beat of the heart. These are usually patients who have an increased pulmonary blood flow, but visible pulsation can occur for similar reasons in patients with an extreme bradycardia such as occurs in heart block.

By dilating during systole, the elastic pulmonary arteries act as a reservoir for a quantity of blood which is subsequently expelled during diastole. The storage function of the arteries may be termed their capacity or, since we are dealing with a pulsatile system, their capacitance (C). The capacity of a system is the same as its volume distensibility. Thus it is the increase in volume per unit increase in pressure. For the sake of simplicity this value is regarded as constant in the examples which follow, but in fact the relation between pressure and volume in arteries is not linear (Appendix J).

The presence of distensibility has an important influence on the relation between pressure and flow in a pulsatile system. The mechanical analogue shown in Figure 10.1 is designed to show its effect. The analogue consists of a rigid metal tube to one end of which is sealed an expansile chamber. The tube and chamber are filled with water. A piston occupies the open end of the tube. It moves in and out in a sinusoidal fashion and thus alternately squeezes water in and out of the

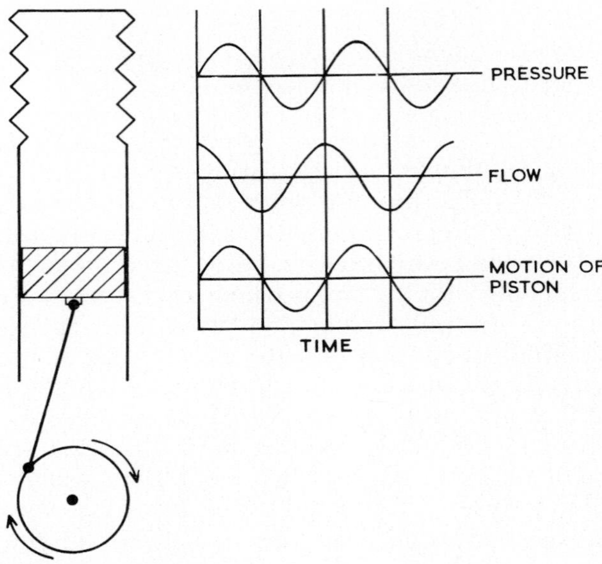

Fig. 10.1 Mechanical analogue to demonstrate how distensibility causes the flow wave to precede the pressure wave. See text for explanation.

chamber. A manometer and flow-meter are incorporated into the tube. If the mass and viscosity of the water and balloon are ignored for the purposes of the illustration, the situation may be thought of as one of a pure capacitance.

The sinusoidal movement of the piston is shown in the lowest tracing. As it moves inwards, so the chamber is distended and the pressure in the water rises. The recording from the manometer which is shown in the upper tracing of Figure 10.1 is, therefore, identical in shape and timing with that of the position of the piston. The recording from the flow-meter also has the same shape as that of the position of the piston, but it differs in its timing. While the piston is moving inwards the flow-meter records the presence of a forward flow which reaches its maximum when the piston is in its mid-position. At the moment when the piston is in the position of maximal insertion the rate of flow becomes zero. Similarly, during the outward movement of the piston, the rate of back-flow reaches its maximum when the piston is in its mid-position, and flow ceases when the piston is at its position of maximal withdrawal. In this way, the curve of flow, which is shown in the middle of Figure 10.1, precedes the curve of pressure by a phase angle of 90° or $\pi/2$ radians (p. 59).

The effect of distensibility is, therefore, to dissociate the phases of the pressure and flow curves so that flow precedes pressure.

The opposition which capacitance offers to the motion of the blood is known as the capacitative reactance (Xc). The lower the distensibility of the storage chamber (*i.e.* the stiffer its walls) the greater will be the amplitude of the pressure wave for a given flow wave. Thus a capacitative reactance varies inversely with the magnitude of the distensibility or capacitance (C):

$$X_C \propto \frac{1}{C}$$

As fluid flows into a storage chamber, the pressure rises. The longer the fluid flows the greater will be the pressure, so that a slow sinusoidal wave of flow is associated with a high amplitude wave of pressure. On the other hand, if fluid flows in and out in small amounts very quickly, it will cause a much smaller change in pressure even although the total volume of fluid displaced per minute is the same. Thus a capacitative reactance also varies inversely as the frequency of the pulse (f):

$$X_C \propto \frac{1}{f}$$

In fact, the complete relation between reactance, distensibility and frequency is:

$$X_C = \frac{1}{2\pi fC}$$

Since the motion of the wheel which drives the piston is a circular one it has to be described in terms of an angular velocity:

$$\omega = 2\pi f$$

This angular velocity also describes the movement of the sinusoidal wave (*cf.* Fig. 5.2, p. 59) so that

$$X_C = \frac{1}{\omega C}$$

Inertia

In order to treat the example given in Figure 10.1 as a pure capacitance, it has been necessary to ignore the viscous resistance to flow offered by the water and the effects of the mass of the water. The presence of this mass introduces forces of inertia (I), which also oppose the movement of the water. The force exerted by inertia is proportional to the change in velocity of the mass. That is to say, it is proportional to the acceleration of the water. It will be remembered from Newton's second law of motion that

$$\text{Force} = \text{mass} \times \text{acceleration}$$

The greatest acceleration of the piston occurs as it changes direction and it is at these times that the forces of inertia are at their maximum. Thus, as the piston turns from its point of maximal withdrawal and starts to move inwards, it meets with an opposition due to the inertia of the column of water. It meets a similar

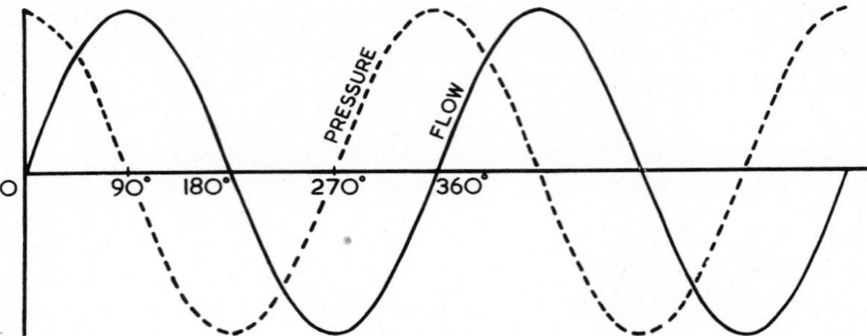

Fig. 10.2 The relation between pressure and flow in the presence of a pure inertial reactance. Inertia causes the pressure wave to precede the flow wave.

opposition but in the opposite direction when it starts to return from the position of maximal insertion. It will be remembered from Figure 10.1 that, at the moment when the piston changes its direction, the rate of flow of water is zero. Hence, if the opposing force exerted by inertia is plotted against time, it will be seen to be 90° out of phase with the curve of flow (Fig. 10.2). In this case, however, the curve of pressure leads the curve of flow. The opposition which inertia offers to the flow of blood may be called an inertial reactance (or an inductive reactance by analogy with electrical circuits).

The inertial reactance varies directly with the mass of liquid that has to be displaced. Like the capacitative reactance, it is also dependent on the frequency of the pulsation. In this case, however, it opposes rapid changes of flow much more than slow ones. Thus the magnitude of the inertial reactance varies directly with the frequency of the pulsation. The complete relation between inertial reactance, mass and frequency is:

$$X_I = 2\pi fm$$

or

$$X_I = \omega m$$

where m is the mass of the fluid.

Impedance

The concept of impedance, which will be developed in the following pages, relates pressure to flow under pulsatile conditions. In so doing it comprises both the properties of reactance and resistance which have so far been discussed separately. The expressions, r sin θ and r cos θ, derived from Figure 5.1 describe only the movement of the 'arm' or 'modulus' r as projected on one of the two axes. This projected motion gives a sinusoidal wave when plotted against the angle θ as in Figures 10.1 and 10.2. Since the angle increases constantly with time the

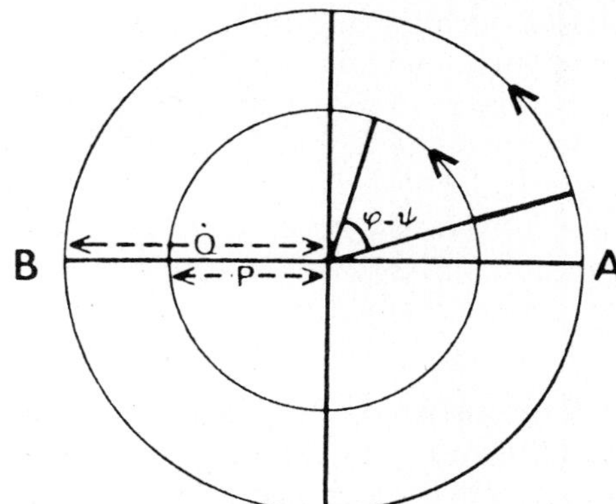

Fig. 10.3 Diagram to illustrate the spatial relation of the moduli of pressure (P) and flow (Q). It is discussed further in the text.

scale of θ can be replaced by a time scale. However, when one is dealing with pressure and flow waves consequent on a driving force (*e.g.* the piston in Fig. 10.1) a zero value for θ does not necessarily correspond with a zero value for time because of the phase angle (ϕ) which is caused by the presence of a reactance.

$$\theta = \omega t + \phi$$

This phase angle will not be the same for pressure as it is for flow. In Figure 10.1, for instance, the pressure wave is in phase with the motion of the piston but the flow wave is $90° = \pi/2$ radians in advance. Because of this difference in phase angle between pressure and flow, the simple ratio of pressure to flow may vary widely throughout a cycle. To take an extreme instance, in the presence of a pure inertial or a pure capacitative reactance, the ratio of pressure to flow will swing between plus and minus infinity.

In Figure 10.3 pressure and flow can be regarded as the sinusoidal waves ($r \cos \theta$) projected on the axis AB by the movement of two arms. The lengths of the two arms are different. That of the pressure arm (pressure modulus) is P and that of the flow arm (flow modulus) is $\dot{Q}$. Both arms are rotating at the same speed, ω, but the phase angle for pressure is φ radians while that for flow is ψ radians so that there is an angle $(\varphi - \psi)$ between them which remains constant as they move round. Thus the ratio of $P \cos \theta$ for pressure to $\dot{Q} \cos \theta$ for flow (which is the ratio of the projections along axis AB) will vary throughout the cycle. On the other hand the length of each modulus (P and $\dot{Q}$) remains the same throughout the cycle and so does the net phase angle $(\varphi - \psi)$ between them so that they form a triangle which remains constant. The situation can, therefore, be characterized by a knowledge of the pressure and flow moduli and of the phase angle between them together with the rate of rotation, ω. It will be seen that the magnitude of each modulus (P and $\dot{Q}$) is given by the maximal value of its projection on AB. We can, therefore, define the relation between pressure and flow for a given frequency by a knowledge of the amplitudes of the pressure and flow waves together with a knowledge of the phase angle between them. The mathematical expression of the relation between these three quantities is given by Z, the impedance. The nature of

Z is described in Appendix K. The expression of Z requires the use of 'complex quantities' which are necessary for the mathematical handling of problems of impedance. Such a mathematical expression is not, however, necessary for the description of impedance which can be achieved by means of a statement of the magnitude of the pressure and flow moduli and the phase angle between them. The description can be simplified by using the ratio of the pressure modulus to the flow modulus (P/Q) which is referred to as the 'impedance modulus'. Thus the impedance may be described in terms of the impedance modulus and the phase angle.

Impedance Spectra

The foregoing considerations have been based on a simple sinusoidal function. The forms of the pressure and flow waves in blood vessels are much more complex. It will, however, be recalled from Chapter 5, page 60 that, according to the Fourier theorem, any complex periodic wave-form may be analysed in terms of its sinusoidal components. Thus both the pressure waves and the flow waves in a blood vessel can be expressed as a series of sinusoidal curves. In each case the chief component will have a frequency equal to that of the heart beat, while the subsequent components of the series will have frequencies corresponding to the harmonics. The impedance of each component can be calculated separately. Since the different components will have different frequencies and amplitudes and phase angles, they will have different values for impedance. It follows that it is not possible to characterize the impedance of such a system by one figure. Instead it is necessary to express it by the relation between frequency and impedance. Thus the full expression of impedance for complex wave forms such as those found in the pulmonary artery has to consist of the magnitude of the pressure (P) and flow ($\dot{Q}$) moduli and phase angle ($\varphi - \psi$) at each harmonic. Alternatively the magnitude

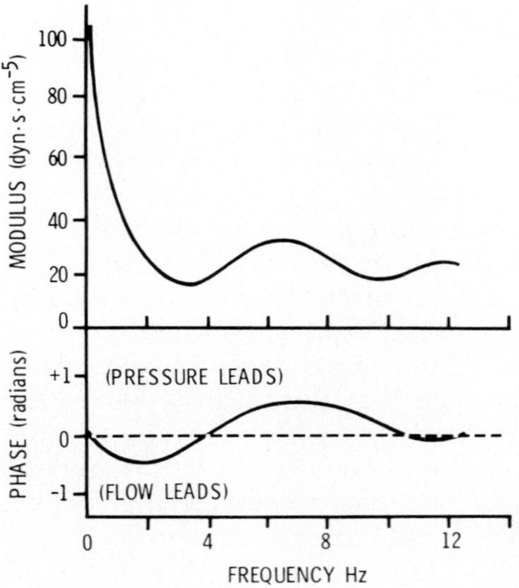

Fig. 10.4 Diagram from Milnor[3] showing the input 'impedance spectrum' in the normal human pulmonary artery.

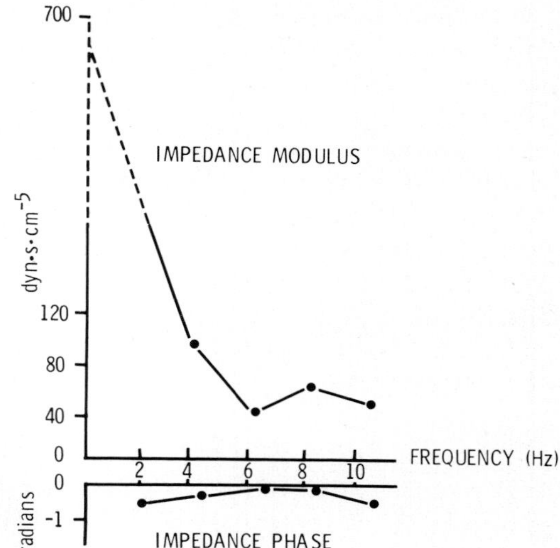

Fig. 10.5 Pulmonary arterial input impedance spectrum from a patient with mitral stenosis and a mean pulmonary arterial pressure of 59 mmHg. Re-drawn from Milnor *et al.*[4]

of the impedance modulus ($P/\dot{Q}$) together with the phase angle ($\varphi - \psi$) may be given for each harmonic. Such an expression would describe the situation for only one heart rate, but, since the various harmonics occur at different frequencies the impedance modulus and phase angle can be plotted against frequency as a continuous relation (Fig. 10.4).

As the frequency becomes slower the conditions become more like those of steady flow, until, when the frequency is zero, steady flow occurs. Under these conditions the phase angle disappears and the impedance modulus ($P/\dot{Q}$) describes resistance.

Pulmonary Input Impedance

The measurement of impedance at the origin of the pulmonary trunk is referred to as the 'input' impedance of the pulmonary circulation. For this purpose, recordings of instantaneous flow and pressure are needed and the wave forms require Fourier analysis. Such measurements have been made in man by Milnor and his colleagues[4] using a differential pressure method for determining flow at the end of a cardiac catheter. The results are similar to measurements made in the dog.[5–7] Figure 10.4 shows typical data from a normal person. Since this diagram is derived from a number of observations of subjects with different heart rates, the moduli and phase angle are plotted as a continuous line against cardiac frequency rather than as a number of individual points against numbered harmonics. The impedance modulus at zero flow ('input' resistance*) is, as would be expected, in the region of 100 dyn · s · cm^{-5}. The modulus falls steeply to a frequency of 1 Hz (frequency per second) after which it shows small oscillations about a relatively constant level. Thus there seems to be a minimum at about 3 Hz followed by a maximum at about 6 Hz and another minimum at about 10 Hz.

* Note that this does not take the pulmonary venous pressure into account.

The phase angle is negative at frequencies lower than 4 Hz and tends to be positive at higher frequencies although variations are noted. Thus flow precedes pressure at low frequencies indicating a predominantly capacitative effect, while pressure precedes flow at high frequencies indicating a predominantly inertial effect. This is what would be expected since capacitance varies inversely as frequency (p. 139) while inertance varies directly as frequency (p. 140).

Figure 10.5, also taken from the work of Milnor and his colleagues,[4] shows results obtained in a patient with mitral stenosis who had a mean pulmonary arterial pressure of 59 mmHg. Here the moduli of impedance are all higher than normal, but the moduli at zero and very low frequencies predominate as in the normal. The phase angle is negative at all frequencies indicating a predominantly capacitative effect throughout.

The Velocity of Propagation of Pulse Waves

The pulse waves of pressure and flow which are generated by the right ventricle pass into the complexities of the pulmonary circulation and a certain amount of information is available concerning their speed of propagation, their degree of attenuation, and their reflection from the periphery.

Suppose a piston fitted into one end of a long rigid tube containing a column of water. If the pressure is suddenly raised at the end by moving the piston inwards it will propagate along the tube at about 1500 $m \cdot s^{-1}$, the speed of sound in water. If the tube is now replaced by one made out of some extensible material such as rubber, the rate of propagation of the pressure wave will be appreciably slower. In this way the propagation of pressure pulse waves along arteries is largely dependent on the extensibility of their walls. The phenomenon was well studied by Thomas Young (of Young's Modulus, p. 44) in 1808[8] in preparation for his Croonian Lecture to the Royal College of Physicians. The equation describing the phenomenon was established from experimental observations by Moens in 1878:[9]

$$s = k\sqrt{\frac{Yh}{2r\rho}}$$

where s is the wave velocity, Y is Young's Modulus for the arterial wall, h is the thickness of the wall, r is the radius of the artery and ρ is the density of the blood. The constant, k, was an arbitrary one for which Moens found the value 0·9. In the same year, Korteweg[10] derived the theoretical formula:

$$s = \sqrt{\frac{Yh}{2r\rho}}$$

The theoretical equation requires the thickness of the vessel wall (h) to be very small in relation to the radius (r) and assumes the fluid to be both incompressible and without viscosity. The presence of viscosity is probably the reason for the value of 0·9 for k in Moen's empirical formula. Bramwell and Hill[11] modified and simplified Korteweg's equation to:

$$s = \frac{3{\cdot}57}{\sqrt{E}}$$

where E is the distensibility coefficient of the vessel (percentage change in volume per mmHg).

In the application of these formulae it is necessary to bear in mind the non-linearity of the relation between tension and extension in the walls of blood vessels (p. 47) and the importance of knowing the absolute dimensions of the wall or volume of the vessel before comparisons can be made.

Measurements of the pressure pulse wave velocity in man have given figures of 2 $m \cdot s^{-1}$ (Ref. 12), 1·8 $m \cdot s^{-1}$ (Ref. 13) and 1·7 $m \cdot s^{-1}$ (Ref. 4). This is less than one half of the velocity in the aorta presumably because of the greater distensibility of the pulmonary artery (p. 47). In the aorta, the pulse wave velocity increases as it progresses distally and the distensibility of the vessels becomes less.[14,15] There is evidence in the rabbit that the distensibility of pulmonary arteries also decreases as the periphery is approached[16] but no information concerning the distribution of the pulse wave velocity. In the aorta an increase in pressure is associated with an increase in pulse wave velocity presumably because the volume distensibility decreases more than the radius (see Appendix J).

Values of 4–5 $m \cdot s^{-1}$ have been found for the pressure pulse wave velocity in the pulmonary artery of patients with acquired pulmonary hypertension.[4,13] Such an increase in velocity would also signify a considerable decrease in distensibility of the pulmonary arteries relative to their increase in radius. Since, in acquired pulmonary hypertension, the physical characteristics of the pulmonary arterial wall appear to be unchanged (Chaps 18, p. 282) one must presume that this is simply the result of the increase in transmural pressure in the presence of a curvilinear relation between tension and extension in the wall. The increased rigidity of the arterial wall is also consistent with the increased capacitative reactance found in patients with acquired pulmonary hypertension (p. 144).

Assessments of the time taken for the flow wave to pass down the arterial tree have been made in man using the body plethysmograph technique for recording pulmonary capillary flow. Assuming that right ventricular ejection starts 0·08 s after the R wave of the electrocardiogram, Kaplan and Kimbel[17] calculated that the foot of the flow wave in the capillaries was 0·12 s after that at the pulmonary valve. Taking a figure of approximately 11 cm (Ref. 18) for the mean distance between the pulmonary valve and the capillaries, this gives a pulse wave velocity of about 90 $cm \cdot s^{-1}$. Reuben[19] calculated the time between the opening of the pulmonary valve (identified by a phonocardiogram) and the foot of the flow wave in the capillaries in a group of patients. When the pulmonary arterial pressure was normal, the time interval was greater than 0·16 s, giving a pulse wave velocity in the region of 70 $cm \cdot s^{-1}$. With increasing levels of pulmonary arterial pressure the conduction time progressively diminished.

Phase Velocity

As has been seen earlier the complex biological wave form in the pulmonary artery may be analysed by the method of Fourier into a number of sinusoidal components comprising the fundamental and a series of harmonics. Thus the velocity of each individual component may be distinguished and is known as the 'phase velocity'. In blood vessels the phase velocity varies with varying frequency[14] so that the shape of the composite pulse wave will tend to change as it passes down the vessel, the higher frequency components travelling faster.

Damping

The presence of viscous properties in the blood and the walls of blood vessels has a damping effect on the pulse waves. Thus the amplitude of the waves will diminish as they travel along the blood vessel. The effect is greater for the higher frequency components, which is a further reason for the change in shape of the composite wave as it proceeds forwards. This subject is examined in greater detail in Appendix L.

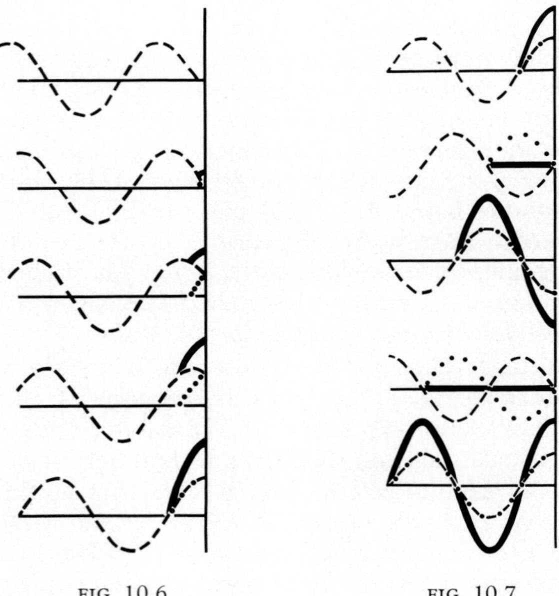

FIG. 10.6 FIG. 10.7

Fig. 10.6 Reflection of a pressure wave from a closed end at successive stages during the first quarter of a cycle. - - - - -, incident wave; · · · · ·, reflected wave; ———, composite wave.

Fig. 10.7 Reflection of a pressure wave from a closed end at quarter cycle stages during $1\frac{1}{4}$ cycles. - - - - -, Incident wave; · · · · ·, reflected wave; ———, composite wave.

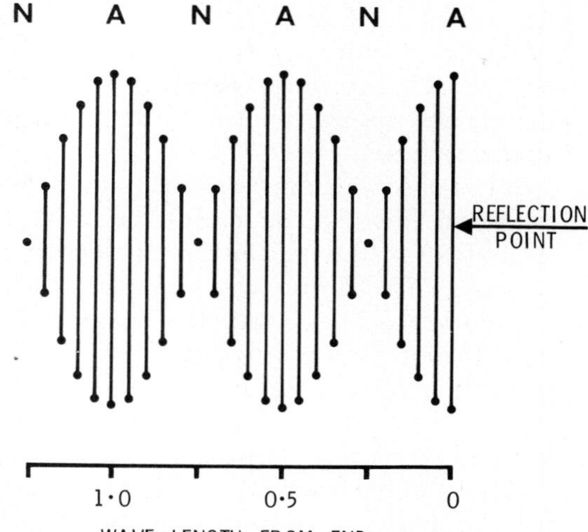

Fig. 10.8 Formation of nodes (N) and antinodes (A) of pressure in the presence of a closed ending.

Wave Reflections

In their passage down the complex branching system of the pulmonary arterial tree the pressure and pulse waves are susceptible to reflection from angulations and from the discontinuities at points of division. It is simplest to consider such effects initially in terms of a single elastic tube with a closed end. We shall assume, for the moment, that neither the wall of the tube nor the fluid which it contains possess viscous properties.

As the wave of pressure meets the closed end, it is subjected to a force equal in magnitude and opposite in direction which stops it. This means that the magnitude of the pressure at the closed end becomes suddenly doubled, while a reflected pressure wave identical in amplitude and frequency is propagated backwards along the tube. As it passes backwards, the magnitude of the reflected pressure wave at any point and at any instant becomes added algebraically to the primary forward wave.

To understand the results of this phenomenon, it is easiest to imagine the moment at which the pressure wave first meets the closed end. This is shown in Figure 10.6 which follows the subsequent course of events for the first quarter of a cycle, during which time the reflected wave travels a quarter of a wavelength. Figure 10.7 shows the wave form which results from the addition of the primary and reflected waves at subsequent intervals of a quarter of a cycle. It will be seen that, at the closed end, the pressure oscillates through twice the amplitude of the primary wave. At a quarter of a wavelength away from the closed end the algebraic addition of the primary and reflected waves results in zero at all times. Such a position of no oscillation is called a 'node'. A position of maximal oscillation such as occurs at the closed end is called an 'antinode'. Figure 10.8 shows that, when there is a closed end, antinodes occur at the end and at successive half wavelengths away from it. Nodes occur half way between the antinodes. The waves which are formed in this way are 'stationary' or 'standing'. The position of antinodes and nodes is fixed and there is no propagation forwards or backwards as is the case with the primary and reflected waves.

In the case of a flow wave passing down such a tube there can be no forward or backward flow at the closed end. The end must, therefore, be a node, while antinodes for flow will occur at a quarter and three quarters of a wavelength away from the end. In this way the impedance modulus, which is the ratio of pressure to flow moduli, will be infinite at the closed end and at every successive half wavelength away from it. At a quarter wavelength, three quarters wavelength etc. the impedance modulus will be zero.

In the case of a tube with an open end, the situation is reversed. The open end imposes a node for pressure and an antinode for flow and maxima for the impedance moduli occur a quarter wavelength, three quarters wavelength etc. away from the end. Appendix L examines in greater detail the nature of reflections at closed and open ends and the relation between the degree of reflection and the change in impedance at a point of discontinuity.

The presence of reflected waves would mean that the amplitudes of pressure and of flow waves would be increased or decreased at various places in the pulmonary arterial tree. If this were so, it would be possible for the amplitude of a pressure wave to be higher downstream than upstream. The fact that such has been found to be the case in the pulmonary arterial tree[4,20] is itself an indication of the presence of reflection. The presence of damping would, however, be expected to cause an attenuation of the reflected wave. The existence of such an attenuation would mean that only relative nodes and antinodes would exist. In addition, it seems likely that the reflection of waves is associated with some phase shift which will tend to obscure the position of nodes and antinodes. Attenuation of reflected waves affects the higher frequency components most so that the impedance found at higher frequencies is closely related to the 'characteristic impedance' which would occur in the absence of a reflected wave (Appendix L).

A knowledge of the approximate phase velocity and the frequency at which the minimum impedance occurs in the proximal pulmonary artery may be used to estimate the approximate site of reflection of waves in the pulmonary circulation.[5,7] If we take 180 $cm \cdot s^{-1}$ as the approximate pulse-wave velocity (p. 145) and 3 Hz as the frequency at which the minimum impedance occurs (Fig. 10.4 and p. 143) the wavelength of this frequency will be approximately 60 cm. If the reflecting system acts as if it were a closed end, it must lie a quarter of this wavelength away from the beginning of the pulmonary artery. This gives a figure of 15 cm, suggesting that the major reflecting sites are in the region of the peripheral pulmonary arterial branches. If the reflecting system acted as if it were an open end, the point of reflection would have to be 30 cm away which would be in the left atrium and seems unlikely. Such calculations are in the nature of interesting speculations rather than accurate measurements. They treat the system as a uniform single tube, while in fact it has a complex anatomy; phase velocity probably increases as the wave passes down the pulmonary arterial tree and increases with frequency, while reflections presumably occur at many widely dispersed points. Nevertheless, the evidence suggests that the reflecting sites are of the closed end type and are mainly situated towards the periphery of the pulmonary arterial tree.

Transmission of Waves

What is not reflected is either dissipated or transmitted. The ratio of amplitude of the transmitted wave to the incident wave may be termed the 'transmission ratio' (Appendix L) just as the ratio of the reflected to the incident wave is termed the 'reflection ratio'.

Caro and his colleagues[21] have studied the transmission of pressure waves through the pulmonary circulation of patients during thoracotomy. Needles were placed in a lobar artery and lobar vein with snares upstream from the arterial needle and downstream from the venous needle. With both snares loose, the arterial pressure tracing in patients with normal mean pressures showed the usual major systolic peak together with a dicrotic notch and dicrotic wave. The simultaneous venous pressure tracing showed two waves of approximately equal amplitude similar to those described on page 72. When the arterial snare alone was tightened, the arterial pressure tracing became flat while the venous pressure tracing was unaltered. When the venous snare alone was tightened, the arterial pressure was unaltered while the venous pressure showed a wave similar in character to that in the artery but delayed and attenuated. The experiment is not quite so simple as it may at first appear, since the application of a snare imposes an antinode for pressure which would have the effect of doubling the amplitude. Nevertheless, it seems clear that the venous pulse wave is normally largely independent of the arterial wave and mainly determined by the mechanical events in the left side of the heart. In so far as transmission of the arterial wave may influence the venous pulse, this would seem to be limited to a slight increase in amplitude of the '*v*'-wave.

In a mixed group of patients with mean pulmonary arterial pressures varying from 17 to 32 mmHg and mean pulmonary venous pressures varying from 1 to 15 mmHg, the forward transmission ratio (amplitude of pulmonary venous pressure as a percentage of amplitude of the pulmonary arterial pressure) was calculated for the fundamental and harmonics after Fourier analysis.[21] Figures of 33 per cent were obtained for frequencies of 1–2 Hz, 25 per cent for 3–4 Hz, 46 per cent for 4–5 Hz and 26 per cent for 5–6 Hz. Presumably such differences imply the presence of stationary waves. Backward transmission tended to be less than forward transmission.

In two patients with pulmonary venous hypertension, with prominent venous '*a*'- and '*v*'-waves, backward transmission of the venous pressure pulse could be clearly identified after snaring the pulmonary artery. In these two patients, forward transmission was 90 per cent and 60 per cent for the fundamental. The increased transmission in the presence of an increased transmural pressure is best explained by the decreased compliance of the conducting vessels which would be expected to accompany an increased degree of distension. Such a decreased compliance follows from the curved nature of the length–tension relation of the walls of blood vessels (p. 44).

Such considerations have a bearing on the evaluation of wedged pressure tracings. It is well known clinically that the venous pressure pulses are transmitted more readily in the presence of venous hypertension. The pressure distal to a main pulmonary arterial branch which has been occluded by a balloon (p. 129) is, by contrast, not usually pulsatile. This is presumably due to the greater compliance of the pulmonary arterial system plus the balloon. A number of similar investigations have been carried out in animals.[5,7,20,22–25]

The body plethysmograph method for measuring instantaneous pulmonary capillary flow (p. 87) has been used in dogs in combination with the measurement of instantaneous flow in the pulmonary artery to determine the transmission of flow waves down the pulmonary arterial tree.[26,27] Each of these two studies employed Fourier analysis. Over the first five harmonics the amplitude decreased progressively both in the pulmonary artery and the capillaries. The amplitudes of higher harmonics were small and within the noise level of the instruments. The percentage transmission from the pulmonary artery to the capillaries was a little over 50 per cent for the first harmonic, declining to about 40 per cent for the third and fourth harmonics.[26] While it was clear that the flow wave was delayed in the capillaries relative to the pulmonary artery, the method was not thought sufficiently accurate to calculate phase differences.

Studies in man have not been so complete. Wasserman *et al.*,[28] computed the shape of the right ventricular outflow and compared this with the pulmonary capillary flow. They calculated that the peak flow in the pulmonary capillaries was 56 per cent of that from the right ventricle.

The transmission of flow waves into the pulmonary venous system has proved an area of debate. Only data on dogs are available. Maloney and his colleagues[29] studied the transmission of sinusoidal flow waves from the pulmonary artery to pulmonary veins in the isolated lung of the dog. The mean pulmonary arterial pressure was maintained higher than the alveolar pressure. The level of the venous pressure was varied but did not greatly affect the results. A sizeable transmission of the flow wave was found only at very low frequencies. For instance, at 0·1 Hz the transmission ratio was about 70 per cent but by 1·0 Hz it had fallen to about 10 per cent. At a frequency of 0·1 Hz the foot-to-foot transmission time was in the region of 10 s.

On the other hand there seems little doubt that pulsatile flow exists in the canine pulmonary veins under normal conditions.[24,25,30,31] There appear to be two main waves of forward flow: one at the end of ventricular systole and the other in the early part of ventricular diastole.[24,31] During atrial contraction there is a diminution in flow[24,31] which may even become reversed after an unusually long diastole.

The origin of the forward flow waves in the pulmonary veins is disputed, but appears on balance to be two-fold. Morgan and his colleagues[31] showed that, when the lung was supplied with blood from the superior vena cava instead of the pulmonary artery, the inflow was constant but the pulmonary venous flow showed a normal pulsatility. Pinkerson[24] and Szidon and his colleagues[25] on the other hand have shown that, when a lobar vein is cannulated so that it becomes disconnected from the left atrium, the venous flow is still pulsatile. Under these conditions, however, it seems that there is only a single forward wave occurring at the end of ventricular systole. It would seem likely, therefore, that the pulsatile flow in the dog's pulmonary veins is determined in part by the forward transmission of the wave from the pulmonary artery and in part by the movements of the left ventricle and the mitral valve.

There can be no doubt that ultimately the intermittency of the outflow from the pulmonary circulation across the mitral valve is imposed by the action of the left ventricle just as the intermittency of the inflow across the pulmonary valve is imposed by the action of the right ventricle, and that these two pulsatile phenomenon are 180° out of phase. The mechanical activity of the heart may also have less direct effects on the wave-forms in the pulmonary circulation, for instance by a reduction of intrathoracic pressure during systole (p. 88). In addition, one needs to bear in mind the quite wide dispersion of lengths of transit pathways in the pulmonary circulation. Thus, a single wave in the pulmonary artery will be transmitted along pathways of different length which will not arrive synchronously in the pulmonary veins. This will have the effect of broadening the venous pulse wave and diminishing its amplitude.

Energy and Power

The energy per unit volume of flowing blood exists in three forms: pressure energy, kinetic energy and gravitational energy. This is the principle of Bernoulli (p. 132):

$$\mathrm{P} + \frac{\rho v^2}{2} + \rho g h = \text{constant}$$

where P is the lateral pressure, ρ is the density of the blood, v is the velocity, g is the acceleration due to gravity and h is the depth of the blood from its highest point. In the following discussion we shall ignore the effects of gravity, the last term of the above equation.

Power is the rate of change of energy so that for a steady rate of blood flow, $\dot{\mathrm{Q}}$, the power is

$$\dot{\mathrm{W}} = \mathrm{P}\dot{\mathrm{Q}} + \frac{\rho v^2}{2}\dot{\mathrm{Q}}$$

the two components representing 'pressure power' and 'kinetic power', respectively. Since $v = \dot{\mathrm{Q}}/\mathrm{A}$, where A is the cross-sectional area of a vessel,

$$\dot{\mathrm{W}} = \mathrm{P}\dot{\mathrm{Q}} + \rho\dot{\mathrm{Q}}^3/2\mathrm{A}^2$$

assuming A to be constant.

Considerations of energy and power are of importance with respect to the movement of blood out of the right ventricle into the pulmonary trunk and with

Table 10.1 Power (mW) associated with pulmonary blood flow in man. Data from Milnor.[3]

	Input	Output	Per cent dissipated
Pressure power			
Constant terms	200	93	54
Oscillatory terms	88	4	95
Kinetic power			
Constant terms	1	1	0
Oscillatory terms	20	5	75
Total power			
Constant terms	201	94	53
Oscillatory terms	108	9	92

respect to the frictional losses which occur during the passage of blood through the pulmonary circulation.

Where flow and pressure are constant the calculation of power presents no difficulty. Where they are changing, as in pulsatile flow, the use of mean values for pressure and flow leads to inaccuracies similar to those discussed for resistance (p. 132). It has, for instance, been customary to calculate the power output of the right ventricle (right ventricular work) by multiplying the mean pulmonary arterial pressure by the mean pulmonary blood flow. Such a calculation not only provides a poor estimate of the pressure power output of the ventricle owing to the inappropriateness of using mean values; it also ignores the kinetic power involved.

In the case of pulsatile blood flow, both pressure and flow can be analysed in terms of a constant term and an oscillatory term. It follows that there will be separate values for pressure power and kinetic power both with respect to the constant term and with respect to the oscillatory term.

Milnor and his colleagues[32] have applied these analytical techniques to the calculation of the hydraulic power associated with pulmonary arterial and venous flow. The former gives an indication of the power output of the right ventricle. The difference between arterial and venous power gives an indication of the rate of loss of energy during the passage of blood through the lungs. Values for the human pulmonary circulation given by Milnor[3] are shown in Table 10.1. Kinetic power is confined mostly to the oscillatory terms and represents only a small fraction of total power either in the pulmonary arteries or pulmonary veins. About one third of the pressure power is associated with the oscillatory motion of the blood at the input while at the output the oscillatory terms account for about 5 per cent. Sixty seven per cent of the total power is dissipated during the passage of blood through the lungs, losses from oscillatory terms being considerably higher than those from the constant terms.

Conceptual Models of Pulsatile Flow

Since the physical properties of the pulmonary circulation are highly complex, simplified models are necessary to aid the understanding of its function. The simplest form of model is that of the pure resistance (Chap. 9). The concept still has considerable practical value and is technically undemanding. Physiologically, it is most closely related to the properties of the peripheral part of the circulation. Nevertheless, it fails completely to take account of pulsatile events which are chiefly a function of the larger vessels.

The need to do so was early seen by the Rev. Stephen Hales (1677–1761) who was the first to appreciate that the large arterial vessels acted as an elastic store for blood during systole, releasing the stored blood during diastole. In this way the pulsatile expulsion of blood from the ventricle was converted to a continuous flow of blood through the tissues. He likened this function to the air-filled compression chamber in early fire-engines which was used to create a steady stream of water from a pulsatile pump. In translation into German this became the 'Windkessel', the theory of which was developed largely by Otto Frank and his School.[33]

The model explains the general shape of the pressure wave in the pulmonary artery—a rapid rise as blood is forced into the 'Windkessel' followed by an exponential fall as the blood escapes through the peripheral resistance at a rate dependent on arterial pressure. It can be represented as a resistance and a capacitance in parallel in an electrical circuit or as a spring and dash-pot in parallel in a mechanical analogue. The equation which describes this relation is

$$\text{Flow} = \frac{\text{rate of change of pressure}}{\text{capacity}} + \frac{\text{pressure}}{\text{resistance}}$$

The limitations of the Windkessel concept are that it ignores the effects of inertia and it treats capacity and resistance as one composite ('lumped') system. In fact inertia has an important influence on the pulsatile motion of blood in large vessels while the system is anatomically a complex one through which the pulse waves take a finite time to travel.

The work of Womersley, McDonald and Taylor, summarized in McDonald's monograph[34] represented an important conceptual advance. Linear equations were derived which described the motion of pulse waves along a blood vessel in which the properties of inertia, capacity and resistance were distributed throughout its length, analogous to electrical transmission lines. In such a model the pulse waves take a finite time to travel and the effects of reflection and standing waves can be taken into account.

There have been many elaborations of these concepts, taking into account some of the many non-linear and non-homogenous properties of the pulmonary vascular system.[23,35] Such endeavour has proved most valuable in aiding physiological understanding. Models are necessarily simplifications. Always less complex than the truth, a new model needs to be a little more complex than our previous understanding. In this way the last decade has achieved a considerable exploration of new and interesting ground. It is only surprising that the physiological concepts and analytical techniques now established have not been applied to any substantial degree to the study of the pulmonary circulation in disease where considerable variations in the properties of pulsatile flow are to be found.

REFERENCES

1. Bergel, D. H. (ed.) (1972) *Cardiovascular Fluid Dynamics*. Academic Press.
2. Gessner, U. (1972) In *Cardiovascular Fluid Dynamics*, ed. Bergel, D. H. Vol. 1, p. 315. Academic Press.
3. Milnor, W. R. (1972) In *Cardiovascular Fluid Dynamics*, ed. Berger, D. H. Vol. 2, p. 299. Academic Press.
4. Milnor, W. R., Conti, C. R., Lewis, K. B. & O'Rourke, M. F. (1969) *Circulat. Res.*, **25**, 637.
5. Caro, C. G. & McDonald, D. A. (1961) *J. Physiol.*, **157**, 426.
6. Patel, D. J., de Freitas, F. M. & Fry, D. L. (1963) *J. Appl. Physiol.*, **18**, 134.
7. Bergel, D. H. & Milnor, W. R. (1965) *Circulat. Res.*, **16**, 401.
8. Young, T. (1808) *Phil. Trans.*, **98**, 164.
9. Moens, A. I. (1878) *Die Pulskurve*. Leiden.
10. Korteweg, D. J. (1878) *Am. Phys. Chem. Ser.* 3, **5**, 525.
11. Bramwell, J. C. & Hill, A. V. (1922) *Proc. Roy. Soc. (B)*, **93**, 298.
12. Fleishner, F. G., Romano, F. J. & Luisada, A. A. (1948) *Proc. Soc. Exp. Biol. (N.Y.)*, **67**, 535.
13. Caro, C. G. & Harrison, G. K. (1962) *Clin. Sci.*, **23**, 317.
14. McDonald, D. A. (1968) *J. Appl. Physiol.*, **24**, 73.
15. Bergel, D. H. (1964) *Pulsatile Blood Flow*, ed. Attinger, E. O. McGraw-Hill.
16. Caro, C. G. & Saffman, P. G. (1965) *J. Physiol.*, **178**, 193.
17. Kaplan, A. S. & Kimbel, P. (1970) *J. Appl. Physiol.*, **28**, 793.
18. Cumming, G., Harding, L. K., Horsfield, K., Prowse, K., Singhal, S. S. & Woldenberg, M. (1970) *NATO Advisory Group for Aerospace Research and Development*. Conference Proceedings, **No. 65**, 23.
19. Reuben, S. R. (1970) *Circulat. Res.*, **27**, 523.
20. Attinger, E. O. (1963) *Circulat. Res.*, **12**, 623.
21. Caro, C. G., Harrison, G. K. & Mognoni, P. (1967) *Cardiovasc. Res.*, **1**, 91.
22. Caro, C. G., Bergel, D. H. & Seed, W. A. (1967) *Circulat. Res.*, **20**, 185.
23. Wiener, F., Morkin, E., Skalak, R. & Fishman, A. P. (1966) *Circulat. Res.*, **19**, 834.
24. Pinkerson, A. L. (1967) *Amer. J. Physiol.*, **213**, 450.
25. Szidon, J. P., Ingram, R. H. & Fishman, A. P. (1968) *Amer. J. Physiol.*, **214**, 10.
26. Karatzas, N. B., Noble, M. I. M., Saunders, K. B. & McIlroy, M. B. (1970) *Circulat. Res.*, **27**, 1.
27. Reuben, S. R., Swadling, J. P., Gersh, B. J. & Lee, G. de J. (1971) *Cardiovasc. Res.*, **5**, 1.
28. Wasserman, K., Butler, J. & Van Kessel, A. (1966) *J. Appl. Physiol.*, **21**, 890.
29. Maloney, J. E., Bergel, D. H., Glazier, J. B., Hughes, J. M. B. & West, J. B. (1968) *Circulat. Res.*, **23**, 11.
30. Morkin, E., Collins, J. A., Goldman, H. S. & Fishman, A. P. (1965) *J. Appl. Physiol.*, **20**, 1118.
31. Morgan, B. C., Dillard, D. H. & Guntheroth, W. G. (1966) *J. Appl. Physiol.*, **21**, 1276.
32. Milnor, W. R., Bergel, D. H. & Bargainer, J. D. (1966) *Circulat. Res.*, **19**, 467.
33. Frank, O. (1899) *Z. Biol.*, **37**, 483.
34. McDonald, D. A. (1960) *Blood Flow in Arteries*. Arnold.
35. Skalak, R., Wiener, F., Morkin, E. & Fishman, A. P. (1966) *Phys. Med. Biol.*, **11**, 437.

11. Normal Variations in Pressure and Flow

Age

The pulmonary blood flow at rest shows a gradual decline from childhood to old age. The average pulmonary blood flow was 4·3 l · min^{-1}/m^2 BSA in a group of ten normal children with an average age of twelve years.[1] Measurements of the cardiac output by the dye-dilution method in a large group of normal people[2] gave an average value of 3·7 l · min^{-1}/m^2 BSA in the early twenties and 2·4 l · min^{-1}/m^2 BSA in the early eighties, the values for the intermediate age groups falling in order between these two figures. There is a wide variation within any age group.

From a series of publications from Karolinska Sjukhuset one may choose a group of studies of 22 normal subjects aged 16–28 (Refs. 3 and 4) and compare this with a group of studies on 16 normal subjects aged 61–83 (Refs. 5 and 6). The details are given in Table 11.1 from which it is clear that in the elderly subjects there is a decrease in the pulmonary blood flow, an increase in the mean pulmonary arterial pressure and an increase in the pulmonary arterial resistance. No significant increase occurred in the wedge pressure. The changes in resistance are small and of physiological rather than pathological interest.

The pulmonary capillary volume has been found to decrease progressively with age.[7]

Anxiety

The effects of anxiety on pulmonary haemodynamics have been recognized since the early years of cardiac catheterization.[8] They are similar to the effects produced by small doses of adrenaline. The pulse rate rises. There is an increase in ventilation and in the rate of uptake of oxygen by the lungs. The increase in ventilation also causes an increased loss of carbon dioxide from the lungs and the respiratory quotient usually rises while the arterial P_{CO_2} decreases. The cardiac output increases proportionately more than the increase in oxygen uptake so that the oxygen saturation of the mixed venous blood becomes raised. The pressure in the pulmonary

Table 11.1 Pulmonary haemodynamics in young and elderly normal subjects. Data from Holmgren *et al.*,[3] Bevegard *et al.*,[4] Granath *et al.*,[5] and Granath and Strandell.[6]

Age (years)	16–28	61–83	
No. of subjects	22	16	*P*
Pulmonary blood flow l · min^{-1}	7·60 ± 1·24	5·59 ± 0·96	< 0·001
Mean pulmonary arterial pressure (mmHg)	13·1 ± 3·1	15·9 ± 2·4	< 0·01
Mean wedge pressure (mmHg)	8·3 ± 2·2	9·4 ± 2·3	> 0·05
Pulmonary arterial resistance ($\Delta P/\dot{Q}$)	0·67 ± 0·36	1·20 ± 0·31	< 0·001

artery becomes elevated and this may be sufficient in a normal person to cause an erroneous diagnosis of pathological pulmonary hypertension to be made. In this area of overlap between the normal and abnormal ranges it is, however, possible for mistakes to be made in the opposite direction. The elevation of the pulmonary arterial pressure due to anxiety is often greater than would be expected from the degree of increase in the pulmonary blood flow. This is particularly evident in patients with acquired heart disease in whom the cardiac output may be fixed, yet the pulmonary arterial pressure can vary according to the state of composure.

Since cardiac catheterization is itself an investigation which is likely to cause anxiety, an awareness of these effects is of great importance in the interpretation of data. It is usual for the pulmonary blood flow and pulmonary arterial pressure to fall gradually during the period of one or two hours over which observations are being made, although it is uncertain whether this is entirely due to decreasing anxiety. In physiological investigations, such systematic changes in the measurement during the period of study make it important, as far as possible, to alternate the sequence of experimental and control observations.

The effects of anxiety are more apparent at rest than during exercise. Thus, in an anxious subject, there may even be a fall in the cardiac output and pulmonary arterial pressure during exercise.

Recently Arvidsson and his colleagues[9] have carried out an interesting investigation of the effects of anxiety induced during hypnosis. In their studies, contrary to what general experience would suggest, there was no demonstrable effect of suggested anxiety on the cardiac output or pulmonary vascular pressures. They note, however, that their subjects did not regard the stimulus as a strong one.

Sleep

Halmágyi *et al.*[10] have studied the effect of sleep on the pulmonary circulation in three patients with mitral stenosis and three with left ventricular failure. In both groups, there was a fall in the systolic pressure in the pulmonary artery (74 to 53 mmHg and 50 to 32 mmHg in respective groups) while the cardiac output did not change substantially. It seems unlikely that such a fall in the pulmonary arterial pressure could be entirely accounted for by a fall in left atrial pressure, and the inference is that a dilatation of the pulmonary vessels occurred during sleep. Hypnosis[9] had no effect on the cardiac output or pulmonary vascular pressures.

Digestion

Lammerant[11] found that digestion increased the pulmonary blood flow from an average of $7{\cdot}1\ \mathrm{l \cdot min^{-1}}$ to an average of $9{\cdot}0\ \mathrm{l \cdot min^{-1}}$. At the same time the pulmonary blood volume measured by a praecordial counter (p. 108) fell from an average value of 1240 ml to 959 ml. The fall in pulmonary blood volume was attributed to a redistribution of the total volume of blood consequent on the increase in splanchnic blood volume which accompanies digestion.

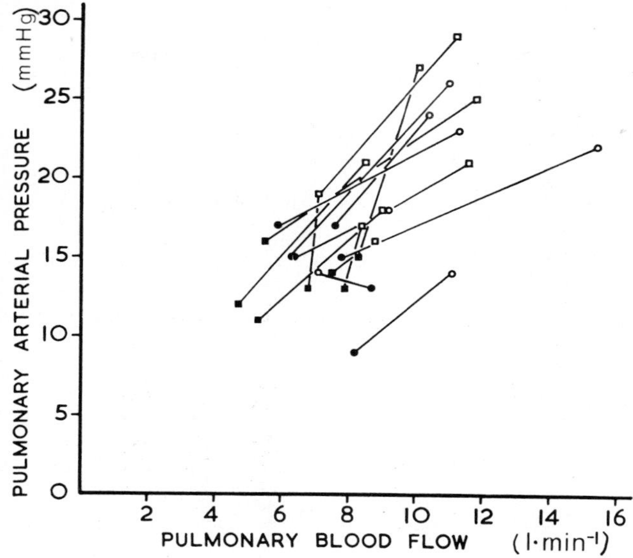

Fig. 11.1 The relation between the pulmonary arterial pressure and the pulmonary blood flow at rest and on exercise in 14 normal adults. Squares represent data from Dexter *et al.*[17]; circles are personal data; solid squares and circles are resting measurements; open squares and circles are measurements taken on exercise. Lines join observations made on an individual subject.

Temperature

Burch and Hyman[12] have studied the effect of a hot humid environment on the human circulation. In three normal subjects such an environment raised the average rectal temperature from 94·5° to 97·1°F. The pulse rate rose from 73 to 97 beats per minute. The pulmonary blood flow increased on the average from 5·0 to 20·2 $\mathrm{l \cdot min^{-1}}$ and the right ventricular systolic pressure rose from 23 to 38 mmHg.

Exercise

In a normal person, exercise increases the cardiac output and consequently the pulmonary blood flow. This is accompanied by an increase in the pulmonary arterial pressure, the magnitude of which depends very roughly on the degree of exertion (Fig. 11.1). In most studies a stationary bicycle has been used for the purpose of exercise and there is some elevation of the pulmonary arterial pressure immediately the feet are placed on the pedals[13] (Fig. 11.2) which may be due to a displacement of blood from the legs. Immediately exercise begins, the pressure rises further.[14] If the degree of exercise is constant, the pressure in the pulmonary artery remains high until about the seventh minute.[13] After this, there is a gradual decline in the level of the pressure until, by the end of a period of exercise lasting thirty minutes,

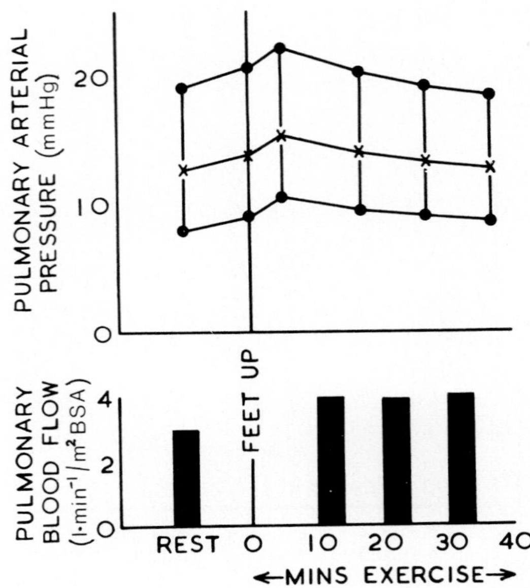

Fig. 11.2 The effect of a prolonged bicycling exercise in the recumbent position in a normal adult. The pulmonary arterial pressure increases when the feet are elevated and placed on the pedals. It rises still further at the beginning of the exercise but returns gradually to its resting level while exercise is continued. Data from Sancetta and Rakita.[13]

it may be lower than its initial resting level (Fig. 11.2). The pulmonary blood flow remains constant throughout this time.[13] The influence of the duration of exercise on the pulmonary arterial pressure may explain some of the differences which have been reported.[15–19] The observations collected in Figure 11.1 are restricted to the first five minutes of exercise. It will be seen that the mean pulmonary arterial pressure rose from an average of 13·9 to 20·9 mmHg, while the pulmonary blood flow rose from an average of 6·9 to 10·1 $l \cdot min^{-1}$.

Although an early report[16] suggested that the pulmonary arterial pressure did not rise during exercise in the upright posture, there is now evidence from several groups of workers that an increase in pulmonary arterial pressure occurs during exercise in both the upright and recumbent postures.[4,20,21]

Part of the rise in pulmonary arterial pressure which accompanies exercise in the recumbent position can be accounted for by an increase in wedge pressure (Fig. 11.3). The degree of elevation of the wedge pressure is variable. Usually the increase in wedge pressure is not more than 4 to 5 mmHg. We have, however, observed wedge pressures up to 23 mmHg in normal subjects. Bevegård and his colleagues[22] found wedge pressures up to 25 mmHg during severe exercise in athletes, while Granath and his colleagues[5,6] observed wedge pressures frequently over 30 mmHg in elderly normal subjects during exercise.

The difference between the mean pressure in the pulmonary artery and the mean wedge pressure (ΔP) tends to increase during exercise. In the observations shown in Figure 11.4, the average pulmonary blood flow rose from 6·9 $l \cdot min^{-1}$ to 10·1 $l \cdot min^{-1}$ during exercise while the average ΔP rose from 5·2 to 8·9 mmHg. Since the increase in ΔP was proportionately greater than the increase in flow, the pulmonary vascular resistance increased during exercise. The difference was not, however, statistically significant. Analysing the data from Karolinska Sjukhuset on the other hand shows changes in the opposite direction[3-6] the resistance falling an average of 27 per cent during exercise in 29 normal subjects ($P < 0{\cdot}001$).

The effect of exercise on the relation between pressure and flow in the normal human pulmonary circulation has been studied by the technique of unilateral occlusion of the pulmonary artery[23] described on page 129. Such a study is illustrated in Figure 11.5. The normal relation between pressure and flow is first established at rest by studying the effects of doubling the flow through the left lung during occlusion of the right pulmonary artery. The observations made during exercise are seen to fall either on this relation or on a rectilinear extension of it. Thus there is no evidence of a change in pulmonary vascular resistance in these studies.

Evidence on the change in pulmonary blood volume during exercise is conflicting. The central blood volume, measured by the conventional dye-dilution technique, has been found to increase.[24] The lack of anatomical precision of this measurement

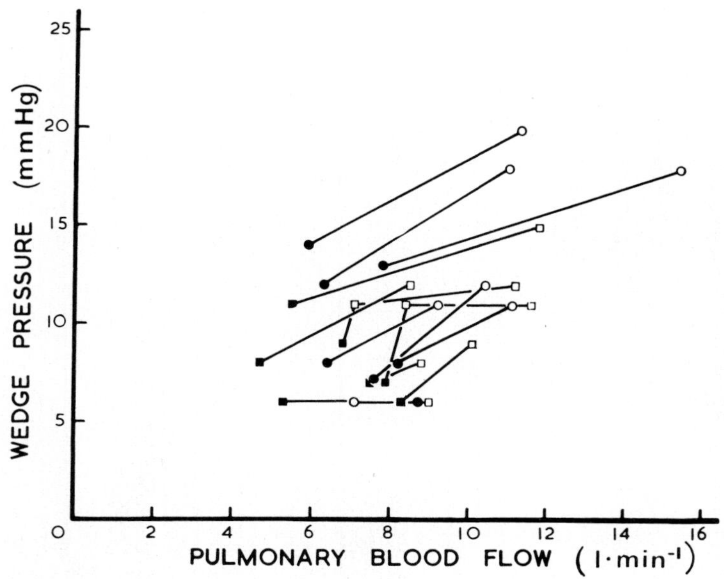

Fig. 11.3 The relation between the wedge pressure and the pulmonary blood flow at rest and on exercise in 14 normal adults. Symbols as in legend to Fig. 11.1.

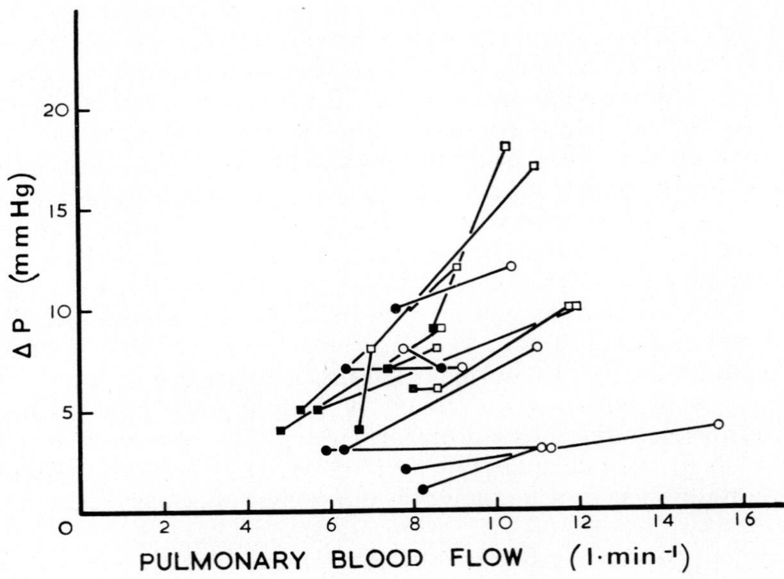

Fig. 11.4 The relation between ΔP and the pulmonary blood flow at rest and on exercise in 14 normal adults. Symbols as in legend to Fig. 11.1.

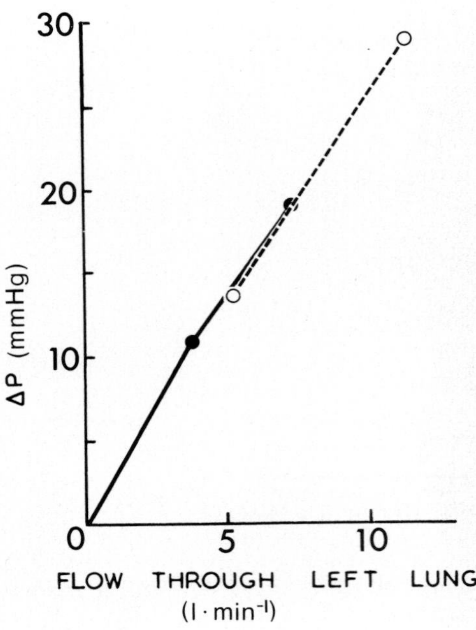

Fig. 11.5 The relation between pressure and flow in the pulmonary circulation of a normal human subject during rest and exercise studied with and without occlusion of the right pulmonary artery.[23] Resting values, ●—●; exercise values ○ - - - ○.

Table 11.2 The effect of pregnancy on the pressures and flow in the pulmonary circulation. Data from Bader *et al.*[65] The figures given are averages, the number of patients studied on each occasion being shown in parentheses.

Weeks of pregnancy	Pulmonary blood flow $l \cdot min^{-1}/m^2$ BSA	Mean pulmonary arterial pressure mmHg	Wedge pressure mmHg
14–24	4·09 (13)	11·2 (14)	5 (2)
25–27	4·26 (15)	11·4 (16)	5 (6)
28–30	3·93 (18)	13·0 (17)	5 (5)
31–35	3·60 (15)	11·8 (17)	6 (4)
36–40	3·44 (20)	11·8 (19)	5 (7)

has been discussed in Chapter 8. During exercise a special inaccuracy may arise in the method.[11] The mean time of arrival of dye to the brachial artery at the elbow may be delayed because of the diminution in the flow of blood through the arms which accompanies exercise of the legs.[25] This will have the effect of increasing the quantity of systemic arterial blood included in the central blood volume. Earlier studies of the pulmonary blood volume by means of praecordial counting (p. 108) showed a 16 per cent fall during exercise.[11] Recent studies with more refined techniques have shown a 9 per cent rise.[26] Measurements of the pulmonary capillary volume by the carbon monoxide method have also shown an increase (Chap. 42, p. 646).

Pregnancy

The pulmonary blood flow is increased early in pregnancy. It reaches its maximum at the 25th to 27th weeks and falls towards the normal by the 31st to 35th weeks (Table 11.2). The pulmonary arterial and wedge pressures appear to be a little low throughout pregnancy. The effect of exercise on the pressures and flow in the pulmonary circulation is normal.

The effects of pregnancy on the pulmonary circulation may be compared with those which accompany any sustained increase in the cardiac output. Among the common causes of such a state of affairs are anaemia and thyrotoxicosis. The pressures in the pulmonary circulation are normal in anaemic patients.[27] The average resting pulmonary arterial pressure is slightly higher than normal in thyrotoxic patients.[27] The reason for this may lie in the anxiety which usually accompanies thyrotoxicosis and it is noteworthy that, during exercise, the pulmonary arterial pressure is not higher than would normally be expected.

Alterations in the Pulmonary Blood Volume by Mechanical Means

The distribution of the blood volume throughout the circulation is determined by the pressure–volume characteristics of each individual section and the transmural pressures existing in that section. A shift of the blood volume from one section to another will occur if their distensibility characteristics are changed. Thus, in general, one may regard the distribution of blood volume between the pulmonary and systemic circuits as being controlled by the relative distensibilities of the two circuits. If, for instance, the distensibility of the systemic circuit were decreased, one would expect a transfer of blood to occur from the systemic into the pulmonary circuit.

Such a decrease in distensibility of the systemic circuit may be caused by the inflation of an antigravity suit and studies on normal people have shown that this is followed by an increase in the 'central' blood volume[28] and the pulmonary blood volume as judged by the external counting of radioactivity from injected ^{131}I-albumin (Ref. 29) (see p. 113). The latter technique has also shown an increase in the pulmonary blood volume during immersion in water.

Manoeuvres which cause blood to be retained in the systemic circuit have the opposite effect. The application of constricting cuffs to the limbs for the purpose of causing venous pooling has been shown, for instance, to decrease the 'central' blood volume[28] and pulmonary blood volume[30] and reduce the radioactivity recorded over the chest after the intravenous injection of ^{131}I-albumin (Ref. 31). Drugs such as the hexamethonium compounds, which also cause pooling of blood in the systemic circuit, will have a similar effect (Chap. 13, p. 191).

The infusion of large volumes of dextran has been shown to cause an increase in the 'central' blood volume[32] and in the pulmonary blood volume measured by radiocardiography.[33] The 'central' blood volume was also found to increase following the infusion of saline.[34] Measurements of the pulmonary blood volume by a dye-dilution method with simultaneous sampling from the pulmonary artery and left atrium,[30] on the other hand, failed to show any increase after the infusion of polyvinylpyrrolidine solution. The use of a similar method for the pulmonary blood volume[35] was also reported as showing no significant increase following the infusion of dextran.

Even within the pulmonary circulation one would expect the distribution of an increased pulmonary blood volume to be determined by the relative distensibilities of the different sorts of vessels. The findings of large changes in the 'central' blood volume[32] and relatively small changes in the more closely defined pulmonary blood volume[30,35] are, therefore, not necessarily inconsistent since the extrapulmonary portion of the 'central' blood volume may be more distensible than the pulmonary portion. A large portion of the 'central' blood volume, for instance, is contributed by the heart, the volume of which has been shown to increase during the inflation of an antigravity suit.[29] Owing to the Laplace law (p. 52) the smallest vessels could well be the least distensible and they, in any case, contribute least to the volume.

The effects on the pulmonary capillary volume of measures designed to increase the pulmonary blood volume have not been consistent. Measurements of DL_{CO} (see p. 637) have shown a slight increase following the infusion of albumin[8] or the application of an antigravity suit.[34] On the other hand, the only study separately to measure the capillary volume gave inconsistent results after the application of an antigravity suit.[36] In one study[34] $D_{L_{CO}}$ was found to increase 18 per cent when the subjects were seated and only 10 per cent when they were lying. The difference might be due to the apical blood vessels being under-filled under normal conditions in the upright posture which would make them more able to expand to accommodate the transfer of blood. In fact, in a similar experiment in which normal people were immersed in water up to the neck, there was an increase in the apical blood flow and decrease in the basal blood flow so that the distribution of flow became even.[37] It should be remembered that percentage changes in $D_{L_{CO}}$ cannot be equated directly with percentage changes in capillary volume (see p. 639).

Infusions of large volumes of dextran,[32,33,35,36,38] saline[34] or polyvinylpyrrolidine[30] cause an increase in both the pulmonary arterial and the left atrial or wedge pressures. Despite this, the pulmonary arteriolar resistance does not greatly change.[30,33,38] Fleming and Bloom,[38] for instance, noted an increase of 266 per cent in the wedge pressure and an increase of 4 per cent in resistance. Giuntini and his colleagues[33] found an increase of 467 per cent in the wedge pressure and a decrease of 12 per cent in the resistance. de Freitas and his colleagues[30] found an increase of 161 per cent in the wedge pressure and an increase of 17 per cent in the resistance. All these studies were carried out in the recumbent position so that there was little scope for redistribution of blood and the opening up of unperfused vessels. It would seem, therefore, that the portion of the pulmonary vasculature which is the chief site of resistance is extremely indistensible.

Posture

The pulmonary blood flow is less in the upright than in the horizontal position.[28,34,39–42] The change from lying to standing is accompanied by a fall of about one third in the cardiac output.[39] Lesser degrees of tilting from the horizontal position are accompanied by a less substantial change,[28,40,41] and the average difference between lying flat in bed and being propped up on pillows at an angle of 70° is only about $0{\cdot}4\ l \cdot min^{-1}$ (Ref. 42).

The volume of blood in the lungs decreases on assuming the upright position.[28,31,41,43] The plethysmographic technique indicated an average fall of 27 per cent in the pulmonary blood volume on standing.[43] This agrees closely with the figure of 28 per cent obtained by studying the changes in radioactivity of the lungs which occurred on standing after the blood stream had been labelled with a radioactive material.[31] The central blood volume (superior vena cava to brachial artery) fell[28] from 2063 to 1598 ml on tilting 60°. The lungs are less opaque to X-rays on standing[43] and the pulmonary capillary volume decreases (Chap. 42, p. 644). The fall in pulmonary blood volume is presumably due to a transfer of blood to the more dependent parts of the systemic circulation.

There are difficulties in comparing the pressures in the pulmonary circulation with the subject in two different positions. With the low intravascular pressures encountered in the lungs, variations in the position of the zero reference point can cause relatively large alterations in the measurements. On standing, the reference point has to be moved with the chest and one cannot be certain how comparable it is in the two positions. With these reservations, it appears that the upright position is accompanied by a slight fall in the pulmonary arterial pressure in normal people [41,42] but a more substantial fall in patients with emphysema or mitral stenosis.[42] In normal subjects a slight fall in wedge pressure has also been observed.[41] The pulmonary vascular resistance appears to increase slightly,[41] an observation which may be explained by the diminution in volume and cross-sectional area of the blood vessels of the lungs. As would be expected, tilting to an angle of 35° with the head down causes an elevation of the pulmonary arterial pressure.[44] This was found to be associated with a decrease in pulmonary arterial resistance.

The important influence of posture on the distribution of pulmonary blood flow is discussed in Chapter 7, page 99.

Effects of Respiratory Movements

Studies on Isolated Lungs

The state of inflation of the lung modifies the size and disposition of the pulmonary blood vessels in a complex way according to their size and their relation to the alveoli. The experiments of Macklin[45] and those of Riley[46] and Howell[47] and their colleagues on isolated lungs have distinguished between the small vessels in proximity to the alveoli on the one hand and the larger arterial and venous vessels on the other. This distinction has been achieved by filling the arteries or veins with latex[45] or kerosene[47] which will not enter vessels of capillary size. When the arterial or venous trees are filled in this fashion it is found that their volume increases with inflation of the lung. The increased volume will occur whether the vascular pressure is maintained constant with reference to the alveolar pressure or with reference to the pressure at the surface of the lung. Presumably the larger arterial and venous vessels are dilated and elongated by the fibrous tissue which tethers them in place within the lung.

Those vessels which are too small to be filled with kerosene behave differently during inflation. If the vascular pressure is initially higher than alveolar pressure, but is maintained constant relative to the pressure at the surface of the lung, the effect of inflation is to diminish their volume.[47] This occurs approximately when the absolute magnitude of the intravascular pressure becomes less than that of the alveolar pressure and it seems reasonable to conclude that the effect is due to compression of the capillaries and possibly other small vessels which are in close relation to the alveoli. The relation between the gas pressure in the alveoli and the blood pressure in the capillaries will be influenced not only by the mechanical properties and disposition of the various structures concerned but also by the forces of surface tension in the fluid lining the alveoli which pull on the alveolar wall tending to diminish alveolar volume and the alveolar–capillary pressure difference.[48]

There have been many studies of the effects of inflation on the resistance to the flow of blood through isolated lungs. Their interpretation is discussed by Burton and Patel.[49] When the difference between the pulmonary arterial pressure and the pulmonary venous pressure is used to calculate the pulmonary vascular resistance, the effects of inflation depend greatly on whether the vascular pressures are held constant with respect to alveolar pressure or with respect to the pressure at the surface of the lung.[50] If the vascular pressures are held constant relative to the pressure at the surface of the lung, inflation causes a substantial increase in vascular resistance. This can be explained by compression of the capillaries and small vessels which lie in the vicinity of the alveoli. If, on the other hand, the vascular pressures are held constant relative to alveolar pressure, such compression cannot occur and the pulmonary vascular resistance shows a slight fall followed by a slight rise.[50] The initial fall in resistance may arise from a dilatation of the larger arteries and veins which, as has been discussed above, are known to increase in volume. Contortion of larger blood vessels may also occur when the lungs are deflated and this could contribute to the increased vascular resistance at this lung volume. The increase in the pulmonary vascular resistance observed at a large lung volume is not so readily explained.

In the above discussion, the effects of inflation of isolated lungs on the pulmonary vascular resistance have been described according to whether the vascular pressures are held constant with respect to the alveolar pressure or with respect to the pressure at the surface of the lung. Whether such isolated lungs are inflated by increasing the alveolar pressure ('positive pressure') or by decreasing the pressure on the visceral pleural surface ('negative pressure') is immaterial. The changes in atmospheric pressure from day-to-day (or place-to-place) may well exceed those changes which are induced in such experiments. Thus a 'positive pressure' inflation on a rainy day (or in Denver) may be associated with the same absolute alveolar pressure and lung surface pressure as a 'negative pressure' inflation on a fine day (or in London).

Studies in the Living Body

In the living body the pulmonary trunk and its main branches and the left atrium and its main venous tributaries lie outside the lungs but within the thoracic cage. It may be supposed, therefore, that the pressure of the blood contained within these structures would be subjected to variations during ventilation similar to those observed in the intrapleural space. In this way, the pulmonary intravascular pressures under normal conditions would tend to be held constant with respect to the intrapleural pressure. During the ventilatory cycle the pulmonary intravascular pressures are in fact observed to undergo changes similar in nature to those found in the intrapleural space, the maximum pressure occurring during expiration. On the other hand, they do not follow completely the changes which occur in intrapleural pressure. In man, the difference between the pulmonary arterial pressure and the intrapleural or oesophageal pressures increases during inspiration and decreases during expiration.[51,52] This effect probably arises from the elastic properties of the walls of the extrapulmonary portions of the pulmonary circulation. As discussed in Chapter 4, p. 44, the relation between length and tension in vessel walls is curvilinear and such that with increasing distension the vessels became progressively less distensible. This means that the transmural pressure increases as the vessel becomes distended. Under normal conditions it seems likely that the extrapulmonary portions of the pulmonary circulation are in a state of near-maximal distension, so that a decrease in the intrapleural pressure, such as occurs during inspiration, causes very little increase in their size and relatively little decrease in intravascular pressure. On the other hand, an increase in the intrapleural pressure, such as occurs during expiration, will more readily reduce the size of such vessels and will be more substantially transmitted to the pressure inside their lumens.

At the same time, fluctuations in the pulmonary arterial and venous pressures will tend to be minimized by movements of blood between the pulmonary and systemic circuits. Measurements of the pulmonary arterial and pulmonary venous blood flows in unanaesthetized dogs with closed chests and normal respiration[53,54] have shown a small increase in the pulmonary arterial flow during inspiration and a decrease during expiration. The pulmonary venous flow showed a similar variation, but delayed in time by approximately one heart beat.[55] There would thus be a small increase in the pulmonary blood volume during inspiration. In man, measurements with the body plethysmograph have been unable to demonstrate a variation of pulmonary capillary blood flow with respiration.[56] However, using blood-flow probes, Gabe and his colleagues[57] have shown that during deep respiratory movements inspiration is accompanied by an increase in pulmonary arterial flow and a decrease in aortic flow.

The physiological mechanisms which underlie such observations are complex. In the first place, the decrease of intrathoracic pressure with inspiration will distend the ventricles. This will have the effect of increasing the output of each ventricle to a degree which depends on its distensibility and its individual Starling relation. In addition the decreased intrathoracic pressure will have the effect of drawing in blood from the extrathoracic portion of the circulation into the intrathoracic portion. In the absence of a cardiac output such a movement would occur through the aorta as well as the venae cavae. In the presence of a cardiac output its effect will be to increase the flow through the venae cavae and diminish the flow through the aorta. The shift of blood between the extrathoracic and intrathoracic portions of the circulation is likely to involve the pulmonary circulation itself to only a limited extent. From the experiments on the effects of inflating isolated lungs discussed earlier (p. 164) one would expect some increase in pulmonary vascular volume. The delay between the increase in pulmonary arterial flow and the increase in pulmonary venous flow is presumably in part due to this uptake of blood and in part due to the transmission time for the passage of flow waves through the pulmonary circulation.

The effects of increasing the alveolar gas pressure on pulmonary haemodynamics have been studied in man by means of a pressure-breathing valve.[58] Such a study is not entirely comparable to one in which isolated lungs are inflated from the trachea. In the body, as discussed above, the pulmonary vascular pressures are not strictly related either to intrapleural or to alveolar pressure. In addition, the presence of the thoracic cage means that when the lung expands from an increase in alveolar pressure it pushes against the chest and increases the intrapleural

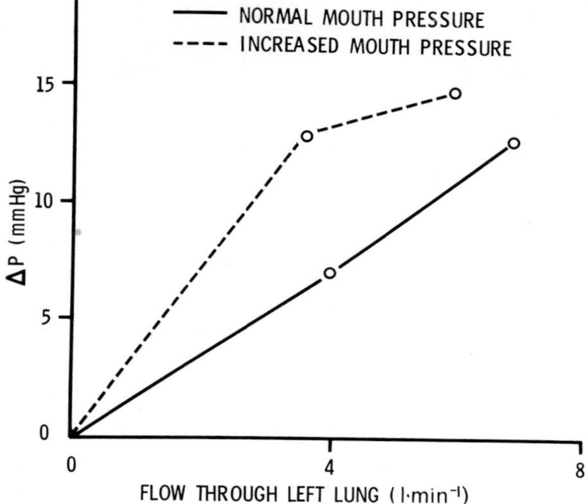

Fig. 11.6 The influence of alveolar pressure on the relation between pressure and flow in the normal recumbent human pulmonary circulation studied by the technique of unilateral pulmonary arterial occlusion (Chap. 9, p. 129). For description, see text.

pressure. This is especially so when the respiratory position is held constant.[58] In the studies carried out in this fashion, the relations between pressure and flow in the pulmonary circulation were observed by the technique of occluding the right main branch of the pulmonary artery with a balloon (p. 129). Figure 11.6 shows the results obtained in a normal subject. The effect of increasing the alveolar pressure is to increase the slope of the pressure–flow relation, indicating an increase in resistance. At the same time the relation itself changes from rectilinear to curvilinear. It seems likely that, under normal circumstances and in the recumbent position, the small vessels of the lung which are the chief site of resistance are in a position of virtually maximal calibre, so that their resistance is fixed. Those vessels which are susceptible to alveolar pressure become compressed when the alveolar pressure is increased. This causes an increase in their resistance and, at the same time, permits them to increase their calibre once more when, with an increased pulmonary blood flow, the transmural pressure returns toward the normal. The vessels which are presumed to be susceptible to alveolar pressure are not necessarily those which are normally the site of major resistance. There are reasons to believe, for instance, that the muscular pulmonary arteries are the chief site of resistance (Chap. 9, p. 128) whereas it would seem likely that the capillaries are most under the influence of alveolar pressure. On the other hand the wedge pressure changes with the left atrial pressure during pressure breathing[58] and even during the Valsalva manoeuvre[59] so that the increased resistance which is measured presumably lies on the arterial side of the capillaries.

The Valsalva Manoeuvre

The Valsalva manoeuvre causes an elevation of the pulmonary arterial and wedge pressures, although in each case this is a little less than the increase in the oesophageal pressure.[60] The pulmonary wedge pressure changes with the left atrial pressure.[58,59] The 'sluice' or 'waterfall' mechanism discussed on page 100 may apply regionally in the lung because of the influence of hydrostatic pressure, and may apply to the whole lung when removed from the body. When the lungs are within the body, however, the elevation of pulmonary venous pressure which accompanies a sudden increase in alveolar pressure will prevent this mechanism having a general application throughout the lung. The raised pulmonary venous pressure is part of the increase in 'static' pressure[61] which accompanies an increased alveolar pressure.[62] During the Valsalva the pulmonary blood volume diminishes[31] and so does the pulmonary capillary volume (Chap. 42, p. 644). After release of the breath-holding there is a rise in both the pulmonary arterial and the wedge pressures whether this is expressed with reference to the oesophageal pressure[60] or the atmospheric pressure. Some authors[63] have observed that this 'overshoot', like that which occurs in the systemic arteries, may be abolished by tetraethylammonium salts, the inference being that it is in part due to an increased tone in the pulmonary vessels. Others[60] have denied that this occurs. Our own observations have been that the overshoot in the pulmonary arterial and wedge pressures still occurs after a dose of guanethidine sufficient to abolish the overshoot in the brachial artery.[64]

REFERENCES

1. Brotmacher, L. & Felming, F. (1957) *Guy's Hosp. Rep.*, **106**, 268.
2. Brandfondbrenner, M., Landowne, M. & Shock, N. W. (1955) *Circulation*, **12**, 557.
3. Holmgren, A., Jonsson, B. & Sjöstrand, T. (1960) *Acta Physiol. Scand.*, **49**, 343.
4. Bevegård, S., Holmgren, A. & Jonsson, B. (1960) *Acta Physiol. Scand.*, **49**, 279.
5. Granath, A., Jonsson, B. & Strandell, T. (1964) *Acta Med. Scand.*, **176**, 425.
6. Granath, A. & Strandell, T. (1964) *Acta Med. Scand.*, **176**, 447.
7. Englert, M. (1967) *Le reseau capillaire chez l'homme*. Masson & Cie.
8. Hickam, J. B., Cargill, W. H. & Golden, A. (1948) *J. Clin. Invest.*, **27**, 290.
9. Arvidsson, T., Åström, H., Bevegård, S. & Jonsson, B. (1970) *Prog. Resp. Res.*, **5**, 365.
10. Halmágyi, D., Felkai, B., Iványi, J., Zsóstér, T., Tényi, M. & Szücs. Zs. (1953) *Brit. Heart J.*, **15**, 15.
11. Lammerant, J. (1957) *Le Volume Sanguin des Poumons chez l'Homme*. Bruxelles: Editions Arscia.
12. Burch, G. E. & Hyman, A. (1957) *J. Clin. Invest.*, **36**, 1138.
13. Sancetta, S. M. & Rakita, L. (1957) *J. Clin. Invest.*, **36**, 1138.
14. Slonim, N. D., Ravin, A., Balchum, O. J. & Dressler, S. H. (1954) *J. Clin. Invest.*, **33**, 1022.
15. Hickam, J. B. & Cargill, W. H. (1948) *J. Clin. Invest.*, **27**, 10.
16. Riley, R. L., Himmelstein, A., Motley, H. L., Weiner, H. M. & Cournand, A. (1948) *Amer. J. Physiol.*, **152**, 372.
17. Dexter, L., Whittenberger, J. L., Haynes, F. W., Goodale, W. T., Gorlin, R. & Sawyer, C. G. (1951) *J. Appl. Physiol.*, **3**, 439.
18. Donald, K. W., Bishop, J. M., Cumming, G. & Wade, O. L. (1955) *Clin. Sci.*, **14**, 37.
19. Reymond, C., Desbaillets, P., Baudraz, B. & Rivier, J. L. (1957) *Cardiologia*, **30**, 259.

20. Epstein, S. E., Beiser, G. D., Stampfer, M., Robinson, B. F. & Braunwald, E. (1967) *Circulation*, **35**, 1049.
21. Messin, R., Degre, S., Demaret, B., Vandermoten, P. & Denolin, H. (1970) *Prog. Resp. Res.*, **5**, 385.
22. Bevegård, S., Holmgren, A. & Jonsson, B. (1963) *Acta Physiol. Scand.*, **57**, 26.
23. Harris, P., Segel, N. & Bishop, J. M. (1968) *Cardiovasc. Res.* **1**, 73.
24. Braunwald, E. & Kelly, E. R. (1960) *J. Clin. Invest.*, **39**, 413.
25. Bishop, J. M., Donald, K. W., Taylor, S. H. & Wormald, P. N. (1957) *J. Physiol.*, **137**, 294.
26. Giuntini, C., Lewis, M. L., Sales Luis, A. & Harvey, R. M. (1963) *J. Clin. Invest.*, **42**, 1589.
27. Bishop, J. M., Donald, K. W. & Wade, O. L. (1955) *Clin. Sci.*, **14**, 329.
28. Weissler, A. M., Leonard, J. J. & Warner, J. V. (1957) *J. Clin. Invest.*, **36**, 1656.
29. Bondurant, S., Hickam, J. B. & Isley, J. K. (1957) *J. Clin. Invest.*, **36**, 59.
30. de Freitas, F. M., Faraco, E. Z., de Azevedo, D. F., Zaduchliver, J. & Lewin, I. (1965) *J. Clin. Invest.*, **44**, 366.
31. Weissler, A. M., McCraw, B. H. & Warren, J. V. (1959) *J. Appl. Physiol.*, **14**, 531.
32. Witham, A. C., Fleming, J. W. & Bloom, W. L. (1951) *J. Clin. Invest.*, **30**, 897.
33. Giuntini, C., Maseri, A. & Bianchi, R. (1966) *J. Clin. Invest.*, **45**, 1770.
34. Doyle, J. T., Wilson, J. S., Estes, E. H., Jn. & Warren, J. V. (1951) *J. Clin. Invest.*, **30**, 345.
35. Varnauskas, E., Korsgren, M., Hoak, P. & Přerovský, I. (1965) *Scand. J. Clin. Lab. Invest.* (Suppl. **86**), p. 81.
36. Schnabel, T. G., Jn., Eliasch, H., Thomasson, B. & Werkö, L. (1959) *J. Clin. Invest.*, **38**, 117.
37. Arborelius, M., Jn., Balldin, U. I., Lilja, B. & Lundgren, C. E. G. (1972) *Aerospace Med.*, **43**, 701.
38. Fleming, J. W. & Bloom, W. L. (1957) *J. Clin. Invest.*, **36**, 1233.
39. McMichael, J. & Sharpey-Schafer, E. P. (1954) *Brit. Heart J.*, **6**, 33.
40. Stead, E. A., Jn., Warren, J. V., Merrill, A. J. & Brannon, E. S. (1945) *J. Clin. Invest.*, **24**, 326.
41. Lagerlöf, H., Eliasch, H., Werkö, L. & Berglund, E. (1951) *Scand. J. Clin. Lab. Invest.*, **3**, 85.
42. Donald, K. W., Bishop, J. M., Cumming, G. & Wade, O. L. (1953) *Clin. Sci.*, **12**, 199.
43. Sjöstrand, T. (1952) *Acta Physiol. Scand.*, **26**, 312.
44. Sancetta, S. M. (1957) *J. Lab. Clin. Med.*, **49**, 684.
45. Macklin, C. C. (1946) *Rev. Can. Biol.*, **5**, 199.
46. Riley, R. L. (1959) In *Pulmonary Circulation*, ed. Adams, W. R. & Veith, I. New York: Grune & Stratton.
47. Howell, J. B. L., Permutt, S., Proctor, D. F. & Riley, R. L. (1961) *J. Appl. Physiol.*, **16**, 71.
48. Lloyd, T. C., Jn. & Wright, G. W. (1960) *J. Appl. Physiol.*, **15**, 241.
49. Burton, A. C. & Patel, D. J. (1958) *J. Appl. Physiol.*, **12**, 239.
50. Roos, A., Thomas, L. J., Jn., Nagel, E. L. & Prommas, D. C. (1961) *J. Appl. Physiol.*, **16**, 77.
51. Lauson, H. D., Bloomfield, R. A. & Cournand, A. (1946) *Amer. J. Med.*, **1**, 315.
52. Heiman, D. F., Rodbard, S., Shaffer, A. B. & Snider, G. L. (1957) *J. Appl. Physiol.*, **10**, 31.
53. Franklin, D. L., Van Cilters, R. L. & Rushmer, R. F. (1962) *Circulat. Res.*, **10**, 17.
54. Morkin, E., Collins, J. A., Goldman, H. S. & Fishman, A. P. (1965) *J. Appl. Physiol.*, **20**, 1118.
55. Morgan, B. C., Dillard, D. H. & Guntheroth, W. G. (1966) *J. Appl. Physiol.*, **21**, 1276.
56. Dubois, A. & Marshall, R. (1957) *J. Clin. Invest.*, **36**, 1566.
57. Gabe, I. T., Gault, J. H., Ross, J., Jn., Mason, D. T., Mills, C. J. Shillingford, J. P. & Braunwald, E. (1969) *Circulation*, **40**, 603.
58. Harris, P., Segel, N., Green, I. & Housley, E. (1968) *Cardiovasc. Res.*, **1**, 84.
59. Björk, V. D., Malmström, G. & Uggla, L. G. (1953) *Ann. Surg.*, **138**, 718.
60. Lee, G. De J., Mathews, M. B. & Sharpey-Schafer, E. P. (1954) *Brit. Heart J.*, **16**, 311.
61. Starr, I. (1940) *Amer. J. Med. Sci.*, **199**, 40.
62. Fenn, W. O., Otis, A. B., Rahn, H., Chadwick, L. E. & Hegnauer, A. H. (1947) *Amer. J. Physiol.*, **151**, 258.
63. Greene, D. G. & Bunnell, I. L. (1950) *J. Clin. Invest.*, **29**, 818.
64. Harris, P., Bishop, J. M. & Segel, N. Unpublished observations.
65. Bader, R. A., Bader, M. E., Rose, D. J. & Braunwald, E. (1955) *J. Clin. Invest.*, **34**, 1524.

12. Structure and Function of Vascular Smooth Muscle

Before turning to the pharmacology of the pulmonary circulation we have thought it helpful first to review recent knowledge concerning vascular smooth muscle and its control. An understanding of the mode of action of drugs on pulmonary blood vessels depends on a knowledge of the intimate mechanisms whereby they affect vascular smooth muscle. It is here, we believe, that the more fundamental advances in the field of pulmonary vascular pharmacology are likely to occur. Most of our knowledge of vascular smooth muscle derives from systemic blood vessels. Even so, it is still remarkably incomplete and it will become apparent that present knowledge of the structure and function of vascular smooth muscle in the pulmonary circulation is rudimentary.

The Structure of Vascular Smooth Muscle[1]

Vascular smooth muscle cells are elongated structures but with an irregularity of shape (Fig. 12.1). They commonly show a great variation in staining on electron microscopy with a division into light cells and dark cells (Figs 12.1 and 12.2). Their diameter is usually in the region of 2·5–5·0 μm. Their length varies greatly. In the aorta their length was found to be in the region of 90–130 μm, while in systemic arterioles it was 30–40 μm (Ref. 2). There is a central, elongated, ellipsoid nucleus with a double membranous envelope (Fig. 12.3). The cytoplasm shows varying numbers of myofilaments (Fig. 12.3) some of which are thick, corresponding to the thick myosin filaments of striated muscle, but most of which are usually thin, corresponding to the thin filaments of striated muscle. Within the cytoplasm varying numbers of spindle-shaped 'dense bodies' may be seen (Fig. 12.2). They are related to the thin myofilaments and may represent the Z-band material of striated muscle.[2] Often they occur at the edge of the cell (Fig. 12.2).

Mitochondria are present (Fig. 12.3), but not in such quantities as in cardiac muscle. They are often particularly located at the ends of the nuclei. Both rough and smooth endoplasmic reticula are apparent.[2] The smooth reticulum may be concerned with the accumulation of calcium[3,4] (p. 177). Close apposition occurs between some portions of the smooth sarcoplasmic reticulum and the plasma membrane and electron-opaque connections have been observed at these sites.[3] The rough endoplasmic reticulum and frequent abundance of ribosomes in the cytoplasm relate to the morphogenetic rôle of the cells[2,5] (see p. 279). In this latter respect a Golgi system occurs adjacent to the nucleus.

The cell is bounded by a plasma membrane about 8 nm thick and a distinct basement membrane (Fig. 12.3). Abundant pinocytotic vesicles occur at or just beneath the plasma membrane (Figs 12.2 and 12.3). They tend not to be seen where a dense body is adjacent to the cell surface. In the rabbit pulmonary artery it was estimated that about 45 per cent of the plasmalemmal surface was occupied by vesiculation.[6]

Each smooth muscle cell is entirely surrounded by plasma membrane and thus distinct from its neighbours. However, the surface of two adjacent cells may come into very close apposition. Sometimes this consists simply of a loss of basement membrane; sometimes there is actual fusion of the plasma membranes to form a nexus.[7] It is thought that nexi provide low-resistance pathways for the transmission

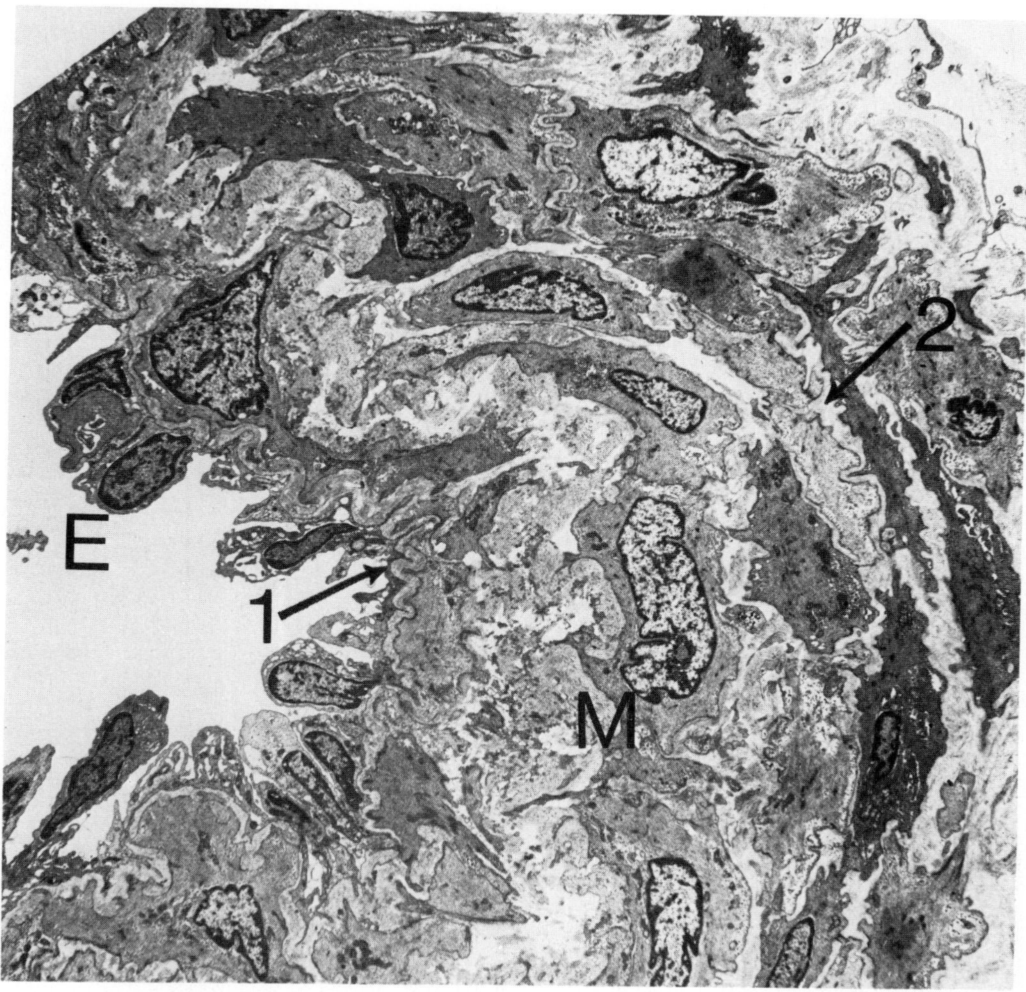

Fig. 12.1 Electron micrograph of part of a transverse section of a muscular pulmonary artery from a girl of eleven years with a ventricular septal defect and severe pulmonary hypertension. The media is delineated by internal (arrow 1) and external (arrow 2) elastic laminae. Within the media are elongated, irregularly-shaped smooth muscle cells, M. Note the light and dark variants. The prominent endothelial cells, E, lie internal to the inner elastic lamina. (Glutaraldehyde, lead citrate, uranyl acetate, × 2800)

of action potentials between cells. They are not generally seen in the aorta,[8,9] but are frequent in systemic arterioles[10] and have been found in veins.[2] They have been observed in the rabbit pulmonary artery[6] but their incidence is low in that vessel.

Innervation of Vascular Smooth Muscle

A detailed study of the autonomic innervation of animals' lungs has been carried out by Hebb.[11] There is no doubt that such innervation exists, whatever its

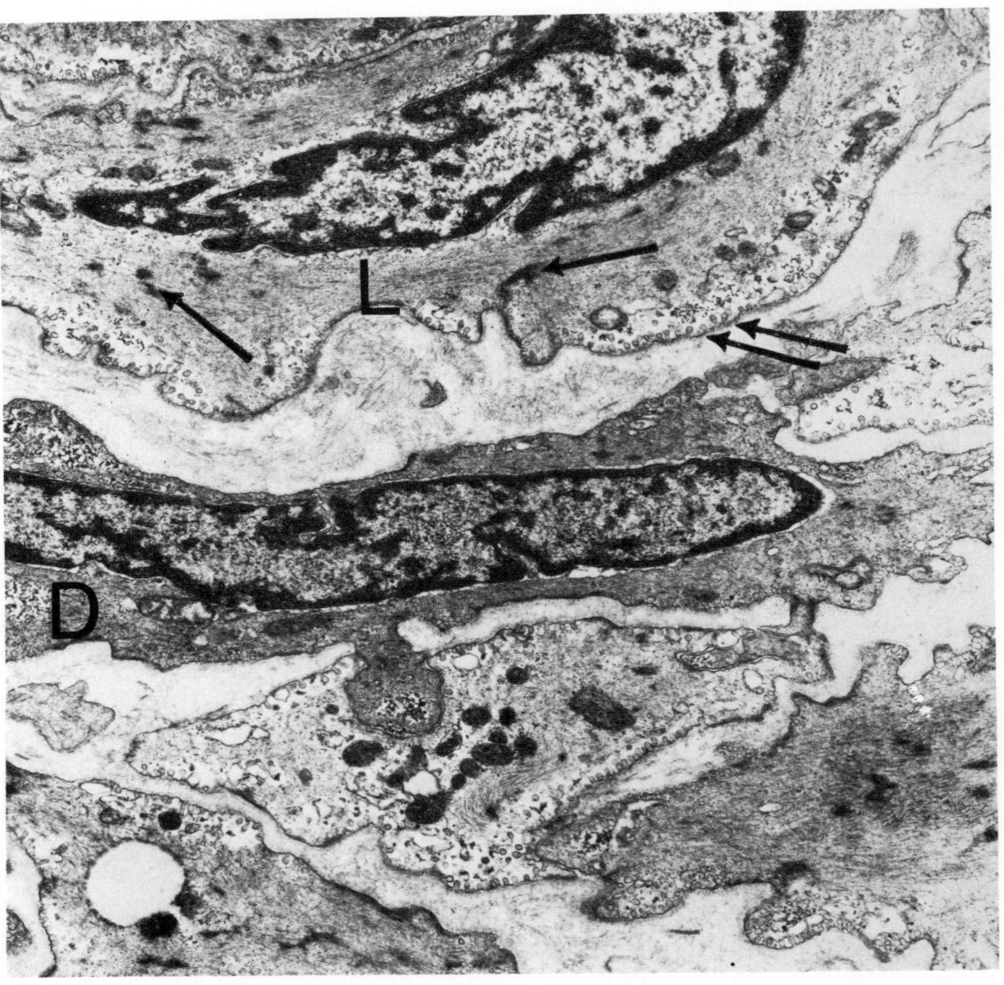

Fig. 12.2 Smooth muscle cells from the media of a pulmonary artery from the same case illustrated in Fig. 12.1. Both light (L) and dark (D) variants are present. Spindle-shaped 'dense bodies' are seen within the cytoplasm (arrows). Abundant pinocytotic vesicles (double arrows) occur at the plasma membrane. (Glutaraldehyde, lead citrate, uranyl acetate, × 14 000)

functional significance. There is wide variation between species but, in general, the autonomic innervation of pulmonary blood vessels is considerably less than that in the systemic circuit and cholinergic innervation is less obvious than adrenergic.

Cholinergic nerves were demonstrated in the extrapulmonary arteries of all species examined: rabbit, sheep, calf and pig.[11] No cholinergic nerves could be shown in the intrapulmonary arteries of the guinea pig. Cholinergic innervation was present in the large (>200 μm) intrapulmonary arteries of the rabbit, cat, sheep, calf and pig. Such innervation extended no further in the pig, as far as vessels of 70–200 μm

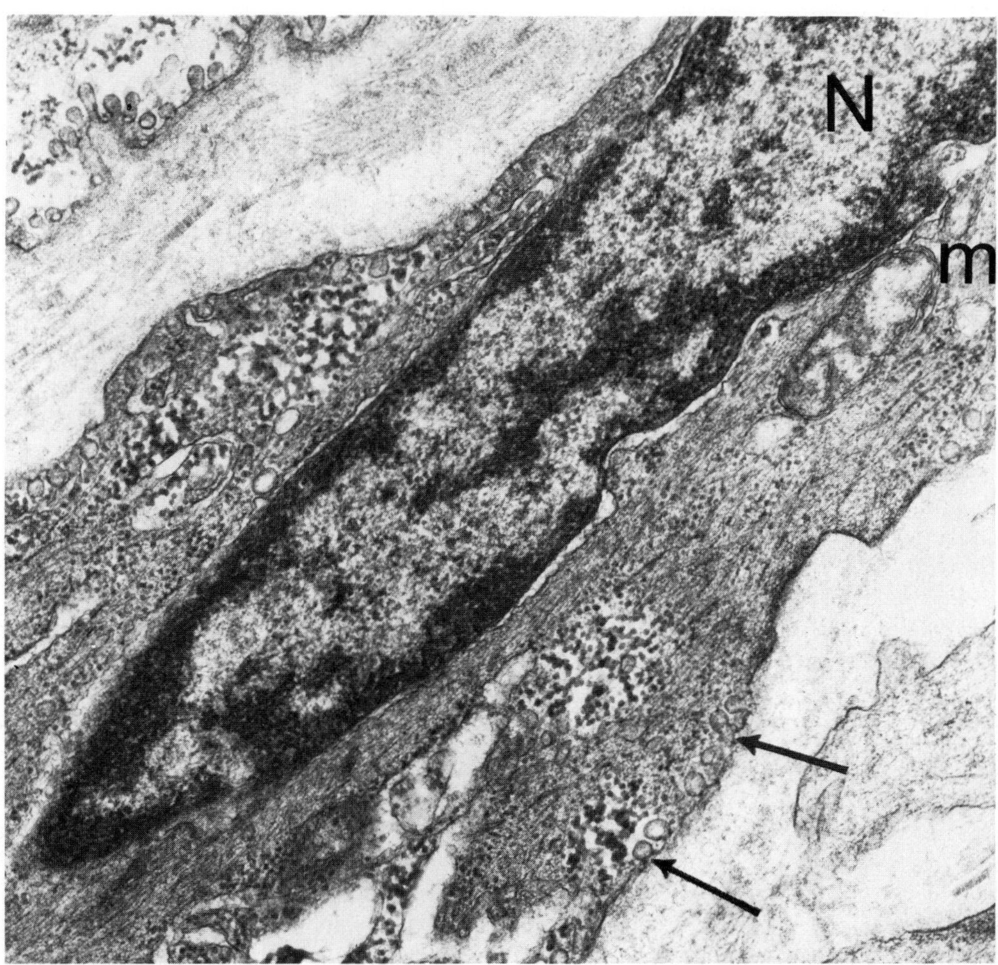

Fig. 12.3 Smooth muscle cell from the media of the artery illustrated in Figure 12.1. There is a central, elongated ellipsoid nucleus, N. Note the thick and thin myofilaments in the cytoplasm. Mitochondria, m, are present at the end of the nucleus. Abundant pinocytotic vesicles occur at or just beneath the plasma membrane (arrows). (Glutaraldehyde, lead citrate, uranyl acetate, × 37 500)

in the rabbit and calf, and down to vessels of less than 70 μm in the cat and sheep. In the larger pulmonary arteries the cholinergic nerves were situated outside the media, but in the smaller arteries some penetration of the media appeared to occur. Cholinergic fibres could be demonstrated only in veins of lobar size and larger.

Vascular adrenergic nerves have been widely studied by the fluorescence technique. Throughout the vascular system they end in a network or 'ground plexus' which is situated at the junction between the adventitia and the media.[2,12,13] Penetration of the media by terminal axons has generally been found to be limited. This has also usually been the case in the arteries of animals' lungs[11,14] although a certain amount of penetration of the media may occur.[11,14,15]

Adrenergic fibres have universally been found in the extra-pulmonary portion of the pulmonary arterial tree.[11,14] Hebb[11] found that in the rat they extend no further down the tree and in the calf only to a limited extent. In the rabbit, cat and sheep an adrenergic supply was demonstrated as far as the smallest arterial branches; in the pig the supply extended as far as vessels of 70 μm in diameter. Adrenergic innervation also extended to a variable extent into the pulmonary venous tributaries.

By fluorescence microscopy the terminal portions of the noradrenergic axons show a number of varicosities. Such varicosities may have a diameter about 1 μm while the diameter of the axon between the varicosities will be about 0·1 μm (Ref. 1). Under the electron microscope the varicosities are seen to contain mitochondria and microvesicles. Many of the microvesicles contain electron-dense material which appears to be composed partly of noradrenaline. The Schwann-cell covering disappears over the varicose area and thus the noradrenaline released from the varicosity has relatively free access to the adjacent smooth muscle cells.[2,6,16]

The minimal separation between the plasma membrane of the adrenergic axon and that of its adjacent smooth muscle was found to be 0·4 μm in the rabbit's pulmonary artery[6] while the average was 1·9 μm. These figures have to be compared with that of 0·05 μm for the synaptic cleft of the motor end-plate of striated skeletal muscle.[17] There is thus a relatively long diffusion pathway for noradrenaline between its point of release at the axonal surface and the receptor site on the smooth muscle cell.

Synthesis and Storage of Noradrenaline in Sympathetic Nerves (Fig. 12.4)

Noradrenaline is synthesised from tyrosine in sympathetic nerve axons.[18,19] The first step, mediated by tyrosine hydroxylase, appears to be rate-limiting. The dopa so formed is decarboxylated to dopamine. These reactions take place in the cytoplasm. Dopamine is taken up by the storage vesicles in which dopamine-β-hydroxylase is located, mediating the conversion to noradrenaline.[20] Dopamine not taken up by the vesicles is destroyed by monoamine oxidase located in the mitochondria. Storage of noradrenaline in the vesicles also protects it against the action of monoamine oxidase.[21]

The storage vesicles are formed in the cell bodies of the sympathetic neurones and pass down the axons, possibly in relation to the microtubular system which exists in the axons.[22,23]

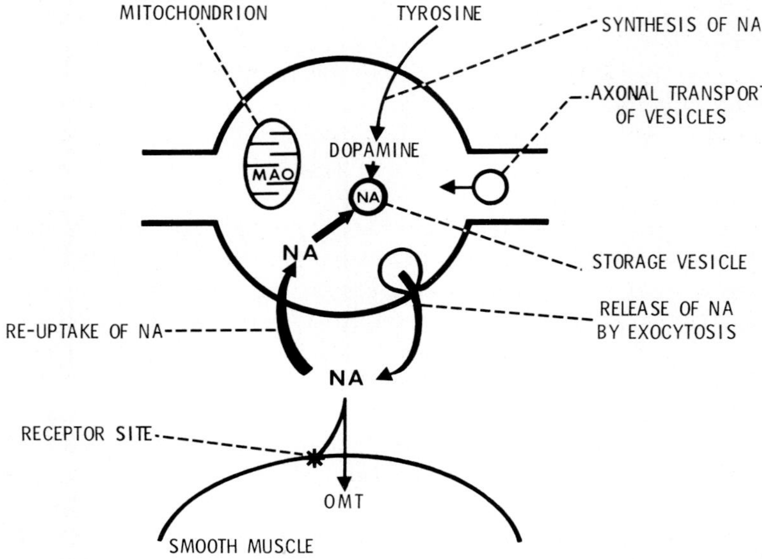

Fig. 12.4 Diagram to show the mechanisms of synthesis, storage, release and re-uptake of noradrenaline at the nerve terminal. NA, noradrenaline; MAO, monoamine oxidase; OMT, catechol-o-methyl transferase.

Noradrenergic Neuromuscular Transmission

Excitation of the nerve causes a release of noradrenaline from its neuro-effector varicosities.[24] This seems to occur by a process of exocytosis of the storage vesicles and depends on the presence of extracellular calcium ions.[25] The released noradrenaline then passes by simple diffusion to its specific receptor sites on the adjacent smooth muscle cells. There is no equivalent of choline esterase to cause a rapid inactivation of the transmitter substance. Monoamine oxidase activity is an intracellular process occurring mainly in the neurones. The other enzyme concerned with the catabolism of noradrenaline, catechol-o-methyl transferase, is located principally in non-neuronal cells. It is concerned with the degradation of circulating noradrenaline but does not seem to have an important influence on the fate of noradrenaline released locally at nerve terminals.

There is a certain degree of uptake of noradrenaline by the smooth muscle cells, but by far the most important function determining the local time-course of concentration of noradrenaline after discharge from the nerve terminal is the active and rapid re-uptake of the transmitter substance by the nerve terminal itself.[26] Cocaine and imipramine prevent this uptake process and thus potentiate the effects of sympathetic stimulation. A diminution in the uptake mechanism by the action of drugs or by a loss of sympathetic nerve terminals will also lead to an increased sensitivity of the smooth muscle tissue to externally added noradrenaline.[27]

Iverson[26] concludes that the rate of removal of circulating noradrenaline is related to the richness of sympathetic innervation of a tissue.

Following the re-uptake of noradrenaline at the surface of the nerve terminal, it is transported once more into the storage vesicles. This process requires energy in the form of ATP and is prevented by reserpine. The process of re-uptake and re-storage of noradrenaline appears to be an important mechanism for the conservation of the transmitter substance.

The distances between the nervous site of release of noradrenaline and its nearest smooth muscle cell are relatively long in blood vessels and this has been found to be particularly so in the pulmonary artery (p. 174). This might be expected to weaken the effect of sympathetic stimulation. In addition, the sympathetic nervous supply is virtually limited to the medial-adventitial junction (p. 174) and the smooth muscle cells of the intimal border of the media are so far removed from neuro-effector sites that no direct transmission seems feasible.

The lack of sympathetic nerve terminations in the inner portion of the media is reflected in the distribution of the noradrenaline content and binding capacity through the arterial wall. In the aorta[28] about three quarters of the total content of noradrenaline is located in the adventitia and some 80–90 per cent of the total capacity to bind noradrenaline is found in the adventitia. The uptake of noradrenaline by the adventitia is inhibited by cocaine, whereas that by the media is not. In the adventitial–medial border, where the sympathetic ground plexus lies, the fate of noradrenaline is determined principally by uptake; while in the media noradrenaline is inactivated mainly by enzymatic breakdown.[29]

Such observations may underlie differences in function between the outer and inner layers of the media. In the perfused ear artery of the rabbit the effects of noradrenaline administered to the outer surface were potentiated by cocaine, while those of noradrenaline administered intra-luminally were not.[30] Differences of action have been observed in arteries between blood-borne and transmitter noradrenaline.[31,32]

The Contractile Mechanism of Vascular Smooth Muscle

The biochemical basis for mechanical contraction appears to be common to all forms of muscle and consists of an interaction between myosin and actin. Knowledge of the contractile process is, however, far more advanced in striated than in smooth muscle. In skeletal and cardiac muscle there is a series of alternating arrays of thick and thin filaments orientated longitudinally within the cell. It is this orderly organisation which gives the striated appearance under the light microscope. The thin filaments, consisting mainly of fibrous actin, arise from each side of transversely disposed Z-lines. They interdigitate with the thick filaments which are composed of myosin molecules. In smooth muscle, both forms of filaments are also present, although the thick filaments are often more difficult to demonstrate than in striated muscle. The two forms of filament are not, however, organized in the orderly arrays found in striated muscle and Z-lines are not present. Thus, under the light microscope, the cells lack striation (Figs 12.1–12.3).

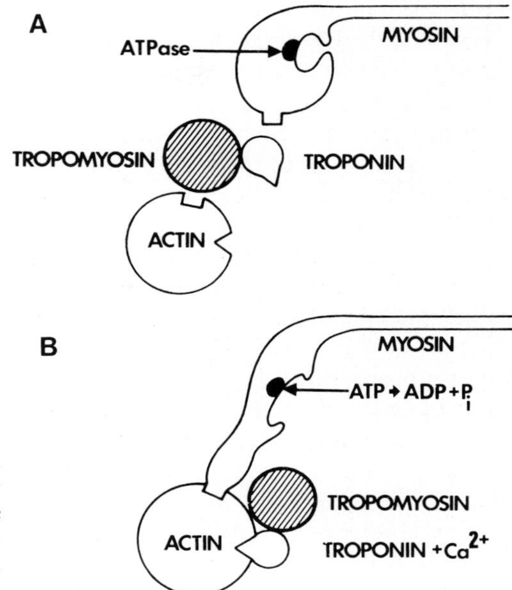

Fig. 12.5 Diagram to show the formation of a cross-bridge. A, When the calcium ion concentration is less than 10^{-7} M, tropomyosin obscures the receptor site for myosin on the actin molecule. B. When the calcium ion concentration is more than 10^{-7} M, the troponins bind to actin, pulling aside tropomyosin and permitting the myosin head to attach to actin.

Contraction consists of a sliding movement between the two sets of filaments.[33,34] This movement is caused by the rapid formation and disengagement of cross-bridges between the heads of the myosin molecules in the thick filaments and sites on the actin molecules in the thin filaments. Attraction between the myosin heads and actin occurs only when the concentration of calcium ions exceeds 10^{-7} M. This is due to the action of the regulatory proteins, tropomyosin and the troponins, which lie on the thin filaments. In the absence of calcium ions the tropomyosin molecule, to which the troponins are attached, appears to block the binding site for myosin on the actin molecule (Fig. 12.5). Calcium ions bind to one of the troponins and, when the concentration of calcium ions exceeds 10^{-7} M, this causes the troponin group to move toward the actin molecules, which in turn displaces the tropomyosin molecule and permits the attachment of myosin to actin.

The conformational change caused by the formation of a cross-bridge activates the ATPase locus which exists in the myosin head and the hydrolysis of ATP provides the energy for the repetitive formation and rupture of cross-bridges on which the sliding movement depends.

In striated muscle, where the process has been more extensively studied, a contraction is initiated by the sudden liberation of calcium ions into the cytoplasm by the sarcoplasmic reticulum. This tubular system ramifies along the contractile mechanism and, in the resting state, actively accumulates calcium ions so that the concentration of calcium ions in the vicinity of the contractile proteins is less than 10^{-7} M. In striated muscle, the release of calcium ions by the sarcoplasmic reticulum follows the action potential and the concentration of calcium ions in the vicinity of the contractile proteins rapidly rises to the order of 10^{-5} M. How this link between depolarisation of the cell membrane and discharge of calcium by the sarcoplasmic reticulum is effected is not certain. In skeletal muscle cells and in many cardiac muscle cells, a system of transverse microtubules passes into the cell at the level of the Z-lines and comes into close contact with portions of the sarcoplasmic reticulum. Such a transverse system is not, however, present in vascular smooth muscle where, in any case, the small diameter of the cells would render it unnecessary.

The origin of calcium ions for contraction in vascular smooth muscle is not so certain. The volume of sarcoplasmic reticulum in the smooth muscle of the main pulmonary artery and aorta of the rabbit is in the region of 5 per cent of the total volume of the cells.[3] Preparations of sarcoplasmic reticulum from aortic smooth muscle have been shown to accumulate calcium,[4,35] but at a rather slower rate than in skeletal muscle. Another possible site of calcium accumulation and release is the mitochondrion. Mitochondria are not as plentiful in vascular smooth muscle as, for instance, in red skeletal muscle or cardiac muscle (Figs 12.1–12.3) and their rôle in the uptake of calcium in aortic smooth muscle is debatable.[4,35]

The concentration of calcium ions in the extracellular fluid is some ten thousand times that in the cytoplasm and a calcium pump mechanism is located in the cell membrane. Contraction could, therefore, be initiated directly by the passage of calcium ions across the plasmalemma. During the action potential there is some influx of calcium in skeletal muscle and more so in cardiac muscle. However, even in cardiac muscle, the total quantity of calcium entering during the action potential is only some fortieth of the quantity required to activate the contractile mechanism and the major source appears to be the sarcoplasmic reticulum.[36] When rhythmically contracting smooth muscle from the portal vein was placed in a bath containing strontium, this electron-dense metal was found in the sarcoplasmic reticulum and mitochondria.[37] However, the quiescent smooth muscle of the rabbit's main pulmonary artery failed to take up the ion unless it was artificially depolarised with a high concentration of potassium or was treated with glycerine to increase the permeability of the cell membrane. There is a possibility that, in smooth muscle and cardiac muscle, a small inward movement of calcium ions triggers the release of further calcium ions from the sarcoplasmic reticulum.[36]

Excitation of Vascular Muscle

The electrophysiology of vascular smooth muscle and its relation to contraction and the maintenance of tone is still an area of uncertainty and some controversy.[2,12,13,38–42]

The resting membrane potential of smooth muscle cells of the main pulmonary artery of the rabbit has been found to be in the region of 50–60 mV both by intracellular electrodes[43,44] and by the sucrose gap technique[45] in which the potential difference is recorded between two segments of a strip of muscle separated by a segment bathed in non-conducting sucrose solution. This is within the range usually found in vascular smooth muscle[2] and somewhat lower than that for skeletal or cardiac muscle. Often there is a tendency for the resting membrane potential to oscillate and the rate of oscillation may be dependent on sympathetic innervation.[46] "Spike" action potentials may arise from the crests of the oscillations when, presumably, the threshold of excitation has been reached. Such cells may be regarded as pacemakers, with an intrinsic capacity for rhythmic depolarisation to excitation threshold. In other studies, stimulation of the splanchnic nerve has given rise to a distinct depolarisation with each stimulus and such "excitatory junction potentials" have initiated spikes.[47]

The contraction of smooth muscle to stimulation is slow and sustained. Thus, contractions elicited by spike action potentials tend to fuse at relatively slow rates of firing and a condition of continuous 'tone' may be produced.[48–51] Such a tone may, therefore, be elicited by the activity of spikes arising either from 'pacemaker' cells or from nervous discharge.

The spread of the excitatory wave between muscle cells must depend on their anatomical connections. If, at one extreme, the muscle cells are entirely separated from each other and come into close apposition with the nerve terminals, the nervous discharge of catecholamine will be expected to affect simply those muscle cells which are related to the nerve terminal. The other extreme may occur towards the intimal aspect of the media where nerve terminals are not found and the muscle cells are connected by nexi. Under those circumstances, transmission may occur from cell to cell. The extent of the propagation of the transmission will presumably depend on the magnitude and dispersal of the initiating action potentials. A large initiating current may become self-propagating; otherwise the spread of excitation will be limited.[12]

In contrast to the above observations, it is clear from a large number of recordings that contraction of vascular smooth muscle, from nervous stimulation or from the application of drugs, can occur in the absence of spike action potentials. That noradrenaline and other vaso-active drugs can cause contraction in cells which have been completely depolarised is well documented.[2] Some workers have found a mechanical response in normally polarised cells associated with only a sustained degree of partial depolarisation and no spikes. For instance,[44] contraction of the main pulmonary artery of the rabbit occurred following the application of noradrenaline while intracellular microelectrodes recorded simply a reduction in the transmembrane potential from a mean of 58 to 44 mV. Such observations have also been made using the sucrose gap technique.[45] Acetylcholine, histamine and 5-hydroxytryptamine have all been found to cause a sustained depolarisation in the smooth muscle of the rabbit pulmonary artery.[52] Other workers have been unable to record any change in the transmembrane potential of the rabbit's main pulmonary artery during contraction following sympathetic nerve stimulation or the application of noradrenaline.[43] The same was found for adrenaline in the carotid sinus.[53] So far, no recording of spike action potentials has been reported from the pulmonary artery, where the vascular smooth muscle cells have been regarded as electrically quiescent.[43]

Somlyo and Somlyo[2,45] have shown that the action potentials of spike-generating vascular smooth muscle can be abolished without depolarisation, while the contractile effects of drugs persist. Different drugs elicit unequal maximal mechanical responses both in the polarised and depolarised state.[2,38] These properties have led to the suggestion that a direct form of pharmaco-mechanical coupling exists in vascular smooth muscle.[2,38]

REFERENCES

1. Burnstock, G. (1970) In *Smooth Muscle*, ed. Bülbring, E., Brading, A. F., Jones, A. W. & Tanita, T. P. 1. Arnold.
2. Somlyo, A. P. & Somlyo, A. V. (1968) *Pharmacol. Rev.*, **20**, 197.
3. Devine, C. E., Somlyo, A. V. & Somlyo, A. P. (1972) *J. Cell. Biol.*, **52**, 690.
4. Fitzpatrick, D. F., Landon, E. J., Debbas, G. & Hunvitz, L. (1972) *Science*, **176**, 305.
5. Pease, D. C. (1962) *Blood Vessels and Lymphatics*. Academic Press.
6. Verity, M. A. & Bevan, J. A. (1967) *Bibl. Anat.*, **8**, 60.
7. Dewey, M. M. & Barr, L. (1962) *Science*, **137**, 670.
8. Karrer, H. E. (1961) *J. Ultrastruct. Res.*, **5**, 1.
9. Keech, M. K. (1960) *J. Biophys. Biochem. Cytol.*, **7**, 533.
10. Rhodin, J. A. G. (1967) *J. Ultrastruct. Res.*, **18**, 181.
11. Hebb, C. (1969) In *The Pulmonary Circulation and Interstitial Space*, ed. Fishman, A. P. & Hecht, H. H. University of Chicago Press.
12. Holman, M. E. (1969) *Rev. Physiol.*, **61**, 137.
13. Speden, R. N. (1970) In *Smooth Muscle*, ed. Bülbring, E., Brading, A. F., Jones, A. W. & Tanita, T. page 558. Arnold.
14. Fillenz, M. (1967) *Bibl. Anat.*, **8**, 56.
15. Cech, S. & Dolezel, S. (1967) *Experientia*, **23**, 114.
16. Verity, M. A., Bevan, J. A. & Ostrom, R. J. (1966) *Nature*, **211**, 537.
17. Eccles, J. C. (1964) *The Physiology of Synapses*. Academic Press.
18. Austin, L., Livett, B. G. & Chubb, I. W. (1967) *Circulat. Res.*, **21**, 111.
19. Nagatsu, T., Levitt, M. & Udenfriend, S. (1964) *J. Biol. Chem.*, **239**, 2910.
20. Levin, E. Y. & Kaufman, S. (1961) *J. Biol. Chem.*, **236**, 2043.
21. Kopin, I. J. (1964) *Pharmacol. Rev.*, **16**, 179.
22. Dahlström, A. & Häggendal, J. (1966) *Acta Physiol. Scand.*, **67**, 278.
23. Banks, P. & Mayor, D. (1972) *Neurotransmitters and Metabolic Regulation*, ed. Smellie, R. M. S. Biochem. Soc. Symposium No. **36**, p. 133.
24. Anden, N. E., Carlsson, A. & Häggendal, J. (1969) *Ann. Rev. Pharmacol.*, **9**, 119.
25. Smith, A. D. (1972) *Neurotransmitters and Metabolic Regulation*, ed. Smellie, R. M. S. Biochem. Soc. Symposium No. **36**, page 103.
26. Iverson, L. L. (1967) *The Uptake and Storage of Noradrenaline in Sympathetic Nerves*. Cambridge University Press.
27. Trendelenburg, U. (1966) *Pharmacol. Rev.*, **18**, 629.
28. Maxwell, R. A., Eckhardt, S. B. & Wastila, W. B. (1968) *J. Pharmacol. Exp. Therap.*, **161**, 34.
29. Levin, J. A. & Furchgott, R. F. (1970) *J. Pharmacol. Exp. Therap.*, **172**, 320.
30. De la Lande, I. S. & Waterston, J. G. (1967) *Nature*, **214**, 313.
31. Glick, G., Epstein, S. E., Wechsler, A. S. & Braunmwald, E. (1967) *Circulat. Res.*, **21**, 217.
32. Brick, I., Hutchinson, K. J. & Roddie, I. C. (1967) *J. Physiol.*, **189**, 27.
33. Huxley, A. F. (1964) *Ann. Rev. Physiol.*, **26**, 131.
34. Huxley, H. E. (1965) In *Muscle*, ed. Paul, W. M., Daniel, E. E., Kay, C. M. & Monckton, G. page 3. Pergamon.
35. Hess, M. L. & Ford, G. D. (1974) *J. Mol. Cell. Cardiol.*, **6**, 275.
36. Nayler, W. G. (1975) In *Mammalian Cell Membranes*, ed. Jamieson, G. A. & Robinson, D. M. Vol. **5**. London: Butterworth.
37. Somlyo, A. V. & Somlyo, A. P. (1971) *Science*, **174**, 955.
38. Somlyo, A. P. (1972) *Physiologist*, **15**, 338.

39. Bohr, D. F. & Uchida, E. (1969) In *The Pulmonary Circulation and Interstitial Space*, ed. Fishman, A. P. & Hecht, H. H. P. 133. University of Chicago Press.
40. Bohr, D. F. (1973) *Circulat. Res.*, **32**, 665.
41. Keatinge, W. R. (1969) In *The Pulmonary Circulation and Interstitial Space*, ed. Fishman, A. P. & Hecht, H. H. page 147. University of Chicago Press.
42. Barr. L. (1969) In *The Pulmonary Circulation and Interstitial Space*, ed. Fishman, A. P. & Hecht, H. H. page 161. University of Chicago Press.
43. Su, C., Bevan, J. A. & Ursillo, R. C. (1964) *Circulat. Res.*, **15**, 20.
44. Haeusler, G. (1972) *J. Pharmacol. Exper. Therap.*, **180**, 672.
45. Somlyo, A. V. & Somlyo, A. P. (1968) *J. Pharmacol. Exper. Therap.*, **159**, 129.
46. Steedman, W. M. (1966) *J. Physiol.*, **186**, 382.
47. Speden, R. N. (1964) *Nature*, **202**, 193.
48. Bozler, E. (1948) *Experientia*, **4**, 213.
49. Bülbring, E. (1955) *J. Physiol.*, **128**, 200.
50. Axelson, J. (1970) In *Smooth Muscle*, ed. Bülbring, E., Brading, A. F., Jones, A. W. & Tomita, T. page 289. Arnold.
51. Ruëgg, J. C. (1971) *Physiol. Rev.*, **51**, 201.
52. Su, C. & Bevan, J. A. (1965) *Life Sci.*, **4**, 1025.
53. Mekata, F. & Niu, H. (1972) *J. Gen. Physiol.*, **59**, 92.

13. Pharmacology of the Pulmonary Circulation

RESISTANCE AND VASOMOTION IN THE PULMONARY CIRCULATION

The long controversy concerning the existence of any active regulation of the pulmonary vascular resistance arose out of the particular difficulties, both practical and theoretical, which encumbered the analysis of this specialised section of the circulation.

The practical difficulties and instrumental limitations are discussed in Chapters 5 and 6. Many of them derive from the low pressures normally encountered in the pulmonary circulation. The pressure in the pulmonary artery is one-sixth of that in the aorta, and the pressure in the left atrium is higher than that in the right atrium, so that the drop in pressure across the lungs (ΔP) is normally often only 5 or 6 mmHg. Under these circumstances, large changes in resistance give rise only to small changes in pressure. A halving of the resistance, for instance, may lead only to a diminution of 3 mmHg in ΔP. Hence, the observed alterations in pressure are often of the same order as the limits of error of the measurements which are made and the range of physiological variation which may normally be encountered from moment to moment.

For this reason the demonstration of a vasodilatory effect may become easier if the nett haemodynamic change affects the pulmonary blood flow more than the intravascular pressures. This has, for instance, proved to be the case with histamine (p. 198), isoprenaline (p. 189) and bradykinin (p. 196) which cause an increase in the pulmonary blood flow; whereas with acetylcholine and aminophylline, which have no effect on the cardiac output, the demonstration of vasodilatation in normals has been more problematic.

The difficulties associated with a small arterio-venous difference in pressure become less in patients with pulmonary hypertension. The increased pulmonary vascular resistance in these patients, together with the muscular hypertrophy which commonly occurs in the muscular pulmonary arteries, provides a more sensitive situation for the testing of drugs than that which exists in the normal lung. This is particularly so in the case of substances causing dilatation. With certain reservations, it seems reasonable to use the results of such pharmacological studies made under pathological conditions in our understanding of the normal pulmonary circulation.

Since the pressure in the left atrium is normally so close to that in the pulmonary artery, it cannot be ignored in assessing the resistance of the pulmonary vessels. For a numerical example of this, we may take a typical effect of hypoxia on the pulmonary circulation (Chap. 30). The breathing of 12 per cent oxygen causes the mean pulmonary arterial pressure to rise from 15 mmHg to say 20 mmHg. The pulmonary blood flow increases from 6 to 8 $l \cdot min^{-1}$. The left atrial pressure remains at 10 mmHg. A measurement of the pulmonary vascular resistance, ignoring the left atrial pressure, shows no change during hypoxia. A measurement of the pulmonary vascular resistance based on ΔP shows that the resistance has increased by about 50 per cent. This has sometimes been a source of confusion.

Such confusion is doubly confounded when the left atrial pressure itself is changed by drugs which affect the systemic circulation or the cardiac output. For this reason we have restricted the following review solely to those studies in which the measurement of wedge or left atrial pressure has been made.

Although direct measurements of the left atrial pressure are possible (Chap. 5, p. 71) they are less convenient than the use of the wedge pressure and more likely to cause anxiety which in itself disturbs pulmonary haemodynamics. Although the evidence suggests that the wedge pressure and the left atrial pressure are closely related (Chap. 5, p. 72), it is possible that drugs might constrict the pulmonary veins and thus cause the wedge pressure to be higher than that in the left atrium. So far there is no evidence that this is so in man.[1]

In addition to such practical considerations, reasonable doubts have been expressed concerning the rectilinearity of the relation between mean flow and mean pressure in the pulmonary circulation. The thin-walled vessels of the lung encouraged the view that they would dilate readily when the pressure within them increased. In this way an increase in the flow of blood through them or an increase in the venous pressure would cause a mechanical decrease in resistance without calling into play any alteration in vasomotor tone.

In essence, pharmacological experiments are measuring changes in the compliance of resistance vessels and relating them to changes in vasomotor tone. Overall compliance is, however, determined by the extensibility characteristics of the non-muscular components of their walls in addition to vasomotor tone. In normal subjects and patients with mitral stenosis in the recumbent posture it seems that the vessels which are on the site of resistance are all open and in a state of low compliance. Such a low degree of compliance might be due to the walls of the resistance vessels being stretched to a relatively rigid portion of their extensibility curve. In this case vasomotor tone would have little effect on their compliance and, in particular, a diminution in vasomotor tone could have little effect on their resistance. This may be another reason why it is difficult to demonstrate vasodilatation in the pulmonary circulation. On the other hand, the fact that some vasodilatation can be demonstrated indicates that the calibre of the resistance vessels is to a certain extent determined by the tone of vascular smooth muscle.

In the recumbent posture, the relation between mean flow and mean pressure in the normal human pulmonary circulation appears to be linear over at least a two-fold increase in the flow (Chap. 9, p. 129). Similarly, manoeuvres which have caused a mechanical increase in the pulmonary venous pressure have not been shown significantly to change the pulmonary arterial resistance (Chap. 11, p. 161). Such observations imply that, in the recumbent position usually chosen for pharmacological investigations, those vessels which are the chief site of resistance in the normal human pulmonary circulation are in a state of virtual indistensibility within physiological limits. This does not, on the other hand, preclude the mechanical effects of an increased intravascular pressure acting in opposition to and preventing the effects of vasoconstriction. Such a possible combination of effects may occur, for instance, during the infusion of noradrenaline (p. 185).

The relation between pressure and flow has been shown also to be rectilinear in patients with mitral stenosis (p. 356), which increases confidence in the results of pharmacological studies in such patients. On the other hand, the relation between pressure and flow is not linear in patients with chronic bronchitis and emphysema (p. 526). The interpretation of pharmacological experiments on such patients, therefore, requires circumspection.

In disentangling the vasomotor effects of drugs on the pulmonary circulation from alterations in pressure secondary to changes in the cardiac output or the total compliance of the systemic circulation, the measurement of the pulmonary blood volume may be helpful.[2] An increase in pulmonary vascular pressure of mechanical origin may be expected to be associated with an increased pulmonary blood volume, while a decrease in pressure of mechanical origin would be expected to be associated with a decreased pulmonary blood volume. Thus, the increase in pulmonary blood volume found in association with a decrease in pulmonary vascular pressures during the administration of acetylcholine[2] (p. 193) or aminophylline[3] (p. 199) supports the occurrence of an active dilatation. Similarly, the decrease in pulmonary blood volume[2] found in association with an increase in pulmonary vascular pressures during the infusion of angiotensin II (p. 196) bespeaks an active vasoconstriction.

In experiments on animals, the isolation or mechanical perfusion of the pulmonary circulation has allowed a greater control of the many variables which may obscure the interpretation of human studies. Nevertheless, such gross interference with the organism brings its own problems, and the application of animal to human pharmacology runs the risk of ignoring species differences both in the structure of the pulmonary circulation (Chap. 26) and in its response to drugs. Since our concern is with the human pulmonary circulation, we shall refer only occasionally to experiments which have been performed on animals an extensive review of which has been given by Aviado.[4]

The tables which form the basis of the following review have been limited to those publications where the mean pulmonary arterial pressure, mean pulmonary wedge or left atrial pressure and mean pulmonary blood flow were measured both before and during the influence of a drug, and to those studies in such papers where these three measurements have been simultaneous. Thus the numbers of observations and mean values together with the conclusions drawn do not always coincide with those presented originally by the authors. Except on rare occasions where only mean values have been published, the data have been re-calculated and analysed statistically by the paired 't' test. We take the occasion to compliment those editors of scientific journals who, in the face of commercial pressures, have ensured that the full numerical data are published in addition to their authors' interpretation.

DRUGS ACTING ON SYMPATHETIC NERVES AND RECEPTORS

In 1948 Ahlquist[5] proposed a solution to the bewilderingly diverse effects of sympathetic stimulation, sympathomimetic drugs and blocking agents on visceral muscle located in different parts of the vascular system or in other organs of the body. He made a comparison of the relative effectiveness of five sympathetic amines (adrenaline and noradrenaline, their α-methyl derivatives and isoprenaline) in stimulating or inhibiting the activity of cardiac muscle and of smooth muscle in different vascular beds, in the uterus and intestine. Cats, dogs, rabbits and rats were studied. An analysis of the responses showed that they could be divided into two groups. In one group, adrenaline was the most powerful agent and isoprenaline the least; in the other group isoprenaline was the most powerful and noradrenaline the least. Ahlquist suggested that these two groups of responses were mediated by two distinct receptors on or in the muscle cells and designated them α and β. As far as the systemic circulation is concerned, the α-receptors are constrictor and the β-receptors dilator.

The adrenergic antagonists available at that time were found to block specifically α-activities. This, together with the subsequent development of agents able specifically to block β-activities, has provided strong support for the theory which is now widely accepted.[6] All adrenergic agonists stimulate both α- and β-receptors, but in varying proportion, so that, at one end of the scale, some are virtually pure α-agonists while, at the other end of the scale, some are virtually pure β-agonists.

A body of evidence is available concerning the action of a number of adrenergic agonists and antagonists in the human pulmonary circulation. These substances include: noradrenaline, (almost pure α-agonist), adrenaline (mixed), isoprenaline (almost pure β-agonist), metaraminol, phenylephrine and methoxamine (almost pure α-agonists), practolol, propranolol and pronethalol (β-antagonists) and phentolamine and tolazoline (α-antagonists). The results are summarized in Tables 13.1 and 13.2.

α-Agonists

Four agents which come into this category have been studied: noradrenaline, methoxamine, phenylephrine and metaraminol.

Noradrenaline The studies reviewed in Table 13.1 show a consistent increase in the pulmonary arterial and wedge pressures during the infusion of noradrenaline with no change in the pulmonary blood flow. The heart rate is decreased and the systemic arterial pressure increased. Presumably the increase in pulmonary venous as well as arterial pressure is due to the displacement of blood from the systemic vascular system by the vasoconstriction caused by stimulation of systemic α-receptors. To this may be added the effects of failure of the left ventricle.

In only one study[7] was there a significant increase in the pulmonary arterial resistance (p. 135). In one other study,[8] the authors claim a significant increase but our own calculations fail to confirm this. The balance of evidence is, therefore,

Table 13.1 Effects of adrenergic agonists on the human pulmonary circulation

Reference	Dose	No. and type of subjects	Mean pulmonary arterial pressure mmHg		Mean wedge or left atrial pressure mmHg		Pulmonary blood flow $l \cdot min^{-1}$ ($/m^2$BSA)		Mean systemic arterial pressure mmHg		Heart rate $bts \cdot min^{-1}$		Pulmonary arterial resistance[a] $dyn \cdot s \cdot cm^{-5}$ ($\times m^2$ BSA)	
			Before	After	Before	After	Before	After	Before	After	Before	After	Before	After
Noradrenaline														
113	0·2–0·4 μg/kg/min in P.A.	9N	16	21****	9	15****	(3·1)	(3·0)	105	124****	70	58***	114	118
114	20 μg/min i.v.	6N	16	27***	11	15**	(4·0)	(4·4)	92	120****	70	53***	(111)	(237)***
114	20 μg/min i.v.	3MS+1P	26	37	11	19	(3·3)	(2·6)	76	111	68	50	(392)	(579)
8	0·2 μg/kg/min i.v.	5N	13	24***	6	11***	6·0	5·4	91	134**	78	69*	101	207
8	0·2 μg/kg/min i.v.	7AI	22	41****	8	29****	5·2	4·7	88	122****	73	75	226	211
9	20–40 μg/min i.v.	13CHD	17	26**	10	16***	(4·7)	(4·3)	85	126****	84	70*	(124)	(176)
115	20–67 μg/min i.v.	9N	14	21****	7	15****	6·7	6·6	89	129****	91	85	87	67
1	4–14 μg/min	7N	15	21**	7	11*	5·7	5·4	104	122**	—	—	119	147
Adrenaline														
116	0·5–0·7 mg i.m.	5P	12	16****	4	4	(3·0)	(4·6)***	—	—	89	99***	131	116
Dopamine														
117	1 μg/kg/min i.v.	9AHD	30	31	22	21	(2·1)	(2·5)***	81	86	83	93***	(304)	(320)
117	5 μg/kg/min i.v.	9AHD	30	31	22	23	(2·1)	(3·4)***	81	91	83	89	(304)	(235)
117	10 μg/kg/min i.v.	9AHD	30	37	22	24*	(2·1)	(3·8)*	81	92	83	104*	(304)	(274)
Isoprenaline														
22	0·2–0·4 μg/kg/min i.v.	21MVD	24	31****	18	23****	(2·3)	(3·3)****	89	89[b]	76	112****	253	203**
22	0·2–0·4 μg/kg/min i.v.	5LVO	23	21	16	13	(3·0)	(5·6)*	104	97	68	89	171	105
23	10–20 mg sub-ling.	1N+6AHD	41	37*	20	17*	(2·6)	(3·0)*	93	92	82	84	(705)	(599)*
24	5–10 μg/min in P.A.	16P	26	23***	6	8	4·4	6·0***	94	94	88	108****	350	236***
25	1·2 μg/min i.v.	2N+2AI+1PH	20	18	9	7***	3·8	5·1****	85	89	80	100	235	181
25	1·2 μg/min i.v.	11MS	32	35*	17	21****	3·4	4·1***	82	83	84	103***	429	351
25	1·2 μg/min i.v.	5MI	19	18	11	8*	3·6	4·8*	86	85	80	98*	186	155
26	0·015–0·027 μg/kg/min	5My	20	14	11	6	(2·3)	(3·4)***	99	89*	80	90	191	106
26	0·015–0·027 μg/kg/min	18MVD	30	36***	19	23***	(2·2)	(2·9)****	91	87	76	98****	314	256**
26	0·015–0·027 μg/kg/min	11LVO	20	18	13	9***	(2·4)	(3·4)****	93	89*	73	92****	127	116
27	3·3–5·0 μg/min in P.A.	15P	27	27	7	6	(3·0)	(4·5)***	98	90**	93	117***	552	368****

Table 13.1 Contd.

Reference	Dose	No. and type of subjects	Mean pulmonary arterial pressure mmHg		Mean wedge or left atrial pressure mmHg		Pulmonary blood flow $l \cdot min^{-1}$ ($/m^2$BSA)		Mean systemic arterial pressure mmHg		Heart rate bts · min^{-1}		Pulmonary arterial resistance[a] dyn · s · cm^{-5} ($\times m^2$ BSA)	
			Before	After	Before	After	Before	After	Before	After	Before	After	Before	After
Metaraminol														
12	0·1–0·3 mg/min in R.V.	5MVD	34	49*	26	33	(2·6)	(2·8)	97	131***	64	67	148	263*
Phenylephrine														
11	0·5–1·0 mg i.v. or in P.A.	8MS	61	81****	24	28	2·9	2·3***	95	121****	82	57**	1130	2071****
Methoxamine														
10	8 mg in P.A.	9AHD	21	23	3	6****	10·8	11·9	131/	171/****	79	61****	333	322
10	8 mg in P.A.	5VSD	15	17	5	10***	11·4	12·7	122/	158/***	77	58***	73	52
2	0·1–0·4 mg/kg in P.A.	3MVD	28	34	20	24	(2·4)	(2·1)	86	107	—	—	209	280

AHD = acquired heart disease; AI = aortic incompetence; CHD = congenital heart disease; LVO = left ventricle overload; MI = mitral incompetence; MS = mitral stenosis; MVD = mitral valve disease; My = myocardial disease; N = normal; P = pulmonary disease; PH = pulmonary hypertension.

* $P < 0{\cdot}05$; ** $P < 0{\cdot}02$; *** $P < 0{\cdot}01$; **** $P < 0{\cdot}001$ (comparing before with after).

[a] See p. 135.

[b] $n = 17$.

against the existence of a substantial vasoconstriction. On the other hand, the impressive increase in the pulmonary venous pressure might possibly have overpowered a pharmacologically induced constriction (p. 162). It is possible, therefore, that the total effect of noradrenaline on the pulmonary circulation is a composite of passive vasodilatation due to an increased transmural pressure and some active vasoconstriction due to the stimulation of α-receptors. Some support for this comes from the observation[9] that, twenty seconds after the beginning of an intravenous infusion of noradrenaline, there is an increase in the pulmonary arterial pressure but not in the wedge pressure. No measurement of flow is available at this time but, since the drug has not been shown to have any effect on the cardiac output, it seems reasonable to suppose that the flow was unchanged.

Methoxamine There have been two reports of the effects of methoxamine (Table 13.1). This α-agonist caused an increase in both the pulmonary arterial and pulmonary venous pressures. There was no consistent effect on the cardiac output. The heart rate slowed and the systemic arterial pressure rose. In neither report was there a significant change in the pulmonary arterial resistance. On the other hand, one study was carried out on patients with congenital shunts in whom the measurement of the pulmonary blood flow is liable to greater error than usual.[10] In the other study, carried out on patients with mitral valvar disease, there was a suggestive increase in the pulmonary arterial resistance and decrease in the pulmonary blood volume.[2] However, the figures relate to only three patients.

Phenylephrine The infusion of phenylephrine into patients with mitral stenosis[11] (Table 13.1) caused an increase in the systemic arterial pressure. There was a slowing of the heart and a decreased cardiac output, attributable to stimulation of baroreceptors. Both the pulmonary venous and pulmonary arterial pressures increased. The pulmonary arterial resistance also increased significantly, becoming approximately doubled. This, in the presence of elevated pulmonary intravascular pressures is strong evidence of pulmonary vasoconstriction. Immediately after the commencement of the infusion of phenylephrine the pulmonary arterial pressure increased while the pulmonary wedge pressure decreased transiently. This finding, also supporting the presence of vasoconstriction, was similar to that found with noradrenaline[9].

Metaraminol In the one report on the effects of metaraminol[12] (Table 13.1) in patients with disease of the mitral valve, there was also a significant increase in the pulmonary arterial resistance.

α-Antagonists

Tolazoline The effects of tolazoline on the pulmonary circulation were first noted by Dresdale[13,14] who described a patient with idiopathic pulmonary hypertension in whom the drug caused the mean pulmonary arterial pressure to fall from 70 to 31 mmHg. The wedge pressure was not measured. The cardiac output was said to have increased. In other patients, tolazoline did not have such a prominent effect on the pulmonary arterial pressure but the cardiac output was increased. There are other sporadic reports of patients with idiopathic pulmonary hypertension in whom tolazoline did[15] or did not[15,16] cause a fall in the pulmonary arterial pressure. There are two reports concerning the action of tolazoline in infants and children with pulmonary hypertension associated with a congenital cardiac defect. In one[16] no effect was observed. Of the studies reported in that paper, three are technically complete and are summarized in Table 13.2. In the other[17] decreases in mean pulmonary arterial pressure ranging from 17 to 40 mmHg were consistently found in eight patients. Measurements of the oxygen uptake were made in only two patients but an increase in the ratio of pulmonary to systemic blood flow occurred in all cases. The wedge pressure, measured in two, was unchanged. Although the gaps in the experimental protocol were considerable, it is difficult to explain these results except in terms of pulmonary vasodilatation.

Support for the vasodilatory action of tolazoline comes from its effects on patients with pulmonary disease[18,19] in which a significant decrease in the pulmonary arterial resistance has been observed (Table 13.2). The presence of an absolute fall in the pulmonary arterial pressure and increase in the wedge pressure makes it unlikely that the decreased resistance is simply the result of the curvilinear relation between pressure and flow which is likely to exist in these patients.

Phentolamine Early studies of phentolamine in a patient with mitral stenosis and a patient with silicosis failed to show any effect on the pulmonary circulation.[20] A more recent publication on normals and patients with acquired and congenital heart disease has, however, given indication of a vasodilatation[21] (Table 13.2). There was a decrease in both the pulmonary arterial and wedge pressures. This, together with the simultaneous observation of an increased pulmonary blood volume and decreased pulmonary arterial resistance speaks strongly against the dilatation being due to any passive mechanical effect. The increase in cardiac output is unexpected for a pure α-antagonist. It might be due to stimulation of the sympathetic system consequent on the fall in systemic arterial pressure, in which case an unopposed reflex stimulation of β-receptors in the pulmonary circulation may have played a part in causing pulmonary vasodilatation. In addition, both phentolamine and tolazoline may have a direct effect on vascular smooth muscle independent of their α-antagonistic activity.

β-Agonists

Isoprenaline The reported effects of isoprenaline, an almost pure β-agonist, are summarized in Table 13.1. In the absence of an anatomical obstruction at the mitral valve the pulmonary venous and arterial pressures tend to fall.[22–27] In the presence of mitral stenosis there is an increase in both the pulmonary venous and the pulmonary arterial pressure.[22,25,26] The cardiac output and the heart rate increase substantially in all the studies in keeping with the β-stimulatory effect of the drug on the heart. The combination of an increased mean flow and a decreased diastolic time presumably underlies the increase in the left atrial pressure in the presence of mitral stenosis. The systemic arterial pressure falls a little or remains unchanged. The pulmonary arterial resistance (p. 135) has consistently decreased. This has been the case whether the pulmonary venous pressure has increased,[22,26]

Table 13.2 Effects of adrenergic antagonists on the human pulmonary circulation

Reference	Dose	No. and type of subjects	Mean pulmonary arterial pressure mmHg		Mean wedge or left atrial pressure mmHg		Pulmonary blood flow $l \cdot min^{-1}$ ($/m^2$ BSA)		Mean systemic arterial pressure mmHg		Heart rate bts min^{-1}		Pulmonary arterial resistance[a] $dyn \cdot s \cdot cm^{-5}$ ($\times m^2$ BSA)	
			Before	After	Before	After	Before	After	Before	After	Before	After	Before	After
Phentolamine														
21	10 mg in P.A.	4N + 14AHD	23	21****	17	15***	3·6	4·1****	89	78****	75	95****	162	129***
Tolazoline														
118	15–50 mg i.v.	3CHD	76	74	5	5	(6·8)	(7·0)	—	—	—	—	(875)	(816)
18	10–30 mg in P.A.	9P	22	18***	5	7	4·7	6·4**	95	97	90	101***	300	130****
19	10–30 mg in P.A.	3P	25	19	9	8	4·3	5·5	94[b]	92	88	92	324	147
Propranolol														
119	0·1 mg/kg in P.A.	7MS	29	24	24	18	8·3	6·8	—	—	110	83	56	72
120	5 mg in P.A.	5MS	30	29	23	22	(3·8)	(3.9)	81	87	106	106	144	144
Practolol														
121	200–600 μg/kg in right heart	19AHD	27	26	18	18	4·4[c]	4·0**	89[d]	88	80	73*	168	152
Pronethalol														
122	1 mg/kg in P.A.	5MS	32	25	20	15*	3·0	2·5*	94	91	84	66*	249	228

Abbreviations as in Table 13.1.
* $P < 0{\cdot}05$; ** $P < 0{\cdot}02$; *** $P < 0{\cdot}01$; **** $P < 0{\cdot}001$ (comparing before with after).
[a] See p. 135.
[b] n = 2; [c] n = 18; [d] n = 15.

decreased[23,26] or remained the same.[24,27] In two studies[23,26] the pulmonary blood volume has been measured by successive injections of dye into the pulmonary artery and left atrium with sampling from the brachial artery (p. 107). The results have shown an increase in the pulmonary blood volume irrespective of whether the left atrial pressure increases or decreases. The combination of a decreased pulmonary arterial resistance in the presence of a decreased left atrial and pulmonary arterial pressure and an increased pulmonary blood volume is strong evidence of an active vasodilatation. An alternative explanation might be that the effects are secondary to a decrease in bronchomotor tone, but this seems unlikely to be of sufficient magnitude to be a determining factor in those subjects with a normal airways resistance.

β-Antagonists

Propranolol, pronethalol, practolol Investigations on the effects of these have been reported (Table 13.2). Pronethalol and propranolol tend to cause a diminution in both the pulmonary arterial and pulmonary venous pressures and there is a tendency for the cardiac output to fall, consistent with blockade of the cardiac β-receptors. No significant effect on the pulmonary arterial resistance has been shown with any of these drugs. In the case of practolol this may not be surprising since the effects of the drug appear to be limited to the myocardium. Even in the systemic circulation, however, the vasoconstrictive action of propranolol and pronethalol does not appear to be a strong one.

Evidence for Adrenoceptor Activity in the Human Pulmonary Circulation

Summarising the preceding evidence one can conclude that there is evidence from the effects of agonists for the existence of α-receptors in the human pulmonary circulation although that from noradrenaline is the least impressive. While antagonists of α-receptors have been shown to cause vasodilatation, this could be due to an action on vascular smooth muscle which is independent of adrenoreceptor activity. The presence of β-receptors seems well established from experiments with the β-agonist isoprenaline. On the other hand, studies with β-antagonists have been negative, suggesting either that the β-receptors are not normally subject to a great deal of stimulation or that the antagonists are not very effective in this section of the vascular system.

Drugs which Block the Sympathetic Efferent Pathway

A number of investigations has been carried out on the effects of the ganglion-blocking drugs, hexamethonium and tetraethylammonium chloride. They are summarized in Table 13.3. The majority of the patients studied has had mitral valvar disease. The effect of the drugs has been to lower the pulmonary arterial and venous pressures and to lower the systemic arterial pressure. The cardiac output has not been consistently affected. In only one report[28] was there a significant decrease in the pulmonary arterial resistance.

Table 13.3 Effects of drugs which interrupt the sympathetic efferent pathways on the human pulmonary circulation

Reference	Dose	No. and type of subjects	Mean pulmonary arterial pressure mmHg		Mean wedge or left atrial pressure mmHg		Pulmonary blood flow $l \cdot min^{-1}$ ($/m^2$ BSA)		Mean systemic arterial pressure mmHg		Heart rate $bts \cdot min^{-1}$		Pulmonary arterial resistance[a] $dyn \cdot s \cdot cm^{-5}$	
			Before	After	Before	After	Before	After	Before	After	Before	After	Before	After
Hexamathonium														
123	10 mg i.v.	3H	10	7	7	2	5·5	4·6	178	105	84	90	52	101
124	25–100 mg i.m.	11AHD	27	22***	18	12***	(3·0)	(2·2)****	104	83***	78[b]	77	188	191
125	10 mg in P.A.	4H	19	12	11	2	5·6	5·1	193	128	82	85	118	142
28	15–75 mg in P.A.	1AHD + 10MS	48	36***	25	20*	(2·5)	(2·6)	96	77***	85	100*	430	315**
126	75 mg in P.A.	5N	18	15***	12	8***	(2·8)	(2·9)	88	82*	73	93**	178	195
126	75 mg in P.A.	5P	33	30*	12	10	(2·6)	(2·6)	85	68****	82	85	666	619
127	5–23 mg in P.A.	19MS	47	39****	29	22****	(2·5)	(2·5)	96[c]	75****	90	92	434	378
21	12·5 mg i.v.	9RHD + 2N	33	28****	22	19***	3·1	2·9	82	74****	89	94	332	318
Tetraethylammonium														
128	5–6 mg/kg i.v.	3N + 4AHD + 3P	23	20*	13	12	4·6	3·9**	—	—	82	97**	180	162
129	5 mg/kg in P.A.	6MS	65	48***	28	22	5·5	4·9	83	74	97	114	585	442
Guanethidine														
30	20–27 mg in P.A.	6N	17	18	9	9	(4·0)	(3·8)	104	103	91	87	98	125
32	10–40 mg i.v.	4N	16	14*	10	9	(4·2)	(4·0)	104	87**	78	80	109	100
32	10–40 mg i.v.	12H	20	18***	10	10	(3·9)	(3·5)	162	130****	87	83	211	186

H = systemic hypertension; RHD = rheumatic heart disease; other abbreviations as in Table 13.1.
* $P < 0·05$; ** $P < 0·02$; *** $P < 0·01$; **** $P < 0·001$ (comparing before with after).
[a] See p. 135.
[b] n = 9; [c] n = 18.

Bretylium and guanethidine block the post-ganglionic sympathetic pathway. There has been one report of the effects of bretylium in which it is said that the pulmonary arterial resistance is increased.[29] There have been three reports on the effects of guanethidine[30-32] (Table 13.3). None showed a significant effect on the pulmonary arterial resistance.

The conclusion seems to be that, in both normal people and patients with pulmonary hypertension, the sympathetic system does not greatly affect the resting pulmonary arterial resistance.

DRUGS ACTING ON THE PARASYMPATHETIC SYSTEM

Acetylcholine is known to be a vasodilator in the systemic circulation. Its action is thought to be a direct one on vascular smooth muscle and independent of the presence of cholinergic nerve endings. It is very rapidly destroyed in the circulating blood by choline esterases. It was introduced into the study of the human pulmonary circulation[33] because it was thought that it might be possible to inject it into the pulmonary artery in such a dose that it would act on the pulmonary vessels but be destroyed by the time it left the lungs. In this way, the complicating effects on the heart and systemic circulation, common to other vasoactive drugs, would be obviated.

In early studies[33-36] it was administered into the pulmonary artery by single injections. In a group of patients with various cardiac and respiratory diseases[33,35] it was found that, when there was a moderate degree of pulmonary hypertension, the injection of acetylcholine caused a transient lowering of the pulmonary arterial pressure. The wedge pressure remained unchanged or, occasionally, showed a transient rise. The systemic arterial pressure and heart rate were unaffected.

Subsequent studies, in which acetylcholine was administered by a continuous infusion into the pulmonary artery, showed that some slight fall in the pulmonary arterial pressure occurred even in normal people[37,38] (Table 13.4). The pulmonary wedge pressure remained unchanged. In a dose of $0{\cdot}5\ mg \cdot min^{-1}$ there was no alteration in cardiac output, heart rate, systemic arterial pressure or ventilation. Although this response to acetylcholine was just discernible under normal conditions, it became more readily apparent if the pulmonary arterial pressure was raised by hypoxia[37,38] (Fig. 13.1, Table 13.4).

A similar enhanced response to continuous infusions of acetylcholine into the pulmonary artery has been found in patients with pulmonary hypertension associated with a number of abnormalities (Table 13.4). The decrease in pulmonary arterial resistance which occurs is accompanied solely by a decrease in the pulmonary arterial pressure, all other haemodynamic measurements remaining constant. While, in the majority of the reports listed in Table 13.4, the effects of acetylcholine did not reach a level of statistical significance, the effect was always one of a decrease in the pulmonary arterial resistance and the overall analysis reveals a significant vasodilatory effect ($P < 0{\cdot}01$). The pulmonary blood volume is increased.[2]

Injection of acetylcholine into one branch of the pulmonary artery has caused vasodilatation in that lung.[39] In patients with mitral stenosis the infusion of

Table 13.4 Effects of drugs acting on the parasympathetic system on the human pulmonary circulation

Reference	Dose	No. and type of subjects	Mean pulmonary arterial pressure (mmHg)		Mean wedge or left atrial pressure (mmHg)		Pulmonary blood flow l · min^{-1} (/m^2 BSA)		Mean systemic arterial pressure (mmHg)		Heart rate bts. min^{-1}		Pulmonary arterial resistance[a] (dyn · s · cm^{-5})	
			Before	After	Before	After	Before	After	Before	After	Before	After	Before	After
Acetylcholine														
130	5–10 mg/min in R.A.	4P	15	13	7	7	4·6	4·7	123	118	—	—	148	110
81	2–12 mg/min in R.A. or P.A.	10MS	46	37*	22	20	(2·6)	(2·8)	82	77	82	78	1002	672
131	0·03–0·08 mg/kg/min in P.A.	5MVD	47	35	25	22	(2·2)	(2·3)	80	72	—	—	491	299
38	0·5 mg/min in P.A.	3N	14	13	8	9	(3·7)	(3·9)	100	98	78	79	128	94
38	0·5 mg/min in P.A.	3NH	9	16	7	7	(5·1)	(5·8)	96	96	95	98	209	129
132	2 mg/min in R.A.	10MS	38	34	20	22	4·5	4·9	105[b]	107	83	81	355	252**
82	0·5 mg/min in P.A.	9MS	42	35***	22	23	(3·3)	(3·2)	99	101	97	97	557	367*
61	83–147 μg/kg/min in R.A.	5N♂	14	13	8	8	7·9	7·2	105	100	74	72	65	62
61	83–147 μg/kg/min in R.A.	7N♀	16	13*	7	7	6·7	6·3	106	103	84	80*	102	76*
80	5–10 mg/min in P.A.	9MS	34	32	18	18	4·3	4·3	93	97	—	—	362	300
Atropine														
41	2–3 mg i.v.	8ND	22	18***	15	10***	8·0	11·7***	—	—	82	115****	121	85***
45	0·8–1·2 mg i.v.	4N	14	12	10	10	6·8	7·0	108	104	86	128	54	43
133	1·2 mg i.v.	6AVD	23	20	13	12	(3·5)	(3·4)	99[c]	100	78	105***	223	182

ND = normals after dextran infusion; NH = hypoxic normals; AVD = aortic valvar disease; other abbreviations as in Table 13.1.
* $P < 0{\cdot}05$; ** $P < 0{\cdot}02$; *** $P < 0{\cdot}01$; **** $P < 0{\cdot}001$ (comparing before with after).
[a] See p. 135.
[b] n = 9; [c] n = 5.

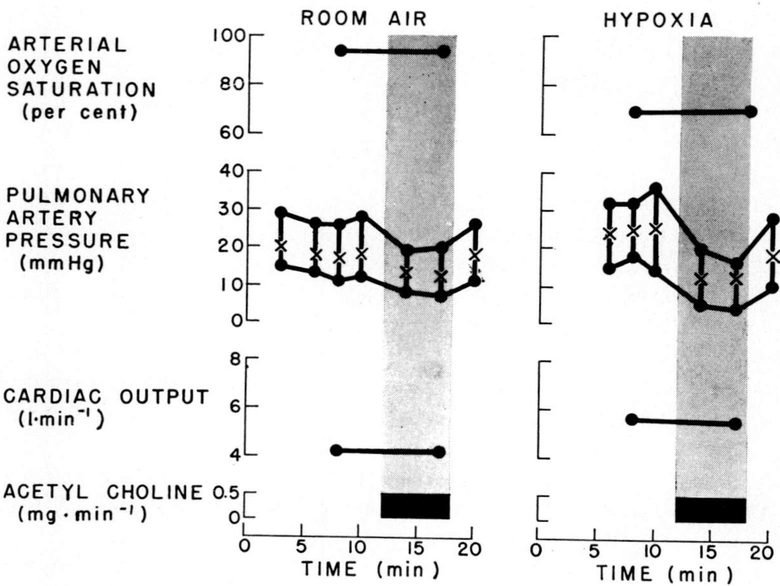

Fig. 13.1 The effects of infusing acetylcholine into the pulmonary artery of a normal subject while breathing room air and while breathing 12 per cent oxygen.[38]

acetylcholine into one lung caused a diminution in the ratio of blood flow to the upper and lower zones[40] on that side (p. 359).

The major circulatory effect of atropine is on the pulse rate (Table 13.4). The effects on the pressures in the pulmonary circulation are small and consist of a tendency to a diminution in the pulmonary arterial pressure and, possibly, in the pulmonary venous pressure. While all three studies reviewed in Table 13.4 showed an average decrease in the pulmonary arterial resistance, this reached statistical significance only in one.[41] This study was carried out in normal subjects who had been given an intravenous infusion of dextran solution. The dose of atropine was large (2–3 mg, i.v.) and this was the only study which showed an increase in the cardiac output. Since atropine is specifically an antagonist of acetylcholine, it is difficult to explain why both should have the same vasodilatory action in the pulmonary circulation.

SUBSTANCES NORMALLY PRESENT IN THE BODY

The possibility that substances which normally occur in the body might exert some control over the pulmonary circulation is an appealing one. Quite apart from the possible physiological importance of such substances, it is conceivable that their appearance in the blood or their production locally in the lungs might be a cause of the pulmonary hypertension which develops in disease. Several natural substances which are known to affect systemic blood vessels have been investigated but none of them has shown itself likely to play a rôle in the development of a pathological increase in pulmonary vascular resistance.

Acetylcholine, adrenaline and noradrenaline These substances have been discussed earlier in the chapter.

Peptides A number of naturally circulating peptide chains of varying length and composition are known to have powerful effects on systemic blood vessels.

Bradykinin causes a decrease in systemic arterial pressure (Table 13.5). This is accompanied by an increase in the heart rate and in the cardiac output, suggesting sympathetic stimulation via the baroreceptor mechanism. In the presence of a normal mitral valve the pulmonary venous pressure is not affected while the pulmonary arterial pressure may rise slightly.[42,43] In the presence of mitral stenosis there is a distinct increase in both the pulmonary venous and pulmonary arterial pressures[44] presumably due to the combination of an increased cardiac output and decreased left ventricular filling time. Two of the three reports found a significant decrease in the pulmonary arterial resistance[43,44] (Table 13.5).

The decapeptide angiotensin I is acted on by a converting enzyme in the pulmonary circulation to form the octapeptide angiotensin II (p. 205). Angiotensin II is a strong vasoconstrictor in the systemic circulation while angiotensin I has no substantial effect. In the circulating blood angiotensin II is inactivated by an angiotensinase.

The intravenous infusion of angiotensin II causes an increase in the systemic arterial pressure (Table 13.5). This is accompanied by a slowing of the heart and a decrease in the cardiac output, presumably the result of stimulation of the baroreceptors. There is a substantial increase in both the pulmonary venous and pulmonary arterial pressures.[2,45,46] The pulmonary arterial resistance increases[2,45,46] (Table 13.5). Presumably the increase in the pulmonary venous pressure is due to the widespread constrictor activity of angiotensin II which reduces the overall compliance of the vascular system. To this may be added the effects on the left ventricle of an increased systemic arterial pressure. Despite the general increase in intravascular pressures throughout the lung, the pulmonary blood volume has been found to be decreased.[2] This supports the occurrence of a vasoconstriction in the pulmonary circulation (p. 184).

The infusion of angiotensin I also caused an increase in systemic arterial, pulmonary arterial and pulmonary venous pressures[47] (Table 13.5). In this case, however, there was no change in the pulmonary arterial resistance. Presumably, during its first passage through the lungs, the angiotensin I was largely converted to angiotensin II which caused systemic vasoconstriction. It is possible that the subsequent destruction of circulating angiotensin II by angiotensinase was sufficiently rapid to prevent a measurable effect on the pulmonary circulation.

The effects of the infusion of vasopressin on the systemic circulation and heart have been contradictory[48,49] (Table 13.5). The pulmonary venous and pulmonary arterial pressures tended to rise but there was no change in the pulmonary arterial resistance (Table 13.5).

Table 13.5 Effects of other naturally occurring substances on the human pulmonary circulation

Reference	Dose	No. and type of subjects	Mean pulmonary arterial pressure mmHg		Mean wedge or left atrial pressure mmHg		Pulmonary blood flow $l \cdot min^{-1}$ ($/m^2$ BSA)		Mean systemic arterial pressure mmHg		Heart rate bts. min^{-1}		Pulmonary arterial resistance[a] $dyn \cdot s \cdot cm^{-5}$	
			Before	After	Before	After	Before	After	Before	After	Before	After	Before	After
Angiotensin II														
45	1·5–2·0 μg/min i.v.	7N	15	22***	10	16***	7·2	5·6***	101	131***	91	75**	66	94*
46	0·015–0·135 μg/kg/min i.v.	16N	12	20****	7	13***	3·8[b]	3·3	87	119****	85	76	73[b]	127***
2	0·03–0·06 μg/kg/min i.v.	10MVD	28	40***	17	27***	(2·5)	(1·8)****	93	126****	—	—	236	424
Angiotensin I														
47	4 U/min	4N + 1E	16	23***	5	12****	(2·7)	(2·9)	86	119****	82	76***	185	175
Bradykinin														
42	0·3–1·0 μg/kg/min i.v.	8N	18	21*	11	10	(4·0)	(5·7)****	114	102***	85	104****	105	91
42	0·3–1·0 μg/kg/min i.v.	7H	43	49	12	13	(3·4)	(4·0)*	122	104***	91	104**	434	424
43	0·45–1·58 μg/kg/min i.v.	6H + 4N	18	18	5	6	(3·9)	(5·9)***	107	79****	80	97****	156	107**
44	0·75–1·42 μg/kg/min i.v.	21MVD	53	64****	23	31****	(2·4)	(3·3)****	89	72****	90	111****	840	656***
Vasopressin														
48	3–5 U/min	8C	23	25*	14	19***	(4·7)	(3·2)****	125	151****	104	88***	164	147
49	20 U in 30 min	5P	13	15	7	8	6·4	6·7	96	85**	—	—	80	91
Histamine														
62	0·1–0·3 μg/kg/min i.v.	8MS	32	36	21	28*	4·6	6·5***	112	94*	73	92*	221	114**
59	0·1–0·4 μg/kg/min i.v.	2N + 2P	12	9*	6	4	8·4	10·0	101	89***	84	95	62	38
60	0·1–0·4 μg/kg/min i.v.	4CP	30	30	21	23	4·6	6·6	107	95	77	86	156	94
61	0·1–0·45 μg/kg/min i.v.	6N♂	15	12*	9	8	8·0	10·4*	101	94*	68	81*	57	34*
61	0·1–0·45 μg/kg/min i.v.	5N♀	15	12*	7	6	6·6	9·1*	97	80*	84	104*	86	46*

H = systemic hypertension; C = cirrhotic; E = emphysema; CP = constrictive pericarditis; other abbreviations as in Table 13.1.
* $P < 0·05$; ** $P < 0·02$; *** $P < 0·01$; **** $P < 0·001$ (comparing before with after).
[a] See p. 135.
[b] n = 55.

5-hydroxytryptamine (serotonin) In animals 5-hydroxytryptamine has been shown to increase the pulmonary vascular resistance to an impressive extent.[50] In man[51–53] this does not appear to be so. Grover and his colleagues[53] report that, in seven patients with a normal pulmonary vascular pressure, the infusion of 5-hydroxytryptamine into the main pulmonary artery caused tachycardia and an increase in the cardiac output. The mean pulmonary arterial pressure rose while the wedge pressure remained unchanged. There was no significant alteration in the pulmonary arterial resistance. In seven normal subjects[51] the infusion of 5-hydroxytryptamine into the main pulmonary artery had no effect on the pulmonary arterial pressure except in one case where an increase in the pulmonary arterial pressure accompanied an increase in the systemic arterial pressure. The cardiac output was not affected in this study.

The pulmonary hypertension which followed the infusion of 5-hydroxytryptamine in animals was found to be associated with the lodging of many small emboli in the pulmonary arteries.[54] The material composing the emboli soon broke up and passed through the capillaries, after which the pulmonary vascular resistance returned to normal. The action of 5-hydroxytryptamine in animals may, therefore, be entirely a mechanical one, and the difference between man and animals may lie in the chemical composition of the blood rather than in the medial musculature of the pulmonary arteries.

It has been suggested[55] that the local liberation of 5-hydroxytryptamine may give rise to pulmonary hypertension in the presence of thromboemboli, but the above data do not support this theory (Chap. 35).

5-hydroxytryptamine is sometimes produced in large quantities by patients with malignant carcinoid tumours. The occurrence of pulmonary hypertension due to 5-hydroxytryptamine in animals has given rise to the expectation that it would also occur in these patients. Pulmonary hypertension is, however, not a feature of this disease[56,57] and has been described in only one patient[58] who was in congestive cardiac failure and who had a history of asthma for twenty-two years.

Histamine Infusions of histamine cause a decrease in the systemic arterial pressure (Table 13.5). The heart rate and cardiac output increase, probably in response to the baroreceptors. In the presence of a normal mitral valve, there is little alteration in the pulmonary venous pressure and a tendency to a slight decrease in the pulmonary arterial pressure[59–61] (Table 13.5). In patients with mitral stenosis both the pulmonary venous and pulmonary arterial pressures increase.[62] As with isoprenaline (p. 189) and bradykinin (p. 196) the increase in pulmonary venous pressure under these circumstances is explicable by the combination of mitral stenosis, an increased cardiac output and a decreased time of diastole. The pulmonary arterial resistance has consistently decreased[50,60–62] whether or not the pulmonary intravascular pressures were increased or decreased. Thus the evidence for an active vasodilatation seems strong.

Prostaglandins These are hydroxy fatty acids comprising 20 carbon atoms with a cyclopentane ring. They are widely synthesized in the tissues, including the lung, from free arachidonic acid and dihomo-γ-linolenic acid. In addition to synthesis, the lung is capable of inactivation of prostaglandins (p. 206). They possess a wide variety of vasoconstrictor and vasodilator actions. We know of no report on their effects in the human pulmonary circulation at the time of writing. In animals, the E and A prostaglandins act as vasodilators of the pulmonary circulation[63-66] whereas prostaglandin $F_{2\alpha}$ constricts.[65-67]

OTHER VASOACTIVE DRUGS

Publications concerning a number of such drugs are summarized in Table 13.6. For the most part they appear to have a direct action on vascular smooth muscle although the intimate mechanisms whereby they affect the activity of the contractile proteins of the smooth muscle cells remain largely unknown.

Aminophylline has been studied by a number of investigators (Table 13.6). It causes a slight fall in systemic arterial blood pressure and some increase in the heart rate. The cardiac output has not usually been affected. There has been a decrease in the pulmonary arterial pressure in patients with acquired heart disease[3,68-70] and usually a decrease in the pulmonary venous pressure. In such patients a consistent decrease in the pulmonary arterial resistance has been found (Table 13.6). The pulmonary blood volume has been found to increase[3] and the combination of diminished pulmonary intravascular pressures, an increased pulmonary blood volume and a decreased resistance is good evidence of active vasodilatation.

Amyl nitrite This drug, given by inhalation, caused a notable decrease in the systemic arterial pressure in patients with mitral stenosis[11] (Table 13.6). An increase in cardiac output and rate occurred, probably as a consequence of baroreceptor response. The pulmonary arterial pressure did no change significantly but there was a substantial increase in the pulmonary venous pressure attributable to the increased cardiac output and diminished diastolic period in the presence of mitral stenosis. The pulmonary arterial resistance showed a highly significant fall.

Glyceryl trinitrate In contrast to the effects of amyl nitrite the effects of sublingual glyceryl trinitrate were negative[71] (Table 13.6). Since there was not any significant decrease in the systemic arterial pressure it is possible that the tablets used were ineffective. Such a lack of effect may occur during storage.

Papaverine, another drug with a known vasodilator action in the systemic circulation, had no significant effect in the pulmonary circulation[72] (Table 13.6).

Procaine In a study on forty two patients with unspecified heart disease, intravenous procaine appeared to cause some decrease in the pulmonary arterial resistance[73] (Table 13.6).

Reserpine Although this drug has a powerful action on nerve terminals and causes a depletion of noradrenaline (p. 176) its dilating action on vascular smooth muscle appears to be an independent and direct one.[74] Evidence from several sources suggests that it is a pulmonary vasodilator[19,75-77] (Table 13.6). There may or may not be a slight lowering of the systemic arterial pressure and increase in the

Table 13.6 The effects of drugs having a direct action on vascular smooth muscle on the human pulmonary circulation

Reference	Dose	No. and type of subjects	Mean pulmonary arterial pressure mmHg		Mean wedge or left atrial pressure mmHg		Pulmonary blood flow $l \cdot min^{-1}$ ($/m^2$ BSA)		Mean systemic arterial pressure mmHg		Heart rate bts. min^{-1}		Pulmonary arterial resistance[a] $dyn \cdot s \cdot cm^{-5}$	
			Before	After	Before	After	Before	After	Before	After	Before	After	Before	After
Aminophylline														
134	0·5 g i.v.	4N	14	14	9	6	(3·2)	(3·2)	104	101	82	104*	130	145
134	0·5 g i.v.	6A	22	18*	12	8*	(2·5)	(3·0)	110	111	78	105***	311	280
70	0·3 g i.v.	17AHD	18	13****	7	6	(2·8)	(3·0)	102	99*	89	96**	232	139**
3	0·25–0·75 g i.v.	17MVD	38	32***	23	19***	(2·2)	(2·2)	94	93	79	82	403	321**
3	0·25–0·75 g i.v.	14AVD	22	17***	12	10***	(2·4)	(2·4)	89	86*	71	77***	186	144*
68	0·24 g i.v.	9MS	44	36***	25	22	(2·8)	(2·9)	—	—	—	—	392	256**
69	0·4 g i.v.	11H	23	19****	14	10***	5·0	5·7***	150	154	78	84**	166	131
Dihydroergotamine														
78	1 mg in P.A.	6N	19	24*	11	16*	(4·0)	(3·7)	117	129	98	90	173	180
Paverine														
72	0·06 g i.v.	7AHD + 3P	16	14***	9	8	(3·1)	(2·9)	109	107	87	86	128	102
Amyl nitrite														
11	inhalation	8MS	62	59	24	32***	2·9	3·9***	92	66****	78	102***	1107	605****
Glyceryl trinitrate														
71	sub-ling.	3N	16	11	10	6	(3·6)	(3·4)	105	99	68	79	75	67
Procaine														
73	0·1 g in R.V.	42NS	31	27***	20	19	(6·3)	(5·9)	112	111	—	—	178	124*
Reserpine														
75	1 mg in P.A.	10MS	31	27	21	19	(3·6)	(3·6)	96	93	—	—	216	148
76	1–2 mg in P.A.	11P	23	20****	6	7	4·4	4·8*	94	94	92	90	342	230***
77	0·02 mg/kg in P.A.	2N + 10AHD	40	34*	20	20	(3·0)	(3·0)	92	87***	83	77	449	291*
19	1–2 mg in P.A.	5P	22	18*	7	9	3·9	4·3	96	93	74	78	322	187*

A = asthma; AVD = aortic valvar disease; NS = not specified; H = systemic hypertension; other abbreviations as in Table 13.1.
* $P < 0{\cdot}05$; ** $P < 0{\cdot}02$; *** $P < 0{\cdot}01$; **** $P < 0{\cdot}001$ (comparing before with after).
[a] See p. 135.

cardiac output. The pulmonary venous pressure is unaffected but the pulmonary arterial pressure falls.

Dihydroergotamine This drug has mild α-blocking properties, but its strong vasoconstrictor action in the systemic circulation seems to be due to an independent effect on vascular smooth muscle. Although it increased both the pulmonary arterial and pulmonary venous pressures[78] (Table 13.6) this would seem to be secondary to systemic vasoconstriction and no change in the pulmonary arterial resistance was noted.

Possible Rôle of Systemic Baroreceptors

Of the drugs which have just been considered, amyl nitrite, histamine and bradykinin all cause a decrease in the systemic arterial pressure and this is accompanied by an increased cardiac rate and output. Conversely, angiotensin II and vasopressin increase the systemic arterial pressure and this is accompanied by a decreased cardiac rate and output. It seems likely that the effects on the cardiac rate and output are mediated by inhibition of the baroreceptors in the first group and by stimulation of the baroreceptors in the second group. The drugs of the first group cause pulmonary as well as systemic vasodilatation. Those of the second group cause systemic vasoconstriction while pulmonary vasoconstriction was demonstrated only with angiotensin II.

While, therefore, the changes in the pulmonary arterial resistance are consistent with the direct effects of these drugs which are known to occur in vascular smooth muscle elsewhere in the circulation, a possible influence of the sympathetic nervous system on the pulmonary blood vessels cannot be excluded. We are not aware of any investigations in which these drugs have been given during sympathetic blockade.

Effects of Pulmonary Vasodilators on Systemic Arterial Oxygen Saturation

Halmagyi and Cotes[79] first noted that the intravenous administration of the bronchodilators adrenaline and aminophylline to patients with chronic pulmonary disease caused a paradoxical fall in the systemic arterial oxygen saturation. They suggested that the drugs had caused pulmonary vasodilatation which had given rise to an increased inequality of ventilation: perfusion ratios (Chap. 36, p. 569). Other substances which cause pulmonary vasodilatation have been shown to have a similar effect: acetylcholine[80–82]; reserpine[19,76]; histamine[59,60,62]; tolazoline[18]; phentolamine.[21] This has not, however, been found with isoprenaline in patients with pulmonary disease[24,27] or with bradykinin in patients with mitral valvar disease.[44] A further, more detailed, consideration of the effects of acetylcholine on the distribution of ventilation:perfusion ratios in patients with mitral stenosis is given in Chapter 23, p. 362.

DRUGS AFFECTING PATHOLOGICAL PROCESSES IN PULMONARY BLOOD VESSELS

Anticoagulant and thrombolytic drugs The effects of drugs on thromboemboli are considered in Chapter 35, p. 556.

Steroids Triamcinolone and prednisone have been given to patients with acquired cardiac disease for up to 13 days but no effect on the pulmonary arterial resistance was found.[83]

Long-term vasodilatation Zoxazolamine, a vasodilator with a central nervous system action[84] has been found to reduce the incidence of hypertensive pulmonary vascular disease in rats treated with monocrotaline.[85]

Anorexigens and primary pulmonary hypertension The possible relation between aminorex fumarate and primary pulmonary hypertension is discussed in Chapter 27, p. 410.

Oral contraceptives and pulmonary vascular disease There has been controversy as to whether or not women taking oral contraceptives show an increased risk of developing pulmonary vascular disease. Three distinct pathological entities have been considered—hypertensive pulmonary vascular disease, non-specific intimal lesions and pulmonary thromboembolism. We shall pay attention to each of these in turn.

Oakley and Somerville[86] found clinical and haemodynamic evidence of a rapid acceleration of hypertensive pulmonary vascular disease in three of their female patients who had taken oral contraceptives. All three were in their twenties and had respectively a large ventricular septal defect, a single atrium with dextrocardia and a cleft anterior cusp of the mitral valve, and a patent ductus arteriosus with reversed flow. Thus all three patients had predisposing causes for severe pulmonary hypertension and the plexogenic variety of hypertensive pulmonary vascular disease. Material from the lung of the young woman with the single atrium was examined by one of us (D.H.) and found to show grade 5 arterial changes with angiomatoid lesions. There was no evidence of superimposed thrombosis or thromboembolism.

Other evidence that oestrogens may lead to an increased pulmonary vascular resistance is indirect. The incidence of spontaneous primary pulmonary hypertension is higher in females (Chap. 28, p. 429). Female rats have been found to have an increased susceptibility to the pulmonary hypertensive effects of chronic hypoxia (Chap. 32, p. 494). Certainly thrombosis does not appear to play a rôle in the pathogenesis of hypertensive pulmonary vascular disease which needs to be considered as a separate and specific pathological entity. So far, the clinical suspicion[86] that the progress of hypertensive pulmonary vascular disease may be hastened by oral contraceptives has not been followed by statistical evidence.

According to Irey and associates[87,88] the pulmonary arteries, like systemic arteries and veins and portal veins, may be vascular target organs of oestrogenic steroids. They studied necropsy material from pregnant and post-partum women and also from women who had taken oral contraceptives. They found non-specific intimal lesions, akin to those which occur in the myometrial arteries in early pregnancy, in sixteen cases. There was a cellular endothelial proliferation of the intima which subsequently became associated with myxomatous or fibrous changes. Although the authors recognized that such vascular lesions are not specific, they point out that they may provoke an overlying thrombosis which may lead to serious sequelae such as myocardial infarction or the development of right ventricular hypertrophy.[87,88] These authors would regard the thrombus in the pulmonary arterial tree of affected patients to be autochthonous rather than embolic in nature. Some authorities are very doubtful as to whether such arterial disease may be induced by oestrogens and regard the lesions described by Irey and his colleagues as non-specific.[89]

The vascular disorder most widely suspected as a complication of taking oral contraceptives is thromboembolism. The main evidence put forward to support the hypothesis that there is a causal relationship between oral contraception and thromboembolic disease is based upon retrospective studies carried out first in Britain and later in the United States. In the first,[90] published in 1968, inquiries about the use of oral contraceptives were made in a series of women where death certificates mentioned thrombosis or embolism of the pulmonary, cerebral or coronary arteries. A matched control series was also studied. It was concluded that a strong association between the use of oral contraceptives and deaths from pulmonary embolism in previously healthy women had been established. These results were considered to be supported by a further retrospective study employing the records of several hospitals outside London.[91]

On the other hand, the results from prospective studies have been entirely negative. Earlier studies compiled by Drill and Calhoun[92] have been criticized.[93] However, such criticisms do not appear to apply to a more recent large-scale prospective investigation, the results of which were also negative.[94]

In his critical review of the subject, Hougie[89] concludes that the positive results found in retrospective studies have been due to the high index of suspicion engendered by the knowledge that the patient is taking oral contraceptives.

There is no doubt that significant increases in prothrombin and Factors VII, IX and X occur in users of oral contraceptives.[89] However, such increases do not necessarily imply that there is a greater tendency to thrombosis. As we have seen elsewhere (Chap. 35, p. 549) a careful histological examination of the lungs in a series of routine necropsies has indicated that pulmonary thromboembolism is a very common condition indeed. The frequency with which it is diagnosed both at the bedside and at routine necropsy is considerably lower. In the face of this, it is difficult to know what importance should be attached to statistics related to pulmonary thromboembolism derived from death certificates, and to minor shifts in incidence from what are obviously erroneously low levels.

From a practical standpoint the increased risk of pulmonary vascular disease from oral contraceptives seems slight, if it exists at all, and has to be measured against the potential morbidity and mortality of unwanted pregnancies and the convenience and effectiveness of other methods of contraception. The lowered oestrogen content of most oral contraceptives during the last few years has also to be borne in mind since statistics based on earlier dosages of oestrogen may no longer be relevant.

MODIFICATION OF ACTIVITY OF CIRCULATING VASOMOTOR SUBSTANCES BY THE PULMONARY CIRCULATION

In addition to the vasomotor action of circulating substances on the pulmonary circulation, there is now evidence that the lungs themselves play an important pharmacokinetic rôle. This has recently been extensively reviewed by Bakhle and Vane[95] and Heinemann and Fishman.[96] A number of vasoactive substances are inactivated, activated or liberated during the passage of blood through the lungs and the present experimental evidence suggests that the pulmonary vascular endothelial cells may often be the site of such metabolic processes. Thus the function of the pulmonary circulation can no longer be considered simply in terms of the exchange of respiratory gases. At first sight the structure of the lungs and its blood vessels does not suggest such an important metabolic activity. However, even at rest, the entire blood volume passes each minute through the lungs where a rich capillary network ensures intimate contact with vascular endothelium. Thus, for the rapid modification of circulating vasoactive substances, the lungs are more advantageously placed than other organs which can receive at each circulation only a fraction of the cardiac output. In retrospect, therefore, it is surprising that a filtration function of the pulmonary circulation, so obvious for particulate matter, was not appreciated earlier for chemical substances.

Catecholamines An uptake of noradrenaline during passage through the pulmonary circulation has been shown in a number of animals[95] and in man[97–99] where it amounts to some 30 per cent. Experiments in animals[95] suggest that the uptake mechanism is saturable. It is inhibited by cocaine, but not by destruction of the sympathetic nerve endings. Only some 20 per cent of the uptake is recoverable as noradrenaline, the rest having been catabolized by monoamine oxidase and catechol-o-methyltransferase activity. Autoradiography and fluorescence microscopy have identified the endothelial cells of the pulmonary capillaries and venules as the site of uptake. It seems, therefore, that noradrenaline is bound initially to binding sites on or in the vascular endothelium and subsequently metabolised. The inhibition of binding by cocaine presumably also occurs in the vascular endothelial cell and the sympathetic nerve terminals are not implicated.

In contrast to its handling of noradrenaline, the pulmonary circulation of animals[95] and man[100] does not remove adrenaline from the circulating blood. The same seems to apply to isoprenaline.[101]

Histamine Experiments on dogs, cats and rats[95] have failed to reveal any uptake of histamine in the pulmonary circulation. On the other hand, lung slices or homogenates from various animals[95] and man[102] readily metabolize added histamine. This apparent discrepancy reflects the inhomogeniety of the cell population of the lung. Different cells have different functions which are carried out according to their location in the tissue. The uptake and metabolism of substances from the blood must depend on the micro-anatomical route which they have to follow. The application of results from lung tissue homogenates or subcellular fractions runs the risk of ignoring this important consideration.

5-hydroxytryptamine It is now half a century since Starling and Verney[103] showed that a substance was present in defibrinated blood which caused such intense vasoconstriction in the kidney that adequate perfusion of the isolated organ became impossible. If, however, the kidney was perfused from a heart–lung preparation, the constrictor substance was removed.

The constrictor substance, now identified as 5-hydroxytryptamine (serotonin), has been shown to be removed during passage through the lungs of a number of animals[95] and of man, in whom some three quarters of injected material were removed on first circulation.[99] Radioautography[104] has shown tritiated 5-hydroxytryptamine to be located in the endothelial cells of arterioles and capillaries in rats' lungs with no labelling of mast cells or smooth muscle cells. The uptake of 5-hydroxytryptamine may be inhibited by amitryptyline and desmethylimipramine which are known to inhibit its uptake by platelets. Hypoxia and cocaine are also inhibitory.[95] The subsequent fate of the 5-hydroxytryptamine taken up by the lungs appears to be oxidative deamination to 5-hydroxyindoleacetic acid, a process which can be inhibited by monoamine oxidase inhibitors.

Angiotensin After release from the kidney renin acts on an α_2-globulin in the plasma to split off a decapeptide, angiotensin I. The decapeptide has little effect on smooth muscle. It can, however, be converted to the highly vasoconstrictor octapeptide, angiotensin II, by the hydrolytic removal of the COOH-terminal dipeptide. The enzyme responsible for this conversion is known as 'converting enzyme'. It was originally discovered in plasma but it is now clear that, in the body, the main site of converting enzyme activity is the pulmonary circulation. This rôle of the pulmonary circulation has been confirmed in man.[105]

Converting enzyme is a peptidase capable of attacking the COOH-terminal dipeptide of a number of naturally occurring and artificial substrates. It has, however, no further effect on angiotensin II and does not attack oxytocin or vasopressin.[95] Its relation to bradykinin is discussed below. It may be inhibited by peptides from certain snake venoms and this action has been shown in man.[106]

When ^{14}C-angiotensin I and blue dextran were injected simultaneously,[107] the dilution curves for radioactivity and dextran after passage through the pulmonary circulation were identical, although some of the angiotensin I had been converted to angiotensin II. The blue dextran molecule is large and does not leave the circulation. The identity of the dilution curves suggests that the two substances occupied the same distribution volume (see Chap. 8, p. 105). This is, therefore, evidence that the site of the pulmonary converting enzyme is on the luminal surface of the pulmonary vascular endothelium.[107]

Angiotensin II is destroyed by an angiotensinase in the blood but it is not specifically affected by passage through the pulmonary circulation.[95,105] Enzymes capable of hydrolyzing the octapeptide are, however, present in lung homogenates.

This is a further example of how inappropriate studies on lung homogenates may be to the handling of substances passing through in the blood.

Bradykinin This vasoactive peptide is also attacked by enzyme hydrolysis during passage through the pulmonary circulation.[108] In this case, however, the result is a loss of physiological activity. A number of peptidases capable of hydrolyzing bradykinin at various peptide bonds has been described. It seems likely that the converting enzyme for angiotensin is also active in splitting bradykinin.[109]

Other peptides The specificity of the attack on angiotensin I and bradykinin is underlined by observations that other peptides pass through the lungs unchanged. These include eledoisin, 'Substance P', physalaemin, oxytocin and vasopressin[95] in animals and vasopressin in man.[110]

Serum α_1-antitrypsin has been shown to be diminished during passage through the lungs in patients with chronic bronchitis but not in normals or patients with non-obstructive pulmonary disease.[111]

Prostaglandins Homogenates of animals' lungs have been shown to be capable of synthesizing prostaglandins E_2 and $F_{2\alpha}$ from arachiodonic acid and prostaglandins E_1 and $F_{1\alpha}$ from dihomo-γ-linolenic acid.[95] It seems likely that an external source of these essential fatty acids would be required since animal tissues are not able to synthesize them.

Prostaglandins of the E and F series and, to a lesser extent, those of the A series are inactivated during passage through the pulmonary circulation in animals.[95,112] Lung tissue contains a number of enzymes capable of attacking prostaglandins in different ways and at different sites. Possibly the most important is 15-hydroxy prostaglandin dehydrogenase inhibitors of which have been found to prevent the inactivation of prostaglandin E_2 during passage through guinea pig lungs.[95]

The ability of the lungs to synthesize, store and release (see later) prostaglandins and to inactivate them implies the existence of discrete locations of these various activities, the nature of which has not been elucidated. It seems. clear, however, that the pulmonary circulation is an important site of control of these substances which are capable of such powerful effects on the cardiovascular system.

Release of vasoactive substances Anaphylaxis causes a release of histamine, prostaglandins and other less well identified or documented substances from animals' lungs.[95] A phospholipase A from bee venom has also been shown to release both histamine and prostaglandins. Histamine itself causes the release of prostaglandins.

A number of chemical substances causes the release of prostaglandins without the release of histamine. These include the fatty acid precursors of prostaglandins (dihomo-γ-linolenic acid and arachidonic acid), acetylcholine, tryptamine, 5-hydroxytryptamine and tyramine.

A variety of physical stimuli can cause the release of prostaglandins and often histamine into the pulmonary circulation. Among such stimuli are over-inflation of the lung, mechanical handling of the lung and the injection of chemically inert pulmonary emboli.

The non-steroid anti-inflammatory drugs, aspirin, indomethacin, phenylbutazone and meclofenamate, have the property of inhibiting the synthesis of prostaglandins in tissues. Such drugs prevent the release of prostaglandins into the pulmonary circulation by anaphylaxis, chemical or physical stimuli but have no effect on the release of histamine.

REFERENCES

1. Luchsinger, P. C., Seipp, H. W. & Patel, D. V. (1962) *Circulat. Res.*, **11**, 315.
2. Oakley, C., Glick, G., Luria, M. N., Schreiner, B. F. & Yu, P. N. (1962) *Circulation*, **26**, 917.
3. Murphy, G. W., Schreiner, B. F. & Yu, P. N. (1968) *Circulation*, **37**, 361.
4. Aviado, D. M. (1965) *The Lung Circulation.* Pergamon.
5. Ahlquist, R. P. (1948) *Amer. J. Physiol.*, **153**, 586.
6. Jenkinson, D. H. (1973) *Brit. Med. Bull.*, **29**, 142.
7. Patel, D. J., Lange, R. L. & Hecht, H. H. (1958) *Circulation*, **18**, 19.
8. Regan, T. J., DeFazio, V., Binak, K. & Hellems, H. K. (1959) *J. Clin. Invest.*, **38**, 1564.
9. Bousvaros, G. A. (1962) *Brit. Heart J.*, **24**, 738.
10. Abrahamson, A. M., Grendahl, H. & Muller, C. (1972) *Acta Med. Scand.*, **191**, 283.
11. Beck, W., Schrire, V. & Vogelpoel, L. (1962) *Amer. Heart J.*, **64**, 631.
12. Eliasch, H., Malmborg, R., Pernow, B. & Zetterquist, S. (1964) *Acta Med. Scand.*, **175**, 167.
13. Dresdale, D. T., Schultz, M. & Mitchtom, R. J. (1951) *Amer. J. Med.*, **11**, 686.
14. Dresdale, D. T., Mitchtom, R. J. & Schultz, M. (1954) *Bull. N.Y. Acad. Med.*, **30**, 195.
15. Gardiner, J. M. (1954) *Aust. Ann. Med.*, **3**, 59.
16. Rudolph, A. M., Paul, M. H., Sommer, L. S. & Nadas, A. S. (1958) *Amer. Heart J.*, **55**, 424.
17. Grover, R. F., Reeves, J. T. & Blount, S. G., Jn. (1961) *Amer. Heart J.*, **61**, 5.
18. Widimský, J., Kasalický, J., Valach, A., Dejdar, R., Vysloužil, Z. & Lukes, M. (1960) *Brit. Heart J.*, **22**, 571.
19. Kasalický, J., Widimský, J. & Dejdar, R. (1963) *Cor et Vasa*, **5**, 264.
20. Storstein, O., Elgvin, T., Helle, I. & Sebelien, J. (1957) *Scand. J. Clin. Lab. Invest.*, **9**, 150.
21. Yoshida, Y. (1969) *Jap. Circ. J.*, **33**, 359.
22. Cox, A. R., Cobb, L. A. & Bruce, R. A. (1963) *Amer. Heart J.*, **65**, 802.
23. McGaff, C. J., Roveti, G. C., Glassman, E. & Milnor, W. R. (1963) *Circulation*, **27**, 77.
24. Williams, J. F., Jn., White, D. H., Jn. & Behnke, R. H. (1963) *Circulation*, **28**, 396.
25. Whalen, R. E., Cohen, A. I., Sumner, R. G. & McIntosh, H. D. (1963) *Circulation*, **27**, 512.
26. Schreiner, B. F., Jn., Murphy, G. W., James, D. H. & Yu, P. N. (1968) *Circulation*, **37**, 220.
27. Ferrer, M. I., Enson, Y., Kilcoyne, M. M. & Harvey, R. M. (1971) *Circulation*, **43**, 528.
28. Balchum, O. J., Gensini, G. & Blount, S. G., Jn. (1957) *J. Lab. Clin. Med.*, **50**, 186.
29. Donald, K. W. & Taylor, S. H. (1960) *Lancet*, **ii**, 389.
30. Harris, P., Bishop, J. M. & Segel, N. (1961) *Clin. Sci.*, **21**, 295.
31. Rockseth, R., Storstein, O., Voll, A., Abrahamsen, A. M. & Ofstad, J. (1962) *Brit. Heart J.*, **24**, 195.
32. Taylor, S. H., Sutherland, G. R., Hutchison, D. C. S., Langford Kidd, B. S., Robertson, P. C., Kennelly, B. M. & Donald, K. W. (1962) *Amer. Heart J.*, **63**, 239.
33. Harris, P. (1955) *Ph.D. Thesis.* University of London.
34. Harris, P. (1955) *Brit. Heart J.*, **17**, 85.
35. Harris, P. (1957) *Brit. Heart J.*, **19**, 272.
36. Wood, P., Besterman, E. M., Towers, M. K. & McIlroy, M. B. (1957) *Brit. Heart J.*, **19**, 279.
37. Harris, P., Fritts, H. W., Jn., Clauss, R. H., Odell, J. E. & Cournand, A. (1956) *Proc. Soc. Exp. Biol. (N.Y.)*, **93**, 77.
38. Fritts, H. W., Jn., Harris, P., Clauss, R. H., Odell, J. E. & Cournand, A. (1958) *J. Clin. Invest.*, **37**, 99.

39. Swenson, E. W., Arborelius, M., Jn., Daicoff, G. R., Bartley, T. D. & Lilja, B. (1974) *Scand. J. Resp. Dis.*, Suppl. **85**, 92.
40. Glazier, J. B., Dollery, C. T. & Hughes, J. M. B. (1968) *Circulation*, **38**, 136.
41. Giuntini, C., Maseri, A. & Bianchi, R. (1966) *J. Clin. Invest.*, **45**, 1770.
42. Bishop, J. M., Harris, P. & Segel, N. (1965) *Brit. J. Pharmacol.*, **25**, 456.
43. de Freitas, F. M., Faraco, E. Z. & de Azevedo, D. F. (1964) *Circulation*, **29**, 66.
44. de Freitas, F. M., Faraco, E. Z., de Azevedo, D. F. & Lewin, I. (1966) *Circulation*, **34**, 385.
45. Segel, N., Harris, P. & Bishop, J. M. (1961) *Clin. Sci.*, **20**, 49.
46. Yu, P. N., Luria, M. N., Finlayson, J. K., Stanfield, C. A., Constantine, H. & Flatley, F. J. (1961) *Circulation*, **24**, 1326.
47. Sancetta, S. M. (1960) *Circulat. Res.*, **8**, 616.
48. Segel, N., Bayley, T. J., Paton, A., Dykes, P. & Bishop, J. M. (1963) *Clin. Sci.*, **25**, 43.
49. Ribot, S., Green, H. & Small, M. J. (1961) *Amer. J. Med. Sci.*, **242**, 612.
50. Aviado, D. M. (1960) *Pharmacol. Rev.*, **12**, 159.
51. Harris, P., Fritts, H. W., Jn. & Cournand, A. (1960) *Circulation*, **21**, 1134.
52. Nemir, P., Jn., Stone, H. H., Mackrell, T. N. & Hawthorne, H. R. (1954) *Surg. Forum*, **5**, 210.
53. Grover, R. F., Olson, S. K. & Blount, S. G., Jn. (1958) *Clin. Res.*, **8**, 62.
54. Kniseley, W. H., Wallace, J. M. & Addison, W. A. (1958) *Fed. Proc.*, **17**, 88.
55. Comroe, J. H., Jn., Van Lingen, B., Stroud, R. C. & Roncoroni, A. (1953) *Amer. J. Physiol.*, **173**, 379.
56. Goble, A. J., Hay, D. R., Hudson, R. & Sander, M. (1956) *Brit. Heart J.*, **18**, 544.
57. Thorson, A. & Nordenfelt, O. (1959) *Brit. Heart J.*, **21**, 243.
58. Sjoerdsma, A., Weissbach, H., Terry, L. L. & Udenfriend, S. (1957) *Amer. J. Med.*, **23**, 5.
59. Bjure, J., Söderholm, B. & Widimský, J. (1966) *Scand. J. Resp. Dis.*, **47**, 53.
60. Lindell, S.-E., Svanborg, A., Söderholm, B. & Westling, H. (1963) *Brit. Heart J.*, **25**, 35.
61. Bjure, J., Helander, E., Lindell, S.-E., Söderholm, B. & Westling, H. (1967) *Scand. J. Resp. Dis.*, **48**, 214.
62. Lindell, S.-E., Söderholm, B. & Westling, H. (1964) *Brit. Heart J.*, **26**, 180.
63. Hauge, A., Lunde, P. K. M. & Waaler, B. A. (1967) *Life Sci.*, **6**, 673.
64. Nakano, J. & McCurdy, J. R. (1968) *Proc. Soc. Exper. Biol. Med.*, **128**, 39.
65. Hyman, A. L. (1968) *Clin. Res.*, **16**, 71.
66. Hyman, A. L. (1969) *J. Pharmacol. Exp. Therap.*, **165**, 267.
67. Änggård, E. & Bergström, S. (1963) *Acta Physiol. Scand.*, **58**, 1.
68. Dulfano, M. J., Yahni, J., Toor, M., Rosen, N. & Langer, L. (1956) *J. Lab. Clin. Med.*, **48**, 329.
69. Werkö, L. & Lagerlöf, H. (1950) *Scand. J. Clin. Lab. Invest.*, **2**, 181.
70. Storstein, O., Helle, I. & Rokseth, R. (1958) *Amer. Heart J.*, **55**, 781.
71. Brachfeld, N., Bozer, J. & Gorlin, R. (1959) *Circulation*, **19**, 697.
72. Rokseth, R., Kjørstad, H., Skaga, E. & Storstein, O. (1960) *Scand. J. Clin. Lab. Invest.*, **12**, 493.
73. Gottsegen, G., Romoda, T. & Matheides, P. (1959) *Acta Cardiologica*, **14**, 149.
74. Goodman, L. S. & Gilman, A. (1970) *The Pharmacological Basis of Therapeutics*. MacMillan.
75. Halmágyi, D., Felkai, B., Czipott, Z. & Kovacs, G. (1957) *Brit. Heart J.*, **19**, 375.
76. Widimský, J., Kasalický, J., Dejdar, R., Vysoužil, Z. & Lukeš, M. (1962) *Brit. Heart J.*, **24**, 274.
77. Faraco, E. Z., Nedel, N., de Azevedo, D. F., de Freitas, F. M. (1963) *Acta Cardiologica*, **18**, 105.
78. Harris, P., Bishop, J. M. & Segel, N. (1963) *Clin. Sci.*, **25**, 443.
79. Halmagyi, D. & Cotes, J. E. (1959) *Clin. Sci.*, **18**, 475.
80. Söderholm, B., Werkö, L. & Widimský, J. (1962) *Acta Med. Scand.*, **172**, 95.
81. Stanfield, C. A., Finlayson, J. K., Luria, M. N., Constantine, H., Flatley, F. J. & Yu, P. N. (1961) *Circulation*, **24**, 1164.
82. Bateman, M., Davidson, L. A. G., Donald, K. W. & Harris, P. (1962) *Clin. Sci.*, **22**, 223.
83. Greene, N. A., Gordon, A. & Boltax, A. J. (1960) *Circulation*, **21**, 661.

84. Burns, J. J., Yu, T. F., Berger, L. & Gutman, A. B. (1958) *Amer. J. Med.*, **25**, 401.
85. Kay, J. M., Smith, P., Heath, D. & Will, J. A. (1976) *Cardiovasc. Res.*, **10**, 200.
86. Oakley, C. & Somerville, J. (1968) *Lancet*, **i**, 890.
87. Irey, N. S. & Norris, H. J. (1973) *Arch. Path.*, **96**, 227.
88. Irey, N. S., Manion, W. C. & Taylor, H. B. (1970) *Arch. Path.*, **89**, 1.
89. Hougie, C. (1973) *Amer. Heart J.*, **85**, 538.
90. Inman, W. H. W. & Vessey, M. P. (1968) *Brit. Med. J.*, **2**, 193.
91. Vessey, M. P. & Doll, R. (1968) *Brit. Med. J.*, **2**, 199.
92. Drill, V. A. & Calhoun, D. W. (1969) *J.A.M.A.*, **207**, 1151.
93. Seltzer, C. C. (1969) *J.A.M.A.*, **207**, 1152.
94. Fuertes, de la Haba, A., Curet, J. O., Pelegrina, I. & Bangdiwala, I. (1971) *Obstet. Gyn.*, **38**, 259.
95. Bakhle, Y. S. & Vane, J. R. (1974) *Physiol. Rev.*, **54**, 1007.
96. Heinemann, H. O. & Fishman, A. P. (1969) *Physiol. Rev.*, **49**, 2.
97. Boileau, J.-C., Campeau, L. & Biron, P. (1972) *Rev. Canad. Biol.*, **31**, 185.
98. Gillis, C. N., Greene, N. M., Cronau, L. H. & Hammond, G. L. (1972) *Circulat. Res.*, **30**, 666.
99. Gillis, C. N., Cronau, L. H., Greene, N. M. & Hammond, G. L. (1974) *Surgery*, **76**, 608.
100. Boileau, J.-C., Campeau, L. & Biron, P. (1971) *Rev. Canad. Biol.*, **30**, 281.
101. Boileau, J.-C., Campeau, L. & Biron, P. (1970) *Canad. J. Physiol. Pharmacol.*, **48**, 681.
102. Lilja, B., Lindell, S. E. & Saldeen, T. (1960) *J. Allergy*, **31**, 492.
103. Starling, E. H. & Verney, E. B. (1925) *Proc. Roy. Soc. (Ser. B.)*, **97**, 321.
104. Strum, J. M. & Junod, A. F. (1972) *J. Cell. Biol.*, **54**, 456.
105. Biron, P., Campeau, L. & David, P. (1969) *Amer. J. Cardiol.*, **24**, 544.
106. Collier, J. G., Robinson, B. F. & Vane, J. R. (1973) *Lancet*, **i**, 72.
107. Ryan, J. W., Smith, U. & Niemeyer, R. S. (1972) *Science*, **176**, 64.
108. Ferreira, S. H. & Vane, J. R. (1967) *Brit. J. Pharmacol. Chemotherap.*, **30**, 417.
109. Ng, K. K. F. & Vane, J. R. (1968) *Nature*, **218**, 144.
110. Crexells, C., Bourassa, M. G. & Biron, P. (1972) *J. Clin. Endocrinol. Metab.*, **34**, 592.
111. Woolcock, A. J., Green, W. & Crockett, A. (1972) *Brit. Med. J.*, **2**, 134.
112. Nakano, J. (1973) In *The Prostaglandins*, ed. Cuthbert, M. F. P. 23. Heinemann.
113. Fowler, N. O., Westcott, R. N., Scott, R. C. & McGuire, J. (1951) *J. Clin. Invest.*, **30**, 517.
114. Patel, D. J., Lange, R. L. & Hecht, H. H. (1958) *Circulation*, **18**, 19.
115. Goldring, R. M., Turino, G. M., Cohen, G., Jameson, A. G., Bass, B. G. & Fishman, A. P. (1962) *J. Clin. Invest.*, **41**, 1211.
116. Witham, A. C. & Fleming, J. W. (1951) *J. Clin. Invest.*, **30**, 707.
117. Beregovich, J., Bianchi, C., Rubler, S., Lonnitz, E., Cagin, N. & Levitt, B. (1974) *Amer. Heart J.*, **87**, 550.
118. Rudolph, A. M., Paul, M. H., Sommer, L. S. & Nadas, A. A. (1958) *Amer. Heart J.*, **55**, 424.
119. Tsolakas, T. C., Davies, J. P. H. & Oram, S. (1965) *Lancet*, **ii**, 416.
120. Bhatia, M. L., Shrivastava, S. & Roy, S. B. (1972) *Brit. Heart J.*, **34**, 638.
121. Finegan, R. E., Marlon, A. M. & Harrison, D. C. (1972) *Amer. J. Cardiol.*, **29**, 315.
122. Howitt, G., Tinker, J. & Wade, E. G. (1965) *Clin. Sci.*, **28**, 417.
123. Werkö, L., Frisk, A. R., Wade, G. & Eliasch, H. (1951) *Lancet*, **ii**, 470.
124. Storstein, O. & Tveten, H. (1954) *Scand. J. Clin. Lab. Invest.*, **6**, 169.
125. Varnauskas, E. (1955) *Scand. J. Clin. Lab. Invest.*, 7, Suppl. 17.
126. Sancetta, S. M. (1957) *J. Lab. Clin. Med.*, **49**, 684.
127. Yu, P. N., Nye, R. E., Jn., Lovejoy, F. N., Jn., Schreiner, B. F. & Yim, B. J. B. (1958). *J. Clin. Invest.*, **37**, 194.
128. Fowler, N. O., Westcott, R. N., Hauenstein, V. D., Scott, R. C. & McGuire, J. (1950) *J. Clin. Invest.*, **29**, 1387.
129. Scott, R. C., Kaplan, S. & Stiles, W. J. (1955) *Amer. Heart J.*, **50**, 720.
130. Söderholm, B. & Widimský, J. (1962) *Acta Med. Scand.*, **172**, 229.
131. Oakley, C., Glick, G., Luria, M. N., Schreiner, B. F., Jn., & Yu, P. N. (1962) *Circulation*, **26**, 917.

132. Bishop, J. M., Harris, P., Bateman, M. & Davidson, L. A. C. (1961) *J. Clin. Invest.*, **40**, 105.
133. Gorlin, R., McMillan, I. K. R., Medd, W. E., Matthews, M. E. & Daley, R. (1955) *Amer. J. Med.*, **18**, 855.
134. Rees, H. A., MacDonald, H. R., Borthwick, R. G., Muir, A. L. & Donald, K. W. (1969) *Clin. Sci.*, **36**, 359.

14. Form and Function in the Foetal Pulmonary Circulation

The Structure of the Pulmonary Vasculature in the Foetus and Newborn

The structure of the pulmonary arterial tree in the foetus is very different from that in the adult. The pulmonary arteries of the foetal lung resemble closely their counterparts in the systemic vasculature, the elastic pulmonary arteries having a pattern of elastic tissue very similar to that of the aorta and the "muscular pulmonary arteries" being thick-walled and muscular. These structural features are associated with the high pulmonary arterial blood pressure which occurs in the foetus. During the first month of extra-uterine life, in babies free of cardiopulmonary disease and born at low altitude, the pressure in the pulmonary artery falls towards its adult value. At the same time the walls of the pulmonary arteries become thin. This is particularly apparent in their muscular component and in this respect the musculature of the lesser circulation may be considered as a continuous tube which includes that of the right ventricle as well as the major pulmonary arteries and small muscular pulmonary arteries.[1] It must be pointed out here that the changes in the pulmonary vasculature described below as occurring at birth and in infancy apply only to babies born at low altitude. These changes do not occur at high altitude where the chronic hypoxia brought about by the diminished barometric pressure leads to the persistence of a mild degree of pulmonary arterial hypertension. The pulmonary circulation of high altitude is discussed in Chapter 32.

The foetal pulmonary trunk At birth the media of the pulmonary trunk is as thick as that of the aorta but in infancy the thickness falls to only 40 to 70 per cent of that of the aorta.

The pattern of the elastic fibrils in the foetal pulmonary trunk is so similar to that in the aorta that, at a glance, the two may be confused with one another (Figs 14.1 and 14.2). Small differences become apparent on careful examination.[1] The elastic fibrils of the foetal aorta are long and run circumferentially. They are uniform in thickness, appearing thicker than those in the adult aorta, and are fairly compactly arranged (Fig. 14.1). The fibrils in the pulmonary trunk also run circumferentially but are fewer and, although mostly parallel to each other, are less regular. They are somewhat coarser than the aortic fibrils and some very short ones may be found. The thickness is less uniform, the ends of some showing small club-like expansions (Fig. 14.2). An appearance of this type is seen in the elastica of the major pulmonary arteries at birth and until the age of six months, when changes which no doubt started at birth become obvious.[1] The elastic fibrils still tend to be parallel but break transversely into numerous, short, stick-like fibrils (Fig. 14.3), some of which show the clubbed terminations referred to in the description of the adult pulmonary trunk of low altitude residents in Chapter 3. Other fragmented foetal elastic fibrils swell and assume grotesque shapes but they are not common. As a result of the fragmentation, the appearance of the elastic

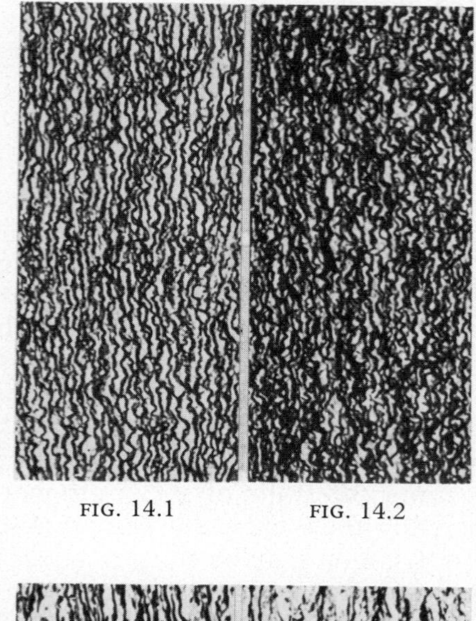

FIG. 14.1 FIG. 14.2

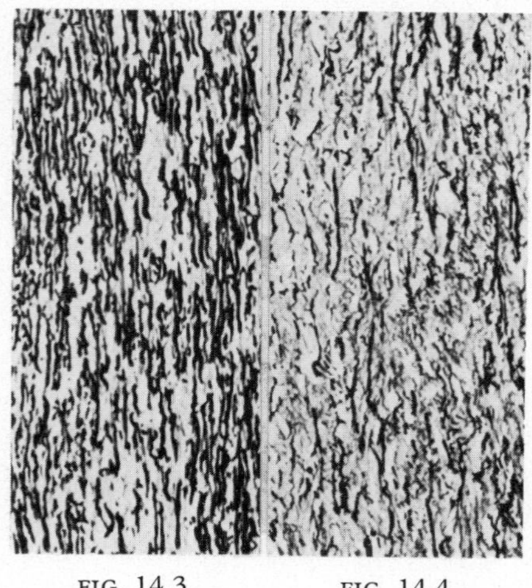

FIG. 14.3 FIG. 14.4

Transverse sections of the normal pulmonary trunk or normal aorta stained to demonstrate elastic tissue. The ratios given in each instance express the thickness of the media of the pulmonary trunk in relation to that of the aorta in the same cases.

Fig. 14.1 Aorta of 7½-month foetus. The elastic fibrils are long, uniform and roughly parallel with one another (× 150). Fig. 14.2 Pulmonary trunk from same case as in preceding figure (ratio 0·9). The appearances are similar to, although not identical with, those of the aorta (× 150). Fig. 14.3 Pulmonary trunk. Male infant aged 9 months (ratio 0·5). The elastic tissue shows a transitional configuration in which the individual fibrils are fragmented into stick-like masses (× 100). Fig. 14.4 Pulmonary trunk. Youth aged 16 years (ratio 0·5). The adult pulmonary appearance of a loosely-arranged network of irregularly-shaped branched fibrils is seen (× 75).

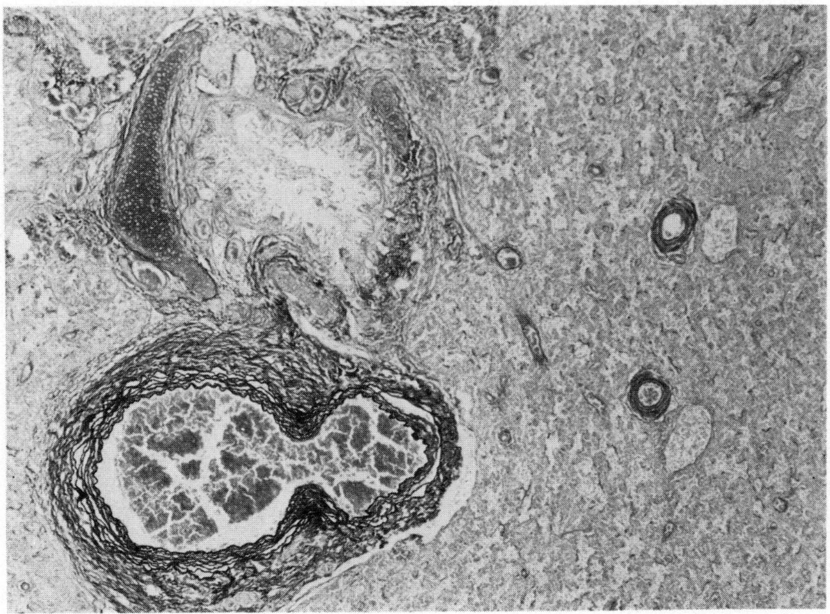

Fig. 14.5 A section of lung from a new-born infant showing the position of interlobular and intralobular arteries in relation to the bronchial tree. (Elastic/Van Gieson, × 40)

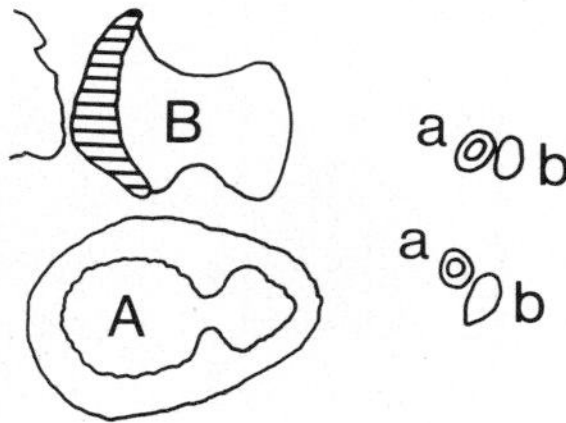

Fig. 14.6 A line-diagram to aid interpretation of Fig. 14.5. Adjacent to a bronchus (B) with cartilage, indicated by cross-hatching, in its walls, is an elastic interlobular pulmonary artery, A, cut in oblique section. Two muscular intralobular pulmonary arteries, a, lie adjacent to bronchioles, b, in the lung lobule.

tissue becomes more open and loose. At this stage the features that later are so characteristic of the elastic tissue of the adult pulmonary trunk (Fig. 14.4) are developing, and a glance at a section of such a vessel at this age is sufficient for recognizing it as pulmonary. However, the elastic fibrils still have a tendency to be parallel to one another and to retain a fair uniformity of width. Between the ages of 6 to 24 months an occasional example of the foetal type of elastic configuration can still be found but in most instances the appearances are the same as in the adult.

The pulmonary lobules of the foetus In the foetus and young infant the muscular pulmonary arteries are also thick-walled and reminiscent of systemic arteries.[2] In the last trimester of pregnancy the foetal lung, in section, appears to be composed of polygonal lobules which are separated from one another by fibrous septa. Within

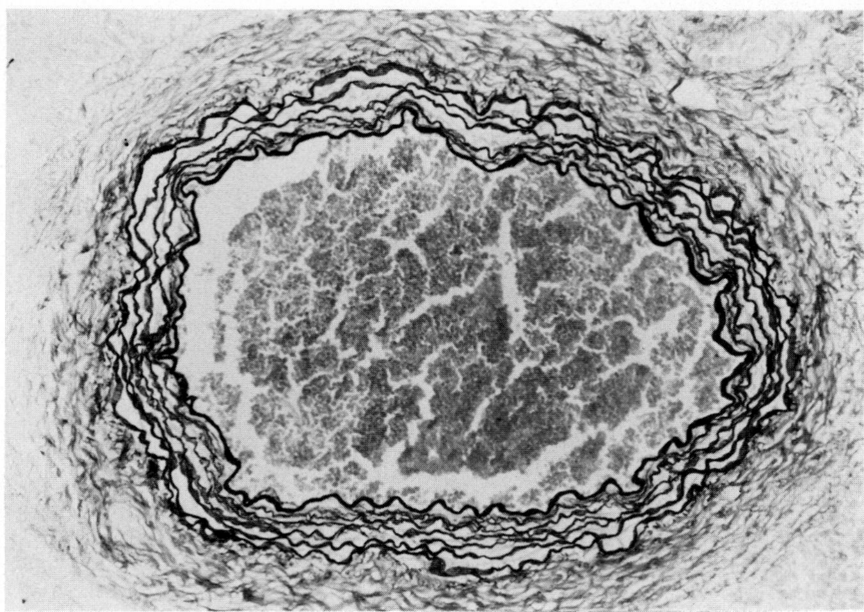

Fig. 14.7 Transverse section of an elastic interlobular pulmonary artery from a new-born infant. The vessel is oval in outline and has a thick media containing many elastic fibrils. (Elastic/Van Gieson, × 129)

each lobule there are one to three bronchioles with adjacent muscular intralobular arteries which are about half the diameter of the bronchioles (Figs 14.5 and 14.6).

At one or more corners of the interlobular septa are bronchi with cartilage in their walls each with its adjacent elastic interlobular artery (Figs 14.5 and 14.6). The interlobular arteries are elastic in type and twice as large as the muscular intralobular arteries. After birth the lobular pattern becomes very much less distinct.

The elastic interlobular arteries These vessels[2] (Fig. 14.7) which develop into the elastic pulmonary arteries of the adult lung, described in Chapter 3, are oval or circular in outline in cross section. The lumen is patent at birth and is lined by endothelium which covers a thick internal elastic lamina. The media comprises circularly-arranged smooth muscle fibres with fragmented elastic fibrils found mainly in the outer third of this coat. There is a thick, fibrous adventitia. In the latter part of the first month of post-natal life the diameter of the lumen exceeds the thickness of the arterial wall. The internal elastic lamina becomes thicker and more wavy and the elastic fibrils in the outer third of the media become much thicker than at birth. The vessels have assumed the 'adult' appearance by the age of one year when the media is composed predominantly of elastic tissue. These elastic arteries increase in size till the age of twenty years.

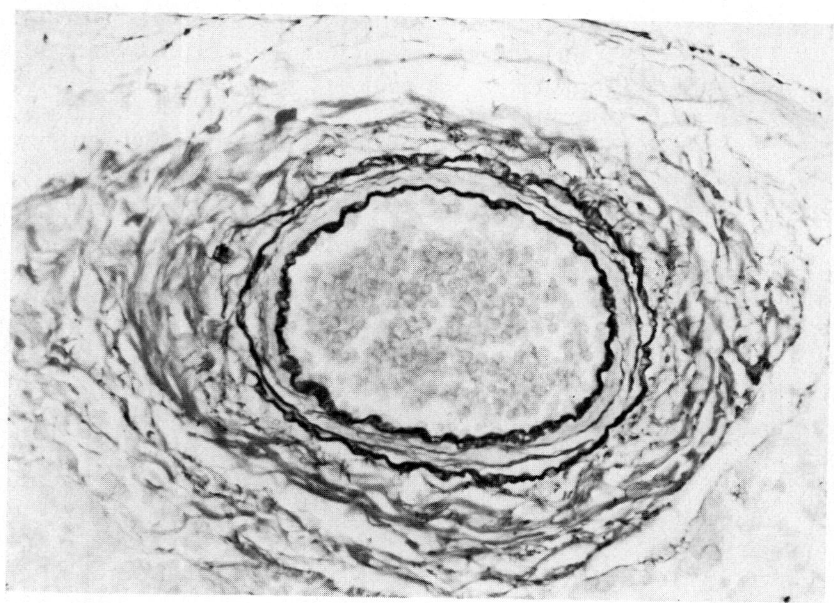

Fig. 14.8 Transverse section of a muscular intralobular pulmonary artery from a new-born infant. There is a thick media of circularly-orientated smooth muscle sandwiched between internal and external elastic laminae. (Elastic/Van Gieson, × 450)

The muscular intralobular arteries These vessels[2] (Fig. 14.8) which develop into the muscular pulmonary arteries of the adult lung, described in Chapter 3, are circular or oval in outline in cross section. The lumen is all but occluded in the last trimester of pregnancy. The cells of the intima are cuboidal and the media consists of circularly orientated smooth-muscle fibres. There is a thick fibrous adventitia. A lumen becomes obvious shortly after birth. The diameters of the lumens of the developing muscular pulmonary arteries increase rapidly in the first six months of post-natal life with an increase in their external diameter. At the same time the media becomes relatively and absolutely thinner than in the foetus or newborn.

Pulmonary arterioles Vessels of this class cannot be identified with certainty in the lung of the foetus or newborn. At the age of one month the arterioles have a small lumen and are lined by endothelium. They are surrounded by a thick fibrous adventitia. With subsequent development there is a progressive increase in the size of the lumen and elastic tissue forms in the walls.

Bronchopulmonary arterial anastomoses In early foetal life the vessels of the lung-buds consist of a plexus of channels connected with both the systemic and pulmonary circulations.[3] Under these circumstances it is not surprising that bronchopulmonary arterial anastomoses form in the foetal lung and are maintained into infancy. They are characteristic of perinatal lungs and probably are of functional importance in the foetal lung but, as we shall see below and in Chapter 39, they undergo occlusion and obliteration in infancy so that, by the time adult life is reached, they are far fewer in number and of much less functional significance. The close interrelation of pulmonary and systemic circulations in the lung-buds leads to a situation in later foetal life where lung parenchyma is supplied by bronchial arteries (bronchopulmonary arteries) and bronchi by pulmonary arteries (pulmobronchial arteries). These are described below.

Bronchopulmonary anastomoses in the foetal lung are to be found in the vicinity of relatively large bronchi in the hilar region or central portions of the lungs.[3] They range from 40 μm to 240 μm in external diameter and from 200 μm to 3000 μm in length. Frequently they run a tortuous course during which they provide branches to bronchial or lung tissue. The vessel comprising the bronchial end of the anastomosis arises from a bronchial artery and has the histological appearances of its parent. That is to say, it has a single internal elastic lamina but no external elastic lamina. In proximity to the elastic or muscular pulmonary artery into which the anastomotic vessel opens it assumes a histological structure like that of a pulmonary artery with distinct internal and external elastic laminae.[3] The medial thickness of different anastomotic vessels varies greatly so that some are thick and narrow and others are thin and wide.

In infancy such vessels show intimal fibrosis which may virtually obliterate the anastomosis.[3] Longitudinal muscle does not occur in foetal bronchopulmonary anastomotic vessels but this is not surprising since longitudinal muscle develops in bronchial arteries only after infancy when they have been subjected to the stimulus of repeated longitudinal stretch brought about by the rhythmic expansion of the lungs during respiration (Chapter 18). Anastomoses between two pulmonary arteries or between a pulmonary artery and a pulmonary vein have not been described in the foetal lung. Arteriovenous anastomoses, however, between bronchial arteries and veins have been seen and venovenous anastomoses of all types are common.[3]

Bronchopulmonary arteries Some branches of bronchial arteries in foetal life and infancy leave the interstitium and enter lung tissue. They do not anastomose with pulmonary arteries but terminate in pulmonary alveolar capillaries.[3] Such bronchopulmonary arteries arise from medium-sized or small bronchial arteries and range in diameter from 20 to 110 μm. They are tortuous and short, although sometimes very long vessels may be found. They do not follow the course of bronchi. Histologically, at their origin they resemble their parent bronchial artery in having one distinct internal elastic lamina but on entering the lung tissue they acquire an external elastic lamina as well, thus resembling a pulmonary artery. Like bronchopulmonary anastomoses, bronchopulmonary arteries are common in the foetus but become much rarer in infancy.

Pulmobronchial arteries In the foetus, some branches of pulmonary arteries leave lung tissue to end in the peribronchial or perivascular connective tissue or to supply the bronchial mucosa.[3] Their calibre varies from 40 to 120 μm and they are much less common than bronchopulmonary arteries. In the initial part of their course they resemble pulmonary arteries in structure but subsequently they lose their external elastic lamina to resemble bronchial arteries. About half of these arteries arise from elastic pulmonary arteries.

The Structure of the Ductus Arteriosus

The muscular nature of the foetal ductus arteriosus The ductus arteriosus of the foetus resembles to some extent a muscular systemic artery. There is a thick media composed predominantly of circularly-arranged smooth muscle, an intimal lining and a fibrous covering, or adventitia (Fig. 14.9). Thus the pulmonary trunk and the aorta, both predominantly elastic, conducting blood vessels, are connected by a highly muscular tube capable of the constriction which leads to physiological closure after birth. The elastic tissue of the ductus is continuous with that in the aorta and pulmonary artery. It is mainly compressed into a thick internal elastic lamina but there is also a zone of elastic fibrils in the outer part of the media (Fig. 14.10).

Longitudinal muscle An interesting feature in the structure of the foetal ductus is the presence of longitudinal muscle beneath the thick internal elastic lamina just described (Figs 14.11 and 14.12). These muscle bundles appear to prevent the over-extension of the ductus. It is also possible that they act indirectly to prevent over-distension of this vessel (Chap. 18, p. 277). Danesino *et al.*[4] found that the superior wall of the ductus was thicker and contained additional longitudinal muscle within the media. They believed this to be associated with the greater tendency of the superior wall to overstretch due to the greater expansion which occurs in it during systole.

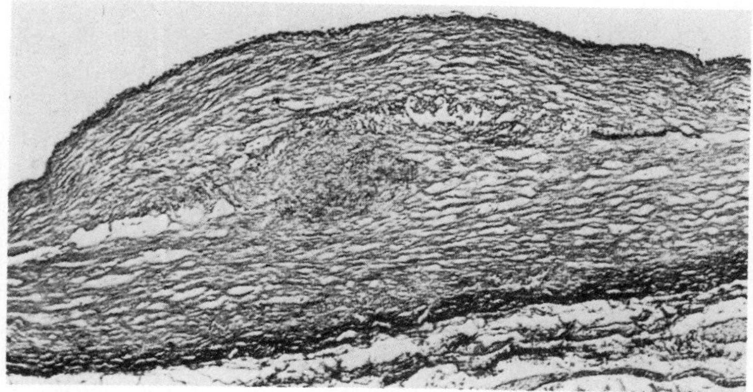

Fig. 14.9 Part of a transverse section of the wall of a patent ductus arteriosus from a new-born female one-day old. The media is thick and composed predominantly of circular muscle. A fasciculus of contracted longitudinal muscle is seen beneath an intimal mound. (Elastic/Van Gieson, × 50)

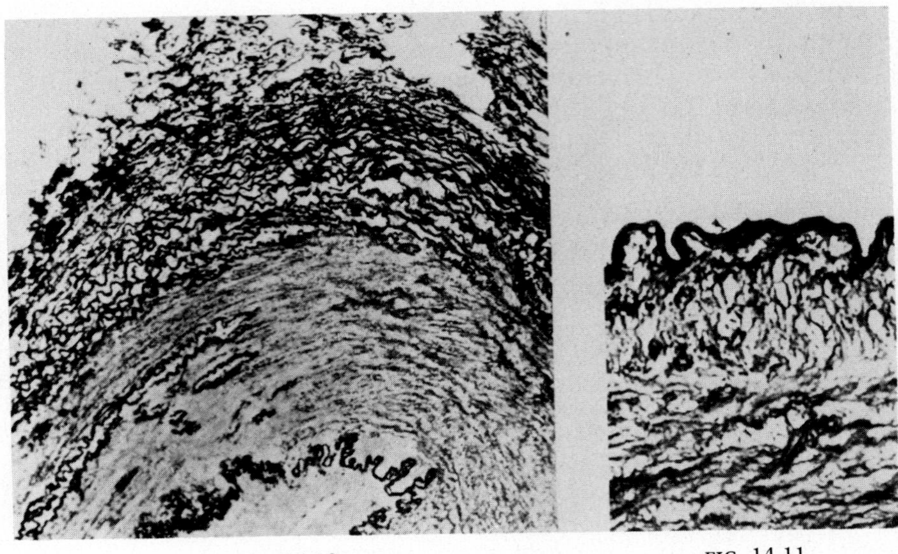

FIG. 14.10 FIG. 14.11

Fig. 14.10 Part of a transverse section of a patent ductus arteriosus, from a male infant aged 3 months, to show the configuration of the elastic tissue. A thick internal elastic lamina is seen at the lower part of the figure. There are also many concentric elastic laminae in the outer part of the media. (Elastic/Van Gieson, × 50)

Fig. 14.11 Part of a transverse section of the wall of a patent ductus arteriosus showing the presence of longitudinal muscle beneath a thick internal elastic lamina. (Elastic/Van Gieson, × 200)

Fig. 14.12 Part of transverse section of a patent ductus arteriosus showing the fibro-elastic intimal mounds and the underlying thick internal elastic lamina. Fasciculi of longitudinal muscle are situated in the inner part of the media beneath the intimal mounds. From a new-born male aged two days. (Elastic/Van Gieson, × 100)

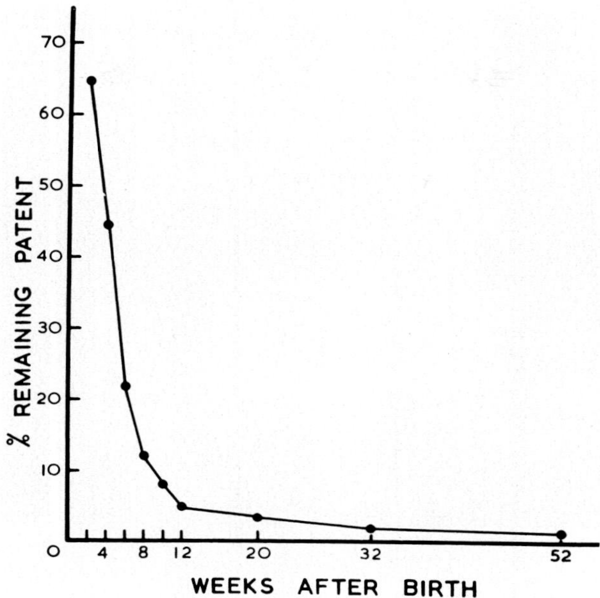

Fig. 14.13 The distribution of the frequency of anatomical closure of the ductus throughout the first year of life. (Data from Christie[8])

Intimal mounds One of the most characteristic features of the foetal ductus arteriosus is the presence of muscular elevations which protrude into the lumen (Figs 14.9 and 14.12). These have been termed 'intimal mounds'[5] or 'sub-endothelial cushions'.[4] Similar structures may be seen in the umbilical artery but only when it is constricted.[6] The intimal mounds of the ductus arteriosus are absent in foetuses which are five-months old[4] but become common and pronounced towards the end of pregnancy. In the newborn, there may be a thin covering of fibrous tissue over these intimal mounds and, as we shall see below, this forms a basis for further fibrous proliferation in early infancy which plays a part in the anatomical closure of the ductus.

Mucoid substance A further component in the ductus arteriosus in the last three months of pregnancy is mucoid material between the muscle fibres. It forms a gel in which the muscle fibres are immersed but sometimes it appears as microcysts.[7] During the last weeks of intra-uterine life, when much elastic tissue is found in the intima and media, there is a gradual reduction in mucoid material.[4]

Anatomical closure of the ductus Two weeks after birth, 35 per cent of ductus arteriosi will not admit a probe. At the end of four weeks, the percentage has risen to 54 (Ref. 8). Figure 14.13 shows the distribution of the frequency of anatomical closure of the ductus throughout the first year of life. The permanent closure of the ductus is affected by a growth of vascular fibrous tissue from the

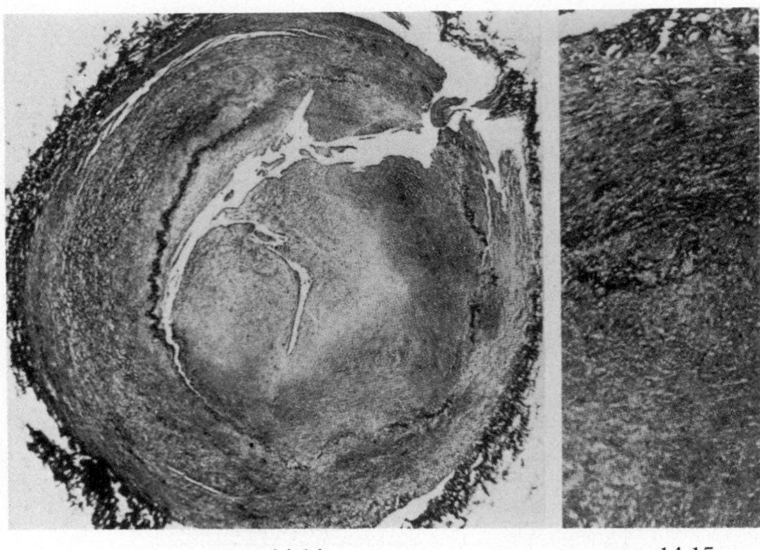

FIG. 14.14 FIG. 14.15

Fig. 14.14 Transverse section of a closing ductus arteriosus from a male infant aged three months. The original lumen is almost totally occluded by fibrous tissue which has proliferated from the intimal mounds and organized blood clot within the lumen. The thick internal elastic lamina is fragmented. (Elastic/Van Gieson, × 30)

Fig. 14.15 Part of Figure 14.14 at higher magnification. Above is the fibrous media. In the centre of the Figure can be seen fragmented remains of the internal elastic lamina. Below is fibrous tissue which has proliferated from the intimal mounds. Near the internal lamina the fibrous tissue is acellular but near the remaining lumen the fibrous tissue is cellular. (Elastic/Van Gieson, × 75)

surface of the intimal mounds and by thrombosis and subsequent organization within the lumen (Figs 14.14 and 14.15). Traces of elastic tissue may be still found in the remnants of the intimal mounds but not in the cellular fibrous tissue occupying the original lumen.

The Abnormally Patent Ductus Arteriosus

The ductus that remains abnormally patent has a thin wall and feels different from the cord-like structure of the closing ductus of the newborn.[7] Its histological features differ from the patent ductus arteriosus of the foetus in the absence of intimal mounds and from the closing ductus of infancy in the absence of obliteration of the lumen by fibrous tissue. In the abnormally patent ductus, there is a concentration of elastic tissue in the inner part of the media (Figs 14.16 and 14.17). The elastic fibrils in this area, in transverse sections of the ductus, have the appearance of being short and stick-like, lining what appear to be lacunae around longitudinally-orientated muscle fibres (Fig. 14.17). Both the muscle and elastic tissue are set in a

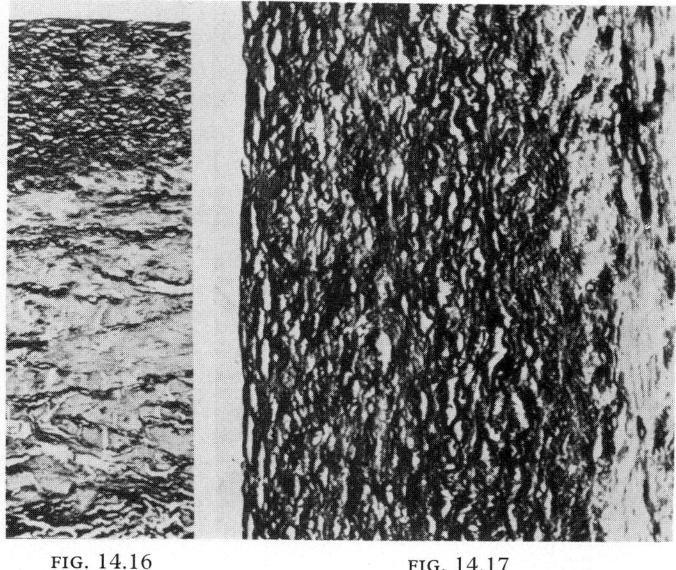

FIG. 14.16 FIG. 14.17

Fig. 14.16 Part of a transverse section of an abnormally patent ductus arteriosus from a girl of three years with severe pulmonary hypertension. The outer part of the media consists of circular muscle but the inner third, shown uppermost, contains much elastic tissue. (Elastic/Van Gieson, × 50)

Fig. 14.17 Part of Figure 14.16 at higher magnification to show inner third of media. Many of the elastic fibrils are short and stick-like and line what appear to be lacunae around longitudinally orientated smooth muscle fibres. (Elastic/Van Gieson, × 100)

ground substance which gives the staining reactions of collagen. The outer portion of the ductus is composed mainly of smooth muscle fibres and associated coarse elastic fibrils, both of which are orientated circularly (Fig. 14.16). In some widely patent ductus arteriosi the arrangement of the muscle and elastic tissue is more complex, as many as four distinct zones being seen in the media.

Physiological Changes in the Pulmonary Circulation at Birth

The classical observations of the foetal circulation in animals by means of angiocardiography[9,10] have been confirmed in the human foetus.[11] Oxygenated blood from the placenta joins the inferior venal caval flow via the ductus venosus. The blood flowing into the heart from the inferior vena cava streams mainly through the foramen ovale into the left atrium and thence into the left ventricle and aorta. Only a small portion flows through the right ventricle and pulmonary artery. Blood from the superior vena cava, on the other hand, passes almost entirely into the right ventricle and pulmonary artery. Most of the blood which enters the main pulmonary artery is diverted through the ductus arteriosus into the aorta and only a very small proportion flows through the lungs. In animals, the pressure in the pulmonary artery is approximately the same as that in the aorta[12] and this is presumably also the case in man. This presumption receives support in the comparable thickness of the two ventricles and in the comparable structure of the pulmonary artery and aorta (p. 211). The structure of the muscular pulmonary arteries is also consistent with the presence of a high vascular resistance in the lungs (p. 295).

At birth, there is a change in the source of supply of oxygen, and the course of the circulation undergoes radical alterations which adapt it to these new circumstances. Experiments on lambs have shown that, within a few minutes of the onset of ventilation, there is a fall in the pulmonary vascular resistance, a fall in the pulmonary arterial pressure and an increased perfusion of the lungs.[13] The fall in the resistance of the vessels of the lungs appears to have two origins: the mechanical effects of the presence of gas in the alveoli and the relief of foetal hypoxia. In their earlier experiments Dawes and his colleagues[13] showed that the fall in pulmonary vascular resistance occurred whether the lungs were filled with oxygen or nitrogen. It did not occur, however, if the lungs were distended with saline. The explanation of these observations would seem to be that, under normal circumstances, the vessels of the lung are pulled open by the outward movement of the chest wall on one side and the surface tension of the alveolar wall on the other. If the alveoli are filled with saline instead of gas, the effect of surface tension in the alveoli is lost.[14] Later work by Dawes and Mott[15] suggested that hypoxic vasoconstriction also played a part in maintaining an increased pulmonary vascular resistance in the foetus. They showed that increasing the arterial oxygen saturation

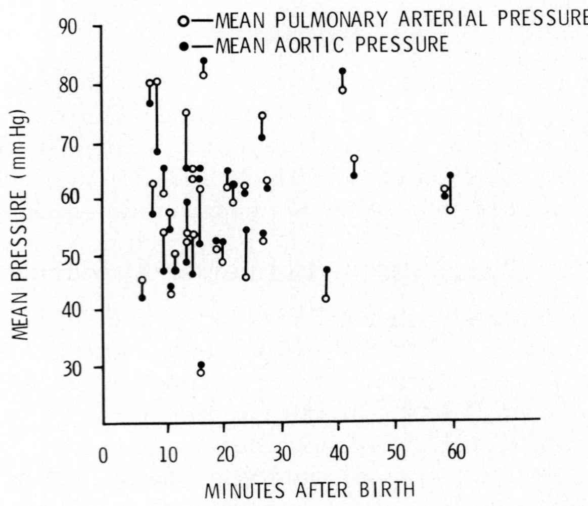

Fig. 14.18 Mean aortic and pulmonary arterial pressure in normal infants studied during the first hour of life.[16]

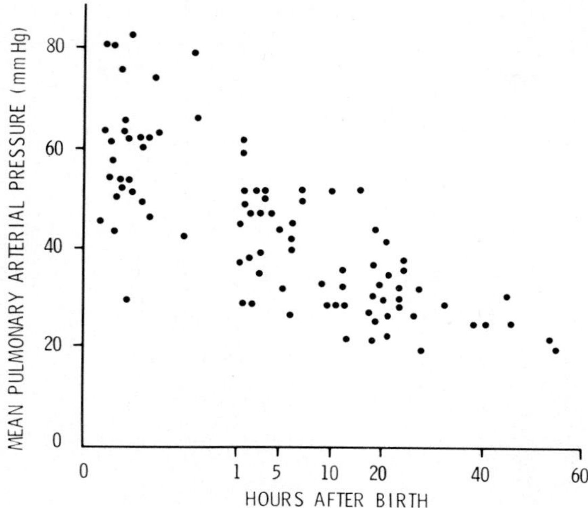

Fig. 14.19 The mean pulmonary arterial pressure in normal infants during the first sixty hours of life.[16,17]

of the foetus, by giving the ewe pure oxygen to breathe, caused pulmonary vasodilatation.

Such rapid changes in the pulmonary vascular resistance at the moment of birth do not appear to occur in man. Saling[16] studied a number of normal infants within one hour of birth and found that, as often as not, the mean pulmonary arterial pressure was as high or higher than that in the aorta (Fig. 14.18). Emmanouilides and colleagues[17] extended these observations with studies on normal infants during the first two days of life. Combining these two sets of figures (Fig. 14.19) it is apparent that the major decrease in the pulmonary arterial pressure has usually occurred during the first twenty-four hours. Rowe and James[18] published values for the pulmonary arterial pressure in mongols up to the age of nine months (Fig. 14.20) from which it is apparent that, by the end of the first month, the pulmonary arterial pressure has reached a level which is normal for the rest of life. The systemic arterial pressure does not change greatly during the first nine months of life, so that the pressure in the pulmonary artery becomes considerably less than that in the aorta by the end of the first month (Fig. 14.20).

The somewhat slow fall in the pulmonary arterial pressure immediately after birth suggests that in the human the main factor determining the high pulmonary vascular resistance in the foetus is hypoxic vasoconstriction. The subsequent further gradual decrease in pressure is similar to what is observed in high altitude dwellers taken to sea-level (Chap. 32, p. 487) and might well have a similar basis.

In newborn infants the oxygen saturation of 'arterialized' capillary blood from the foot is lower than that from the right hand,[19] which suggests the presence of a right-to-left shunt through the as yet unclosed ductus arteriosus. This suggestion

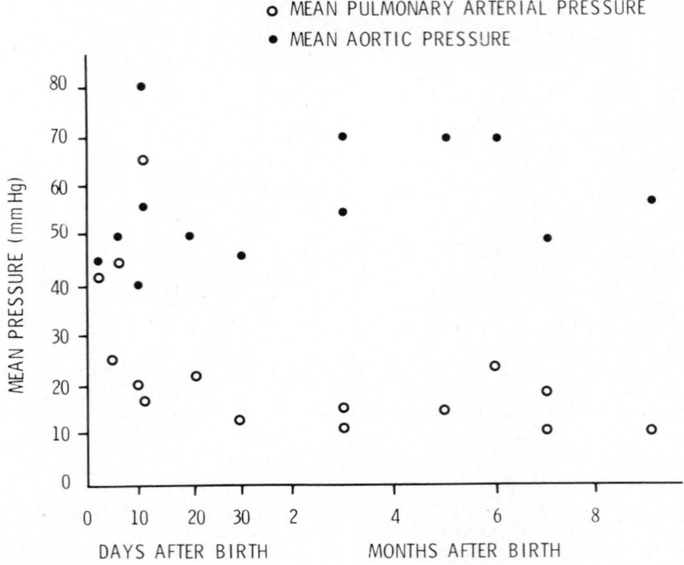

Fig. 14.20 Mean aortic and pulmonary arterial pressures in mongols during the first nine months of life.[18]

has received direct support from the studies of Saling[16] who found that the right-to-left shunt averaged 52 per cent of the systemic flow during the first hour of life.

Emmanouilides *et al.*[17] found direct evidence of a left-to-right shunt through the ductus arteriosus in the great majority of infants between one and fifteen hours after birth. Beyond this time the existence of a left-to-right shunt was uncommon. Dye-dilution curves have also given evidence of a left-to-right shunt in infants in the first fifteen hours of life.[20]

It would seem, therefore, that the ductus remains functionally patent for usually about fifteen hours after birth. Closure is then presumably due to muscular constriction since permanent anatomical closure comes some time later (Fig. 14.13). During the first hour of life the pressure in the pulmonary artery is of the same magnitude as that in the aorta and there is a substantial right-to-left shunt through the ductus arteriosus. Beyond that time the pulmonary arterial pressure falls below the aortic and the shunt becomes left-to-right until the moment of physiological closure of the ductus.

The factors which determine the physiological closure of the ductus are not entirely clear.[21] Presumably it is due to a contraction of the smooth muscle in the wall of the vessel and possibly the complex arrangement in the wall has some importance. In the guinea-pig[22] and the lamb[23,24] the ductus has been shown to constrict in response to an increased arterial Po_2. This does not, however, appear to be a universal finding[25] and it has been suggested that torsion of the ductus when the lungs become inflated with air may be a factor. In human infants it has been shown that inducing alveolar hypoxia can open the ductus under the age of three days.[26] Another piece of evidence suggesting that the arterial Po_2 influences the closure of the human ductus is the observation that persistent patent ductus arteriosus is more common in people born at high altitude.[27]

In those infants between two- and twenty-six hours old who had no evidence of shunt in the dye-dilution curve,[20] the calculated cardiac output averaged 548 ml · min^{-1} with a range of 186–854 ml · min^{-1}. Expressed in terms of body surface area this amounted to an average of 2·5 l · min^{-1}/m^2 BSA with a range of 0·9 to 3·7 l · min^{-1}/m^2 BSA. Owing to the low pulmonary blood flow the calculated pulmonary vascular resistance is high in infancy even after the pulmonary arterial pressure has fallen to an adult level. This is simply an expression of the smallness of the vascular bed and it has to be borne in mind when interpreting haemodynamic data in infants.

REFERENCES

1. Heath, D., Dushane, J. W., Wood, E. H. & Edwards, J. E. (1959) *J. Path. Bact.*, **77**, 443.
2. Civin, W. H. & Edwards, J. E. (1951) *Arch. Path.*, **51**, 1972.
3. Wagenvoort, C. A. & Wagenvoort, N. (1967) *Lab. Invest.*, **16**, 13.
4. Danesino, V. L., Reynolds, S. R. M. & Rehman, I. H. (1955) *Anat. Rec.*, **121**, 801.
5. Jager, B. V. & Wolfenman, O. J. (1942) *Amer. J. Path.*, **18**, 595.
6. Chacko, A. W. & Reynolds, S. R. M. (1954) *Contr. Embryol. Carneg. Instn.*, **35**, 135.
7. Edwards, J. E. (1953) In *Pathology of the Heart*, ed. Gould, S. E. Springfield, Ill.: Thomas.
8. Christie, A. (1930) *Amer. J. Dis. Child.*, **40**, 323.
9. Barclay, A. E., Barcroft, J., Barron, D. H. & Franklin, K. J. (1939) *Brit. J. Radiol.*, **12**, 505.
10. Barclay, A. E., Barcroft, J., Barron, D. H., Franklin, K. J. & Pritchard, M. M. L. (1941) *Amer. J. Anat.*, **69**, 383.
11. Lind, J. & Wegelius, C. (1954) *Cold Spring Harbor Symposium. Quart. Biol.*, **19**, 109.
12. Hamilton, W. F., Woodbury, R. A. & Woods, E. B. (1937) *Amer. J. Physiol.*, **119**, 206.
13. Dawes, G. S., Mott, J. C., Widdicombe, J. G. J. & Wyatt, D. G. J. (1953) *J. Physiol.*, **121**, 141.
14. Burton, A. C. (1959) In *Pulmonary Circulation*, ed. Adams, W. R. & Veith, I. page 202. New York, N.Y.: Grune & Stratton.
15. Dawes, G. S. & Mott, J. C. (1962) *J. Physiol.*, **164**, 465.
16. Saling, E. (1960) *Arch. Gynäk*, **194**, 287.
17. Emmanouilides, G. C., Moss, A. J., Duffie, E. R. Jn. & Adams, F. H. (1964) *J. Pediat.*, **65**, 327.
18. Rowe, R. D. & James, L. S. (1957) *J. Pediat.*, **51**, 1.
19. Edlridge, F. L. & Hultgren, H. N. (1955) *J. Clin. Invest.*, **34**, 987.
20. Prec, K. J. & Cassels, D. E. (1955) *Circulation*, **11**, 789.
21. Rudolph, A. (1970) *Circulation*, **41**, 343.
22. Kennedy, J. A. & Clark, S. L. (1942) *Amer. J. Physiol.*, **136**, 140.
23. Born, G. V. R., Dawes, G. S., Mott, J. C. & Rennick, B. R. (1956) *J. Physiol.*, **132**, 304.
24. Assali, N. S., Morris, J. A., Smith, R. W. & Manson, W. A. (1963) *Circulat. Res.*, **13**, 478.
25. Barron, D. H. (1944) *Physiol. Rev.*, **24**, 277.
26. Moss, A. J., Emmanouilides, G. C., Adams, F. H. & Chuang, K. (1964) *Pediatrics*, **33**, 937.
27. Alzamora-Castro, V., Battilana, G., Abugattas, R. & Sialer, S. (1960) *Amer. J. Cardiol.*, **5**, 761.

15. Causes of Pulmonary Arterial Hypertension

Pulmonary arterial hypertension is associated with many diseases. In the present classification they are considered in groups each of which is characterized by a common aetiological factor. While these factors are recognized, the actual mechanism by which pulmonary hypertension develops in each group is frequently obscure.

Pre-Tricuspid Shunts

A persistently increased pulmonary blood flow for a prolonged period, due to a large left-to-right shunt entering the systemic venous stream before it enters the right ventricle, eventually leads to pulmonary arterial hypertension in most cases. In this book we shall refer to patients in this group as having 'pre-tricuspid shunts'. Diseases accompanied by this haemodynamic abnormality include those forms of high inter-atrial communication such as septum secundum or sinus venosus defects which do not involve abnormality of the lower part of the inter-atrial septum and the mitral valve.[1] Another group of congenital anomalies producing pre-tricuspid shunts are anomalous pulmonary venous drainage into the right atrium or superior vena cava.[2] Young patients with such diseases usually have a normal pulmonary arterial pressure. However, the existence of an increased pulmonary blood flow for many years may cause them eventually to develop pulmonary hypertension, most usually in middle age or less often in young adult life (Chap. 21). When pulmonary hypertension becomes established, it is associated with a florid form of hypertensive pulmonary vascular disease showing the whole range of structural changes from medial hypertrophy and intimal fibroelastosis, to plexiform and angiomatoid lesions, and in some instances to necrotizing arteritis. This form of pulmonary vascular disease is described in detail in Chapter 16.

Post-Tricuspid Shunts

A large communication between the left ventricle or aorta and the right ventricle or pulmonary arteries will also lead to an elevation of the pulmonary arterial pressure.[3] We shall refer collectively to patients included in this group as having 'post-tricuspid shunts'. The diseases in this group differ distinctly in their natural history from those of the previous group in that pulmonary hypertension is usually present from birth and not acquired in later life. A high vascular resistance is maintained from birth and there is a retention of thick-walled small pulmonary arteries similar to those seen in the foetal lung (Chap. 14). The reason for this distinction from the previous group may be that there is an increased pulmonary blood flow right from the earliest stages of extra-uterine life (Chap. 18). In order for this course of events to occur, the communication must be large and free.

Patients, for instance, with a small defect, or those in whom the flow is impeded by pulmonary stenosis, do not develop pulmonary hypertension.

Most of the diseases with post-tricuspid shunts are congenital anomalies of the heart. This group includes large ventricular septal defects. They may be defects of the membranous septum, high in the ventricle, which may be isolated or associated with other congenital diseases such as corrected or uncorrected transposition of the great arteries.[4] They may be defects of the muscular portion of the ventricular septum, in which case they frequently appear near the apex[5] and may be multiple. The ventricular septal defect may be so large as to constitute a single ventricle[6] or may be associated with a persistent ostium primum. Other diseases included in this group are the widely patent ductus arteriosus of 'window-type',[7] a large aorto-pulmonary septal defect,[8] a cardio-aortic fistula arising usually from rupture of an aneurysm of a sinus of Valsalva,[9] and a persistent truncus arteriosus.[10] Not all the members of this group, however, are congenital diseases of the heart. Rupture of an aortic aneurysm, usually syphilitic, into one of the main pulmonary arteries is a rare example of an acquired disease to be included in this group.[11] So is rupture of the interventricular septum following a myocardial infarction.[12] In these unusual cases the pulmonary hypertension is acquired and the elastic tissue pattern of the media of the pulmonary trunk is of adult pulmonary type[12] (Chap. 17). The hypertensive pulmonary vascular disease associated with post-tricuspid shunts is the same as that found in pre-tricuspid shunts and may progress to dilatation lesions and necrotizing arteritis.

The Common Atrioventricular Canal and Pre- and Post-Tricuspid Shunts

Sometimes a large atrial septal defect of ostium primum type is associated with two distinct atrioventricular valves and a cleft in the anterior cusp of the mitral valve without a co-existent ventricular septal defect. This is a partial persistent common atrioventricular canal[13] which is characterized by a pre-tricuspid shunt so that there is a late onset of moderate pulmonary hypertension following a long period of high pulmonary blood flow. This congenital anomaly gives rise to mild hypertensive pulmonary vascular disease and is consistent with remarkable longevity.[14] In contrast, patients with the complete form of persistent common atrioventricular canal, in which a ventricular septal defect is part of the congenital anomaly, have a post-tricuspid shunt. They are exposed to the haemodynamic stresses and complications of direct transmission of left ventricular pressure and flow into the pulmonary circulation and usually die during the first year of life.

Prolonged Left Atrial Hypertension

An elevation of the pressure in the left atrium would be expected to cause a similar rise in the pressure in the pulmonary artery simply by backward transmission. When the elevation in left atrial pressure is severe and persistent, however, the pulmonary arterial pressure rises more than would be anticipated from this mechanism. Why this occurs is unknown and is discussed further in Chapter 23.

Mitral stenosis is the commonest lesion which gives rise to severe left atrial and pulmonary arterial hypertension and associated changes in the pulmonary blood vessels.[15] Usually this valvular disease is due to rheumatism, but the congenital type leads to identical haemodynamic and morbid anatomical abnormalities in the pulmonary circulation.[16] Mitral incompetence will also cause a rise in left atrial and pulmonary arterial pressures, although the effect on the latter is somewhat less than is the case with a pure stenosis of the valve. The main causes of mitral incompetence are ischaemic heart disease causing rupture of the chordae or papillary muscle dysfunction, rheumatism,[17] 'floppy' mitral valve and bacterial endocarditis.[17] Trauma is a much rarer cause.[17] When chronic rheumatic heart disease of the mitral valve is associated with the development of aneurysmal dilatation of the left atrium, hypertensive pulmonary vascular disease is less severe and the patient's prognosis is accordingly better.[18]

Large tumours of the left atrium such as the myxoma[19,20] and compression of the large pulmonary veins by a mediastinal granuloma[21] are rare causes of elevation of blood pressure in the pulmonary veins and associated pulmonary arterial hypertension.

Systemic arterial hypertension, aortic stenosis and aortic incompetence all increase the work of the left ventricle and will tend to raise the end diastolic pressure in this chamber. This may cause an increase of the left atrial pressure. In less severe cases the elevation of the left atrial pressure will occur only during exercise. A similar effect results from the partial dysfunction of the myocardium by ischaemia[22] or from myocardial disease. Those patients with an increased work or weakness of the left ventricle who have left atrial hypertension do not usually develop such severe pulmonary arterial hypertension as occurs in mitral stenosis, but exceptions to this have been reported.[23] The pulmonary arteries in cases of aortic stenosis have been shown to be abnormally thick on account of associated pulmonary hypertension.[24] The pulmonary vascular disease associated with prolonged pulmonary venous hypertension consists of medial hypertrophy of the muscular pulmonary arteries, and muscularization of the pulmonary arterioles with intimal fibrosis in these classes of vessel (Chap. 22). Sometimes necrotizing arteritis occurs but it is characteristic of the hypertensive pulmonary vascular disease of sustained left atrial hypertension that dilatation lesions, such as the plexiform and angiomatoid lesions, never occur. In other words, the grades of vascular change encountered are 1 to 3 and 6, the intermediate grades 4 and 5 never being seen in the lung in this group of diseases (Chap. 22).

Chronic Hypoxia

All states associated with chronic hypoxia lead to pulmonary arterial hypertension and an associated hypoxic hypertensive pulmonary vascular disease (Chap. 33). This is very different from the forms of pulmonary vascular disease already referred to in this chapter. It consists of a triad of muscularization of the terminal portions of the pulmonary arterial tree, the development of longitudinal muscle in the intima, and a characteristic sparsity of intimal fibrosis (Chap. 33). Since the pulmonary vascular disease is mainly muscular in nature both the pulmonary hypertension and the anatomical abnormalities in the pulmonary vasculature appear to be reversible (Chap. 33).

The commonest diseases in Western Europe and the United States which give rise to hypoxic hypertensive pulmonary vascular disease are chronic bronchitis and emphysema, including both alveolar and centrilobular forms (Chap. 33). Pulmonary hypertension and muscularization of the terminal portions of the pulmonary arterial tree also occur in those people who live at high altitudes in such regions as the Andes or the Himalayas. As well as occurring in normal healthy people living at high altitude similar pulmonary vascular disease is said to be found in sufferers from Monge's disease, the so-called 'chronic mountain sickness' (Chap. 32). Other states of chronic hypoxia pre-disposing to hypoxic hypertensive pulmonary vascular disease are the Pickwickian syndrome, kyphoscoliosis, and chronic hypoxia secondary to enlarged adenoids (Chap. 33).

Pulmonary Fibrosis

Pulmonary fibrosis may be massive or interstitial in type and both forms may give rise to pulmonary arterial hypertension and associated vascular disease of the lung (Chap. 41). Massive pulmonary fibrosis is usually produced by silicosis or one of the other pneumoconioses and leads to fibrous occlusion and ablation of the small pulmonary arteries. Interstitial fibrosis (fibrosing alveolitis) is produced by a whole range of diseases which are considered in Chapter 41 and which include such widely differing conditions as rheumatoid disease, scleroderma, sarcoidosis, the Hamman-Rich syndrome, and berylliosis. Many cases of interstitial fibrosis of the lung progress to 'honeycomb lung' and the abnormalities of the alveolar walls and bronchioles become associated with pulmonary vascular disease. This has two stages, an early stage of muscularization of the pulmonary arterial tree and a late stage of fibrous occlusion and ablation of small pulmonary arteries. The change from a predominantly muscular to a fibrous vascular disease is reflected in a change of the reversibility of the associated pulmonary hypertension. This subject is considered in detail in Chapter 41. Bronchiectasis has to be severe and widespread to cause pulmonary hypertension and even then is usually associated with only a moderate elevation of pulmonary arterial pressure. A characteristic structural abnormality of this disease is hypertrophy of the bronchial arteries and the development of broncho-pulmonary anastomoses (Chap. 39). Other diseases such as pulmonary tuberculosis which are associated with destruction of lung parenchyma and the formation of fibrotic areas may cause some pulmonary hypertension, if they are extensive enough.[25]

Recurrent Pulmonary Embolism

A variety of emboli including thromboemboli, fat,[26] tumour particles (Fig. 15.1) and bilharzia ova[27] may all lead to organic pulmonary vascular occlusion and pulmonary hypertension (Chap. 35). The ova of *Schistosoma mansoni* which give

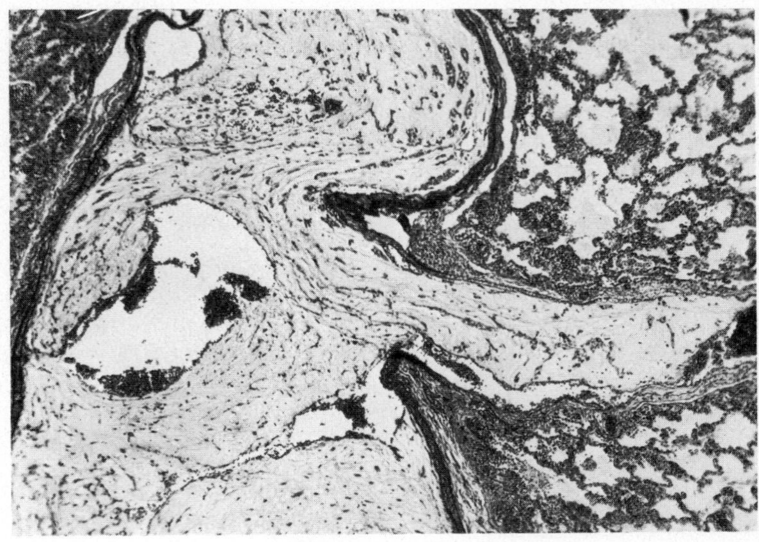

Fig. 15.1 Section of lung from a 35 year old woman with a myxoma of the right atrium which had given rise to pulmonary emboli. Included in the Figure is part of a transverse section of a large muscular pulmonary artery and a thin-walled arteriolar branch which passes to the right. Both are largely occluded by an embolus of atrial myxoma which contains large thin-walled vessels. (Haematoxylin & eosin, × 40)

rise to pseudotubercles in the lung parenchyma (Fig. 15.2), appear to produce an elevation of pulmonary arterial pressure directly by widespread pulmonary vascular occlusion (Fig. 15.3). Collateral angiomatoid vessels similar to those of the late stages of hypertensive pulmonary vascular disease develop as a result of the fibrotic occlusion stimulated by egg embolism[27] (Fig. 15.4). It has been suggested that the pulmonary hypertension associated with thromboembolism is in part due to constriction of pulmonary arteries which may lead to 'concentric intimal fibrosis'.[28] Physiological evidence for this theory is, however, lacking.[29]

Of the various diseases that may lead to recurrent pulmonary embolism it has become clear during the last few years that the most important is that due to recurrent pulmonary thromboembolism (Chap. 35). Not all pulmonary embolism is of the classical type in which large thromboemboli may give rise to sudden death or to red infarcts in the lung. Pulmonary thromboembolism may also be recurrent and silent, showers of small, even minute, emboli passing into the pulmonary circulation and producing an elevation of pulmonary arterial pressure. The pathology of this disease is considered in Chapter 35. Clinically, it may mimic closely the disease variously termed 'primary', 'idiopathic' or 'essential' pulmonary hypertension (Chap. 28).

Primary Pulmonary Hypertension

In a minority of cases there is no apparent cause for the development of pulmonary arterial hypertension in a patient. There is no evidence of a primary disease of the heart or lungs, of any disease or condition predisposing to chronic hypoxia, of parasitic disease involving the lung or of underlying cirrhosis of the liver or portal vein thrombosis. Finally, and most important, there is nothing to substantiate a diagnosis of recurrent pulmonary thromboembolism. When all these diseases have been excluded by clinical and laboratory investigation a diagnosis of 'unexplained pulmonary hypertension' may be entertained (Chap. 28). The clinical features of 'unexplained pulmonary hypertension' may be produced by two distinct pathological entities. One is the classical primary pulmonary hypertension in which the brunt of the pathology falls on the pulmonary arterial tree. The other is pulmonary veno-occlusive disease in which the pathology involves primarily the pulmonary veins. Both diseases are considered in detail in Chapter 28.

Diet

One of the most interesting advances in the pathology of the pulmonary vasculature during the past few years has been the demonstration that pulmonary hypertension and hypertensive pulmonary vascular disease may be induced by diet. This subject

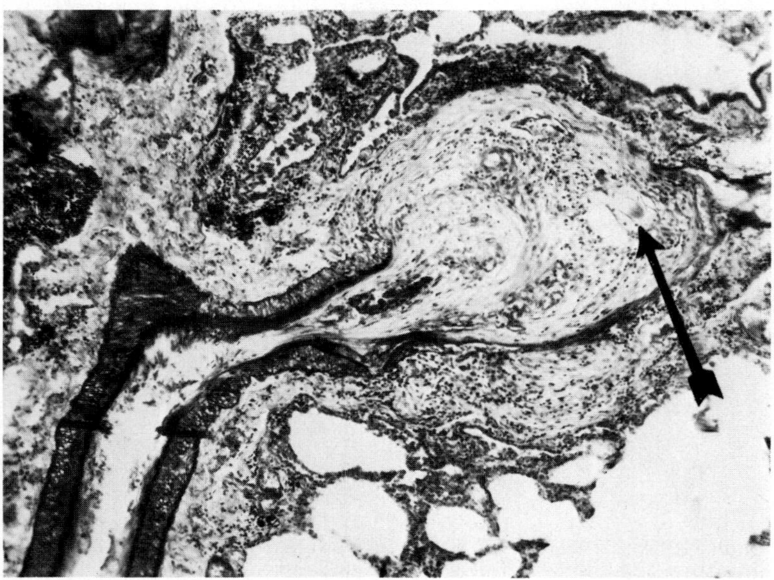

Fig. 15.2 Pulmonary bilharziasis. A longitudinal section of a muscular pulmonary artery is shown. It terminates abruptly in a pseudotubercle which has formed around ova of *Schistosoma mansoni*; one of these is indicated by a black arrow. Most of the granuloma is formed by fibrous tisue but a chronic inflammatory exudate and a foreign body giant cell can also be seen. (Elastic/Van Gieson, × 95)

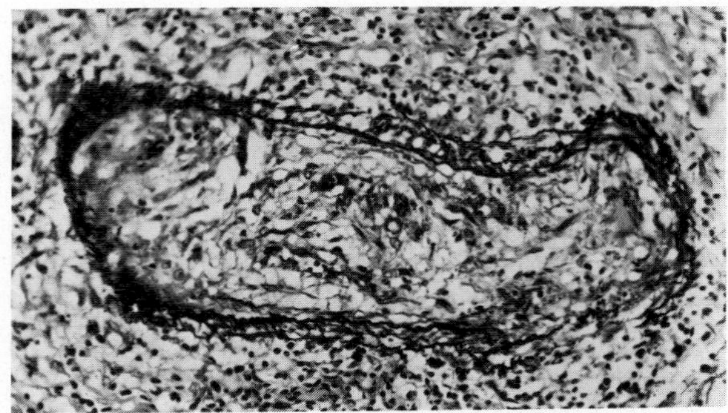

Fig. 15.3 Oblique section of a small muscular pulmonary artery from a case of pulmonary bilharziasis. The vessel is totally occluded by vascular fibrous tissue. (Elastic/Van Gieson, × 100)

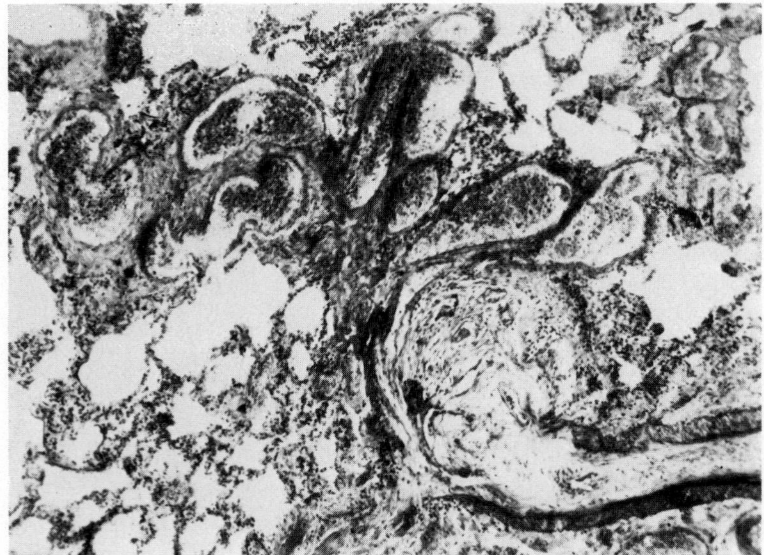

Fig. 15.4 A longitudinal section through a muscular pulmonary artery. As in Figure 15.2 this ends abruptly in an area of granulomatous reaction around ova of *Schistosoma mansoni*. Beyond the granuloma is an 'angiomatoid' lesion. These dilated, thin-walled branches of the muscular pulmonary artery arise proximal to the occluded segment of the parent vessel. They provide a collateral flow to the pulmonary capillaries thus compensating for the occlusion of the small pulmonary arteries. The lesion bears a striking similarity to grade 5 hypertensive pulmonary vascular disease described in Chapter 16. (Elastic/Van Gieson, × 85)

is considered in Chapter 27. The substances incriminated in this respect so far have been pyrrolizidine alkaloids such as monocrotaline, fulvine and senecionine found in the plants *Crotalaria spectabilis, Crotalaria fulva, Senecio jacobaea* and *Crotalaria laburnoides.* So far, the demonstration of the induction of pulmonary hypertension by diet has been confined to experimental animals, although in one case of primary pulmonary hypertension occurring in an African youth there was a strong suspicion that he had ingested a herbal infusion containing *Crotalaria laburnoides* (Chap. 27). The whole subject has recently stimulated great interest in cardiological circles with the suggestion that a recent epidemic of primary pulmonary hypertension in Switzerland, Austria and Western Germany was due to the ingestion of a slimming drug aminorex fumarate which was marketed only in these three countries. As yet there is no convincing evidence that prolonged administration of the drug may produce hypertensive pulmonary vascular disease in animals. Nevertheless it is clear that substances taken by mouth may induce pulmonary hypertension and this concept is discussed at length in Chapter 27.

Hepatic Disease and Pulmonary Hypertension

In rare instances, patients with cirrhosis of the liver may develop pulmonary arterial hypertension and hypertensive pulmonary vascular disease characterized by dilatation lesions, and die in congestive cardiac failure. Workers have postulated that some haemodynamic or biochemical abnormality resulting from the hepatic cirrhosis itself is responsible for the pulmonary complications. It should be noted, however, that some substances, like the pyrrolizidine-alkaloid fulvine, will affect the liver and pulmonary circulation apparently independently, producing hepatic necrosis and cirrhosis on the one hand, and hypertensive pulmonary vascular disease on the other. This problem of the association of hepatic and pulmonary vascular disease is considered at length in Chapter 29. It may be noted here that the pulmonary vascular disease reported in patients with cirrhosis of the liver is very similar to that found in congenital pre- and post-tricuspid shunts and in classical primary pulmonary hypertension, being characterized by the development of plexiform and angiomatoid lesions.

Filariasis and Pulmonary Hypertension

In Chapter 27 we refer to an epidemic of primary pulmonary hypertension which began in Germany, Switzerland and Austria in 1968. The great interest which has been taken in this epidemic has prompted workers to see if similar epidemics have occurred in other areas of the world. It became apparent that there was a higher prevalence of unexplained pulmonary hypertension in Sri Lanka (previously Ceylon) when compared with Britain.[30,31] In the five years between 1967 and 1972, roughly the same period during which the epidemic occurred in Western Europe, no fewer than 65 patients were diagnosed as having 'primary pulmonary hypertension' in a consecutive series of 2500 patients investigated with cardiovascular disease, a frequency of 2·6 per cent.[31] This contrasts with a frequency of 0·17 per cent found by Wood[32] in a series of 10 000 patients seen over a period of ten years. There were unusual features in the cases occurring in Sri Lanka. A disproportionately large number of men were affected by this disease which is classically known to involve young women (Chap. 28). The severity of the pulmonary hypertension was unusual. There was a frequent association with eosinophilia and there was a significant fall in the eosinophil counts, which may exceed 4000 per mm^3, when the patients were treated with diethyl carbamazine.[31,33] These unusual clinical features of cases of primary pulmonary hypertension in Sri Lanka suggested to Obeyesekere and his co-authors[30,31] a causal relationship with filariasis. This was considered by them to be corroborated by the finding of *Wuchereria bancrofti* in an enlarged lymph node from a woman of 30 years with the disease and in the epididymis of a man of 35 years with pulmonary hypertension although it should be noted that the finding of the parasite in lymph nodes in this country must be common. Filariasis due to *W. bancrofti* infestation was said by Obeyesekere and Peiris[31] to be endemic along the south-west coastal border of Sri Lanka and it is this area in which cases of hitherto unexplained pulmonary hypertension are also frequent.[31] Tropical pulmonary eosinophilia is also common in this region.

W. bancrofti is a parasite which is widespread in tropical and sub-tropical countries. The adult worms, male and female, are thin, filiform organisms which are a little thicker than coarse hairs. The female is some three inches in length while the male is shorter and thinner.[34] Several worms lie coiled together in the thoracic duct or in the large lymphatic vessels of the pelvis or groins. The females are viviparous and produce microfilariae which pass by the lymphatics to the blood stream where they are readily found on microscopic examination.[34] The microfilariae, 300×8 μm, are enclosed in a loose sheath in which they move backwards and forwards. The microfilariae of *W. bancrofti* appear in the blood in the evening and are thus termed *Microfilaria nocturna*.[34] Their disappearance during the daytime is thought by some to indicate that the microfilariae collect in the pulmonary vasculature. Others believe that they are quickly destroyed and that their periodic nocturnal appearance is due to daily discharge of larvae by female worms in the lymphatics. The intermediate host is a female mosquito, usually of the genus *Culex*. The mosquito ingests microfilariae in infected blood and these escape from their sheaths in the insect's stomach, pass to its muscles and hence to its labium from whence they regain access to the man being bitten. The adult worms in man physically obstruct lymphatics or liberate substances which damage the walls of the lymphatics closing these vessels permanently. This may lead to lymphatic varicosities, elephantiasis, scrotal enlargement and so on. Hypereosinophilia is absent in this form of the disease.

In tropical pulmonary eosinophilia the lesions are not confined to the lymphatic system and are found in the lung, liver, and spleen and there are associated hypereosinophilia, enlargement of lymph nodes and pulmonary symptoms such as chronic cough and wheezing.[31] It is believed that this condition represents hypersensitivity to a specific filarial antigen so that while adult worms produce microfilariae they are destroyed rapidly in the blood. According to Obeyesekere and Peiris[31] it is quite possible that many of these microfilariae are destroyed continually in the lung leading to widespread blockage of pulmonary arterioles and capillaries and thus leading to severe pulmonary hypertension. They think that there is reason to believe that the cases of 'primary pulmonary hypertension' in Sri Lanka are in fact secondary to filariasis.[31] This view is not shared by Walloopillai who is of the opinion that the cases in Sri Lanka are examples of primary pulmonary hypertension unrelated to *Filaria* (personal communication). Wagenvoort (personal communication) says that the histopathology in these cases is characterized by plexiform lesions, a finding which is consistent with the views of Walloopillai.

Filarial Worms and Pulmonary Hypertension in Animals

Filarial worms are known to cause pulmonary hypertension in animals. Dissanaike and Paramananthan[35] described a new filarial worm *Brugia buckleyi* in the right ventricle and pulmonary arteries of the Ceylon wild hare (*Lepus nigricollis singhala*). In these animals there was electrocardiographic evidence of right ventricular hypertrophy with gross hypertrophy and dilatation of the right ventricle at necropsy and evidence of pulmonary infarction.[36] Similar findings have been reported in the dog due to infestation with *Darofilaria immitis*.[37,38]

The Lung Worm

Cats infested with the lung worm, *Aelurostrongylus abstrusus*, may show pronounced hypertrophy and hyperplasia of arteries in the lung which on cursory examination resemble bronchial arteries. According to Hamilton,[39] however, they are pulmonary arteries and the change within them he ascribes to the presence of the lung worm. Pulmonary vascular disease of this type was found in 34·7 per cent of 256 randomly selected cats that he examined.[39] *Aelurostrongylus abstrusus* is a nematoid parasite which has a complex life cycle. The male is 7·5 mm in length and the female 10 mm. The adult worms live in the pulmonary arteries and terminal bronchioles although there is disagreement amongst various authors as to their usual habitat. Eggs, measuring 80×70 μm, are deposited singly but continuously by the female into the pulmonary arteries and alveolar spaces. The eggs embryonate and develop into first stage larvae which migrate up to the respiratory bronchioles where they cause mild irritation and are coughed up in the sputum. They are swallowed and pass out unchanged as threads, some $0{\cdot}36 \times 0{\cdot}015$ mm, in the faeces. The intermediate host is the snail (*Epiphragmorphora* species, *Helminthoglypta* species or *Helix aspersa*) or slug (*Agriolimax agrestis* or *Agriolimax columbianus*). The second and third stage larvae live in the musculature of the intermediate host. Sometimes third stage larvae infect mice or birds as paratenic hosts. When the paratenic host is eaten by a cat the third stage infective larvae burrow through the wall of the intestine to reach the mesenteric lymph nodes where they moult to produce fourth stage larvae. These drift in venous blood to pass through the right ventricle into the pulmonary arterial tree. Here a final ecdysis produces adult worms.

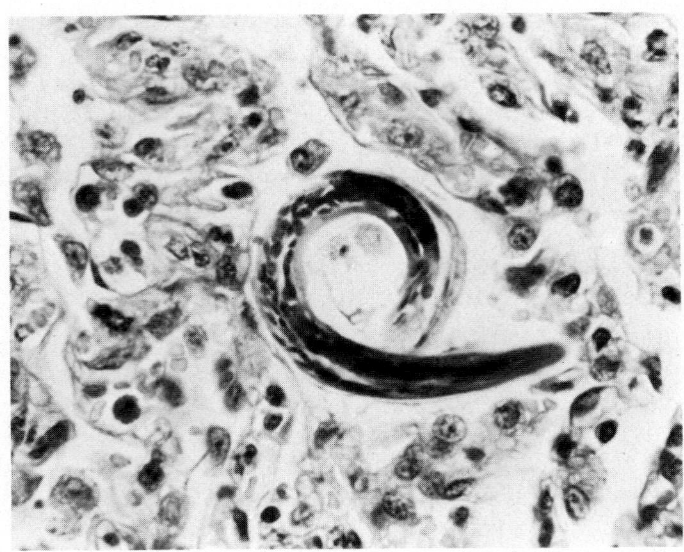

Fig. 15.5 Section of lung of cat showing infestation with the nematode parasite *Aelurostrongylus abstrusus*. (Haematoxylin & eosin, × 600)

The lung worm may produce pulmonary hypertension by occluding pulmonary arteries or by producing hypertrophy and hyperplasia of their muscle coats by means of chemical substances derived from the worms, eggs or first stage larvae. Lepage[40] believes that the worms have a vascular habitat and the observation of eggs in the pulmonary arterioles[41] supports this view. When eggs are released in large numbers, they produce small pulmonary infarctions due to thrombus which forms around the eggs occluding the pulmonary arteries.[40]

We have had the opportunity of studying sections of lung from cats infested with the parasite (Fig. 15.5) and are able to confirm the presence of very thick-walled and tortuous arteries running through the lungs (Fig. 15.6). The affected arteries show hyperplasia of smooth muscle running circularly and obliquely and in the intima there is longitudinally orientated smooth muscle. The histological appearances appear to be reminiscent of bronchial rather than pulmonary arteries but according to Hamilton[39] they are definitely pulmonary. We were impressed by the pronounced hyperplasia of smooth muscle in the lung parenchyma and bronchial tree as well as in the vasculature (Fig. 15.7). This suggests to us that the muscular hyperplasia may be induced by a substance diffusing from the adult worms, eggs or larvae.

Cotton-Wool Granulomata of Pulmonary Arteries

In this chapter we have described the many causes of pulmonary hypertension and have made brief references to the type of pulmonary vascular disease which

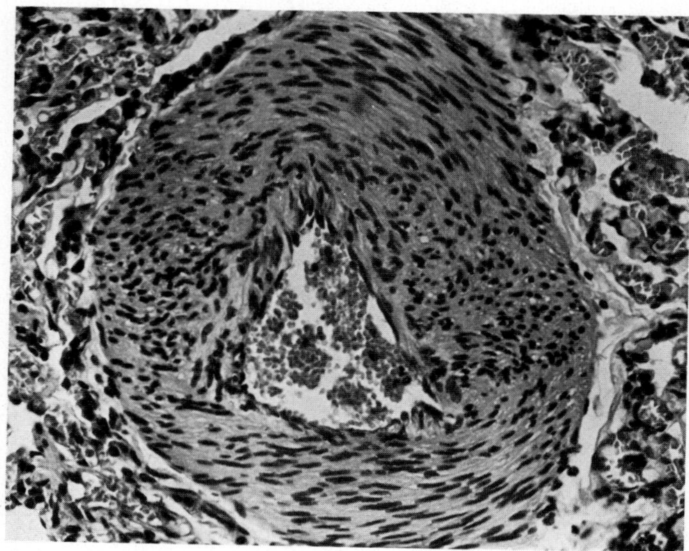

Fig. 15.6 Transverse section of a muscular pulmonary artery from a cat infested with *Aelurostrongylus abstrusus*. There is pronounced medial hypertrophy. (Haematoxylin & eosin, × 270)

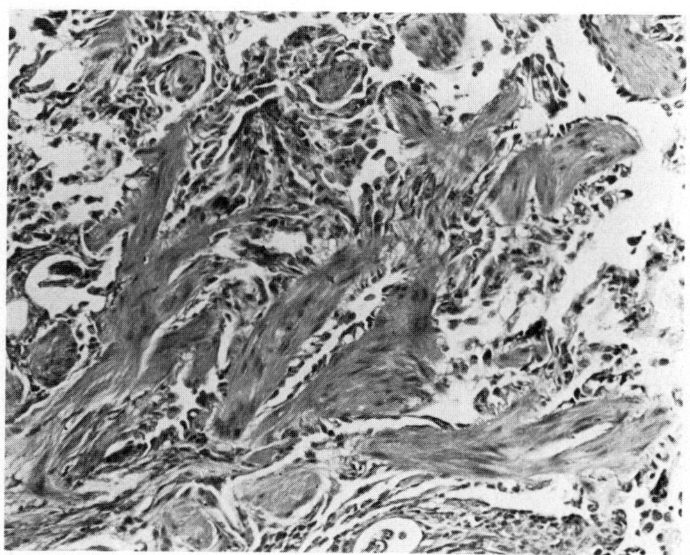

Fig. 15.7 Section of lung from a cat infested with *Aelurostrongylus abstrusus*. There is pronounced hyperplasia of smooth muscle in the lung parenchyma. (Haematoxylin & eosin, × 150)

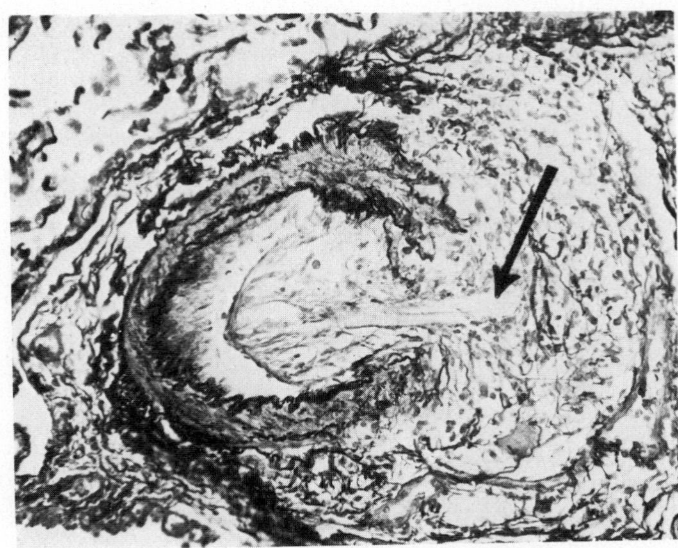

Fig. 15.8 Cotton-wool granuloma of pulmonary artery, occurring in a woman of 49 years who had ligation of a patent ductus arteriosus following investigation by cardiac catheterization. The catheter had been sterilized by autoclaving in thick cotton-wool gauze. The Figure shows a transverse section of a hypertrophied muscular pulmonary artery. A cotton-wool fibre, indicated by an arrow, has impacted in the wall of the artery and has penetrated the media. A granulomatous reaction has taken place around the fibre forming a dumb-bell shaped mass protruding into the lumen and adventitia of the artery. Note the frayed ends of the media the continuity of which has been interrupted by the passage through it of the granuloma surrounding the fibre. (Elastic/Van Gieson, × 150)

complicates each of the main groups of diseases listed. It seems appropriate here to consider a histological lesion that may be seen by the pathologist called upon to give an opinion on the state of the pulmonary vasculature in a lung biopsy specimen. If he is not familiar with the cotton-wool granuloma of the pulmonary artery[42] the condition may lead to confusion and perhaps even to a faulty diagnosis. This condition is not a cause of pulmonary hypertension but it is not infrequently seen in cases of pulmonary hypertension where cardiac catheterization has been carried out to establish the diagnosis of the underlying cause.

The lesion is caused by fragments of cotton wool introduced into the vascular system. They may have adhered to the tip of a cardiac catheter especially if it was stored or sterilized in gamgee tissue. Another source of entry of fragments of cotton wool into the systemic veins is contamination of a syringe needle used for intravenous injection. Fragments of cotton wool are carried into the pulmonary arteries where they impinge into the media, eventually working their way through the wall. They appear as doubly refractile rod-shaped bodies (Fig. 15.8). Commonly a granuloma forms around the fibre. This is composed of granulation and fibrous tissue, with scattered chronic inflammatory cells and foreign-body giant cells. The condition affects other arteries in the body,[43] but it is probably of no clinical significance in the sense that it does not produce vascular occlusion and pulmonary hypertension. Its importance lies rather in the fact that it may cause perplexity to the pathologist unfamiliar with the lesion, even leading to a mistaken diagnosis of some granulomatous arteritis involving the lung.

Pulmonary Arterial Stenosis

A rare cause of pulmonary arterial hypertension is the presence of congenital narrowings of the pulmonary artery.[44–46] Such narrowings may affect the pulmonary trunk, its main branches or their more distal divisions. The abnormality is particularly associated with congenital rubella.[47–49] The anatomical nature of the lesions may be demonstrated angiographically[50] (Fig. 15.9). An increased pulmonary arterial pressure is found proximal to the lesions and this particularly affects the systolic pressure.[51] Withdrawal of the catheter across the stenosis clearly reveals the local nature of the haemodynamic abnormality (Fig. 15.10). The arterial narrowing gives rise to a systolic ejection murmur.

The Effects of Pulmonary Hypertension on the Pulmonary Circulation

The pulmonary arterial hypertension of pre- and post-tricuspid congenital cardiac shunts is associated with the development of a characteristic form of hypertensive pulmonary vascular disease referred to briefly above. We may consider the pathology of this form of pulmonary vascular disease at this point first because

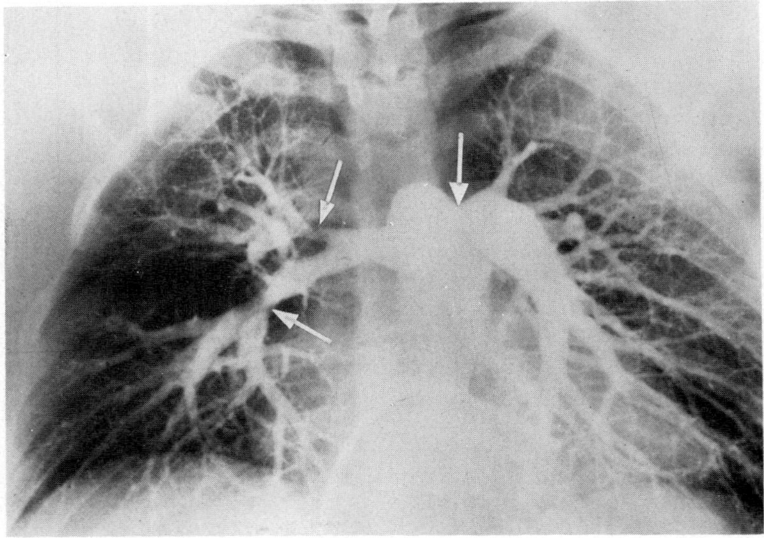

Fig. 15.9 Pulmonary arteriogram in a patient aged 21 with multiple pulmonary arterial narrowings shown by arrows. See also Fig. 15.10.

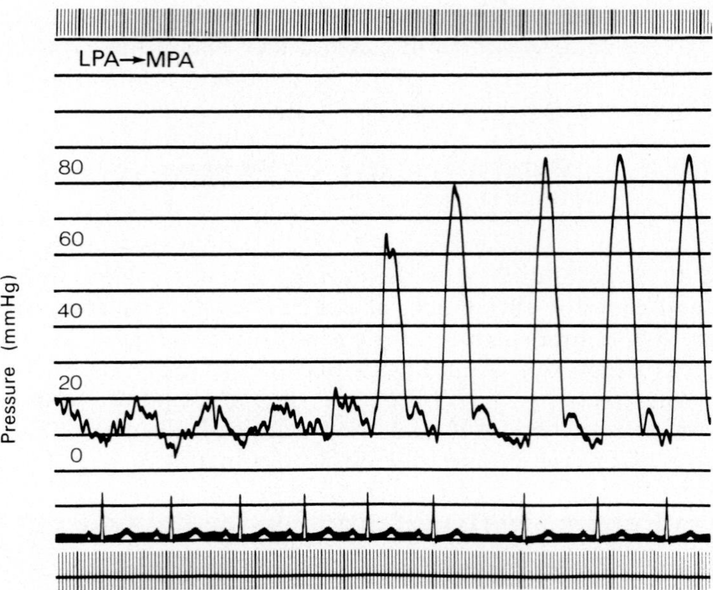

Fig. 15.10 Pressure tracing on withdrawal of a cardiac catheter from the left pulmonary artery into the pulmonary trunk in a patient aged 21 with multiple pulmonary arterial stenoses. See also Figure 15.9.

it presents the widest spectrum of histological changes and second since the chapters following refer to it specifically. Progressive medial hypertrophy, vascular occlusion and dilatation follow on in a stereotyped fashion so that six grades may be recognized. These are described in detail in Chapter 16. The development of these abnormalities in the small pulmonary blood vessels can, to a large extent, be related to the changes which occur in the haemodynamics of the pulmonary circulation and this relation is elaborated in Chapter 19. There is also a relation between the extent of the occlusive pulmonary vascular disease and the degree of immediate reversibility of the elevated pulmonary vascular resistance after surgical correction of the underlying septal defect. This subject is discussed in Chapter 20. Patients with pulmonary arterial pressures that are chronically elevated to levels of the order of systemic magnitude develop characteristic clinical features which are described in Chapter 21. Changes in structure in the major elastic pulmonary arteries associated with severe pulmonary hypertension are described in Chapter 17.

REFERENCES

1. Heath, D. & Whitaker, W. (1957) *Brit. Heart J.*, **19**, 327.
2. Whitaker, W. (1954) *Brit. Heart J.*, **16**, 177.
3. Edwards, J. E. (1957) *Circulation*, **15**, 164.
4. Brown, J. W., Heath, D. & Whitaker, W. (1955) *Brit. Heart J.*, **17**, 273.
5. Heath, D., Brown, J. W. & Whitaker, W. (1956) *Brit. Heart J.*, **18**, 1.
6. Heath, D. (1957) *Circulation*, **15**, 701.

7. Whitaker, W., Heath, D. & Brown, J. W. (1955) *Brit. Heart J.*, **17**, 121.
8. Fleming, H. A. (1956) *Thorax*, **11**, 71.
9. Brown, J. W., Heath, D. & Whitaker, W. (1955) *Circulation*, **12**, 819.
10. Hicken, P., Evans, D. & Heath, D. (1966) *Brit. Heart J.*, **28**, 284.
11. Heath, D., Parker, R. L. & Edwards, J. E. (1958) *Brit. J. Clin. Pract.*, **12**, 701.
12. Shillingford, J. P., Kay, J. M. & Heath, D. (1970) *Amer. Heart J.*, **80**, 562.
13. Fontana, R. S. & Edwards, J. E. (1962) In *Congenital Cardiac Disease*. Philadelphia & London: Saunders.
14. Heath, D. (1968) *Brit. J. Dis. Chest.*, **62**, 207.
15. Henry, E. W. (1952) *Brit. Heart J.*, **14**, 406.
16. Walton, K. W. & Heath, D. (1960) *Brit. Heart J.*, **22**, 440.
17. Becker, D. L., Burchell, H. B. & Edwards, J. E. (1951) *Circulation*, **3**, 230.
18. Best, P. V. & Heath, D. (1964) *Brit. Heart J.*, **26**, 312.
19. Van Buchem, F. S. P. & Eerland, L. D. (1957) *Dis. Chest.*, **31**, 61.
20. Heath, D. (1968) *Amer. J. Cardiol.*, **21**, 315.
21. Edwards, J. E. & Burchell, H. B. (1951) *Arch. Intern. Med.*, **87**, 372.
22. Müller, O. & Rorvik, K. (1958) *Brit. Heart J.*, **20**, 302.
23. Heath, D., Cox, E. V. & Harris-Jones, J. N. (1957) *Thorax*, **12**, 321.
24. Smith, R. C., Burchell, H. B. & Edwards, J. E. (1954) *Circulation*, **10**, 801.
25. Heath, D. & Best, P. V. (1958) *J. Path. Bact.*, **76**, 165.
26. Taquini, A. C., Roncoroni, A. J. & Aramendia, P. (1956) *Amer. Heart J.*, **51**, 468.
27. Brewer, D. B. (1955) *J. Path. Bact.*, **70**, 299.
28. Barnard, P. J. (1954) *Circulation*, **10**, 343.
29. Marshall, R. (1965) In *Pulmonary Embolism: Mechanism and Management*. Springfield, Ill. Thomas.
30. Obeyesekere, I. & De Soysa, N. (1970) *Brit. Heart J.*, **32**, 524.
31. Obeyesekere, I. & Peiris, D. (1974) *Brit. Heart J.*, **36**, 676.
32. Wood, P. (1956) In *Diseases of the Heart and Circulation* 2nd Ed. London: Eyre & Spottiswoode.
33. Obeyesekere, I. (1973) *Singapore Med. J.*, **14**, 311.
34. Cappell, D. F. & Anderson, J. R. (1971) In *Muir's Textbook of Pathology*—9th Ed. page 292. London: Arnold.
35. Dissanaike, A. S. & Paramananthan, D. C. (1961) *J. Helminth.*, **35**, 209.
36. Jayasinghe, J. B., Fernando, S. D. A. & Dissanaike, A. S. (1964) *Ann. Trop. Med. Parasit.*, **58**, 328.
37. Detweiler, D. K., Hubben, K. & Patterson, D. F. (1960) *Amer. J. Vet. Res.*, **21**, 329.
38. Patterson, D. F. & Luginbuhl, H. R. (1963) *J. Amer. Vet. Med. Ass.*, **143**, 619.
39. Hamilton, J. M. (1966) *J. Comp. Path.*, **76**, 133.
40. Lepage, G. (1968) In *Veterinary Parasitology*. page 235. Edinburgh & London: Oliver & Boyd.
41. Cameron, T. W. M. (1934) In *The Internal Parasites of Domestic Animals*. page 123. London: Black.
42. Heath, D. & MacKinnon, J. (1962) *Brit. Heart J.*, **24**, 518.
43. Kay, J. M. & Wilkins, R. A. (1969) *Clin. Radiol.*, **20**, 410.
44. D'Crus, I. A., Agustsson, M. H., Bicoff, J. P., Weinberg, M. & Arcilla, R. A. (1964) *Amer. J. Cardiol.*, **13**, 441.
45. McCue, C. M., Robertson, L. W., Lester, R. G. & Mauck, H. P. (1965) *J. Pediat.*, **67**, 222.
46. Eldredge, W. J., Tingelstad, J. B., Robertson, L. W., Mauck, H. P. & McCue, C. M. (1972) *Circulation*, **45**, 404.
47. Rowe, M. D. (1963) *Pediatrics*, **32**, 180.
48. Emmanoulides, G. B., Linde, G. M., Crittenden, H. J. (1964) *Circulation*, **29**, 514.
49. Wasserman, M. P., Varghese, P. J. & Rowe, R. D. (1968) *Amer. Heart J.*, **76**, 638.
50. Gay, B. B., Franch, R. H., Shuford, W. H. & Rogers, J. V. (1963) *Amer. J. Roentgenol.*, **90**, 599.
51. Agustsson, M. H., Arcilla, R. A., Gasul, B. M., Bicoff, J. P., Nassif, S. I. & Lendrum, B. L. (1962) *Circulation*, **26**, 421.

16. The Pathology and Electron Microscopy of Hypertensive Pulmonary Vascular Disease in Congenital Cardiac Septal Defects

Progressive changes develop in the structure of the pulmonary arteries and arterioles as a complication of the chronically elevated pulmonary arterial pressure associated with large congenital septal defects of the heart. This progression runs a stereotyped course irrespective of the underlying cardiac anomaly. Heath and Edwards,[1] were able to define six grades on the basis of structural alterations in the media and intima of the small pulmonary arterial vessels. These are summarized in Table 16.1. While the whole process must be regarded as a continuous one, its division into grades is of practical value since it enables the pathologist to express a group of complex abnormalities in a succinct manner as a grade number. In this chapter we are concerned solely with the alterations found in small pulmonary blood vessels. The changes in the intima and media of the larger, elastic pulmonary arteries are considered in Chapter 17.

While the changes found in grades 2 to 6 are identical in patients with 'pre-tricuspid' and 'post-tricuspid' shunts (Chap. 15), the earliest (grade 1) abnormalities seen in the small pulmonary blood vessels tend to differ in the two groups. Grade 1 of the classification presented in this chapter refers to patients with post-tricuspid shunts. The corresponding grade seen in patients with pre-tricuspid shunts is dealt with at the end of the chapter.

Table 16.1 Basis of grades of hypertensive pulmonary vascular disease

This system of grading is applicable only to the form of pulmonary vascular disease ('plexogenic pulmonary arteriopathy') which occurs with large congenital cardiac septal defects, with the classical form of primary pulmonary hypertension and in rare cases of cirrhosis of the liver and portal vein thrombosis.

	Grade of hypertensive pulmonary vascular disease					
	1	2	3	4	5	6
Type of intimal reaction	← None →	← Cellular	→	→	→	→
			← Fibrous and fibroelastic	→	→	→
				← 'Plexiform lesion'	→	→
State of media of arteries and arterioles	← Hypertrophied	→	→	→	→	→
			← Some generalized dilatation	→	→	→
				← Local 'dilatation lesions'	→	→
					← PH[a]	→
						← NA[b] →

[a] Pulmonary haemosiderosis associated with distended, thin-walled arterial vessels throughout the lung
[b] Necrotizing arteritis

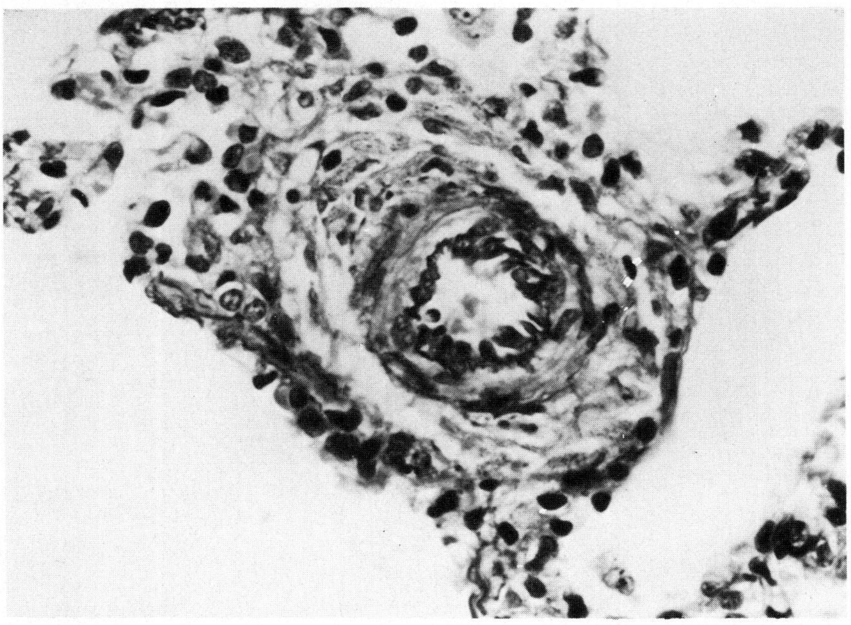

Fig. 16.1 Transverse section of a pulmonary arteriole from a boy aged 6 years with a persistent truncus arteriosus and pulmonary hypertension. It has a thick muscular media in which the plump nuclei of the muscle fibres can be seen. There is no intimal proliferation of any type. Hypertensive pulmonary vascular disease (HPVD: grade 1). (Elastic/Van Gieson, $\times 600$)

Grade 1. The Stage of Retention of Foetal-Type Pulmonary Arteries

The definitive histological features lie in the pulmonary arterioles and the muscular pulmonary arteries. This grade is the earliest ever found in large post-tricuspid shunts.

The walls of pulmonary arterioles (<100 μm in diameter) normally have a distinct muscular media only at the point of origin from a parent muscular pulmonary artery (Chap. 3), and elsewhere in their course comprise only a single elastic lamina. In grade 1 hypertensive pulmonary vascular disease they have a thick muscular media sandwiched between distinct internal and external elastic laminae (Fig. 16.1). Even arterial vessels as small as 30 μm in diameter look like small muscular pulmonary arteries instead of venules as they do in the normal lung. These small thick-walled arterial vessels resemble closely the intra-lobular pulmonary arteries of the foetus (Chap. 14) and in this connexion it should be remembered that comparable classes of vessels differ greatly in size in the foetus and the adult.

It has already been pointed out in Chapter 3 that small arterial vessels less than 100 μm in diameter with a distinct media are found occasionally in the normal

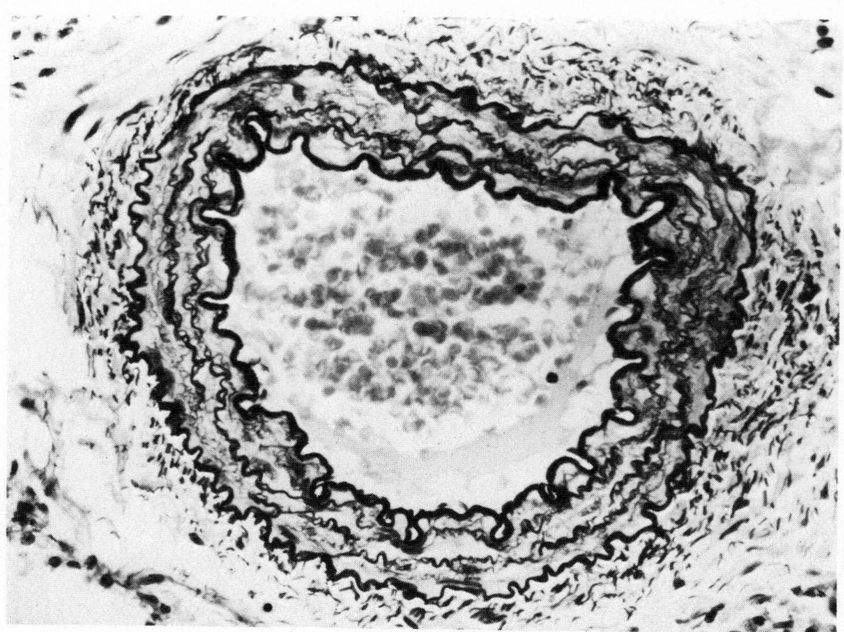

Fig. 16.2 Transverse section of a muscular pulmonary artery from the same case illustrated in Figure 16.1. There is medial hypertrophy with crenation of elastic laminae consistent with vasoconstriction. No form of intimal proliferation is present. HPVD: grade 1. (Elastic/Van Gieson, × 360)

human lung, especially in the region of the lingula. This may lead to confusion since one of the most helpful histological criteria in the recognition of early hypertensive pulmonary vascular disease is the appearance of a muscular media in arterial vessels below 100 μm in diameter. It is much better to select tissue from the upper and lower lobes. For reasons to be discussed in Chapter 22 it is further suggested that the lower lobe is the more suitable of the two for pulmonary biopsy.

The media of the muscular pulmonary arteries (100 to 1000 μm in external diameter) is also very thick (Fig. 16.2) and, as in the case of the vessels of arteriolar dimension, may be as thick as 25 per cent of the external diameter of the vessel. Fasciculi of longitudinal muscle may develop external to the outer elastic lamina (Fig. 16.3) and internal to the inner elastic lamina as described later in the chapter. In both classes of vessel there is no intimal fibrosis but the adventitia is thick and fibrous. There is a gradual increase in medial thickness in muscular pulmonary arteries from grade 1 to 3, generally speaking, but there is much variation in the thickness of individual muscular pulmonary arteries in any one case. There is no direct relation between medial thickness and the level of pulmonary arterial pressure.

The pulmonary veins are normal in cases with post-tricuspid shunts associated with pulmonary hypertension.

The appearances which have just been described represent the persistence of the muscular blood vessels found in the foetal lung. It is presumed that this thickened musculature persists because of an active constriction of the arteries and forms an inherent component of ventricular septal defect and other forms of post-tricuspid shunt. In contrast, the abnormalities to be described in grades 2 to 6 may be thought of as representing the pathological effects of pulmonary hypertension on these thick blood vessels.

Grade 2. Stage of Medial Hypertrophy with Cellular Intimal Proliferation

Cellular intimal proliferation is seen in both the smallest muscular pulmonary arteries, less than about 300 μm in diameter, and in the arterioles. It is restricted to these small arterial vessels and there is no intimal reaction elsewhere in the pulmonary vasculature. In some arterioles the endothelial cells are rounded and form a prominent vascular lining. In others, there is a cellular intimal proliferation to form eccentric masses with underlying material which stains brown with Van Gieson's stain. In other cases the cellular intimal proliferation may form a

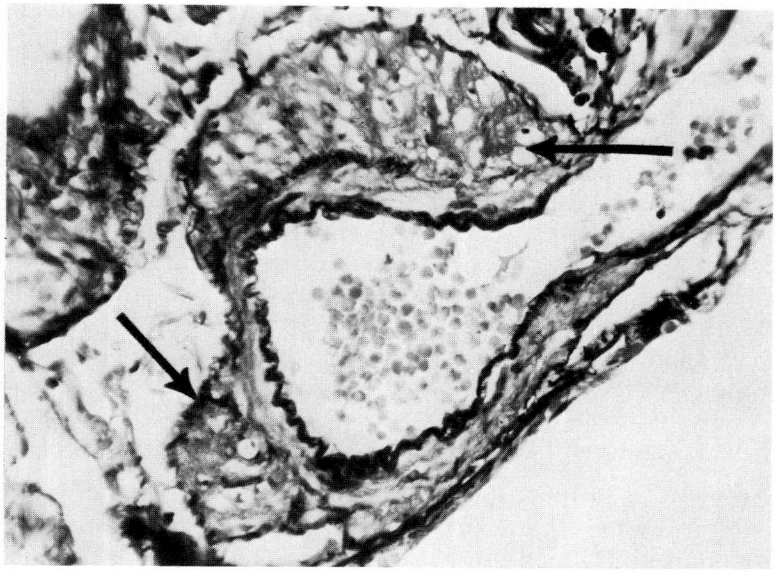

Fig. 16.3 Transverse section of a muscular pulmonary artery from a woman of 38 years with a persistent truncus arteriosus and pulmonary hypertension. Large fasciculi of longitudinally-orientated smooth muscle fibres (arrows) have developed external to the outer elastic lamina of the original media of circular muscle. HPVD: grade 1. (Elastic/Van Gieson, ×450)

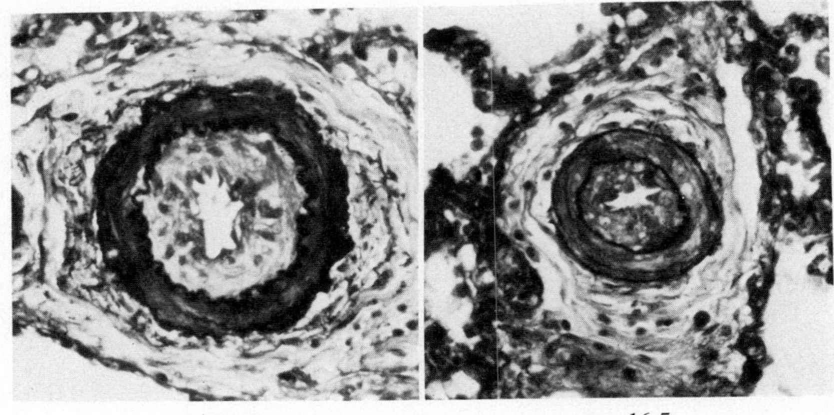

FIG. 16.4 FIG. 16.5

Fig. 16.4 Transverse section of a small muscular pulmonary artery from a boy of 6 years with a persistent truncus arteriosus and pulmonary hypertension. There is hypertrophy of the media and a pronounced cellular proliferation of the intima which has produced almost total occlusion of the lumen. HPVD: grade 2. (Elastic/Van Gieson, × 300)

Fig. 16.5 Transverse section of a pulmonary arteriole from the same case as in Figure 16.4. A thick muscular media is present between distinct internal and external elastic laminae. The lumen of the arteriole is almost totally occluded by a cellular intimal proliferation and a material which stains brown with Van Gieson's reagents. HPVD: grade 2. (Elastic/Van Gieson, × 400)

concentric rim around the circumference of both small muscular pulmonary arteries (Fig. 16.4) and arterioles (Fig. 16.5). The prominence of the endothelium in these small vessels may be due to hyperplasia or to contraction of the underlying smooth muscle of the media. In time, collagen, recognizable by its property of staining red with Van Gieson's stain, forms underneath the endothelium and this constitutes the earliest stage of grade 3. The nature of the cellular intimal proliferation is considered at the end of the chapter where we give an account of the ultrastructural changes in the pulmonary arteries of dogs subjected to the creation of a systemic-pulmonary anastomosis.

Grade 3. Stage of Progressive Fibrous Vascular Occlusion

There is progressive intimal fibrosis in the smaller muscular pulmonary arteries and pulmonary arterioles with a change in the nature of the intimal proliferation and an extension of it into medium-sized arteries (300 to 500 μm).

Early in grade 3, cellular fibrous tissue develops under the endothelial lining (Fig. 16.6). Later lesions are characterized by concentric or eccentric masses of less cellular fibrous tissue that stains bright red with Van Gieson's stain. Finally, the intimal fibrotic lesions show an admixture of fine or even coarse elastic fibrils

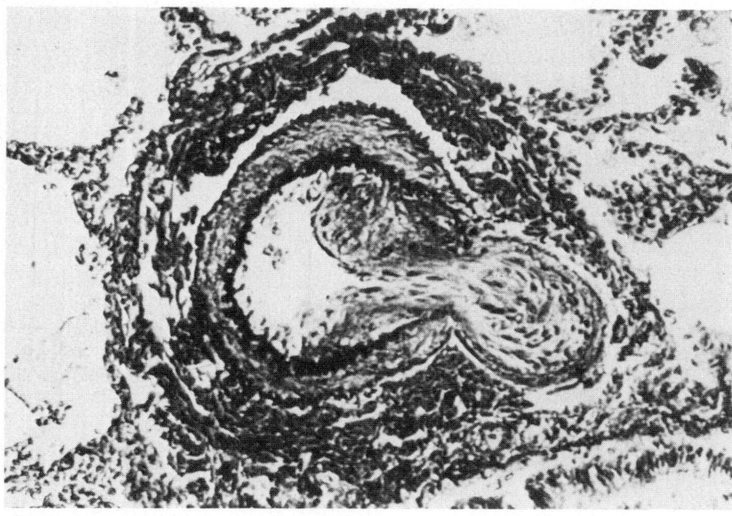

Fig. 16.6 Transverse section of a small muscular pulmonary artery with an oblique section of an arteriolar branch. There is medial hypertrophy. Cellular fibrous tissue forms eccentric masses in the artery and occludes the arteriole. From a 9 year old boy having cor triloculare biatriatum without pulmonary stenosis. HPVD: grade 3. (Elastic/Van Gieson, × 160)

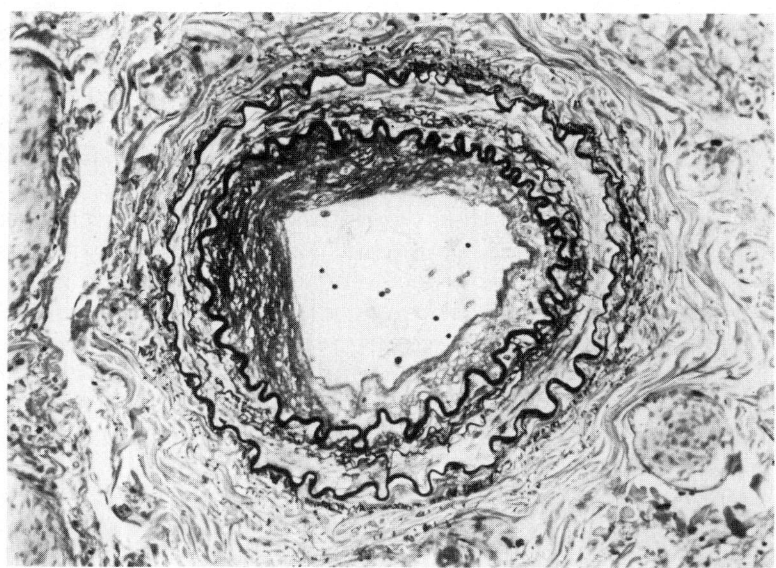

Fig. 16.7 Transverse section of a muscular pulmonary artery from a young woman aged 26 years with a widely patent ductus arteriosus and severe pulmonary hypertension. There is medial hypertrophy and crenation of elastic laminae suggestive of vasoconstriction. There is severe intimal fibroelastosis. HPVD: grade 3. (Elastic/Van Gieson, × 185)

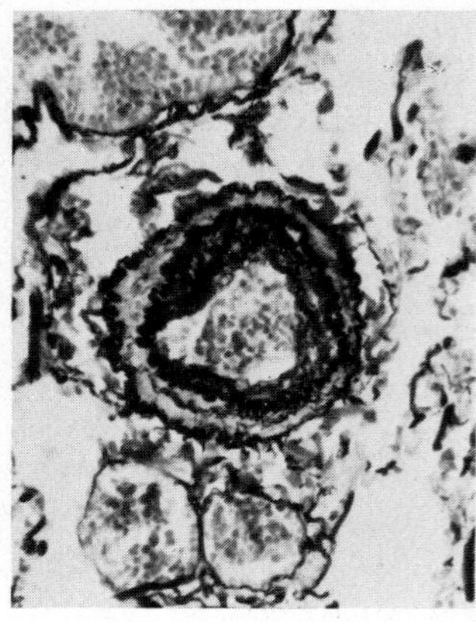

Fig. 16.8 Transverse section of a pulmonary arteriole from a woman aged 39 years with an atrial septal defect and severe pulmonary hypertension. A distinct muscular media is present. There is also severe intimal fibroelastosis. HPVD: grade 3. (Elastic/Van Gieson, × 150)

and some splitting or elastosis of the internal elastic lamina (Figs 16.7 and 16.8). The intimal fibrous tissue eventually becomes hyaline.

Most of the intimal lesions are found first in the arterioles and smaller muscular pulmonary arteries and extend back around the mouths of origin of the vessels to involve the parent arteries (Fig. 16.6). It will be remembered from Chapter 3 that arterioles occur not only as terminations of the smallest muscular pulmonary arteries but may arise more proximally in the pulmonary vascular tree as right-angled branches of fairly large muscular arteries. Pulmonary arterioles show intimal fibrosis irrespective of their site of origin in the pulmonary vascular tree. Severe intimal fibrosis is common in the smallest muscular pulmonary arteries under 300 μm in diameter, but is found much less frequently in the medium-sized arteries between say 300 and 500 μm in diameter. Only in unusually severe hypertensive pulmonary vascular disease is intimal fibrosis widespread in the latter class of vessel. The largest muscular pulmonary arteries show atherosclerosis rather than intimal fibrosis. The fibrosis is focal and is sometimes continuous with the fibrous tissue in the smaller muscular pulmonary arteries and arterioles and sometimes not. Finally, the concentric or eccentric masses of avascular fibrous tissue in the muscular arteries and arterioles may occlude the vessel completely, but a small endothelium-lined channel with an irregular course frequently remains.

The intimal fibrosis due to age is easily distinguishable from that due to pulmonary hypertension for it consists of a narrow layer of acellular fibrous tissue which stains only faintly with eosin and is not admixed with elastic fibrils (Chap. 3, Figs 3.14 and 3.17).

In grade 3, the media of muscular arteries and arterioles reaches the limit of its capacity for hypertrophy so that its thickness may be up to 30 per cent of the external diameter of the vessel. In the medium-sized and large muscular arteries the increase in medial thickness is brought about to some extent by the development of fasciculi of longitudinal muscle. This subject is discussed below.

Grade 4. The Stage of Progressive Generalized Arterial Dilatation with the Formation of Complex 'Dilatation Lesions'

In the later stages of grade 3 the media tends to become thinner in the muscular pulmonary arteries and pulmonary arterioles throughout the lungs. This generalized dilatation progresses through grades 4 to 6 and may be regarded as the effect of a sustained and progressive elevation of the transmural pressure. Such dilatation occurs not only in patent vessels but also in those showing focal areas of occlusion. In the latter case, the dilatation and thinning of the media is found in smaller and medium-sized muscular arteries and in pulmonary arterioles. In the smaller arteries and in the arterioles, the thinning is found either at, or distal to, a focus of fibrotic occlusion in a parent muscular artery, whereas in the medium-sized arteries it is seen proximal to the foci of occlusion. The dilatation of hypertrophied muscular-arteries may be more pronounced over short segments. This occurs shortly after the origin of a smaller arterial branch. A distended sac is formed, the wall consisting of a thin but still recognizable arterial structure with a distinct media and internal and external elastic laminae. At such dilatations, fibrous intimal thickening may occur, the fibres and nuclei tending to be arranged concentrically to give a so-called onion-layering appearance. Beyond the distended segment the normal arterial structure is resumed, usually with super-added intimal fibrosis. In spite of the generalized dilatation and thinning of the media which occurs in grades 4 to 6, many muscular

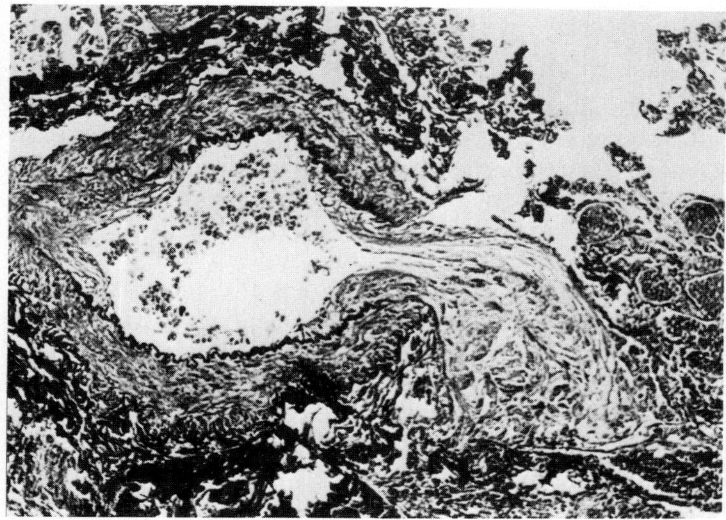

Fig. 16.9 Transverse section of a muscular pulmonary artery from a woman aged 27 years with an atrial septal defect and severe pulmonary hypertension. There is hypertrophy of the media and excessive dilatation of an arteriolar branch to form a plexiform lesion. The intimal proliferation in the distended sac is cellular indicating the dilatation lesion to be of recent formation. HPVD: grade 5. (Elastic/Van Gieson, × 150)

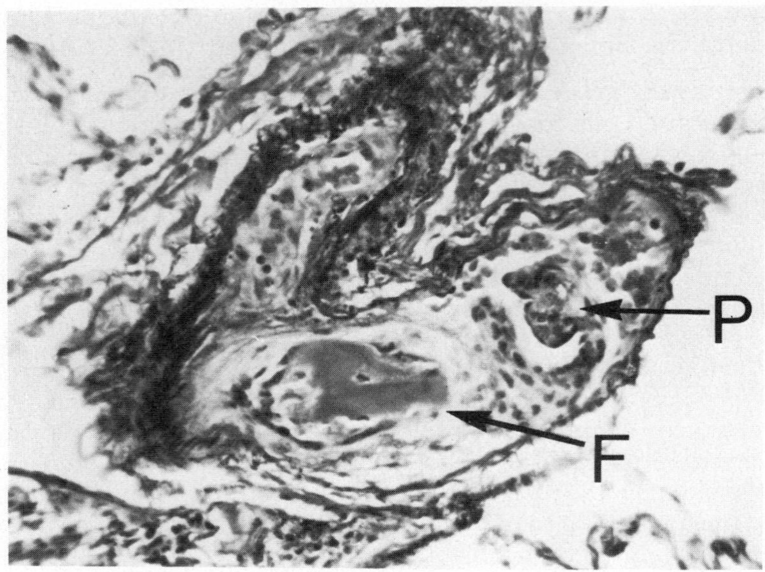

Fig. 16.10 Plexiform lesion in a section of lung from a young woman of 21 years with a large ventricular septal defect and severe pulmonary hypertension. The proliferated cells in the dilated sac are arranged in a plexiform manner (arrow P). Fibrinoid substance is also seen in the dilated arterial branch (arrow F). HPVD: grade 5. (Elastic/Van Gieson, × 160)

pulmonary arteries and arterioles still show a marked increase in medial thickness with gross intimal fibroelastosis.

In addition to the generalized dilatation, the severer grades are accompanied by local dilatations of small arterial vessels which have been termed '*dilatation lesions*'.[1] These assume complex shapes and three main types may be distinguished: (a) plexiform lesions, (b) vein-like branches of hypertrophied, usually occluded, muscular pulmonary arteries and (c) angiomatoid lesions.

The plexiform lesion Some pulmonary arterioles and smallest muscular pulmonary arteries are greatly distended to form sacs, the walls of which are thin, consisting of a single elastic lamina or an exceedingly thin layer of muscle between two ill-defined elastic laminae (Figs 16.9–16.11). Large, similarly thin-walled channels leave these dilated sacs and terminate as capillaries that pass to the alveolar walls. In some instances vessels of capillary-size leave the sacs and pass directly to the alveolar capillaries. As a result of endothelial proliferation and thrombosis in these dilated vessels, three zones may often be distinguished. Proximally there is fibrous tissue continuous with that in the intima of the parent muscular pulmonary artery. In early lesions this fibrous tissue is cellular, in late lesions it is acellular. There is a central zone of proliferative cellular endothelial tissue which often assumes a characteristic plexiform pattern. In the distal portion of the distended sac there is frequently a thrombus. As the lesion ages, the thrombus becomes organized and

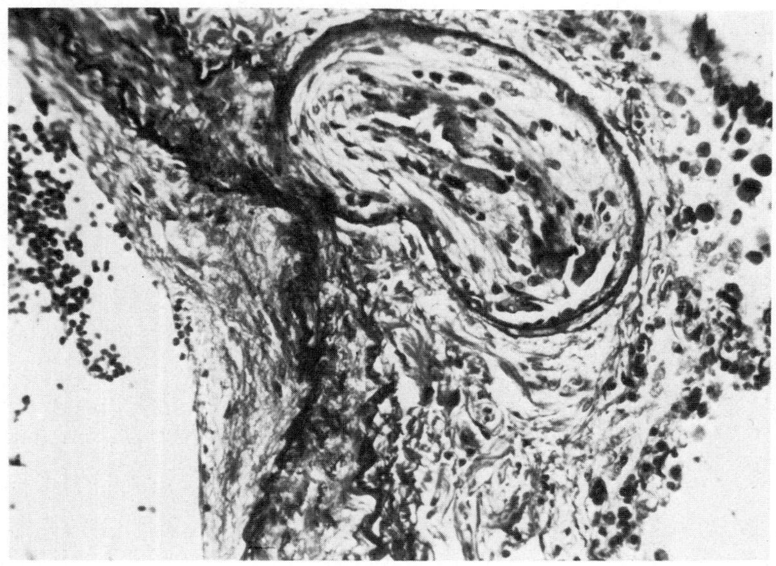

Fig. 16.11 Arc of a hypertrophied muscular pulmonary artery showing intimal fibrosis from a case of patent ductus arteriosus with pulmonary hypertension. A thin-walled dilated branch arises to the right and contains cellular proliferation consistent with being part of a plexiform lesion. HPVD: grade 4. (Elastic/Van Gieson, × 190)

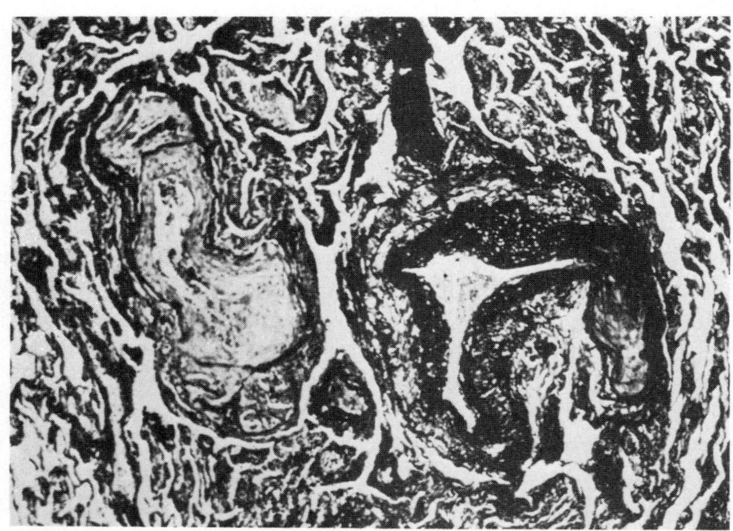

Fig. 16.12 Transverse section of a muscular pulmonary artery from a woman aged 20 years with a patent ductus arteriosus and severe pulmonary hypertension. There is medial hypertrophy and very severe elastosis of the internal elastic lamina. Two plexiform lesions are present. That to the right of the picture is old for the proliferated tissue in the dilated sac has been totally replaced by fibroelastic tissue. HPVD: grade 5. (Elastic/Van Gieson, × 75)

M

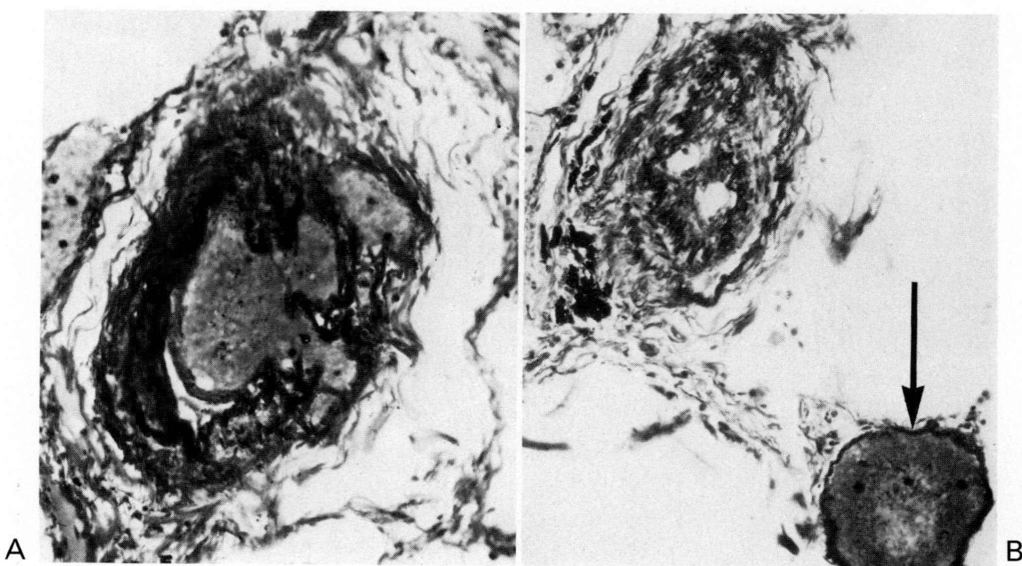

Fig. 16.13 Serial sections of a lung from a woman aged 38 years with a large ventricular septal defect and severe pulmonary hypertension. They show the origin of a thin-walled branch of a hypertrophied muscular pulmonary artery, and demonstrate that such vessels are entirely arterial in nature and do not represent arteriovenous shunts. (Both Elastic/Van Gieson, ×150.) A, Muscular pulmonary artery showing emergence of thin-walled branches proximal to obstruction of vessel by fibroelastic tissue. Note ragged edges of media at the origin of the branch. B, The same vessel at a more distal site where it is almost occluded by fibroelastic tissue only two small channels remaining patent. Below it is a thin-walled vessel (arrow) which resembles a vein but which is in fact a continuation of the arterial branch seen emerging in A.

finally fibroelastic tissue forms (Fig. 16.12). We consider the nature of the plexiform lesion in Chapter 18. We may note here that, since the form of hypertensive pulmonary vascular disease complicating congenital cardiac shunts has a natural history to develop plexiform lesions, it may be termed 'plexogenic pulmonary arteriopathy' (Chap. 28, p. 418). This form of vascular disease occurs also in the classical form of primary pulmonary hypertension and the very rare cases of severe pulmonary hypertension complicating cirrhosis of the liver and portal vein thrombosis.

Vein-like branches of hypertrophied muscular pulmonary arteries Muscular pulmonary arteries showing medial hypertrophy and gross intimal fibroelastosis may give rise to thin-walled branches resembling veins (Figs 16.13A and B), and these end as capillaries in the alveolar walls. These vein-like vessels usually emerge from the parent artery proximal to a point of obstruction and have been thought to provide a collateral pulmonary blood flow to the alveolar walls.[2] Similar lesions are found in pulmonary vascular occlusion due to Bilharzia (Chap. 15, Fig. 15.4). In the cases of pulmonary hypertension associated with congenital heart disease these

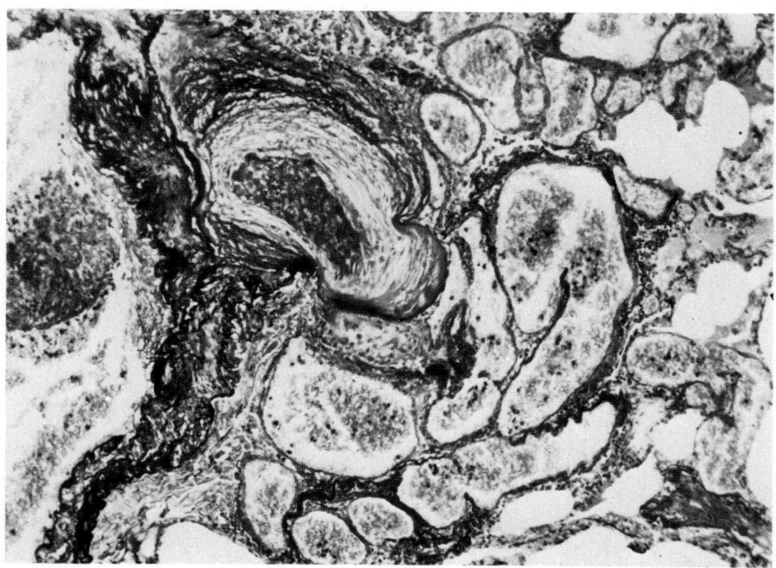

Fig. 16.14 The edge of an oblique section of a muscular pulmonary artery from a woman of 26 years with a widely-patent ductus arteriosus and severe pulmonary hypertension. To the right lies a complex of thin-walled, dilated branches of the artery. HPVD: grade 5. (Elastic/Van Gieson, × 75)

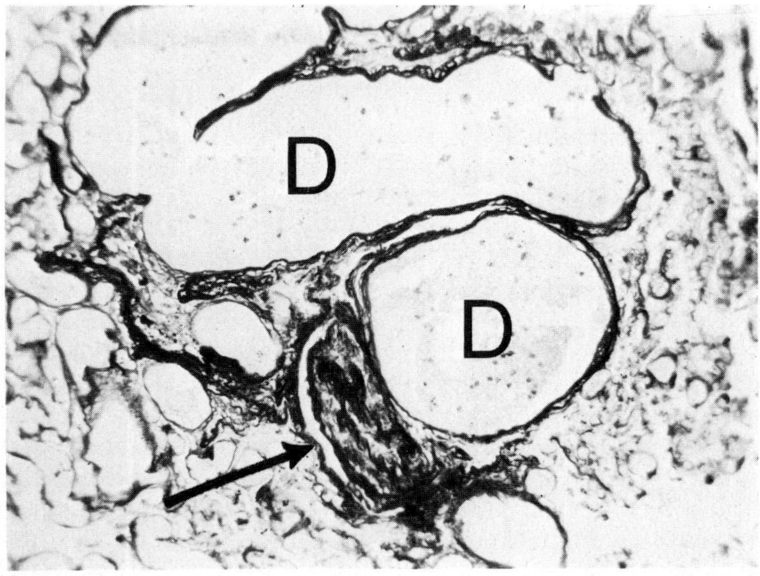

Fig. 16.15 Section of muscular pulmonary artery and its branches in a young woman aged 21 years with a large muscular ventricular septal defect and severe pulmonary hypertension. The parent vessel (arrow) shows medial hypertrophy. It is distorted and occluded by intimal fibroelastic tissue. Above it lie its dilated branches (D) arising proximal to the point of occlusion. HPVD: grade 5. (Elastic/Van Gieson, × 135)

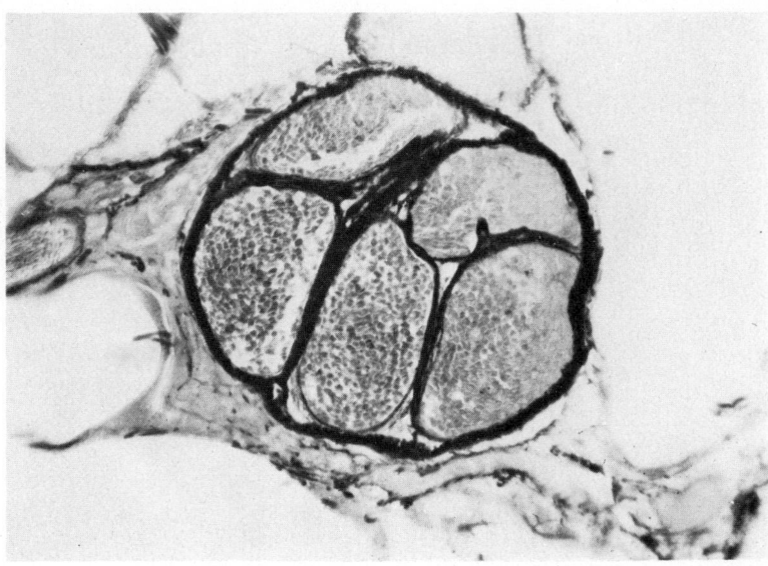

Fig. 16.16 Section of a small angiomatoid lesion from the same case illustrated in Figure 16.15. HPVD: grade 5. (Elastic/Van Gieson, × 140)

dilated branches are, however, occasionally found to arise from blood vessels with patent lumina. The appearances at the site of the origin of thin-walled branches of hypertrophied muscular pulmonary arteries (Figs 16.14 and 16.15) have been misinterpreted by some workers as arterio-venous anastomoses in the lung. Serial sections demonstrate conclusively that the thin-walled vessels are entirely arterial in nature and end as pulmonary capillaries.[2]

The angiomatoid lesion This lesion (Figs 16.6–16.18) appears to arise in a small muscular pulmonary artery just proximal to a fibrotic occlusion. At this point small capillaries develop in the wall of the artery in proximity to a lateral branch. They pass into the lateral branch by which time they have become dilated vessels lying in a sheath which is composed of the wall of the lateral branch. The walls of these vessels are extremely thin and consist of a single elastic lamina (Figs 16.16 and 16.18). At a short distance from the parent artery the dilated vessels form an angiomatoid mass from which thin-walled vessels ramify in all directions to end in capillaries which pass to the alveolar walls (Fig. 16.18). The diameter of the angiomatoid lesion may be as large as 1 mm. The lesion is rare and has been seen only in ventricular septal defect with pulmonary hypertension.[3] If the intimate connexion between parent muscular pulmonary artery, thin-walled branch and angiomatoid lesion is not established by examination of serial sections, one may mistakenly consider the angiomatoid mass to be an independent, separate entity in the lung.

All three types of 'dilatation lesion' appear to be severer and more complex expressions of the generalized dilatation that occurs throughout the pulmonary arterial tree as a result of the persistently high intravascular pressure. The accurate designation of these thin-walled vessels as branches of muscular pulmonary arteries is a good example of the principle stated in Chapter 3 that the recognition of the various classes of pulmonary blood vessel is only achieved with certainty by the examination of serial sections. On the examination of single sections, such vessels would be regarded almost certainly as veins, but the accurate spatial relationships and connexions of such peculiar arterial vessels have been demonstrated by the laborious but rewarding technique of drawing reconstructions from serial sections.[2]

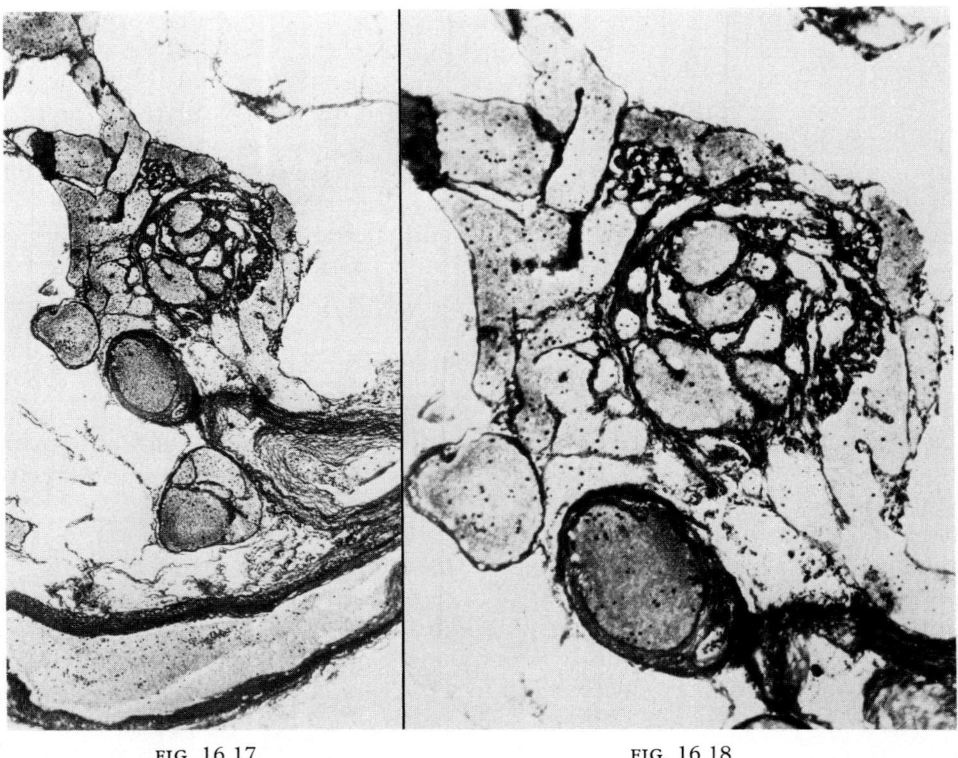

FIG. 16.17 FIG. 16.18

Fig. 16.17 A muscular pulmonary artery, shown in the lower part of the Figure, with a branch that shows much intimal fibrosis. A secondary branch seen in transverse section is divided by fibrous trabeculae into parallel tubes, forming an angiomatoid lesion, from which thin-walled channels arise to provide a collateral circulation. HPVD: grade 5. From a woman aged 38 years with a large ventricular septal defect associated with severe pulmonary hypertension. (Elastic/Van Gieson, × 35)

Fig. 16.18 Detail of Figure 16.17. Central vessel of angiomatoid lesion with sub-divided lumen surrounded by thin-walled dilated branches. (Elastic/Van Gieson, × 100)

In summary, grade 4 is characterized by generalized dilatation of the pulmonary arterial vessels accompanied by a thinning of the media. At this stage the complex 'dilatation lesions' begin to appear. The advent of the plexiform lesion is arbitrarily chosen to define this grade, the other forms of dilatation lesion occurring in grade 5.

Grade 5. Stage of Chronic Dilatation with Formation of Numerous Dilatation Lesions and Pulmonary Haemosiderosis

In grade 5, all three types of dilatation lesion previously described are found and give rise to thin-walled, dilatated vessels which ramify throughout the lung rendering it highly vascular. The origins and connexions of these small blood vessels in the lungs are illustrated diagrammatically in Figure 16.19. It would seem that they are fragile and either burst or allow diapedesis of blood, for foci of macrophages which contain haemosiderin are scattered throughout the lung. Generalized dilatation of the pulmonary arterial tree progresses. At this stage fibrosis occurs in the media as well as the intima and the blood vessels appear to be rigidly dilated. The intimal fibrous tissue is acellular or even hyaline. In grades 3 and 4, as previously stated, the lumina of some arteries with intimal fibrosis become all but obliterated by fibrous tissue leaving a small endothelium-lined channel. In grade 5, however, some of these central channels are widely dilated and surrounded by what appears to be a rigid tube consisting largely of acellular fibrous tissue and a thin, fibrosed media. The arterioles show a similar dilatation with fibrosis.

Grade 6. Stage of Necrotizing Arteritis

Necrotizing arteritis occurs rarely but nevertheless has been described in cases of atrial septal defect,[4] ventricular septal defect,[5] mitral stenosis,[6] and primary pulmonary hypertension.[7] It is usually associated with a very high pulmonary artery blood pressure.

Some of the muscular pulmonary arteries undergo acute fibrinoid necrosis, and, when stained with haematoxylin and eosin, the muscle of the media shows a glassy or 'smudgy' appearance (Fig. 16.20). There is a loss of nuclei and appropriate straining (Chap. 3) demonstrates fibrinoid substances. The necrotic muscle induces an inflammatory reaction around it which consists predominantly of polymorphonuclear leucocytes with a few eosinophils (Fig. 16.21). Thrombosis is found in some arteries, many of which show gross hypertrophy.

In the subacute, healing phase of arteritis, the dead muscle becomes replaced by granulation tissue, staining basophilically, which also forms masses in the intima and adventitia adjacent to the area of necrosis in the media. The granulation tissue may replace the entire vessel, only parts of the elastic laminae remaining (Fig. 16.22). In other cases only a small area of the media is replaced by fibrous tissue so that, lying between the bulbous expansions in the intima and adventitia, this gives the lesion a dumb-bell shape. In the connecting bar of fibrous tissue in the media, the long axes of the fibroblast nuclei are radial. The adventitial masses of granulation

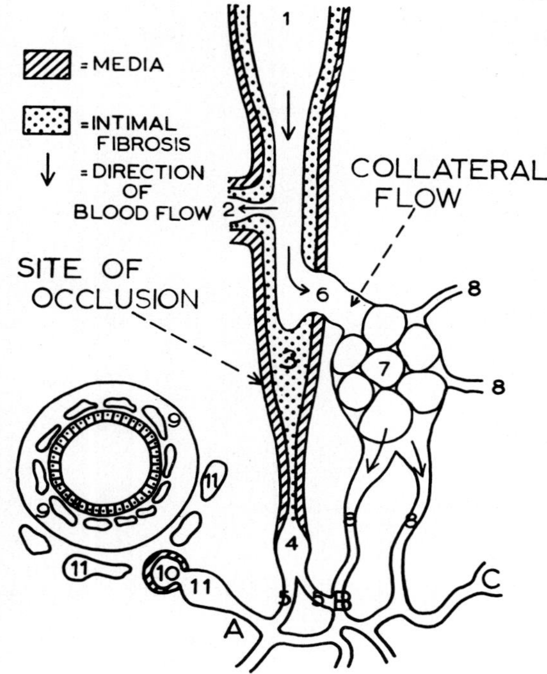

Fig. 16.19
Diagram to show the origin and probable connexions of small, thin-walled blood vessels in the lung in grade 5 hypertensive pulmonary vascular disease.

1 = Dilated muscular pulmonary artery with thin media and intimal fibrosis: this is part of the generalized dilatation proximal to the site of vascular occlusion.
2 = Hypertrophied muscular pulmonary artery arising as a side branch of 1 with heaped-up intimal fibrous tissue at the site of origin.
3 = Terminal muscular pulmonary artery totally occluded by fibrous tissue: the media may be thick, as shown, or abnormally thin.
4 = Terminal dilated pulmonary arteriole.
5 = Capillaries in alveolar walls arising from pulmonary arteriole.
6 = Dilated, thin-walled, vein-like branch of hypertrophied parent muscular pulmonary artery.
7 = Localized 'dilatation lesion': an angiomatoid lesion is shown.
8 = Capillaries in alveolar walls arising from dilatation lesions.
9 = Dilated thin-walled vessel in sub-mucosa of small bronchus.
10 = Small bronchial artery in fibrous coat of small bronchus giving rise to thin-walled branches shown as 11.
A = Broncho-pulmonary anastomosis at capillary level.
B = Anastomosis between capillaries arising from parent muscular pulmonary artery and from 'dilatation lesions'.
C = Possible anastomosis between thin-walled vessels derived from pulmonary artery and those derived from pulmonary vein.

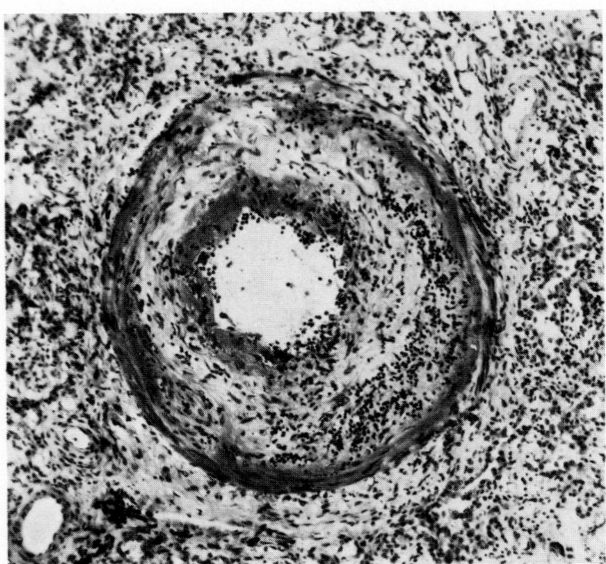

Fig. 16.20 Transverse section of a muscular pulmonary artery from a man aged 26 years with primary pulmonary hypertension. The vessel shows fibrinoid necrosis. The media has a glassy appearance and is brightly eosinophilic. An acute inflammatory exudate is scattered throughout the arterial wall. HPVD: grade 6. (Haematoxylin and eosin, × 100)

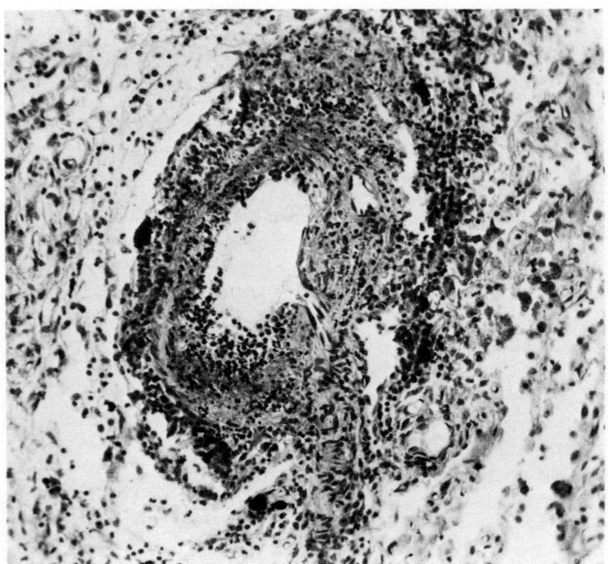

Fig. 16.21 Transverse section of a muscular pulmonary artery from the same case as in Figure 16.20. Necrotizing arteritis is present, all layers of the vessel wall being infiltrated by numerous acute inflammatory cells. HPVD: grade 6. (Haematoxylin and eosin, × 150)

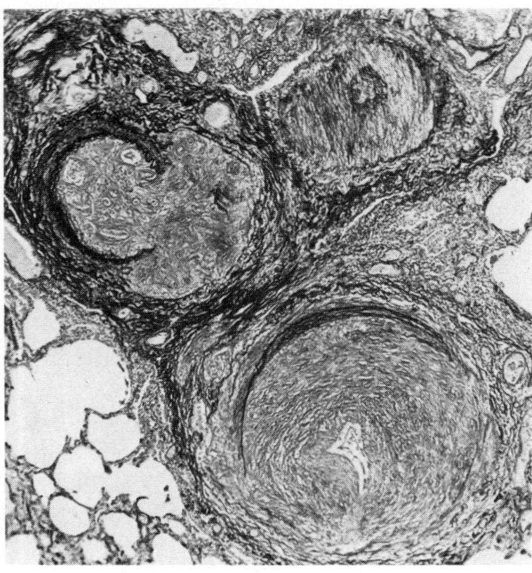

Fig. 16.22 Transverse section of two muscular pulmonary arteries from a girl aged 12 years with cor triloculare biatriatum. The healing stage of necrotizing arteritis is seen. In both cases large arcs of the media have been destroyed and replaced by granulation and fibrous tissue which occludes the lumen of the artery. In the case of the artery in the upper part of the figure the granulation tissue fans out to form a mass in the adventitia. HPVD: grade 6. (Elastic/Van Gieson, ×50)

tissue frequently occur at the sites of origin of pulmonary arterioles. Many small capillaries, lined by plump endothelium, ramify throughout the basophilic fibrous tissue and a few thin-walled vessels leave this tissue to lie between the old acellular collagen fibres of the adventitia. This imparts a characteristic picture of many dilated vein-like structures lying scattered throughout the adventitia of the larger muscular pulmonary arteries.

GRADE 1 IN CASES OF PRE-TRICUSPID SHUNT

In atrial septal defect, and those other forms of congenital heart disease characterized by a high pulmonary blood flow over a prolonged period prior to the onset of pulmonary hypertension (Chap. 21, p. 319), the changes in structure in grade 1 differ from those seen in ventricular septal defect and other types of post-tricuspid shunt. Before the onset of pulmonary hypertension, the arterioles are lined by a single elastic lamina, as in the normal lung. Both they and the small muscular pulmonary arteries are widely dilated. The onset of pulmonary hypertension is associated with a pronounced cellular endothelial proliferation in the arterioles and the smallest muscular pulmonary arteries. Once pulmonary hypertension is established, a distinct muscular media forms in the arterioles and there is hypertrophy of the media of the muscular pulmonary arteries. These histological features are the same as those seen in grade 2 associated with post-tricuspid shunts and from

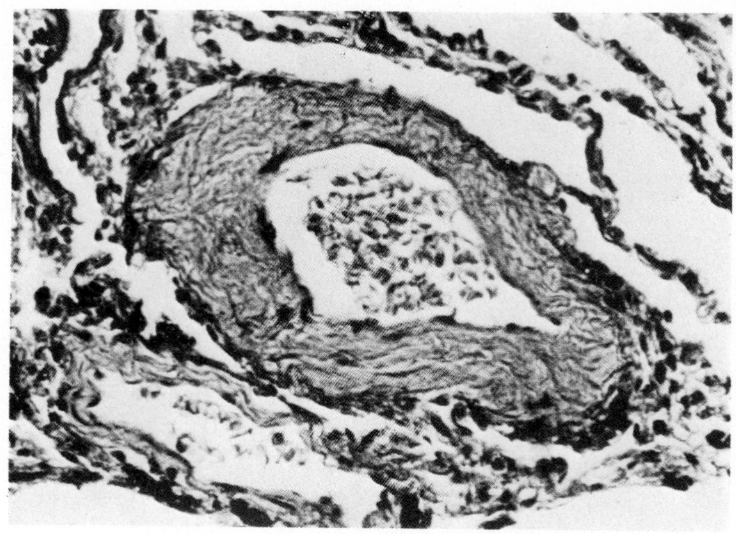

Fig. 16.23 Transverse section of a pulmonary vein from a man aged 50 years with atrial septal defect. There is severe acellular intimal fibrosis which is characteristically associated with high pulmonary blood flow. (Elastic/Van Gieson, × 365)

this point the chain of events is identical with that already described. Even when the pulmonary arterial pressure is normal or only slightly elevated, there is a marked intimal acellular fibrosis in the pulmonary veins (Fig. 16.23). This remains characteristic of atrial septal defect no matter what grade of hypertensive vascular disease is present in the pulmonary arteries.

Longitudinal Muscle in Pulmonary Arteries

Longitudinally oriented smooth muscle fibres develop in the muscular pulmonary arteries (Fig. 16.3) in the presence of pulmonary hypertension irrespective of its underlying cause.[8] Thus, they have been reported in examples of pulmonary hypertension due to congenital cardiac shunts, an elevated left atrial pressure, chronic hypoxia and primary pulmonary hypertension.[8] Longitudinal muscle is seen in association with any grade of hypertensive pulmonary vascular disease. It may form isolated bundles or a complete coat around the circumference of the vessel. Within these bundles small groups of fibres are demarcated from one another by elastic fibrils or rarely by collagen. Usually the longitudinal muscle fibres are found in the outer part of the media in apposition to the outer elastic lamina (Fig. 16.3). Occasionally it is found internal to the inner elastic lamina but this is more characteristic of hypoxic hypertensive pulmonary vascular disease as described in

Chapter 33. Sometimes longitudinal muscle is found in both situations in one artery.

Pulmonary Vascular Disease in Lung Biopsy Specimens

Most biopsy specimens of lung from cases of congenital cardiac septal defect will show only early changes in the pulmonary vasculature since such material is derived from cases regarded as operable.[9] Thus, although cases of atrial septal defect coming to necropsy will commonly show severe hypertensive pulmonary vascular disease, those subjected to thoracotomy and lung biopsy, may show no changes at all in the pulmonary vasculature.[9] Cases of patent ductus arteriosus may show only increased intimal fibrosis in muscular pulmonary arteries.[9] Only in cases of ventricular septal defect will an increase in the thickness of both media and intima be expected even in those cases regarded as suitable for operation.[9]

Post-Mortem Pulmonary Arteriography

This technique consists of the radiographic examination of the lungs after the pulmonary arteries have been injected with a radio-opaque material.[10] The site and extent of thrombosis within the larger arteries may be shown and the territory supplied by such an artery is demonstrated by the absence of opaque material. In addition to such localized occlusion of larger arteries, the arteriogram of lungs affected by severe pulmonary hypertension shows a less finely branched appearance than that which occurs in the normal lung.[11] This is probably related to the widespread vascular occlusion described in this chapter. Since the opaque material is of such consistency as will not pass through capillaries, the injection into the pulmonary artery may be of value histologically in distinguishing arterioles from venules. Injection into the aorta is of value in demonstrating anastomoses between the bronchial and pulmonary circulation (Chap. 39).

'*Arteriosclerosis*' In the preceding account we have avoided the use of the term 'arteriosclerosis of small pulmonary vessels' and have preferred in each grade to designate precisely the class of blood vessel concerned and the nature of the process affecting it.

'*Ayerza's disease*' According to Brenner,[12] Ayerza of Buenos Aires described in 1901 in an unpublished clinical lecture, a case of heart failure with such marked cyanosis that the patient was almost black—a 'cardiac Negro'. At necropsy there was dilatation of the bronchi, peribronchitis and dilatation of the right atrium and ventricle but the pulmonary vessels were not mentioned. Eight years later Marty described a similar case as 'Ayerza's disease'. Arrillaga[13] was the first worker to comment on the presence of pulmonary arterial lesions in the syndrome and he later (1924) believed them to be syphilitic in origin. The relative importance of chronic lung disease, syphilis and pulmonary vascular lesions in 'Ayerza's disease' was never defined.

The Application of the Grading System

Since the first edition of this book was published it has come to our attention in the literature that some workers have attempted to apply the grading system just described to forms of hypertensive pulmonary vascular disease other than plexogenic pulmonary arteriopathy. This is not appropriate since other forms of vascular disease have their own characteristic histological features, as we describe in other places in this volume, which do not correspond to the six grades described.

Some of our colleagues like Professor Wagenvoort of Amsterdam believe that the grading system does not adequately describe the different histological appearances that may occur. Thus, he points out that grade 3 changes encompass moderate intimal fibrosis in a few pulmonary arteries to severe intimal fibrotic changes in most of the vessels. While we accept this to be a valid criticism, we hold that the grading system is a method of describing a complex collection of changes in a succinct manner. It is better, in our opinion, for the pathologist to employ a grade number than shy away altogether from description of the pulmonary vasculature because it entails quantitative studies of the pulmonary vessels more suited to institutions with a research interest in the field.

As we describe elsewhere (Chap. 18, p. 281) some authorities would argue that fibrinoid necrosis (grade 6) accompanies rather than follows plexiform lesions (grade 4). This controversy is set out in our consideration of the nature of the plexiform lesion (Chap. 18, p. 280).

Electron Microscopy

In the account given above of the histopathology of hypertensive pulmonary vascular disease complicating congenital septal defects we refer to cellular intimal proliferation. To gain insight into the possible nature of this proliferation in man we may consider the ultrastructural changes which occur in the pulmonary arteries of animals in which left to right shunts have been created experimentally. The account of the electron microscopy of hypertensive pulmonary vascular disease secondary to a post-tricuspid shunt that we give here is based on the investigations of Esterley and his colleagues[14] who studied the ultrastructure of lung biopsy specimens from 12 young adult dogs of both sexes with anastomoses created between the left subclavian and left main pulmonary arteries, and of Hatt *et al.*[15] who studied pulmonary biopsy specimens from 47 cases of congenital cardiac septal defects including both pre- and post-tricuspid shunts.

Ultrastructure of the Normal Pulmonary Artery

Depending on the state of vascular distension the endothelial cells are flat, ovoid or spherical and they form a single layer in close apposition to the focally fenestrated internal elastic lamina. There is an intervening subendothelial space which contains amorphous material, fine fibrillary strands and occasional collagen and elastic fragments. Rarely, smooth muscle cells occur in this space adjacent to gaps in the internal elastic lamina. The surface of the internal elastic lamina directed towards the intima is more irregular than that directed towards the media. The sub-endothelial space is continuous with the interstitial space of the media. The smooth muscle cells of the media are disposed in two or three circumferential layers, and there are associated collagen fibres and fragments of elastic tissue. The external elastic lamina has fewer fenestrations than the internal. The adventitia consists of dense collagen bundles with scattered fibroblasts.

Endothelial cells in the pulmonary arteries adhere by overlapping cytoplasmic extensions with attachments consisting of focal thickenings. Pinocytotic vesicles are moderately abundant in endothelial cells which, however, contain only small numbers of elongated mitochondria, few microsomes and only small cytoplasmic vacuoles. According to Esterley *et al.*[14] no intracellular cytoplasmic fibrils are seen in pulmonary endothelial cells. In contrast to this, there are abundant myofilaments, with dense bodies, in the cytoplasm of smooth muscle cells as we illustrate in Chapter 12. Abundant pinocytotic vesicles are seen in the cytoplasm. However, smooth endoplasmic reticulum, free ribosomes, elongated mitochondria, and small Golgi complexes are infrequent and largely confined to perinuclear zones. The fibroblasts among the abundant collagen fibres of the adventitia contain much rough endoplasmic reticulum with many mitochondria and Golgi formations.

Early Ultrastructural Responses of the Pulmonary Artery to Increased Pulmonary Arterial Pressure and Flow

Soon after the creation of a systemic-pulmonary anastomosis in dogs, ultra-structural changes take place in the walls of the pulmonary arteries as a reaction to the altered haemodynamic circumstances.[14] Increased cellular metabolism and protein synthesis within the endothelial cells is indicated by an increase in micropinocytosis, rough endoplasmic reticulum, ribosomes, mitochondria and Golgi formations. The endothelial cells develop cytoplasmic vacuolation and villiform processes project from the luminal surfaces of many of them.[14] The accumulation of vacuoles and the widening of the subendothelial space suggests an increased passage of materials from the vessel lumen. Similar cytological changes in the endothelial cells were noted by Hatt *et al.*,[15] who attached the same functional significance to them. As we shall see below, the continued hyper-reactivity of the endothelial cells to the sustained haemodynamic stimuli appears to be injurious. Their capacity to deal with increased filtration appears to be inadequate and they die. The smooth muscle cells of the media seem to be stimulated to increased protein synthesis and energy production corresponding to increased medial tension. Their cytoplasm shows an increase of ribosomes, rough endoplasmic reticulum, Golgi formations, mitochondria and myofibrils. The interstitial spaces of the media are enlarged and contain poorly defined granular material. The presumed increase in filtration through the intima appears to be diverted to the intercellular ground substance of the media. In the adventitia, circumferential orientation of fibroblasts becomes prominent and there is an increase of rough endoplasmic reticulum within them.

Ultrastructure of Intimal Proliferation

Experimental studies on dogs suggest that, after systemic-pulmonary anastomoses have been present for two to three months, the changes of hyper-activity in the endothelial cells described above are translated into those of 'intimal proliferation'.[14] It is of immediate interest to realize that, in experimental dogs, the intimal thickening is not due to any proliferation of pulmonary endothelial cells. Hatt *et al.*,[15] from a study of lung biopsy specimens from cases of congenital cardiac septal defect in man, make the same point stating that the early proliferation of endothelial cells does not lead to a significant thickening of the intima since many of the cells desquamate into the lumen. In fact, endothelial cells show diffuse changes of degeneration and involution. Many of the endothelial cells become 'shrivelled' and contain dense irregular osmiophilic cytoplasmic clumps and few recognizable organelles with scattered dilated cisternae of the endoplasmic reticulum. Other cells show diffuse vacuolation.

The cells which give rise to 'intimal proliferation' arise in fact in the sub-endothelial space. Three distinct cell groups are to be found. We may dismiss immediately subendothelial blood cells which are neutrophil polymorphs and monocytes. The second more important group of cells are smooth muscle cells which are to be found near the gaps in the internal elastic lamina. They are undoubtedly smooth muscle cells since they contain cytoplasmic myofilaments and dense bodies. Furthermore, many are partly medial and partly subendothelial in situation with connecting cytoplasmic bridges occupying fenestrations in the internal elastic lamina. Similar extrusions of smooth muscle cells from the media into the adventitia also occur. It is clear that such extrusions account for the layers of longitudinal muscle found in close apposition to the internal and external aspects of the hypertrophied media of circularly orientated smooth muscle described in the account of the histopathology of hypertensive pulmonary vascular disease given above.

Much of the focal intimal thickening, however, is brought about by accumulations of less differentiated cells situated between locally degenerating endothelium and the intimal smooth muscle cells situated as just described near fenestrations in the internal elastic lamina. In these less differentiated cells there are cytoplasmic fibrils without dense bodies.[14] Hatt *et al.*[15] refer to the same fibrillary cytoplasm in the cells causing intimal proliferation in their human case of congenital cardiac septal defect. We shall now consider the nature of these cells.

The Nature of the Cells Leading to Cellular Intimal Proliferation

The cytoplasmic filaments in the cells involved in the cellular intimal proliferation led Esterley and his associates[14] to believe that the cells were de-differentiated smooth muscle cells. It is of considerable interest to note that the same controversy has surrounded the nature of the type cell of the atrial myxoma which is also characterized by an abundance of cytoplasmic filaments.[16] Thus, Merkow *et al.*[17] concluded that the atrial myxoma is composed of 'myoid-type cells'. It should, however, be noted that, in unequivocal muscle cells, cytoplasmic filaments are associated with focal condensations (Chap. 12, p. 170).

In fact cells with cytoplasmic filaments are widespread throughout the lining of the heart and vascular systems. Stein and his associates[18] believe that these cells constitute 'subendothelial vasoformative reserve cells'. As well as being concerned in the formation of atrial myxoma and obliterative vascular disease, they are concerned in the thickened endocardium overlying hypertrophied infundibular muscle in Fallot's tetrad, or in the thickened aortic valve cusps in rheumatic aortic stenosis. They think that these reserve cells can undergo hyperplasia and differentiation into smooth muscle, fibrocytes and endothelial cells. Subsequently such cells produce their own secretions so that the differentiated cells become associated with a stroma containing collagen, elastic and acid mucopolysaccharide. It will thus be seen that, once there is proliferation of subendothelial vasoformative reserve cells, the path is open to intimal fibrosis and fibroelastosis or the development of fasciculi of longitudinal muscle, all characteristic at one stage or other of plexogenic pulmonary arteriopathy (p. 418), as we have seen earlier in this chapter. We may also note in passing that cells with cytoplasmic filaments are to be expected deep in thrombi,[19] where they have been interpreted as myoid in nature. Subendothelial vasoformative reserve cells may be closely related to, or even identical with, 'myofibroblasts' which are to be found in granulation tissue and account for its contractility.[20]

REFERENCES

1. Heath, D. & Edwards, J. E. (1958) *Circulation*, **18**, 533.
2. Brewer, D. B. (1955) *J. Path. Bact.*, **70**, 299.
3. Brewer, D. B. & Heath, D. (1959) *J. Path. Bact.*, 77, 141.
4. Shepherd, J. T., Edwards, J. E., Burchell, H. B., Swan, H. J. C. & Wood, E. H. (1957) *Brit. Heart J.*, **19**, 70.
5. Old, J. W. & Russell, W. O. (1950) *Circulation*, **2**, 545.
6. Hicks, J. D. (1953) *J. Path. Bact.*, **65**, 333.
7. Aitchison, J. D. & Richmond, H. G. (1955) *Brit. Heart J.*, **17**, 312.
8. Heath, D. (1963) *J. Path. Bact.*, **85**, 407.
9. Wagenvoort, C. A., Nauta, J., Van der Schaar, P. J., Weeda, H. W. H. & Wagenvoort, N. (1967) *Circulation*, **35**, 1028.
10. Evans, W., Short, D. S. & Bedford, D. E. (1957) *Brit. Heart J.*, **19**, 93.
11. Evans, W. (1951) *Proc. Roy. Soc. Med.*, **44**, 600.
12. Brenner, O. (1935) *Arch. Intern. Med.*, **56**, 211.
13. Arrillaga, F. C. (1913) *Arch. Mal. Coeur*, **6**, 312.
14. Esterley, J. A., Glagor, S. & Ferguson, D. J. (1968) *Amer. J. Path.*, **52**, 325.
15. Hatt, P. Y., Rouiller, C. & Grosgogeat, Y. (1959) *Path. Biol.*, **7**, 515.
16. Stovin, P. G. I., Heath, D. & Khaliq, S. U. (1973) *Thorax*, **28**, 273.
17. Merkow, L. P., Kooros, M. A., Magovern, G., Hayeslip, D. W., Weikers, N. J., Pardo, M. & Fisher, D. L. (1969) *Arch. Path.*, **88**, 390.
18. Stein, A. A., Mauro, J., Thibodeau, L. & Alley, R. (1969) In *Pathology Annual*, ed. Sommers, S. C. Vol. **4**, page 293. London: Butterworths.
19. Davies, M. J., Ballantine, S. J., Robertson, W. B. & Woolf, N. (1972) Paper Synopsis, *J. Path.*, **107**, vi.
20. Gabbiani, G., Hirschel, B. J., Ryan, G. B., Statkov, P. R. & Majno, G. (1972) *J. Exp. Med.*, **135**, 719.

17. The Effects of Hypertension on the Structure of the Elastic Pulmonary Arteries

The 'elastic pulmonary arteries' are the pulmonary trunk and those pulmonary arteries greater than 1 mm in diameter[1] (Chap. 3). As the term implies, these blood vessels have considerable amounts of elastic tissue within their media which is largely composed of smooth muscle. Smaller amounts of collagen are also present. The three connective tissue elements are embedded in a ground substance containing acid mucopolysaccharide. All of the medial components show changes, either of a qualitative or quantitative nature, in association with pulmonary arterial hypertension.[2] The intima of the elastic pulmonary arteries comprises an endothelial lining, with an underlying 'subintima' of collagen in the pulmonary trunk and the major elastic arteries outside the lung. Like the media it undergoes structural alterations in the presence of a high pulmonary arterial pressure. The adventitia consists of fibrous tissue and does not appear to be affected by pulmonary hypertension.

Muscle Fibres

In pulmonary arterial hypertension there is an increase in the thickness of the media of the elastic arteries. Normally the ratio of the thickness of the media of the pulmonary trunk to that of the aorta is in the range of 0·4 to 0·7 but in the presence of significant chronic pulmonary hypertension the ratio approaches, or even exceeds, unity.[3] Since at the same time there is also an obvious dilatation of the elastic arteries, the increased medial thickness can only be due to an increase in the volume of tissue. Most of the thickening of the media is due to an increase in the bulk of muscle and this runs parallel with the hypertrophy of the right ventricle. It is of interest to note, however, that increased medial thickness of the pulmonary trunk is not always accompanied by medial hypertrophy of the 'muscular pulmonary arteries' as defined in Chapter 16. Concomitant hypertrophy of the elastic and muscular pulmonary arteries does take place in such conditions as pre- and post-tricuspid congenital cardiac shunts, mitral stenosis and any pathology leading to sustained left atrial pressure, and primary pulmonary hypertension where right ventricular hypertrophy is associated with florid hypertensive pulmonary vascular disease. However, it does not in chronic bronchitis and emphysema, in subjects living at high altitude, in kyphoscoliosis and in experimental animals subjected to reduced atmospheric pressure.[4] This is because hypoxic hypertensive pulmonary vascular disease is characterized by muscularization of the pulmonary arterioles alone without increased medial thickness of the 'muscular pulmonary arteries' (Chap. 33). In addition to the circularly orientated muscle fibres, fasciculi of longitudinal muscle develop in approximation to the external elastic lamina. This is clearly the same process as that described in the muscular pulmonary arteries in the preceding chapter and must have the same functional significance. The development of longitudinal muscle in pulmonary arteries in association with pulmonary arterial hypertension is of interest in showing that new muscle is formed as a response to the increased pressure. This does not support the view sometimes put forward that the pathological condition of 'medial hypertrophy' may be spurious and that its histological appearances are merely those of vasoconstriction.[5]

Elastic Fibrils

In the foetus the appearance of the elastic tissue of the media of the pulmonary trunk is very similar to that of the aorta (Chap. 14). In both arteries the elastic fibrils are long, uniform, non-branched and parallel with one another (Figs 14.1 and 14.2, p. 212). In subjects not living at high altitude these long fibrils fragment into stick-like portions during infancy to give rise to the transitional pattern of elastic tissue (Fig. 14.3, p. 212). In early childhood in dwellers at sea level or low altitude the transitional pattern changes once again so that by the age of two years the adult pulmonary configuration of elastic tissue is established.[3] In this there is a loose network of branched, fragmented elastic fibrils which often show club-like terminal expansions. This appearance persists throughout adult life in people who live at sea level or at low altitude (Figs 17.1 and 17.2 and Fig. 14.4, p. 212).

Such a transition does not occur in congenital heart diseases which give rise to pulmonary hypertension from birth. A list of the diseases with post-tricuspid shunts is given in Chapter 15. The arrangement of the elastic tissue in the pulmonary trunk in these diseases is like that of the aorta[3] (Figs 17.3–17.9 and Fig. 17.19, p. 272). When pulmonary hypertension is acquired in adult life, as in the secundum type of atrial septal defect or in rheumatic mitral stenosis, the transition to the adult configuration of elastic tissue in the pulmonary trunk has already occurred (Figs 17.10–17.13).

The arrangement of the elastic tissue does not appear to be determined by the magnitude of the pulmonary blood flow.[6] For example, the arrangement of the elastic tissue in the pulmonary trunk was of foetal type in a child of 1½ years with a ventricular septal defect and a pulmonary blood flow of 7·4 $\text{l} \cdot \text{min}^{-1}/\text{m}^2$ BSA (Fig. 17.7). However, in a woman of twenty-seven years with an atrial septal defect and a pulmonary blood flow of comparable magnitude (6·7 $\text{l} \cdot \text{min}^{-1}/\text{m}^2$ BSA) the configuration was of adult type (Fig. 17.10). Both of these patients had pulmonary hypertension.

The pattern of the elastic tissue also appears unrelated to the absolute levels of mean or pulse pressure in the pulmonary artery. For instance, the pressure in the pulmonary artery in patients with rheumatic mitral stenosis may ultimately equal that in the aorta and yet the configuration of the elastic tissue in the pulmonary artery is normal (Fig. 17.13). Hence the same pressure in the two great arteries is associated with a completely different pattern of elastic tissue.

It seems most likely from such evidence that the appearance of the elastic tissue of the pulmonary trunk is related to the time of onset of the elevated blood pressure. When the hypertension is present from birth, the arrangement of elastic tissue in the

All the figures in this chapter are transverse sections of the pulmonary trunk or aorta stained by Verhoeff's or Weigert's methods to demonstrate elastic tissue. The ratios in the legends express the thickness of the media of the pulmonary trunk in relation to that of the aorta in the same cases. The magnification is × 75 except in Figures 17.1, 17.2, and Figures 17.14 to 17.18 where it is × 150.

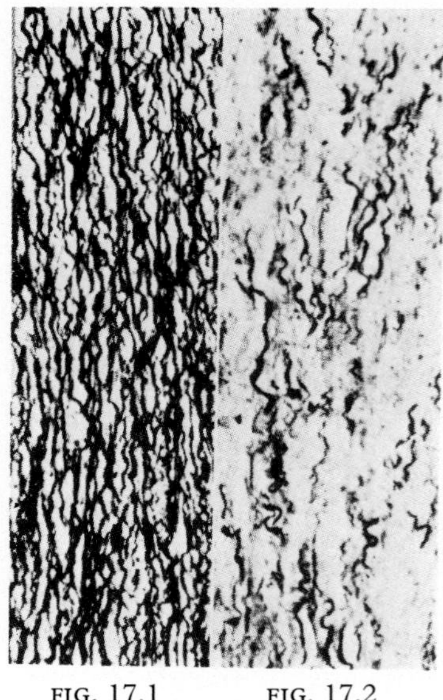

FIG. 17.1 FIG. 17.2

Fig. 17.1 Ascending aorta in a fifty-three year old man, showing the normal aortic configuration of the elastic tissue of the media.

Fig. 17.2 Pulmonary trunk in a fifty-three year old man, showing the normal adult pulmonary configuration of the elastic tissue of the media.

foetal pulmonary trunk is retained and resembles that of the aorta (Figs 17.3–17.9 and Fig. 17.19). When the elevation of the pulmonary arterial pressure occurs after the normal transition of the pattern into the adult form (Figs 17.10–17.13), the pulmonary trunk thickens but the foetal pattern is not regained.

Since the existence of pulmonary arterial hypertension from birth modifies the normal evolution of the elastic tissue pattern of the pulmonary trunk, one might anticipate that the normal transition seen in normal subjects living at sea level would not occur in healthy people living at high altitude. In mountain dwellers, a moderate pulmonary hypertension persists from birth on account of the exposure to chronic hypoxia due to diminished barometric pressure. This leads to retention of a 'persistent pattern' of elastic tissue in the media of the pulmonary trunk well into adult life as described in detail in Chapter 32. Thus two very different histological pictures in the pulmonary trunk may both be regarded as normal, depending on the altitude at which the subject lives.

In all cases of primary pulmonary hypertension occurring in adults that we have studied, the elastic tissue pattern in the media of the pulmonary trunk was of adult pulmonary type (Figs 17.14–17.18). This suggests that in adults the idiopathic elevation of pulmonary arterial pressure is acquired.[6] In some cases of the disease occurring in children, however, examination of the elastic tissue pattern in the pulmonary trunk suggests that the pulmonary hypertension may be present from the neonatal period.[7]

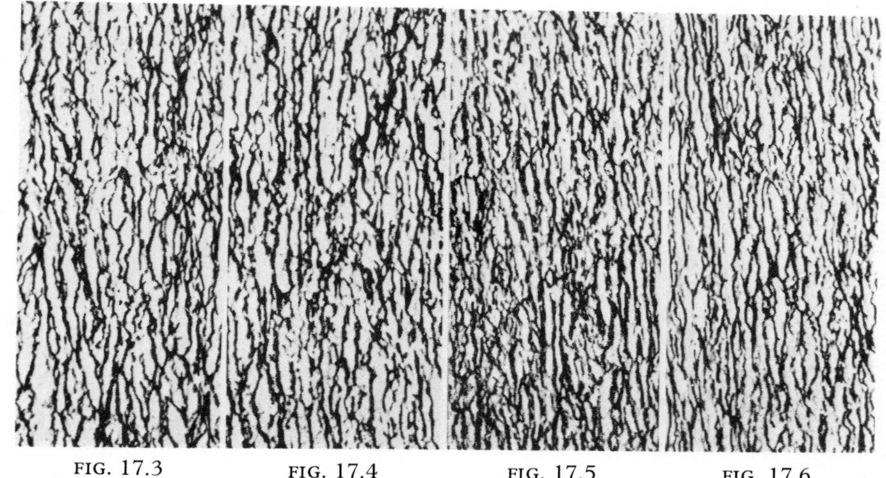

FIG. 17.3 FIG. 17.4 FIG. 17.5 FIG. 17.6

Fig. 17.3 Pulmonary trunk. Woman aged thirty-four years with a widely patent ductus arteriosus and pulmonary hypertension from birth (mean pulmonary arterial pressure 84 mmHg). Aortic configuration (ratio 0·7).

Fig. 17.4 Aorta from the same case as in Figure 17.3.

Fig. 17.5 Pulmonary trunk. Girl aged eleven years with a large ventricular septal defect and pulmonary hypertension from birth (mean pulmonary arterial pressure 69 mmHg). Aortic configuration (ratio 1·3).

Fig. 17.6 Aorta from the same case as in Figure 17.5.

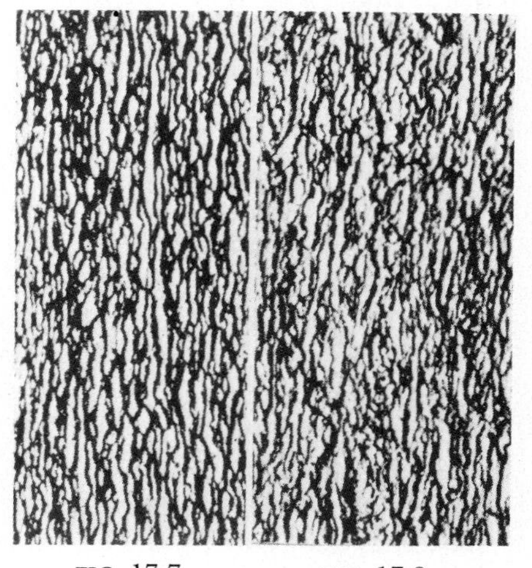

FIG. 17.7 FIG. 17.8

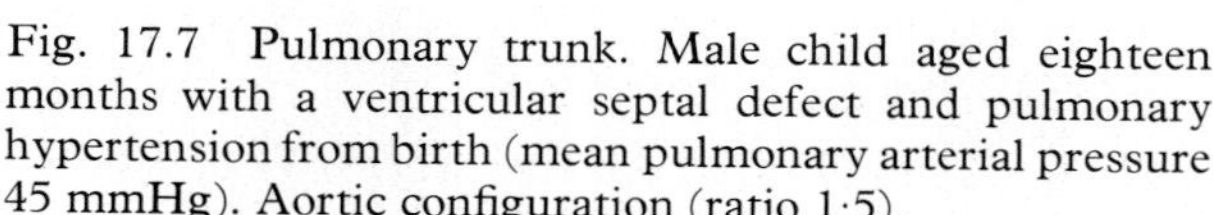

Fig. 17.7 Pulmonary trunk. Male child aged eighteen months with a ventricular septal defect and pulmonary hypertension from birth (mean pulmonary arterial pressure 45 mmHg). Aortic configuration (ratio 1·5).

Fig. 17.8 Pulmonary trunk. Boy of thirteen years with corrected transposition of the great vessels associated with large ventricular septal defect and pulmonary hypertension from birth. Aortic configuration (ratio 0·9).

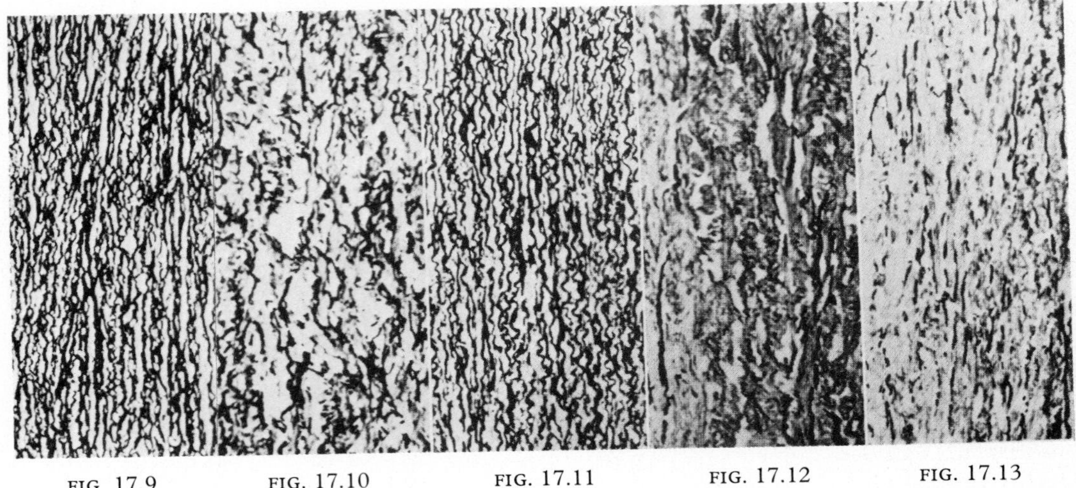

FIG. 17.9 FIG. 17.10 FIG. 17.11 FIG. 17.12 FIG. 17.13

Fig. 17.9 Pulmonary trunk. Boy aged nine years with cor triloculare biatriatum and pulmonary hypertension from birth (mean pulmonary arterial pressure 80 mmHg). Aortic configuration (ratio 0·9).

Fig. 17.10 Pulmonary trunk. Woman aged twenty-seven years with an atrial septal defect and acquired pulmonary hypertension (mean pulmonary arterial pressure 67 mmHg). Adult pulmonary configuration (ratio 1·2).

Fig. 17.11 Aorta from the same case as in Figure 17.10.

Figure 17.12 Pulmonary trunk. Man aged thirty-eight years with rheumatic mitral stenosis and acquired pulmonary hypertension (mean pulmonary arterial pressure 71 mmHg). Adult pulmonary configuration (ratio 1·0).

Fig. 17.13 Pulmonary trunk. Woman aged thirty-five years with rheumatic mitral stenosis and acquired pulmonary hypertension (mean pulmonary arterial pressure 76 mmHg). Adult pulmonary configuration (ratio 1·0).

Ground Substance

The elastic, muscle and collagen fibres are embedded in a mucopolysaccharide ground substance related to chondroitins B and C. In the presence of severe, chronic pulmonary hypertension this material is more prominent, so that not infrequently sections of the pulmonary trunk from such cases show areas of the media which stain metachromatically with toluidine-blue and positively with alcian-blue. Such staining reactions reveal acid mucopolysaccharide. Hence the mere presence of this material does not imply the existence of pulmonary hypertension but an excessive accumulation does.

Areas of media showing such accumulations of acid mucopolysaccharide tend to become cystic[8,9] and present the appearance of 'cystic medial necrosis' identical to that which occurs in the aorta in dissecting aneurysm. The development of this condition is of considerable gravity since parts of the pulmonary trunk have the consistency of wet blotting paper at the very time that the vessel is exposed to increased tension. Rupture of the pulmonary trunk may occur under these conditions[9] but fortunately this is rare. Cystic medial necrosis of the pulmonary trunk also predisposes to saccular or dissecting aneurysms.[7]

Intima

Pulmonary atherosclerosis is characteristic of all conditions associated with pulmonary arterial hypertension. It will even be found in young children with Fallot's tetrad on the rare occasions when this abnormality is associated with a raised pulmonary arterial pressure (Fig. 17.19). We studied the incidence and severity of atheroma in the pulmonary arteries in relation to age, the pulmonary arterial blood pressure and the pulmonary blood flow in sixty-five cases of congenital and acquired heart disease.[10] At the same time the incidence and severity of atheroma in the ascending and thoracic aorta in these cases were studied in relation to age and the mean blood pressure in the radial artery. The series consisted of twenty-one cases of congenital heart disease associated with pulmonary stenosis, twenty-two cases of congenital heart disease associated with pulmonary

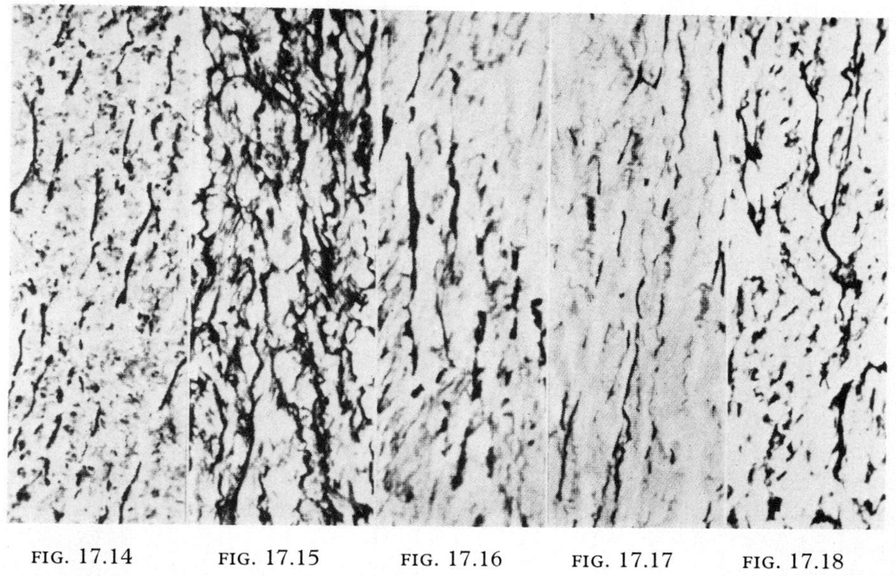

FIG. 17.14 FIG. 17.15 FIG. 17.16 FIG. 17.17 FIG. 17.18

Figs 17.14–17.18 In each instance the Figure is part of a transverse section of pulmonary trunk from a case of primary pulmonary hypertension. All the patients were female; their ages at death were, consecutively, twelve, twenty-one, thirty, thirty-six and forty years. In each case the configuration of the elastic tissue is of adult pulmonary type suggesting that the elevated pulmonary arterial pressure was acquired.

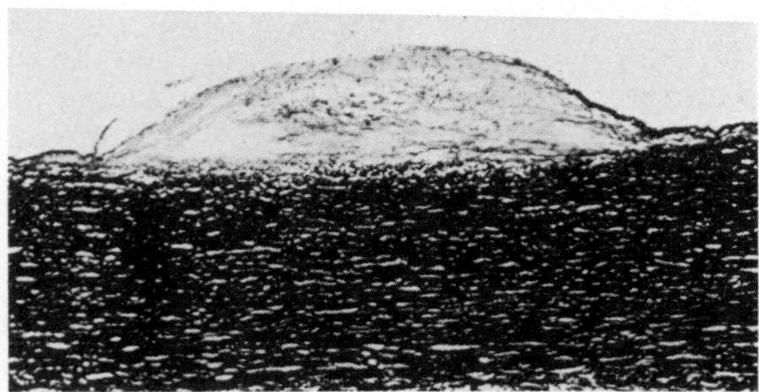

Fig. 17.19 Transverse section of a major elastic pulmonary artery from a boy aged four years with Fallot's tetrad, who had a pulmonary arterial mean pressure of 37 mmHg and an abnormally high pulmonary blood flow of 11·3 $l \cdot min^{-1}/m^2$ BSA. A plaque of superficial atheroma is present. The configuration of the elastic tissue of the media is of aortic type, found in patients who have pulmonary hypertension from birth. The ratio of the thickness of the media of the pulmonary trunk relative to that of the aorta is 0·7, a value at the upper limit of normal. (× 50)

hypertension from birth (*i.e.* post-tricuspid shunts) and twenty-two cases of congenital pre-tricuspid shunts or acquired heart disease in some of which there was an elevated pulmonary arterial blood pressure acquired after birth. The results demonstrated the importance of pulmonary hypertension and high pulmonary blood flow in the aetiology of pulmonary atheroma. Atherosclerosis of the lesser circulation was found in only two of the cases of pulmonary stenosis and in both of these the valvular obstruction was slight and there was an associated ventricular septal defect. Pulmonary atheroma occurred in all but one of the sixteen patients dying after the age of 3½ years in whom pulmonary hypertension had been present from birth. It occurred in all twenty-one of the cases of acquired pulmonary hypertension in which the age at death was 20 years or more. In six cases of acquired pulmonary hypertension in which death occurred after the age of 40 years, pulmonary atheroma developed with only a moderately increased pulmonary arterial pressure, but in four of these six the pulmonary blood flow was high.

Atheroma in the pulmonary circulation is in no sense specific for pulmonary hypertension and is commonly found in the middle-aged and elderly who die from diseases unassociated with haemodynamic abnormalities in the lesser circulation. Its incidence, however, is considerably less and its onset later in the pulmonary arteries than in the aorta where it is present in most people by the second decade of life. This difference in the incidence of atheroma between the two circulations might well be attributed to the differences in blood pressure to which they are subjected. A further instance of the importance of mechanical factors in the causation of atheroma is the frequent appearance in childhood of atheroma in the region of the aortic valve, the anterior cusp of the mitral valve and the root of the aorta. All these sites are exposed to turbulent and mechanical stresses. The above considerations demonstrate the importance of local mechanical factors in the development of atherosclerosis.

REFERENCES

1. Brenner, O. (1935) *Arch. Intern. Med.*, **56**, 211.
2. Whitaker, W. & Heath, D. (1959) *Progr. Cardiovasc. Dis.*, **1**, 380.
3. Heath, D., Wood, E. H., Dushane, J. W. & Edwards, J. E. (1959) *J. Path. Bact.*, **77**, 443.
4. Heath, D., Edwards, C., Winson, M. & Smith, P. (1973) *Thorax*, **28**, 24.
5. O'Neal, R. M., Thomas, W. A. & Hartroft, P. M. (1955) *Arch. Path.*, **60**, 267.
6. Heath, D. & Edwards, J. E. (1960) *Circulation*, **21**, 59.
7. Wagenvoort, C. A., Heath, D. & Edwards, J. E. (1964) *The Pathology of the Pulmonary Vasculature*. Springfield, Ill.: Thomas.
8. Wade, G. & Ball, J. (1957) *Quart. J. Med.*, **26**, 83.
9. Whitaker, W., Heath, D. & Brown, J. W. (1955) *Brit. Heart J.*, **17**, 121.
10. Heath, D., Wood, E. H., Dushane, J. W. & Edwards, J. E. (1960) *Lab. Invest.*, **9**, 259.

18. The Relation Between Structure and Function in the Blood Vessels of the Lung in Pulmonary Hypertension

MUSCULAR PULMONARY ARTERIES AND ARTERIOLES

Circular Muscle

It may be said as a generalization that there is a relation between the structure of a blood vessel of a certain size and the blood pressure which exists within it over a prolonged period. In this respect it has been possible from time to time in the preceding chapters to draw a comparison between the pulmonary and systemic circulations. The adult pulmonary trunk, for instance, contains blood at a lower pressure than that in the aorta while its wall is more distensible and contains less elastic tissue than that of the aorta (Chap. 4). On the other hand, in foetal life, where the pressures in the pulmonary trunk and aorta are identical, the structure of their walls is similar (Chap. 14). The resistance of the adult pulmonary circulation to the flow of blood is much lower than it is in the systemic circulation and this is related to the meagreness of the circular muscle in the smaller muscular pulmonary arteries (Chap. 3). *In utero*, however, the resistance to the flow of blood through the pulmonary circulation is of the same order as that in the systemic circulation and the foetal interlobular and intralobular pulmonary arteries are found to have a thick coat of circular muscle (Chap. 14).

In diseases where a high resistance to flow develops in the smaller branches of the pulmonary arterial tree, the media of these vessels is also found to be excessively muscular. As is shown in Chapters 16 and 22, this applies not only to those conditions where pulmonary arterial hypertension exists from birth, but also to diseases such as rheumatic mitral stenosis which arise later in life.

Superficially, such a conformity between structure and function has an appealing logic, but beyond this it raises questions which invite teleological thought. In particular this is true when we consider why the structure of the pulmonary arterial tree changes under different circumstances. Why, for instance, does the muscular coat of the muscular pulmonary arteries become thinner during the first year of life? The temptation is to say that it does so because there is no longer any necessity for it to be there. The more mechanistic view would be that it is a property of muscle to waste if it is not used and hence the wasting of the muscular coat implies a lack of stimulus to contraction possibly due to the increase in local Po_2. Similarly the hypertrophy of the medial muscle which occurs in various diseases is not the *cause* of arterial constriction but its *effect*. An excess of muscle tissue is universally the expression of an increased muscular work. Thus, hypertrophy of the muscle of the media of a vessel must imply active constriction occurring intermittently or continuously for a prolonged time.[1] The mere presence of an excess of muscle does not cause constriction, although it is true that the thicker a muscle is, the more strongly it can contract when stimulated.

Such considerations leave unanswered the question as to what is the nature of the stimulus that initially causes the thin musculature of the media to contract and then sustains this contraction while the muscle hypertrophies. Theoretically, the origin of the stimulus might be neural, humoral or myogenic. It has been known for many years that nerve fibres end in the pulmonary vessels (Chap. 12) but the function of these nerves is unknown. In animals, there is evidence that the tone of the pulmonary vessels can be influenced by vasomotor nerves but such evidence is so far lacking in man. As far as humoral factors are concerned, certain naturally occurring substances appear capable of altering the tone of the arteries which are the site of resistance in the pulmonary circulation (Chap. 13, p. 195). No humoral agent has, however, been implicated in the development of pulmonary hypertension in disease with the exception of chronic hypoxia (Chaps 32 and 33). Chronic hypoxia will give rise to an increased quantity of smooth muscle in the terminal portion of the pulmonary arterial tree, but does not simulate the histological changes found, for instance, in hypertensive pulmonary vascular disease due to cardiac shunts.

The myogenic theory of pulmonary arterial hypertension may be stated as follows.[1] In the majority of patients with severe pulmonary arterial hypertension the primary abnormality would be likely to cause a slight rise in pulmonary arterial pressure. For instance, in mitral stenosis the pressure in the left atrium is elevated and this will cause a slight rise in the pulmonary arterial pressure by simple backward transmission. Similarly, the increased pulmonary blood flow which is associated with certain congenital abnormalities of the heart (Chap. 21) might also be expected to produce a slight elevation in the pulmonary arterial pressure. Although this elevation of pressure may not occur at rest, it may become apparent under conditions of stress such as exercise.

Hence the possibility arises that the initial stimulus for the production of severe pulmonary arterial hypertension is a purely mechanical slight elevation in pressure which is common to these otherwise very dissimilar groups of patients. In the case of mitral stenosis, the magnitude of this mechanical rise in pressure may be assessed from the increase in left atrial or pulmonary arterial wedge pressure. When the wedge pressure is compared with that in the pulmonary arteries in patients with mitral stenosis (Fig. 23.3, p. 355), it is found that the arterial pressure increases to a disproportionately great extent as the wedge pressure rises[2,3] and such a relation is consistent with the view that the mechanical rise in pressure itself stimulates a constriction of the small pulmonary arteries.

Following the original work of Bayliss,[4] Folkow[5] and Folkow and Löfving[6] there is now a great deal of evidence that vessels of the systemic arterial tree will constrict in response to a sudden increase in pressure[7–9] and that active tension of vascular smooth muscle increases with stretch.[10] The basis of this effect is unknown, but it may be caused by the stretching allowing the influx of calcium ions from the extracellular liquid across the membrane of the vascular smooth muscle cells (Chap. 12, p. 178). Under normal conditions this mechanism must necessarily be dominated

N

by the purely elastic properties of the vessel wall, otherwise its 'positive feedback' effect would lead to great instability of the blood pressure.[11]

When the underlying abnormality is acquired after infancy, as in rheumatic mitral stenosis, the initial stages of the development of pulmonary arterial hypertension are, therefore, seen as small and probably transient increases in the pressure in the pulmonary arteries, causing distension of their walls and evoking constriction in the medial muscle. The constriction is at first weak because the medial muscle is small in bulk. Frequently repeated or continued constriction eventually causes this muscle to hypertrophy. This in turn increases the power of constriction so that what was originally an insignificant function assumes importance. As the constriction increases in power, so the pressure in the pulmonary artery is raised still further to create a vicious circle of hypertension and constriction.

In patients with large post-tricuspid shunts (Chap. 15) pulmonary hypertension exists from birth. Here, there is an increased pulmonary blood flow from the onset of extra-uterine life. The media of the muscular pulmonary arteries at birth is still thick and muscular as in the foetus (Chap. 14). These vessels are thus able to respond with unusual power to the mechanical stimulus which, it is proposed, arises from distension. In this way, the vicious circle of hypertension and constriction is entered at an already advanced stage. In their study of lung biopsy specimens Wagenvoort and his colleagues[12] concluded that medial hypertrophy of the muscular pulmonary arteries was related to pressure and not flow, a conclusion which is consistent with the foregoing theory.

Patients with large pre-tricuspid shunts do not develop severe pulmonary hypertension until later in life (Chap. 21). It seems likely that these patients do not have a greatly increased pulmonary blood flow in early infancy. The direction of flow through an atrial septal defect is determined by the relative distensibility of the ventricles during diastole. Normally the right ventricle is much more easily distended than the left, and hence blood flows preferentially into the right ventricle. At birth, however, the wall of the right ventricle is nearly as thick as that of the left ventricle, so that the distensibility of the two chambers becomes nearly equal. Thus, even though the atrial septal defect may be large, the left-to-right shunt at birth is probably small. In this way, the walls of the elastic and muscular pulmonary arteries are allowed to undergo the involution which normally occurs during the first few months of life (Chap. 14), and, by the time the left-to-right shunt becomes large, the media of the muscular pulmonary arteries is thin.

Grover and his colleagues[13] have pointed out the wide variability of the responsiveness of the pulmonary circulation between individuals and between species. They give as examples: mitral stenosis, in which 25–30 per cent of patients develop severe pulmonary hypertension;[14] congenital absence of one pulmonary artery, in which some 20 per cent of patients develop severe pulmonary hypertension;[15] and congenital cerebral arteriovenous fistula which causes pulmonary vascular abnormalities in 25 per cent. Personal experience of the effects of acute hypoxia in normal people confirms the existence of a wide variation in the degree of response of the pulmonary arterial pressure. Grover and his colleagues[13] found a similar variation at high altitude. Peñaloza *et al.*[16] found a great variation in the electrocardiographic evidence of right ventricular hypertrophy in a high altitude population.

In an interesting series of studies, the susceptibility of cattle to hypoxia has been shown to be genetically determined. The pulmonary arterial pressure was measured in a group of 49 healthy cattle residing at an altitude of 3000 m. The fifteen animals with the lowest pressure were selected as a 'resistant' group. Ten animals with 'brisket disease' at the same altitude were taken as 'susceptible' to pulmonary hypertension. Both groups were removed to an altitude of 1500 m and each group was bred within itself. The pulmonary vascular resistance increased to a much greater extent in the offspring of the 'susceptible' group than in the offspring of the 'resistant' group when they were transferred to high altitude.[17,18] The same was found with the second generation offspring.[19]

It seems clear, therefore, that there is a wide variability in the responsiveness of the pulmonary circulation to various physiological and pathological stimuli and that such responsiveness may well be partly determined by genetic factors. Such considerations may be important in determining the occurrence, for instance, of familial primary pulmonary hyptertension (p. 430) or of primary pulmonary hypertension in a very small group of patients taking anorexigens (p. 410).

Longitudinal Muscle

Burton,[20] on theoretical grounds, concluded that circularly orientated smooth muscle was inefficient in withstanding increased circumferential tension as it is even more distensible than elastic tissue and tends to yield. On the other hand, longitudinally orientated muscle fibres would remove kinks in circumferential collagen fibres and tighten up the fibrous tissue network of the artery, so reducing the effective unstretched circumference of the vessel and making it more stable. The only force available to stretch fasciculi of longitudinal muscle would be that very small component of the circumferential tension in the media resolved through the angle of nearly 90° made by the long axis of the nearly circumferential collagen fibres with the long axis of the vessel. Burton[20] points out that leverage of this type is used in some pointer movements in electrical instruments since it affords such a big mechanical advantage. It seems clear from such theoretical speculations that longitudinal muscle in pulmonary arteries exposed to hypertension may help to prevent their overdistension. Turnbull[21] was aware that a high pressure within an artery predisposes to the formation of longitudinal muscle which he found to be 'extremely conspicuous' in the arcuate and interlobular arteries of the kidney in systemic hypertension.

A clue to an additional factor is suggested by the distribution of longitudinal muscle in the bronchial arteries. Considerable amounts are found in the bronchial arteries but *only in the intrapulmonary part of their course* and *only in post natal life*. From aorta to lung they have the usual thick media of circular muscle with a thick internal elastic lamina, characteristic of any systemic artery (Chap. 38). However, once they enter the lung and come to lie in the walls of the bronchi they develop a very thick layer of longitudinal muscle internal to a thin coat of circular muscle (Fig. 38.3). Here they are subjected to the additional stress of repeated stretching during respiration. Longitudinal muscle is not found in the foetal bronchial arteries when the lung is immobile. Hence in the bronchial arteries it would appear that the essential combination of factors in the aetiology of the development of longitudinal muscle is high intravascular pressure and repeated stretch. It is of interest in this respect that the mesenteric arteries of the rat have been found to develop adventitial longitudinal muscle when they are connected to the diaphragm by a thread in such a way as to subject them to rhythmic traction with ventilatory movements.[22]

Although normal pulmonary arteries are subjected to repeated stretching, they conduct blood at a pressure only one-sixth of that in the systemic circulation. A high pulmonary arterial pressure is physiological in the foetus, but the lung and its contained vessels are immobile. When pulmonary hypertension develops from any cause in post-natal life, however, the critical combination of high intravascular pressure and repeated stretch occurs and acts as a stimulus for the development of longitudinal muscle in pulmonary arteries.

It seems likely that the layers of longitudinal muscle internal and external to the media must arise from a few pre-existing normal longitudinal fibres. This is in keeping with the view of Turnbull[21] who regarded the development of longitudinal muscle in the intima of the aorta as a hypertrophy of the normally occurring but sparse longitudinal muscle layer in the aorta. Although longitudinal muscle is not normally regarded as a feature of the structure of a muscular pulmonary artery (Chap. 3), it seems likely that a few longitudinal muscle fibres are to be found in the media. Such fibres could hypertrophy under the combined stimulus of hypertension and repeated stretch to give rise to the apparently new coats of longitudinal muscle.

Intimal Proliferation and Fibrosis

Cellular intimal proliferation begins in grade 2 of hypertensive pulmonary vascular disease (p. 245) and affects in the first place the arterioles and smaller muscular pulmonary arteries. As the disease progresses through stage 3, intimal fibroelastosis occurs in the same region and extends to the medium sized muscular pulmonary arteries. It is natural to think of this as a reaction of the tissue to mechanical stress. Rudolph[23] has suggested that the stress arises from the forces of sheer, due to the increased pulmonary blood flow, and quotes the experimental work of Fry[24] who demonstrated the effect of sheer on vascular endothelium. From their correlations between haemodynamics and histology, however, Wagenvoort and his colleagues[12] concluded that intimal fibrosis was related to pressure and not to flow. A high flow may exist for many years in patients with an atrial septal defect without an intimal reaction occurring.

On the other hand, it is not entirely clear how an increased transmural pressure acts. Since endothelial cells are virtually incompressible they will not undergo an increased mechanical stress with an increased pressure unless the vessel dilates. Yet

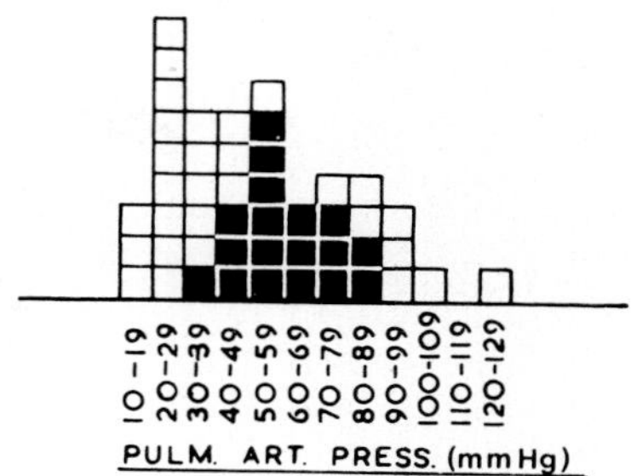

Fig. 18.1 Histogram to show the effect of a single injection of acetylcholine on the pulmonary arterial pressure in a group of patients with various diseases.[25] The patients are arranged according to the level of the initial mean pressure in the pulmonary artery. Each black square represents a patient in whom the pressure in the pulmonary artery fell after the injection. Each white square represents a patient in whom no fall was apparent.

general dilatation of muscular pulmonary arteries and arterioles appears to occur at stages subsequent to the appearance of intimal proliferation and fibrosis. In addition, the dilatation is not localized to this class of vessels. At the same time it is observed that the localized areas of dilatation of muscular pulmonary arteries tend to be associated with severe intimal fibrosis (Chap. 16, p. 249). Another region which seems particularly prone to intimal fibrosis is the point of origin of an arteriole from a muscular pulmonary artery. Here it could be argued either that there is a localized increase in the sheer forces or that the effects of a mechanical weakness of the wall are operating.

The medial coat of the muscular and elastic pulmonary arteries contains only smooth muscle cells and the intima normally contains only vascular endothelial cells. The production of collagen and elastin must, therefore, arise from one or both of these types of cells. Such a morphogenetic function of vascular smooth muscle has been demonstrated in the systemic circulation.[22]

Response to Drugs

As fibrosis develops throughout the wall of the small arterial branches, there is a progressive disappearance of muscle from the media. The turning point at which muscular hypertrophy reaches its maximum only to decline with the onset of fibrosis lies between grades 3 and 4. Such a sequence of events sheds light on certain inconsistencies in the action of dilator drugs on these vessels. As has been discussed in Chapter 13, acetylcholine appears to act as a dilator in the pulmonary circulation.[25] When given as a single rapid injection into the pulmonary artery it will usually cause a noticeable fall in the pulmonary arterial pressure in patients with a moderate degree of pulmonary hypertension. On the other hand, when the initial pressure in the pulmonary artery is normal and when it is very high, this fall in pressure does not occur (Fig. 18.1). An explanation of these findings in terms of the structure of the small pulmonary arteries[25] would be that, when the pulmonary arterial pressure is normal, the muscle of the media of these vessels is thin and its tone slight, so that the response to acetylcholine is too feeble to have any unequivocal effect on the pressure in the pulmonary artery. When the pulmonary arterial pressure becomes raised, the dilating activity of acetylcholine will become increasingly apparent because the muscular coat is thicker and presumably its tone is increased. Finally, with predominant fibrosis, the small pulmonary arteries become rigid tubes and are once more unable to respond to the drug.

Similar results were observed following the inhalation of 100 per cent oxygen in patients with ventricular septal defects and in this study the results were related to the histological appearances of the pulmonary vessels.[26] The inhalation of 100 per cent oxygen caused a substantial fall in the pulmonary vascular resistance in patients with grade 1 to 3 lesions. In patients with grade 4 and 5 lesions this fall was less impressive or absent (Chap. 19).

The development of fibrosis in the walls of the small pulmonary arterial branches appears to be a progressive and irreversible process. In patients with pulmonary hypertension associated with intracardiac shunts the pulmonary vascular resistance increases progressively beyond a certain stage to reduce and finally reverse the shunt which initially caused the pulmonary arterial hypertension (Chap. 19). Similarly, as will be described in Chapter 20, the closure of such an intra-cardiac defect results in an immediate substantial fall in the ratio of the pulmonary arterial pressure to the systemic arterial pressure if the vascular abnormalities are of grades 1 to 3, but has no effect on this ratio if they are of grades 5 and 6.

The Nature of the Plexiform Lesion

The 'plexiform lesion' is the most striking histopathological change to occur in the lung in certain varieties of severe pulmonary hypertension. Its nature and, allied to this, the mechanism of its formation, are not well understood and this shortcoming in pulmonary vascular pathology has recently assumed considerable practical importance in relation to the epidemic of primary pulmonary hypertension in Germany, Switzerland and Austria from 1968 to 1972 (Chap. 27, p. 410). These cases were characterized by the development of plexiform lesions and it seems likely that, if we knew more about the mode of development of this lesion, we might gain insight into the nature and aetiology of the epidemic itself.

Plexiform lesions occur only in the presence of severe pulmonary arterial hypertension and even then they are found in only a few well-defined types of hypertensive pulmonary vascular disease. Thus they occur most characteristically in patients with large pre- and post-tricuspid shunts such as are described in Chapter 16. They are found in primary pulmonary hypertension but they do not occur in pulmonary veno-occlusive disease or recurrent pulmonary thromboembolism, which constitute the other two causes of clinically 'unexplained pulmonary hypertension'. What is so intriguing is that they develop in the very rare cases of cirrhosis of the liver or portal vein thrombosis which become associated with severe pulmonary hypertension.

Plexiform lesions will occur in cases of Fallot's tetrad where severe pulmonary hypertension has developed as a result of too large a shunt being created between the systemic and pulmonary circulations.[27] When such shunts are created experimentally in dogs, they will also lead to plexiform lesions.[28] Pulmonary vascular changes similar to plexiform lesions sometimes also occur in cases of pulmonary schistosomiasis (Chap. 15). In this disease the dilated thin-walled vessels arise from muscular pulmonary arteries containing ova of *Schistosoma mansoni*.

In its early cellular form, the plexiform lesion consists of a plexiform network of capillary-like channels within a dilated short segment of a muscular pulmonary artery. The channels are separated by proliferating endothelial cells. Within these channels and the remaining lumen of the parent artery, fibrin thrombi, eventually mixed with platelets, are often recognizable.[29] The media of the parent artery frequently shows fibrinoid necrosis and Wagenvoort believes that the network of capillary channels may constitute recanalization of a fibrin thrombus.[29]

There is some experimental work[30,31] to support the idea that fibrinoid necrosis and arteritis are concerned in and precede the development of plexiform lesions. However, it is clear that the organization and recanalization of a fibrin thrombus complicating severe pulmonary hypertension and fibrinoid necrosis of muscular pulmonary arteries cannot totally explain the development of plexiform lesions. The combination of greatly elevated pulmonary arterial pressure, necrotizing pulmonary arteritis, and fibrin thrombi in pulmonary arteries occurs in mitral stenosis but in this disease, and indeed any characterized by pulmonary venous hypertension, plexiform lesions never occur. It is clear that additional haemodynamic factors are also concerned.

Distal to the plexus, the arterial branch in which it has arisen shows pronounced dilatation. This appearance of a thin-walled dilated vessel showing continuity with a thick-walled parent muscular pulmonary artery has misled some workers into believing that these plexiform lesions represent some form of arteriovenous anastomosis.[32,33] As plexiform lesions age the proliferated endothelial cells are replaced by fibrous tissue and then fibroelastic tissue as shown in Figure 16.2. Although quite different in histological structure, such vascular changes merely represent an aging fibrous plexiform lesion.

The fact that plexiform lesions occur in episodes supports the generally accepted view that plexiform lesions are acquired rather than congenital. Some observers,[34,35] have expressed the view that these lesions are congenital but most authorities would think that this hypothesis in untenable. There is no doubt that plexiform lesions can occur in infancy but this should be taken as an indication that the pulmonary haemodynamics suitable for their development came about unusually early in life rather than confirming their congenital origin. Plexiform lesions have been reported in an 8-week old girl with ventricular and atrial septal defects and a patent ductus arteriosus[36] and in a 53-day old girl with a patent ductus arteriosus and mitral atresia.[37] The fact that plexiform lesions can be induced in the lungs of adult dogs by the experimental creation of shunts[28] also points to their acquired rather than congenital nature.

Necrotizing Arteritis

The essential lesion is fibrinoid necrosis of the media of arterioles or muscular pulmonary arteries around which an inflammatory reaction occurs. It is associated with an extremely high pulmonary arterial pressure and probably intense vasospasm.

If so, it implies a high concentration of calcium ions in the region of the contractile proteins of the smooth muscle cells (Chap. 12, p. 177). If the normal constrictor response of vascular smooth muscle to stretch is mediated by an influx of calcium ions across the stressed cell membrane (p. 178) it is feasible that with a severe stress the inward movement of calcium ions could be overwhelming. In this case there will be an intense contraction associated with a rapid rate of hydrolysis of ATP by myosin ATPase. The increased concentration of ADP caused by the hydrolysis of ATP may liberate more ionized calcium from the sarcoplasmic reticulum[38] and thus a vicious circle of increasing calcium ion concentration and decreasing ATP concentration may be established. Such a vicious circle will end in the death of the cell in rigor.

LARGE ELASTIC PULMONARY ARTERIES

Studies on Arterial Strips

In patients with large post-tricuspid defects and pulmonary hypertension from birth, the pulmonary trunk retains its foetal pattern of elastic tissue which is similar to that in the adult aorta (Chap. 17, p. 267). On the other hand, when pulmonary hypertension starts later in life, the pulmonary trunk seems unable to increase its content of elastic tissue and its histological appearances are those of the normal pattern. This difference between the histological appearances of the pulmonary trunk in acquired and congenital pulmonary hypertension is reflected by differences in the extensibility of the tissue composing the media of the wall.[39]

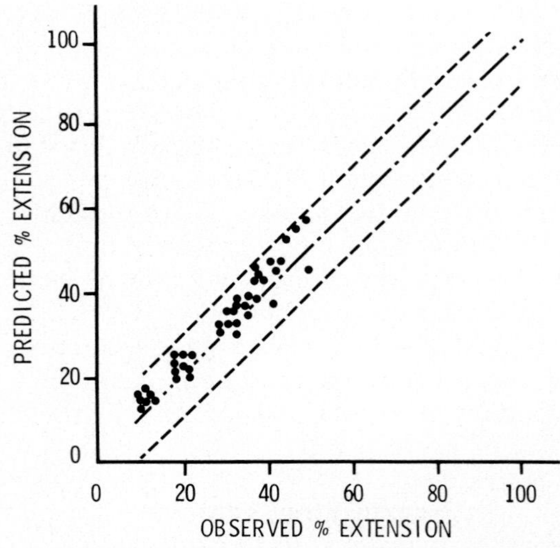

Fig. 18.2 The extensibility of the pulmonary trunk in patients with disease of the mitral valve. The observed degree of extension is plotted against that predicted by a formula derived from normal subjects. The line of identity is given together with lines at twice the standard error of the estimate.[39]

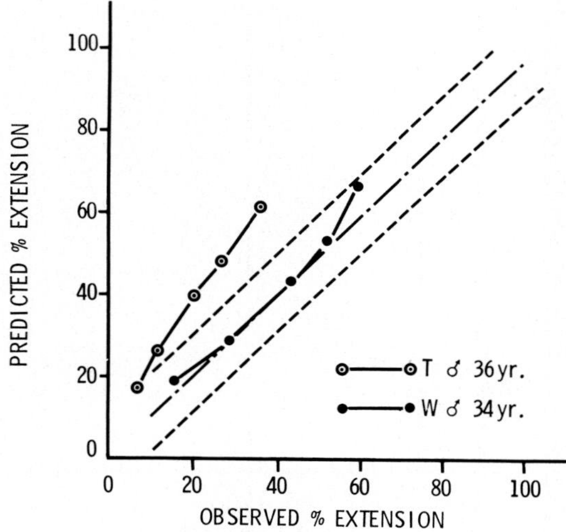

Fig. 18.3 The extensibility of the pulmonary trunk in two patients with ventricular septal defect plotted as in Figure 18.2. For discussion, see text.[39]

Figure 18.2 plots the observed degree of extension in strips of the pulmonary trunk taken from a group of subjects with disease of the mitral valve against that predicted from normal data for a given age and load.[39] It demonstrates that the extensibility of the tissue of the pulmonary trunk in these subjects with acquired pulmonary hypertension is the same as normal. This is consistent with the normal configuration of the elastic tissue in these patients (Chap. 17, p. 267). Since the wall

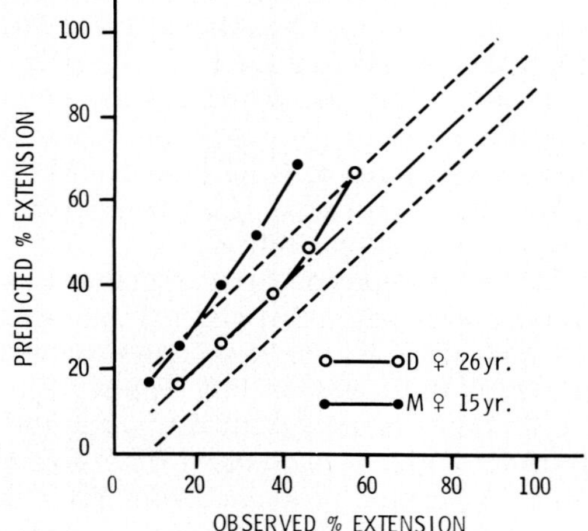

Fig. 18.4 The extensibility of the pulmonary trunk in two patients with primary pulmonary hypertension, plotted as in Figure 18.2. For discussion, see text.[39]

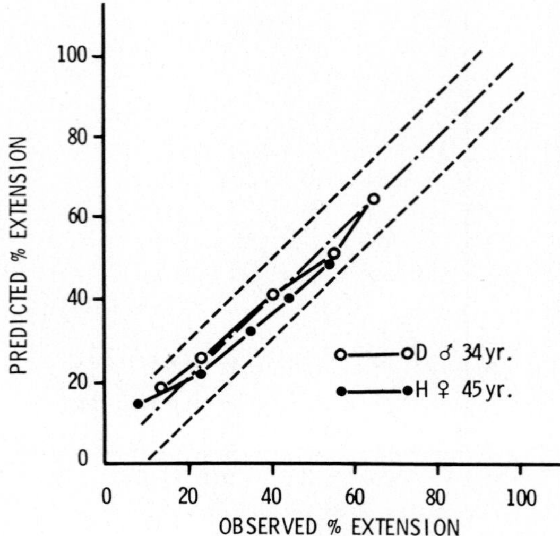

Fig. 18.5 The extensibility of the pulmonary trunk in two patients with atrial septal defect[39] plotted as in Figure 18.2.

of the pulmonary trunk is thicker in patients with disease of the mitral valve than in normals, the extensibility of the entire wall is less than that of the normal.

Figure 18.3 plots the observed degree of extension against that predicted for the normal in two subjects with a ventricular septal defect. One (subject T) had a large ventricular septal defect with severe pulmonary hypertension and the elastic tissue of the pulmonary trunk had an aortic pattern. The extensibility of the tissue of the pulmonary trunk was less than normal. The other subject (W) had a small defect of the Roger type and a normal pulmonary arterial pressure; the elastic tissue was of the adult pulmonary pattern and the extensibility was normal.

Figure 18.4 plots the observed degree of extension against the predicted in two cases of primary pulmonary hypertension. One (subject M) had an aortic pattern of elastic tissue and a reduced extensibility. The other (subject D) had a normal pattern of elastic tissue and normal extensibility.

Figure 18.5 shows similar observations on two subjects with an atrial septal defect. In both, the configuration of the elastic tissue and the extensibility were normal.

In people indigenous to high altitude, the foetal aortic pattern of the elastic tissue persists in the pulmonary trunk until later in life. Figure 18.6 shows the extension observed in a group of pulmonary trunks with the aortic pattern of elastic tissue taken from five high altitude subjects in Peru.[40] The group as a whole have a significant lower extensibility than that predicted from Peruvian low level normals. In these specimens, measurements of elastin showed a concentration which was inappropriately high for the age (Fig. 18.7). The collagen content of the specimens was normal. If, as suggested by Roach and Burton[41] (Chap. 4, p. 44), the initial part

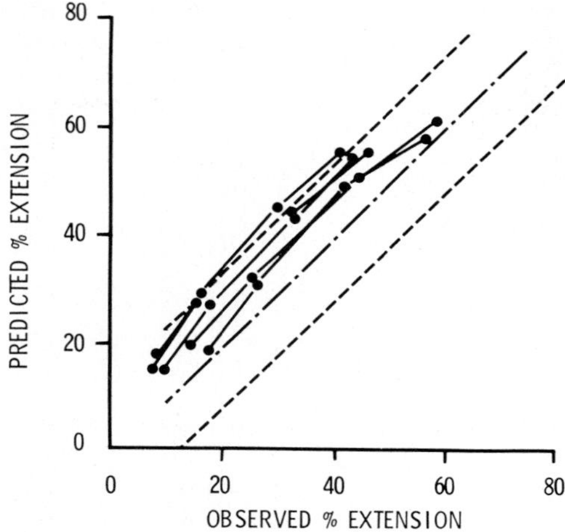

Fig. 18.6 The extensibility of the pulmonary trunk in five Peruvian subjects with an 'aortic' pattern of elastic tissue,[40] plotted as in Figure 18.2.

of the length–tension curve is dictated mainly by elastin, one might predict that the extensibility of the high altitude tissue would be particularly reduced at low loads. Figure 18.8 shows that this was so. Among the specimens with a normal elastic pattern, there is a decrease in extensibility with age, but the specimens with an aortic pattern show a degree of extension which is inappropriate for their age.

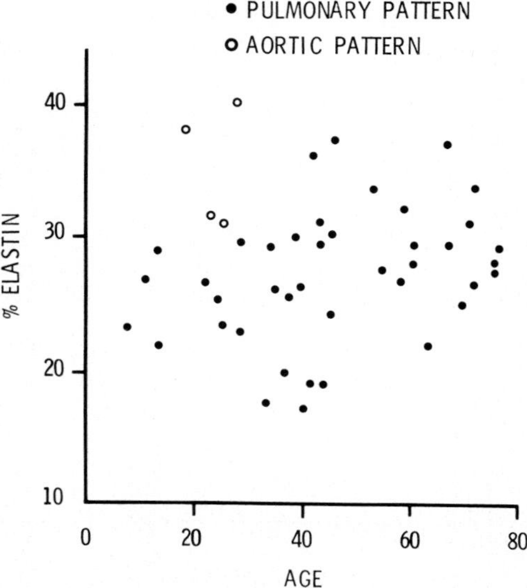

Fig. 18.7 The relation between age and the content of elastin (per cent dry weight) in the pulmonary trunk in Peruvian subjects.[40]

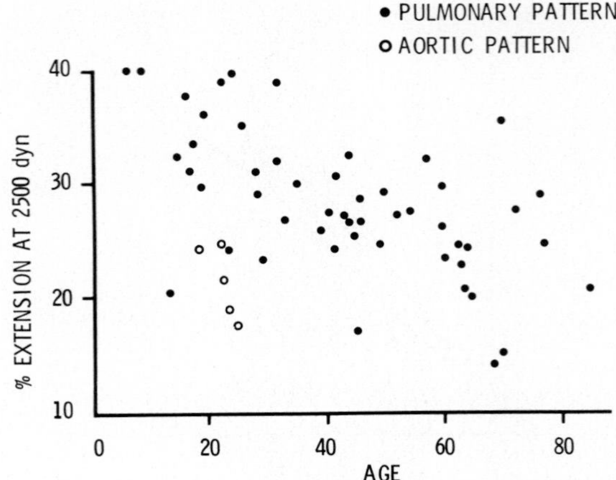

Fig. 18.8 The relation between age and the degree of extensibility of the pulmonary trunk at a low load in Peruvian subjects.[40]

When the percentage content of elastin is plotted against the degree of extension at low load (Fig. 18.9) there is, as would be anticipated, no distinction between those with an aortic type of elastic pattern and those with the normal pulmonary pattern.

The preceding plots of extensibility show the absolute deviation of the observations

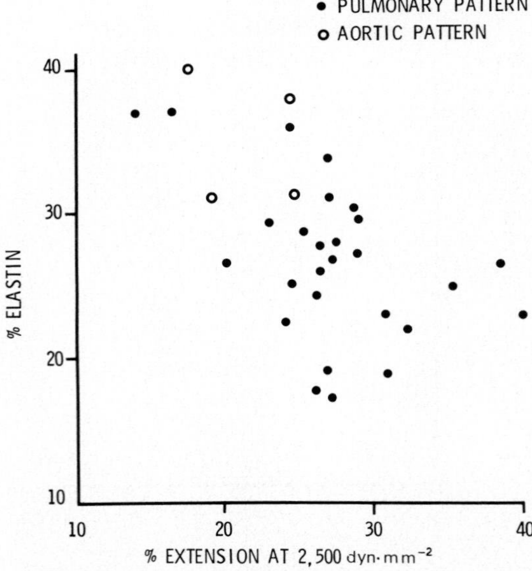

Fig. 18.9 The relation between the content of elastin (per cent dry weight) and the extensibility of the pulmonary trunk at a low load in Peruvian subjects.[40]

from the normal values. When the degree of extension is expressed as a percentage of that predicted (Fig. 18.10) the maximal decrease in extensibility, both in the high altitude subjects and in the subjects with an aortic pattern due to congenital heart disease, is seen to occur at the lesser degrees of extension. This is consistent with the thesis of Roach and Burton.[41] For contrast, Figure 18.10 shows the average of a group of specimens from cases of Fallot's tetrad. Here the extensibility decreases with an increasing degree of extension and this is consistent with an increased proportion of collagen (Chap. 37, p. 586).

The histological and physical characteristics which distinguish the elastic pulmonary arteries of patients with pulmonary hypertension of neonatal origin from those of patients in whom pulmonary hypertension arises later in life may provide an explanation of the difference in size of the elastic pulmonary arteries which is commonly observed radiologically between these two groups. Patients with a ventricular septal defect and pulmonary hypertension from early life tend to have only a limited radiological enlargement of the elastic pulmonary arteries (see Fig. 21.5, p. 314), whereas patients with an atrial septal defect in whom pulmonary hypertension has developed later in life may show an enormous dilatation of these vessels (see Fig. 21.10, p. 323).

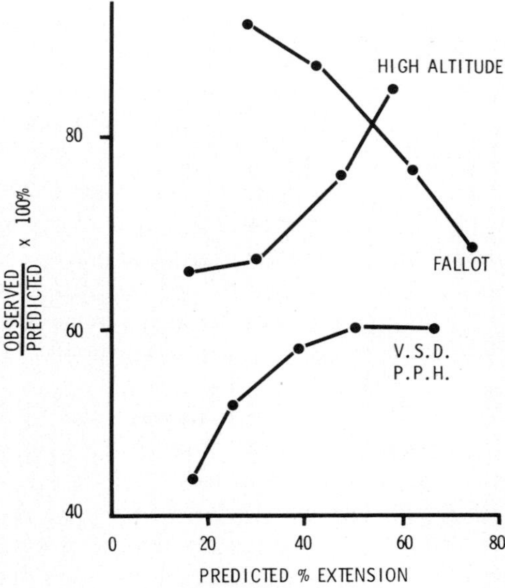

Fig. 18.10 The ratio of observed to predicted degree of extension of the pulmonary trunk is plotted against that predicted from normals. Average values of three groups are shown: 'aortic' elastic pattern due to high altitude; 'aortic' elastic pattern due to ventricular septal defect or primary pulmonary hypertension; and Fallot's tetrad.[40]

Studies of Volume Distensibility

One of the difficulties in interpreting data concerning the volume distensibility of blood vessels is the complicated relation which exists between the distensibility of a vessel and the circumferential extensibility of its wall. A small vessel, for instance, would have a lower distensibility than a large one even though the structure of the walls were the same. This is partly because the injection of the same volume of liquid into a small vessel causes a proportionately greater degree of stretch of the walls. Even if the percentage change in volume is the same, however, the distensibility of the small vessel will be less than that of the larger because the smaller radius is associated with less tension in the vessel wall (Chap. 4, p. 52). This dependence of the coefficient of distensibility on the size of a vessel will account for at least some of the differences which have been estimated to occur between childhood and maturity (p. 53). It has equally to be taken into account when comparing the distensibility coefficient of the pulmonary arteries in pulmonary hypertension with the values found in normal people. Since the coefficient of extensibility of the vessel wall is not constant, the distensibility of the vessel is also dependent on the degree to which the circumference is held beyond its unstretched length. This is likely to be different in a normal person from what it is in a patient with pulmonary hypertension. The wall of an artery becomes less extensible the more it is stretched from its natural length (Chap. 4, p. 44) so that an increased stretching of the circumference will tend to diminish the distensibility of the vessel. On the other hand, as has just been seen, the increase in radius due to the stretching of the arterial wall will simultaneously tend to increase the distensibility. The relation between the coefficient of distensibility of a vessel and of the extensibility of its wall is, therefore, a complex one (Appendix J).

Using the Windkessel formula, Deuchar and Knebel[42] estimated that in two adult patients with a ventricular septal defect and pulmonary hypertension the distensibility coefficients of the pulmonary arterial tree were 0·23 and 0·27 ml/mmHg. This compared with a value for the normal adult of 1·9 ml/mmHg. Since both the volume and the pressure within the elastic pulmonary arteries are increased in this condition, an abnormally low coefficient of distensibility will certainly mean a diminished extensibility of the arterial wall. This statement, however, ignores the difficulties inherent in comparing two vessels, the walls of which are stretched different degrees beyond their natural lengths.

Lasser and Amram[43] made similar estimations of the distensibility of the pulmonary arterial tree in patients with mitral stenosis and found an average value of 1·00 ml/mmHg with a range of 0·37 to 2·8. The average value is thus lower than normal but the range of values extends into the normal. These authors comment that, on exercise, the mean pulmonary arterial pressure and pulse pressure increase while the stroke volume may stay the same or even decrease. This was taken to indicate a decreased distensibility of the pulmonary arteries on exercise due to distension from an increased pulmonary blood volume. The average calculated value for the distensibility coefficient of the pulmonary arterial tree in these patients during exercise was 0·38 ml/mmHg.

Reuben[44] has studied the compliance of the whole pulmonary arterial tree in a group of patients with varying degrees of severity of acquired heart disease and mean pulmonary arterial pressures extending from 12 to 60 mmHg. The method used was based on the assumption that the pulmonary arterial system behaved as a 'lumped' system (Chap. 10, p. 153). The downslope of the pulmonary arterial pressure during diastole approximated to an exponential curve which would be regarded as being determined by a time constant equal to the resistance multiplied by the capacity of the system. Since the resistance could be calculated in the conventional way, the capacity could also be calculated. In these studies the capacity was found to decrease with an increasing mean pulmonary arterial pressure. Such a result would be predicted from the curved relation between length and tension known to exist even in the normal pulmonary artery (Chap. 4, p. 44). No information could be gained regarding the specific changes in the characteristics of the arterial wall and, since the subjects had acquired disease, the elastic tissue in the walls of the elastic pulmonary arteries must be expected to be normal.

The study gave an interesting insight into the relative effects of capacity and resistance in transmitting the flow wave to the capillary bed in patients with pulmonary hypertension. Transmission of the flow wave is favoured by a low resistance and a low capacity. An increased resistance tends to distend the elastic pulmonary arteries and, with an increasing volume, these vessels become less distensible. Thus, an increased resistance would be expected to be associated with a decreased capacity. In the dog[45] this opposite relation between resistance and capacity is such that, with an increasing mean pulmonary arterial pressure, the time constant remains unchanged and the transmission of the flow wave is unaffected. In patients, however, Reuben[44] found that, at the higher levels of mean pulmonary arterial pressure, the capacity decreased to a lesser proportion than the increase in resistance. Thus, the time constant increased and this was associated with a diminution in the transmission of the flow wave to the capillaries.

The most direct observations of the distensibility of human pulmonary arteries have been made by Meyer and Schollmeyer[46] who carried out measurements of volume and pressure in the pulmonary trunk and its two main branches after death in patients with mitral stenosis and in patients of the same age who had had a normal pulmonary circulation. They found that for the same increase in pressure there was a proportionately greater increase in volume in the subjects with mitral stenosis than in the control group. Thus the volume distensibility of the pulmonary trunk and its two main branches was increased in patients with mitral stenosis. In view, however, of the complex relation between distensibility and extensibility which has just been discussed, this does not necessarily mean that the walls of these vessels are more extensible than normal.

The Influence of Turbulence

Roach and her colleagues have published evidence that a turbulent blood flow in an artery causes vibration in the wall which makes it more distensible.[47–49] Using a combination of angiography and pulmonary arterial catheterization, the systolic and diastolic pressures could be related to the changes in radius of the main divisions of the pulmonary artery.[50] Using the Laplace equation and assuming a linear relation between length and tension, the radius at zero pressure could be estimated and wall tension could then be plotted against the ratio of the radius observed to the radius at zero pressure. Expressed in this way the extensibility of the pulmonary arterial wall was greater than normal in patients with a pulmonary valvar stenosis and in patients with an atrial septal defect. Boughner and Roach[50] suggest that the increased extensibility is due to the presence of a murmur. The dilatation of the pulmonary artery is confined to the trunk in pulmonary valvar stenosis, but extends further down into the major branches in the presence of an atrial septal defect. This was thought to be explicable by the propagation of the murmur further down the pulmonary arterial tree in patients with an atrial septal defect.

The results run somewhat contrary to those just reported on isolated strips of the pulmonary trunk.[39] They are, however, derived in a different way and three points need to be taken into consideration. In the first place the results of Boughner and Roach[50] relate to dynamic extensibility during life, not static extensibility after death. Secondly, they include the adventitia and not just the media. Finally, they presuppose a linear relation between length and tension within the range studied.

PULMONARY CAPILLARIES

The pulmonary capillaries are normal in patients with pulmonary arterial hypertension associated with an intracardiac shunt, but they are dilated and show alterations in their structure (Chap. 22) when the elevation of pulmonary arterial pressure is secondary to prolonged pulmonary venous hypertension. Although capillaries appear to be highly indistensible structures within the time limits of physiological experiment (Chap. 11, p. 162), it is difficult to explain their dilatation in mitral stenosis except as a result of a prolonged increase in distending pressure. Capillaries, however, will dilate readily in the presence of chemical stimuli and such a stimulus remains a possibility. A dilatation of the capillaries has the effect of increasing the diffusing capacity of the lungs (Chap. 42, p. 639). This is partly because there is a larger volume of blood to accept oxygen or other gases from the alveoli and partly because there is an increased surface over which diffusion can occur. In patients with mitral stenosis, this tendency to increase the diffusing capacity may counteract the increased resistance to the passage of respiratory gases across a thickened alveolar-capillary membrane. However, even in the earlier stages of mitral stenosis, physiological measurements of the pulmonary capillary volume have shown only a modest increase, while in the later stages the capillary volume has decreased (Chap. 42, p. 648).

PULMONARY VEINS

Patients with pre-tricuspid shunts without severe pulmonary arterial hypertension frequently develop intimal fibrosis of the pulmonary veins (Chap. 16). Since these are the patients in whom the highest levels of sustained pulmonary blood flow occur, it is probable that this change in structure is related to the increased flow. Intimal fibrosis in pulmonary veins is not nearly so characteristic of post-tricuspid shunts and in these patients the level of pulmonary blood flow is not in general so high. Intimal fibrosis also occurs in the pulmonary veins in patients with mitral stenosis, where it is probably an expression of an increased pressure in these vessels. The hypertrophy of the media of the pulmonary veins which sometimes accompanies intimal fibrosis in this disease may, as in the arteries, be a response to prolonged stretch.

REFERENCES

1. Harris, P. (1955) *Brit. Heart J.*, **17**, 85.
2. Harris, P. (1955) *Ph.D. Thesis*, University of London.
3. Dexter, L., Dow, J. W., Haynes, F. W., Whittenberger, J. L., Ferris, B. G., Goodale, W. T. & Hellems, H. K. (1950) *J. Clin. Invest.*, **29**, 602.
4. Bayliss, W. M. (1902) *J. Physiol.*, **28**, 220.
5. Folkow, B. (1949) *Acta Physiol. Scand.*, **17**, 289.
6. Folkow, B. & Löfving, B. (1956) *Acta Physiol. Scand.*, **38**, 37.
7. Johnson, P. C. (1967) *Gastroenterology*, **52**, 435.
8. Johnson, P. C. (1968) *Circulat. Res.*, **22**, 199.
9. Speden, R. N. & Freckelton, D. J. (1970) *Circulat. Res.*, **27**, Suppl. II, 99.
10. Lundholm, L. & Mohme-Lundholm, E. (1966) *Acta Physiol. Scand.*, **68**, 347.
11. McDonald, D. A. & Taylor, M. G. (1959) *Progr. Biophys.*, **9**, 107.
12. Wagenvoort, C. A., Nauta, J., Van der Schaar, P. J., Weeda, H. W. H. & Wagenvoort, N. (1967) *Circulation*, **35**, 1028.
13. Grover, R. F., Vogel, J. H. K., Averill, K. H. & Blount, S. G., Jn. (1963) *Amer. Heart J.*, **66**, 1.
14. Wood, P. (1957) In *Diseases of the Heart and Circulation*, 2nd Ed. page 541. Eyre and Spottiswoode.
15. Pool, P. E., Vogel, J. H. K. & Blount, S. G., Jn. (1962) *Amer. J. Cardiol.*, **10**, 705.
16. Peñaloza, D., Gamboa, R., Marticorena, E., Echevarria, M., Dyer, J. & Gutierrez, E. (1961) *Amer. Heart J.*, **61**, 101.
17. Will, D. H., Card, C. S., Vandlandingham, G. D. & Alexander, A. F. (1967) *The Physiologist*, **10**, 347.
18. Will, D. H., Hicks, J. L., Card, C. S. & Alexander, A. F. (1970) *Fed. Proc.*, **29**, 591.
19. Weir, E. K., Tucker, A., Reeves, J. T., Will, D. H. & Grover, R. F. (1974) *Cardiovasc. Res.*, **8**, 745.
20. Burton, A. C. (1954) *Physiol. Rev.*, **34**, 619.
21. Turnbull, H. M. (1914) *Quart. J. Med.*, **8**, 201.
22. Somlyo, A. P. & Somlyo, A. V. (1968) *Pharmacol. Rev.*, **20**, 197.
23. Rudolph, A. (1971) In *The Natural History and Progress in Treatment of Congenital Heart Defects*, ed. Langford Kidd, B. S. & Keith, J. D. page 289. Thomas.
24. Fry, D. L. (1968) *Circulat. Res.*, **22**, 165.
25. Harris, P. (1957) *Brit. Heart J.*, **19**, 272.
26. Heath, D., Helmholz, H. F., Jn., Burchell, H. B., Dushane, J. W. & Edwards, J. E. (1958) *Circulation*, **18**, 1155.
27. Wagenvoort, C. A., Dushane, J. W. & Edwards, J. E. (1960) *Mayo Clin. Proc.*, **35**, 186.
28. Heath, D., Donald, D. E. & Edwards, J. E. (1959) *Brit. Heart J.*, **21**, 187.
29. Wagenvoort, C. A. (1973) *Cardiovasc. Clin.*, **5**, 43.
30. Downing, S. E., Vidone, R. A., Brandt, H. M. & Liebow, A. A. (1963) *Amer. J. Path.*, **43**, 739.
31. Harley, R. A., Friedman, P. J., Saldaña, M., Liebow, A. A. & Carrington, C. B. (1968) *Amer. J. Path.*, **52**, 52a.

32. Kucsko, L. (1953) *Frankfurt Z. Path.*, **64**, 54.
33. Hufner, R. F. & McNicol, C. A. (1958) *Arch. Pathol.*, **65**, 554.
34. Moschcowitz, E., Rubin, E. & Strauss, L. (1961) *Amer. J. Path.*, **39**, 75.
35. Stanisic, M. (1967) *Zentralbl. Allg. Pathol.*, **110**, 367.
36. Wagenvoort, C. A. (1962) *Med. Thorac.*, **19**, 354.
37. Kanjuh, V. I., Sellers, R. D. & Edwards, J. E. (1964) *Arch. Path.*, **78**, 513.
38. Hasselbach, W. & Suko, J. (1974) *Biochem. Soc. Spec. Publ.*, **4**, 159.
39. Harris, P., Heath, D. & Apostolopoulos, A. (1965) *Brit. Heart J.*, **27**, 660.
40. Castillo, Y., Krüger, H., Arias-Stella, J., Hurtado, A., Harris, P. & Heath, D. (1967) *Brit. Heart J.*, **29**, 120.
41. Roach, M. R. & Burton, A. C. (1957) *Canad. J. Biochem. Physiol.*, **35**, 681.
42. Deuchar, D. & Knebel, R. (1952) *Brit. Heart J.*, **14**, 225.
43. Lasser, R. P. & Amram, S. S. (1956) *Amer. Heart J.*, **51**, 749.
44. Reuben, S. R. (1971) *Circulat. Res.*, **29**, 40.
45. Reuben, S. R., Swadling, J. P., Gersh, B. J. & Lee, G. de J. (1970) *Cardiovasc. Res.*, **4**, 473.
46. Meyer, W. W. & Schollmeyer, P. (1957) *Klin. Wschr.*, **35**, 1070.
47. Roach, M. R. (1963) *Amer. J. Cardiol.*, **12**, 802.
48. Roach, M. R. (1963) *Circulat. Res.*, **13**, 537.
49. Roach, M. R. & Harvey, K. (1964) *Canad. J. Physiol. Pharmacol.*, **42**, 53.
50. Boughner, D. R. & Roach, M. R. (1971) *Circulat. Res.*, **28**, 415.

19. The Relation of Hypertensive Pulmonary Vascular Disease to Haemodynamics

The Relation of Haemodynamics to Hypertensive Pulmonary Vascular Disease in Patients with Post-Tricuspid Shunts

Figures 19.1 to 19.3 review the findings of a study[1] relating pressure, flow and resistance in the pulmonary circulation with the grade of vascular abnormality. In patients with abnormalities of grade 1 severity, a range of 40–70 mmHg is found in the mean pulmonary arterial pressure (Fig. 19.1). By grade 3, the pressure increases only slightly to a range of 50–80 mmHg. At this stage severe intimal fibrosis develops. In the subsequent stages obstructive and dilatation lesions develop and, by grade 5, there is a sharp increase in the mean pulmonary arterial pressure to a range of 80–100 mmHg.

The relation to pulmonary blood flow is in the reverse direction, there being a gradual reduction in the flow with an increase in the severity of the structural abnormality (Fig. 19.2). Patients with congenital defects of the cardiac septa and early hypertensive pulmonary vascular disease have an abnormally high pulmonary blood flow of 5 to 17 $l \cdot min^{-1}/m^2$ BSA (Fig. 19.2). Those with grade 5 lesions usually have a pulmonary blood flow which is within the normal range or which is abnormally low (1·5 to 4 $l \cdot min^{-1}/m^2$ BSA) (Fig. 19.2). In grade 6 the flow is always diminished.

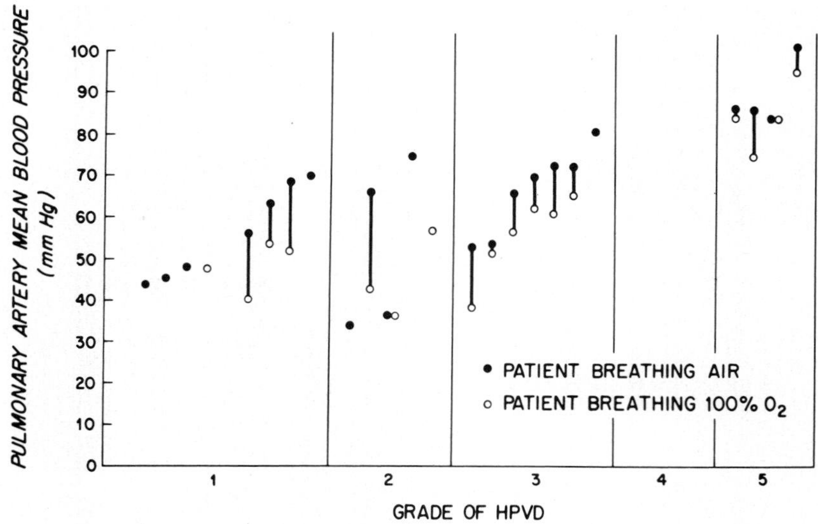

Fig. 19.1 Relation between grade of hypertensive pulmonary vascular disease (HPVD) and mean blood pressure in pulmonary artery in 24 patients with post-tricuspid shunts.

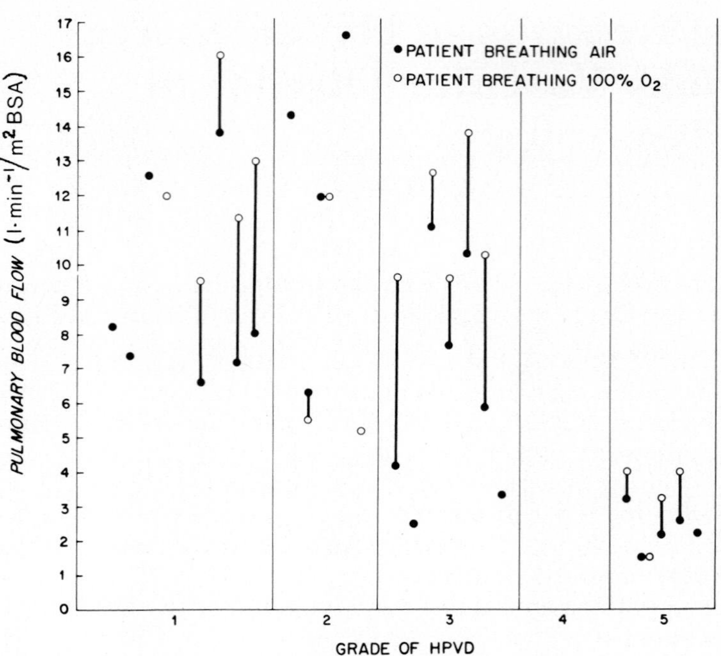

Fig. 19.2 Relation between grade of hypertensive pulmonary vascular disease (HPVD) and pulmonary blood flow in 25 patients with post-tricuspid shunts.

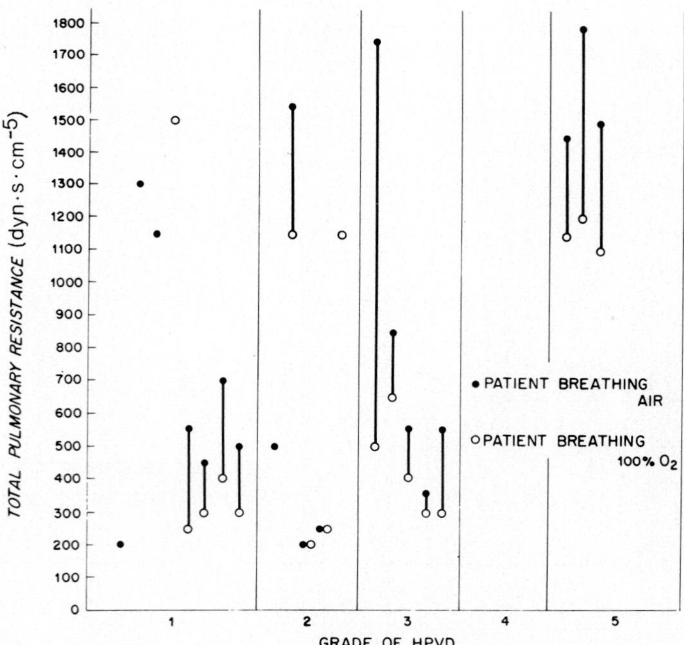

Fig. 19.3 Relation between grade of hypertensive pulmonary vascular disease (HPVD) and total pulmonary resistance in 21 patients with post-tricuspid shunts.

The pulmonary vascular resistance shows a rise with an increasing grade number, there being once more a substantial rise between grades 3 and 5 (Fig. 19.3). It is difficult to compare resistances in infants and adults since the normal resistance in infants is high (Chap. 14). It can be seen, for instance, in Figure 19.3 that three infants with post-tricuspid shunts and grade 1 vascular lesions have a total pulmonary resistance over 1000 dyn · s · cm^{-5}. If we exclude infants on this account, the majority of patients with post-tricuspid shunts and lesions of grade 1 to 3 severity in the lungs have a total pulmonary resistance of less than 700 dyn · s · cm^{-5}. Most patients with grade 5 lesions have a total pulmonary resistance which exceeds 1450 dyn · s · cm^{-5}.

The Relation of Haemodynamics to Hypertensive Pulmonary Vascular Disease in Patients with Pre-Tricuspid Shunts

Figures 19.4–19.6 show the results obtained in a study of 15 patients with pre-tricuspid shunts.[1] As in the previous group, there is a rise in the pulmonary arterial pressure (Fig. 19.4) and pulmonary vascular resistance (Fig. 19.5) and a fall in the flow of blood through the lungs (Fig. 19.6) as the degree of abnormality in the pulmonary arteries increases.

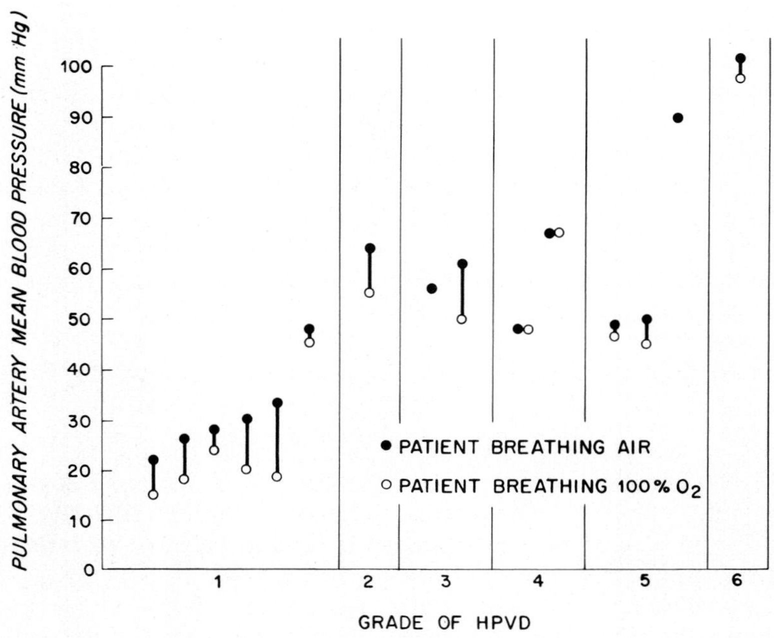

Fig. 19.4 Relation between grade of hypertensive pulmonary vascular disease (HPVD) and mean blood pressure in pulmonary artery in 15 patients with pre-tricuspid shunts.

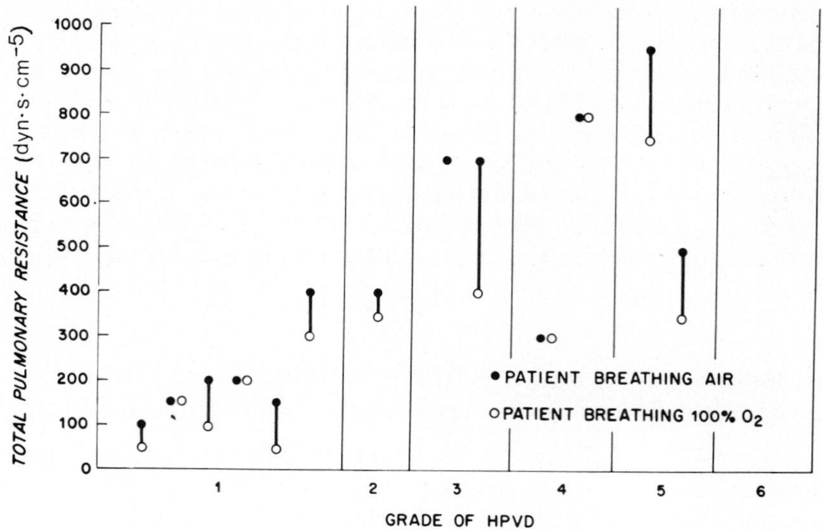

Fig. 19.5 Relation between grade of hypertensive pulmonary vascular disease (HPVD) and total pulmonary resistance in 13 patients with pre-tricuspid shunts.

Grade 1 lesions are usually associated with a normal resistance of about 200 dyn · s · cm^{-5}, although there may be a slight elevation to 400 dyn · s · cm^{-5} (Fig. 19.5). The resistance rises again to about 700 dyn · s · cm^{-5}, with an increase in severity to grade 3. Resistances of the order of 2900 dyn · s · cm^{-5} may be found with grade 6 lesions. While the total resistance tends to rise with progressive vascular abnormality, there is a considerable variation in the level of resistance found in association with any one grade (Fig. 19.5). The overall elevation in pressure and resistance throughout the range of grades is steeper than in the previous group, since in patients with pre-tricuspid shunts the pressure is often normal in grade 1.

The Severity of the Pulmonary Vascular Lesion and the Influence of Inhalation of 100 per cent Oxygen

In the work on which most of this chapter is based,[1] the haemodynamic effects of inhaling 100 per cent oxygen were compared with the histological grade of hypertensive pulmonary vascular disease. The effect of such inhalation in patients with shunts due to congenital heart disease is, in general, to lower the pulmonary arterial pressure and increase the pulmonary blood flow.[1,2] Oxygen appears, therefore, to act as a dilator in the pulmonary circulation (Chap. 30). In patients with grade 1 lesions, the inhalation of oxygen may lower the pulmonary vascular resistance to normal levels. With increasing grades of vascular abnormality, oxygen still causes a fall in resistance but cannot reduce it to a normal level. Patients with grade 5 lesions, for instance, maintain a pulmonary vascular resistance of more than five times normal even during the inhalation of 100 per cent oxygen.

Such data suggest that the total pulmonary resistance is compounded of two elements, one with a functional and the other with an organic basis. The functional element, represented by that part of the total pulmonary resistance removed completely or partially on the inhalation of 100 per cent oxygen, is of major importance in grade 3 lesions and is still present in some patients with grade 4 and 5 lesions. In the severest grades, even after administration of 100 per cent oxygen, there is still a residual resistance which, wholly or in part, probably has its basis in organic changes in the pulmonary arteries.

The Progressive Nature of Pulmonary Vascular Occlusion

The concept which underlies this chapter is one of progressive vascular occlusion which in the early stages is reversible but in the later stages becomes irreversible.[1,2] In grades 1 to 3 the most striking feature is an increase in thickness of the media of the muscular pulmonary arteries. In such grades, the pulmonary hypertension is largely reversible pharmacologically and we shall see in the following chapter how

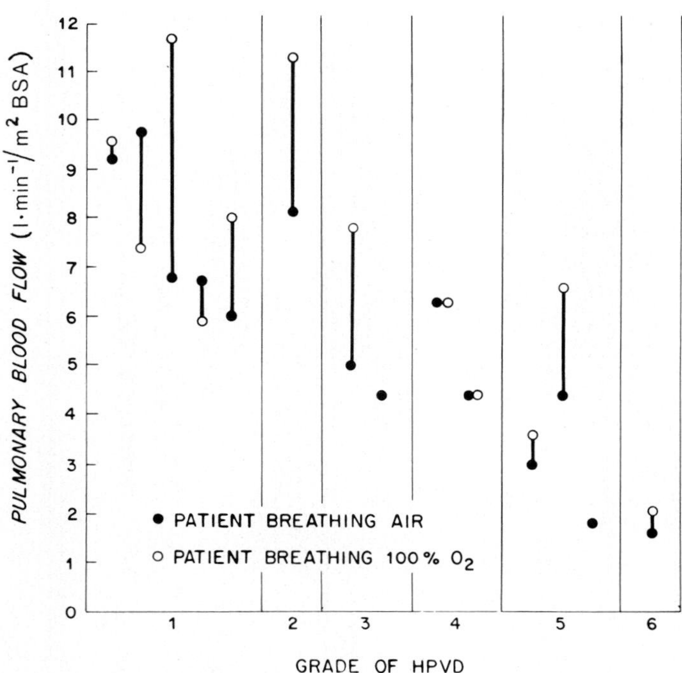

Fig. 19.6 Relation between grade of hypertensive pulmonary vascular disease (HPVD) and pulmonary blood flow in 14 patients with pre-tricuspid shunts.

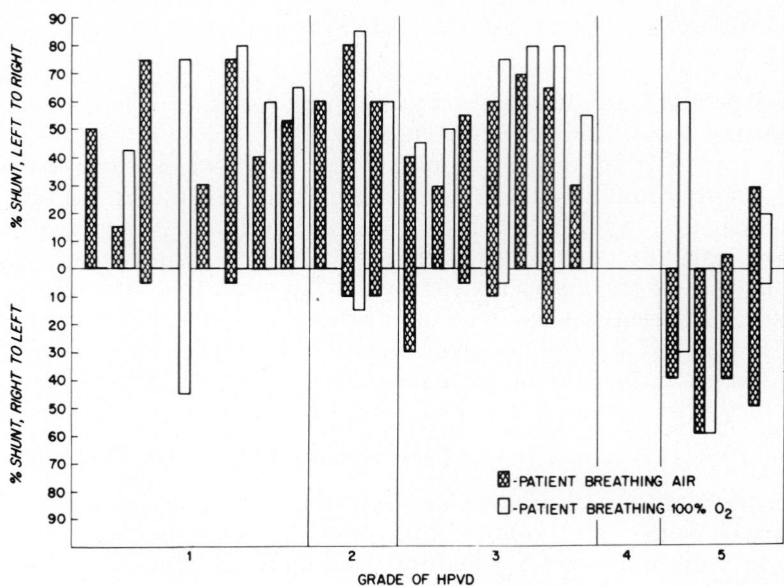

Fig. 19.7 Relation between grade of hypertensive pulmonary vascular disease (HPVD) and percentage of blood shunted in each direction through ventricular septal defect or patent ductus arteriosus in 22 patients with post-tricuspid shunts.

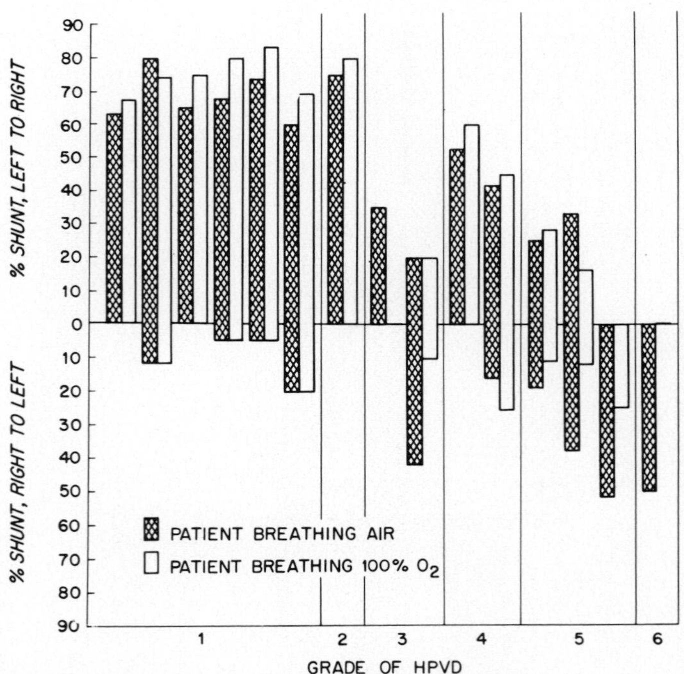

Fig. 19.8 Relation between grade of hypertensive pulmonary vascular disease (HPVD) and percentage of blood shunted in each direction through atrial septal defect in 15 patients with pre-tricuspid shunts.

the surgical closure of the defect brings the pulmonary arterial pressure back to normal or nearly so. These patients have large left-to-right shunts which increase on the inhalation of 100 per cent oxygen (Figs 19.7 and 19.8). The shunts are in the region of 30 to 80 per cent of the systemic blood flow in cases of post-tricuspid shunts but are even greater in pre-tricuspid shunts such as atrial septal defect. Some of these patients also have a right-to-left shunt but this is usually small and tends to disappear on the inhalation of 100 per cent oxygen.

The onset of generalized vascular dilatation in the late stage of grade 3 and the subsequent appearance of complex localized 'dilatation lesions' in grade 4 appears to represent an important transition stage in the progression of hypertensive pulmonary vascular disease. From this point onwards the pulmonary vascular resistance becomes very high and leads to a diminution in the pulmonary blood flow until eventually the flow through the lungs is less than that through the systemic circuit. These patients have predominantly right-to-left shunts which may be as high as 60 per cent of the total systemic flow. In the higher grades of hypertensive vascular disease the pulmonary vasculature appears to become rigid with increasing fibrosis and unable to respond to the dilating effects of 100 per cent oxygen. Similarly, it will be seen in the following chapter than the closure of the defect at this stage does not cause much, or any, fall in the pulmonary arterial pressure.

REFERENCES

1. Heath, D., Helmholz, H. F., Jn., Burchell, H. B., Dushane, J. W. & Edwards, J. E. (1958) *Circulation*, **18**, 1155.
2. Barratt-Boyes, B. G. & Wood, E. H. (1958) *J. Lab. Clin. Med.*, **51**, 72.

20. The Influence of Hypertensive Pulmonary Vascular Disease on the Selection of Patients for Closure of Septal Defects

Techniques of operating on patients with congenital defects giving rise to an increased pulmonary blood flow have advanced to such an extent that the immediate mortality for operating on an uncomplicated atrial or ventricular septal defect is negligible in children and young adults. The extension of these skills into infancy and the neonatal period progresses and the more complicated anomalies are becoming susceptible to radical correction.

It is in the early months of life that the effects of the surgical treatment of intra-cardiac shunts are most dramatic. The lung, subjected to a great increase in blood flow and possibly to an increase in venous pressure as a result of the congenital septal defect, develops oedema which impairs the exchange of oxygen and threatens life. In these circumstances the removal of the shunt is life-saving and the necessity for surgery is obvious, provided the appropriate technique is available at a risk which is less than that of the disease itself.

At this early time of life, the muscular pulmonary arteries have not developed the severer grades of hypertensive pulmonary vascular disease which complicates the natural history of the disease after infancy. The rate of evolution of severe hypertensive pulmonary vascular disease varies according to the congenital anomaly. It is slow in atrial septal defect (p. 321) and may not appear until late in life. It is faster in ventricular septal defect (p. 310) where dilatation lesions have been found from the age of two years. It is even faster in transposition of the great vessels associated with a post-tricuspid shunt (p. 324) under which circumstances dilatation lesions have been described as early as one year of age.

After infancy, therefore, the objective of surgery is not only the immediate relief of respiratory or cardiac distress due to a large pulmonary blood flow but also the prevention of the development of severe hypertensive pulmonary vascular disease. In addition, the severity of hypertensive pulmonary vascular disease has an influence on the risks of operation. We have, therefore, to consider three aspects: the risks of operation, the immediate results of surgical correction and the long-term changes which occur in the pulmonary circulation after surgery.

Influence of Hypertensive Pulmonary Vascular Disease on Surgical Mortality

Grosse-Brockhoff and Loogen[1] have presented figures from a series of 281 patients operated on for a ventricular septal defect. When the pulmonary vascular resistance was less than 200 $\text{dyn} \cdot \text{s} \cdot \text{cm}^{-5}$, the mortality was 1·3 per cent; between 201 and 800 $\text{dyn} \cdot \text{s} \cdot \text{cm}^{-5}$ the mortality was 10·0 per cent; over 800 $\text{dyn} \cdot \text{s} \cdot \text{cm}^{-5}$ the mortality was 32 per cent. Rahimtoola and his colleagues[2] reported a similarly high mortality in patients operated on for an atrial septal defect who had a high pulmonary vascular resistance. They divided a group of 55 patients with a systolic pulmonary arterial pressure greater than 60 mmHg into two groups according to whether the pulmonary vascular resistance was greater or less than 640 dyn · s · cm^{-5}. Of the 35 with a resistance less than 640 dyn · s · cm^{-5} there were 3 deaths in hospital. Of the 20 with a resistance more than 640 dyn · s · cm^{-5} there were 10 deaths in hospital. All those of the higher resistance group who survived the operation were left with disability, while the majority of the survivors of the low-resistance group were free from symptoms.

Such immediate surgical risks have to be weighed against the natural history of severe hypertensive pulmonary vascular disease. Morch[3] reviewed 19 patients who had been followed since early childhood with a ventricular septal defect, a systolic pulmonary arterial pressure within 10 mmHg of the systolic systemic arterial pressure and evidence of some right to left shunt. Seven of these patients had died at an average age of 29 years. Twelve were still living with an average age of 32 years. Admittedly many of the patients were short of breath, some severely so. Nevertheless, in the light of such figures, the immediate risks of surgery in these patients are not justifiable and this has been the generally accepted view.

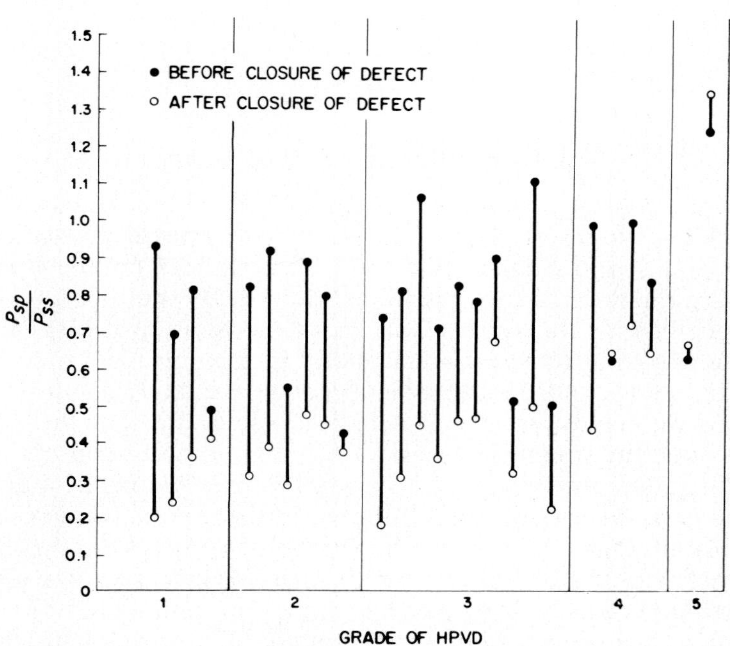

Fig. 20.1 The relation between the grade of hypertensive pulmonary vascular disease (HPVD) and the ratio of the systolic blood pressure in the lesser circulation to that in the systemic circulation (P_{SP}/P_{SS}) before and after closure of a ventricular septal defect in 26 patients.

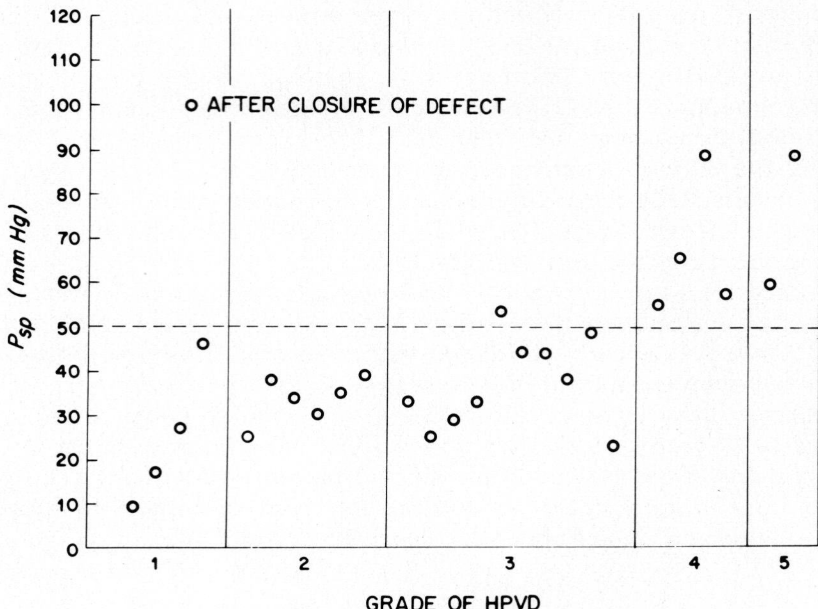

Fig. 20.2 The relation between the grade of hypertensive pulmonary vascular disease (HPVD) and the residual systolic blood pressure in the lesser circulation (P_{SP}) following closure of a ventricular septal defect in 26 patients.

The Immediate Effects of Surgery

Simultaneous changes in pulmonary blood flow and systemic blood pressure make it difficult to interpret changes in pulmonary arterial pressure which occur after closure of a septal defect while the patient is still on the operating table. However, using the ratio of the systolic pressure in the pulmonary artery (P_{SP}) to the systolic pressure in the systemic arteries (P_{SS}) as an index, there is a relation between the grade of histological abnormality in the small pulmonary arteries, as defined in Chapter 16, and the immediate change in pulmonary arterial pressure.[4]

In patients with ventricular septal defect, it was found that the ratio $P_{SP/SS}$ fell substantially when the grade of hypertensive pulmonary vascular disease was 1 to 3 (Fig. 20.1). The immediate post-operative systolic pressure in the pulmonary artery was, with one exception, less than 50 mmHg in these patients (Fig. 20.2). This is thought to indicate that, when medial hypertrophy alone (grade 1) or in association with intimal proliferation of a cellular (grade 2) or fibrous (grade 3) nature is present, the pulmonary hypertension is associated with a high pulmonary blood flow and is largely reversible as a result mainly of elimination of a large left-to-right shunt. In cases with hypertensive pulmonary vascular disease of grade 5 severity the ratio P_{SP}/P_{SS} did not fall and the residual systolic blood pressure in the pulmonary circulation exceeded 50 mmHg (Fig. 20.2). This suggests that, when severe generalized vascular occlusion, with dilation and localized 'dilatation lesions' proximal to the obstructed arterial segments, is present, the pulmonary hypertension is mainly of an organic basis and irreversible, at least immediately after closure of the septal defect. In 3 of 4 cases with grade 4 hypertensive pulmonary vascular disease the ratio P_{SP}/P_{SS} fell. This suggests that an increased pulmonary blood flow is still of some importance even in some patients with grade 4 lesions when dilatation lesions are seen in addition to widespread vascular occlusion. However, all four has a residual systolic pulmonary arterial pressure exceeding 50 mmHg. Hence the onset of grade 4 hypertensive pulmonary vascular disease marks the important transition from the stage when the pulmonary arterial pressure falls immediately after closure of the defect to the stage when it does not.

Similar findings were obtained in patients with atrial septal defect. In two of the three cases with grade 1 or 2 hypertensive pulmonary vascular disease, the residual systolic blood pressure after closure fell below 50 mmHg but in the two cases with grade 5 changes, the level of systolic blood pressure in the pulmonary artery after operation exceeded 50 mmHg.

The Long Term Effects of Surgery

Figure 20.3 shows the changes which occurred in the total pulmonary vascular resistance in patients studied for periods of time up to four years after the closure of an atrial septal defect.[5,6] The mean age of these patients was 34 years with a

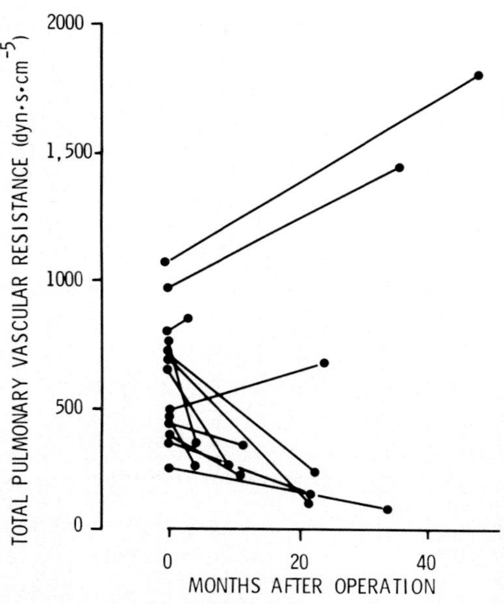

Fig. 20.3 Total pulmonary vascular resistance before and after closure of atrial septal defects. Mean age at operation, 33·7 years (range 6–48 years). Data from Reeve *et al.*[5] and Beck *et al.*[6]

range of 6–48 years. The three patients who had a resistance higher than 750 $dyn \cdot s \cdot cm^{-5}$ before the operation showed an increase in resistance after closure of the defect. All except one of the rest showed a fall in resistance. It is of interest that, in those patients in whom the resistance fell, it achieved a level which was within the normal range. These figures suggest that the hypertensive pulmonary vascular disease recovers completely if it is in its early stages, while, if it is in its late stages, it continues to progress.

Similar data for ventricular septal defect have been given by Dushane.[7] Figure 20.4 shows his results in 36 patients on whom an operation was carried out after the age of two and a half years for ventricular septal defect and pulmonary hypertension. Most of these patients were children and the value for the total pulmonary vascular resistance is given in terms of body surface area. In all except one there was a fall in the ratio of pulmonary arterial to systemic arterial pressure during the operation. However, taking the paired observations during the haemodynamic investigations before and after the operation, there is no significant difference. Inspection of Figure 20.4 shows that the pulmonary vascular resistance has increased substantially in some patients and decreased substantially in others. In general, those patients who have developed a high resistance are those who have become dyspnoeic. Those patients who develop symptoms stand out as a distinctive group with respect to their final pulmonary vascular resistance ($P = 6 \times 10^{-8}$) but are indistinguishable from the rest from the point of view of their initial resistance ($P = 0{\cdot}95$). It is clearly impossible to set any practical upper limit for the pulmonary vascular resistance below which an operation is likely to be advantageous and above which it should not be performed.

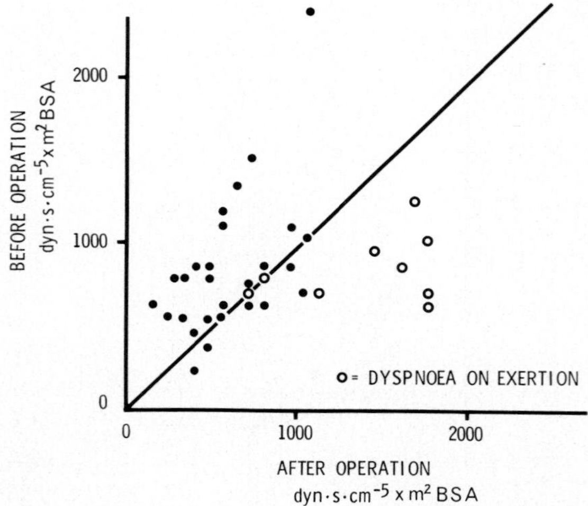

Fig. 20.4 Total pulmonary vascular resistance (/m^2 BSA) before and after closure of ventricular septal defects associated with pulmonary hypertension in patients over the age of two years. Mean age at operation, 8·0 years (range 2·5–35 years). Data from Dushane.[7]

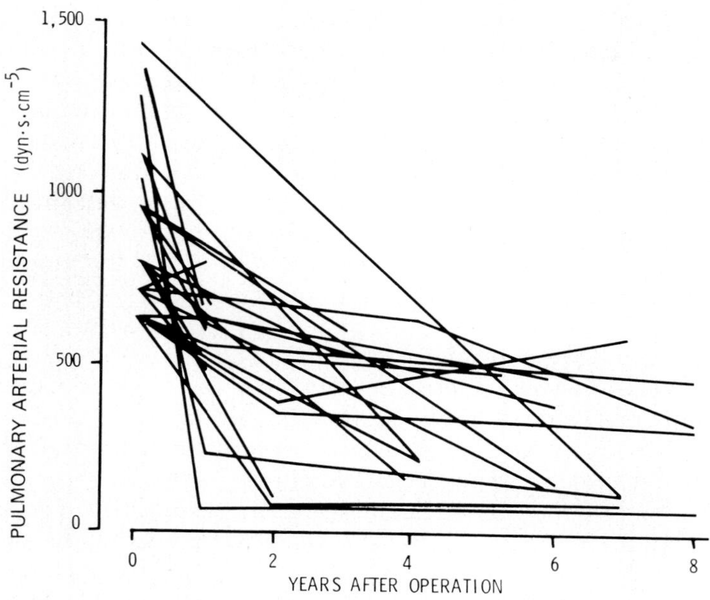

Fig. 20.5 Pulmonary arterial resistance before and after closure of ventricular septal defects associated with pulmonary hypertension in children. Mean age at operation, 7·2 years (range 3–12 years). Data from Hallidie-Smith *et al.*[8]

The results of a similar study reported by Hallidie-Smith and her colleagues[8] were more optimistic (Fig. 20.5) and all except one of 25 patients showed a decrease in pulmonary arterial resistance after operation.

Such data underline the great practical difficulties which are often involved in deciding whether or not to advise an operation in these patients. Patients with a systolic pulmonary arterial pressure equal to the systolic systemic arterial pressure and with cyanosis should clearly not be advised surgery. Those with a large pulmonary blood flow and low pulmonary vascular resistance equally clearly should be advised to have an operation. It is in the group of patients between these two extremes that the dilemma occurs.

The clinician has to weigh on one hand the possibility that an operation will prevent the development of fatal hypertensive pulmonary vascular disease, and on the other hand the possibility that the closure of the defect will deprive the right ventricle of an escape mechanism should severe hypertensive disease occur. In coming to a decision we believe that the clinical, electrocardiographic and radiological evidence needs to be taken carefully into account and that action should not be taken on haemodynamic data alone. It is of interest, for instance, that a third heart sound and mid-diastolic murmur was heard in all the patients reported by Hallidie-Smith and her colleagues.[8] The clinician should not accept uncritically the numbers that come from the haemodynamic laboratory. In particular, measurements of flow are liable to great error. Using the Fick method, the measurement of the oxygen uptake is often faulty and difficult to carry out in children. Even if this is avoided by using the pulmonary : systemic ratio of flow, the errors of blood-sampling can still be enormous. The use of vena caval samples for the estimation of the mixed venous blood is full of imponderables. The existence of streaming in the pulmonary artery, particularly in the presence of a post-tricuspid shunt, renders the measurement of mixed pulmonary arterial blood inaccurate. At the same time, the small arterio-venous difference in oxygen content across the lungs magnifies the effects of such inaccuracies on the subsequent calculations.

Vogel *et al.*[9] suggest that the use of tolazoline in patients with a ventricular septal defect and pulmonary hypertension may distinguish between those who will benefit from surgery and those who will not. They find that, when an injection of tolazoline causes a fall in the total pulmonary vascular resistance, surgical closure of the defect also leads to a reduction in the total pulmonary vascular resistance. Conversely when tolazoline has no effect, surgery is also ineffective.

One factor of great importance in deciding on the advisability of surgery is the age of the patient. Dilatation lesions have not been observed below the age of two years in simple ventricular septal defects (Chap. 21, p. 311). Dushane *et al.*[10] report that, in children below the age of two, surgical correction was always followed by a fall in the total pulmonary vascular resistance. There is, therefore, a strong argument in favour of closing all large ventricular septal defects before that age.

The fact that, in some patients, the pulmonary vascular resistance increases to high levels after surgery implies strongly that hypertensive vascular disease is progressing autonomously despite correction of the cardiac defect. There is, however, as yet no histological proof that this is so. In dogs, hypertensive pulmonary vascular disease has been produced by forming a fistula between the aorta and a pulmonary artery and increasing the local pulmonary blood flow by a combination of proximal constriction of the pulmonary artery and removal of one lobe of the lung.[11] When the anastomosis was subsequently closed and the constriction removed from the pulmonary artery, the pressure perfusing the affected lobe could be returned to normal. Under these circumstances it was observed that a histological regression of the hypertensive pulmonary vascular disease occurred in the first three grades. On the other hand, when the process had reached grade 4 or beyond, no regression occurred.

REFERENCES

1. Grosse-Brockhoff, F. & Loogen, F. (1968) *Circulation*, **37–38**, Suppl. V, 13.
2. Rahimtoola, S. H., Kirklin, J. W. & Burchell, H. B. (1968) *Circulation*, **37–38**, Suppl. V, 2.
3. Morch, J. E. (1971) In *The Natural History and Prognosis in Treatment of Congenital Heart Defects*, ed. Langford-Kidd, B. S. & Keith, J. D. page 26. Thomas.
4. Heath, D., Helmholz, H. F., Jn., Burchell, H. B., Dushane, J. W. & Edwards, J. E. (1958) *Circulation*, **43**, 1167.
5. Reeve, R., Selzer, A., Popper, R. W., Leeds, R. F. & Gerbode, F. (1966) *Circulation*, **33–34**, Suppl. I, 107.
6. Beck, W., Swan, H. J. C., Burchell, H. B. & Kirklin, J. W. (1960) *Circulation*, **22**, 938.

7. Dushane, J. W. (1971) In *The Natural History and Prognosis in Treatment of Congenital Heart Defects*, ed. Langford-Kidd, B. S. & Keith, J. D. page 14. Thomas.
8. Hallidie-Smith, K. A., Hollman, A., Cleland, W. P., Bentall, H. H. & Goodwin, J. F. (1969) *Brit. Heart J.*, **31**, 246.
9. Vogel, J. H. K., Grover, R. F., Jamieson, G. & Blount, S. G., Jn. (1974) *Adv. Cardiol.*, **11**, 108.
10. Dushane, J. W., Weidman, W. H. & Ritter, D. G. (1972) *Birth Defects*, **8**, 63.
11. Glass, B. A., Geer, J. C. & Albert, H. M. (1965) *Ann. Thoracic Surg.*, **1**, 159.

21. The Influence of Hypertensive Pulmonary Vascular Disease on the Natural History of Patients with Congenital Cardiac Shunts

The occurrence and degree of hypertensive pulmonary vascular disease influences the natural history of patients with congenital shunts. In doing so, it has an important bearing on the development of clinical signs and haemodynamic changes and needs to be taken carefully into account in assessing the correct clinical management. In this chapter we shall be considering the influence of hypertensive pulmonary vascular disease and its clinical implications in a number of varieties of congenital cardiac abnormalities.

VENTRICULAR SEPTAL DEFECT

This lesion, the commonest of all congenital cardiac defects, may be taken as the prototype of the post-tricuspid shunt (p. 227).

Factors Determining the Shunt

The immediate factors which determine the size of the shunt are the size of the defect and the difference in pressure between the left and right ventricles during systole. In the absence of any other abnormality the difference in pressure between the two ventricles during systole will be determined by the relation between the input impedances of the systemic and pulmonary arterial circulations. Since the major components of these impedances are the resistance values (input impedance at zero frequency, p. 143) the resistances of the two circuits may, for practical purposes, be taken as the factors which, together with the size of the defect, control the magnitude of the shunt. The haemodynamics may be further complicated by stenosis of the pulmonary valve or the outflow-tract of the right ventricle or by obstruction to the outflow of blood from the left ventricle. A stenosis at, or below, the pulmonary valve will add a resistance in series to that of the pulmonary circulation and thus reduce the left-to-right shunt. An obstruction to the outflow of blood from the left ventricle will add a resistance in series to that of the systemic circulation and thus increase the left-to-right shunt. For the present purposes we shall consider the condition in which the two outflow-tracts are initially normal, and, since the haemodynamic effects of small defects are unimportant, we shall confine ourselves to the large ones.

Natural History in Early Infancy

In foetal life, there is little difference in the resistance of the two circuits which are, in any case, connected by the ductus arteriosus (Chap. 14, p. 222). It seems unlikely, therefore, that any substantial shunt occurs across the ventricular septal defect *in utero*. Following birth there is normally a rapid fall in the pulmonary vascular resistance followed by a more delayed decrease over the succeeding two or three weeks (Chap. 14, p. 223). There is evidence[1] that the fall in pulmonary vascular resistance is delayed in infants with a large ventricular septal defect. As it takes place, however, the left-to-right shunt increases. Thus the pulmonary blood flow and the output of the left ventricle increase.

This sequence of events is probably the reason why such infants do not usually develop symptoms in the first four weeks of life.[1] By that time, however, the magnitude of the shunt has reached such proportions that pulmonary oedema is liable to develop. There are three reasons for this. The greatly increased pulmonary blood flow may itself cause an increased transudation of liquid through the walls of the pulmonary arterioles and muscular pulmonary arteries (Chap. 24). In addition, the left ventricle may fail, leading to a raised left atrial pressure.[1,2] Under these circumstances the syndrome of congestive cardiac failure is liable to occur, with the retention of water and sodium ions by the kidneys and the expansion of the extra-cellular space. To these factors may be added the susceptibility of the oedematous lung to air-borne infection.

Clinical Features of the Phase of Greatly Increased Pulmonary Blood Flow

The dominating symptom is of dyspnoea with the secondary difficulties which this imposes on feeding. The front of the chest develops a bulge (Fig. 21.1) possibly due in part to the high end-expiratory volume of the congested and rigid lung (Chap. 25). There is a vigorous beat caused by the over-active left ventricle. The defect gives rise to a systolic murmur and there is often a third sound and mid-diastolic murmur due to the torrential flow through the mitral valve. With congestive failure the liver enlarges. The chest radiograph shows a large heart with plethoric and oedematous lungs.

Subsequent Natural History

Some infants are so severely affected at this stage as to require an operation (see below, p. 316). Others respond to digitalis and diuretics. However, during the succeeding months many infants recover spontaneously and the symptoms regress. There are three distinct reasons why this improvement may happen, concerning the septal defect, the outflow tract of the right ventricle and the pulmonary vasculature. In a certain number of infants the septal defect will close[1,3,4] either by apposition of the septal cusp of the tricuspid valve[2] or by fibrous or muscular overgrowth.[5] Even if closure is not complete, a decrease in the size of the orifice may occur[1] or the orifice may remain unchanged while the rest of the heart and body

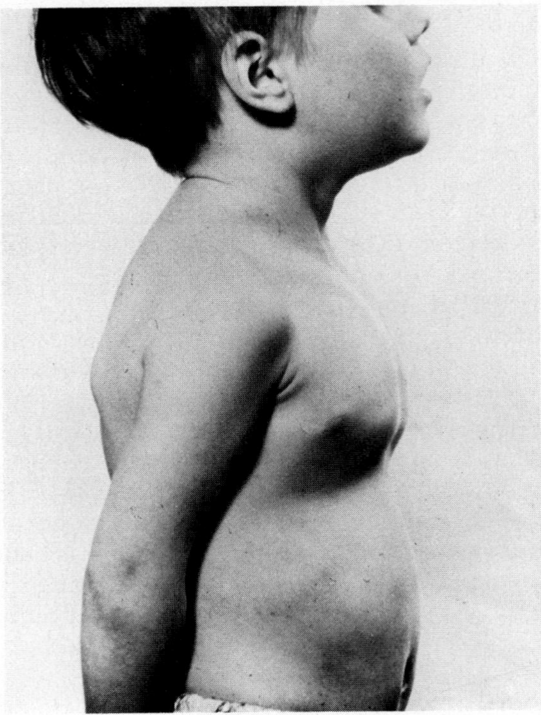

Fig. 21.1 Bulged chest of child due to an increased pulmonary blood flow during infancy.

grow so that the shunt becomes less relative to the cardiac output. In a proportion of cases a stenosis develops in the outflow tract of the right ventricle below the pulmonary valve.[4,6] This raises the resistance to outflow from the right ventricle and diminishes the shunt. Finally, in a group of patients, the pulmonary vascular resistance may increase and thus reduce the pulmonary blood flow.

The Rôle of Hypertensive Pulmonary Vascular Disease

Evidence for the rôle of hypertensive pulmonary vascular disease in the natural history of patients with a large ventricular septal defect comes both from serial physiological[1,4,7-11] and morbid anatomical studies.[12-14] Changes in the muscular pulmonary arteries and their resistance affect the course of events at two stages. In the presence of a large ventricular septal defect, they delay the decrease in pulmonary vascular resistance[1] and medial musculature of the muscular pulmonary arteries[12] which normally occurs after birth (Fig. 21.2). At a later stage they can give rise to a progressive rise in pulmonary vascular resistance[1,4,7] which accompanies a progression through the grades of hypertensive pulmonary vascular disease discussed in Chapter 16.[12-14] It is this latter phase which helps reduce the pulmonary blood flow after the first six months of life. Thus, in these patients, the muscular pulmonary arteries are subjected to two opposing influences during the first year of life. There is the natural involutionary process which, during the first weeks of life, reduces both the resistance and the bulk of medial muscle, possibly owing to the effects of alveolar oxygen tension (Chap. 14, p. 223). Opposing this is the stimulus to an increased resistance and an increased bulk of medial muscle which derives in some not well understood fashion from a raised pulmonary blood flow (Chap. 18, p. 275). This latter influence at first delays the process of normal involution and then operates gradually to reduce the pulmonary blood flow.

The second course of events at first helps reduce the pulmonary blood flow from the dangerous levels which it has reached in the first few months after birth and subsequently may progress so to restrict the pulmonary blood flow as to be incompatible with life. Thus a process which is initially life-saving becomes eventually life-threatening. The progress of the pathological changes of hypertensive pulmonary vascular disease under these circumstances takes place over several years. Among a group of subjects with a ventricular septal defect, the youngest age at which Wagenvoort and his colleagues[12] found dilatation lesions at necropsy was two and a half years. Such considerations may be important when considering the time for surgery (p. 306) since, before the age of two years, one can be reasonably certain that the hypertensive pulmonary vascular disease has not reached an irreversible stage.

Clinical Features After Infancy

Those children who were born with a small ventricular septal defect or those in whom the defect has become smaller will have no symptoms. In a certain number an increased pulmonary blood flow will persist, causing dyspnoea on exertion and

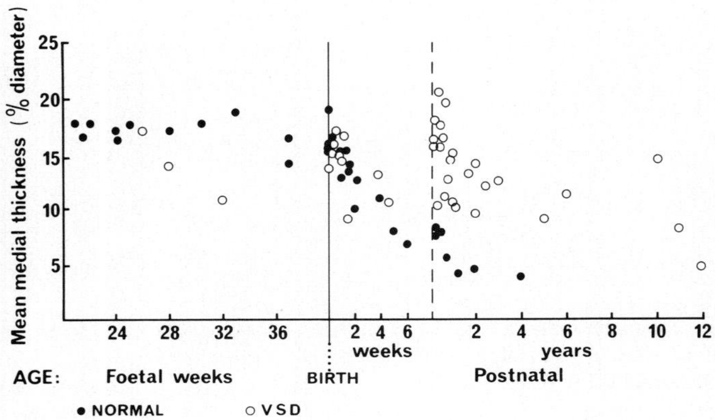

Fig. 21.2 Diagram re-drawn from Wagenvoort *et al.*[12] to show the effects of a ventricular sep defect on the involution of the media of the muscular pulmonary arteries after birth.

a susceptibility to respiratory infections.[15] To the systolic murmur of the septal defect will be added a mid-diastolic murmur at the apex indicating an increased flow through the mitral valve (Fig. 21.3). The chest radiograph will show cardiac enlargement with some dilatation of the pulmonary arteries extending into the periphery of the lungs (Fig. 21.4).

With an increasing severity of hypertensive pulmonary vascular disease, the pulmonary vascular resistance comes to equal and then exceeds the systemic vascular resistance. Thus the shunt becomes reversed and cyanosis appears. In patients with a post-tricuspid defect such a state of affairs will usually have developed before the end of the second decade.

The dominant complaint is one of breathlessness on exertion.[15,16] Haemoptysis occurs in about a third of the patients with this syndrome and is found most commonly with advancing age and the development of grade 4 hypertensive vascular disease. Most haemoptyses are probably arterial in origin, arising from rupture of

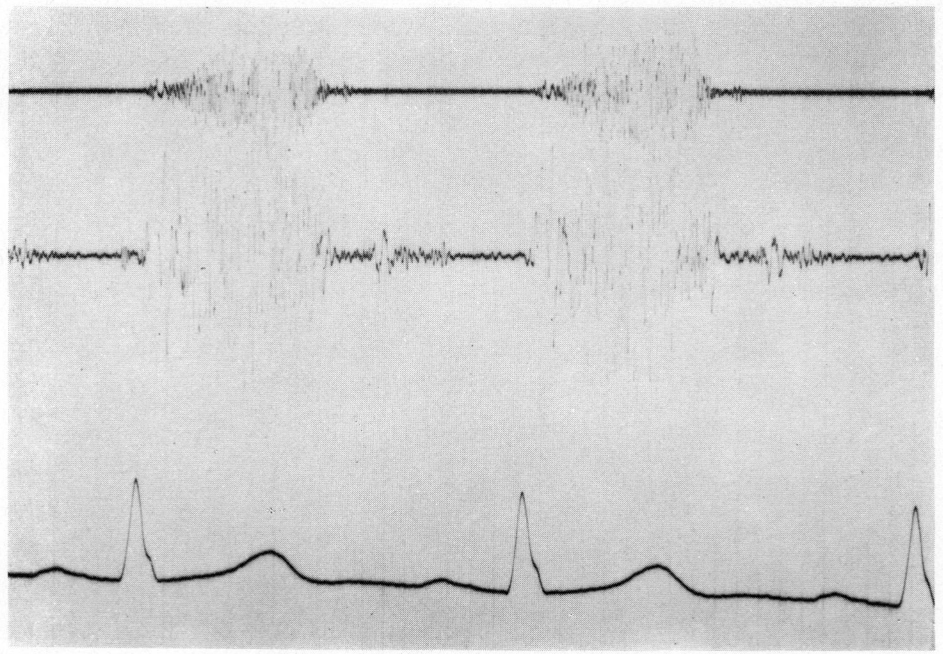

Fig. 21.3 Phonocardiogram from a boy of eight years with a ventricular septal defect and high pulmonary blood flow. The upper tracing is from the pulmonary area and shows a murmur throughout systole. The middle tracing is from the mitral area and shows, in addition, a third heart sound followed by a mid-diastolic murmur due to the increased flow through the mitral valve. The bottom tracing is the electrocardiogram. The vertical lines are at 0·04 s. Pulmonary arterial pressure, 52/14 mmHg; wedge pressure, 12 mmHg. Pulmonary blood flow, $11{\cdot}2\ \mathrm{l \cdot min^{-1}}$; systemic blood flow, $3{\cdot}8\ \mathrm{l \cdot min^{-1}}$.

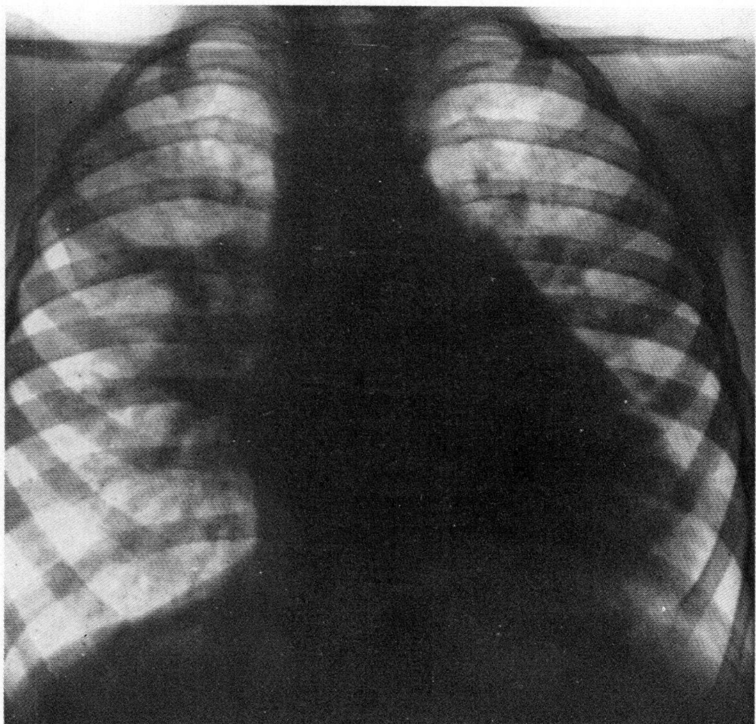

Fig. 21.4 Chest radiograph of a boy aged two years with a ventricular septal defect and a high pulmonary blood flow. Pulmonary arterial pressure, 60/15 (30) mmHg; wedge pressure, 10 mmHg. Pulmonary blood flow, $7{\cdot}2\ l \cdot min^{-1}$; systemic blood flow, $2{\cdot}2\ l \cdot min^{-1}$.

the aneurysmal dilatations of thin-walled branches of muscular pulmonary arteries described in Chap. 16. Rarely, a left recurrent laryngeal palsy, producing hoarseness and aphonia, may be caused by pressure from a greatly dilated pulmonary artery. Occasionally there is a complaint of pain in the chest on effort. The pain is situated beneath the front of the chest and is described in the same terms as the pain of myocardial ischaemia, often being referred to as a 'tightness'. It does not spread into the arms or the neck, however, and it is said that glyceryl trinitrate fails to give relief.[17] It is always accompanied by dyspnoea and disappears soon after resting. Some authors have thought that this pain is due to ischaemia of the right ventricle.[18] Others have suggested that it arises from the pulmonary artery.[17]

Syncope may also occasionally accompany effort in patients with the severest degrees of pulmonary vascular disease.[19–21] This symptom is more common in patients with primary pulmonary hypertension who have no abnormal communications. Syncope may sometimes be due to paroxysmal tachycardia.[22]

The reversal of the shunt causes cyanosis and, if this is severe, it is accompanied

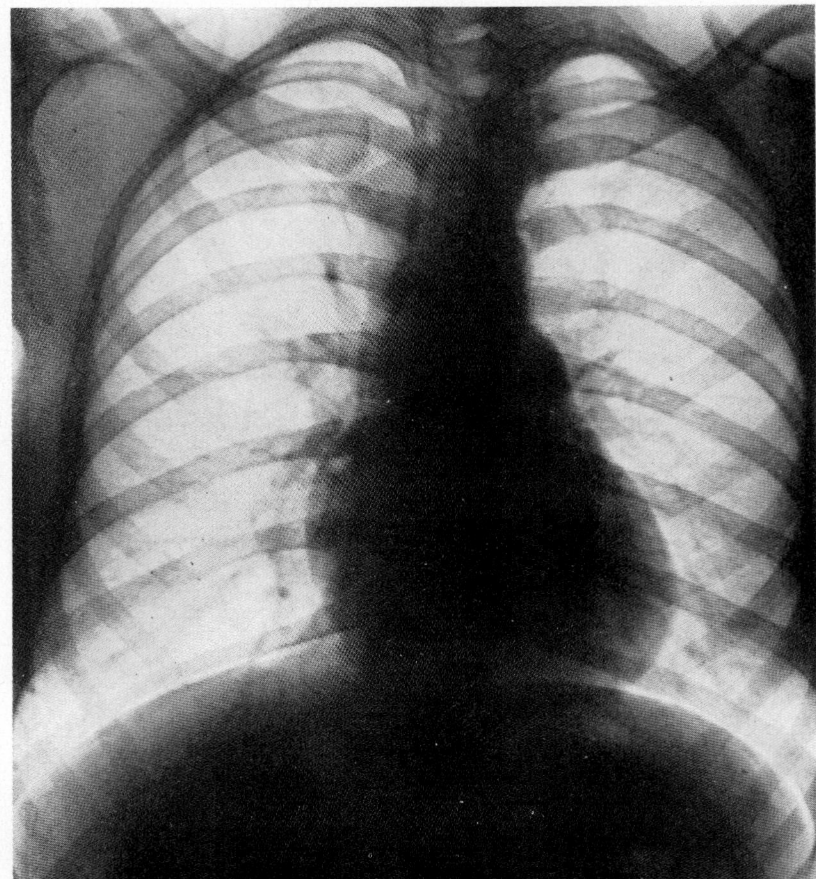

Fig. 21.5 Chest radiograph of a girl of 15 years with a ventricular septal defect and pulmonary hypertension (130/70 mmHg). Cyanosis and dyspnoea had developed at the age of nine years. The clarity of the periphery of the lung fields may be contrasted with the appearance in Figure 21.4.

by clubbing. There is hypertrophy of the right ventricle which causes a systolic lift to the left of the sternum. A prominent atrial wave in the jugular venous pulse may also be evidence of right ventricular hypertrophy. The second sound in the pulmonary area is often palpable. The high pulmonary arterial pressure causes the pulmonary valve to close earlier than it would normally. This leads to a decrease in the separation of the two components of the second sound which may sound single. When the two components can be heard separately, the pulmonary is louder than the aortic. The systolic murmur of the defect disappears. The mid-diastolic murmur, which is present when there is an increased flow through the mitral valve, also disappears as the pulmonary blood flow diminishes. A murmur of pulmonary incompetence may develop.

The electrocardiogram shows evidence of increasing right ventricular hypertrophy. Radiologically, there is enlargement of the pulmonary trunk and its main and lobar branches but diminution in the size of the peripheral arteries. The increase in size of the pulmonary trunk and its main branches tends to be less than that found in atrial septal defect[23] (compare Figs 21.5 and 21.10) and these vessels may be within normal limits. The existence of pulmonary hypertension from early in life in such patients prevents the involution of elastic tissue which normally occurs in elastic pulmonary arteries during the first year of life (Chap. 17, p. 267) and their extensibility remains low (Chap. 18, p. 282). This may explain why these vessels are not in general so enlarged as those of patients with atrial septal defect (p. 321) in whom pulmonary hypertension occurs later in life and at a time when the extensibility of the elastic pulmonary arteries has achieved normal adult proportions.

The management of such patients is purely supportive, cardiac failure being treated with conventional therapy when it occurs. The particular risk of pregnancy in these patients should be noted. Morgan-Jones and Howitt[24] found a mortality of 27 per cent in a group of patients with reversed shunt due to hypertensive pulmonary vascular disease, death occurring most often just after labour.

Relative Importance of the Different Factors Determining the Natural History

At this point we need to consider the relative importance and frequency of the various factors which have been shown to influence the natural history of patients with a ventricular septal defect. In his survey of 1500 cases of isolated ventricular septal defect of all sizes Keith[25] comes to the following conclusions. Some 20 to 25 per cent of all defects will eventually close spontaneously, while 50 per cent of patients will be left with a small defect. Five per cent will develop infundibular stenosis, 5 per cent will die in childhood and 5 per cent will ultimately die from the effects of advanced hypertensive pulmonary vascular disease. These figures take into account the entire range of size of defect.

It will be recalled (Chap. 17, p. 267) that patients dying with severe hypertensive vascular disease from a large ventricular septal defect show a pattern of elastic tissue in the pulmonary trunk which is similar to that found in the foetus. The reason for this is believed to be the maintenance of a high pulmonary arterial pressure from the time of birth which prevents the normal involution of the elastic tissue in the elastic pulmonary arteries. Such an explanation is not incompatible with the natural history which has just been outlined. It does presuppose, however, that in these severely affected cases there is little fall in the pulmonary arterial pressure at any time. It is possible that such cases may not present to the physician in infancy and that they will not be revealed by the serial prospective studies which have just been reviewed. Somerville[26] carried out a retrospective study of 65 patients with reversal of shunt due to a high pulmonary vascular resistance aged from six to twenty-four years. She found that in only 7 per cent was there a history of thriving problems in infancy and only 5 per cent showed the bulged chest characteristic of a phase of greatly increased pulmonary blood flow during infancy. Such observations suggest that many or most of these patients may follow a natural history rather different from that described above and do not come under the care of the physician during infancy. Possibly they represent the extreme of a spectrum in which the pulmonary vascular resistance falls little if at all at any stage of life.

Surgical Management

According to the stage in the natural history of the disease, the surgical management of these patients is directed to the immediate relief of a torrential pulmonary blood flow or the longer term prevention of the progression of hypertensive pulmonary vascular disease. Relief of the increased pulmonary blood flow in infancy may be effected either by banding the pulmonary trunk or by closing the ventricular septal defect. The operation of banding the pulmonary trunk has been widely used. The theoretical basis for it was suggested by Civin and Edwards[27] who observed that a naturally occurring pulmonary stenosis protected the pulmonary vasculature from hypertensive pulmonary vascular disease in patients with a large ventricular septal defect. Muller and Damman[28] first reported on the operation and later showed[29] that it was effective in protecting the pulmonary blood vessels against the effects of pulmonary arterial hypertension. A certain degree of regression of abnormalities may even be observed.[29] A number of authors have now confirmed the protective effect of the operation.[30-33]

Although life-saving, the operation is only palliative and a further operation is required, usually after the age of two years, in which the band is removed and the defect closed.[32,34-36] In the meantime, the orifice created by the constriction fails to grow with the heart and the stenosis becomes, therefore, relatively more severe as time goes on. In addition, a hypertrophy and stenosis may develop in the infundibulum of the right ventricle.[35] Both these factors will diminish further the pulmonary blood flow and may eventually cause a reversal of the shunt. In a small proportion of cases a spontaneous closure of the ventricular septal defect will occur.[36-39] Removal of the band will nevertheless still be necessary.

In the largest series so far reported,[33] the remarkably low mortality of 3 per cent was achieved in the preliminary banding procedure. To this, however, has to be added, during the second stage operation, a mortality of 28 per cent (Ref. 36) the magnitude of which was in part due to the large proportion of children requiring banding who had multiple septal defects which were difficult to repair.

The alternative surgical approach is to carry out a corrective closure of the defect in one stage.[40-43] Opinions differ concerning the relative merits of the two approaches. Kirklin[44] has argued the case for primary repair of the defect and it seems likely that, as surgical techniques advance, this will become more and more the operation of choice. For the moment, however, banding is regarded as the best treatment for infants in pulmonary oedema under the age of six months in many centres. After this age the indication for primary repair becomes progressively stronger.

In the older child, the indication for operation is usually taken as a pulmonary blood flow which is twice the systemic. By the time the pulmonary blood flow has been reduced to the magnitude of the systemic, the pulmonary vascular disease has entered on a course which is autonomously progressive whatever is done to the cardiac defect and operation is, therefore, contraindicated (p. 301). There remains a group of patients who lie between these opposing indications for and against surgery and in whom it is difficult to decide what is for the best.

PATENT DUCTUS ARTERIOSUS

A persistently patent ductus arteriosus is another cause of a post-tricuspid shunt. In full-term infants it is seldom large enough to give rise to symptoms. In premature infants, however, physiological closure of the ductus is often delayed and may be associated with respiratory symptoms.[45] Apart from this the presence of symptoms usually suggests the presence of other lesions such as ventricular septal defect,

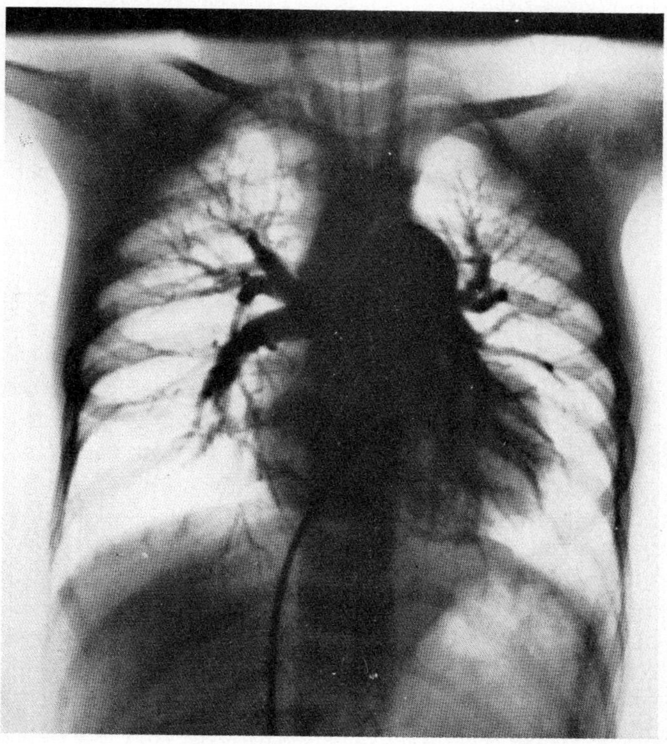

Fig. 21.6 Pulmonary arteriogram of a boy aged four years with a ventricular septal defect and patent ductus arteriosus and reversed shunt. The narrowness of the peripheral branches of the pulmonary artery contrasts with the dilatation of its main branches. Pulmonary arterial pressure, 90/60 mmHg; wedge pressure, 4 mmHg. Pulmonary blood flow, 1·6 $l \cdot min^{-1}$; systemic flow, 3·2 $l \cdot min^{-1}$.

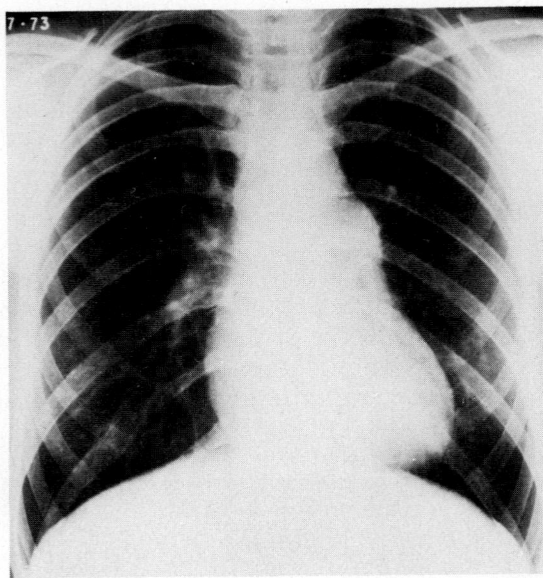

Fig. 21.7 Chest radiograph of female patient of 43 years with a patent ductus arteriosus and pulmonary hypertension causing a reversal of shunt. The cardiac size is not abnormally large. The diameter of the aortic arch is increased. The pulmonary trunk is greatly enlarged and there is calcification in its wall. The right pulmonary artery is moderately enlarged. The peripheral vessels are small.

coarctation or aortic stenosis which act to increase the left-to-right shunt or embarrass the left ventricle.[46,47] The effects are then similar to those described in infants with a large ventricular septal defect. If surgical treatment is necessary, the ligation of the ductus will probably need to be accompanied by banding of the pulmonary artery in the presence of a ventricular septal defect or by the resection of a coarctation.

A certain number of patients with a large patent ductus will develop progressive hypertensive pulmonary vascular disease.[48] Such patients will present with dyspnoea, haemoptysis and cyanosis. The dyspnoea has been said to be somewhat less severe in patients whose pulmonary hypertension is caused by a patent ductus.[49] This has been attributed to the systemic distribution of the shunt which maintains a relatively normal oxygen tension in the blood which is supplied to the chemoreceptors of the head and neck, the unsaturated blood passing down the descending aorta.[49]

On physical examination they have the signs of severe pulmonary hypertension: a prominent venous '*a*'-wave, a systolic lift over the right ventricular outflow tract, and a loud second sound due to the pulmonary component. A continuous murmur is not heard, but a murmur of pulmonary incompetence[48] is usual. Cyanosis may be severe enough to cause clubbing and may be restricted to the lower limbs or to the toes and the fingers of the left hand.

The electrocardiogram shows right ventricular hypertrophy. On the chest radiograph the cardiac shadow is often not enlarged.[23] The arch of the aorta is large. The pulmonary trunk is usually considerably enlarged (Figs 21.6 and 21.7) but this extends only to a limited degree into the lobar arteries.[23] The extreme increase in size of the pulmonary trunk in this condition may be due to the vibration caused in its wall by the turbulence of the blood in that area.[50,51] The only moderate enlargement of the lobar arteries is consistent with their having preserved a foetal type of elastic tissue (Chap. 17, p. 267) which renders them relatively indistensible (Chap. 18, p. 282). Calcification may be visible in the ductus.

ATRIAL SEPTAL DEFECT

An uncomplicated atrial septal defect may be taken as the prototype of a pre-tricuspid shunt. In this condition, the factor which determines the relative magnitude of the flow through the pulmonary and systemic circuits is the relative distensibility of the two ventricles during diastole. At birth the ventricles are of equal size[52] so that their distensibilities are not likely to differ greatly. Under these circumstances no great nett flow of blood will occur across the atrial septal defect, which accounts for the fact that this lesion gives no trouble in the new born. However, since the pulmonary arterial pressure falls after birth, the right ventricle has less work to do and does not grow to the same extent as the left ventricle. Its wall becomes relatively thinner and its distensibility greater than that of the left ventricle. Thus a nett flow of blood from left to right will develop between the atria and the pulmonary blood flow will increase. Judging by the electrocardiogram[53] the adult balance between the two ventricles is not normally reached until the early teens, so that the distinction between the two ventricles develops rather more slowly than the distinction between the two sets of peripheral arterial vessels. Perhaps this is due to the relatively greater importance of pulsatile work in the right ventricle, which means that the ratio of right to left ventricular work is greater than the ratio of pulmonary to systemic resistance. In the presence of an atrial septal defect, the right ventricle will remain relatively enlarged by the development of the shunt and volume overload.

Unlike patients with post-tricuspid shunts, patients with an uncomplicated atrial septal defect do not, therefore, present as an urgent clinical problem in infancy. Perhaps for this reason there is little information concerning the pulmonary haemodynamics and structure of the pulmonary blood vessels in this condition during infancy. Information is available, however, on the pulmonary arterial pressure of patients with transposition of the great vessels complicated with only an atrial septal defect[54] (p. 324), in which condition the fall in pulmonary arterial pressure follows the same course as in a normal infant.

When, with an increasing compliance of the right ventricle, the pulmonary blood flow begins to increase, it does so gradually and at a time by which the normal involution of the muscular pulmonary arteries has probably mainly occurred. Another factor which distinguishes the haemodynamic effects of atrial septal defect from those of a post-tricuspid defect is the position of the overloaded ventricle relative to the pulmonary venous return. With a post-tricuspid shunt the blood from the pulmonary circulation returns to the overloaded left ventricle so that the greater the shunt, the higher the left ventricular filling pressure and the higher the pulmonary venous pressure. With an atrial septal defect, however, the pulmonary venous blood drains primarily into the left atrium, from which its subsequent movement is determined by the distensibility of the left ventricle on the one side and by the distensibility of the right ventricle plus the resistance of the septal defect on the other. Thus, should the overloaded right ventricle fail, the pulmonary venous return still has the option of proceeding in the normal fashion through the left ventricle. In this way the pulmonary venous pressure need not be increased and, at the same time, the magnitude of the shunt will be decreased.

Most children and young adults with a simple secundum atrial septal defect have a normal pulmonary arterial pressure.[55] The pulmonary vascular resistance is decreased. There may be some breathlessness on effort but the majority can carry out their normal day's activities with little or no awareness of any restriction. Some give a history of excessive susceptibility of respiratory infection. The increased flow through the outflow tract of the right ventricle and the pulmonary trunk gives rise to a systolic 'ejection' murmur at the left sternal edge and in the pulmonary area (Fig. 21.8). It is not usually of sufficient amplitude to be palpable. There may, in addition, be a soft mid-diastolic murmur, increasing on inspiration, to the left of the base of the sternum due to the increased flow through the tricuspid valve (Fig. 21.8). Characteristically, the two components of the second sound are widely separated (Fig. 21.8), the second component being due to the closure of the pulmonary valve and the first to the closure of the aortic valve. This is attributed to the presence of both a delayed activation and a delayed emptying of the right ventricle. The degree of separation of the two components of the second sound remains fixed throughout the respiratory cycle. In the normal person, the act of inspiration causes a greater fall in left atrial pressure than in right atrial pressure because of the flow of blood into the right atrium from the venae cavae. This causes the volume load on the right ventricle temporarily to exceed that on the left ventricle. The delay in the closure of the pulmonary valve to which this gives rise increases the separation of the two components of the second sound. In the presence of a large atrial septal defect the pressures in the two atria are equilibrated and the differential effect of inspiration on the filling of the ventricles is lost. In some patients a clicking noise occurs early in systole in the pulmonary area at the time when the right ventricle begins to discharge into the pulmonary artery.[56] A similar systolic click can be heard in many patients with a dilated pulmonary trunk or aorta whatever the origin of the enlargement. It is probably caused by the inertia of the increased mass of blood present in the dilated vessel (Chap. 10, p. 139).

The chest radiograph characteristically shows an enlargement of the pulmonary trunk, of the right and left pulmonary arteries, and of their branches far into the

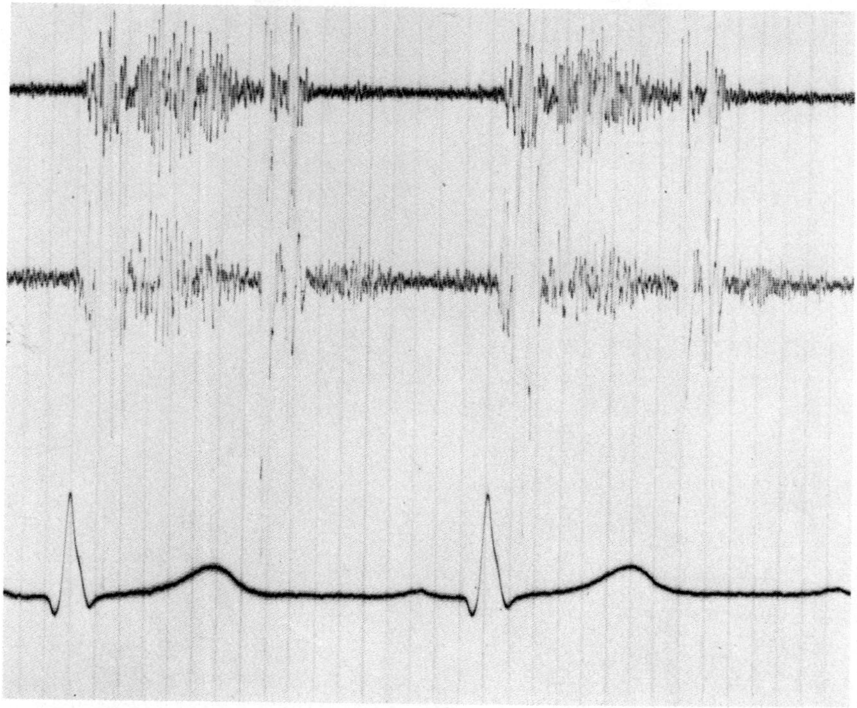

Fig. 21.8 Phonocardiogram from a girl of seven years with an atrial septal defect, a normal pulmonary arterial pressure and a pulmonary blood flow twice the systemic flow. The top tracing is from the pulmonary area. It shows a systolic murmur and a widely split second sound. The middle tracing is from the left sternal border and shows, in addition, a tricuspid flow murmur. The bottom tracing is the electrocardiogram. The vertical lines are at 0·04 s.

periphery of the lungs[57] (Fig. 21.9). Some of these enlarged vessels will be seen end-on as rounded shadows. On screening, a systolic expansile pulsation is usually readily visible in the pulmonary trunk and the two main pulmonary arteries. The electrocardiogram usually shows some degree of right bundle branch block.[58]

A certain number of such patients will eventually develop serious pulmonary hypertension. This is usually delayed until the fourth decade or later,[59,60] but may occasionally occur in childhood or early adult life.[55] When it occurs, it is accompanied by the appearance of the severer grades of hypertensive pulmonary vascular disease (Chap. 16). As the hypertensive pulmonary vascular disease develops, the patient becomes increasingly disabled with dyspnoea and cyanosis appears. Haemoptyses are frequent. The final period is complicated by congestive failure often precipitated by atrial fibrillation. The chest radiograph at this stage will show increasing cardiac enlargement. The pulmonary trunk and its main divisions and lobar arteries may become enormously dilated, while the periphery of the lungs appears avascular[23]

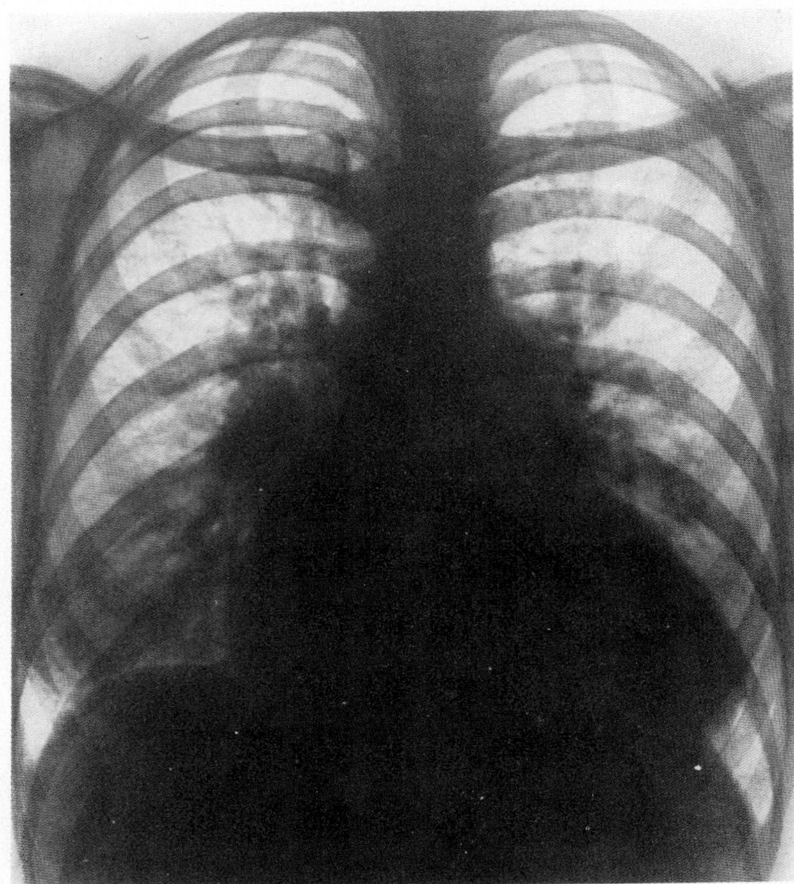

Fig. 21.9 Chest radiograph of a woman of 32 years with an atrial septal defect and a high pulmonary blood flow. Pulmonary arterial pressure, 30/15 (20) mmHg; wedge pressure, 7 mmHg; pulmonary flow, $12{\cdot}0\ \mathrm{l \cdot min^{-1}}$; systemic flow, $3{\cdot}5\ \mathrm{l \cdot min^{-1}}$.

(Fig. 21.10). Thrombosis may occur in the dilated pulmonary arteries. The shadow of the arch of the aorta is characteristically small.

In atrial septal defect, the onset of severe pulmonary hypertension is delayed until the normal involutional changes in the elastic tissue of the elastic pulmonary arteries (Chap. 17, p. 267) have increased their distensibility (Chap. 18, p. 284) and this may explain their often extreme dilatation (Fig. 21.10).

The rôle of surgery in patients with atrial septal defects is the prevention of hypertensive pulmonary vascular disease, since the acute infantile problems associated with post-tricuspid shunts do not occur.

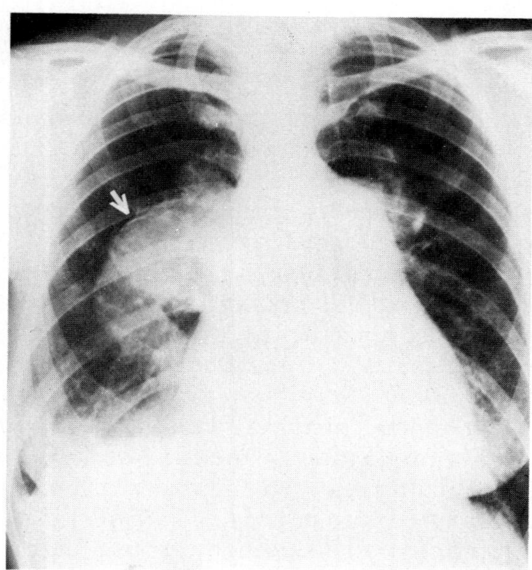

Fig. 21.10 Chest radiograph of female patient of 47 years with an atrial septal defect and pulmonary hypertension causing a reversal of shunt. The heart is enlarged. The diameter of the aortic arch is small. The pulmonary trunk, its primary divisions and lobar branches are greatly dilated. There is calcification in the right pulmonary artery, indicated by the arrow. The peripheral vessels are small. Contrast with Figure 21.9.

TRANSPOSITION OF THE GREAT VESSELS

Although a wide and complex range of abnormal anatomical dispositions is included under this heading, we shall confine our discussion to two distinct groups of patients: those with and those without a complete ventricular septum. In the presence of transposition, the systemic and pulmonary circuits function in parallel instead of in series. The transfer of oxygenated blood from the pulmonary to the systemic circuit and the transfer of under-oxygenated blood from the systemic to the pulmonary circuit depend on the presence of shunts inside the heart or between the great vessels. The magnitude of the shunt has to be the same in each direction otherwise the volume of one circuit would expand indefinitely at the expense of the other. In the absence of a post-tricuspid shunt, the mixing between the two circulations takes place in the atria. In the presence of a ventricular septal defect, mixing occurs in the ventricles with possible additional mixing in the atria.

The magnitude of the bi-directional shunt determines the immediate survival of the patient. Life is impossible in the absence of mixing and inadequate mixing is the major cause of neonatal death. On the other hand the relative magnitude of the pulmonary and systemic flows are, in the presence of transposition, not related to the size of the bi-directional shunt. In this respect, therefore, the haemodynamics of transposition differs fundamentally from that which obtains when the great vessels have a normal ventricular origin.

Given a large ventricular septal defect, the factor determining the distribution of ventricular outflow between the pulmonary and systemic circulations in transposition is still the ratio of the resistances of the two circuits. On the other hand, in the presence of transposition, the venous return to the 'pulmonary' ventricle is the pulmonary blood flow and the venous return to the 'systemic' ventricle is the systemic blood flow. Thus it is possible for the pulmonary blood flow to differ from the systemic blood flow without any nett shunt of blood.

Similarly, given a large atrial septal defect, the factor determining the distribution of ventricular inflow will be the ratio of the distensibility of the two ventricles. The venous return to the 'pulmonary' atrium is, however, the pulmonary flow, while the venous return to the 'systemic' atrium is the systemic flow.

The natural history of transposition in the first weeks after birth is dominated more by the adequacy of mixing between the two circulations than by the events in the pulmonary circulation. Failure to provide sufficient exchange of oxygen leads to death and, without treatment, the condition carries a high neonatal mortality. It is in this respect that the introduction of balloon atrioseptostomy has made such an important contribution.[61]

Thereafter, the factors which determine the natural history are those common to pre-tricuspid and post-tricuspid shunts. If there is a ventricular septal defect, a sequence of events similar to that described earlier in this chapter will take place. The tempo of the changes in the pulmonary circulation is, however, in general increased.[62] Of 30 patients with a ventricular septal defect and transposition, Viles and colleagues[63] found 11 with dilatation lesions with ages ranging from ten months to five years. A similarly high incidence of higher grades of hypertensive pulmonary vascular disease was observed by Ferencz.[64] Newfeld and colleagues[65] studied 57 patients under one year of age with transposition and a ventricular septal defect. Of these, eight had grade 3 and one (aged two months) had grade 4 hypertensive pulmonary vascular disease. There were 36 patients between the age of one and sixteen years of age of whom as many as 26 showed grade 4 abnormalities. Nine of this latter group were between the ages of one and two. Wagenvoort and colleagues[66] noted an increased medial musculature of the muscular pulmonary arteries, after allowance had been made for the normal effects of age, and the frequent occurrence of concentric intimal proliferation and fibrosis. They also comment on the rapidity with which hypertensive pulmonary vascular disease progresses in this condition. Stenosis may develop in the outflow tract of the right ventricle and closure of the ventricular septal defect may occur[62] with haemodynamic effects similar to those where the origin of the great vessels is normal. Stenosis at or below the pulmonary valve protects the pulmonary vasculature and increases the life expectancy.[67]

When there is no post-tricuspid shunt the factors determining pulmonary haemodynamics must be similar to those which obtain with an uncomplicated atrial septal defect. The pressure in the pulmonary circulation falls in the normal fashion during the first few months of life[54] and this is not affected by enlargement of the atrial septal defect with balloon septostomy. A great diversity of pulmonary blood flow appears to occur.[54] Morbid anatomical studies have provided divergent results. Wagenvoort and colleagues[66] found some degree of atrophy of the media of the muscular pulmonary arteries in such patients together with occasional cushion-like proliferation of the intima which suggested a thrombotic origin. They likened the appearances to those found in pulmonary stenosis. On the other hand, both Ferencz[64] and Viles *et al.*[63] noted the development of hypertensive pulmonary vascular disease and even occasionally of dilatation lesions. Newfeld *et al.*[65] studied 58 infants with transposition and a complete ventricular septum or small ventricular septal defect. None had pulmonary vascular lesions above grade 2, the pathological significance of which may be difficult to assess at this age. There were 26 patients with the same combination of abnormalities between the ages of one and sixteen years. Four of them showed grade 4 hypertensive pulmonary vascular disease, the youngest being two years old.

A number of principles underlie the application of surgery to patients with transposition. A sufficient admixture of blood between the two circuits has to be ensured and this may be effected by various procedures in the atria. The pulmonary blood flow may require reduction by banding the pulmonary artery. Occasionally, the presence of severe pulmonary stenosis requires a procedure to increase the pulmonary blood flow. Finally the two circuits may be reconstructed in series either by operating on the great vessels or by transposing the venous return. From the point of view of the pulmonary circulation the same considerations guide the choice of surgery as those which have been discussed in ventricular and atrial septal defects. The more rapid development of hypertensive pulmonary vascular disease in these patients has, however, to be borne in mind.

TOTAL ANOMALOUS PULMONARY VENOUS DRAINAGE

Gross Anatomy

Anomalous drainage of the pulmonary veins (see Chap. 2, p. 17) may occur directly into the right atrium or into any of its tributary vessels.[68,69] The most common site of entry into the systemic venous system is the left innominate vein, the next most common is into the right atrium, with entry into the right superior cava or coronary sinus occurring somewhat less frequently. Among the other less common sites of entry are the portal vein and the ductus venosus.[69] Usually the pulmonary veins converge to empty at a single anatomical region. When the site of entry is peripheral to the right atrium, coronary sinus or superior vena cava, the pulmonary veins usually combine to form a single vessel,[69] but this may not always be so.

Haemodynamics

Physiologically, life is possible only if there is adequate transfer of blood and oxygen from the right to the left atrium. The mixing of systemic and pulmonary venous blood also impairs the transport of oxygen to the body.

As with a pure atrial septal defect, the factors determining the ratio of pulmonary to systemic blood flow are the relative distensibility of the two ventricles and the size of the atrial septal defect. The size of the defect, however, operates in the opposite sense between these two anomalies. Where the pulmonary venous return is through its normal channels into the left atrium, the larger the atrial septal defect the larger will be the ratio of pulmonary to systemic flow. Where, on the other hand, the pulmonary venous return is through abnormal channels into the right atrium, the larger the atrial septal defect the smaller will be the ratio of pulmonary to systemic flow. When the atrial septal defect is small, the presence of total anomalous pulmonary venous drainage can give rise to pulmonary hypertension due simply to an increased flow.[70-72]

Pulmonary Venous Obstruction

The association of pulmonary venous obstruction with total anomalous pulmonary venous drainage is an important aspect of any consideration of this condition. It affects particularly those pulmonary venous pathways which pass below the diaphragm.[69,71,73,74] The longer the venous pathway, the greater the likelihood of localized obstruction apart from the increased resistance inherent in a long, narrow, tortuous vessel. If the anomalous pulmonary venous drainage is directly into the right atrium, the coronary sinus or the right superior vena cava, obstruction is unusual.[69,73] In addition to the occurrence of fibrous strictures along the course of the venous pathways a number of other extrinsic or intrinsic causes of vascular obstruction may operate. The diaphragm itself may constrict the vein passing through it. The vein may drain into a narrow ductus venosus or it may enter the portal system and be subjected to the resistance of the hepatic vascular bed. When the drainage is through a vein ascending towards the left innominate vein constriction may occur as it passes between the left pulmonary artery and the left bronchus.[73,75-77]

The presence of venous obstruction causes pulmonary venous hypertension.[70,71,73,75,78,79] This may be demonstrable, occasionally, by the retrograde passage of the catheter past the pulmonary venous obstruction (Fig. 21.11). More commonly it is assessed by the wedge pressure, although an acceptable wedge pressure is often difficult to obtain. In addition, many patients have an increased pulmonary vascular resistance[70,80-82] which may be of systemic magnitude. In the series reported by Gathman and Nadas,[70] 43 out of 52 cases with pulmonary hypertension had an increased pulmonary resistance. Of the 43 with an increased pulmonary vascular resistance, 40 had pulmonary venous obstruction. The occurrence of a high pulmonary vascular resistance appears, therefore, to be related to the presence of pulmonary venous obstruction.

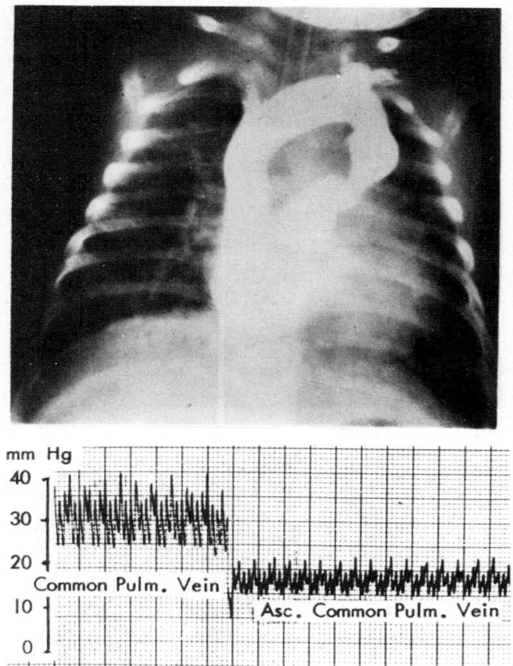

Fig. 21.11 Angiogram of infant with total anomalous pulmonary venous drainage entering an ascending common pulmonary vein. A stenosis is shown on the angiogram and a fall in pressure occurred on withdrawal of the catheter across the stenosis.

Hypertensive Pulmonary Vascular Disease

Ferencz and her colleagues[83] reported on the histology of the muscular pulmonary arteries in 22 patients at ages ranging from 2 weeks to 7 years with a median of 11 months. Only two cases were regarded as normal. The majority had only grade 1 changes. Two had grade 3 changes (aged 1 and 7 years) while one, aged 5 years, had plexiform lesions. In this group of cases, no distinction appears to have been made between those with and those without venous obstruction.

Pulmonary Oedema

In this condition the pulmonary venous blood returns primarily to the overloaded ventricle, as in post-tricuspid shunts, although the usual presence of a fairly wide communication between the atria will minimize the effects of failure of the right ventricle on the pulmonary circulation. The presence of obstruction in anomalous pulmonary veins also produces a combination of an increased pulmonary blood flow and increased pulmonary venous pressure similar to, or even more severe than, that which occurs in post-tricuspid shunts. For this reason pulmonary oedema is common.

Clinical Features in the Absence of Venous Obstruction

The clinical features[70,84] depend greatly on whether or not there is pulmonary venous obstruction. In the absence of venous obstruction and the presence of a large inter-atrial communication, some patients survive into adult life.[85] The majority, however, die within the first year. Tachypnoea develops within the first few weeks of life. Cyanosis is not usually prominent. Congestive failure appears usually within the first six months. The heart is large and overactive, with a prominent left parasternal heave. The first sound is loud. The two components of the second sound are separated to the normal extent but the separation does not usually vary with respiration. The second, pulmonary, component is the louder. A moderate ejection systolic murmur is heard best to the left of the sternum, and there is often a low-pitched mid-diastolic murmur at the lower end of the sternum due to the increased flow of blood through the tricuspid valve. A continuous murmur may be heard over the anomalous vessel.

The electrocardiogram shows right axis deviation, right ventricular hypertrophy and right atrial enlargement. The chest radiograph usually shows an enlarged cardiac shadow with increased pulmonary vascular markings. In those patients with drainage into the left innominate vein who survive infancy, a characteristic enlargement of the upper mediastinal shadow occurs.[85,86] This has a rounded appearance which, together with the cardiac shadow, gives the shape of a figure-of-eight. The left border of the upper mediastinal shadow is formed by the vertical pulmonary vein, while the right border is formed by the dilated superior vena cava.

Clinical Features in the Presence of Pulmonary Venous Obstruction

Patients with pulmonary venous obstruction[70,84] present earlier than those without obstruction. Without surgical correction few survive the first two or three months of life. Tachypnoea is again the prominent symptom and congestive heart failure occurs early.

In contrast to the severity of the symptoms, the clinical findings in the heart are often surprisingly unimpressive. The heart is usually not enlarged, the sounds may be normal and there is usually either no murmur or a soft ejection systolic murmur. Crepitations may be heard in the lungs. A continuous murmur may be heard over the anomalous trunk.

The electrocardiogram shows right axis deviation and right ventricular hypertrophy but evidence of right atrial enlargement is not usual. The chest radiograph (Fig. 21.12) shows a cardiac shadow of normal size. The pulmonary vascular markings are increased and the lung fields have a 'ground glass' or mottled appearance due to oedema. Kerley's B-lines have been described.[87]

Management

If pulmonary venous hypertension is found to be present by clinical and radiological criteria and by the existence of a wedge pressure which exceeds the right atrial pressure, then the prognosis[71,72,75,78,88] is so bad that the risks of

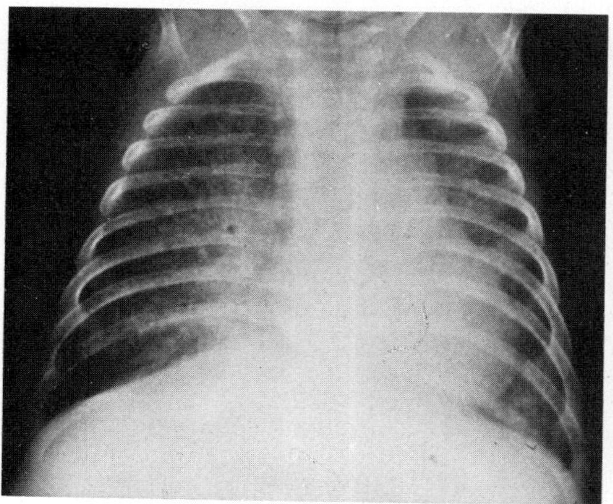
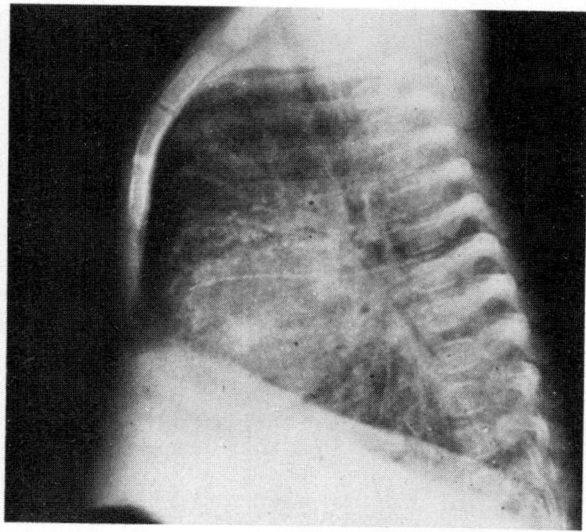

Fig. 21.12 Chest radiograph of infant with total anomalous pulmonary venous drainage with obstruction showing pulmonary oedema.

surgical correction have to be taken.[88] Even in the absence of pulmonary venous obstruction, many infants will also be so gravely ill that corrective surgery is necessary. When the right atrial pressure exceeds the left, a certain number of infants may be helped by balloon atrioseptostomy[78,89] provided that there is no pulmonary venous obstruction. A proportion of patients without venous obstruction will survive infancy and surgery can be elected at a time when its risk is less. The presence or absence of severe pulmonary hypertensive vascular disease will then, as in the other conditions already discussed, have an important bearing on the decision to operate.[80]

REFERENCES

1. Hoffman, J. I. E. & Rudolph, A. M. (1965) *Amer. J. Cardiol.*, **16**, 634.
2. Bloomfield, D. K. (1964) *Circulation*, **29**, 914.
3. Li, M. D., Collins, G., Disenhouse, R. & Keith, J. D. (1969) *Canad. Med. Ass. J.*, **100**, 737.
4. Keith, J. D., Rose, V., Collins, G. & Kidd, B. S. L. (1971) *Brit. Heart J. Suppl.*, page 81.
5. Hoffman, J. I. E. & Rudolph, A. M. (1970) *Advances in Pediatrics*, **17**, 57.
6. Gasul, B. M., Dillon, R. F., Vrla, V. & Hait, G. (1957) *J.A.M.A.*, **164**, 847.
7. Lucas, R. V., Jn., Adams, P., Jn., Anderson, R. C., Meyne, N. G., Lillehei, C. W. & Varco, R. L. (1961) *Circulation*, **24**, 1372.
8. Stanton, R. E. & Fyler, D. C. (1961) *Pediatrics*, **27**, 621.
9. Areilla, R. A., Agustsson, M. H., Bicoff, J. P., Lynfield, J., Weinberg, M., Jn., Fell, E. G. & Gasul, B. M. (1963) *Circulation*, **28**, 560.
10. Auld, P. A. M., Johnson, A. L., Gibbons, J. E. & McGregor, M. M. (1963) *Circulation*, **27**, 257.
11. Weidman, W. N., DuShane, J. W. & Kincaid, O. W. (1963) *Amer. Heart J.*, **65**, 148.
12. Wagenvoort, C. A., Neufeld, H. N., DuShane, J. W. & Edwards, J. E. (1961) *Circulation*, **23**, 740.
13. Damman, J. F., Jn. & Ferencz, C. (1956) *Amer. Heart J.*, **52**, 210.
14. Heath, D., Swan, H. J. C., DuShane, J. W. & Edwards, J. E. (1958) *Thorax*, **13**, 267.
15. DuShane, J. W. & Kirklin, J. W. (1960) *Circulation*, **21**, 13.

16. Heath, D. & Whitaker, W. (1956) *Circulation*, **14**, 323.
17. Viar, W. N. & Harrison, T. R. (1952) *Circulation*, **5**, 1.
18. Dresdale, D. T., Schultz, M. & Michtom, R. J. (1951) *Amer. J. Med.*, **11**, 686.
19. Eisenmenger, V. (1897) *Z. Klin. Med.*, **32** (Suppl.), p. 1.
20. Howarth, S. & Lowe, J. B. (1953) *Brit. Heart J.*, **15**, 47.
21. Werkö, L. & Eliasch, H. (1952) *Cardiologia*, **21**, 403.
22. Wood, P. (1952) *Brit. Med. Bull.*, **8**, 348.
23. Jefferson, K. & Rees, S. (1973) *Clinical Cardiac Radiology*. London: Butterworths.
24. Morgan-Jones, A. & Howitt, G. (1965) *Brit. Med. J.*, **i**, 1627.
25. Keith, J. D. (1971) In *The Natural History and Progress in Treatment of Congenital Heart Defects*, ed. Kidd, B. S. L. & Keith, J. D. page 5. Thomas.
26. Somerville, J. (1972) Paper presented to the American College of Cardiology.
27. Civin, W. H. & Edwards, J. E. (1950) *Circulation*, **2**, 545.
28. Muller, W. H., Jn. & Damman, J. F., Jn. (1952) *Surg. Gyn. Obst.*, **95**, 213.
29. Damman, J. F., Jn., McGeachen, J. A., Thompson, W. M., Smith, R. S. & Muller, W. H., Jn. (1961) *J. Thorac. Cardiovasc. Surg.*, **42**, 722.
30. Boruchow, I., Waldhausen, J. A., Miller, W. W., Rashkind, W. J. & Friedman, S. (1969) *Arch. Surg.*, **99**, 716.
31. Goldblatt, A., Bernhard, W. F., Nadas, A. S. & Gross, R. E. (1965) *Circulation*, **32**, 172.
32. Hallman, G. L., Cooley, D. A. & Bloodwell, R. D. (1966) *J. Thorac. Cardiovasc. Surg.*, **52**, 476.
33. Stark, J., Aberdeen, E., Waterston, D. J., Bonham-Carter, R. E. & Tynan, M. (1969) *Surgery*, **65**, 808.
34. Dobell, A. R. C., Murphy, D. R. & Bibbons, J. E. (1968) *Ann. Thorac. Surg.*, **5**, 435.
35. Ebert, P. A., Canent, R. V., Spach, M. S. & Sabiston, D. C., Jn. (1970) *J. Thorac. Cardiovasc. Surg.*, **60**, 516.
36. Stark, J., Tynan, M., Aberdeen, E., Waterston, D. J., Bonham-Carter, R. E., Graham, G. & Somerville, J. (1970) *Surgery*, **67**, 536.
37. Billig, D. M., Kreidberg, M. B. & Chernoff, H. L. (1971) *Chest*, **59**, 581.
38. Edgett, J. W., Jn., Nelson, W. P., Johnke, E. J. & Abay, G. V. (1968) *Amer. J. Cardiol.*, **22**, 729.
39. Nghiem, Q. X., Harris, L. C. & Tyson, K. R. T. (1969) *J. Pediat.*, **75**, 694.
40. Ching, E., DuShane, J., McGoon, D. C. & Davidson, G. K. (1971) *Ann. Thorac. Surg.*, **12**, 1.
41. Daicoff, G. R. & Miller, R. H. (1970) *Circulation*, **41–42**, Suppl. 2, 110.
42. Sigmann, J. M., Stern, A. M. & Sloan, H. E. (1967) *Pediatrics*, **39**, 4.
43. Kirklin, J. W. & DuShane, J. W. (1961) *Pediatrics*, **27**, 961.
44. Kirklin, J. W. (1971) *Circulation*, **43**, 321.
45. Rudolph, A. (1974) *Congenital Diseases of the Heart*. Year-Book Medical Publishers.
46. Cooley, D. A. & Hallman, G. L. (1964) *J. Cardiovasc. Surg.*, **5**, 584.
47. Stark, J., Hucin, B., Aberdeen, E. & Waterston, D. J. (1971) *Surgery*, **69**, 483.
48. Whitaker, W., Heath, D. & Brown, J. W. (1955) *Brit. Heart J.*, **17**, 121.
49. Wood, P. (1958) *Brit. Med. J.*, **ii**, 701 and 755.
50. Roach, M. R. (1963) *Circulat. Res.*, **13**, 537.
51. Roach, M. R. (1963) *Amer. J. Cardiol.*, **12**, 802.
52. Keen, E. N. (1955) *J. Anat.*, **89**, 484.
53. Hollman, A. (1958) *Brit. Heart J.*, **20**, 129.
54. Tynan, M. (1972) *Circulation*, **46**, 809.
55. Evans, J. R., Rowe, R. D. & Keith, J. D. (1961) *Amer. J. Med.*, **30**, 345.
56. Leatham, A. & Vogelpoel, L. (1954) *Brit. Heart J.*, **16**, 21.
57. Campbell, M. (1951) *Brit. Heart J.*, **13**, 438.
58. Barber, J. M., Magidson, O. & Wood, P. (1950) *Brit. Heart J.*, **12**, 277.
59. Campbell, M., Neill, C. & Suzman, S. (1957) *Brit. Med. J.*, **i**, 1375.
60. Markham, P., Howitt, G. & Wade, E. G. (1965) *Quart. J. Med.*, **34**, 409.
61. Rashkind, W. J. & Miller, W. W. (1968) *Circulation*, **38**, 453.
62. Plauth, W. H., Jn., Nadas, A. S., Bernhard, W. F. & Fyler, D. C. (1970) *Circulation*, **42**, 131.

63. Viles, P. H., Ongley, P. A. & Titus, J. L. (1969) *Circulation*, **40**, 31.
64. Ferencz, C. (1966) *Circulation*, **33**, 232.
65. Newfeld, E. A., Paul, M. H., Muster, A. J. & Idriss, F. S. (1974) *Amer. J. Cardiol.*, **34**, 75.
66. Wagenvoort, C. A., Nauta, J., Van der Schaer, P. J., Weida, H. W. H. & Wagenvoort, N. (1968) *Circulation*, **38**, 746.
67. Ankeney, J. L. & O'Grady, T. J. (1968) *Ann. Thorac. Surg.*, **5**, 262.
68. Darling, R. C., Rothney, W. S. & Craig, J. M. (1957) *Lab. Invest.*, **6**, 44.
69. Burroughs, J. T. & Edwards, J. E. (1960) *Amer. Heart J.*, **59**, 913.
70. Gathman, G. E. & Nadas, A. S. (1970) *Circulation*, **42**, 143.
71. Gomes, M. R., Feldt, R. H., McGoon, D. C. & Danielson, G. K. (1970) *J. Thorac. Cadiovasc. Surg.*, **60**, 116.
72. Gersony, W. M., Bowman, F. O., Jn., Steeg, C. N., Hayes, C. J., Jesse, M. J. & Malm, J. R. (1971) *Circulation*, **43**, Suppl. 1, 19.
73. Elliot, L. P. & Edwards, J. E. (1962) *Circulation*, **25**, 913.
74. Mustard, W. T., McKeon, W. J. & Trusler, G. A. (1968) *Progr. Cardiovasc. Dis.*, **11**, 145.
75. Behrendt, D. M., Aberdeen, E., Waterston, D. J. & Bonham-Carter, R. E. (1972) *Circulation*, **41**, 347.
76. Kauffman, S. L., Ores, C. N. & Anderson, D. H. (1962) *Circulation*, **25**, 376.
77. Hastreiter, A. R., Paul, M. N., Molthan, M. E. & Miller, R. A. (1962) *Circulation*, **25**, 916.
78. Engle, M. A. (1972) *Circulation*, **46**, 209.
79. Scott, L. P. & Welch, C. C. (1965) *Amer. J. Cardiol.*, **16**, 286.
80. Leachman, R. D., Cooley, D. A., Hallman, G. L., Simpson, J. W. & Dear, W. E. (1969) *J. Thorac. Surg.*, **7**, 5.
81. Levy, A. M., Naeye, R. L., Talakin, B. S. & Hanson, J. S. (1965) *Amer. J. Cardiol.*, **16**, 280.
82. Rosenberg, H. S., McNamara, D. G. & Colin, C. D. (1963) *Arch. Path.*, **76**, 177.
83. Ferencz, C., Greco, J. M. & Libi-Sylova, M. (1971) In *The Natural History and Progress in Treatment of Congenital Heart Defects*, ed. Kidd, B. S. L. & Keith, J. D. page 300. Thomas.
84. Gasul, B. M., Arcilla, R. A. & Lev, M. (1966) *Heart Diseases in Children.* page 469. Lippincott.
85. Whitaker, W. (1954) *Brit. Heart J.*, **16**, 177.
86. Snellen, H. A. & Albers, F. H. (1952) *Circulation*, **6**, 801.
87. Robinson, A. E., Chen, J. T. T., Bradford, W. D. & Lester, R. G. (1969) *Amer. J. Cardiol.*, **24**, 436.
88. Billig, D. M. & Kreidberg, M. B. (1973) *The Management of Neonates and Infants with Congenital Heart Disease.* Grune & Stratton.
89. Serratto, M., Bucheleres, H. G., Bicoff, P., Miller, R. A. & Hastreiter, A. R. (1968) *J. Pediatrics*, **73**, 734.

22. Structural Changes in the Lung Associated with Pulmonary Venous Hypertension

In this chapter we shall be concerned with the characteristic changes that develop in the lung parenchyma and in the pulmonary arteries, veins and lymphatics in patients who have chronic pulmonary venous hypertension from birth or who acquire it in adult life.[1] All these lesions appear to be the result directly or indirectly of the raised pressure in the pulmonary veins.

Those diseases in which pulmonary venous hypertension is present from birth may or may not be associated with a communication between the systemic and pulmonary circulations. The group with a septal defect includes mitral atresia with patent foramen ovale and a single ventricle. The group without a septal defect includes cor triatriatum, congenital mitral stenosis, congenital stenosis of all the pulmonary veins at the left atrial ostia, constrictive endocardial sclerosis, and congenital mitral incompetence. A third group of diseases in which pulmonary venous hypertension is acquired later in life includes rheumatic mitral stenosis and incompetence, non-rheumatic mitral incompetence consequent upon either healed bacterial endocarditis or ruptured chordae tendinae and mediatinal granuloma constricting pulmonary veins. Of all the diseases included in these groups, rheumatic disease of the mitral valve is by far the most common.

The Ultrastructure of the Alveolar Wall in Mitral Stenosis

There have been several electron microscopic studies of the alveolar wall in mitral stenosis[2–6] and the ultrastructural changes reported are unlikely to be restricted to this single valvular lesion but may be regarded as characteristic of chronic pulmonary venous hypertension. Changes occur in the endothelial cells of the pulmonary capillaries, in the interstitial space of the lung and in the epithelial cells lining the alveolar spaces.

The endothelial cells of the pulmonary capillaries become oedematous so that their cytoplasm is swollen and abnormally lucent; it contains large irregularly-shaped clear vacuoles measuring up to 400 nm in diameter.[6] Sometimes the endothelial swelling is so severe as to give rise to intra-luminal projections of clear, oedematous cytoplasm measuring up to 1600 nm in diameter. The inter-cellular junctions remain intact. The oedematous swelling of the endothelial cells of the pulmonary capillaries has been reported by a number of authors.[2,4,5] Aggregates of protein, fat and iron in the endothelial cells have also been reported.[3]

Most authors report a thickening of the basal lamina of the endothelial cells.[2–5] Kay and Edwards[6] are of the opinion that thickening of the basal lamina does not affect the thinnest convex portions of the blood-airway barrier where the capillary bulges into the alveolar lumen. Sometimes the basal lamina is split to enclose disintegrating fragments of extravasated erythrocytes (Fig. 22.1).

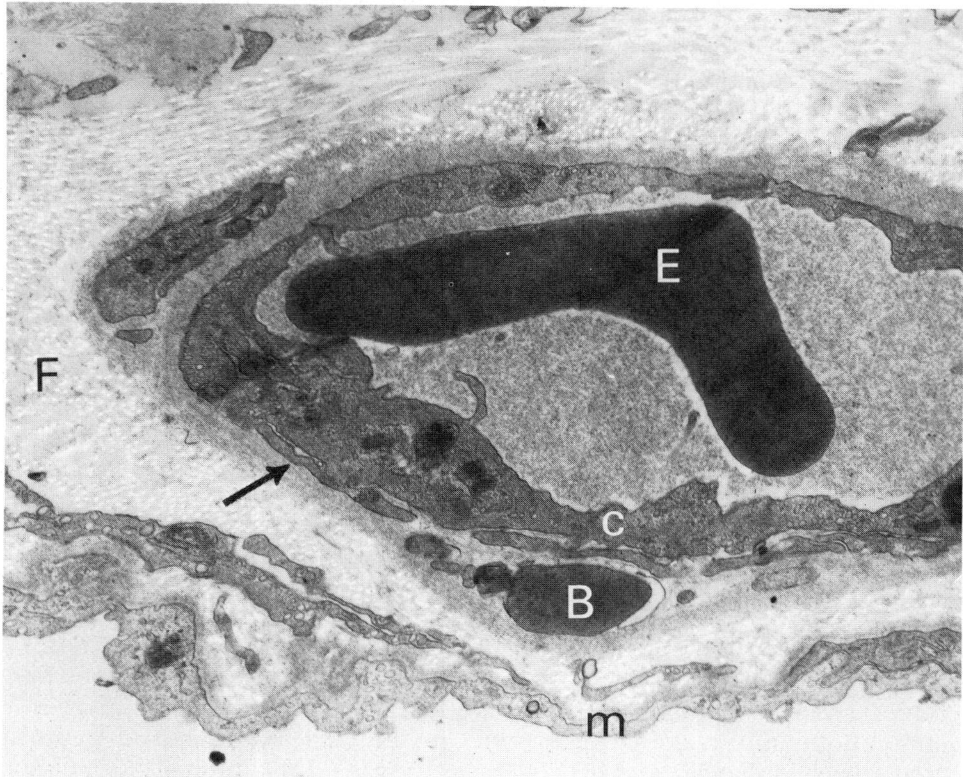

Fig. 22.1 Alveolar wall in mitral stenosis. A capillary containing an erythrocyte (E) is surrounded by dense proliferated connective tissue fibrils (F) which separate endothelial cell (C) from membranous pneumocyte (m) lining alveolar wall. The endothelial basement membrane (arrow) is thickened and split to enclose a fragmenting extravasated erythrocyte (B). (× 14 060)

Interstitial pulmonary oedema is characteristic of mitral stenosis and other diseases associated with pulmonary venous hypertension. Ultrastructurally, it appears as irregular lucent areas in the alveolar wall causing wide separation of groups of connective tissue fibrils and septal cells. According to Kay and Edwards,[6] the oedema fluid is restricted to the collagen-containing portions of the alveolar wall and does not accumulate in the thinnest portions of the blood–air barrier over the convexities of the alveolar cap where the interstitial space is devoid of collagen and consists only of fused basal laminae. They believe that the distribution of interstital pulmonary oedema depends on whether it is produced by haemodynamic changes or the action of toxic substances on the alveolar wall. In contrast to pulmonary oedema of haemodynamic origin, that produced by ammonium sulphate[7] or α-naphthyl thiourea[8] accumulates in the thinnest part of the blood-air barrier leading to the detachment of endothelial cells with the formation of oedema vesicles which protrude into the pulmonary capillaries. We would point out in this connexion that high-altitude pulmonary oedema is characterized by the formation of such endothelial vesicles which project into pulmonary capillaries,[9] so they cannot be regarded as being restricted to pulmonary oedema produced by toxic substances.

With persistence of oedema in the alveolar walls there is a proliferation of reticular and elastic fibrils[2–5] so that the alveolar capillaries become embedded in dense connective tissue.[6]

Over wide areas, membranous type 1 pneumocytes lining the alveolar walls are lost and replaced by granular type 2 pneumocytes (Chap. 3). This ultrastructural change corresponds to the 'cuboidal-cell metaplasia' seen on light microscopy.[10] Some of the remaining membranous pneumocytes are thickened due to the formation of clear intra-cytoplasmic vesicles.[6] The majority of cells within the alveolar spaces are granular pneumocytes the remainder being macrophages. Hyperplasia and shedding of granular pneumocytes into the alveolar spaces is in no way specific for mitral stenosis or chronic pulmonary venous hypertension. As described in Chapter 41, this sequence of events is also characteristic of the transition from the cellular to the mural stage of fibrosing alveolitis.

Pulmonary Capillary Pressure and Permeability of the Alveolar Wall

Kay and Edwards[6] have discussed the experiments of Szidon, Pietra and Fishman[11] and conclude that the permeability of inter-endothelial junctions is dependent on intra-luminal pressure and that alveolar epithelium rather than capillary endothelium is the critical barrier to the entry of water and solutes into the alveolar spaces. Szidon and his colleagues[11] studied the influence of pulmonary capillary pressure on the movement of macromolecules across the alveolar-capillary wall in an isolated dog lung preparation. This was perfused *in vivo* with solutions of horseradish peroxidase (mol. wt. 40 000; diameter 2·5 nm) or haemoglobin (mol. wt. 64 000; diameter 6·5 nm). When the perfusion pressure was 15 to 20 mmHg neither horseradish peroxidase nor haemoglobin escaped from the capillaries but when it was raised (peroxidase, 30 mmHg; haemoglobin, 40 mmHg) both tracers escaped through inter-endothelial junctions to enter the interstitial space of the alveolar septum. However, the tight junctions between the alveolar epithelial cells prevented tracers entering the alveolar spaces. Only when the perfusion pressure exceeded 50 mmHg did leakage occur.

Early Histological Changes in the Lung Parenchyma

The earliest changes demonstrable histologically in the lung in the presence of pulmonary venous hypertension occur in the capillaries and parenchyma of the lung and correspond to the ultrastructural changes described above. Macroscopically, the lung is engorged with blood. The pulmonary capillaries are distended and red blood cells pass through their walls with splitting of their basement membranes as described above and illustrated in Figure 22.1. This process leads to the presence

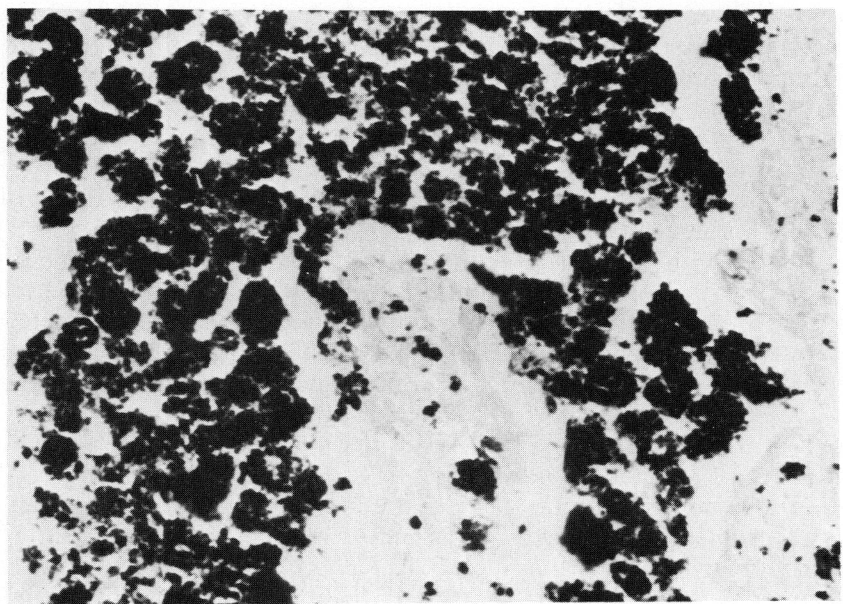

Fig. 22.2 Section of lung from a young woman with mitral stenosis. The section has been stained with Perls's reagents to demonstrate ferric iron. There is severe pulmonary haemosiderosis with numerous collections of haemosiderin-containing macrophages in the lung substance. (Perls's reagents, × 375)

of disintegrating erythrocytes in the alveolar spaces. They are ingested by macrophages which group together in the lung, often in a subpleural position, and give rise to pulmonary haemosiderosis (Fig. 22.2). As we have seen above not all free intra-alveolar cells are macrophages. The majority are granular pneumocytes.

Pulmonary Haemosiderosis

The relation between pulmonary haemosiderosis (Fig. 22.2) and the degree of hypertension in the pulmonary arteries and veins has been investigated in patients with mitral stenosis.[12] The degree of haemosiderosis was graded according to the average size of siderotic nodules found in lung tissue obtained at biopsy or necropsy. No direct relation was found between the occurrence and degree of pulmonary haemosiderosis and the level of blood pressure in either the pulmonary arteries or veins. While haemosiderosis was found in the majority of patients with severe pulmonary arterial hypertension and associated pulmonary venous hypertension, it also occurred commonly when the pulmonary arterial pressure was only moderately raised. The biopsies used in this investigation were resected from the lingula since this area is easily accessible to the surgeon at thoracotomy. However, it is probably preferable to study a portion of the upper lobe since in severe pulmonary haemosiderosis the lingula and the base of the lung may contain much less pigment than the rest of the lung and may in fact be entirely free of it.[13]

The source of the bleeding in pulmonary haemosiderosis consequent to pulmonary venous hypertension appears to be the alveolar capillary bed. We shall see later in this chapter that pulmonary arterial disease in mitral stenosis progresses only to the stage of grade 3. Hence there are no thin-walled branches of muscular arteries to account for the bleeding into the lung and subsequent pulmonary haemosiderosis as occurs in the late stages of hypertensive pulmonary vascular disease associated with congenital septal defects of the heart. Some believe that the bleeding takes place from bronchopulmonary anastomoses[14] but we think this is very unlikely. In the investigation referred to above,[12] pulmonary haemosiderosis was found in a few patients with mitral stenosis who had either a normal pulmonary arterial pressure or only mild pulmonary hypertension. Even allowing for the fact that such measurements of pressure are taken at rest and that in these patients the pulmonary arterial pressure would almost certainly rise abnormally on exercise, such occurrence of pulmonary haemosiderosis supports the views of Wood[15] who believed that the condition occurs early in the life history of mitral stenosis.

There is a gradual change from pulmonary haemosiderosis to what Lendrum terms 'siderofibrosis'.[16] This may be accompanied by the siderotic impregnation of elastica (Figs 22.3 and 22.4) and reticulin in the lung, and also with crystal formation and foreign body giant cell reaction.[16] These changes are comparable with

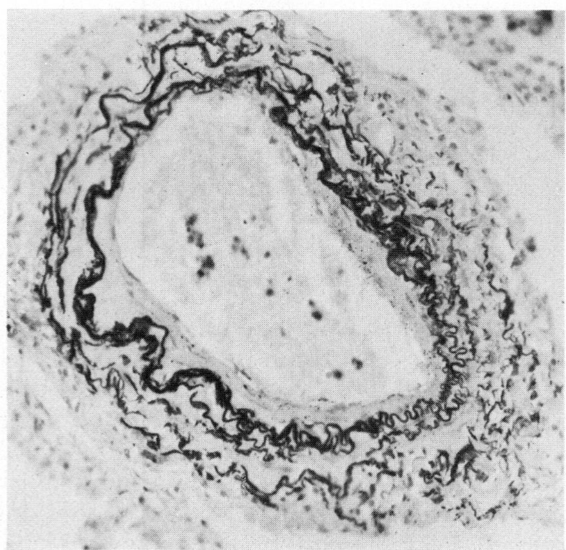

Fig. 22.3 Transverse section of a muscular pulmonary artery from a boy aged six-and-a-half years with congenital mitral stenosis showing incrustation of the elastic laminae with ferric iron. (Perls's reagents, × 150)

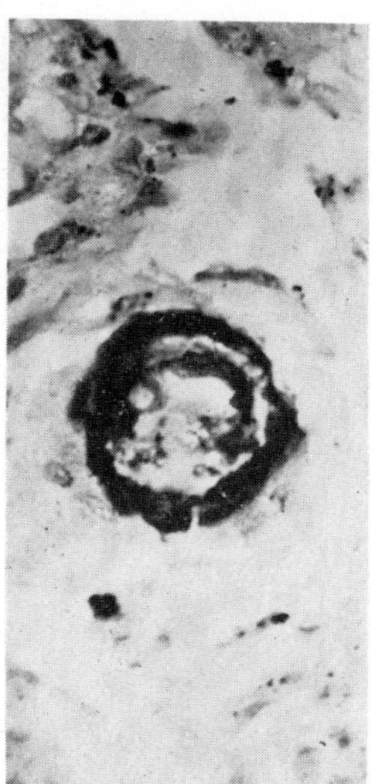

Fig. 22.4 Transverse section of a pulmonary arteriole from a boy aged six-and-a-half years with congenital mitral stenosis showing incrustation of the elastic laminae with ferric iron. (Perls's reagents, ×570)

those seen in the splenic stroma in cases of haemolytic anaemia. Occasionally, incrustation of the elastic laminae of the pulmonary blood vessels with ferric iron in cases of pulmonary venous hypertension may be severe.[17] Examination of a lung biopsy specimen showing these histological features may lead one to suspect the presence of a heart disease associated with pulmonary venous hypertension even when this has been undetected by clinical examination or special laboratory investigations.[17]

In cardiac failure with elevation of the pulmonary venous pressure, digitate clumps of fibrin may form in the alveolar ducts.[16] These are similar in appearance to those described as occurring in uraemia by Doniach[18] who related them to the 'bat's wing shadows' in the radiograph. Lendrum[16] believes that similar deposits of fibrin may be related to the formation of connective tissue in the ducts and alveoli of patients with systemic hypertension who have received hexamethonium compounds.[19]

Late Changes in the Lung Parenchyma

These changes are referred to classically as 'brown induration'. Fresh haemorrhages are seen in the lung and focal collections of cells are scattered throughout the lung. Some of these cells are macrophages and have ingested haemosiderin but, as we have seen above, others are granular pneumocytes which have been shed from the linings of the alveolar spaces. Many alveolar spaces contain oedema coagulum. Some of this is organized so that there is widespread fibrosis in the alveolar spaces and walls (Fig. 22.5). The interstitial oedema, distension of pulmonary capillaries and mural fibrosis contribute to the characteristic thickening

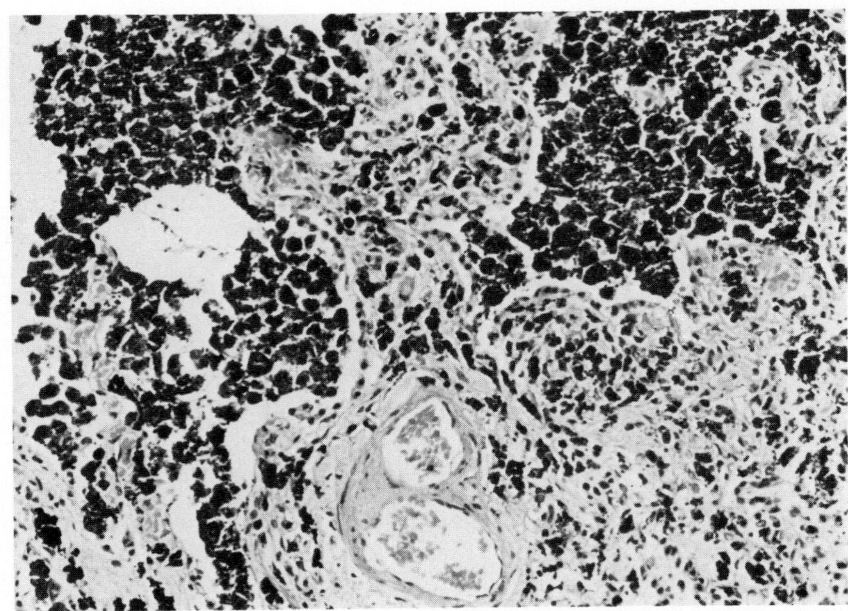

Fig. 22.5 Section of lung from the same case illustrated in Figure 22.2. Groups of haemosiderin-laden macrophages are present. There is pronounced interstitial fibrosis of the lung leading to thickening of alveolar walls which are covered by granular pneumocytes. The small pulmonary vein included in the section shows intimal fibrosis. The combination of interstitial fibrosis and pulmonary haemosiderosis produces the appearance of 'brown induration of lung'. (Haematoxylin & eosin, × 150)

of the alveolar walls. The thin membranous pneumocytes are lost from areas of the alveolar walls and are replaced by prominent granular pneumocytes which give rise to the appearance of so-called 'cuboidal metaplasia'. Many of the intra-alveolar masses of fibrous tissue become lined by flat cells. None of the histological components of 'brown induration' is pathognomonic of pulmonary venous hypertension but together they are characteristic of it. They may be produced by old pulmonary infarcts and for this reason, when the changes are focal, they should be interpreted with caution. On the other hand, some workers consider that such advanced changes in the lung in mitral stenosis are generally focal and not truly representative of the entire lung.[20]

The nature and site of the pulmonary fibrosis are themselves dependent upon the severity and chronicity of the predisposing pulmonary oedema. When the oedema is severe and acute as, for instance, in pneumonia or rupture of an aortic aneurysm into the pulmonary artery,[21] organization of the oedema coagulum usually takes place in the alveolar spaces and the fibrous tissue is cellular. Pulmonary venous hypertension, however, is usually chronic and it is more common for oedema coagulum to collect and be organized in the alveolar walls. This occurs in the repeated sub-clinical attacks of pulmonary oedema seen in mitral stenosis, myxoma, or thrombus of the left atrium occluding pulmonary veins, congenital stenosis of the pulmonary veins or mediastinal granulomata interfering with pulmonary venous return.[1] In such diseases, pulmonary interstitial fibrosis develops,[22] the fibrous tissue becoming relatively acellular.

Bone Formation and Calcification

Ossification in the alveolar spaces is seen frequently in cases of mitral stenosis,[23,24] or mitral incompetence (Figs 22.6 and 22.7). However, on rare occasions it may occur even in primary pulmonary hypertension[16] or in association with congenital septal defects when there is no associated pulmonary venous hypertension. The persistence of the fibrin clumps described above in cases with pulmonary venous hypertension is a possible explanation of these osseous bodies,[16] although transitional stages have not been seen.

A much rarer manifestation in the lungs of patients with mitral stenosis is microlithiasis.[25] In this condition, extensive calcification occurs around foci of alveolar exudate to form numerous calcospherities (Fig. 22.8). These are uniform in size and consist largely of stratified concretions of calcium phosphate which dissolve in hydrochloric acid to leave an onion-shaped organic envelope which

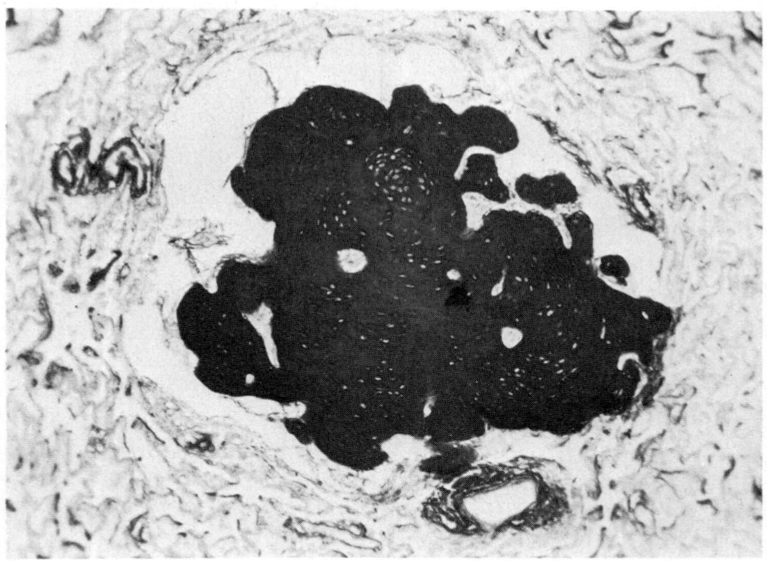

Fig. 22.6 Section of lung from a woman aged thirty-one years with congenital mitral incompetence associated with a corrected transposition of the great vessels without a ventricular septal defect. There is an osseous nodule in the lung tissue. (Elastic/Van Gieson, × 85)

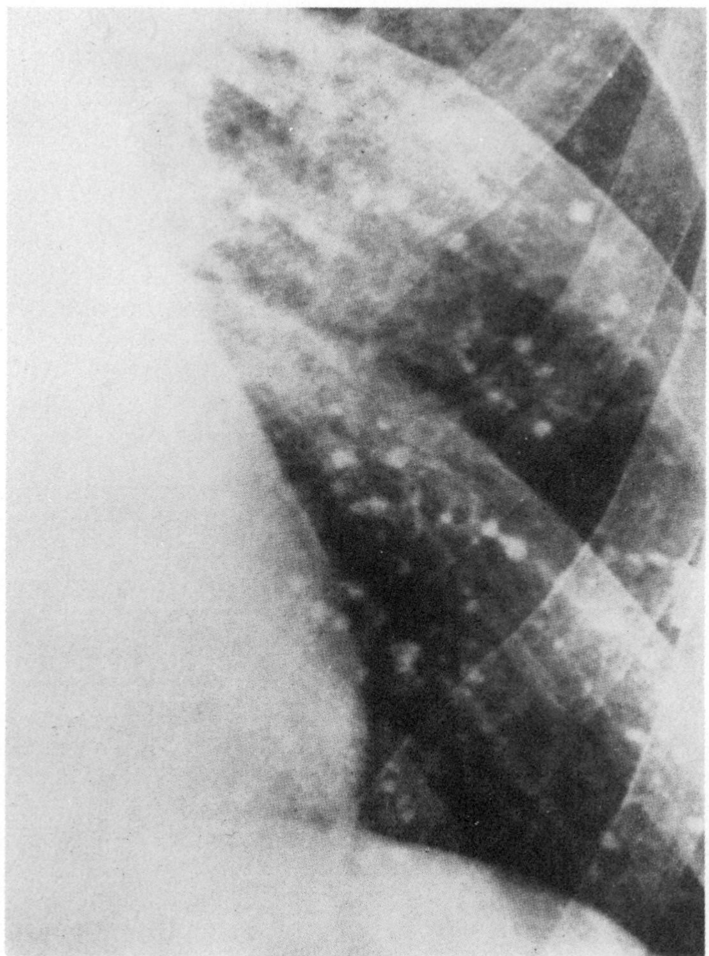

Fig. 22.7 Radiograph of the base of the left lung in a patient with mitral stenosis showing pulmonary ossification.

contains iron.[26] Each calcospherite is 250 to 750 μm in diameter, is roughly spherical in shape, and contains about 15 rings of calcium phosphate.[25] The microliths produce miliary opacities in radiographs. The lungs are stiff or even stony-hard and may require cutting with a saw during necropsy. Whole sections of lung from such a case resemble sandpaper.

Pulmonary Mast Cells

Pulmonary mast cell counts in cases of mitral stenosis and chronic left ventricular failure confirm Ehrlich's original observation that there is a proliferation of such

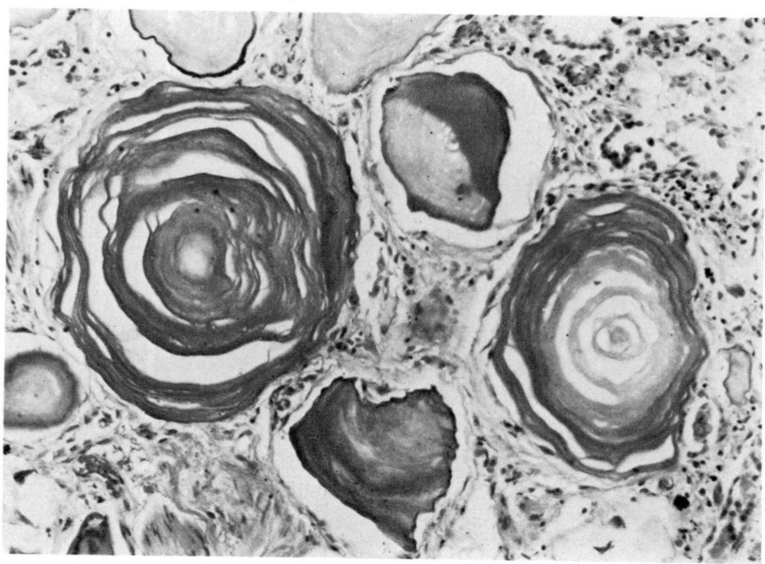

Fig. 22.8 Section of lung from a woman aged 50 years with rheumatic mitral stenosis and microlithiasis alveolaris pulmonum. The alveoli contain microliths which are composed of concentric lamellae of calcium phosphate. (Haematoxylin & eosin, × 145)

cells in brown induration of the lung.[27] We have carried out such counts on 27 necropsy specimens of lung. In twelve cases in which the lungs were normal or showed acute oedema, the mean mast cell count was 3·67 per mm^2 of lung. In one case with sub-acute pulmonary oedema the count was 12·36. In 14 cases with brown induration due to mitral stenosis or chronic left ventricular failure the count was 41·90 per mm^2 (Fig. 22.9). The mast cell hyperplasia in brown induration associated with pulmonary venous hypertension is associated with the laying down of fibrous tissue after chronic lymphatic obstruction with oedema of alveolar walls.[27]

Distension of Pulmonary Lymphatics

Persistent or transient horizontal lines are seen frequently at the bases of the lung in radiographs of patients with mitral stenosis[28] (Fig. 22.10). The persistent variety appears to be due to the deposition of haemosiderin in the fibrous tissue septa between the secondary lobules.[29] The transient lines occur during periods of cardiac failure and disappear with recovery. They are said to be caused by oedema of the connective tissue of the septa together with distension of the lymphatics[30] (Fig. 22.11). Transient basal horizontal lines are accompanied by a raised left atrial pressure. Rossall and Gunning[31] found that the lines appeared when the mean pressure in that chamber exceeded 24 mmHg but elevation of pulmonary arterial pressure alone appeared to play little part in their production.

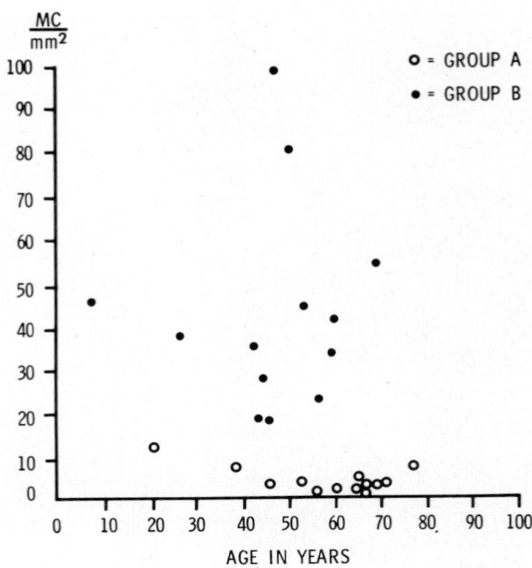

Fig. 22.9 The relation between pulmonary mast cell counts expressed as mast cells per mm^2 of lung (MC/mm^2) and age in the lungs of 27 cases coming to necropsy. The cases in Group A had normal lungs or acute pulmonary oedema at necropsy. The cases in Group B had most of the histological components of 'brown induration' of the lungs described in the text.

The degree of distension of the pulmonary lymphatics has been assessed in lung biopsies resected from patients with mitral stenosis in whom the pulmonary arterial and wedge pressures were known.[32] Two methods of assessment of lymphatic distension may be employed. The diameters of the largest single lymphatics seen in the pleura, the connective tissue septa between the secondary lobules and around the muscular pulmonary arteries may be measured. The calibre of these lymphatic vessels varies very considerably over short segments of their length which can make this method extremely misleading and yet at the same time gives a spurious impression of accuracy by the use of numbers.[32] An alternative method is to note the incidence of the overall appearance of obviously distended lymphatics around pulmonary arteries ('pulmonary lymphangiectasis') (Fig. 22.11). In the investigation quoted,[32] pulmonary lymphangiectasis was observed in seven of the twenty cases of mitral stenosis studied and in six of these the pulmonary venous pressure was 30 mmHg or more.

Changes in the Pulmonary Veins

Veins, like arteries, exhibit medial hypertrophy and intimal fibrosis as a reaction to an elevation in their intraluminal pressure[1] (Fig. 22.12).

Normally the muscle in the vein wall is arranged in an irregular fashion intermingled with collagen and elastic fibrils (Fig. 3.16, p. 37). In the presence of a

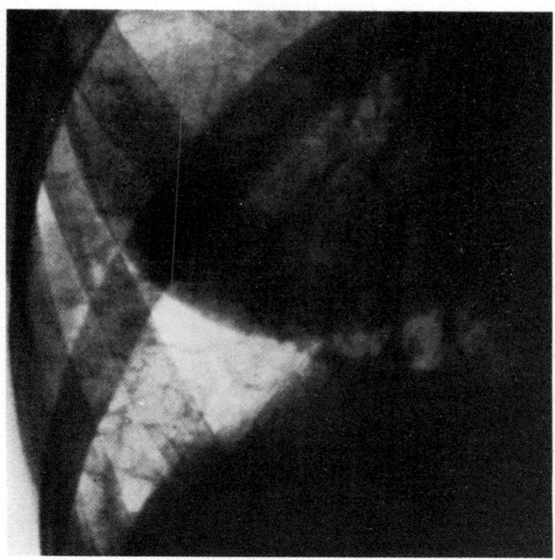

FIG. 22.10

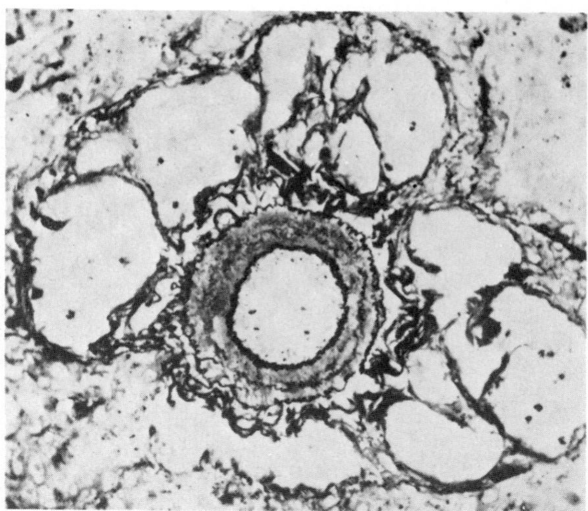

FIG. 22.11

Fig. 22.10 Radiograph of the base of the right lung in a patient with mitral stenosis showing 'Kerley's B lines' due to distension of the lymphatics and oedema of the connective tissue septa of the lung.

Fig. 22.11 Transverse section of a muscular pulmonary artery from a boy aged six-and-a-half years with congenital mitral stenosis. Distended lymphatic vessels are clustered around the abnormally thick-walled vessel to give the appearance of 'pulmonary lymphangiectasis' referred to in the text. (Elastic/Van Gieson, × 150)

severe, chronic pulmonary venous hypertension the muscle is condensed into a distinct muscular media devoid of collagen and fragmented elastic fibrils and is sandwiched between internal and external elastic laminae, so that in some instances the appearance of an arterial media is produced (Fig. 22.12).

Severe intimal fibrosis, usually acellular or even hyaline, is as characteristic of pulmonary veins subjected to hypertension as it is of pulmonary arteries (Fig. 22.12). Furthermore, in pulmonary veins, as in the arteries, the intimal fibrosis increases in severity with increasing age of the patient and increasing duration of hypertension.

The hypertrophy and condensation of smooth muscle in the pulmonary veins is pathognomonic of pulmonary venous hypertension, but the intimal fibrosis, while characteristic of a raised pressure in the pulmonary veins, is not specific. Severe intimal fibrosis in pulmonary veins is found commonly in diseases associated with high pulmonary blood flow, such as atrial septal defect (Chap. 16).

Changes in the Pulmonary Arteries

Pulmonary venous hypertension is associated with a raised pressure in the pulmonary arteries (Chap. 23). This association occurs in mitral stenosis,[33] left

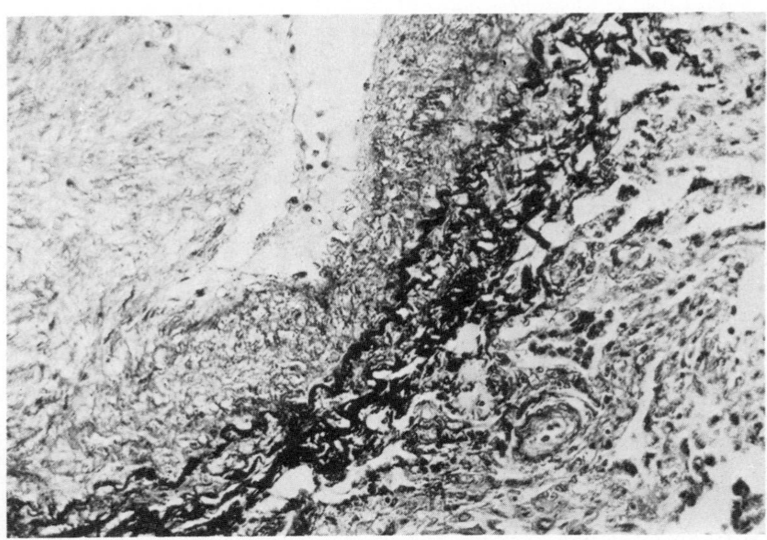

Fig. 22.12 Part of a transverse section of a pulmonary vein from a woman aged twenty-six years with a granuloma of the mediastinum which had compressed most of the pulmonary veins and led to pulmonary venous hypertension. A distinct muscular media is seen between distinct internal and external elastic laminae. These appearances mimic the structure of an artery. (Elastic/Van Gieson, × 200)

ventricular failure,[33] myxoma of the left atrium,[34] myocardial fibrosis[35] and mediastinal granuloma pressing on pulmonary veins.[36] Pulmonary venous hypertension is usually acquired owing to the great frequency of rheumatic mitral stenosis but may more rarely be present from birth in association with the congenital diseases of the heart already listed in the opening paragraph of this chapter.

When hypertension is present from birth in the pulmonary veins, it implies that it is also present in the pulmonary trunk. Hence, as we have seen in Chapter 17, the appearance of the elastic tissue of the pulmonary trunk in such an instance resembles that of the foetal pulmonary trunk or the adult aorta (Fig. 22.13). Similarly, in patients who have acquired pulmonary venous hypertension, the appearance of the elastic tissue in the pulmonary trunk is of adult pulmonary type (Fig. 22.14).

In patients with mitral stenosis who develop pulmonary arterial hypertension associated with an elevated pulmonary venous pressure, the structural alterations in the muscular pulmonary arteries and pulmonary arterioles (Figs 22.15 to 22.17) usually develop only to the stage of medial hypertrophy and intimal fibrosis represented by grade 3 of the classification described in Chapter 16. This observation has also been made by Wagenvoort,[37] who notes that there appears to be only one authenticated case of mitral stenosis in which the structures that we call

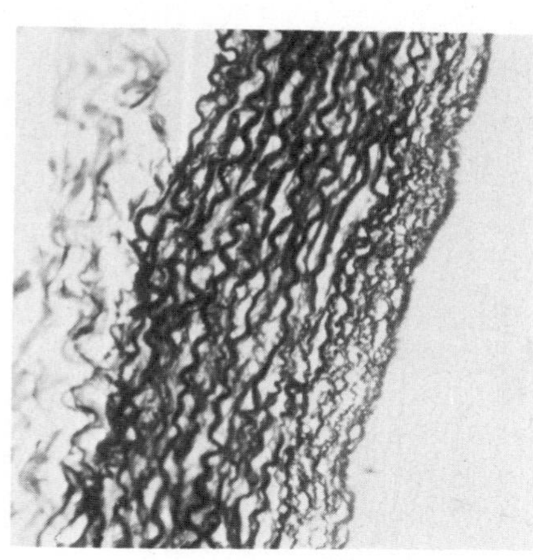

FIG. 22.13

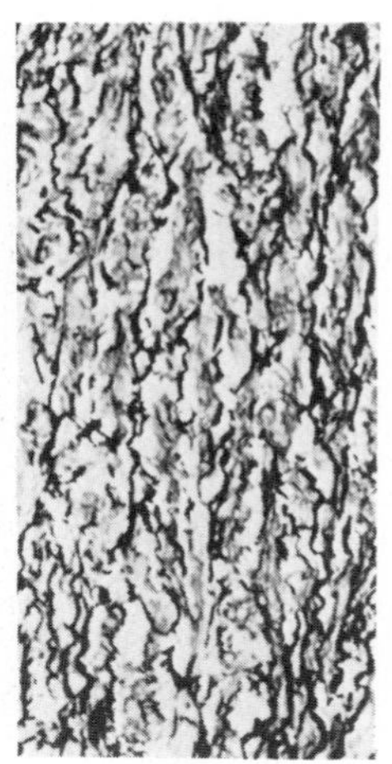

FIG. 22.14

Fig. 22.13 Part of a transverse section of an elastic pulmonary artery from a boy aged six-and-a-half years with congenital mitral stenosis. Presumably this patient had hypertension in his pulmonary veins and arteries from birth. The configuration of the elastic tissue is of aortic type. (Weigert-Sheridan, Lawson modification; × 150)

Fig. 22.14 Transverse section of pulmonary trunk of a woman aged forty-five years with non-rheumatic mitral incompetence consequent upon healed bacterial endocarditis. This woman had acquired pulmonary venous hypertension. The configuration of the elastic tissue is of adult pulmonary type. (Weigert-Sheridan, Lawson modification; × 150)

'dilatation lesions' had developed in the lung.[38] The reason for this is not apparent. The fact that grade 5 pulmonary vascular disease has been seen in patients with pulmonary venous hypertension in association with a congenital septal defect[1] shows that obstruction to pulmonary venous return does not prevent the development of the higher grades of structural change in the pulmonary arteries. Although the lesions of grades 4 and 5 do not occur in mitral stenosis, grade 6 hypertensive pulmonary vascular disease, characterized by necrotizing arteritis, is seen occasionally.

Patients with systemic hypertension or aortic stenosis can develop an increase of medial thickness of the muscular pulmonary arteries, probably as a result of an elevated left atrial pressure.[39]

Post-mortem angiographs of lungs in cases of mitral stenosis show moderate dilatation of the main pulmonary artery in most cases. However, the size of the elastic pulmonary arteries supplying lobes, segments and sub-segments of lung varies according to their site. Those in the upper part of the lungs are either dilated or normal in size, but those in the lower parts of the lungs are narrowed.[40] Harrison[40] thinks it likely that the narrowing is due to arterial tonus persisting after death and he found that on histological examination the muscular pulmonary

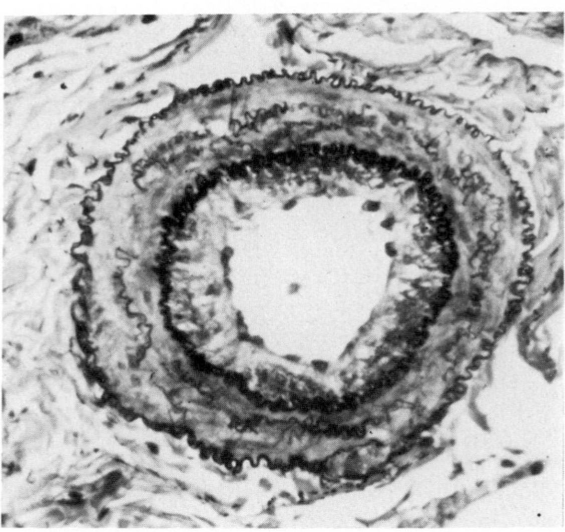

Fig. 22.15 Transverse section of a muscular pulmonary artery from a woman with acquired mitral stenosis of rheumatic aetiology. The media and the internal elastic lamina are abnormally thick. There is cellular intimal proliferation. The lining endothelial cells are prominent. Hypertensive pulmonary vascular disease of grade 2 severity (Elastic/Van Gieson, × 340)

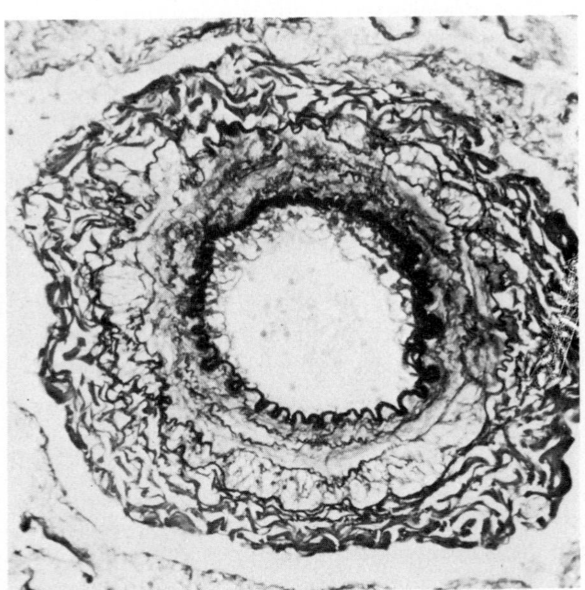

Fig. 22.16 Transverse section of a muscular pulmonary artery from a boy of six-and-a-half years with congenital mitral stenosis. The media and the internal elastic lamina are abnormally thick. Fasciculi of longitudinally orientated muscle fibres are seen in apposition to the external elastic lamina. Hypertensive pulmonary vascular disease grade 1. (Elastic/Van Gieson, × 150)

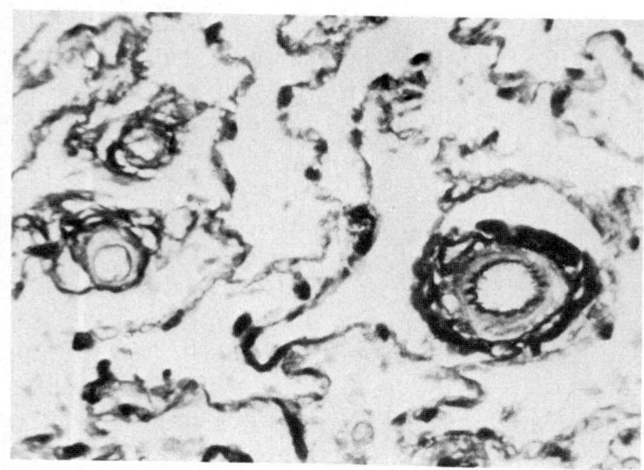

Fig. 22.17 Transverse sections of three pulmonary arterioles from a boy aged six-and-a-half years with congenital mitral stenosis. All three arterioles have a muscular media. The two arterioles to the left are far too small to be regarded as constricted muscular pulmonary arteries. Appearances of this type favour the hypothesis of the development of new muscle in arteriolar walls. (Elastic/Van Gieson, × 250)

arteries in the lower lobes appeared severely hypertrophied. Those in the upper lobes showed only slight increase in medial thickness. In the lower zones there was focal narrowing as well as the more generalized arterial narrowing; this focal change was due to atherosclerosis. As with pulmonary haemosiderosis (p. 335), pulmonary congestion and oedema are maximal in the posterior part of the upper lobe, where there is minimal arterial hypertrophy and narrowing.[40] The hypertrophy of the media of pulmonary veins referred to above (p. 343) is also more prominent in the lower lobes. Similar studies in cases of congenital heart disease with a septal defect show dilatation of the main pulmonary arteries and their segmental divisions. Considerable narrowing is seen in the lobular arteries but, unlike mitral stenosis, this is uniform throughout upper and lower lobes, and this is confirmed on histological examination when the degree of medial hypertrophy is the same throughout the lung.[40]

Fibrinous Vasculosis

Lendrum[41] has shown that in cases of mitral stenosis associated with severe pulmonary hypertension there may be a deposition of fibrin in the walls of the pulmonary arteries ranging from 450 μm to 50 μm. He believes that fibrinogen enters from the lumen and fibrin is deposited under the endothelium. In the areas of intimal thickening, fibrin is piled up on the inner side of the internal elastic lamina. The fibrin appears to break through the elastica, traverse the media and be partially held up at the external elastic lamina. This means that the fibrin may spread laterally on the inner surface of the external elastic membrane. The fibrin eventually fans out into the adventitia. It is presumed that the substance which spreads through the media is fibrinogen for the observed material stains positively by the picro-Mallory method mentioned in Chapter 3. Lendrum assumes that in mitral stenosis it is the high pulmonary arterial blood pressure that forces fibrinogen into the media.

Similar appearances are seen in the systemic circulation in the renal arteries in cases of malignant hypertension, in cases of hypersensitivity angitis induced by drugs, and in tissues that have undergone infarction or torsion.[41]

Brenneman and Liebow[42] were unable to reproduce these appearances by elevating the intravascular pressure in a single lobe of a normal dog's lung for periods up to twenty minutes. However, Harrison[43] has shown that on injecting broken-up human blood clot into the systemic veins of rabbits the fragments of fibrin are treated occasionally as foreign bodies and they migrate through the wall of the artery into the adventitia leaving a gap in the internal elastic lamina with scarring of the media and a fibrous mass in the adventitia. Cotton-wool fibres and filter paper fragments are treated in the same way. We have seen granulomata in and around the walls of muscular pulmonary arteries which have apparently followed the impaction of cotton-wool fibres into these vessels following their introduction into the pulmonary circulation during cardiac catheterization (Chap. 15). Such granulomata consist of doubly refractile fibres surrounded by fibrous tissue, foreign body giant cells, and a chronic inflammatory exudate. They have been seen by von Glahn and Hall[44] in both man and experimental animals.

Electron Microscopy of the Pulmonary Vasculature in Mitral Stenosis

The electron microscopy of the pulmonary vasculature in mitral stenosis has been studied by Hatt and Rouiller.[45] They studied the ultrastructure of the muscular pulmonary arteries, pulmonary arterioles, pulmonary capillaries and pulmonary veins in lung biopsy specimens resected during the course of commisurotomy in 25 cases of tight mitral stenosis.

The pulmonary capillaries showed constant and pronounced changes. The thickness of the basement membrane, normally in the range of 8 to 10 nm was commonly increased to between 15 and 30 nm and in extreme cases reached 50 nm. There was a sub-endothelial infiltration of a hyaline substance which merged into a similar substance seen in the pulmonary arteries and veins. The lining endothelial cells were in general swollen. In four of the cases studied the endothelial cells contained haemosiderin which occurred either diffusely or focally in large aggregates in their cytoplasm. The endothelial cells were continuous with only narrow intercellular hiatuses separating one cell from its neighbour. In a quarter of the cases there was a reduplication of the endothelial cells so that supernumerary cells appeared deep to the single layer of endothelium. The cytoplasm of these deeper cells was altered and in extreme cases this progressed to degeneration to a cytoplasmic debris set in the sub-endothelial hyaline substance referred to above. In the endothelial cells there was no noticeable abnormality of the nucleus, the Golgi apparatus or the rough endoplasmic reticulum. The mitochondria were sparse. There was an increase in size and number of intra-cytoplasmic vacuoles. Inclusion bodies, normally found in the endothelium of pulmonary capillaries and composed of structureless osmiophilic material which is probably lipid in nature, were neither increased nor diminished in numbers. The adventitial cells, possibly pericytes, were normal in those cases where the alterations in the endothelial cells were minimal. On the other hand, in cases where the endothelial cells of the pulmonary capillaries were severely damaged, there was also considerable alteration to the adventitial cells to the extent that it became difficult to distinguish the cellular damage from debris arising from other origins. Interestingly enough, there was no relation between the severity of the lesions in the pulmonary capillaries and the levels of pulmonary arterial pressure.

There were striking changes in the ultrastructure of the muscular pulmonary arteries but in this case there was a relation to the degree of pulmonary arterial hypertension present. When the elevation of pulmonary arterial pressure was only moderate, the endothelial cells showed but little change, and the alterations were limited to an infiltration of the sub-endothelial zone with a hyaline material similar to that which we have described above as existing at the level of the pulmonary capillaries. Commonly, the internal elastic lamina was thinner than normal but was set in a hyaline material which frequently extended and insinuated into the media.

In the presence of frank pulmonary arterial hypertension, however, there were striking changes in intima, media, and adventitia. So far as the intima was concerned, there was an increase of intra-cytoplasmic vacuolation and deposition of haemosiderin similar to that described above in the endothelium of the pulmonary capillaries. A most interesting observation recorded by Hatt and Rouiller[45] was that the cytoplasm of the endothelial cells showed a fibrillar structure reminiscent of that of the smooth muscle cell. In Chapter 16 we refer to the report of a similar finding in lung biopsy specimens from twelve young adult dogs subjected to the creation of a significant systemic-pulmonary shunt. There we consider at length the nature of such cells with intra-cytoplasmic fibrils. In cases of mitral stenosis such cells were found to be capable of ingesting haemosiderin. Their relation to smooth muscle cells is considered in Chapter 16. These sub-endothelial cells of controversial nature and origin were found to be enmeshed in a hyaline material between elastic fibrils which appears to be derived from the fragmentation and reduplication of the internal elastic lamina.

As one would anticipate, in the presence of pulmonary arterial hypertension, the ultrastructure of the muscular pulmonary arteries showed evidence of medial hypertrophy. There was an increase in the number of layers of smooth muscle cells. These cells were orientated regularly in parallel layers separated by interstices containing hyaline substance, elastic fibrils and collagen fibres. Very occasional muscle cells showed disintegration with disappearance of the intra-cytoplasmic fibrillar structure, clarification of the cytoplasm, nuclear breakdown and inclusion of amorphous material. The muscle cells which showed no sign of disintegration but which were involved in the process of hypertrophy showed an increase in density of the intra-cytoplasmic fibrillar structure. Areas of infiltration with connective tissue were found in the inner half of the media. The external elastic lamina was not changed. There was fibrous thickening of the adventitia. In the adventitia, there were occasional detached smooth muscle cells some of which showed evidence of disintegration.

The pulmonary veins showed constant ultrastructural changes irrespective of the existence or not of pulmonary arterial hypertension. There was some swelling of the venous endothelium. The endothelial cells showed an enhancement of intra-cytoplasmic fibrillar structure and vacuolization. In the pulmonary veins, as in the capillaries, there was ultrastructural evidence of muscularization supporting the histological appearance described earlier in this chapter. There was also evidence of thickening of the adventitia by fibrocytes.

In general terms we see, therefore, that the ultrastructural changes in the pulmonary circulation in mitral stenosis confirm the histological appearances described earlier in this chapter. What is of interest is the fact that the hyperplastic endothelial cells show the development of a pronounced fibrillar change in their cytoplasm. Superficially reminiscent of a transformation into a myoid type of cell, this fibrillary cytoplasmic appearance is considered at greater length in Chapter 16.

The Relation of Pathological Changes in the Lungs to Clinical and Radiological Features in Cases of Mitral Stenosis

We have had the opportunity to carry out a histological study of lingular biopsies from 20 patients with mitral stenosis and relate the pathological changes found to the radiological appearances of the lungs, and to abnormalities in pulmonary function and pulmonary haemodynamics.[46] Medial hypertrophy in the small muscular pulmonary arteries, defined as a medial thickness exceeding 6·8 per cent of the external diameter of the vessel, and muscularization of the pulmonary arterioles were found when the pulmonary vascular resistance exceeded only 260 $dyn \cdot s \cdot cm^{-5}/m^2$ BSA. There was no linear relation between the degree of medial hypertrophy and the height of pulmonary vascular resistance. Pulmonary haemosiderosis was found in only one-third of the patients, most of whom also had radiological evidence of haemosiderosis. Its presence was not related to the height of the pulmonary venous pressure. Radiological evidence of enlargement of the main pulmonary arteries was found to be an indication of the presence of pulmonary arterial hypertension and associated hypertensive pulmonary vascular disease but not of its degree. 'Pulmonary lymphangiectasis' did not occur with only moderate rises in left atrial pressure. Horizontal lines on the chest radiograph were related to the presence of alveolar fibrosis. Both conditions are probably the result of oedema in the lung tissue. The relation between structural changes in the alveolar wall and respiratory function is poor. Diffusing capacity appeared to be more closely related to pulmonary vascular disease than to changes in the alveolar walls. The severity and duration of dyspnoea was related to the grade of hypertensive pulmonary vascular disease.

REFERENCES

1. Heath, D. & Edwards, J. E. (1959) *Brit. J. Dis. Chest.*, **53**, 8.
2. Schulz, H. (1959) In *Die submikroskopische Anatomie und Pathologie der Lunge*. page 114. Berlin.
3. Gieseking, R. (1960) *Beitr. Path. Anat.*, **123**, 333.
4. Asano, H. (1964) *Jap. Circul. J.*, **28**, 787.
5. Coalson, J. J., Jaques, W. E., Campbell, G. S. & Thompson, W. M. (1967) *Archs. Path.*, **83**, 377.
6. Kay, J. M. & Edwards, F. R. (1973) *J. Path.*, **111**, 239.
7. Hayes, J. A. & Shiga, A. (1970) *J. Path.*, **100**, 281.
8. Meyrick, B., Miller, J. & Reid, L. (1972) *Brit. J. Exp. Path.*, **53**, 347.
9. Heath, D., Moosavi, H. & Smith, P. (1973) *Thorax*, **28**, 694.
10. Parker, F. & Weiss, F. (1936) *Amer. J. Path.*, **12**, 573.
11. Szidon, J. P., Pietra, G. G. & Fishman, A. P. (1972) *New Engl. J. Med.*, **286**, 1200.
12. Heath, D. & Whitaker, W. (1956) *J. Path. Bact.*, **72**, 531.
13. Gough, J. (1960) In *Recent Advances in Pathology*, ed. Harrison, C. V. 7th ed., p. 54. London: Churchill.
14. Lendrom, A. C., Scott, L. D. W. & Park, S. D. S. (1950) *Quart. J. Med., NS.*, **19**, 249.
15. Wood, P. (1954) *Brit. Med. J.*, **1**, 1051.
16. Lendrum, A. C. (1960) *Proc. R. Soc. Med.*, **53**, 338.
17. Walton, K. W. & Heath, D. (1960) *Brit. Heart J.*, **22**, 440.
18. Doniach, I. (1947) *Amer. J. Roentgenol.*, **58**, 620.
19. Doniach, I., Morrison, B. & Steiner, R. E. (1954) *Brit. Heart J.*, **16**, 101.
20. O'Neal, R. M., Thomas, W. A., Lee, K. T. & Rabin, E. R. (1957) *Circulation*, **15**, 64.
21. Heath, D., Parker, R. L. & Edwards, J. E. (1958) *Brit. J. Clin. Pract.*, **12**, 701.
22. Andrews, E. C., Jn. (1957) *Johns Hopk. Hosp. Bull.*, **100**, 28.
23. Hicks, J. D. (1953) *J. Path. Bact.*, **65**, 333.
24. Whitaker, W., Black, A. & Warrack, A. J. N. (1955) *J. Fac. Radiol. (Lond.)*, **7**, 29.
25. Wagenvoort, C. A., Heath, D. & Edwards, J. E. (1964) *The Pathology of the Pulmonary Vasculature*. Springfield, Ill.: Thomas.
26. Sharp, M. E. & Danino, E. A. (1953) *J. Path. Bact.*, **65**, 389.
27. Heath, D., Trueman, T. & Sukonthamarn, P. (1969) *Cardiovasc. Res.*, **3**, 467.
28. Shanks, S. C. & Kerley, P. (eds.) (1951) *A Textbook of X-ray Diagnosis by British Authors*. London: Lewis.
29. Fleischner, F. G. & Reiner, L. (1954) *New Engl. J. Med.*, **250**, 900.
30. Gough, J. (1955) *Lancet*, **i**, 161.
31. Rossall, R. E. & Gunning, A. J. (1956) *Lancet*, **i**, 604.
32. Heath, D. & Hicken, P. (1960) *Thorax*, **15**, 54.
33. Dexter, L., Dow, J. W., Haynes, F. W., Whittenberger, J. L., Ferris, B. G., Goodale, W. T. & Hellems, H. K. (1950) *J. Clin. Invest.*, **29**, 602.
34. Van Buchem, F. S. P. & Eerland, L. D. (1957) *Dis. Chest*, **31**, 61.
35. Heath, D., Cox, E. V. & Harris-Jones, J. N. (1957) *Thorax*, **12**, 321.
36. Edwards, J. E. & Burchell, H. B. (1951) *Arch. Intern. Med.*, **87**, 372.
37. Wagenvoort, C. A. (1959) *J. Path. Bact.*, **78**, 503.
38. Gordon, A. J., Donoso, E., Kulm, L. A., Ravitch, M. M. & Himmelstein, A. (1954) *New Engl. J. Med.*, **251**, 923.
39. Smith, R. C., Burchell, H. B. & Edwards, J. E. (1954) *Circulation*, **10**, 801.
40. Harrison, C. V. (1958) *Brit. J. Radiol., NS.*, **31**, 217.
41. Lendrum, A. C. (1956) In *Pulmonary Circulation and Respiratory Function*. University of St. Andrews. Edinburgh: Livingstone.
42. Brenneman, A. R. & Liebow, A. A. (1959) *Yale J. Biol. Med.*, **31**, 271.
43. Harrison, C. V. (1948) *J. Path. Bact.*, **60**, 289.
44. von Glahn, W. C. & Hall, J. W. (1949) *Amer. J. Path.*, **25**, 575.
45. Hatt, P. Y. & Rouiller, C. (1958) *Path. Biol.*, **6**, 1371.
46. Jordan, S. C., Hicken, P., Watson, D. A., Heath, D. & Whitaker, W. (1966) *Brit. Heart J.*, **28**, 101.

23. Pulmonary Haemodynamics of Mitral-Valve Disease

Left Atrial Pressure

The normal mitral valve[1] opens to approximately 4 to 6 cm^2. In mitral stenosis the area of the opening is often less than 1 cm^2. Since the valve is normally open for somewhat less than half the cardiac cycle, the actual rate of volume flow through it during this time is more than twice the mean cardiac output. The narrowing of the valve increases the velocity with which the particles of blood pass through it and causes turbulence. The turbulence in turn increases the resistance to the flow of blood (Chap. 9) so that the resistance of the valve is not a simple function of its area.

The obstruction placed by stenosis of the mitral valve between the left atrium and the left ventricle causes an elevation of the mean left atrial pressure. In general, the degree of elevation increases with the severity of the stenosis, and may reach a level of 40 mmHg (Fig. 23.1, Table 23.1).

In addition to the increase in mean pressure, the presence of mitral stenosis alters the shape of the left atrial pulse-wave.[2–5] In the normal heart, the opening of the mitral valve allows blood to pass rapidly into the left ventricle with a consequent sharp fall in the left atrial pressure (y-descent) (Chap. 5, p. 71 and

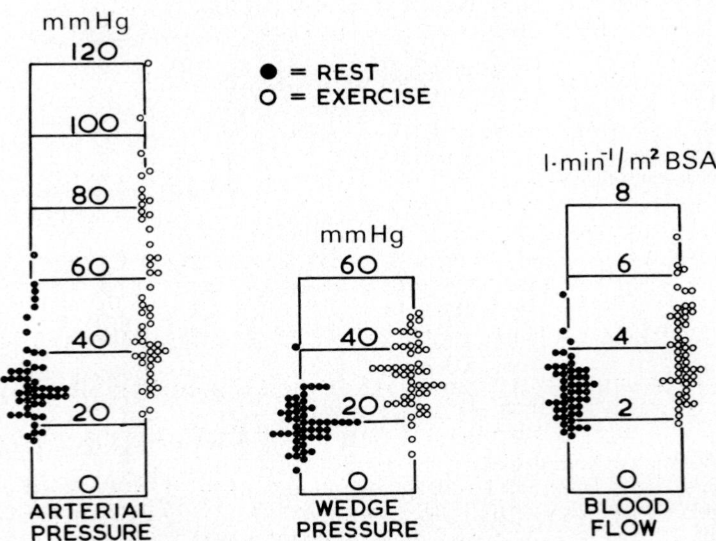

Fig. 23.1 The pulmonary arterial pressure, wedge pressure and blood flow in a group of fifty patients with mitral stenosis studied at rest and during exercise.

Table 23.1 The effects of exercise on the pulmonary circulation in fifty patients with mitral stenosis

		Pulmonary arterial pressure (mmHg)	Wedge pressure (mmHg)	Pulmonary blood flow ($l \cdot min^{-1}/m^2$ BSA)
Rest	Mean	33·5	20·3	2·90
	s.d.	12·5	6·3	0·78
Exercise	Mean	56·7	33·0	4·02
	s.d.	23·3	8·9	1·21

Fig. 5.14). By mid-diastole the pressure begins to rise again due to distension of the ventricle and this has been called 'diastasis'.[3] In the presence of mitral stenosis, the high pressure in the left atrium may tend to open the mitral valve earlier in diastole than it would normally.[6,7] The subsequent flow of blood through the narrow valve orifice is slow and this causes the *y*-descent of the left-atrial pressure tracing to be less steep than normal (Fig. 23.2). Finally, the rate of filling of the left ventricle is so slow that 'diastasis' does not occur. When there is atrial fibrillation, the *a*-wave disappears.

In the presence of pure mitral incompetence, the *v*-wave of the left atrial tracing is unusually high, the *y*-descent is rapid owing to the ease with which blood can pass into the left ventricle, and diastasis is present. Mitral incompetence does not, as a rule, elevate the mean left atrial pressure so much as mitral stenosis.

The distinction between stenosis and incompetence of the mitral valve is one of great practical importance, but, although analysis of the shape of the left atrial pressure tracing may distinguish pure stenosis from pure incompetence, it has proved of little value in assessing the relative importance of the two abnormalities when they occur together.[5] To some extent this may be due to the fact that the shape of the pulse wave is also affected by the size and distensibility of the left atrium and pulmonary veins.

Similar alterations have been observed in the shape of the pulmonary wedge tracing[8] (Fig. 23.2). However, the damping due to the catheter and to the system of vessels through which the pulse waves are transmitted often renders these tracings even more ambiguous than those from the left atrium.

Pulmonary Arterial Pressure

If the pulmonary blood flow and pulmonary vascular resistance remained unchanged, the elevation of left atrial pressure due to mitral stenosis would cause an equal elevation in pulmonary arterial pressure. The situation in patients with mitral stenosis is quite different. The elevation in left atrial pressure develops over the

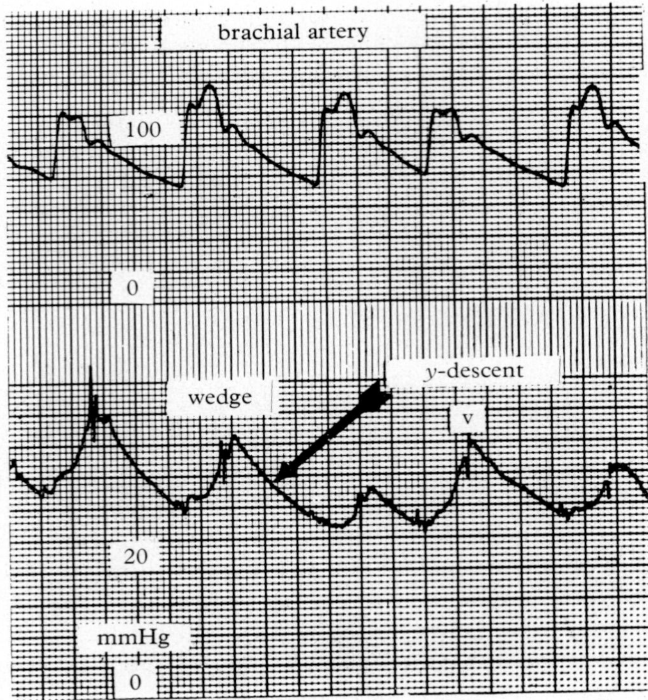

Fig. 23.2 Simultaneous wedge and brachial arterial pressure tracings from a patient with pure mitral stenosis and atrial fibrillation.

course of years, and the muscular pulmonary arteries undergo the changes described in Chapter 22. There is an increase in the pulmonary arterial resistance which may exceed 1000 dyn · s · cm^{-5} and thus the pulmonary arterial pressure rises to a greater extent than the pressure in the left atrium[9] and may approach that in the systemic arteries. Dexter and his colleagues[9] concluded that, while the wedge pressure was rising to a value of 25 mmHg, the pulmonary arterial pressure rose proportionately. Beyond this point the pulmonary arterial pressure increased to a disproportionate extent. Since 25 mmHg is approximately the osmotic pressure of the plasma, it was suggested that these results gave evidence of a protective mechanism whereby the narrowing of the pulmonary arteries tended to prevent the pressure in the pulmonary capillaries from exceeding the osmotic pressure of the plasma and thus causing pulmonary oedema.

Figure 23.3 shows the relation between the wedge and pulmonary arterial pressures in a group of patients with mitral stenosis.[10] Drawn on the diagram are a curved regression line calculated to fit the data and a straight line representing the relation which would be expected if the resistance remained constant. Such observations give no evidence that any sudden alteration occurs in the shape of the relation between the two pressures. Neither is it clear how the suggested protective mechanism acts. The pressure in the left atrium is determined by the size of the mitral valve orifice, the diastolic pressure in the left ventricle, the proportion of time during which the mitral valve is open, the flow of blood coming from the lungs, and the distribution of blood between the systemic and pulmonary circulations. The resistance of the pulmonary arteries is not directly concerned. An increased resistance in the muscular pulmonary arteries may, however, lower the left atrial pressure indirectly by reducing the flow of blood through the mitral valve.

There are two ways in which this might happen. In the first place, an increased resistance in the muscular pulmonary arteries would cause the pulmonary trunk and its elastic branches to dilate, so that, during the time that this was happening, the flow of blood out of the lungs would be less than the output of the right ventricle. It is not credible, however, that this minute difference would be of any significance particularly if it occurred over a long period of time. Secondly, the high pressure in the pulmonary artery might so increase the work of the right ventricle that its output is reduced. There is little doubt that this does happen

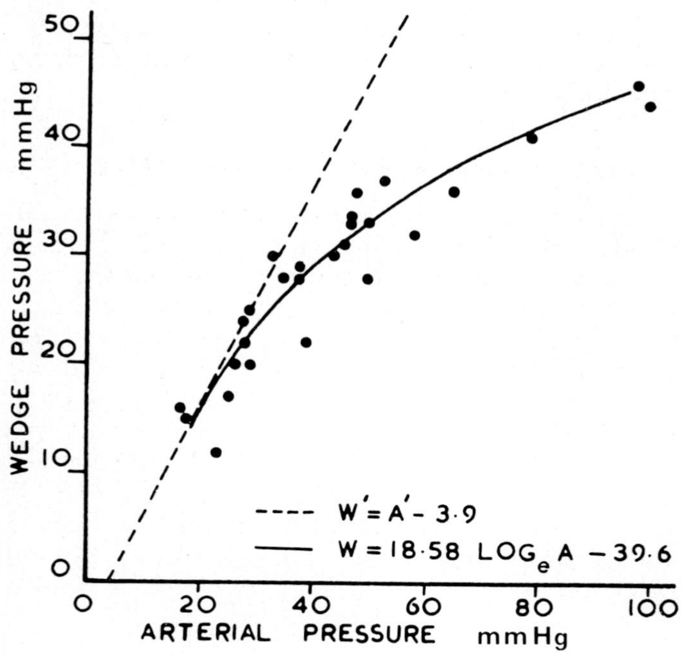

Fig. 23.3 The relation between the mean pulmonary arterial and mean wedge pressure in a group of twenty-seven patients with mitral stenosis.[10] The curved regression line has been calculated to fit the data by the method of least squares. The straight line is a tangent to the curved line and represents the relation which would be expected if resistance and flow remained constant.

in many patients during exercise and, in the more severely affected patients, even while at rest (Fig. 23.1, Table 23.1). In so far as this is true, the increased resistance in the pulmonary circulation may be said to 'protect' the pulmonary capillaries against oedema.

It will be recalled that the changes in the muscular pulmonary arteries in patients with disease of the mitral valve are virtually confined to the first three grades of hypertensive pulmonary vascular disease (Chap. 22). Dilatation lesions are not seen. Rarely, however, necrotizing arteritis may occur. The mildness of the changes in the muscular pulmonary arteries is consistent with the mild increase in pulmonary vascular resistance found usually in haemodynamic studies. Thus both the histological changes and the pulmonary vascular resistance differ from observations made in patients with severe pulmonary hypertension associated with congenital cardiac defects. It is possible that, in order to produce the degree of resistance associated with dilatation lesions, the left atrial pressure would have to reach a level which has so serious effect on the lungs as to be incompatible with life. Another determining factor may be the effect of the pulmonary arterial pressure on the output of the right ventricle. If severe hypertensive pulmonary vascular disease were associated with an extreme elevation of the left atrial pressure, the total resistance to flow from the right ventricle might cause the output of that ventricle to decrease beyond what is compatible with life. In patients with congenital defects, the right ventricle is able to profit by the ability to reverse the shunt and, in this way, the total systemic flow of blood is not rigidly restricted by the pulmonary blood flow.

Relations Between Pressure and Flow in the Pulmonary Circulation

Studying a group of patients with mitral valvar disease of differing severity provides information, such as that presented in Figure 23.3, from which deductions may be made concerning the natural history of the haemodynamic changes in the pulmonary circulation during the evolution of the disease. It does not tell us what is the relation between pressure and flow in the pulmonary circulation in a particular patient at a particular time. This information has been derived using the technique of occluding the right branch of the pulmonary artery by means of an inflatable balloon (see Chap. 9, p. 129). The results of such studies[11] are shown in Figure 23.4. Compared with normal subjects (Fig. 9.13, p. 130) the relation between pressure and flow tends to be steeper, indicating an increased resistance. The linearity of the relation is preserved, suggesting that, within a two-fold increase in flow, there is no change in the calibre of those vessels which are the site of resistance. From this point of view the behaviour of the pulmonary circuit is similar to that found in normal people.

Effects of Exercise

Since the original observations of Hickam and Cargill[12] there has been a number of consistent reports on the effects of exercise in patients with mitral

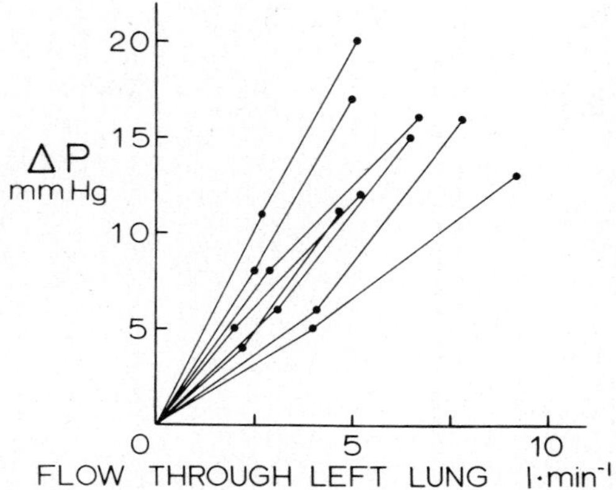

Fig. 23.4 Relation between the flow of blood through the left lung and the difference between the pulmonary arterial and wedge pressure (ΔP) in patients with mitral stenosis. Each line is based on two points. These represent observations made under normal resting conditions and when the flow of blood through the left lung has been increased by blocking the right pulmonary artery with a balloon (see p. 129).

stenosis.[13–17] Figure 23.1 and Table 23.1 show the effects of bicycling exercise in a series of fifty consecutive patients with mitral stenosis. Exercise causes the wedge pressure to increase. It often exceeds 40 mmHg and is frequently above the osmotic pressure of the plasma. In patients with very mild stenosis, the wedge pressure may be normal at rest but rises an abnormal amount with exercise. The pulmonary arterial pressure usually increases to a greater extent than the wedge pressure. The response of the cardiac output to exercise is usually less than normal in these patients and becomes more impaired the greater the degree of pulmonary hypertension. In the most severely affected patients the cardiac output may not increase at all. From the data given in Table 23.1 it may be deduced that the pulmonary arterial resistance rose on the average during exercise. Experiments using the technique of occluding the right pulmonary artery with a balloon have, however, failed to show any substantial effect of exercise on the relation between pressure and flow.[11] In Figure 23.5 the observations made during exercise fall on the resting pressure: flow line or on a rectilinear extrapolation of it.

The elevation in left atrial pressure during exercise is at least partly due to the increase in the flow of blood through the stenosed valve. The limitation in the response of the cardiac output to exercise which develops in the more severely affected patients may thus prevent the left atrial pressure reaching levels which must cause pulmonary oedema. It is the high resistance offered by the muscular pulmonary arteries which appears to limit the response of the cardiac output by overburdening the right ventricle.

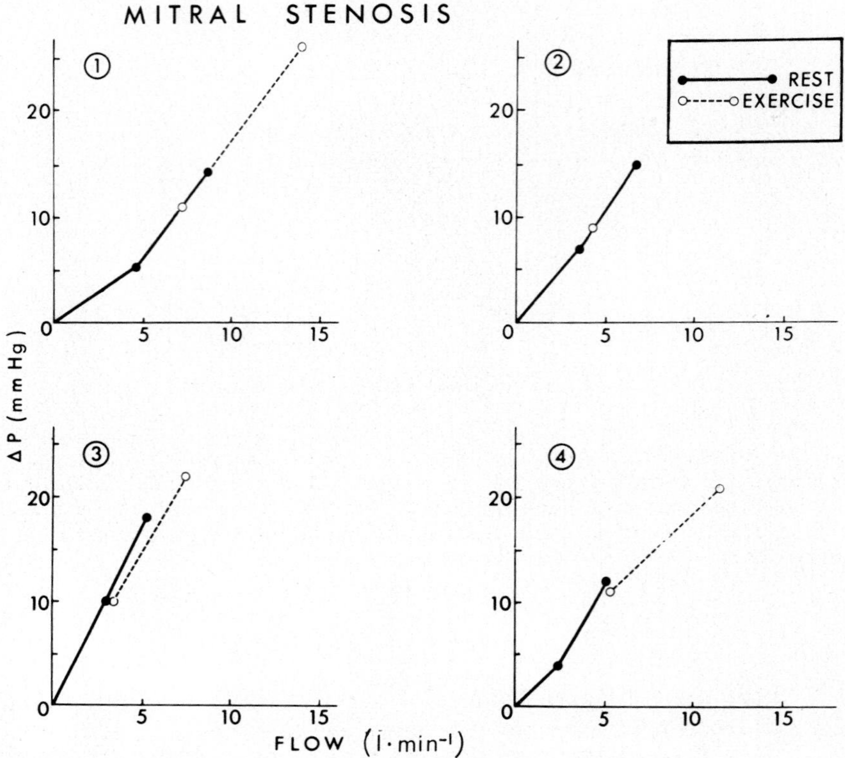

Fig. 23.5 Observations at rest and on exercise on four patients with mitral stenosis using the same technique as in Figure 23.4.

The Pulmonary Blood Volume

From the sustained increase which occurs throughout the pulmonary circulation in patients with disease of the mitral valve, one would anticipate an increase in the pulmonary blood volume. Of the studies which have been published on this point we shall omit the measurements of the 'central' blood volume which includes the volume of blood in the left atrium and left ventricle. The results of more precise investigations of the pulmonary blood volume by dye dilution techniques[18–25] are summarized in Table 8.1 (p. 105). In a number of these publications,[19–21,23,25] comparisons have been made between subjects with a normal pulmonary circulation and those with rheumatic disease of the mitral valve. Four out of five of these publications showed the pulmonary blood volume to be increased in disease of the mitral valve, while the fifth[23] showed a decrease. The average value of all these studies was 256 ml/m^2 BSA in 48 normal subjects and 351 ml/m^2 BSA in 112 patients, with rheumatic disease of the mitral valve. Using an analogue computer analysis of radiocardiographic data, Perasalo and Heiskanen[26] found an average of 204 ml/m^2 BSA for the pulmonary blood volume in 15 normal subjects and 211 ml/m^2 BSA in 10 patients with mitral stenosis.

There are many imponderables in evaluating the possible effects of mitral valvar disease on the errors inherent in the dye-dilution methods. These patients have a lower cardiac output than normal which will increase the mean transit time in the lungs and diminish proportionately the error introduced by sampling through catheters.[18] The increased size of the pulmonary artery may increase the degree of streaming following an injection at that site, and this needs to be related to the specific changes in the distribution of the flow of blood in the lungs which accompany mitral stenosis. An enlarged left atrium in the presence of mitral stenosis may decrease the efficiency of mixing in that chamber, while the presence of mitral regurgitation may improve mixing.

Taking the published data as a whole, it seems likely that the pulmonary blood volume does increase in disease of the mitral valve but that this is unlikely to be more than by about one third on the average. Such an increase may seem smaller than one would expect. A number of factors, however, needs to be taken into account. First the relation between pressure and volume in all sections of the system is not linear and distensibility decreases as pressure rises. To be set against this is the possibility that a prolonged increase in transmural pressure might cause a vessel to enlarge to an extent that would not occur under brief physiological conditions. The issue is further complicated by the changes in the structure of the blood vessels induced by the disease (Chap. 22). The walls of the pulmonary trunk, for instance, where we have information concerning both the structure and the mechanical properties, are thickened but the material composing the media has the same histological appearance (p. 267) and the same degree of extensibility (Chap. 18, p. 283) as the normal. Finally, as is discussed in Chapter 8, not all sections of the pulmonary circulation will have the same characteristics of distensibility. Different classes of vessels possess walls of different structures and their wide range of calibre implies a wide variation in the Laplace effect (p. 52).

The Distribution of Blood Supply to the Lungs

A number of studies has been made concerning the distribution of pulmonary blood flow in patients with mitral stenosis. The techniques used have been the inhalation of $C^{15}O_2$ (Ref. 27) or the intravenous injection of ^{133}Xe (Refs 28 and 29) or the use of ^{131}I-labelled macro-aggregated albumin.[30] Although expressed in slightly different ways, all are agreed that there is a redistribution of blood flow so that the upper portions of the lungs tend to become more perfused than the bases. Friedman and Braunwald[30] found a close correlation between this effect and the pulmonary arterial and left atrial pressures and a negative correlation with the cardiac output.

Although a tendency to a similar redistribution of flow may be found in patients with other forms of pulmonary arterial hypertension, the redistribution for a given level of pulmonary arterial pressure is greater in patients with mitral valvar disease than in those with a normal left atrial pressure.[30] The careful studies of Hughes and his colleagues[31] demonstrated that the distribution of flow at residual lung volume was similar to that in normals, showing a gradual decrease from apex to base (Chap. 7, p. 101). The difference between patients with mitral valvar disease and normal subjects became most apparent at total lung capacity when the point of maximal regional blood flow was 7 cm nearer the apex in the patients than in the normals.

The reason for the change in distribution of blood flow remains enigmatic. An equalization of the distribution of flow would be expected to follow an increase in pulmonary arterial pressure (Chap. 7, p. 100) since a high pressure in the pulmonary artery would overcome the effects of gravity. What is difficult to explain is the reversal of the normal distribution. There is radiographic evidence that both the pulmonary arteries and pulmonary veins are narrowed at the bases of the lungs while they are enlarged at the apices.[32-35] Histologically, the abnormalities in the muscular pulmonary arteries are most severe at the bases (Chap. 22, p. 347). There is, therefore, an anatomical basis for the physiological observations. On the other hand, the reason why the structural changes affect predominantly the vessels to the lower lobes remains obscure. It seems unlikely that hypoxia due to under-ventilation of the bases of the lungs is a determining factor since the regional distribution of ventilation has been found to be normal[28] and since the structural changes found in the blood vessels are not those associated characteristically with hypoxia. It has been suggested that perivascular oedema could compress the more dependent blood vessels.[36] The physical basis for this suggestion, however, does not seem rigorously to have been established and one would have expected that the increase in hydrostatic tissue pressure from apex to base would be matched by a similar increase in intra-luminal vascular pressure. Moreover, the normal distribution of ventilation speaks against alterations in compliance and small airways resistance such as would be expected if there were basal oedema.

Alternatively, it might be inferred that there is, in the muscular pulmonary arteries of the lowest parts of the lungs, an increased tone which leads both to an increased resistance and to an increased muscularity. If the increased tone were itself stimulated by an increased intravascular pressure (Chap. 18, p. 275) it would be reasonable to expect it to be greatest at the bottom of the lungs where, in the upright position, the hydrostatic pressure is greatest. The infusion of acetylcholine into one main branch of the pulmonary artery caused a relative increase in the perfusion of the base of the lung on that side and no change in the distribution of flow on the other side.[29] The inhalation of oxygen also caused a relative increase in basal perfusion.[28] It is not permissible, however, to interpret such experiments simply in terms of the distribution of tone. The distribution of calibre may be just as important, since a given change in medial muscular tension will have a proportionately greater effect on resistance in a vessel with a small lumen.

The physiological shunt and physiological dead space (Chap. 36) have been found to be increased in patients with mitral stenosis.[37] This is evidence of an unequal distribution of the ventilation: perfusion ratio.

Table 23.2 The diffusing capacity for carbon monoxide and haemodynamics in (sitting) patients with rheumatic disease of the mitral valve. The values from the same laboratory for normal subjects sitting and lying are also given. Data from Yu.[56] Only mean values are given. II, III and IV are functional classification.

	Mitral valvar disease			Normal	
	II	III	IV	Sitting	Lying
Number of cases	11	45	13		
Cardiac index ($l \cdot min^{-1}/m^2$ BSA)	2·6	2·2	1·5		
Mean pulmonary arterial pressure (mmHg)	26	32	49		
Wedge pressure (mmHg)	15	21	26		
Pulmonary arterial resistance ($dyn \cdot s \cdot cm^{-5}$)	200	284	855		
D_L ($ml/mmHg/min/m^2$ BSA)	16	13	8	16	18
D_M ($ml/mmHg/min/m^2$ BSA)	39	28	21	43	39
Vc (ml/m^2 BSA)	49	49	26	37	52

Diffusion

The effects of mitral stenosis on the diffusing capacity are complex and are discussed in Chapter 42, p. 648. Jordan and his colleagues,[38] in a study which attempted to relate physiological measurements with morbid histology, concluded that the impairment of the diffusing capacity 'depends less on the structure of the alveolar wall than on the presence of occlusive pulmonary vascular changes'. Of the two components of the diffusing capacity (p. 639) the membrane component, D_M, shows a progressive decrease with an increasing severity of the disease. The capillary volume (Vc) may be somewhat increased in the early stages, but ultimately becomes diminished. The values reported by Yu[56] are summarized in Table 23.2.

The Effects of Mitral Stenosis on Respiratory Mechanics

Many workers have found a decreased distensibility ('compliance') of the lungs in patients with mitral stenosis.[39–42] The rigidity of the lungs may be due to fibrosis and chronic oedema which accompanies severe mitral stenosis. It may also be partly due to an increased distending pressure in the pulmonary vessels (Chap. 25).

Pulmonary Oedema

In the more severely affected patients, the pressure in the pulmonary capillaries must often exceed the osmotic pressure of the plasma during exercise or excitement, and pulmonary oedema (see Chap. 24) is prone to develop. It is surprising that it does not occur more frequently. Possibly the reason for this lies in the abundant lymph drainage,[43] evidence for which may be found in the presence of Kerley's B lines on the radiograph (Fig. 22.10, p. 343) and in the observations of dilated lymph vessels on the surface of the lungs at thoracotomy or in the substance of the lungs in histological sections (Fig. 22.11, p. 343). It seems likely that the rate of development of left atrial hypertension is important. When this occurs gradually, as in rheumatic disease of the mitral valve, there is time for the development of an augmented lymphatic drainage system. Where left atrial hypertension arises suddenly, as in ruptured chordae tendineae, there is no time for the development of lymphatics and pulmonary oedema is more likely to occur.

The pressure in the pulmonary capillaries is obviously dependent on the ratio of flow to resistance at the mitral valve. Sarnoff *et al.*[44–46] have shown how the pulmonary capillary pressure is also dependent on the state of the systemic circulation. Widespread constriction of systemic arteries and veins will cause blood to be displaced from the systemic into the pulmonary circulation and thus increase the intravascular pressures in the lungs. This may be the prime cause of the pulmonary oedema which is associated with damage to the brain and seems to be at least an important contributory cause of the pulmonary oedema which occurs in left-ventricular failure from various lesions. Widespread peripheral vasoconstriction often occurs in patients with mitral stenosis. Their cold, white skin is witness to this and is particularly noticeable in the presence of congestive failure or pulmonary oedema. Pulmonary oedema associated with systemic vasoconstriction may be alleviated by giving ganglion-blocking drugs which cause the systemic vessels to dilate and drain blood away from the lungs.[47]

With the onset of acute pulmonary oedema, there is a rise in the pulmonary arterial and wedge pressures and in the right atrial pressure.[48] The cardiac output falls. There is an increase in the rate of uptake of oxygen by the lungs, presumably due to the combination of an increased ventilation and a decreased distensibility of the lungs which together increase the work of breathing. There is a decrease in the arterial oxygen saturation. With subjective improvement, all these measurements return to their previous levels, the arterial oxygen saturation being the last to do so. These changes are observed irrespective of whether the pulmonary oedema is associated with mitral stenosis or left ventricular failure.[48]

Pharmacology of the Pulmonary Circulation in Mitral Stenosis

The muscular hypertrophy of the muscular pulmonary arteries in mitral stenosis and the high resistance to the flow of blood through them has provided an ideal situation for the testing of dilator drugs. There is evidence that acetylcholine, oxygen, amyl nitrate, aminophylline, histamine, bradykinin, isoprenaline and reserpine (Chap. 13) have a dilating effect.

The dilating effects of acetylcholine in the circulation have been used to investigate the distribution of the ventilation:perfusion ratio in mitral stenosis. The infusion of this substance was noted to cause a fall in the arterial oxygen saturation[49] and it was suggested that acetylcholine had released local vasoconstriction in under-ventilated areas of the lung and thus increased the perfusion through these areas. Measurements of the alveolar–arterial difference in oxygen tension (Chap. 36) during the breathing of high concentrations of oxygen[37,50] have confirmed that, in patients with mitral stenosis, the infusion of acetylcholine often causes an increase in the physiological shunt. Since the total pulmonary blood flow remains unchanged during the infusion of acetylcholine, an increased flow of blood through under-ventilated areas must necessarily mean a decreased flow through areas with a higher ventilation:perfusion ratio. This is presumably the cause of the increase in physiological dead space which was also observed in these patients. The anatomical shunt measured with 100 per cent oxygen is unaffected by acetylcholine.[50]

In patients with a mean pulmonary arterial pressure over 45 mmHg, acetylcholine may have the reverse effect. In these patients, the physiological shunt and dead space are greatest and this is presumably due to the increasing mal-distribution of blood flow which develops as the pulmonary hypertension becomes more severe (p. 359). Under these circumstances, it is possible that acetylcholine acts preferentially on those vessels where the media is most hypertrophied and the lumen most narrowed. In this case the action of the drug would be to increase the flow of blood through areas with a high ventilation:perfusion ratio and to decrease the flow through areas with a low ratio. Thus the effect would be to diminish both the physiological shunt and the dead space (Fig. 23.6).

The Effects of Valvotomy

There have been several series of observations on this subject.[51-55] Measurements of the immediate effects of valvotomy on the operating table may be misleading

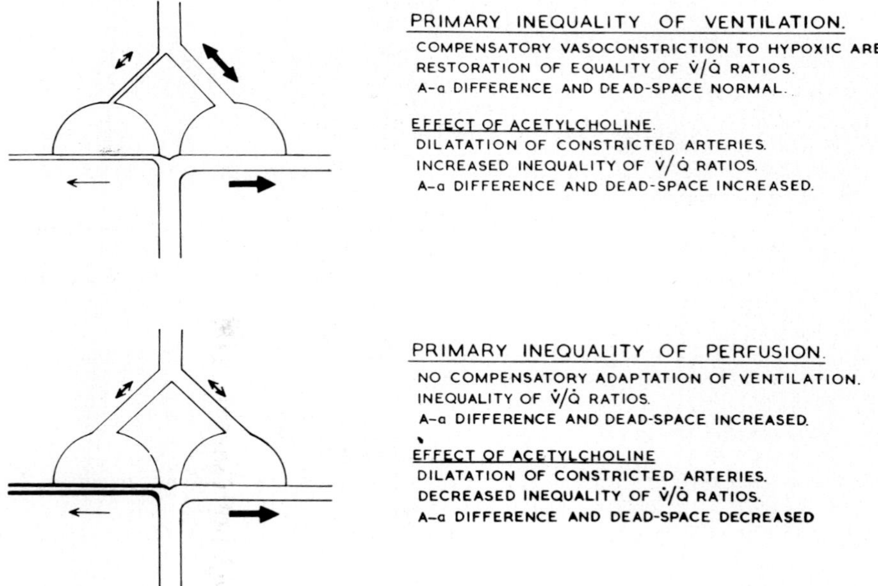

Fig. 23.6 Diagram to illustrate the explanation of the varying effects of acetylcholine on respiratory gas exchange in patients with mitral stenosis.

owing to the changes within the myocardium and the systemic circulation which accompany the manipulation. Cardiac catheterization a few weeks after the operation usually shows a fall in the pulmonary arterial and wedge pressures and this is generally observed in studies made up to two years after the operation. In a study of twelve patients,[55] for instance, the average pulmonary arterial and wedge pressures were 52 and 28 mmHg, respectively, a week before the operation, 33 and 17 mmHg within three months after the operation, and 29 and 18 mmHg between eight and thirty months after the operation. Most authors have found little change or slight increase in the cardiac output after valvotomy, although in one study[54] there was a diminution. Calculations of the pulmonary arterial resistance usually show that a diminution occurs after the operation. Since the mechanical effect of a lowered left atrial pressure would be to increase resistance and since the pulmonary blood flow has usually changed very little, there is every reason to believe that this represents an increased distensibility of the vessels which are the site of the resistance. Presumably these are the muscular pulmonary arteries. The increased distensibility may in part be due to a diminution in the tone of their medial musculature but there may also be a regression of the structural abnormalities themselves. We know of no information on this point. Presumably in those very rare instances where a necrotizing arteritis occurs in the muscular pulmonary arteries, the anatomical changes and resistance are irreversible.

Physiological measurements made two to five years after mitral valvotomy have shown a tendency to the re-development of the pulmonary venous and arterial hypertension in nine out of twelve reported cases.[54,55]

REFERENCES

1. Gorlin, R. & Gorlin, S. G. (1951) *Amer. Heart J.*, **41**, 1.
2. Allison, P. R. & Linden, R. J. (1955) *Lancet*, **i**, 9.
3. Braunwald, E., Moscovitz, H. L., Amram, S. S., Lasser, R. P., Sapin, S. O., Himmelstein, A., Ravitch, M. M. & Gordon, A. J. (1955) *Circulation*, **12**, 69.
4. Fox, I. J., Wakai, C. S., Connolly, D. C. & Wood, E. H. (1956) *Proc. Mayo Clin.*, **31**, 126.
5. Marrow, A. G., Braunwald, E., Haller, J. A. & Sharp, E. H. (1957) *Circulation*, **16**, 399.
6. Messer, A. L., Counihan, T. B., Rappaport, M. B. & Sprague, H. B. (1951) *Circulation*, **4**, 576.
7. Wells, B. (1954) *Brit. Heart J.*, **16**, 261.
8. Owen, S. G. & Wood, P. (1955) *Brit. Heart J.*, **17**, 41.
9. Dexter, L., Dow, J. W., Haynes, F. W., Whittenberger, J. L., Ferris, B. G., Goodale, W. T. & Hellems, H. K. (1950) *J. Clin. Invest.*, **29**, 602.
10. Harris, P. (1955) *PhD. Thesis.* University of London.
11. Harris, P., Segel, N. & Bishop, J. M. (1968) *Cardiovasc. Res.*, **2**, 73.
12. Hickam, J. B. & Cargill, W. H. (1948) *J. Clin. Invest.*, **27**, 10.
13. Draper, A., Heimbecker, R., Daley, R., Carroll, D., Mudd, G., Wells, R., Falholt, W., Andrus, E. C. & Bing, R. J. (1951) *Circulation*, **3**, 531.
14. Gorlin, R., Sawyer, C. G., Haynes, F. W., Goodale, W. T. & Dexter, L. (1951) *Amer. Heart J.*, **41**, 192.
15. Eliasch, H. (1952) *Scand. J. Clin. Lab. Invest.* Suppl. **4**.
16. Lukas, D. S. & Dotter, C. T. (1952) *Amer. J. Med.*, **12**, 639.
17. Donald, K. W., Bishop, J. M. & Wade, O. L. (1954) *J. Clin. Invest.*, **33**, 1146.
18. Milnor, W. R. & Jose, A. D. (1960) *J. Appl. Physiol.*, **15**, 177.

19. Dock, D. S., Kraus, W. L., McQuire, L. B., Hyland, J. W., Haynes, F. W. & Dexter, L. (1961) *J. Clin. Invest.*, **40**, 317.
20. McGaff, C. J., Roveti, G. C., Glassman, E. & Milnor, W. R. (1963) *Circulation*, **27**, 77.
21. Roy, S. B., Bhardwaj, P. & Bhatia, M. L. (1965) *Brit. Med. J.*, **ii**, 1466.
22. Samet, P., Bernstein, W. H., Medow, A. & Levine, S. (1965) *Dis. Chest*, **47**, 632.
23. Schreiber, B. F., Jn., Murphy, G. W. & Yu, P. N. (1966) *Circulation*, **34**, 249.
24. Levinson, G. E., Frank, M. J. & Hellems, H. K. (1964) *Amer. Heart J.*, **67**, 734.
25. de Freitas, F. M., Faraco, E. Z., Nedel, N., de Azevedo, D. F. & Zaduchliver, J. (1964) *Circulation*, **30**, 370.
26. Perasalo, J. & Heiskanen, T. (1971) *Cardiovasc. Res.*, **5**, 260.
27. Dollery, C. T. & West, J. B. (1960) *Circulat. Res.*, **8**, 765.
28. Dawson, A., Kaneko, K. & McGregor, M. (1965) *J. Clin. Invest.*, **44**, 999.
29. Glazier, J. B., Dollery, C. T. & Hughes, J. M. P. (1968) *Circulation*, **38**, 136.
30. Friedman, W. F. & Braunwald, E. (1966) *Circulation*, **34**, 363.
31. Hughes, J. M. B., Glazier, J. B., Rosenzweig, D. Y. & West, J. B. (1969) *Clin. Sci.*, **37**, 847.
32. Goodwin, J. F., Steiner, R. E. & Lowe, K. G. (1952) *J. Fac. Radiol. (Lond.)*, **4**, 21.
33. Avedsson, H. & Odman, P. (1957) *Acta Radiol.*, **47**, 97.
34. Doyle, A. E., Goodwin, J. F., Harrison, C. V. & Steiner, R. E. (1957) *Brit. Heart J.*, **19**, 353.
35. Steiner, R. E. (1958) *Brit. J. Radiol.*, **31**, 188.
36. West, J. B., Dollery, C. T. & Heard, B. E. (1965) *Circulat. Res.*, **17**, 191.
37. Bishop, J. M., Harris, P., Bateman, M. & Davidson, L. A. G. (1961) *J. Clin. Invest.*, **40**, 105.
38. Jordan, S. C., Hicken, P., Watson, D. A., Heath, D. & Whitaker, W. (1966) *Brit. Heart J.*, **28**, 101.
39. Mead, J., Frank, N. R., Lindgren, I., Gaensler, E. A. & Whittenberger, J. L. (1953) *Proc. Amer. Fed. Clin. Res.*, **1**, 116.
40. Brown, C. C., Fry, D. L. & Ebert, R. V. (1954) *Amer. J. Med.*, **17**, 438.
41. Marshall, R., McIlroy, M. B. & Christie, R. V. (1954) *Clin. Sci.*, **13**, 137.
42. White, H. C., Butler, J. & Donald, K. W. (1958) *Clin. Sci.*, **17**, 667.
43. Drinker, C. K. (1945) In *Pulmonary Edema and Inflammation*. Harvard University Press.
44. Sarnoff, S. J. & Sarnoff, L. C. (1952) *Circulation*, **6**, 51.
45. Sarnoff, S. J., Berglund, E. & Sarnoff, L. C. (1953) *J. Appl. Physiol.*, **5**, 367.
46. Sarnoff, S. J. & Berglund, E. (1952) *Amer. J. Physiol.*, **170**, 588.
47. Sarnoff, S. J., Goodale, W. T. & Sarnoff, L. C. (1952) *Circulation*, **6**, 63.
48. Fejfar, Z., Fejfarova, M., Bergmann, K. & Brod, J. (1958) *Abstracts of the IIIrd World Congress of Cardiology*, p. 171.
49. Söderholm, B. & Werkö, L. (1959) *Brit. Heart J.*, **21**, 1.
50. Bishop, J. M., Harris, P., Bateman, M. & Raine, J. M. (1962) *Clin. Sci.*, **22**, 53.
51. Carlotti, J., Joly, F., Sicot, J. R. & Voci, G. (1953) *Sem. Hop. Paris*, **29**, 2079.
52. Werkö, L., Biorck, G., Crafoord, C., Wulff, H., Kroak, H. & Eliasch, H. (1953) *Amer. Heart J.*, **45**, 477.
53. Goodale, F., Jn., Sanchez, G., Friedlich, A. L., Scannell, J. G. & Myers, G. S. (1955) *New Engl. J. Med.*, **252**, 979.
54. Donald, K. W., Bishop, J. M., Wade, O. L. & Wormald, P. N. (1957) *Clin. Sci.*, **16**, 325.
55. Lyons, W. S., Tompkins, R. G., Kirklin, J. W. & Wood, E. H. (1959) *J. Lab. Clin. Med.*, **53**, 499.
56. Yu, P. N. (1969) In *Pulmonary Blood Volume in Health and Disease*. Lea & Febiger.

24. The Interstitial Space of the Lung and Pulmonary Oedema

Anatomy of the Interstitial Space

The walls of the pulmonary capillaries are composed of a single layer of endothelial cells resting upon a basement membrane (Fig. 24.1). At the site of the nucleus, the endothelial cell bulges into the lumen of the capillary but elsewhere its cytoplasm forms a thin sheet (Figs 24.1 and 24.2). For the most part, the alveolar wall is lined by the flat membranous pneumocytes which are sometimes termed squamous or type 1 pneumocytes. Their cytoplasm also forms an exceedingly thin layer covering the fused basement membrane common to the alveolar and pulmonary capillary wall (Figs 24.1 and 24.2). In the corners of the alveoli are to be found the granular or type 2 pneumocytes which are larger and project like demilunes into the alveolus (Fig. 24.3). Unlike pulmonary macrophages, their surface microvilli are short and regular and their cytoplasm contains the characteristic lamellar bodies which are thought to be the source of pulmonary surfactant (Fig. 24.3). The extensions of the cytoplasm of the granular pneumocytes frequently overlap that of the membranous pneumocyte.

Close apposition and fusion of basement membranes occur where the convexities of capillary and alveolus touch. In the corners between these rounded structures, the basement membranes of the pulmonary capillary and alveolar walls separate to leave interstitial spaces. Such minute tissue spaces are in continuity with spaces of increasing size which surround the airways and blood vessels and accompany them into the mediastinum. Thus dye injected under the pretracheal fascia after death penetrates readily into the perivascular and peribronchial spaces of the lung.[1] Conversely, dye injected by micropipettes into the region of the subpleural alveoli of the cat[2,3] spreads rapidly along the perivascular and peribronchial spaces and into the lymphatics which arise in them.

Since the pulmonary capillaries are supported by strands of the connective tissue framework of the lung, they have a thin wall and a thick wall (Fig. 24.4). The thin wall consists of the attenuated cytoplasm of membranous pneumocytes, the fused basement membrane of alveolar epithelium and pulmonary capillary, and the cytoplasm of the capillary endothelium (Fig. 24.4). It is concerned with the exchange of respiratory gases. The thick wall has a layer of interstitial tissue between the separated basement membranes (Fig. 24.4). This part of the alveolar wall is concerned with the movement of tissue fluid. As we shall see later in the chapter, this division of the alveolar wall into thick and thin parts is of importance with regard to the anatomical situation and function of 'J-receptors' which appear to be stimulated by pulmonary congestion and oedema.

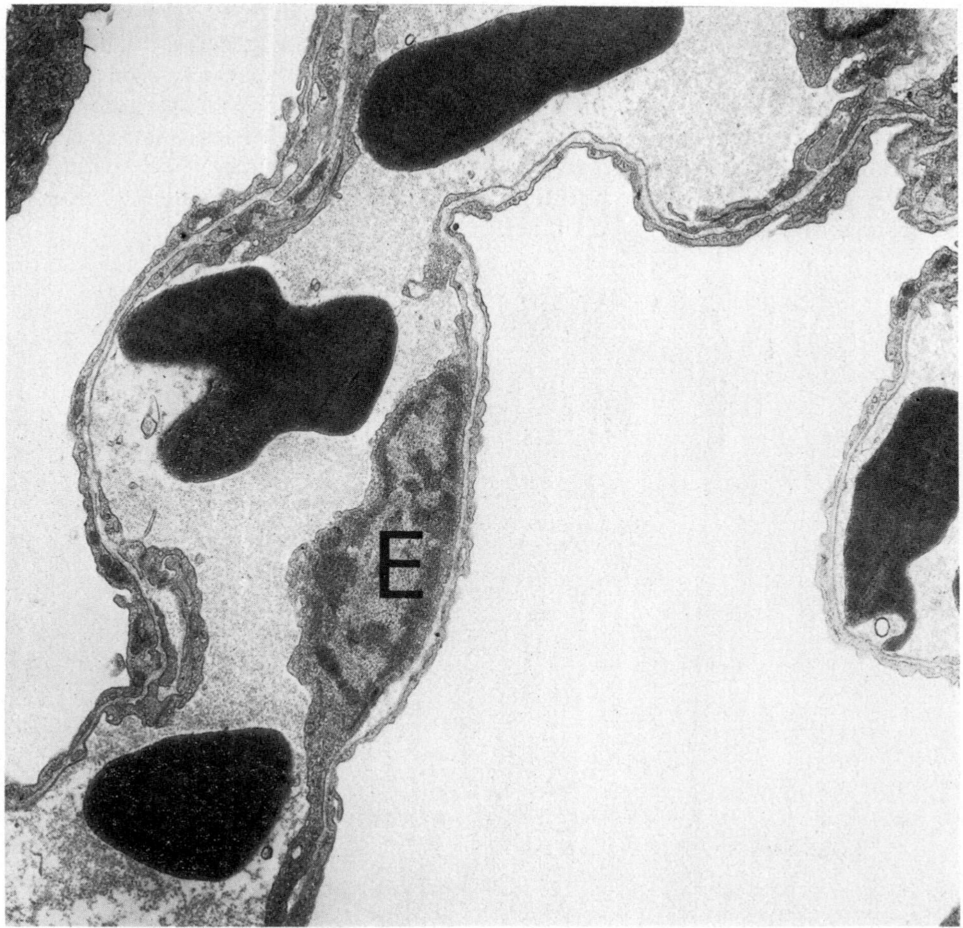

Fig. 24.1 Electron micrograph of lung from a normal Wistar albino rat. The pulmonary capillary is lined by a single layer of endothelial cells, E. The basement membranes of capillary and alveolar walls are fused but in places these are expanded into small blebs due to small collections of fluid in the interstitium. The alveolar aspect of the fused membranes is lined by thin cytoplasmic extensions of membranous pneumocytes. (× 7500)

Composition of the Interstitial Space

The regions of close opposition between alveolar epithelium and capillary endothelium are too thin to contain formed elements. In the larger tissue spaces at the corners of alveoli and capillaries and in the thick walls of the capillaries, fibrils of collagen and elastin occur together with various mesenchymal cells. The perivascular and peribronchial spaces consist of loose connective tissue in which small lymphatic vessels appear to arise.

It would seem that the space between the visible structures of the interstitium is not simply filled with a watery solution. Instead, the greater portion of it is occupied by a gel-like structure.[4] Mucopolysaccharides, especially hyaluronic acid, play an important rôle in the formation of this structure, probably cross-linking strands of collagen to form a mesh-work.[5–7] The rate of diffusion of small molecules and the bulk flow of water is greatly reduced through such gel-like structures[8] so that the free movement of tissue liquid probably occurs through that small proportion of the space which is unoccupied by gel.[9,10]

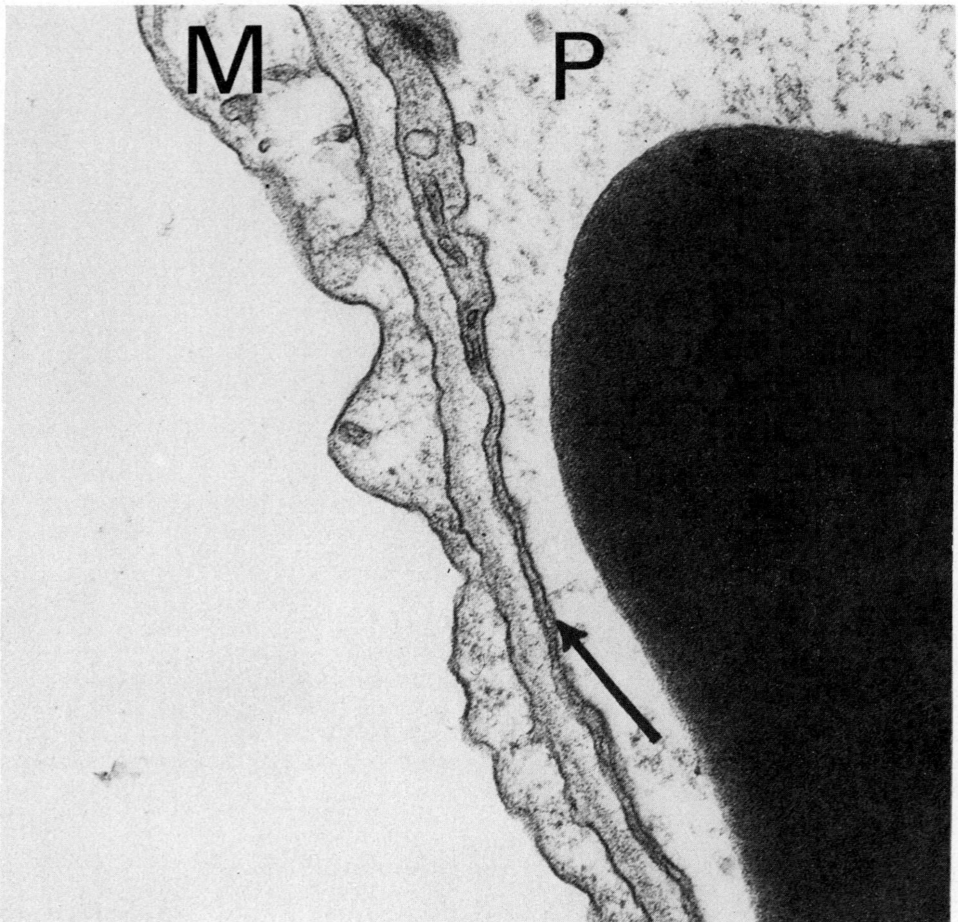

Fig. 24.2 Electron micrograph of alveolar-capillary wall of rat at high magnification. The thin layer of cytoplasm from a membranous pneumocyte, M, is seen covering the alveolar aspect of the fused basement membrane. The attenuated cytoplasmic lining of an endothelial cell (arrow) lines the capillary. The dark mass in the lower right-hand corner is an erythrocyte surrounded by plasma, P. (× 50 000)

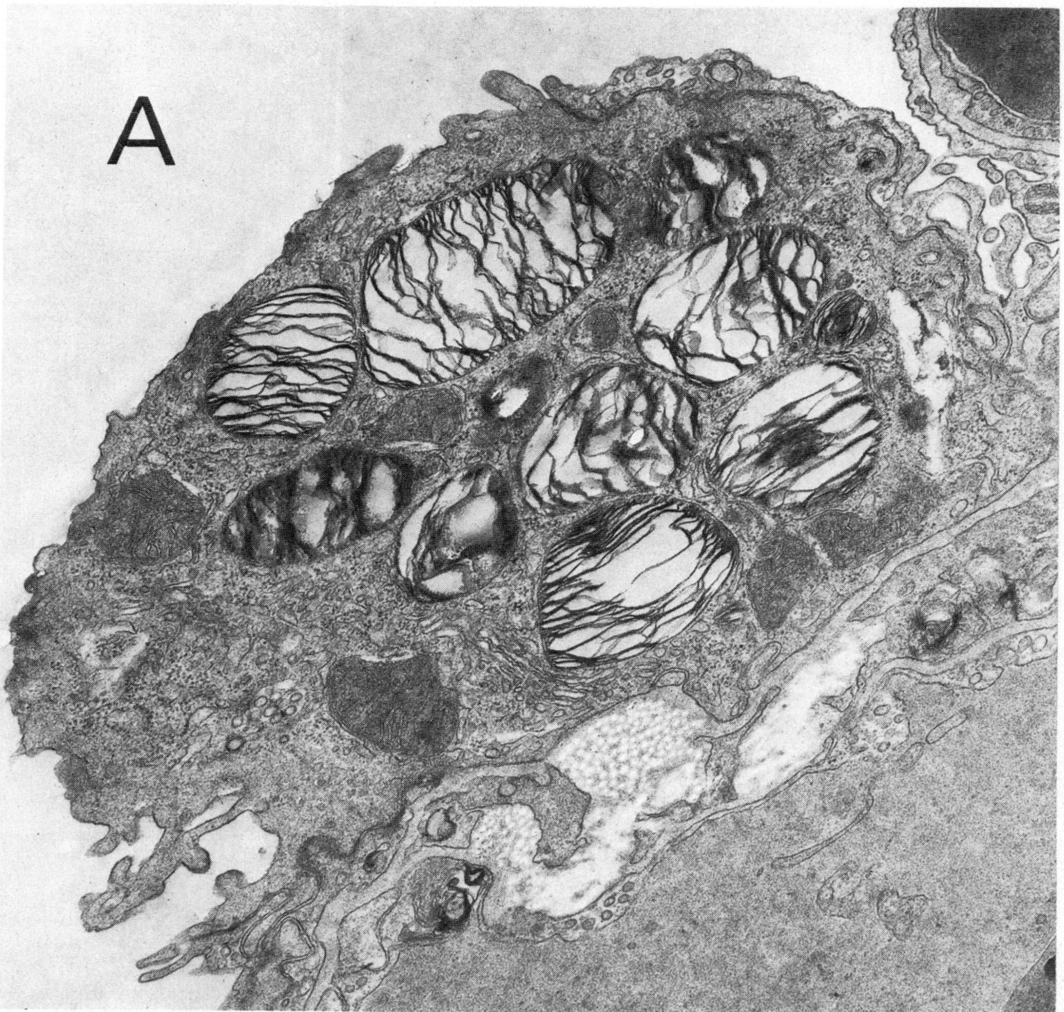

Fig. 24.3 Electron micrograph of lung from a Wistar albino rat. Into the alveolar space, A, projects a granular type 2 pneumocyte. Its cytoplasm contains lamellar bodies. (× 18 750)

Physical Properties of the Interstitial Space

The fibrous structures, collagen and elastin, of the interstitium form a complex system of restraints linking the visceral pleural surface with the blood vessels and respiratory passages. The mechanical effect of this system is to maintain the patency of the blood vessels in the inflated lung. The effect will be mainly on the larger blood vessels and those surrounded by a distinct perivascular space. The patency of the capillaries will be largely determined by local forces arising from the alveoli.

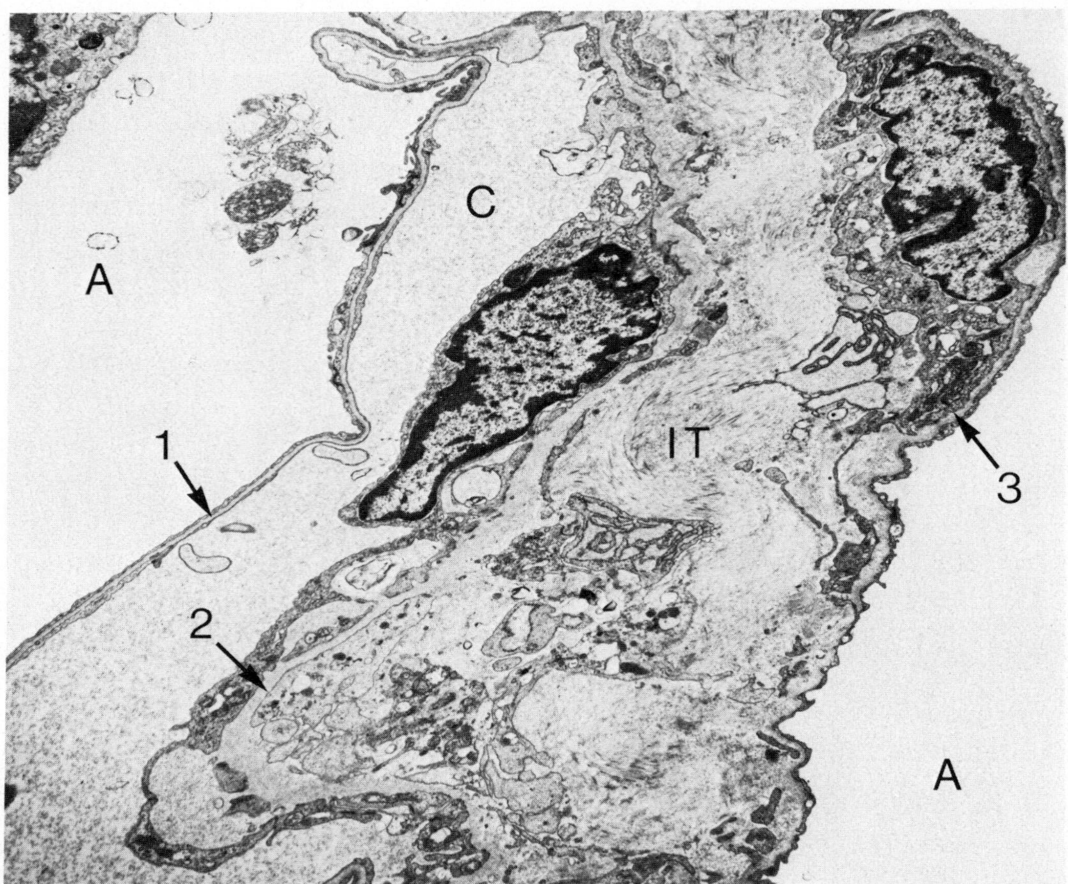

Fig. 24.4 Electron micrograph of lung from a Wistar albino rat. It shows that the alveolar wall is composed of thin and thick-walled parts. The thin wall is concerned with exchange of respiratory gases with the alveolar space, A. It consists, from without inwards, of the attenuated cytoplasm of membranous pneumocytes, the fused basement membrane of alveolar epithelium and pulmonary capillary (arrow 1) and the cytoplasm of the capillary endothelium. The lumen of the pulmonary capillary is indicated as C. The thick portion of the alveolar wall has a layer of collagenous interstitial tissue, IT, situated between the separated basement membranes (arrows 2 and 3). This part of the alveolar wall is concerned with the movement of tissue fluid. (× 5625)

The interstitial gel substance presumably possesses a bulk modulus of elasticity which will cause it to maintain the disposition of the vascular and respiratory structures and which will, in general, supply forces which are in the opposite direction to those generated by the fibrous network. Thus extension of the fibrous network will pull on vessels and tend to dilate them while the presence of a gel will tend to limit the dilatation. Doubtless, this antagonistic arrangement will add to the stability of the vessel wall.

The physical properties of the gel would be expected to be affected by its degree of hydration, while the hydrostatic pressure of the free interstitial liquid will in turn vary in a complex fashion according to the proportion of gel-substance to water. The structural network of cross-linked polymers which constitutes the gel-substance creates a complex system of pores in which extremely high forces of capillary attraction may be developed. This causes the gel to 'imbibe' water. Let us imagine, first, a lump of gel equilibrated with, and suspended in, an excess of water in a distensible bag (Fig. 24.5a). Then the hydrostatic pressure in the free water surrounding the gel will be the same as that in the pores of the gel and will be greater than atmospheric to a degree determined by the elasticity of the bag and the effects of gravity. Now imagine that water is gradually withdrawn from the bag. The volume of free water will decrease with perhaps very little change in pressure until the walls of the bag come into contact with the surface of the gel. If the process of withdrawing water continues beyond this point (Fig. 24.5b) there will be a sharp decrease in the hydrostatic pressure of the water in the bag. The volume of the bag will, however, tend to be maintained by the bulk forces of elasticity developed by the gel together with such elastic forces as might arise from the wall of the bag itself.

Recent research by Guyton,[4] using capsules embedded into tissues, and by Scholander,[11] using fine wicks introduced into tissues, has shown that an analogous situation exists in most normal interstitial spaces. In the lungs of living dogs, the hydrostatic pressure of the interstitial liquid was found to average about 6 mmHg less than atmospheric pressure[12] at a mid antero-posterior level.

The distribution of this hydrostatic pressure from the top to the bottom of the lung will be affected by gravity according to the height of the column of liquid supported. In this respect it will increase linearly from the apex to the base. With the exception of the apical portion of the lung, which may not be perfused with

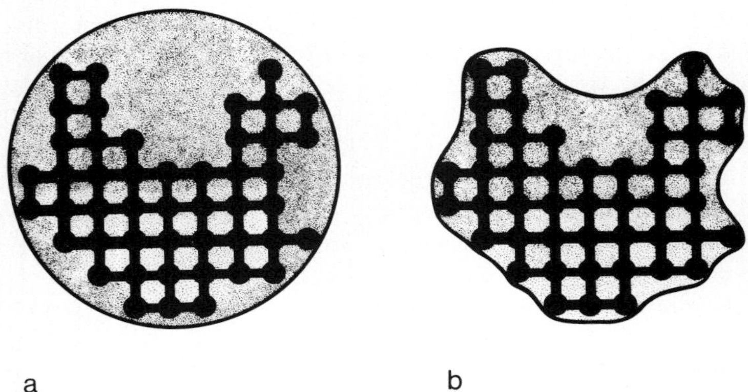

Fig. 24.5 The diagrams illustrate a model consisting of a gel (shown as a grid) suspended in water within a distensible bag. For description, see text.

blood (Chap. 7, p. 160), this linear increase will be of the same magnitude as the linear increase in intravascular pressure as the base is approached. Thus the difference between intravascular pressures and tissue liquid hydrostatic pressure (which largely determines the size of vessels and the bulk movement of liquid across their walls) is maintained constant at all perfused levels of the lung.

Movement of Water Through the Interstitial Space

It seems likely, as has been described above, that free movement of water occurs only in those limited spaces of the interstitium which are not occupied by gel matrix. Such spaces, however, form a continuum whereby water and solutes may pass readily throughout the lung. Bulk movement of water into and out of the interstitium is controlled by balances between hydrostatic and osmotic pressures either side of the vascular wall according to the Starling equation. In addition, water is being lost all the time through vaporization in the alveoli and by lymphatic drainage. Only a minute quantity of water can be formed *in situ* from oxidative processes. The permeability of the alveolar epithelium is considerably less than that of the capillary endothelium.[13]

It may be helpful to consider the order of magnitude in the lung of the forces of the classical Starling equation describing the algebraic relation between hydrostatic pressure, osmotic pressure and the movement of water across the wall of a vessel. We may take a figure of 28 mmHg for the colloid osmotic pressure of the plasma and 6 mmHg for that of the interstitial liquid.[14] The colloid osmotic pressure difference across the vessel wall is, therefore, about 22 mmHg and this will be so throughout the lung. The average pressure of free interstitial liquid in the dog's lung was found by Meyer *et al.*,[12] to be about 6 mmHg less than atmospheric at the mid antero-posterior line but various technical considerations led those authors to suggest a figure of 10 mmHg less than atmospheric to be more realistic. The average pulmonary capillary pressure in man, as judged by the wedge pressure, is about 9 mmHg above atmospheric measured from a similar reference point (p. 71). One may calculate, therefore, a transmural difference in pressure of about 19 mmHg. Such a difference will, as discussed above, remain constant at all levels.

It seems likely, therefore, that there is a close balance in the capillaries between the forces of osmotic pressure and those of hydrostatic pressure and that this balance is not affected by the height above the base of the lung. It may be expected that the higher transmural pressure on the arteriolar side will favour a movement of water into the interstitium while the lower transmural pressure on the venular side will favour a movement of water into the blood stream.

That the capillaries are not the only site of loss of water into the interstitial space is shown by the experiments of Iliff[15] on isolated dogs' lungs. In these experiments, the pulmonary capillaries were held shut by maintaining the alveolar pressure (25 cm water) greater than the pulmonary arterial or venous pressures (p. 164). Under these conditions the weight of the lung rose substantially when either the pulmonary arterial or the pulmonary venous pressures were increased to 20 cm water. The rate of loss of water into the interstitial space was about three times as great on the venous side as on the arterial side.

Physical Factors Underlying the Development of Pulmonary Oedema

While it is usual to consider the formation of interstitial liquid in terms of the Starling equation, it is important to appreciate that the immediately relevant equation is composed of rates of flow of liquid and not simply of pressures. On one side of this equation there is the net rate of entry of water into the interstitial space from the blood stream. On the other side is the sum of the rate of re-absorption into the blood stream and the rate of removal by the lymphatics and the rate of loss by vaporization in the alveoli. The accumulation of interstitial liquid occurs when the rate of entry exceeds the sum of the factors on the other side of the equation. The expression of the equation in terms of rates of flow reveals the importance of time in the course of events. It also keeps us mindful of the rôle of lymphatic drainage.

Under physiological conditions the magnitude of lymphatic drainage does not seem sufficient to modify the balance of the equation to any substantial degree.[16] On the other hand, during acute pulmonary oedema, there is an increase in lymphatic drainage and this must determine the severity and rapidity of development of the oedema. In addition, in patients with chronic venous hypertension, an increase in the size of the lymphatic system develops (p. 341) which plays an important rôle in the prevention of oedema. During chronic experimental pulmonary venous hypertension in dogs, the flow of lymph has been found to increase up to 28 times.[17]

In practice the primary cause of pulmonary oedema is always an increase in the rate of passage of water from the blood stream into the interstitium. The two ways in which this arises are: (1) an increase in the intraluminal pressure of the pulmonary capillaries and almost certainly the muscular pulmonary arteries, arterioles and venules; (2) an increase in the permeability of the walls of these vessels. In each case the distribution of the water which is retained in the lung appears to be determined by the same physical factors. Thus, in the experimental animal, the sequence of accumulation of water in the lung is the same irrespective of the cause of the oedema.[18] The experiments of Staub[18] on dogs showed that water accumulated first in the peribronchial and perivascular interstitial spaces. This is presumably because the compliance of these parts of the interstitial space is greatest. Next there was a small increase in the alveolar-capillary distance. These two layers are closely apposed and their cell surfaces may even share a common basement membrane (p. 366) so that it is understandable that a relatively high pressure will be required to separate them. Finally the alveoli filled with fluid.

Changes also occur in the cellular anatomy of the pulmonary capillary endothelium. In early pulmonary oedema, fluid collecting in the interstitial space balloons into the lumen of the pulmonary capillary as an 'endothelial vesicle' (Fig. 24.6). These vesicles are covered by the attenuated cytoplasm of the endothelial cells of the pulmonary capillary and are filled with oedema fluid (Fig. 24.6). They tend to take the shape of the pulmonary capillaries and become sausage-shaped

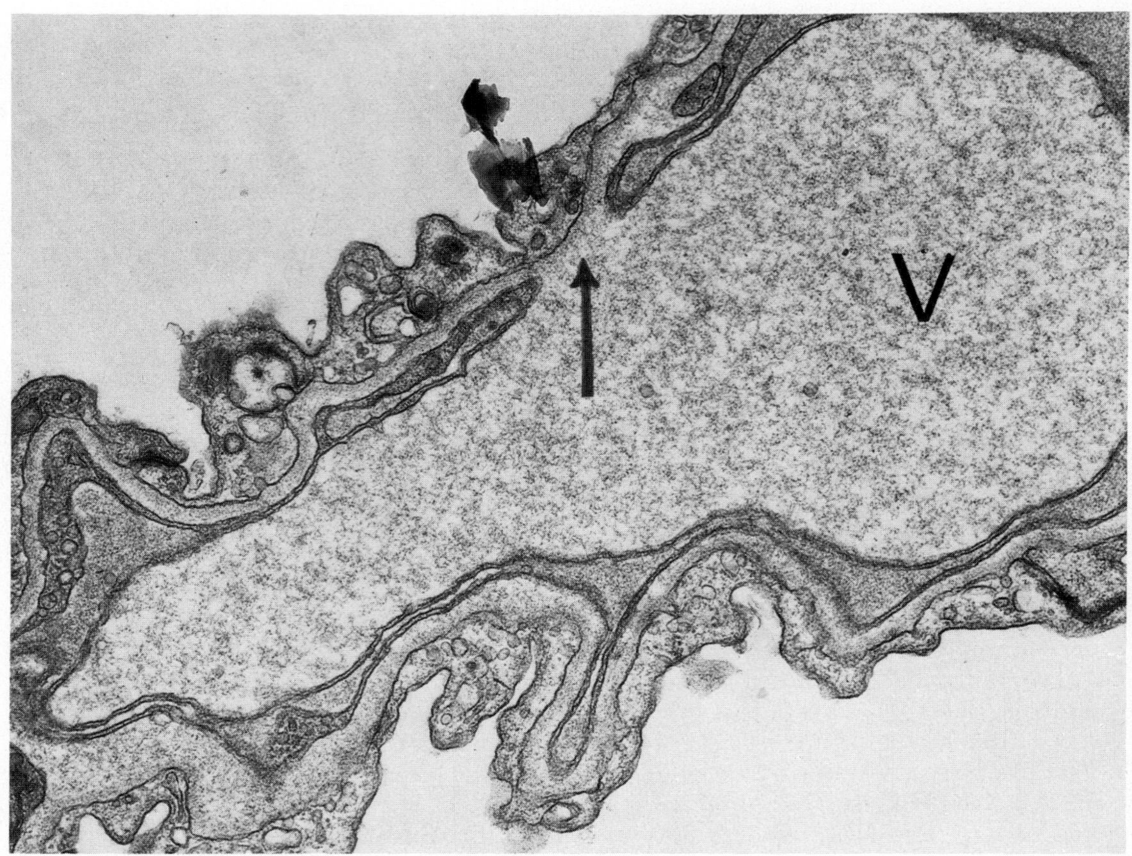

Fig. 24.6 Electron micrograph of lung from a Wistar albino rat in early pulmonary oedema after exposure to acute hypoxia due to reduced barometric pressure. An endothelial vesicle, V, projects into a pulmonary capillary assuming its elongated shape. The site of formation of the vesicle is indicated by an arrow. (×25 000)

(Figs 24.6 and 24.7). When cut in transverse section, however, they appear circular and, if their pedicle is not fortuitously included in the section, give the spurious impression of being free-floating within the capillary (Fig. 24.7).

Measurement of the Interstitial Spaces

Direct gravimetric measurements of the total content of water in the lungs can be made by drying to a constant weight. To estimate the extravascular water, allowance has to be made for the water present in the blood and this may be calculated from the quantity of haemoglobin present. Such measurements on the lungs of normal individuals dying suddenly of accidental death have given an average value for the extravascular water of 198 ml/m^2 BSA with a range of 149 to 249 ml.[19] Cander and Forster[20] give an average value of 580 ml for normal adult lungs. Assuming a body surface area of 1·8 m^2 this amounts to 320 ml/m^2 BSA.

Attempts to measure this volume in life have been made by means of indicator substances both from the blood phase and the gas phase. Both methods are similar in principle. In each case, two substances are added to the phase in question, one of which can diffuse out of the phase and into the lung tissue, while the other cannot do so. The degree of loss of diffusible indicator can be calculated by reference to the concentration of the non-diffusible indicator.

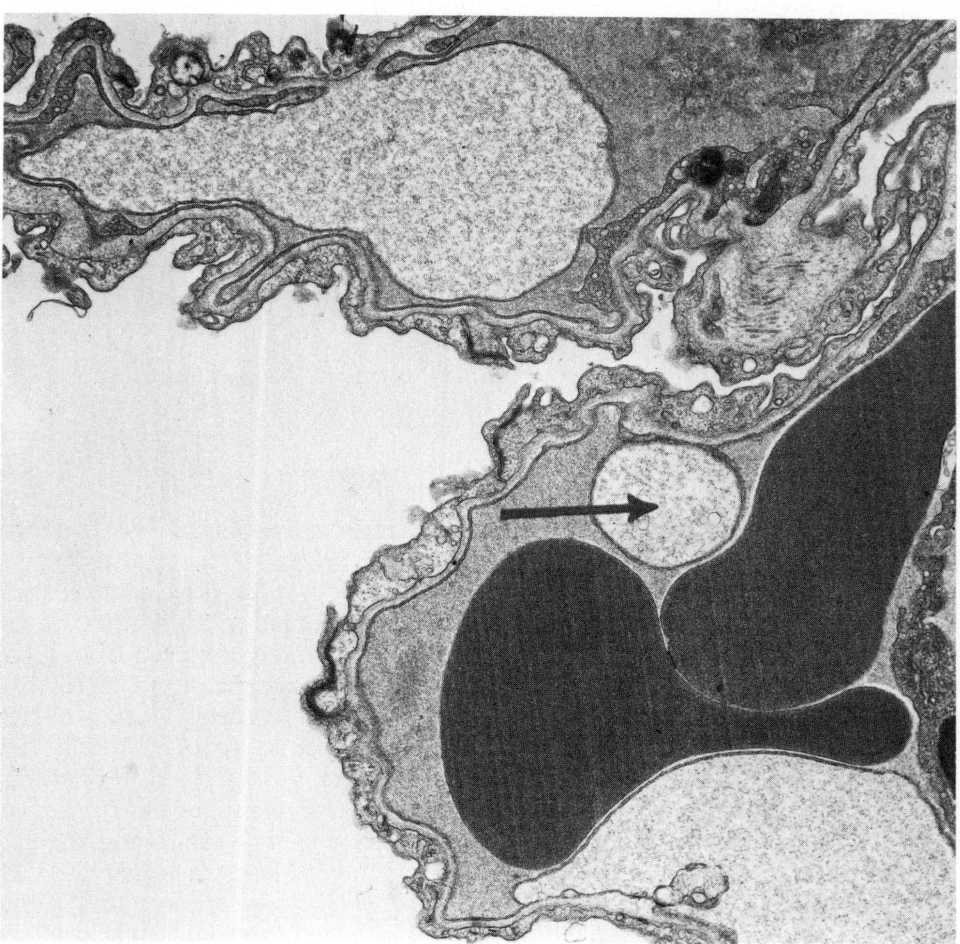

Fig. 24.7 Electron micrograph of lung from the same animal illustrated in the preceding Figure. The endothelial vesicle shown there is included again. Also present is a vesicle cut in transverse section (arrow). (× 12 500)

Measurement of the Interstitial Space from the Blood Phase

In the case of the blood phase, Evans' blue or ^{131}I-labelled albumen has been used as the indicator which does not leave the blood stream while deuterium or tritiated water have been used to measure the extravascular water space. The two indicators are injected simultaneously into the right heart and dilution curves derived from systemic arterial samples. The curve for Evans' blue or labelled albumen may be used to calculate the pulmonary blood flow ($\dot{Q}$) (p. 82). If none of the labelled water left the blood stream during its passage through the lungs, the dilution curve for labelled water would have the same form as that for Evans' blue, the ratio of the concentration of the two indicators being at any time their ratio in the injected solution. Since, however, some of the labelled water passes out from the capillaries into the pulmonary tissue spaces, its dilution curve becomes modified, reaching a lower and later peak than that for Evans' blue. The mean transit time for the labelled water ($\bar{t}_{H_2O}$) is, therefore, greater than that for Evans' blue ($\bar{t}$) and, when multiplied by the pulmonary blood flow, it gives a volume

$$V' = \dot{Q}\bar{t}_{H_2O}$$

which is greater than the central blood volume

$$V = Q\bar{t}$$

The difference between these two volumes is taken as a measurement of the interstitial water space:

$$V_i = V' - V = \dot{Q}(\bar{t}_{H_2O} - \bar{t})$$

In order to define $\dot{Q}$, $\bar{t}$ and $\bar{t}_{H_2O}$ a semi-logarithmic extrapolation has to be made to the downslope of each dilution curve (Chap. 8, p. 105).

Such a calculation regards the interstitial space as a simple physical extension of the blood space. The movement of indicator between blood and tissue is, however, determined by diffusion more than mass flow. It will be remembered from Chapter 8, page 107, and Appendix H that intravascular volumes are measured correctly only if the distribution of indicator is proportional to the distribution of flow. With an indicator which passes out of the blood stream, its extravascular distribution is determined by diffusion in a volume where there is no flow. Appendix M analyzes the discrepancies between the real and measured interstitial spaces which derive from this anomaly. When the rate of diffusion is high relative to the rate of capillary flow a large interstitial space will be entered and the estimated space approximates to the real. When the rate of diffusion is low relative to the rate of capillary flow, only a small interstitial space will be entered and this small space will tend to be over-estimated.

There can be no doubt that the method under-estimates total pulmonary extra-vascular water and experiments on animals have shown that the value estimated by

Table 24.1 Measurements of the pulmonary extravascular water in man by the double indicator technique

Condition	Reference	Number of subjects	Wedge or left atrial pressure mmHg	Pulmonary extra-vascular water mean ± SD ml/m² BSA
Normal subjects	24	7	—	108 ± 50[a]
	53	8	—	121 ± 32[a]
	25	9	9	107 ± 22
	30	6	—	86 ± 5
Rheumatic valvar disease				
mitral valvar disease	25	21	21	193 ± 87
aortic valvar disease	25	18	12	154 ± 64
mitral and aortic disease	29	15	22	157 ± 52
mitral and aortic disease	28	3	16	178
Systemic hypertension or ischaemic heart disease with congestive cardiac failure	24	6	—	156 ± 44[a]
Primary or thrombo-embolic	26	8	10	105 ± 37
pulmonary hypertension	28	1	—	73
Obstructive airways disease				
without history of oedema	26	12	7 (in 4)	113 ± 27
with history of oedema	26	8	13 (in 5)	157 ± 55

[a] Assuming BSA = 1·8 m².

the method amounts only to some 50–70 per cent of the extravascular water estimated from a comparison of the wet and dry weights of the lung.[21–23]

Several groups of workers have applied this method to man and their observations are summarized in Table 24.1. There is remarkable consistency between the various publications. The average value for the normal pulmonary extravascular water is 106 ml/m² BSA. Patients with rheumatic mitral or aortic valvar disease had an average value of 170 ml/m² BSA. A similar elevation in the pulmonary extravascular water was found by Lilienfield *et al.*[24] in patients with congestive cardiac failure due to systemic hypertension or ischaemic heart disease. McCredie[25] found no correlation between the pulmonary extravascular water and the pulmonary blood flow or the pulmonary vascular resistance. On the other hand, there was a distinct correlation between the pulmonary extravascular water and the mean pressure in either the pulmonary artery or the left atrium. Patients with primary or thrombo-embolic pulmonary hypertension showed normal values.[26]

In patients with chronic bronchitis and no history of congestive cardiac failure, the pulmonary extravascular water has been found to be normal[26] or sometimes low.[27] There is an inverse relation between the extravascular water and the residual volume of the lungs and the smallest volumes of extravascular water occurred in patients with severe panacinar emphysema. In chronic bronchitic patients with a history of congestive cardiac failure the pulmonary extravascular water was increased.[26,27] In individual patients with chronic bronchitis the pulmonary extravascular water increased substantially during the occurrence of congestive cardiac failure.[27]

The effect of exercise has been studied in both normal subjects and patients with disease of the mitral valve.[28–30] Marshall *et al.*[30] in six normal subjects found a consistent increase in the pulmonary extravascular water during exercise, the average changing from 155 to 229 ml/m^2 BSA. Turino *et al.*[29] exercised six patients with rheumatic disease of the mitral valve and found the average value of the pulmonary extravascular water to increase from approximately 180 to 230 ml/m^2 BSA. In the three patients with rheumatic disease of the mitral valve studied by Korsgren *et al.*[28] the average value increased from 178 to 301 ml/m^2 BSA.

Marshall *et al.*[30] found that the pulmonary extravascular water of normal subjects was slightly lower in the sitting position than in the supine position, the average values for six subjects being 126 and 155 ml/m^2 BSA, respectively. Such a difference might be expected since, in the upright posture, the apices of the lungs may not be well perfused (p. 99) and the extravascular water in un-perfused areas will not be recognized by the method. Such a change in the distribution of blood flow may account for some of the increase in pulmonary extravascular water found during exercise, when the increased intravascular pressures perfuse the lungs more evenly. It seems unlikely, however, that such a mechanism entirely accounts for the observations since the changes noted during exercise in normal subjects were substantially greater than those due to posture and since an increase was also observed in patients in whom the pulmonary arterial pressure was elevated sufficiently to perfuse the entire lung. There seems little doubt, therefore, that the pulmonary extravascular water increases during exercise in reponse to an increase in pulmonary intravascular pressures.

Measurement of the Pulmonary Tissue Volume from the Gas Phase

Cander and Forster[20] have attempted to measure the pulmonary parenchymal tissue volume by introducing indicators into the respiratory gases. In this case, helium was used as the indicator which did not leave the gas phase and nitrous oxide or acetylene were used as indicators which could pass from the alveolar gas into the pulmonary parenchyma. The main uptake of these soluble gases from the alveoli is by the blood flowing through the capillaries and the method was originally developed to measure capillary blood flow (Chap. 6, p. 88). A deep breath of air containing small quantities of helium and, say, nitrous oxide is taken and the breath held for a measured length of time before an end-expired 'alveolar' sample of gas is taken. The original alveolar concentration of nitrous oxide can be calculated from the concentration of helium in the end-expired sample by assuming that no helium is lost from the alveoli and that the ratio of concentrations of nitrous oxide to helium at the beginning of the breath-holding period was the same as in the inspired air. In this way, the 'alveolar' concentration of nitrous oxide after a period of breath-holding can be expressed as a percentage of the initial 'alveolar' concentration. If a series of measurements are taken after varying lengths of breath-holding, the 'alveolar' concentrations expressed as percentages of the initial concentration lie on a straight descending line when plotted semi-logarithmically against time until recirculation starts to occur. If this straight line is extrapolated backwards it intercepts the zero-time ordinate at less than 100 per cent. This is interpreted as implying an initial rapid uptake of nitrous oxide from the tissues. Since both the volume of this initial uptake of soluble gas and its partial pressure at the time can be calculated, the volume of the pulmonary parenchymal tissue can be derived using the solubility constant of the gas in this tissue. The average value for the pulmonary parenchymal tissue volume calculated in this way was 606 ml for normal subjects.[20] This figure includes the volume of the pulmonary capillaries which amounts to about 100 ml. Thus (assuming BSA $\simeq 1{\cdot}8$ m^2) the volume of the extravascular tissue was about 280 ml/m^2 BSA which is rather higher than the magnitude calculated from indicators introduced into the blood phase.

Whether the apparent initial rapid uptake of soluble gas is entirely due to its solution in the pulmonary parenchyma might be doubted. There is evidence that the act of sudden deep inspiration leads to a transient increase in the flow of blood through the lungs (p. 166) which might account for some of the initial rapid uptake of gas. In addition, the inhomogeneity of ventilation–perfusion in the lungs may cause the fall in alveolar concentration of the gas to deviate from a straight line when plotted semilogarithmically. In this case, the extrapolation along a straight line is in error.

Causes of Pulmonary Oedema

A large number of substances can cause pulmonary oedema by damaging the pulmonary capillary endothelium and thus increasing its permeability. A review is given by Frejaville.[31] We shall concern ourselves chiefly with the commoner haemodynamic causes of pulmonary oedema.

Of these, the largest group consists of abnormalities associated with an increase in the pulmonary venous pressure. Failure of the left ventricle from systemic hypertension or ischaemic heart disease is probably the commonest cause. Failure of the left ventricle may also be due to aortic valvar disease, while elevation of the pulmonary venous pressure may be due specifically to mitral valvar disease. All these conditions are liable to give rise to pulmonary oedema when the mean left atrial pressure exceeds 30 mmHg (Refs 32–36). The duration of the pulmonary venous hypertension is, however, important—a reminder that the relevant equation is concerned with rate of transfer of water and not just pressure (p. 373). In general, the raised venous pressure needs to last for at least one hour before pulmonary oedema develops. A transient elevation of the pulmonary venous pressure above 30 mmHg is common, for instance, during exercise in such patients but, although there is some increase in the pulmonary extravascular water (p. 378), this is not usually sufficient to give rise to clinical pulmonary oedema. On the other hand, the presence of a long-standing pulmonary venous hypertension of lesser degree is associated with the development of an increase in the lymphatic drainage system (p. 341) which tends to prevent the formation of oedema. Thus, an acute incompetence of the mitral valve due to rupture of the chordae tendineae or to infective endocarditis is more likely to give rise to oedema than an incompetence of similar degree which has developed gradually over many years from rheumatic disease. Possibly this is why pulmonary oedema tends to be more common in aortic valvar disease than mitral valvar disease. Among patients with mitral valvar disease, pulmonary oedema is especially prone to affect patients with severe stenosis who remain in sinus rhythm. All patients with a chronic elevation of the pulmonary venous pressure are particularly liable to breathlessness in bed. This may probably be explained by the elevation of pressure in the pulmonary circulation which accompanies the recumbent posture (p. 163).

Another group of haemodynamic causes of pulmonary oedema consists of patients with an increased pulmonary blood flow. In these patients, it would seem likely that the transudation of liquid into the lung occurs in the arterioles and possibly the muscular pulmonary arteries as well as in the capillaries (p. 372). As with the patients with pulmonary venous hypertension, pulmonary oedema is more likely to arise if the increase in pulmonary blood flow has developed acutely. Thus, it is found especially in patients with a ruptured ventricular septum from myocardial infarction or a ruptured congenital aneurysm of the sinus of Valsalva. It is also found commonly in new-born infants with left-to-right shunts of congenital origin. When an increased pulmonary blood flow persists for a long period, the development of pulmonary hypertensive vascular disease tends eventually to reduce the flow and thus the pressure in the arterioles and capillaries so that the likelihood of pulmonary oedema is diminished.

The mechanism of production of high altitude pulmonary oedema, discussed on page 501, presents particular features. Here there is a normal pressure in the capillaries but a high pulmonary arterial pressure. The major site of resistance appears from morphological evidence to be in the pulmonary arterioles and the oedema would seem to be due to a transudation across the walls of the muscular pulmonary arteries.

Clinical Features of Pulmonary Oedema

These are too well-known to warrant extensive treatment here. The outstanding symptom is dyspnoea, associated with a feeling of suffocation and of oppression in front of the chest. This is often accompanied by an awareness by the patient of rhonchi in the chest or even by wheezing. There is commonly a dry cough which may be the first symptom. The presence of pink, frothy sputum must represent an extensive alveolar oedema. The patient sits upright, grasping the side of the bed or the arms of the chair, or he may prefer to stand, supporting himself with his hands. The skin is moist and pale due to cutaneous vasoconstriction. The lips are blue. Auscultation reveals, classically, the presence of wide-spread fine crepitations. Commonly, however, there are also coarser crepitations and rhonchi.

Radiological Features of Pulmonary Oedema

The chest radiograph allows a distinction between alveolar oedema and interstitial oedema. Alveolar oedema gives rise to fluffy opacities up to about an inch in diameter which may become confluent. Characteristically they are predominant in the region of the hilum giving rise to the classical 'bat's wing' symmetrical shadow (Fig. 24.8). The distribution of the opacities is, however, by no means always symmetrical or even bilateral.

Interstitial pulmonary oedema may be acute or chronic. It is characterized by a fuzziness of the outline of the larger pulmonary arteries, presumably due to an accumulation of liquid in the perivascular space. The classical appearances in the parenchyma were described by Kerley.[37] The 'B'-lines which he described (Fig. 22.9) are short, straight, fine lines occurring at the bases of the lungs and best seen in the costo-phrenic angle. They extend inwards from, and at right angles to, the pleural surface. They are due primarily to oedema of pulmonary septa, but in the presence of chronic pulmonary venous hypertension an enlargement of the lymphatics, fibrosis or a deposition of haemosiderin may contribute to the shadow.[38,39] In patients with chronic venous hypertension the presence of 'B'-lines indicates a pulmonary wedge pressure greater than 20 mmHg (Refs 40 and 41). A small layer of pleural liquid visible along the thoracic wall at the costo-phrenic angle commonly accompanies the presence of 'B'-lines. The 'B'-lines seen in acute pulmonary interstitial oedema are less well-defined than those seen in chronic pulmonary interstitial oedema and they disappear rapidly. When a chronically elevated left atrial pressure is reduced, for instance by mitral valvotomy, the 'B'-lines also tend to disappear. Under these circumstances, however, linear shadows may persist due to the presence of fibrosis or the deposition of haemosiderin.

The lines which Kerley[37] designated 'A' are a less common feature of pulmonary interstitial oedema. They are longer, passing from the periphery of the lung towards the hilum, and are not restricted to the bases.

The Effects of Pulmonary Oedema on Respiratory Function

The presence of pulmonary oedema reduces the compliance of the lung.[42] The small increase in the distance between the alveolus and its adjacent capillary is insufficient to impair the diffusion of oxygen to any important degree.[19] The reduction in arterial P_{O_2} which occurs with alveolar oedema is predominantly due to an inhomogeneity of ventilation: perfusion ratios[43] (Chap. 36). Blood passing through an alveolus which is filled with oedema liquid acts as a shunt. In addition, the abnormalities of the distribution of ventilation may be exacerbated by an increased resistance to flow through the smaller airways.[44] In the terminal stages of pulmonary alveolar oedema there is a failure of total ventilation and a retention of carbon dioxide with respiratory acidosis.[45-47] Metabolic acidosis, due to tissue hypoxia, also contributes to the low pH of the blood.[45-47]

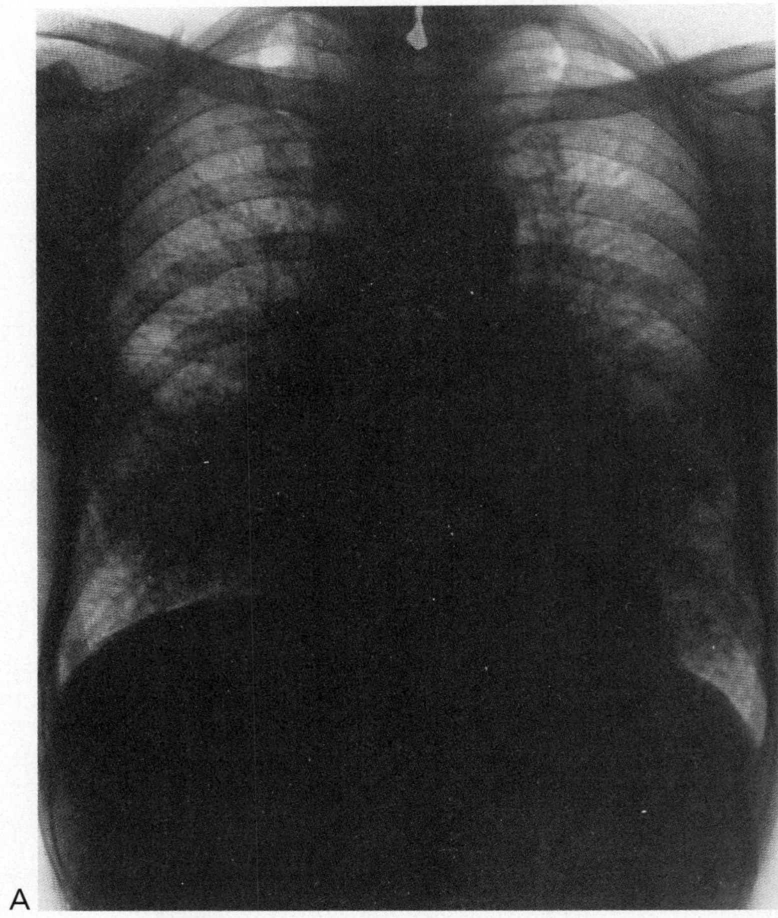

FIG. 24.8A

Figs 24.8A and B Chest radiographs of a patient during and after recovery from acute pulmonary oedema. The patient had aortic incompetence with an infective endocarditis which caused rupture of the chordae tendineae and mitral incompetence.

J-Receptors

In the alveolar walls in the lung there appear to be afferent nerve endings which are stimulated by pulmonary congestion irrespective of its cause. Paintal[48] states that the sensory nerve fibers would have a diameter of between 0·1 and 0·3 μm. They are said to be situated in the interstitial tissue composed of collagen and reticulin fibres which is bounded by the basement membrane of the alveolar epithelium and by that of the endothelium of the pulmonary capillary. The thick

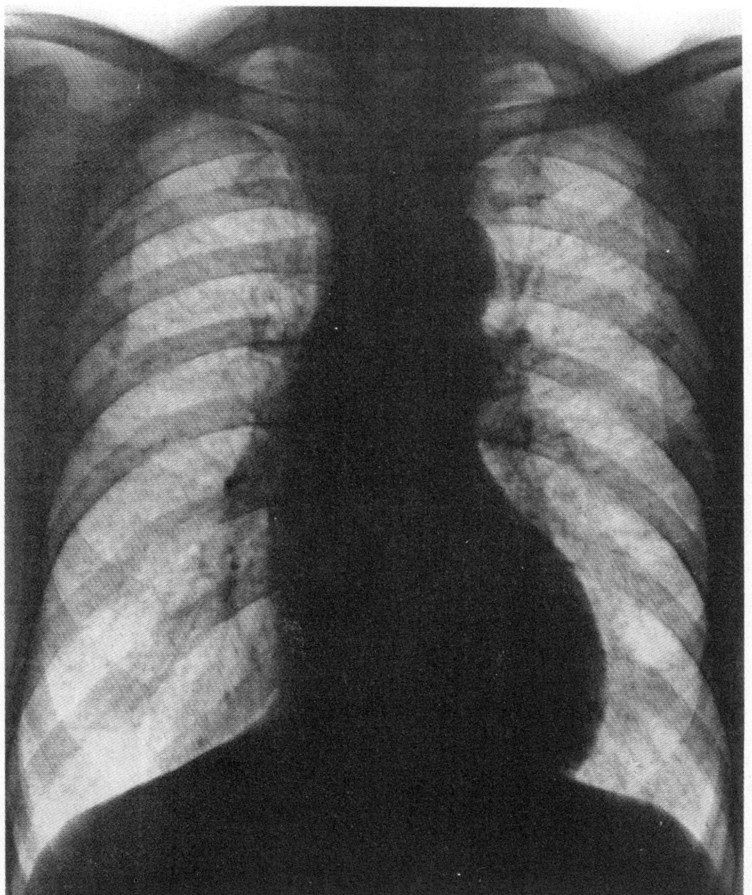

FIG. 24.8B

and thin portions of the alveolar wall have already been described at the beginning of this chapter and are illustrated in Figure 24.4. The J-receptors lie in the interstitial tissue, as indicated by IT in that figure. Since they are situated near the pulmonary capillaries they are termed 'juxtapulmonary capillary receptors' or, more succinctly, 'J-receptors'.

The function of these receptors appears to be to respond not to increased pulmonary capillary pressure *per se* but to a reduction in pulmonary compliance brought about by oedema of the interstitial tissue. The nerve endings are probably connected to collagen fibres and stimulated when fluid enters the interstitial tissue which acts like a sponge. Excitation occurs whatever the basis for the pulmonary congestion, be it mitral stenosis or even the inhalation of chlorine. Congestion for even short periods increases the activity of the endings. Increased receptor activity can continue for days, if congestion persists.

Experimental evidence is available which indicates that the J-receptors are situated where they can be rapidly excited by stimuli arising from the pulmonary capillaries or alveolar spaces. Thus, the endings are stimulated within 2·5 seconds of injection of phenyl diguanide into the right atrium or ventricle or within 0·3 seconds of insufflation of volatile anaesthetics into the lungs.[48] The average impulse frequency is intense compared with that found in the non-medullated fibres of chemoreceptors. In pulmonary oedema, there is an early accumulation of oedema fluid in the peribronchial and perivascular tissues but fluid in this situation will not stimulate the J-receptors.[49]

Paintal[48] believes the J-receptors have a physiological rôle in subjects at high altitude. He bases his view on the evidence that there is an elevation of pulmonary capillary pressure and an increase in cardiac output during exercise at high altitude.[50,51] He believes that these haemodynamic changes are associated with congestion of pulmonary capillaries and conditions likely to stimulate the J-receptors. This would lead to a sensation of breathlessness and the initiation of what he calls the 'J-reflex'. Stimulation of the J-receptors does not reflexly lower pulmonary arterial pressure by reducing either pulmonary vascular resistance or input into the right ventricle. Deshpande and Devanandan[52] studied the reflex effect of stimulating J-receptors on the monosynaptic reflexes of hind-limb muscles and found that stimulating the endings produced inhibition of monosynoptic reflexes of both flexor and extensor muscles of the hind limb.

REFERENCES

1. Marchand, P. (1951) *Thorax*, **6**, 359.
2. Staub, N. C. (1966) *Physiologist*, **9**, 294.
3. Staub, N. C. (1967) *Fel. Proc.*, **26**, 442.
4. Guyton, A. C., Granger, A. H. & Taylor, A. E. (1971) *Physiol. Rev.*, **51**, 527.
5. Fessler, J. H. (1960) *Biochem. J.*, **76**, 124.
6. Mathews, M. B. (1965) *Biochem. J.*, **96**, 710.
7. Schubert, M. (1966) *Fed. Proc.*, **25**, 1047.
8. Ogston, A. G. & Sherman, T. F. (1961) *J. Physiol.*, **156**, 67.
9. McMaster, P. D. & Parsons, R. J. (1939) *J. Exper. Med.*, **69**, 247.
10. McMaster, P. D. (1946) *J. Exper. Med.*, **84**, 473.
11. Scholander, P. F., Hargens, A. R. & Miller, S. L. (1968) *Science*, **161**, 321.
12. Meyer, B. J., Meyer, A. & Guyton, A. C. (1968) *Circulat. Res.*, **22**, 263.
13. Taylor, A. E., Guyton, A. C. & Bishop, V. S. (1965) *Circulat. Res.*, **16**, 353.
14. Guyton, A. C. (1969) In *The Pulmonary Circulation and Interstitial Space*, ed. Fishman, A. P. & Hecht, H. H. page 3. The University of Chicago Press.
15. Iliff, L. D. (1971) *Circulat. Res.*, **28**, 524.
16. Levine, O. R., Mellins, R. B., Senior, R. M. & Fishman, A. P. (1967) *J. Clin. Invest.*, **46**, 934.
17. Uhley, H. N., Leeds, S. E., Sampson, J. J. & Friedman, M. (1962) *Circulat. Res.*, **11**, 966.
18. Staub, N. C., Nagano, H. & Pearce, M. L. (1967) *J. Appl. Physiol.*, **22**, 227.
19. Gump, F. E., Mashima, Y., Ferenczy, A. & Kinney, J. M. (1971) *J. Trauma*, **11**, 474.
20. Cander, L. & Forster, R. E. (1959) *J. Appl. Physiol.*, **14**, 541.
21. Goresky, C. A., Cronin, R. F. P. & Wangel, B. E. (1969) *J. Clin. Invest.*, **48**, 487.
22. Levine, O. R., Mellins, R. B. & Fishman, A. P. (1965) *Circulat. Res.*, **17**, 414.
23. Levine, O. R., Mellins, R. B. & Senior, R. M. (1970) *J. Appl. Physiol.*, **28**, 116.
24. Lilienfield, L. S., Freis, E. D., Partenope, E. A. & Morowitz, H. J. (1955) *J. Clin. Invest.*, **34**, 1.

25. McCredie, R. M. (1967) *Circulation*, **36**, 381.
26. McCredie, R. M. (1970) *Brit. Heart J.*, **32**, 66.
27. Turino, G. M., Edelman, N. H., Senior, R. M., Richards, E. C. & Fishman, A. P. (1968) *Bull. Physio-Path. Resp.*, **4**, 47.
28. Korsgren, M., Lueper, R., Liander, B. & Varnauskas, E. (1969) *Cardiovasc. Res.*, **3**, 1.
29. Turino, G. M., Pine, M. B., Shubrooks, S. J. & Carey, J. P. (1971) *Bull. Physio-Path. Resp.*, **7**, 1161.
30. Marshall, B. E., Teichner, R. L., Kallos, T., Sugerman, H. J., Wyche, M. Q., Jn. & Tantum, K. R. (1971) *J. Appl. Physiol.*, **31**, 375.
31. Frejaville, J. P. (1971) *Bull. Physio-Path. Resp.*, **7**, 1279.
32. Lenègre, J., Scebat, L. & Renais, J. (1960) *Arch. Mal. Coeur*, **53**, 834.
33. Gorlin, R., Lewis, B. M., Haynes, F. W., Spiell, R. J. & Dexter, L. (1951) *Amer. Heart. J.*, **41**, 834.
34. Hayward, G. W. (1955) *Brit. Med. J.*, **i**, 39.
35. Fejfar, Z., Fejfarova, M., Bergmann, K. & Brod, J. (1959) *Cardiologica*, **34**, 233.
36. Finlayson, J. K., Luria, M. N., Stanfield, C. A. & Yu, P. N. (1961) *Ann. Int. Med.*, **54**, 244.
37. Kerley, P. (1933) *Brit. Med. J.*, **ii**, 594.
38. Jordan, S. C., Hicken, P., Watson, D. A., Heath, D. & Whitaker, W. (1966) *Brit. Heart. J.*, **28**, 101.
39. Fleischner, F. G. & Reiner, L. (1954) *New Engl. J. Med.*, **250**, 900.
40. Rossall, R. E. & Gunning, A. J. (1956) *Lancet*, **i**, 604.
41. Grainger, R. G. (1958) *Brit. J. Radiol.*, **31**, 201.
42. Sharp, J. T., Griffith, G. T., Bunnell, I. L. & Greene, D. G. (1958) *J. Clin. Invest.*, **37**, 11.
43. Said, S. I., Longacher, J. W., Davis, R. K., Banerjee, C. M., Davis, W. M. & Woodell, W. J. (1964) *J. Appl. Physiol.*, **19**, 403.
44. Milic-Emili, J. & Ruff, F. (1971) *Bull. Physio-Path. Resp.*, **7**, 1181.
45. Anthonisen, N. R. & Smith, H. J. (1965) *Ann. Intern. Med.*, **62**, 991.
46. Lissac, J., Guize, L., Letac, B., Labrousse, J., Fabiato, A. & Copper-Royer, F. (1971) *Coeur et Méd. Int.*, **10**, 47.
47. Avery, W. G., Samet, P. & Sackner, M. A. (1970) *Amer. J. Med.*, **48**, 320.
48. Paintal, A. S. (1970) In *The Mechanism of Excitation of Type J Receptors, and the J Reflex*, Hering-Breuer Centenary Symposium. page 59. London: Churchill.
49. Staub, N. C., Nagano, J. & Pearce, M. L. (1967) *J. Appl. Physiol.*, **22**, 227.
50. Peñaloza, D., Sime, F., Banchero, N. & Gamboa, R. (1963) In *Progress in Research in Emphysema and Chronic Bronchitis*, ed. Grover, R. F. & Herzog, H. Vol. 1, p. 257. New York: Karger.
51. Vogel, J. H. K., Weaver, W. F., Rose, R. L., Blount, S. G. & Grover, R. F. (1963) In *Progress in Research in Emphysema and Chronic Bronchitis*, ed. Grover, R. F. & Herzog, H. Vol. 1, p. 269. New York: Karger.
52. Deshpande, S. S. & Devanandan, M. (1970) *J. Physiol. (Lond.)*, **26**, 345.
53. Ramsey, L. H., Puckett, W., Jose, A. & Lacy, W. W. (1964) *Circulat. Res.*, **15**, 275.

25. The Influence of the Pulmonary Circulation on the Mechanics of the Lung

When an isolated lung is perfused through the pulmonary artery, it increases in size, rising up from the surface on which it is placed and drawing in air through the trachea. This erectile property of the pulmonary circulation was first fully investigated by von Basch at the end of the last century.[1] He showed that increasing the vascular pressure in the lung caused it to become more rigid ('Lungenstarre'). During this century a number of investigations of the phenomenon has been made *in vivo* in animals and in normal and diseased human lungs.

During normal ventilatory movements of the lungs there are phasic variations in the difference in pressure between the pleural space and the atmosphere. These differences arise partly because of the changes in the degree of distension of the lung, partly because of the resistance to the flow of air through the air passages and partly because of the viscous properties of the tissues of the lung. The same three factors determine the relation between pressure and flow of air into and out of the isolated lung. The last two factors (resistance to air-flow and tissue viscosity) are dependent on the rate of change of volume of the lung; while the first factor

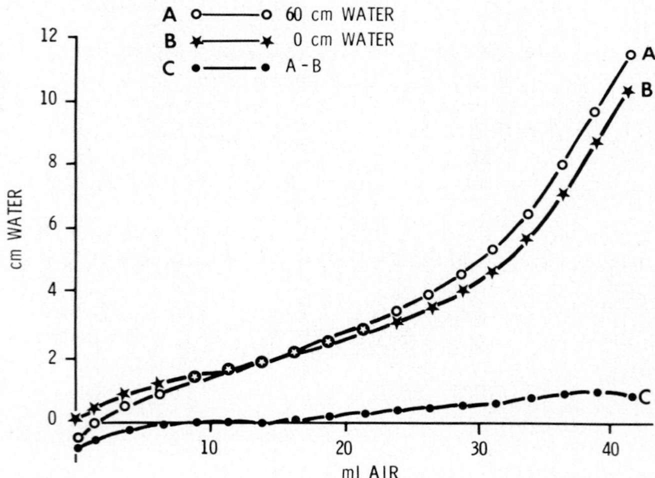

Fig. 25.1 The static pressure–volume relation of the isolated lung of the rabbit and the effects of pulmonary perfusion. The experiment was started with the lungs inflated and the distending pressure measured with and without perfusion through the pulmonary artery at a pressure of 60 cm water. Thereafter, successive small quantities of air were removed and, after stabilization, the distending pressure measured with and without perfusion at each lung volume. Left atrial pressure was maintained at zero.[18]

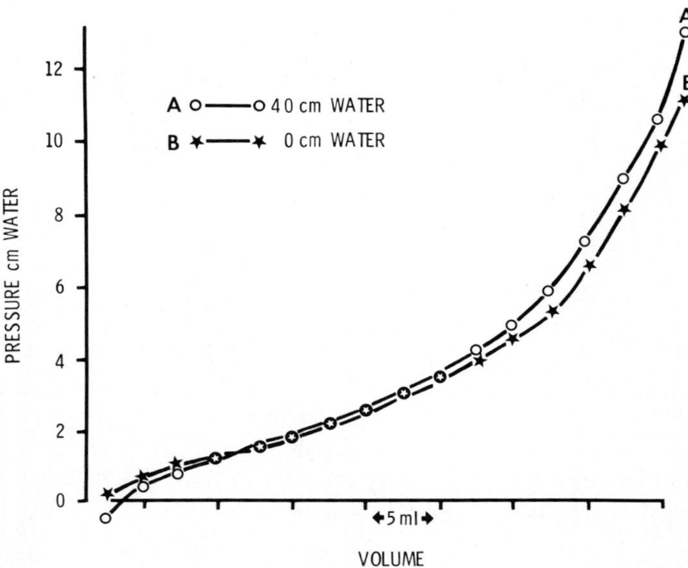

Fig. 25.2 The effects of retrograde perfusion through the left atrium on the static pressure–volume relation of the isolated rabbit lung.[18] The technique was as described in Figure 25.1 except that perfusion was through the left atrium at a pressure of 40 cm water.

(degree of distension) is independent of the time taken to reach a particular lung volume. If, therefore, the lung is inflated in small stages of long time intervals the relation between pressure and volume is determined only by the mechanical retractile forces of the lung which are brought into play by its distension. Such a 'static' pressure : volume relation is shown in Figure 25.1 for the isolated rabbit lung (curve B).

If the lung is now perfused through the pulmonary artery the 'static' pressure : volume relation is changed (curve A). It becomes steeper so that there is a larger change in pressure for a given change in volume, indicating a greater rigidity or decreased compliance. Where the two curves cross is the point of inflation towards which the erectile forces of the pulmonary circulation tend to bring the lung. The reversal in sign of the erectile forces at this point of inflation is shown by curve C (equals A minus B). At greater lung volumes the perfused pulmonary circulation will tend to expel air from the lung; at lower lung volumes it will tend to draw air in.

A similar effect obtains if the pulmonary circulation is perfused retrogradely from the left atrium (Fig. 25.2). Thus, either the venous system has erectile properties which are similar to those of the arterial system or the mechanical effects are due to the filling of the capillaries which is common to both circumstances.

Figure 25.3 shows a series of pressure : volume curves taken at different pulmonary intravascular pressures, the pressure in the left atrium being maintained the same as that in the pulmonary artery. With an increasing intravascular pressure the

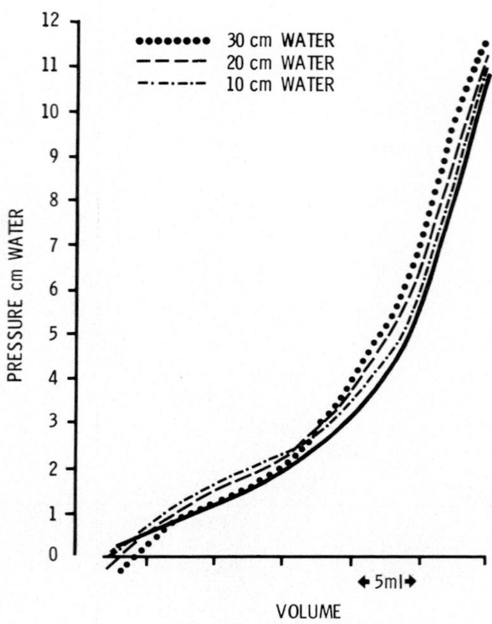

Fig. 25.3 The effects of pulmonary vascular congestion on the static pressure–volume relation of the isolated rabbit lung.[18] In this case the technique was as described in Figure 25.1 except that both the pulmonary arterial and left atrial pressures were increased to the same extent. Congestion at three levels of pressure was studied: 10, 20 and 30 cm water.

curves become progressively steeper, indicating an increasing rigidity or decreasing compliance of the lung. The point of crossing of the curves obtained during finite intravascular pressures is, however, situated some distance away from the pressure:volume curve obtained when the intravascular pressure is zero. The horizontal distance between the point of crossing and the pressure:volume curve at zero intravascular pressure may represent the volume of air occupied by the pulmonary capillaries when they swell and protrude into the alveoli.

The investigation of such phenomena in normal and diseased humans has required the measurement of intrapleural pressures and lung volume as well as the measurement of pressures in the pulmonary circulation. In the early studies of Christie and Meakins[2] the intrapleural pressure was measured directly by needle, and a decreased compliance of the lung reported in patients with cardiac disease. Subsequent studies have used the pressure registered in a balloon introduced into the oesophagus as an indication of intrapleural pressure. In the earlier work, using this technique, a decreased compliance of the lung was found in patients with cardiac disease.[3,4] White *et al.*[5] studied a group of patients with rheumatic disease of the mitral valve and found an average value of 0·12 l/cm water for the pulmonary compliance, the average normal figure being 0·24. There was, however, no impressive correlation

Table 25.1 Lung compliance in Pulmonary Hypertension[7]

Type of pulmonary hypertension	Lung compliance
Pulmonary venous	Low
Hyperkinetic	Low
Reversed shunt	Normal
Primary	Normal
Thromboembolic	Normal
High altitude	Normal

between the compliance and the wedge pressure, although compliance decreased during exercise as the wedge pressure rose.

Hywall-Davies and colleagues[6] investigated a group of patients with intra-cardiac communications. They found a decreased compliance in patients with pulmonary arterial hypertension associated with an increased pulmonary blood flow. When, however, the pulmonary vascular resistance in such patients had increased sufficiently to prevent a left-right shunt, the compliance was normal. Patients with an increased pulmonary blood flow but normal pulmonary arterial pressure had a normal pulmonary compliance.

This and subsequent literature has recently been reviewed by Gazetopoulos *et al.*[7] and their conclusions are presented in Table 25.1. It is clear that a decreased compliance is not found when there is pulmonary arterial hypertension alone, as in 'primary' pulmonary hypertension or thromboembolic pulmonary hypertension or high altitude pulmonary hypertension. It is found in patients with a raised pulmonary venous pressure and in patients with a considerable left-right shunt giving rise to pulmonary arterial hypertension. The common factor appears to be an increased pressure in the pulmonary capillaries.

One could not be sure, from such studies, whether the decreased compliance arose simply because of the erectile properties of the pulmonary capillary bed or whether the accumulation of oedema or fibrosis of alveolar walls which occurs under chronic conditions made a contribution. A similar fall in compliance, however, has been noted to occur transiently during an attack of angina[8] which would suggest that the intravascular pressure itself is a factor. The studies were carried out during the induction of angina by atrial pacing. With the onset of angina there was an increase in left ventricular end-diastolic pressure which coincided with a decrease in pulmonary compliance. On recovery both these measurements returned to normal.

A similar transient decrease in pulmonary compliance has been shown to accompany the increase in 'central venous pressure' which occurs during the inflation of an antigravity suit[9,10] (see Chap. 11, p. 162). During these transient changes, the pulmonary compliance is inversely related to the 'central venous pressure'. Submersion in water[9] and the infusion of dextran had a similar effect.[11]

It seems likely that, in addition, the accumulation of oedema liquid will contribute to a decreased pulmonary compliance. The accumulation of excess liquid in the interstitial space may be expected to have some influence, but probably the accumulation of excess liquid in the alveoli would have a more important effect.[12] Patients with pulmonary oedema were found to have values for the pulmonary compliance which were only 25 per cent of the normal.[12] This is considerably less than would be expected from simple distension of pulmonary blood vessels. The formation of bubbles with a small diameter inside the alveoli may contribute to the decrease in compliance under these conditions.[12]

From the studies on isolated lungs, described at the beginning of the chapter, one would expect changes in compliance due to an increased pulmonary capillary pressure to be accompanied by a change in the functional residual capacity of the lung. The direction of such a change would depend on whether the point of inflation to which the erectile forces of the capillaries tended to bring the lungs was greater or less than the functional residual capacity. In infants and young children with pulmonary arterial hypertension associated with a greatly increased pulmonary blood flow[6] there is a notable increase in the antero-posterior diameter of the chest (Fig. 21.1, p. 310) suggesting that the resting lung volume is increased. Presumably the fact that it is not found in patients with acquired heart disease such as mitral stenosis is due to the greater rigidity of the thoracic wall in later life.

In addition to the effects of the pulmonary circulation on pulmonary compliance, there is evidence that an increased pulmonary venous pressure will increase the airways resistance. The airways resistance is increased in patients with mitral stenosis.[13] An increased resistance was found in patients with pulmonary oedema[12] when it was attributed to swelling of the mucosa of the airways or to the presence of oedema fluid or bubbles within them. A transient increase in airways resistance, however, has been found to accompany angina induced by atrial pacing.[8] The increased resistance to air-flow coincided with the transient increase in left ventricular end-diastolic pressure and decrease in pulmonary compliance. This suggests that the lumen of an airway may be reduced by the filling of its mucosal capillaries or venules. Pepine and Weiner[8] put forward the interesting theory that part of the sensation of suffocation associated with angina may be due to the changes in pulmonary mechanics which follow the sudden increase in left ventricular end-diastolic pressure.

Occlusion of one main branch of the pulmonary artery has been found to cause a diminution of the ventilation to that lung in dogs and man.[14-16] Using broncho-spirometry,[14] the ventilation of the lung with an occluded blood supply could be shown to fall from 45 per cent to 29 per cent of the total ventilation, while the anatomical dead space of the affected side was diminished. After occlusion of one main branch of the pulmonary artery there is a slight increase in total ventilation. The arterial P_{CO_2} is not greatly affected and the physiological dead space (p. 570) increases much less than would be expected. Normally, toward the end of expiration, the expired P_{CO_2} shows a gently rising plateau. Under these circumstances, however, a downward sloping pattern develops, which suggests that the functional lung is emptying before the occluded one[14,16] and implies an inequality of ventilatory time-constants. The airways resistance is increased and dynamic compliance reduced.[16,17]

The re-distribution of ventilation which follows occlusion of one pulmonary artery is prevented by giving 6 per cent carbon dioxide to the occluded side[14,17] or to both sides.[16] Severinghaus and his colleagues[17] suggested that the reduction of ventilation to the affected side was due to the constriction of peripheral airways which resulted from local hypocarbia. The larger airways are supplied with blood from the bronchial arteries which would have a normal arterial P_{CO_2} and would not, therefore, be subjected to hypocarbia. Even and his colleagues,[16] however, present evidence that there is, in addition, some reflex narrowing of larger airways.

REFERENCES

1. Von Basch, S. (1887) *Klin. Z. Streitf.*, **1**, 81.
2. Christie, R. V. & Meakins, J. C. (1934) *J. Clin. Invest.*, **13**, 323.
3. Brown, C. C., Fry, D. L. & Ebert, R. V. (1954) *Amer. J. Med.*, **17**, 438.
4. Frank, N. R., Lyons, H. A., Siebens, A. A. & Nealon, T. F. (1957) *Amer. J. Med.*, **22**, 516.
5. White, H. C., Butler, J. & Donald, K. W. (1959) *Clin. Sci.*, **17**, 667.
6. Hywall-Davies, H., Williams, J. & Wood, P. (1962) *Brit. Heart J.*, **24**, 129.
7. Gazetopoulos, N., Salonikides, N. & Davies, H. (1974) *Brit. Heart J.*, **36**, 19.
8. Pepine, C. J. & Weiner, L. (1972) *Circulation*, **46**, 863.
9. Bondurant, S., Hickham, J. B. & Isley, J. K. (1957) *J. Clin. Invest.*, **36**, 59.
10. Bondurant, S., Mead, J. & Cook, C. D. (1960) *J. Appl. Physiol.*, **15**, 875.
11. Giuntini, C., Maseri, A. & Bianchi, R. (1966) *J. Clin. Invest.*, **45**, 1770.
12. Sharp, J. T., Griffith, G. T., Bunnell, I. L., Ivan, L. & Green, D. G. (1958) *J. Clin. Invest.*, **37**, 111.
13. Nisell, O., Carlberger, G. & Bevegård, S. (1958) *Acta Med. Scand.*, **162**, 277.
14. Swenson, E. W., Finley, T. N. & Guzman, S. V. (1961) *J. Clin. Invest.*, **40**, 828.
15. Ruff, F., Duroux, P., Caubarrere, I. & Even, P. (1971) *J. Physiol. (Paris)*, **63**, 94.
16. Even, P., Duroux, P., Caubarrere, I., Ruff, F., Butez, J. & Brouet, G. (1972) *Bull. Physio-Path. Resp.*, **8**, 467.
17. Severinghaus, J. W., Swenson, E. W., Finley, T. N., Lategola, M. T. & Williams, J. (1961) *J. Appl. Physiol.*, **16**, 53.
18. Harris, P. (1955) Ph.D. Thesis. University of London.

26. The Pulmonary Blood Vessels of Animals

In the first edition of this book we confined our attention to the human pulmonary circulation, but recent important advances in this field such as the concept of dietary hypertension, which is based largely on animal experiments at the present time, have made consideration of pulmonary blood vessels in animals necessary.

The Course of the Pulmonary and Bronchial Vasculature

In some animals the course of the pulmonary and bronchial blood vessels may differ considerably from that in man. Thus, in some species like the cow, sheep, pig and mouse, the pulmonary veins closely follow the bronchial tree. In others, the pulmonary veins run an independent course towards the hilum as in the human lung. These different relationships of blood vessels to bronchial tree depend on differences in the anatomy of the lung in different species and have been studied by McLaughlin and his associates.[1,2]

The Structure of Pulmonary Arteries in Animals

The appearance of normal pulmonary arteries in some species is very similar to that of the earliest stage of hypertensive pulmonary vascular disease in man. In the human lung, the presence of significant numbers of small muscular pulmonary arterial vessels less than 100 μm in diameter with a distinct media of circularly oriented smooth muscle sandwiched between internal and external elastic laminae is pathognomonic of hypertensive pulmonary vascular disease (Chap. 16). However, this is a normal finding in the lungs of many laboratory and domesticated animals especially if they are small (Fig. 26.1). It is clear from this that, when laboratory animals are used for experiments on the pulmonary circulation and the vasculature of the lung studied subsequently, great care must be taken in assessing the significance of small muscular blood vessels analogous to the 'muscularized pulmonary arteriole' of human disease. Such small muscular vessels may be of true pathological significance such as the vessel illustrated in Figure 16.1. On the other hand, they may represent merely the smallest muscular pulmonary arteries found normally in that species and have no pathological significance. It is obvious that, when histological studies are carried out on the pulmonary arteries from an animal, human pulmonary arteries must not be used mentally as the controls. Careful control studies of the same species must be undertaken. Conclusions drawn from experiments on the pulmonary circulation of animals, particularly concerning vasomotor responses, should be applied to human disease critically, when such conclusions are based on the muscular nature of the pulmonary vasculature of animals.

The muscular pulmonary arteries of several domesticated and laboratory animals appear thick-walled, especially if the lungs have not been fixed in distension. We have studied the structure of the small pulmonary blood vessels in several species and have found a considerable range in the medial thickness of their pulmonary arteries.[3] In some species the highest values found for medial thickness exceeded 10 per cent of the external diameter and such values in man would indicate medial hypertrophy. There is still place for further studies to determine whether the thicker muscular pulmonary arteries of animals relate to higher pulmonary arterial pressures than in man. It is known that in some species the pulmonary arterial pressure is slightly higher than in man. In cattle a systolic pressure in the pulmonary artery has been recorded of 24 mmHg (Ref. 4) or 28 ± 4 mmHg (Ref. 5). In a giraffe the pulmonary arterial pressure was found to vary between 38/13 and 48/22 mmHg (Ref. 6). While resting pulmonary pressures of certain animals may be similar to those in man, there may be peculiar situations in animals during which pulmonary vasospastic responses are great and attended by higher levels of pressure than those obtained in normal man.[7]

In the case of reptiles such as the crocodile or turtle, the thick-walled pulmonary arteries may be related to the anatomy of the heart.[8] In such species, the pulmonary circulation may be exposed to haemodynamic stresses similar to those found in certain congenital cardiac diseases in man such as a large ventricular septal defect. Thus, in the crocodile and alligator, the pulmonary trunk and second aorta both arise from the right ventricle. In the turtle, functional phenomena similar to those in man with a single ventricle and without pulmonary stenosis, including high levels of pulmonary arterial pressure have been demonstrated.[9]

In some species the pulmonary arteries have a histological structure quite unlike that seen in the human lung. Thus, the peculiar arrangement of smooth muscle in the media of the muscular pulmonary arteries of the guinea-pig suggests that these vessels may have different physiological potentialities from human thin-walled pulmonary arteries.[7] Sphincter-like structures and longitudinal muscle bundles have also been reported in pulmonary arteries of the cow[10] and horse.[11]

Pulmonary Arterial Disease in Animals

In spite of what has been said above, one must exercise caution before dismissing thick-walled pulmonary arteries as a characteristic of the normal histology of the species rather than as evidence of pulmonary vascular disease. Thus, we have found the pulmonary arteries of the healthy low-altitude cat to be thin-walled,[12] whereas in the North of England many cats have thick-walled arteries in the lungs. These are regarded as hypertrophied pulmonary arteries by workers who have studied them and are regarded as a response to infection by the lung worm, *Aelurostrongylus abstrusus* (Chap. 15, p. 235).

Another controversy of the same type has arisen in connection with the normal structure of the pulmonary arteries of monkeys. A quantitative histological study of the pulmonary trunk and muscular pulmonary arteries of five vervet monkeys (*Cercopithecus aethiops sabaeus*) led Jones[13] to conclude that the normal pulmonary

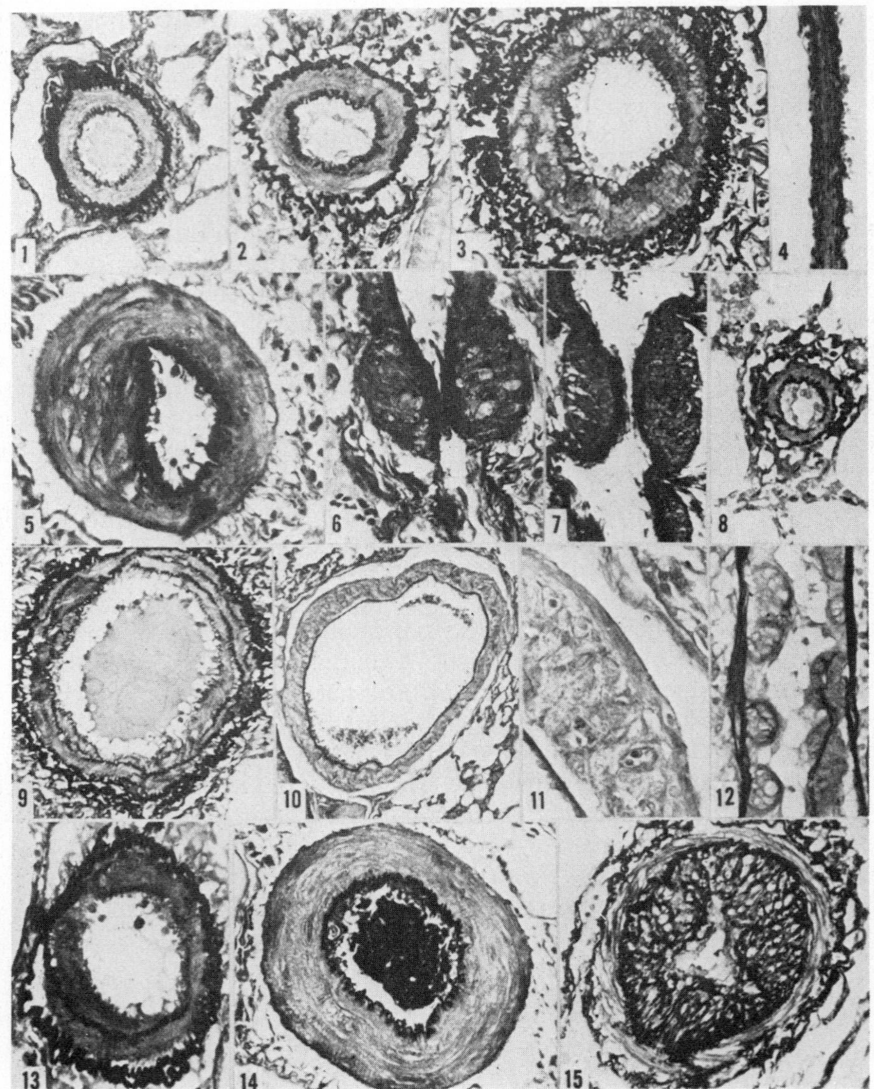

Fig. 26.1 Pulmonary and bronchial blood vessels from a variety of animal species. All sections were stained by the Lawson modification of the Weigert-Sheridan method for elastic tissue and counter-stained with Van Gieson's stain.

1, Transverse section of muscular pulmonary artery from a cow. Both the media and the internal elastic lamina are thick. The degree of medial thickness shown here and in 2 and 3 would be taken as evidence of hypertensive pulmonary vascular disease in a human muscular pulmonary artery. (× 142)

2, Transverse section of a small muscular pulmonary artery from a pig. The media and the internal and external elastic laminae are very thick. (× 255)

3, Transverse section of a large muscular pulmonary artery from a pig. The media is thick. (× 127)

4, Longitudinal section of a muscular pulmonary artery from a goat. The media and the internal and external elastic laminae are thin as in the llama or as in the normal human lung (× 142)
5, Transverse section of muscular pulmonary artery from a guinea-pig. The media is thick and irregular. This section has been taken through one of the sphincter-like masses of circular muscle illustrated in longitudinal section in 6 and 7. (× 255)
6, Longitudinal section of muscular pulmonary artery from a guinea-pig. Above, the internal elastic lamina is thick, and circularly orientated smooth muscle forms a sphincter. Below, the wall of the arterial vessel appears to consist solely of a single elastic lamina with small sub-endothelial prominences protruding into the vascular lumen. (× 142)
7, Longitudinal section of muscular pulmonary artery from a guinea-pig. The internal elastic lamina is thick. Sphincter-like masses of circularly orientated smooth muscle are seen at intervals along the artery. Between these masses the wall of the artery is thin. (× 142)
8, Transverse section of a very small muscular pulmonary artery from a pig. Internal and external elastic laminae and a thick muscular media are seen clearly. Such appearances in an arterial vessel of this small size in the human lung are pathognomonic of hypertensive pulmonary vascular disease. (× 255)
9, Transverse section of large pulmonary vein from a pig. In contrast to the pulmonary artery there is no thick internal elastic lamina. The media consists of circularly arranged smooth muscle with concentric elastic laminae. Many of the elastic laminae are crowded together at the junction between media and adventitia. (× 120)
10, Transverse section of large pulmonary vein from a rat. The internal elastic lamina is thick. The vessel is enveloped by cardiac muscle. (× 57)
11, Part of the transverse section of the large pulmonary vein of the rat shown in 10 at higher magnification to show the cardiac muscle. (× 255)
12, Longitudinal section of small pulmonary vein of a pig. The vessel has a beaded appearance due to the discrete fibromuscular masses protruding into the lumen. (× 255)
13, Transverse section of small pulmonary vein from a pig. There is a thick elastic lamina and internal to this is one of the fibromuscular prominences shown in the preceding figure, cut in transverse section. The protruding mass gives the vessel the appearance of being partially occluded. (× 255)
14, Transverse section of bronchial artery of a guinea-pig. A very thick media composed of circularly arranged smooth muscle is lined on its inner aspect by a thick internal elastic lamina. (× 255)
15, Transverse section of bronchial artery of a pig. There is an outer layer of circularly orientated smooth muscle, a thick elastic lamina internal to this, and a thick inner layer of longitudinally arranged smooth muscle. (× 255)

vasculature in this species is relatively more muscular than that of man. He also found in at least three of these animals heavy right ventricles, but did not regard this as secondary to pulmonary vascular disease. The monkeys were not subjected to cardiac catheterization to confirm that they had a normal pulmonary arterial pressure. Subsequently, we found the pulmonary vasculature to be thin-walled (3·3 per cent of the external diameter) and the pulmonary arterial pressure to be low (21/18 mmHg) in a military monkey (*Erythrocebus patas patas*).[14] We also found the pulmonary arterial pressure to be low and the pulmonary arteries to be thin-walled in two baboons, *Papio papio*.[15] In the face of these conflicting results it is of interest to speculate that the group of vervet monkeys reported by Jones may have developed pulmonary hypertension and early hypertensive pulmonary vascular disease. He notes that the vervet monkeys had been used in a psycho-pharmacological study and had been given frequent injections of 'various psychoactive drugs'. Recently in Western Europe an epidemic of primary pulmonary hypertension has been ascribed to certain appetite-suppressing drugs which exert their effects directly on the brain (Chap. 27, p. 410).

The Structure of Pulmonary Veins in Animals

There are also differences in structure among the pulmonary veins of different species. An example of this is the existence of striated muscle of cardiac type around the larger intrapulmonary veins in the rat (Fig. 26.1, section 11), squirrel and mouse. Human pulmonary veins outside the lung have a prolongation of cardiac muscle from the left atrium along them but there is no intrapulmonary extension of such muscle.[7] In rodents, intrapulmonary cardiac muscle possibly contracts rhythmically in life and this introduces the possibility of haemodynamic factors and reflexes not present in man.[7] In some animals, such as the cow, pig and rat, the small pulmonary veins have irregular fibro-muscular prominences into the lumen (Fig. 26.1).

The Pulmonary Arteries of Animals and Evolutionary Adaptation

The pulmonary arteries of the llama are thin-walled[12] and among the animals which we have studied at high altitude in Peru this species appears to be uniquely lacking in the long term response of constriction and hypertrophy of pulmonary arteries to chronic hypoxia. Such a species difference may represent an evolutionary adaptation of life in the Peruvian Altura, the lack of reaction to hypoxia preventing an increase in the pulmonary vascular resistance which limits the cardiovascular performance of other animals.

Although the small pulmonary arteries of the llama are thin-walled the media of its pulmonary trunk presents a highly muscular appearance, quite unlike that seen in man, with thick discrete bundles of muscle separated by bands of coarse elastic fibrils.[16] The pulmonary trunk of cattle and sheep show the same histological features. Studies have been carried out on the histological appearances, extensibility, and content of collagen and elastin in the pulmonary trunk and aorta of the dog, sheep, cattle, pig and llama living at an altitude of 14 200 ft (4330 m) above sea level.[16] All vessels showed a curved relation between the degree of extension and the extensile load such that, with an increasing load, the tissue became less extensible.[16] The tissue of the aorta was always less extensible than that of the pulmonary trunk of the same animal. The proportion of elastin was always greater in the aorta than in the pulmonary trunk from the same animal, but there was no substantial difference between the proportion of collagen in the two vessels. No clear correlation emerged between the physical properties and chemical composition of the pulmonary trunks or aortae of different animals.

Blocking Mechanisms

Some species of mammals have blocking mechanisms in their pulmonary arteries which appear to bring about their physiological closure. According to Wagenvoort *et al.*[7] blocking mechanisms have not been described in the adult human lung but have been reported in a wide variety of species. These include the horse,[11] cow,[17] cat,[18] rabbit and dolphin.[19] Most of these blocking mechanisms take the form of sphincters in the course of the artery. We have already referred to their presence in cattle, horses and guinea-pigs.[3,20] The sphincters may be situated in the intima or media.

Wagenvoort[7,21] describes two other types of blocking mechanism. One occurs particularly at the origin of a branch from a larger artery. This takes the form of a ring of smooth muscle in the intima which protrudes into the lumen of the parent vessel. Such rings are to be found in the inter- and intralobular pulmonary arteries of the normal foetus and newborn. They are, however, fewer and less well developed than in animals.

The other type takes the form of small groups of short longitudinal muscle fibres which occur in the intima of foetal and neonatal pulmonary arteries. Wagenvoort[7] states that he has seen such structures repeatedly in foetuses and infants without any congenital defect, as well as in subjects who died with congenital heart disease. This leads him to reject the concept that they are arterial malformations.[22] He is not sure of their functional significance. Earlier, Von Hayek[23] had described them as 'epithelioid cells' and had suggested that they might swell in response to histamine blocking the lumen of the artery.

REFERENCES

1. McLaughlin, R. F. Jn., Tyler, W. S. & Canada, R. O. (1961) *Amer. J. Anat.*, **108**, 149.
2. McLaughlin, R. F. Jn., Tyler, W. S. & Canada, R. O. (1961) *J.A.M.A.*, **175**, 694.
3. Best, P. V. & Heath, D. (1961) *Circulat. Res.*, **9**, 288.
4. Doyle, J. T., Patterson, J. L., Jn., Warren, J. V. & Detweiler, D. K. (1960) *Circulat. Res.*, **8**, 4.
5. Reeves, J. T., Grover, R. F., Will, D. H. & Alexander, A. F. (1962) *Circulat. Res.*, **10**, 166.
6. Goetz, R. H., Warren, J. V., Gauer, O. H., Patterson, J. L. Jn., Doyle, J. T., Keen, E. N. & McGregor, M. (1960) *Circulat. Res.*, **8**, 1049.
7. Wagenvoort, C. A., Heath, D. & Edwards, J. E. (1964) In *The Pathology of the Pulmonary Vasculature*. page 140. Springfield, Ill.: Thomas.
8. Edwards, J. E. (1955) In *Cardiovascular Surgery*, International Symposium. Henry Ford Hospital. Philadelphia: Saunders.
9. Steggerda, F. R. & Essex, H. E. (1954) *Fed. Proc.*, **13**, 145.
10. Castigli, G. (1947) *Monit. Zool. Ital.*, **56**, 112.
11. Heidenreich, J. (1960) *Zbl. Vet. Med.*, **7**, 794.
12. Heath, D., Castillo, Y., Arias-Stella, J. & Harris, P. (1969) *Cardiovasc. Res.*, **3**, 75.
13. Jones, E. L. (1969) *J. Path.*, **99**, 181.
14. Heath, D., Jones, E. L. & Housley, E. (1970) *Cardiovasc. Res.*, **4**, 515.
15. Smith, P., Heath, D., Wright, J. S. & McKendrick, C. S. (1973) *J. Path.*, **111**, 43.
16. Heath, D., Harris, P., Castillo, Y. & Arias-Stella, J. (1968) *J. Path. Bact.*, **96**, 161.
17. Dubreuil, G. (1923) *C.R. Soc. Biol.*, **75**, 1166.
18. Bariatti, R. & Conti, G. (1952) *Chir. Ital.*, **7**, 333.
19. Lacoste, A. & Baudrimont, A. (1926) *C.R. Soc. Biol.*, **78**, 1148.
20. Baudrimont, A. & Maugein-Merlet, A. M. (1933) *Bull. d'Hist.*, **10**, 201.
21. Wagenvoort, C. A. (1954) *Acta Anat.*, **21**, 70.
22. Rubin, E. & Strauss, L. (1961) *Amer. J. Path.*, **39**, 145.
23. Von Hayek, H. (1949) *Z. Anat. Entwicklungsgesch.*, **114**, 9.

27. Dietary Pulmonary Hypertension

Pulmonary hypertension may be dietary in origin. The substances incriminated in this respect so far have all been pyrrolizidine alkaloids found in the foliage and seeds of *Crotalaria* and *Senecio* species. As yet, the association between diet and pulmonary hypertension has been demonstrated only in experimental animals. However, a recent epidemic of primary pulmonary hypertension in West Germany, Austria and Switzerland has been ascribed to the ingestion of the anorexigen aminorex fumarate. These facts raise the interesting possibility that some cases of primary pulmonary hypertension in man may follow the ingestion of herbal remedies or drugs. As described below, in one case that we saw in East Africa in a youth of 19 years there was a strong suspicion that he had ingested an infusion containing a *Crotalaria* species.

THE PYRROLIZIDINE ALKALOIDS

Crotalaria spectabilis

Crotalaria spectabilis is an annual shrub which is widely distributed throughout the tropical and subtropical regions of the world (Fig. 27.1). The genus is a member of the family *Papilionaceae* which consists of some 550 to 650 species.[1] The plant is believed to have originated in India and it was introduced into the Southern United States in 1921 for use as a cover crop and green manure in agricultural practice. Its flowers are somewhat reminiscent of the laburnum and twenty to forty blossoms are carried on racemes measuring up to 30 cm in length (Fig. 27.1). The plant bears pods containing hard, black, shiny seeds which are kidney-shaped and measure $4 \times 3 \times 2$ mm (Fig. 27.2). When the seeds are ripe, they become loose and rattle giving the plant its vernacular name of 'rattlebox'.

The stems, foliage and seeds of this shrub contain a pyrrolizidine alkaloid, monocrotaline, the formula of which is shown in Figure 27.3. This alkaloid is concentrated in the seeds which contain 3 to 5 per cent of monocrotaline.

Monocrotaline or other closely related pyrrolizidine alkaloids are found in other *Crotalaria* species and, when these plants are eaten by farm or experimental animals, they give rise to various diseases which usually affect predominantly the liver or the lung.[1] Poisoning by *C. spectabilis* has been reported in hens, turkeys, pigs, cattle, monkeys and rats. *C. sagittalis* gives rise to 'Missouri river-bottom disease' of horses in the United States. 'Walkabout disease' in horses in Western Australia is produced by the ingestion of *C. retusa*. *C. crispata* gives rise to a similar condition in Northern Australia. Jagziekte is a disease of horses in South Africa brought on by eating *C. dura*. In these diseases, the liver shows changes ranging from necrosis of parenchymal cells, to cirrhosis. The lesions which have been reported in the lungs include oedema, haemorrhage and a reactive proliferation

Fig. 27.2 The seeds of *C. spectabilis*.

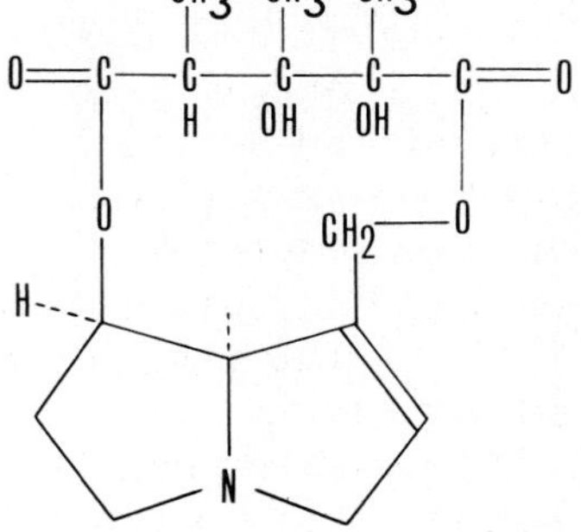

Fig. 27.1 *Crotalaria spectabilis*.

Fig. 27.3 Formula of monocrotaline.

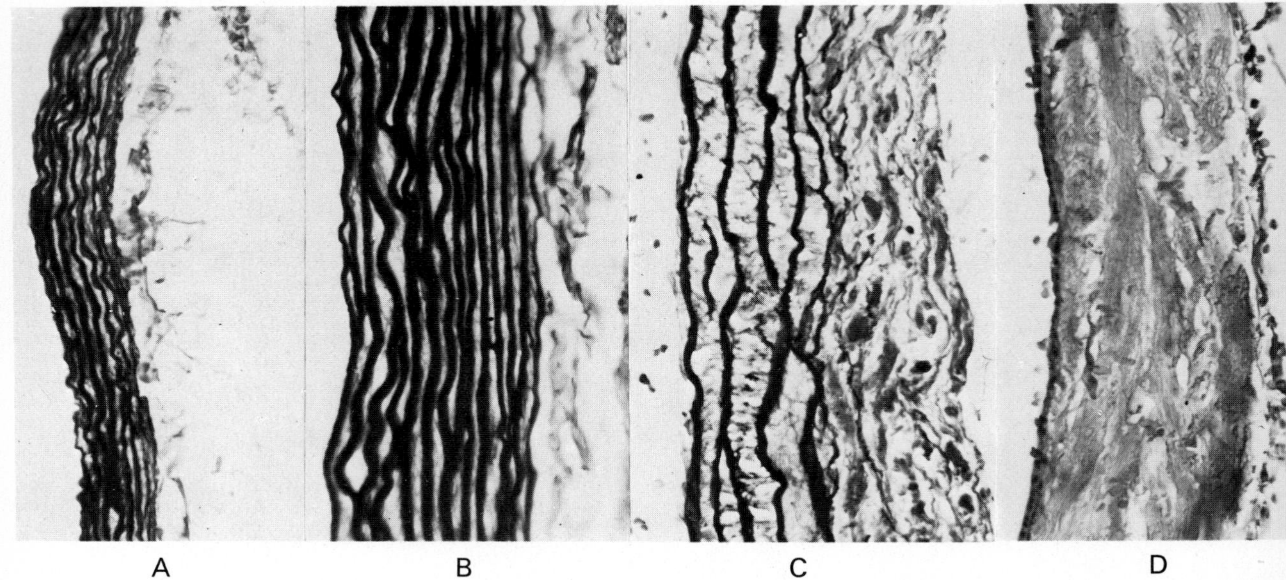

Fig. 27.4 A. Part of transverse section of pulmonary trunk of control Wistar albino rat. Note the thin media containing parallel elastic fibrils packed tightly together. The adventitia is to the right in this and the remaining three parts of this Figure. B. Part of transverse section of aorta of control rat. The media is thick and contains parallel elastic fibrils packed tightly together. C. part of transverse section of pulmonary trunk of a test rat fed on a diet containing ground *C. spectabilis* seeds. The media is hypertrophied, the elastic fibrils being forced apart by hyperplastic muscle fibres. D. Part of transverse section of pulmonary vein of control rat. The wall is largely composed of cardiac muscle fibres. (All Elastic/Van Gieson, × 250)

of both the epithelial and connective tissues. *Crotalaria* poisoning also occurs in man. In Jamaica veno-occlusive disease of the liver may follow the drinking of 'bush-tea' which is an infusion prepared from various *Crotalaria* species including *C. fulva*. The relation between the alkaloid fulvine in this plant and pulmonary hypertension is considered below.

Young rats fed on a diet containing powdered *C. spectabilis* seeds do not gain weight as rapidly as normal animals. Their breathing becomes laboured and they develop cyanosis and die. If the seeds are added to the diet to give a concentration of 0·1 per cent by weight, all the animals die within 36 to 60 days.[2] At necropsy, there are serous effusions, cardiac enlargement, induration of the lungs, and a liver showing the 'nutmeg' mottled appearance of centrilobular congestion and necrosis.[2] These clinical and pathological features indicate that the rats die from congestive cardiac failure.

When the individual ventricles of the heart are dissected by the method of Fulton, Hutchinson and Morgan Jones,[3] the cardiomegaly is found to be due to dilatation and hypertrophy of its right ventricle.[2] The only histological abnormality in the heart comprises small foci of myocarditis in the right ventricle and it seems likely that these represent areas of ischaemic change following the hypertrophy of the cardiac muscle fibres.

The right ventricular hypertrophy is secondary to pulmonary vascular disease. This consists of hypertrophy of the smooth muscle of the pulmonary trunk[4] (Fig. 27.4) and muscular pulmonary arteries (Fig. 27.5), and the development of a muscular media in the pulmonary arterioles[2] (Fig. 27.6). As in man, the normal pulmonary arteriole in the rat is a thin-walled structure devoid of smooth muscle. Quantitative investigation shows that the increase in medial thickness of the pulmonary trunk and muscular pulmonary arteries is comparable in degree to the increase in right ventricular weight.[4] About a third of the rats fed on the *C. spectabilis* seeds develop acute pulmonary arteritis (Fig. 27.7) which may show evidence of partial healing.[2] The intimal fibro-muscular prominences which are a normal anatomical feature of the small pulmonary veins in the rat are increased in size[2] (Fig. 27.8).

As will be seen by reference to Chapters 16 and 22, the morbid anatomical changes observed in the hearts and pulmonary arterial blood vessels of rats fed on *C. spectabilis* seeds are the same as those associated in man with pulmonary hypertension. The organic basis for the increased pulmonary vascular resistance is clearly the abnormal muscularization of the small pulmonary arterial vessels. The

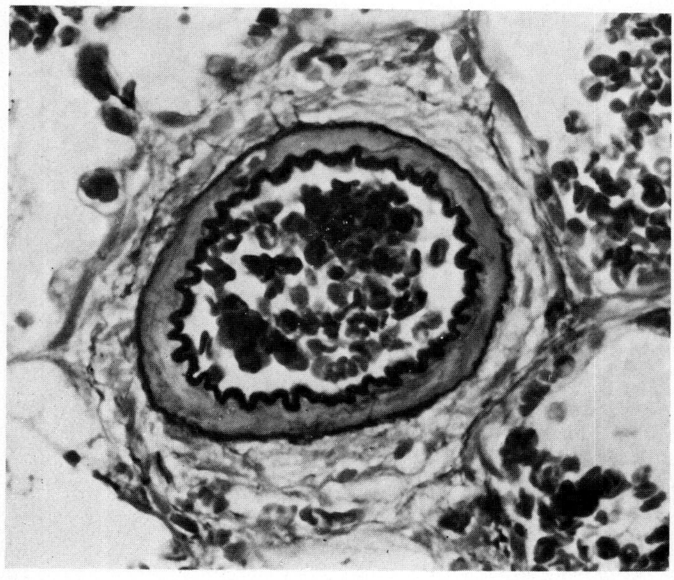

Fig. 27.5 Transverse section of muscular pulmonary artery from a rat fed on *C. spectabilis* seeds. There is medial hypertrophy. (Elastic/Van Gieson, × 600)

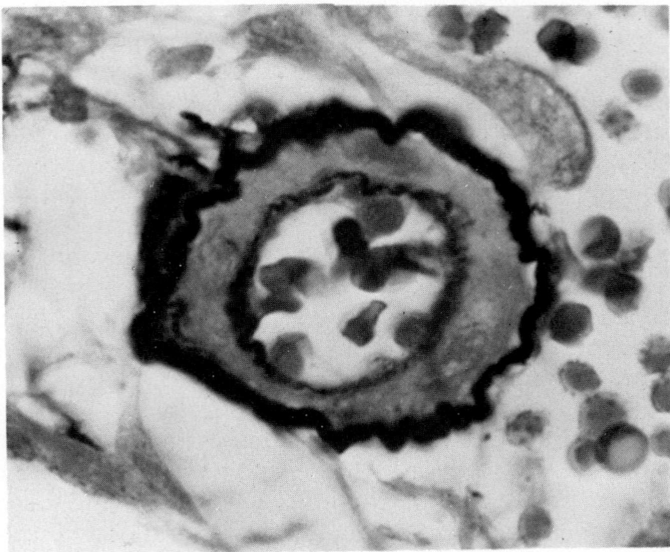

Fig. 27.6 Transverse section of pulmonary arteriole from a rat fed on *C. spectabilis* seeds. The vessel is muscularized with a distinct media of smooth muscle bounded by a thick outer and a thin inner elastic lamina. (Elastic/Van Gieson, × 1500)

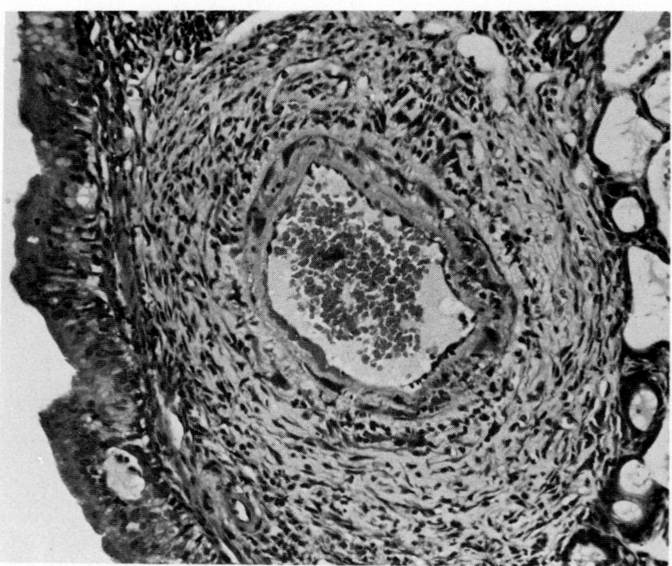

Fig. 27.7 Transverse section of muscular pulmonary artery from a rat fed on *C. spectabilis* seeds. There is fibrinoid necrosis of the media which is surrounded by a thick band of granulation tissue infiltrated with an acute-on-chronic inflammatory exudate. (Elastic/Van Gieson, × 150)

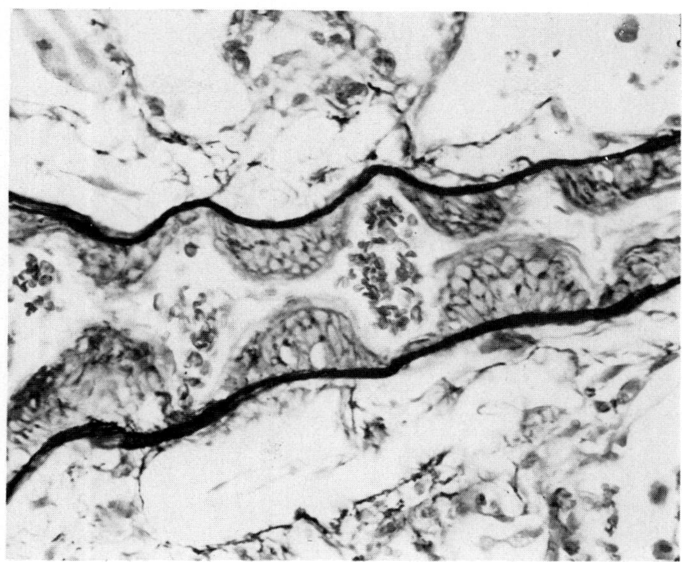

Fig. 27.8 Longitudinal section of pulmonary vein from a rat fed on *C. spectabilis* seeds. The muscular pads in the intima, normal features of the pulmonary vein in the rat, are hypertrophied. (Elastic/Van Gieson, × 375)

pulmonary arteritis is probably due to necrosis of the media consequent upon a sudden, severe increase in the intraluminal blood pressure.

Rats eating a diet containing *C. spectabilis* show multiple exudative changes in the lung parenchyma.[5] Pulmonary oedema is prominent. Electron microscopy of the lung reveals interstitial oedema of the alveolar-capillary wall with the protrusion of endothelial vesicles into the lumens of the pulmonary capillaries[5] (Fig. 27.9). These probably represent the early ultrastructural phase of pulmonary oedema and are more likely to be an effect than a cause of the pulmonary hypertension. As well as oedema, the exudative lesions in the acute stage include haemorrhage, interstitial fibrosis and alveolar cell metaplasia. Such lesions appear to be the direct or indirect result of chronic exudation of blood or plasma from the small pulmonary blood vessels into the alveolar walls and spaces. These changes together resemble the 'brown induration' of the lungs found in patients with pulmonary venous hypertension and may be due to increased intraluminal pressure in the small pulmonary blood vessels resulting from increased vascular resistance in the small pulmonary veins. Alternatively they may be due to exudation from small pulmonary arterial vessels proximal to a site of increased resistance.

The alveolar cell metaplasia referred to above shows as enlarged and proliferated cells which line the alveolar walls or lie free within the alveolar spaces (Fig. 27.10). Electron microscopy shows these cells to be enlarged granular (type 2) pneumocytes containing prominent, electron-dense, lamellar secretory inclusions[5] (Fig.

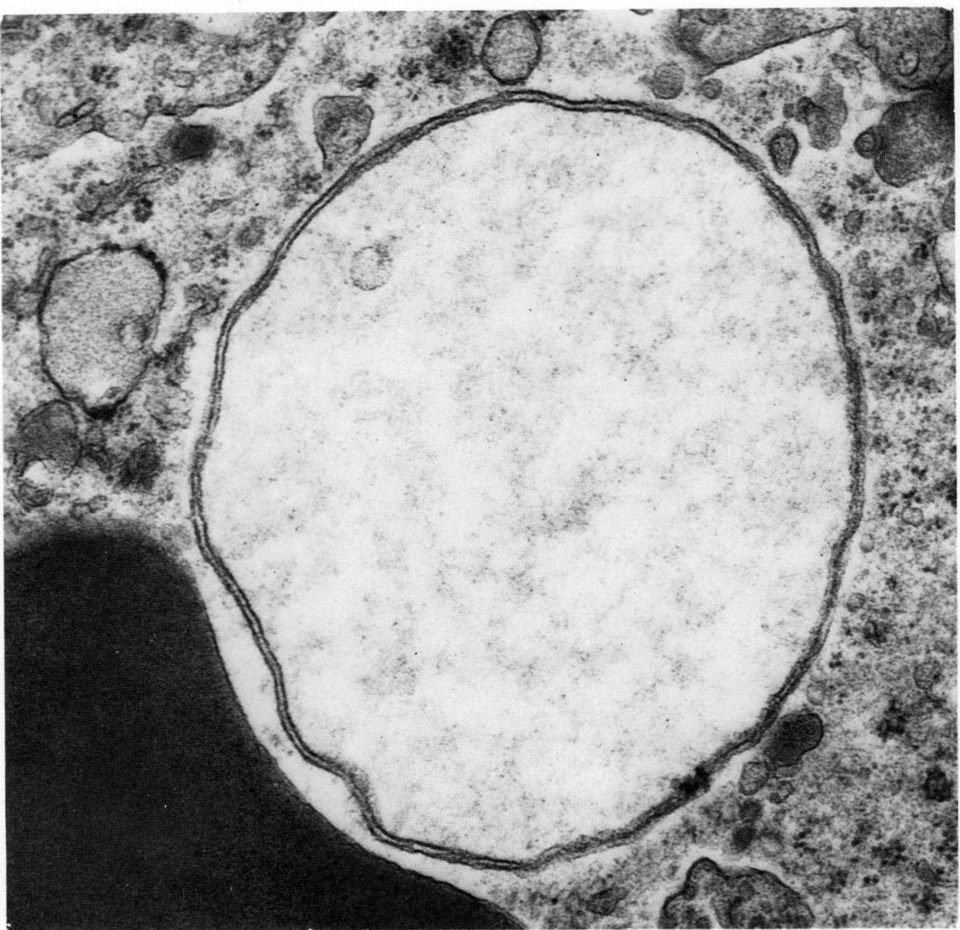

Fig. 27.9 Electron micrograph of lung from a rat fed on *C. spectabilis* seeds. The edge of an erythrocyte is seen in the lower left-hand corner of the Figure. In the centre is an endothelial vesicle which has projected into the lumen of a pulmonary capillary and been sectioned transversely. It is an ultrastructural feature of early pulmonary oedema. (× 37 500)

27.11). The alveolar spaces contain scanty macrophages as well as an excessive number of myelin figures and lattices. These structures resemble phospholipid membranes and may be related to pulmonary surfactant. It is likely that the proliferation of granular pneumocytes is a non-specific reaction of the alveolar walls to injury.

When very small oral doses of *C. spectabilis* seeds amounting to only 0·02 per cent by weight of the diet are administered to rats over a prolonged period of 140 to 288 days the exudative lesions become chronic and further lesions appear.[6] These include osseous nodules in the lung parenchyma (Fig. 27.12) and cartilaginous metaplasia in the elastic pulmonary arteries (Fig. 27.13) (Ref. 6). Even after prolonged administration of *C. spectabilis,* dilatation lesions, such as plexiform or angiomatoid lesions, do not occur in the lung. The lack of intimal fibrosis in dietary hypertensive pulmonary vascular disease in the rat is probably a species difference.

It is possible to confirm directly by catheterization and manometry of the right side of the rat heart that the pulmonary vascular disease produced by eating *C. spectabilis* seeds is associated with pulmonary hypertension.[7] In eight normal rats we found that the right ventricular systolic pressure ranged from 22 to 36 mmHg with a mean value of 29 mmHg. In five rats fed the seeds the corresponding pressure ranged from 62 to 112 mmHg with a mean of 86 mmHg (Ref. 7).

Intraperitoneal and intramuscular injections of monocrotaline, the toxic constituent of *C. spectabilis,* fail to produce an immediate elevation of the right ventricular pressure in rats, indicating that the alkaloid does not itself directly constrict small pulmonary blood vessels.

There is a proliferation of mast cells in a proportion of rats fed on *C. spectabilis* seeds.[8] Although mast cells in the rat are rich in serotonin (5-hydroxytryptamine) there is no evidence that mast cells are concerned in the genesis of the pulmonary

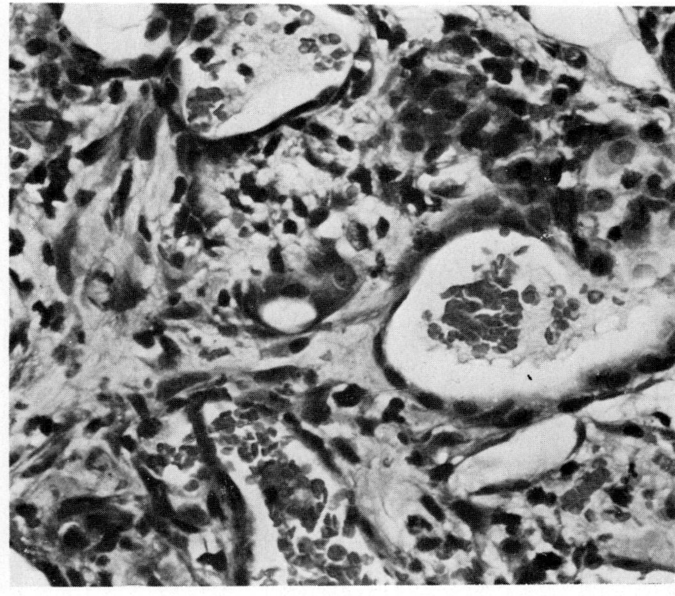

Fig. 27.10 Section of lung from rat fed on *C. spectabilis* seeds. There is fibrosing alveolitis and the alveolar spaces are lined by prominent cells which on electron microscopy prove to be granular pneumocytes (see Fig. 27.11). (Haematoxylin & eosin, × 375)

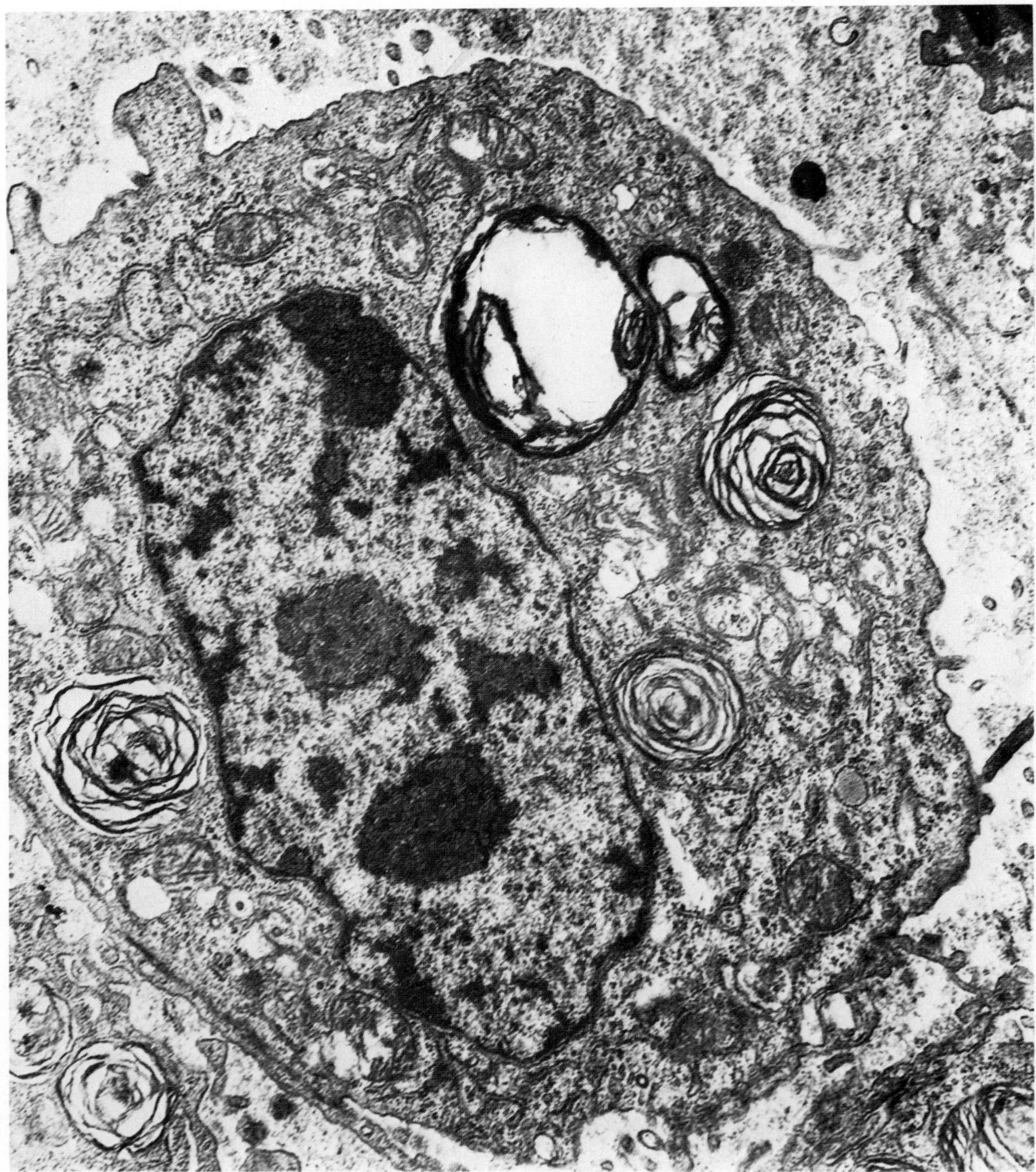

Fig. 27.11 Electron micrograph of lung from a rat fed on *C. spectabilis* seeds. The prominent cells lining alveolar spaces are granular pneumocytes characterized by lamellar bodies. (× 12 500)

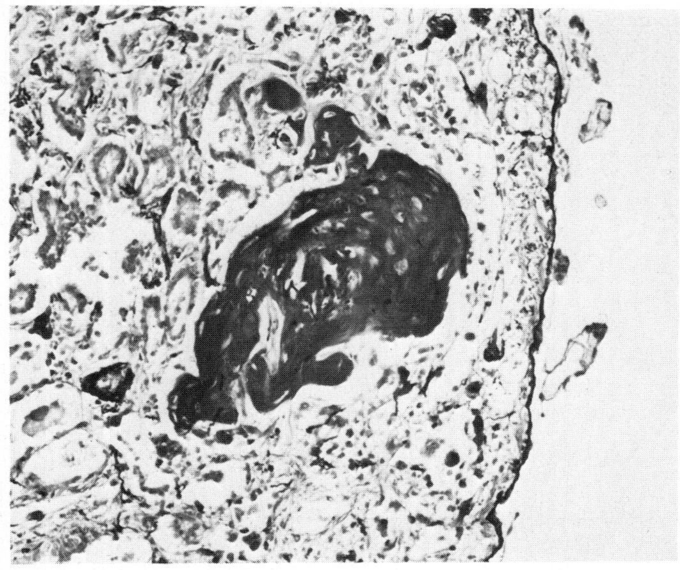

Fig. 27.12 Section of lung from a rat fed on *C. spectabilis* seeds. Within the lung substance is an osseous nodule. (Elastic/Van Gieson, × 150)

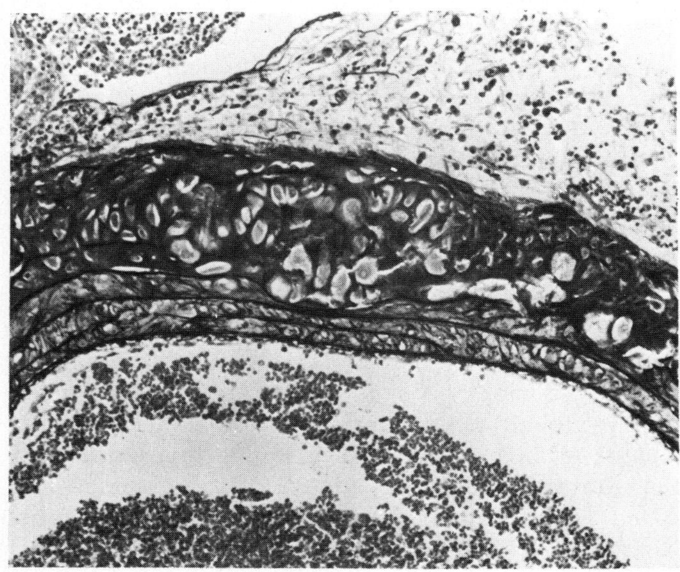

Fig. 27.13 Part of transverse section of elastic pulmonary artery from a rat fed on *C. spectabilis* seeds. There is cartilaginous metaplasia within the adventitia. (Elastic/Van Gieson, × 150)

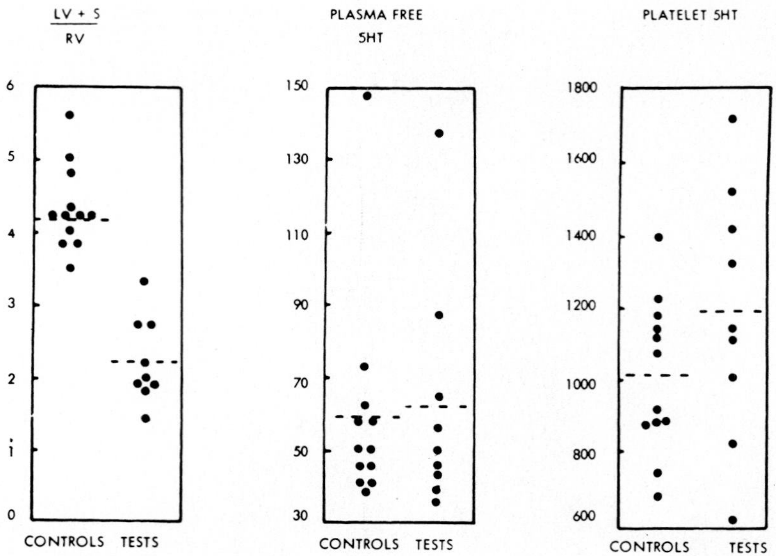

Fig. 27.14 The ratio of left to right ventricular weight, (LV + S)/RV, and the levels of plasma free and platelet bound 5-hydroxytryptamine (5-HT; serotonin) in 12 control rats and in 9 rats fed on *C. spectabilis* seeds. The plasma free 5-HT is measured in ng/ml and the platelet 5-HT in ng/10^9 platelets. There is no statistically significant difference in the level of plasma free and platelet bound 5-HT in the test and control animals.

hypertension induced by the seeds. The mast cell hyperplasia seems to be a secondary phenomenon related to the development of exudative lesions in the lung parenchyma. A study of the concentration of serotonin in the platelets, plasma and lungs of rats fed on the seeds has not indicated that ingested monocrotaline interferes with the metabolism or transport of this amine[9] (Fig. 27.14).

Crotalaria fulva

This is one of the many plants used in Jamaica to prepare bush tea. It contains the pyrrolizidine alkaloid fulvine which has a structural formula very similar to that of monocrotaline, differing only in the absence of one hydroxyl group. Fulvine, and possibly other pyrrolizidine alkaloids, are now generally accepted as causing veno-occlusive disease of the liver in Jamaica, and a programme of health education on the island has now reduced the incidence of the disease. The condition was originally described as a syndrome of hepatomegaly and ascites in Jamaican children and was regarded as a hepatitis of unknown aetiology.[10] Subsequently the disease was called serous hepatosis.[11] The occurrence of occlusion of the small hepatic vein radicals in children with this clinical syndrome was first described by Bras, Jelliffe and Stuart[12] in 1954 and they proposed the name veno-occlusive disease by which the condition is now widely known. Stuart and Bras[13] in 1957 described three clinical stages of the disease.

The similarity of the structural formulae of monocrotaline and fulvine suggested to us that fulvine might also be a cause of pulmonary hypertension and hypertensive pulmonary vascular disease. When single doses of fulvine are administered to Wistar albino rats by the intraperitoneal or intragastric route, in a dosage of 50 mg or 80 mg, respectively, of the alkaloid per kg of body weight, some of the animals die after two or three weeks from severe acute hepatic necrosis. However, those rats which survive for longer than a month develop right ventricular hypertrophy, medial hypertrophy of the pulmonary trunk, pulmonary vascular disease, and exudative changes in the lungs.[14] The pulmonary vascular disease and exudative changes encountered are the same as those produced by monocrotaline. There is hypertrophy of the muscular pulmonary arteries and muscularization of the pulmonary arterioles. Some of the muscular pulmonary arteries show fibrinoid necrosis, but dilatation lesions, such as plexiform and angiomatoid lesions do not occur.[14] The exudative lesions are very similar to those found in *Crotalaria spectabilis* poisoning. So far as we are aware, pulmonary hypertension has not yet been reported in any human cases of veno-occlusive disease of the liver in Jamaica.

Senecio jacobaea

The 'ragwort' (*Senecio jacobaea*) is a familiar plant of the British countryside. Its seeds and foliage contain several pyrrolizidine alkaloids which include senecionine, jacobine, jacoline and jacozine.[15] When the diet of rats is adulterated with powdered ragwort plants, including seeds and foliage, to give a concentration of 5 or 10 per cent by weight of the diet, they develop hypertrophy of the right ventricle, pulmonary trunk, and muscular pulmonary arteries.[16] This suggests that ragwort contains an agent which produces pulmonary hypertension. *Senecio jacobaea* is freely available to the public in dried chopped form as a commodity available in 'Health Stores'. This material is meant to be taken in the form of an infusion to cure a variety of ailments.

Crotalaria laburnoides (C. bagamoyoënsis)

On a recent visit to Tanzania one of the authors was shown necropsy material from an African youth of 19 years who had died from primary pulmonary hypertension. He was suspected of having ingested a herbal remedy containing the seeds of the plant *Crotalaria laburnoides* (*C. bagamoyoënsis*) which grows in the coastal area around the small township of Bagamoyo which was an important centre of the African slave trade in the last century. David Livingstone knew this town and was almost certainly familiar with the plant. In view of the association between the *Crotalaria* species and pulmonary hypertension in rats, we fed powdered seeds of this plant to Wistar albino rats to see if this would induce right ventricular hypertrophy and associated hypertensive pulmonary vascular disease.[17] At the end of the experimental period, right ventricular hypertrophy, medial hypertrophy of the pulmonary trunk and 'muscular pulmonary arteries', and muscularization of the pulmonary arterioles had developed in a proportion of the test animals.[17] These are the morbid anatomical features pathognomonic of a raised pulmonary arterial pressure and show that the seeds of *C. laburnoides* contain an agent capable of inducing pulmonary hypertension in rats.

THE EFFECT OF APPETITE-SUPPRESSANTS

Aminorex fumarate

So far we have seen that certain pyrrolizidine alkaloids contained in *Crotalaria* and *Senecio* species may give rise to pulmonary hypertension and associated pulmonary vascular disease in animals. Extracts of *C. fulva* and *S. jacobaea* may be included in the human diet but as yet there have been no reported cases of pulmonary hypertension following the ingestion of pyrrolizidine alkaloids in man. However, recently it has been postulated that a slimming drug, aminorex fumarate, may produce the clinical picture of 'primary' pulmonary hypertension leading to a rapid death from congestive cardiac failure.

'Primary' pulmonary hypertension is a rare disease and accounts for less than one per cent of adult patients studied by cardiac catheterization. In the latter half of 1967, however, a dramatic and sudden change in the incidence of this disease was noticed at the University Medical Clinic in Berne.[18] The incidence of primary pulmonary hypertension in adults subjected to cardiac catheterization increased from 0·87 per cent observed during the 12-year period 1955 to 1966 to 15·4 per cent during the years 1967 and 1968.[19] A comparable increase in incidence was noticed in every clinical centre in Switzerland.[20] Similar observations were made in Austria[21] and Germany,[22] where the rise in incidence was less pronounced.

Gurtner and his colleagues were convinced that the sudden twenty-fold increase in the incidence of primary pulmonary hypertension in their clinic was not due to chance nor to improved diagnostic procedures.[18] They noted that the majority of patients studied since 1967 differed from their earlier cases in that the recent patients tended to be older, showed a more rapid progress of the disease, and were frequently obese. Furthermore, a considerable proportion of the individuals studied since the beginning of 1967 had tried to reduce weight by taking aminorex, a potent appetite-suppressing drug.

Aminorex (2-amino-5-phenyl-2-oxazoline) resembles adrenaline and amphetamine in its chemical structure (Fig. 27.15) and suppresses the appetite in most individuals by acting directly on the brain.[23] It was introduced on to the Swiss market in November 1965 under the proprietory name of Menocil. Gurtner[24] noted that of 70 patients (62 females and 8 males) with primary pulmonary hypertension investigated between January 1967 and March 1970, 55 gave a history of having aminorex. In these patients, the first symptoms appeared between 6 and 12 months after commencing the drug. Aminorex was withdrawn from the market

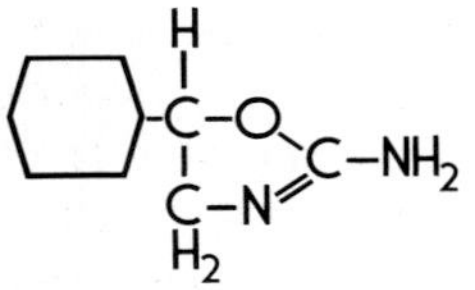

Fig. 27.15 Formula of aminorex.

in October 1968 and since that date there has been a pronounced decline in the incidence of primary pulmonary hypertension.[25,26] These workers have, however, noticed a recent 3-to-5 fold increase in the incidence of primary pulmonary hypertension in Switzerland unassociated with aminorex ingestion. It is not certain whether this increase of pulmonary hypertension unassociated with aminorex is due to an increased awareness of the disease resulting from wide publicity, or to a possible concealment of aminorex consumption, or whether it reflects the operation of other unsuspected aetiological factors.

Apart from the temporal relationship between the availability of aminorex and the incidence of primary pulmonary hypertension, there is also a geographical coincidence between the market of the drug and the changed incidence of the disease. Thus an increased incidence of primary pulmonary hypertension has been reported only in countries where the drug has been commercially available (Austria, Germany and Switzerland); the incidence of the disease does not appear to have changed in countries where the drug has not been marketed.

THE PULMONARY VASCULAR DISEASE ASSOCIATED WITH THE INGESTION OF AMINOREX

Histological examination of the lungs from patients who have taken a course of aminorex has been carried out on both biopsy[27] and necropsy material.[28] Through the kindness of Professor Gurtner of Berne and Dr. Widgren of Geneva we have been able to examine such material.

All the histological lesions could be interpreted as occurring as part of a spontaneous primary pulmonary hypertension the detailed pathological features of which we describe in Chapter 28 and elsewhere.[29] The elastic pulmonary arteries are atheromatous. There is medial hypertrophy of the muscular pulmonary arteries. These latter vessels also show intimal fibrosis and fibroelastosis which may be so severe as to be of the 'onion-skin' type leading to total vascular occlusion. In contrast to the pulmonary vascular disease in animals with dietary pulmonary hypertension, described above, there are dilatation lesions including plexiform and angiomatoid lesions. The pulmonary arterioles are hypertensive in type with a distinct media of circular muscle bounded by internal and external elastic laminae and showing intimal fibrosis and fibroelastosis.

As some of the patients who have taken the anorexigen aminorex have naturally been obese it has been postulated that their pulmonary hypertension and hypertensive pulmonary vascular disease is of the hypoxic type described in Chapter 33, such as might occur in the Pickwickian syndrome. Reference to the description above of the pulmonary vascular disease associated with the ingestion of aminorex and to the description of hypoxic hypertensive pulmonary vascular disease in Chapter 33 will show that such is not the case.

AMINOREX AND PULMONARY HYPERTENSION IN LABORATORY ANIMALS

Some workers have reported that an intravenous injection of aminorex to dogs may produce a transient rise in the pulmonary arterial pressure.[30] Others have been more concerned to see if prolonged administration of the drug in the diet of laboratory animals can produce pulmonary vascular disease similar to that in patients who have taken the drug in Western Europe.

We have added aminorex fumarate to the diet of 39 female Wistar albino rats and 4 female beagle dogs. The dose of the drug given to the rats was 840 mg per kg of diet and that given to the dogs was 6 mg per kg of body weight. The rats received the drug for periods ranging from 24 to 302 days. The dogs received it for 20 weeks. None of these animals developed right ventricular hypertrophy or pulmonary vascular disease even after such prolonged administration of aminorex.[31] It might be argued that such results are not valid because the drug was given to animals of normal body weight rather than to obese rats and dogs. However, it should be noted that in the series of cases of pulmonary hypertension associated with appetite suppressants reported by Gurtner and his colleagues the majority of patients were only slightly overweight.[18] It seems unlikely that obesity as such played an important role in the development of the pulmonary hypertension in these patients. Nevertheless, it has been suggested that the basis for the sporadic occurrence of pulmonary hypertension in patients taking aminorex is that in a small

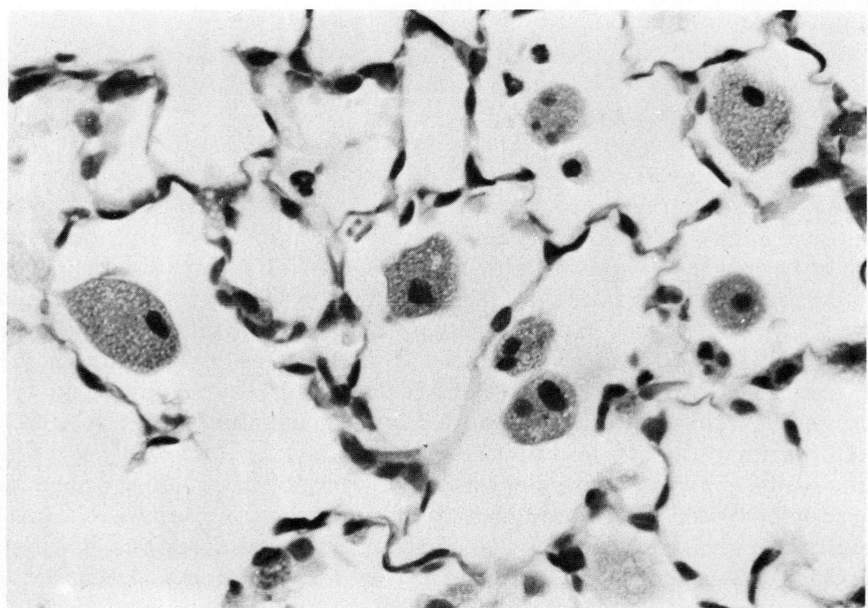

Fig. 27.16 Section of lung from rat given chlorphentermine hydrochloride. The alveolar spaces are filled with 'foam cells'. (Haematoxylin & eosin, × 600)

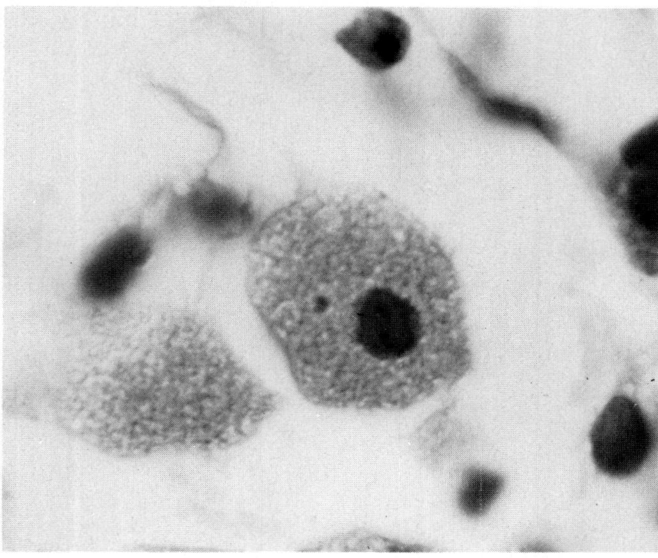

Fig. 27.17 'Foam cells' in an alveolar space of a rat treated with chlorphentermine. (Haematoxylin & eosin, × 1500)

number of them the pulmonary arterial tree is 'sensitized' to its action by some pre-existing abnormality such as the cardiopulmonary changes associated with obesity and chronic hypoxia. This seems unlikely because it has proven impossible to induce a raised pulmonary arterial pressure by injecting aminorex into calves subjected to the chronic hypoxia of living at a high altitude where the barometric pressure was only 625 mmHg (Ref. 32).

Pharmacologists have demonstrated slight transient increases in pulmonary vascular resistance in rats and dogs given aminorex. An intravenous infusion of the drug into dogs produces pulmonary hypertension and increased pulmonary vascular resistance which reaches a maximum 15 min after the start of the infusion and which remains for the duration of the infusion.[30] Kraupp and his associates[30] believe the action of aminorex to correspond to the alpha-type of sympathomimetic vasomotor action (p. 185). Other authors have reported a transient pressor effect of the drug on the pulmonary circulation of dogs similar in action to adrenaline and lasting for a period of hours.[33,34]

As yet, however, no one has succeeded in producing sustained pulmonary hypertension and associated hypertensive pulmonary vascular disease by prolonged administration of a diet containing aminorex to rats or dogs. Perivascular oedema and lymphocytic infiltration in the lungs of rats receiving a diet adulterated with the drug have been reported but this was not associated with hypertrophy of the right ventricle or the pulmonary arterial tree.[35] Prolonged administration of

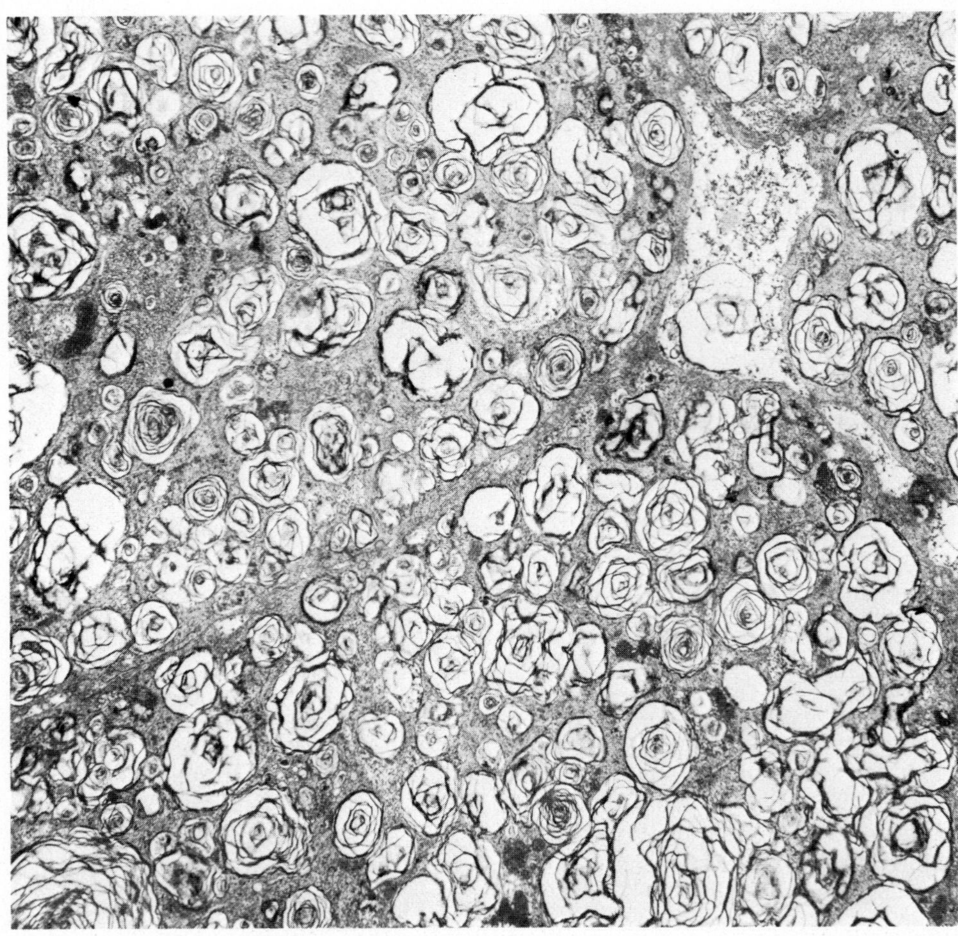

Fig. 27.18 Electron micrograph of intra-alveolar 'foam cells' in chlorphentermine-treated rats. The cells contain numerous osmiophilic lamellar inclusions but also lysosomal bodies indicating them to be alveolar macrophages. The osmiophilic material is derived from hyperplastic granular pneumocytes which liberate their lamellar bodies into the alveoli. (× 18 750)

aminorex to Patas monkeys does not lead to a raised pulmonary arterial pressure or to hypertensive vascular changes in the lung.[36]

In summary, the present position with regard to aminorex fumarate appears to be that, while there is statistical evidence linking the drug with pulmonary hypertension in man, there is no proof that it causes hypertensive pulmonary vascular disease. The failure of administration of aminorex to animals to produce lesions in the pulmonary arterial tree does not exclude the possibility that this substance may produce pulmonary hypertension in man. The negative results may reflect a species

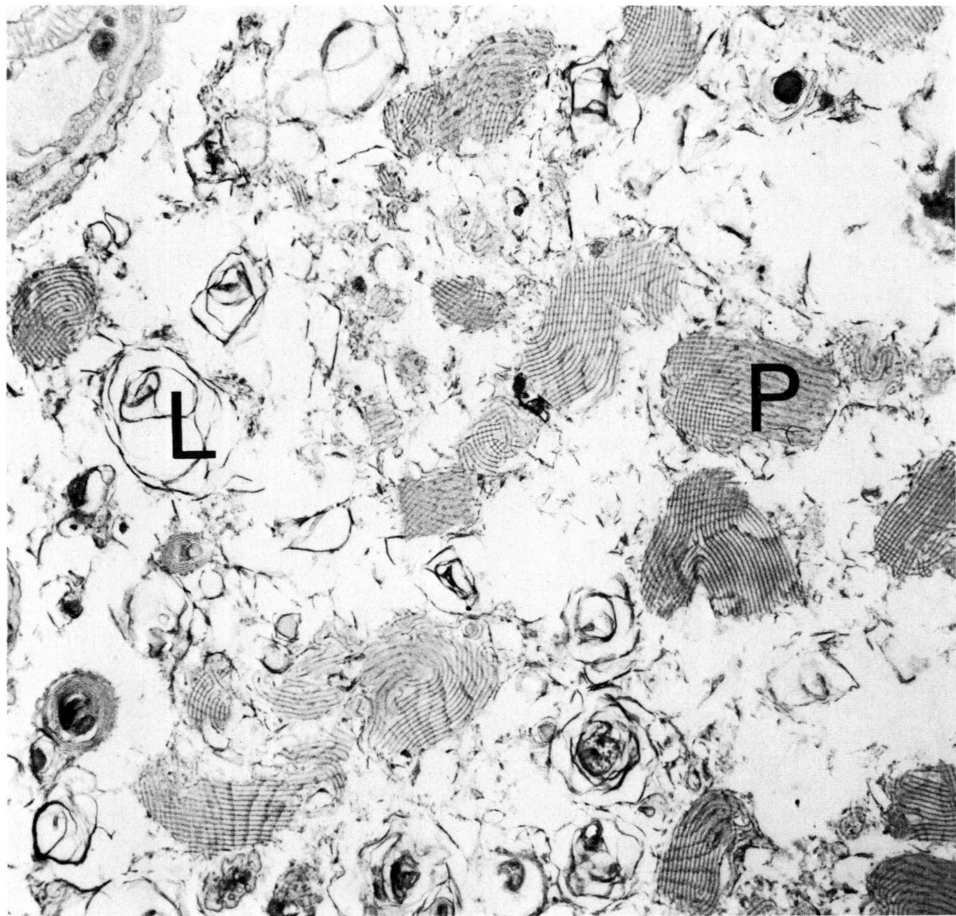

Fig. 27.19 Electron micrograph of alveolar debris in a rat given chlorphentermine. It consists of lamellar material, L, and phospholipid lattices, P. (× 12 500)

difference in the behaviour of the pulmonary vasculature. It should also be kept in mind that only one in 2000 patients taking the drug were affected by pulmonary hypertension. This low incidence of pulmonary hypertension needs to be considered in relation to the negative results in animals.

Chlorphentermine. Disease of the Lung Parenchyma in Rats

Chlorphentermine hydrochloride is an appetite-suppressant which is chemically closely related to amphetamine. At the time of writing, it is available on the British market. When given to rats daily for 50 days by intraperitoneal injection in a dosage of 50 mg per kg body weight it also fails to give rise to the morbid anatomical associations of pulmonary arterial hypertension namely right ventricular hypertrophy, medial hypertrophy of the pulmonary trunk and hypertensive pulmonary vascular disease.[37] However, while chlorphentermine produces no pathological changes in the pulmonary arteries, it gives rise to striking changes in the lung parenchyma. These include a hyperplasia of type 2 granular pneumocytes with the appearance in the alveolar spaces of great numbers of pulmonary histiocytes (Figs 27.16 and 27.17) which have ingested lamellar bodies no doubt derived from the hyperplastic granular pneumocytes (Fig. 27.18) (Ref. 38). The alveoli become filled with lamellar bodies, myelin figures and phospholipid lattices (Fig. 27.19) (Ref. 38). Osmiophilic lamellar inclusions also appear in bronchiolar Clara cells, type 1 (membranous) pneumocytes, and endothelial cells of pulmonary capillaries. The phospholipid content of the lung increases remarkably, dipalmitoylphosphatidylcholine being particularly affected.[39] Such findings make it clear that, while as yet there is no proof that anorexigens can lead to pulmonary vascular disease, there is no doubt that they can exert deleterious effects on the lung parenchyma and pulmonary capillary bed.

REFERENCES

1. Kay, J. M. & Heath, D. (1969) *Crotalaria Spectabilis, the Pulmonary Hypertension Plant.* Springfield, Ill.: Thomas.
2. Kay, J. M. & Heath, D. (1966) *J. Path. Bact.*, **92**, 385.
3. Fulton, R. M., Hutchinson, E. C. & Jones, A. M. (1952) *Brit. Heart J.*, **14**, 413.
4. Heath, D. & Kay, J. M. (1967) *Cardiovasc. Res.*, **1**, 74.
5. Kay, J. M., Smith, P. & Heath, D. (1969) *Thorax*, **24**, 511.
6. Smith, P., Kay, J. M. & Heath, D. (1970) *J. Path.*, **102**, 97.
7. Kay, J. M., Harris, P. & Heath, D. (1967) *Thorax*, **22**, 176.
8. Kay, J. M., Gillund, T. D. & Heath, D. (1967) *Amer. J. Path.*, **51**, 1031.
9. Kay, J. M., Crawford, N. & Heath, D. (1968) *Experientia*, **24**, 1149.
10. McFarlane, A. L. & Branday, W. J. (1945) *Brit. Med. J.*, **1**, 838.
11. Hill, K. R., Rhodes, K., Stafford, J. L. & Aub, R. (1953) *Brit. Med. J.*, **1**, 117.
12. Bras, G., Jelliffe, D. B. & Stuart, K. L. (1954) *Arch. Path.*, **57**, 285.
13. Stuart, K. L. & Bras, G. (1957) *Quart. J. Med. (NS)*, **26**, 291.
14. Kay, J. M., Heath, D., Smith, P., Bras, G. & Summerell, J. (1971) *Thorax*, **26**, 249.
15. Bull, L. B., Culvenor, C. C. J. & Dick, A. T. (1968) *The Pyrrolizidine Alkaloids. Their chemistry, pathogenicity and other biological properties.* Amsterdam: North Holland.
16. Burns, J. (1972) *J. Path.*, **106**, 187.
17. Heath, D., Shaba, J., Williams, A., Smith, P. & Kombe, A. (1975) *Thorax*, **30**, 399
18. Gurtner, H. P., Gertsch, M., Salzmann, C., Scherrer, M., Stucki, P. & Wyss, F. (1968) *Schweiz. Med. Wschr.*, **98**, 1579 & 1695.
19. Gurtner, H. P. (1969) *Deutsch. med. Wschr.*, **94**, 850.
20. Rivier, J. L. (1970) *Schweiz. med. Wschr.*, **100**, 143.
21. Lang, E., Haput, E. J., Kohler, J. A. & Schmidt, J. (1969) *Müch. med. Wschr.*, **8**, 405.
22. Kaindl, F. (1969) *Wein. Z. inn. Med.*, **50**, 451.
23. Peters, L. & Gourzis, J. T. (1974) In *Obesity, Circulation, Anorexigens*, ed. Blankart, R. page 61. Berne: Hans Huber.
24. Gurtner, H. P. (1970) *Proceedings of 12th Annual Meeting of the European Society for the Study of Drug Toxicity.* Uppsala, Sweden, June 1970. Amsterdam: Excerpta Medica.
25. Gurtner, H. P. (1969) *Bull. de Physio-Pathologie Respiratoire*, **5**, 435.

26. Blankart, R. (1974) In *Obesity, Circulation, Anorexigens*, ed. Blankart, R. page 187. Berne: Hans Huber.
27. Obiditsch-Mayer, I. (1969) *Wein. Z. inn. Med.*, **50**, 486.
28. Jornod, J., Widgren, S. & Fischer, G. (1970) *Schweiz. med. Wschr.*, **100**, 151.
29. Wagenvoort, C. A., Heath, D. & Edwards, J. E. (1964) In *The Pathology of the Pulmonary Vasculature*. page 172. Springfield, Ill.: Thomas.
30. Kraupp, O., Stühlinger, W., Raberger, G. & Turnheim, K. (1969) *Naunyn-Schmeideberg's Arch. Pharmak.*, **264**, 389.
31. Kay, J. M., Smith, P. & Heath, D. (1971) *Thorax*, **26**, 262.
32. Byrne-Quinn, E. & Grover, R. F. (1974) In *Obesity, Circulation, Anorexigens*, ed. Blankart, R. page 155. Berne: Hans Huber.
33. Engelhardt, A., Kronberg, G., Steopel, K. & Stötzer, H. (1970) *Proceedings of the 12th Annual Meeting of the European Society for the Study of Drug Toxicity*. Uppsala, Sweden, June 1970. Amsterdam: Excerpta Medica.
34. Brunner, H. & Stepanek, J. (1970) *Proceedings of the 12th Annual Meeting of the European Society for the Study of Drug Toxicity*. Uppsala, Sweden, June 1970. Amsterdam: Excerpta Medica.
35. Backmann, R., Haschemian, A., Kemper, F. & Morgenroth, K., Jn. (1970) In *Obesity, Circulation, Anorexigens*, ed. Blankart, R. Berne: Hans Huber.
36. Smith, P., Heath, D., Kay, J. M., Wright, J. S. & McKendrick, C. S. (1973) *Cardiovasc. Res.*, **7**, 30.
37. Heath, D., Smith, P. & Haselton, P. S. (1973) *Thorax*, **28**, 551.
38. Smith, P., Heath, D. & Haselton, P. S. (1973) *Thorax*, **28**, 559.
39. Gloster, J., Heath, D., Hasleton, P. & Harris, P. (1976) *Thorax*, **31**, 558.

28. Unexplained Pulmonary Hypertension

The many well-defined pathological causes of pulmonary arterial hypertension have been listed in Chapter 15. In the great majority of patients with pulmonary hypertension, clinical examination together with the relevant investigations provides a precise diagnosis of the cause. In some cases, however, the elevation of pulmonary arterial pressure remains unexplained even after exclusion of all known predisposing diseases of the heart and lungs by careful clinical and radiological examination and by detailed investigation at cardiac catheterization. This clinical condition of 'unexplained pulmonary hypertension' may be produced by three distinct pathological entities. They are 'plexogenic pulmonary arteriopathy' (which is the underlying pathology of classical primary pulmonary hypertension), pulmonary veno-occlusive disease, and recurrent pulmonary thromboembolism. These causes are summarized in Table 28.1. We consider the first two of these diseases in this chapter while we discuss pulmonary embolism in Chapter 35. It should be appreciated that the clinician may sometimes be able to distinguish between these three entities but frequently this is not possible. Under such circumstances the diagnosis has to be 'unexplained pulmonary hypertension' with the realization that the term embraces the possibility of classical primary pulmonary hypertension, pulmonary veno-occlusive disease and recurrent pulmonary thromboembolism.

Table 28.1 Causes of unexplained pulmonary hypertension.

1. Classical primary pulmonary hypertension (due to plexogenic pulmonary arteriopathy)
2. Pulmonary veno-occlusive disease
3. Recurrent pulmonary thromboembolism

The Three Pathological Entities

The histopathological lesions which are found in a case of classical primary pulmonary hypertension comprise increased medial thickness of muscular pulmonary arteries, muscularization of pulmonary arterioles, the development of intimal fibrosis and fibroelastosis in a characteristic 'onion-skin' configuration, the development of dilatation lesions especially plexiform lesions (Chap. 18) and in some instances necrotizing arteritis. The last may be seen in an acute form with fibrinoid necrosis of the media infiltrated by neutrophil polymorphs or in a sub-acute form with granulomatous changes in the arterial walls and overlying thrombosis. These changes are described in greater detail below but we may note here that they may be termed succinctly 'plexogenic pulmonary arteriopathy', a form of pulmonary arterial disease with the natural history of forming plexiform lesions, although these will not be found in every case.

This term was accepted by a Working Party of the World Health Organization on Primary Pulmonary Hypertension[1] held in Geneva in October 1973. It will be immediately recognized that 'plexogenic pulmonary arteriopathy' while highly characteristic of classical primary pulmonary hypertension is not pathognomonic of the disease. In Chapter 16 we have seen that this is the form of hypertensive pulmonary vascular disease which is found in pre-and post-tricuspid congenital cardiac shunts. It also occurs very rarely in association with portal hypertension as produced by cirrhosis of the liver or portal vein thrombosis (Chap. 29) (Table 28.2).

Table 28.2 Causes of plexogenic pulmonary arteriopathy.

1. Pre- and post-tricuspid congenital cardiac shunts
2. Classical primary pulmonary hypertension
3. Portal hypertension (very rarely), *e.g.* portal vein thrombosis, cirrhosis of the liver

The second distinct entity that may give rise to the clinical picture of unexplained pulmonary hypertension is pulmonary veno-occlusive disease. In this condition, which is described more fully later in the present chapter, the brunt of the pathology falls on the pulmonary veins, the pulmonary arteries being involved only secondarily. The disease may sometimes be diagnosed clinically, largely on radiological grounds, but this is not always the case.

The third entity to be reckoned with is recurrent pulmonary thromboembolism in which small muscular pulmonary arteries and pulmonary arterioles become progressively occluded by impaction and subsequent organization of repeated small thromboemboli. This disease is described in Chapter 35. Wagenvoort and Wagenvoort[2] in their detailed study of the pathology of the lung vessels in 156 clinically diagnosed cases of 'primary pulmonary hypertension' accept a clear distinction between recurrent pulmonary thromboembolism and primary pulmonary hypertension. The distinguishing histological features are described below (Table 28.3), but it may be noted here that in their 31 cases of recurrent pulmonary thromboembolism the Wagenvoorts[2] found no plexiform lesions, no fibrinoid necrosis, and no onion-skin intimal proliferation, all highly characteristic of plexogenic pulmonary arteriopathy underlying classical primary pulmonary hypertension.

The Accuracy of the Diagnosis of Primary Pulmonary Hypertension

The Wagenvoorts[2] carried out a meticulous histological and morphometric study of the pulmonary blood vessels in lung tissue from 156 patients from 51 medical centres throughout the world in whom the diagnosis of primary pulmonary hypertension had been made. Although clinical and even necropsy examination had been carried out in every one of these collected cases, the diagnosis was incorrect in no fewer than 46 instances. The conditions incorrectly diagnosed as primary pulmonary hypertension (with plexogenic arteriopathy as its underlying pathology)

Table 28.3 Histopathological differentiation between three diseases which may present clinically as 'unexplained pulmonary hypertension'

Disease	Muscular pulmonary arteries					Pulmonary veins and venules	
	Type of intimal proliferation	Medial hypertrophy	Plexiform lesions	Fibrinoid necrosis	Arteritis	Intimal fibrosis	State of media
Primary pulmonary hypertension	Concentric onion-skin type. Occasional thrombi near fibrinoid necrosis	Severe in early stages Less severe in late stages	Common	Frequent	Frequent	Age change only	Normal
Recurrent pulmonary thromboembolism	Fresh, organizing and re-canalized thrombi. Eccentric pads of intimal fibroelastosis	Slight	Absent	Absent	Rare	Age change only	Normal
Pulmonary veno-occlusive disease	Usually absent or slight	Slight	Absent	Rare	Rare	Loose fibrosis leading to widespread pronounced occlusion. Re-canalization common	Mimics that of muscular pulmonary artery

were chronic pulmonary thromboembolism (31 cases), pulmonary veno-occlusive disease (five cases), chronic pulmonary venous hypertension (five cases), sarcoidosis (one case), pulmonary schistosomiasis (one case) and chronic bronchitis and emphysema (three cases). It is clear from this investigation that the condition is mis-diagnosed frequently and is most likely to be confused with chronic pulmonary thromboembolism and to a much less extent with pulmonary veno-occlusive disease.

CLASSICAL PRIMARY PULMONARY HYPERTENSION

The occurrence of a 'primary' vascular disease has been suspected since 1891 when Romberg[3] reported a case in which right ventricular hypertrophy and 'pulmonary arterial sclerosis' were found at necropsy in the absence of any apparent causal lesion. In 1951, Dresdale and his associates[4] confirmed by cardiac catheterization that the essential haemodynamic abnormality was a raised pulmonary arterial pressure. They were able to collect 39 cases characterized by pulmonary hypertension without any apparent cause.[4] By 1956, Wood[5] had recognized the condition 17 times and he described the clinical features which he regarded as distinctive of the disease. In the following year 25 cases of the disease, comprising three series, were reported in the British Heart Journal.[6–8] By 1971, the Wagenvoorts[2] were able to find in the literature 602 cases scattered over 260 publications. From 1968 to about 1972 an epidemic of primary pulmonary hypertension occurred in Western Europe yielding many cases for clinical and pathological examination (Chap. 27). Apart from this and a suspected epidemic in Sri Lanka at the same time the disease has remained very rare elsewhere.

Clinical Features

The haemodynamic abnormalities of the disease are pulmonary arterial hypertension with a normal pulmonary venous pressure. No abnormal communications can be demonstrated in the heart although, in the later stages, a patent foramen ovale may allow passage of blood from right to left. As the condition progresses, the cardiac output becomes reduced. While cardiac catheterization provides the haemodynamic diagnosis, there is a distinct risk of sudden death during the procedure.[9–11] This particularly applies to angiocardiography[12] which should be avoided. The signs and symptoms may be similar to those found in a congenital cardiac shunt associated with severe hypertensive pulmonary vascular disease.[13] The symptoms are usually of short duration at first presentation. Commonly about two years,[14,15] they may be as short as a few months[16] but may extend up to 12 years.[17] Dyspnoea and fatigue on exertion are common. Many patients have substernal pain on exercise. The origin of this pain is still in some doubt. It may be due to relative ischaemia in a hypertrophied right ventricle. On the other hand it is often difficult to distinguish it from the constricting praecordial sensation which may accompany severe dyspnoea. The pain radiates to the neck but not, characteristically, to the arms. Fainting and syncope on effort are common and are

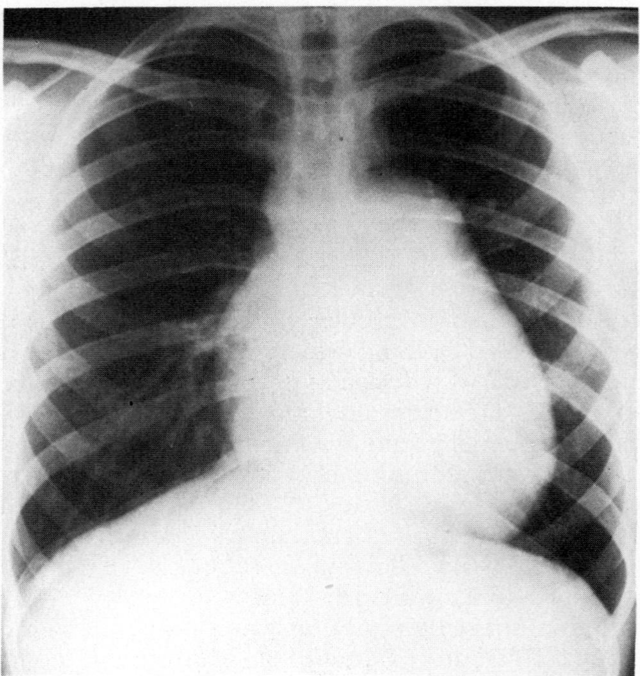

Fig. 28.1 Radiograph of the chest of a woman of 23 years with classical primary pulmonary hypertension proven at necropsy. Dyspnoea and attacks of syncope had occurred for one year. On physical examination there was a left parasternal lift, a loud pulmonary component of the second sound and the murmur of pulmonary incompetence. The radiograph shows considerable enlargement of the pulmonary trunk and enlargement of its major divisions. The peripheral vascular shadows are within normal limits.

This was a patient of the late Dr Paul Wood and we are glad to take the opportunity of paying tribute to his unsurpassed contribution to our knowledge of the clinical implications of pulmonary vascular disease.

thought to be due to transient cerebral ischaemia resulting from a sudden inadequacy of output of the right ventricle. Haemoptysis is uncommon and probably occurs as a result of rupture of dilated plexiform lesions.[18] Fatal haemoptysis has, however, been reported in this disease.[19]

Most of the clinical signs are those of pulmonary arterial hypertension. They include prominent '*a*'-waves in the jugular venous pulse, a right ventricular heave, and a palpable second heart sound in the pulmonary area. On ausculation there is accentuation of the pulmonary component of the second sound. A Graham-Steell murmur of pulmonary incompetence and possibly an early systolic ejection click may be present. Most of these signs were first listed by Bedford[20] and they have been repeatedly reported in patients with primary pulmonary hypertension.[21]

The electrocardiogram will reveal varying degrees of right ventricular and right atrial hypertrophy. In the early stages of the disease, the chest radiograph may be within normal limits. As the disease progresses, cardiac enlargement develops and the pulmonary trunk and its larger branches become prominent. The vascular pattern in the periphery of the lungs appears often to be remarkably normal. There is no radiographic evidence of pulmonary venous hypertension (Fig. 28.1).

Histopathology

The histopathology of primary pulmonary hypertension is identical with that of advanced hypertensive pulmonary vascular disease complicating a large congenital cardiac shunt (Chap. 16). All the various hypertensive arterial lesions may occur in one case as illustrated in the reports by Wagenvoort and his co-workers[22] and by Gilmour and Evans.[14] The various lesions which have been reported in primary pulmonary hypertension include medial hypertrophy of elastic pulmonary arteries,[8] medial hypertrophy of muscular pulmonary arteries[7,8,23] (Fig. 28.2), and the development of longitudinal muscle.[21] Intimal fibrosis of all grades of severity is

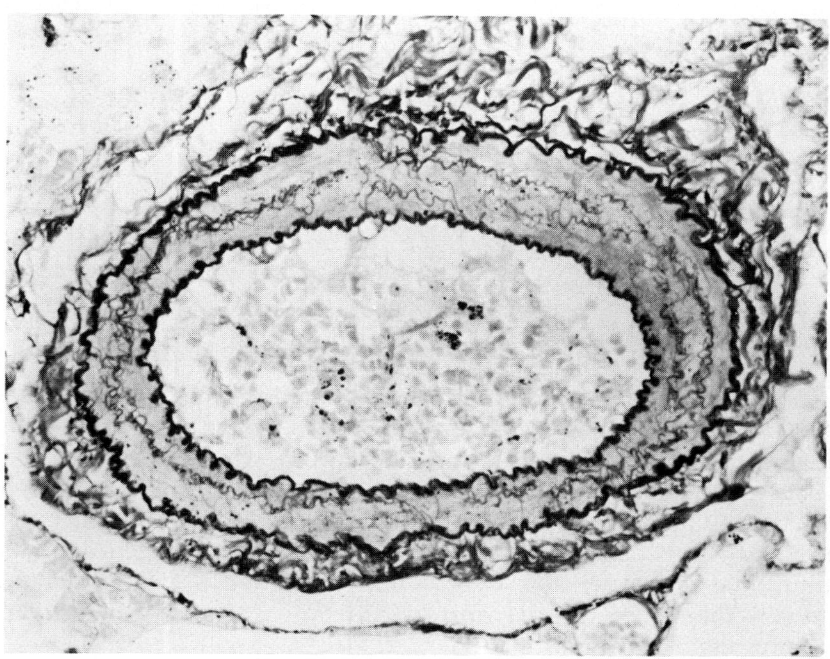

Fig. 28.2 Transverse section of a muscular pulmonary artery from a case of primary pulmonary hypertension occurring in a young woman who had taken the anorexigen aminorex fumarate. The vessel shows medial hypertrophy and crenation of the elastic laminae consistent with vasoconstriction. (Elastic/Van Gieson, × 300)

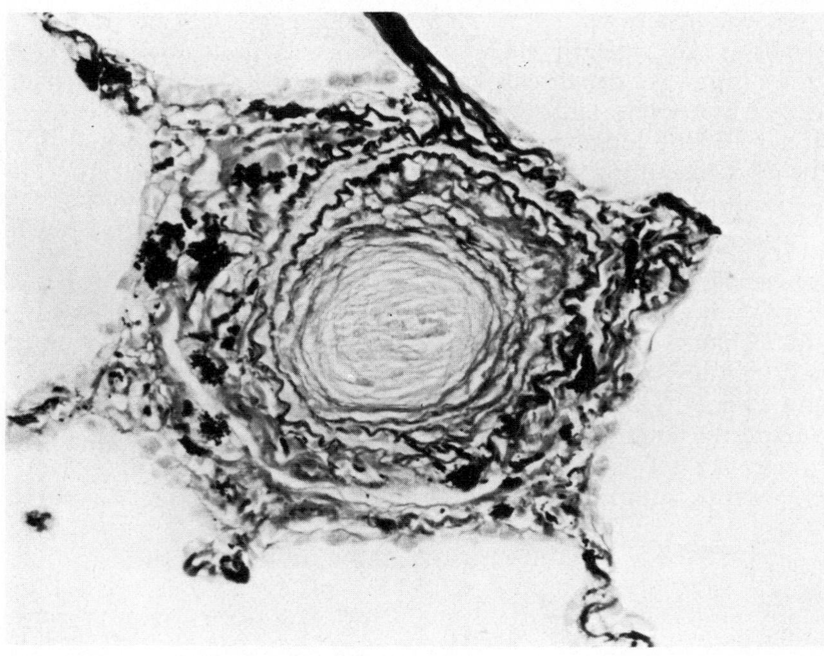

Fig. 28.3 Transverse section of muscular pulmonary artery from a case of primary pulmonary hypertension in a man of 50 years. There is intimal fibroelastosis of 'onion-skin' type with atrophy and disruption of the underlying media. (Elastic/Van Gieson, × 375)

common[4,7,8,21,23] and leads to a 'pruning effect' in the post-mortem angiogram of the lung. The intimal fibrosis of primary pulmonary hypertension is characteristically of the concentric 'onion-skin' variety[2] (Fig. 28.3). Dilatation lesions are common[14,18,24,25] (Fig. 28.4). Bleeding may occur from dilatation lesions leading to pulmonary haemosiderosis and the impregnation of elastic laminae and reticulin fibrils with ferric iron, perhaps with an associated foreign body giant cell reaction Necrotizing arteritis is common in primary pulmonary hypertension[7,8,21,23,26] probably because the elevation of the pulmonary arterial pressure is unusually rapid and severe. As in all forms of hypertensive pulmonary vascular disease, muscularized pulmonary arterioles occur (Fig. 28.5). Very characteristic of the histopathology of primary pulmonary hypertension are medial hypertrophy of muscular pulmonary arteries, 'onion-skin' type intimal fibrosis, dilatation lesions especially plexiform lesions, and pulmonary arteritis.

Thromboses may occur over necrotic areas of the muscular pulmonary arteries and these may give rise to thromboemboli which pass to occlude more distal muscular pulmonary arteries and pulmonary arterioles.[8,21] Such thrombi may re-canalize with the formation of intra-arterial septa (Fig. 28.6). This may produce

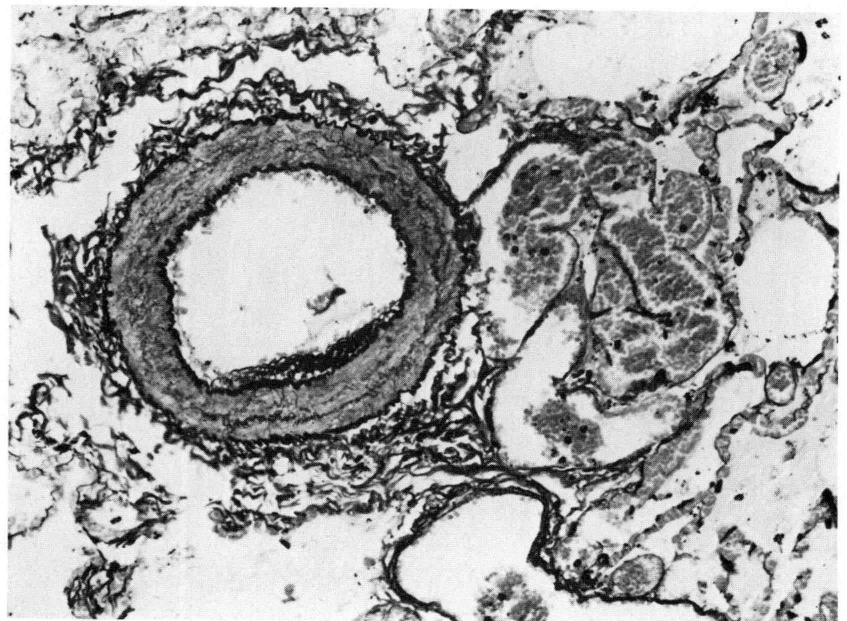

Fig. 28.4 Transverse section of muscular pulmonary artery from the same case of primary pulmonary hypertension illustrated in Figure 28.2. The vessels show pronounced medial hypertrophy. To the right lies a thin-walled branch of the parent artery. It shows an angiomatoid lesion which is a variety of dilatation lesion. (Elastic/Van Gieson, × 375)

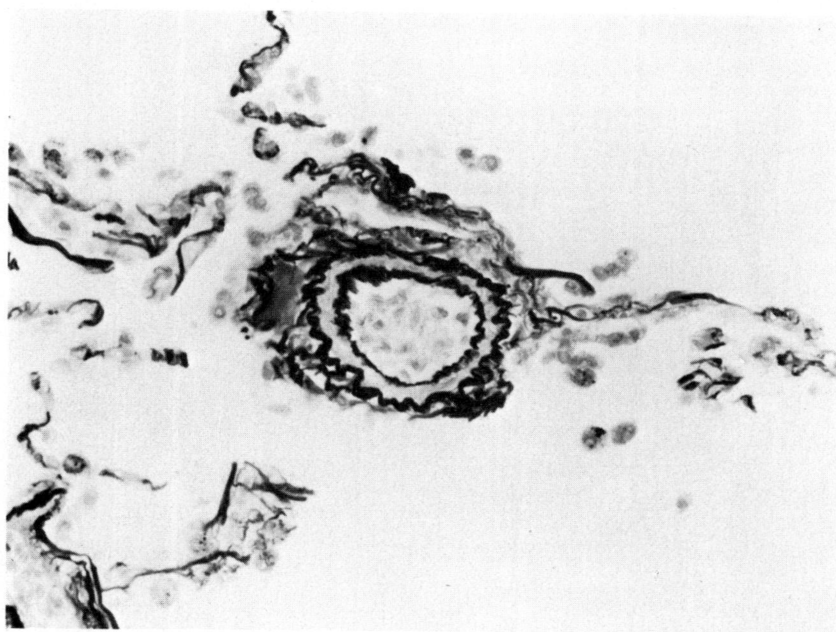

Fig. 28.5 Transverse section of pulmonary arteriole from the same case of primary pulmonary hypertension illustrated in Figure 28.3. The vessel is abnormal and muscularized, showing a distinct media of circular muscle sandwiched between internal and external elastic laminae. (Elastic/Van Gieson, × 375)

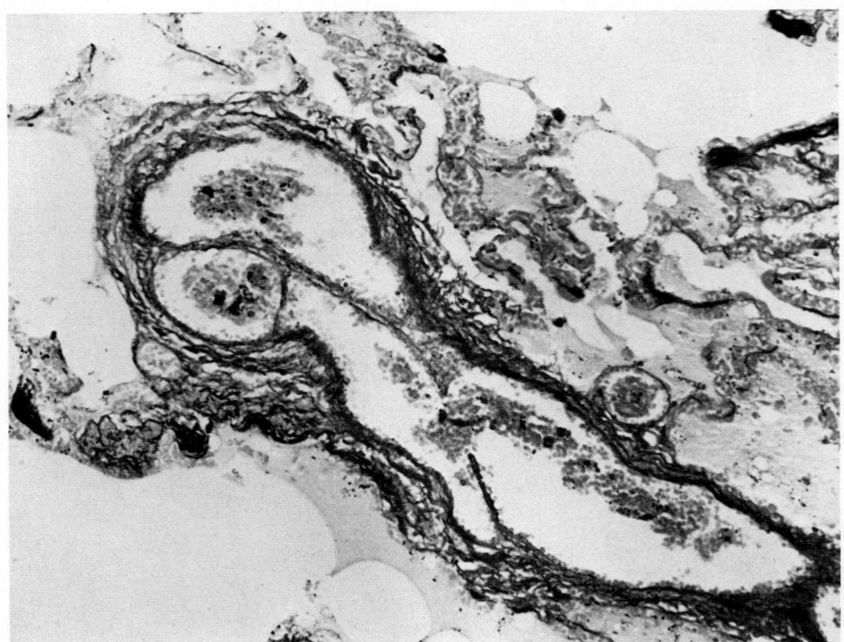

Fig. 28.6 Oblique section of a muscular pulmonary artery from the same case of primary pulmonary hypertension illustrated in Figure 28.2. It contains intra-arterial septa resulting from old re-canalized thrombus. (Elastic/Van Gieson, × 150)

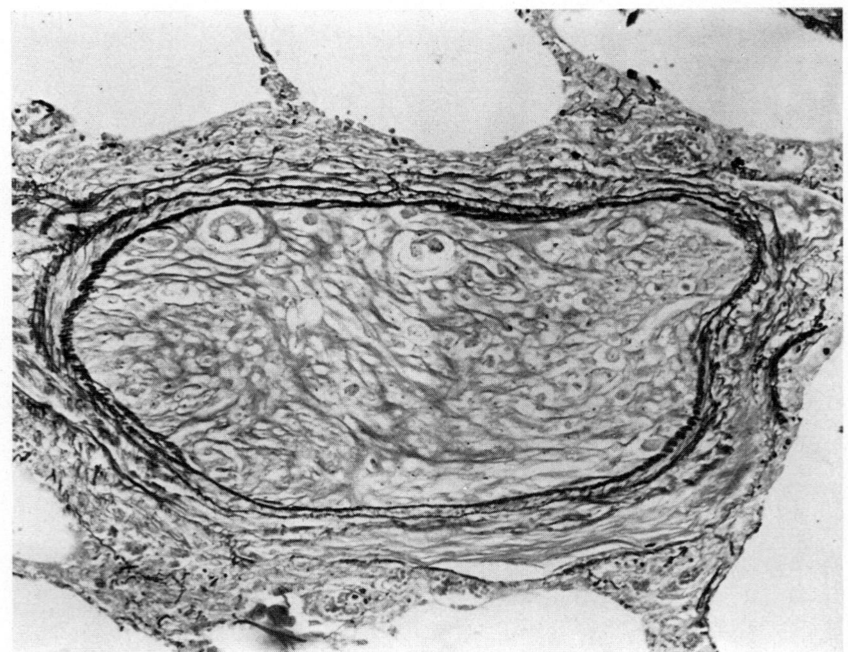

Fig. 28.7 Oblique section of muscular pulmonary artery from a case of recurrent pulmonary thromboembolism occurring in a woman of 62 years. The vessel is occluded by recent thrombus. There is thinning of the underlying media. (Elastic/Van Gieson, × 150)

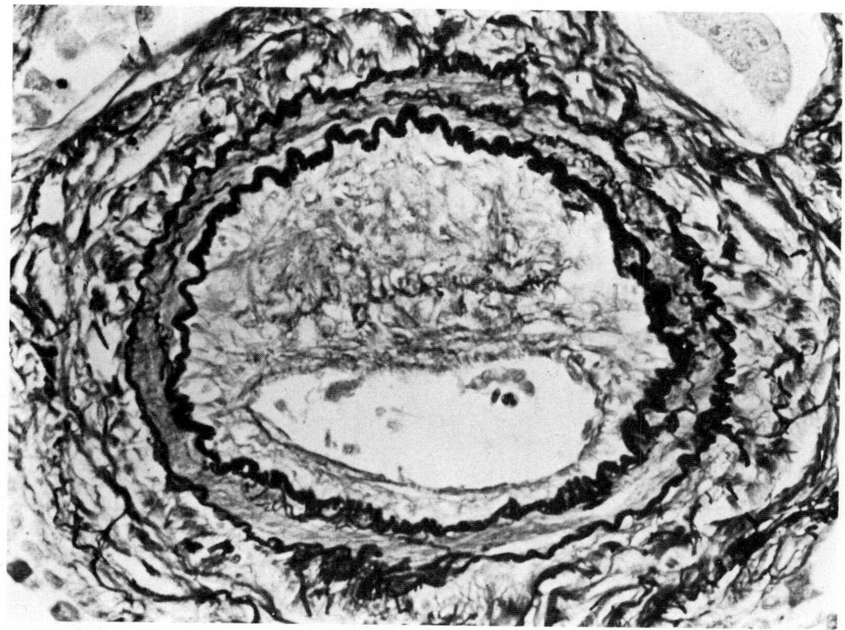

Fig. 28.8 Transverse section of muscular pulmonary artery from the same case of recurrent pulmonary thromboembolism. There is hypertrophy of the media with crenation of the elastic laminae consistent with some degree of vasoconstriction. The lumen is almost totally occluded by recently organized thrombus apart from one re-canalization channel. Contrast this type of intimal proliferation with the 'onion-skin' intimal fibrosis of primary pulmonary hypertension shown in Figure 28.3. (Elastic/Van Gieson, × 375)

histological appearances that may give rise to difficulties in making a clear differential diagnosis from recurrent pulmonary thromboembolism. However, fresh and organizing thrombus is much less common in primary pulmonary hypertension. In recurrent pulmonary thromboembolism, as will be described in Chapter 35, the pulmonary arteries contain much recent (Fig. 28.7) or organizing thrombus (Figs 28.8 and 28.9) which eventually gives rise to cushion-like excentric patches of intimal fibrosis (Fig. 28.10). Sometimes intimal fibrosis in pulmonary thromboembolism may be total or present with a central lumen but the onion-skin pattern of the intimal fibrosis of primary pulmonary hypertension is not seen. Recanalization may give rise to a colander-like lesion in some pulmonary arteries and care must be taken not to confuse such intra-arterial septa with dilatation lesions.

The Pulmonary Trunk in Primary Pulmonary Hypertension

As already stated in Chapter 17, examination of the pattern of elastic tissue of the pulmonary trunk may help determine whether pulmonary hypertension was present from infancy or was acquired in later life. When this technique is employed

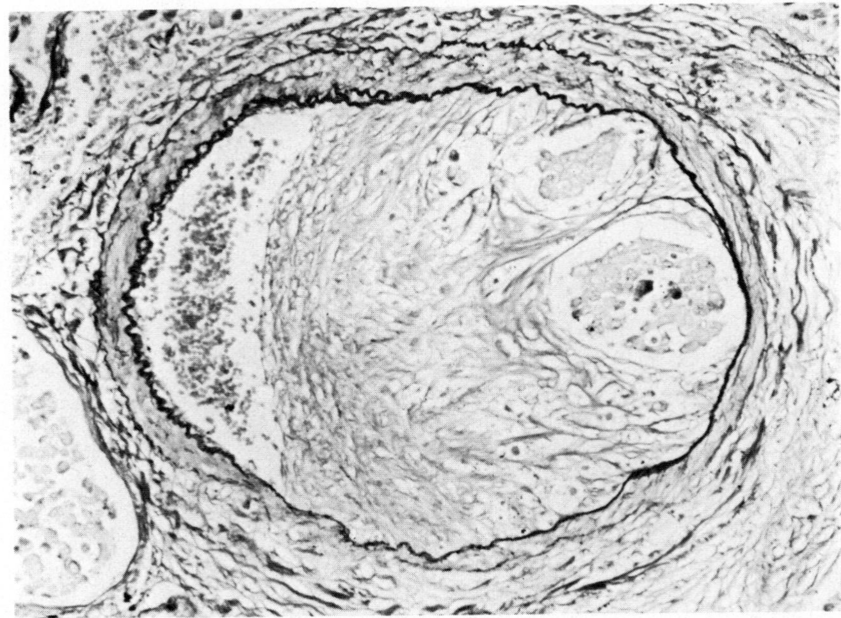

Fig. 28.9 Transverse section of muscular pulmonary artery from the same case of recurrent pulmonary thromboembolism. This vessel shows multiple recanalization channels which would eventually lead to the formation of a colander lesion. There is fibrosis of the underlying media which shows some fibrosis. (Elastic/Van Gieson, ×150)

in cases of primary pulmonary hypertension, it reveals that most cases show an adult pattern of elastic tissue consistent with the pulmonary hypertension having been acquired in adult life.[27] However, in some cases of primary pulmonary hypertension, the raised pulmonary arterial pressure appears to be present from infancy[28] for in such patients the pulmonary trunk has an aortic pattern of elastic tissue.

Aetiological Factors in Primary Pulmonary Hypertension

AGE

Most patients with primary pulmonary hypertension are young adults or children. Of the 110 cases collected by the Wagenvoorts[2] 71 cases were in the age range of 16 to 69 years with an average age of 33 years. Examination of the pulmonary trunk from cases in young adults suggests that in this group the pulmonary hypertension is acquired.

However, a considerable number of cases occur in children[2,10,25,28–32] and cases have been described as occurring in infants under nine months of age.[33,34] No fewer than 39 of the 110 cases of primary pulmonary hypertension collected and

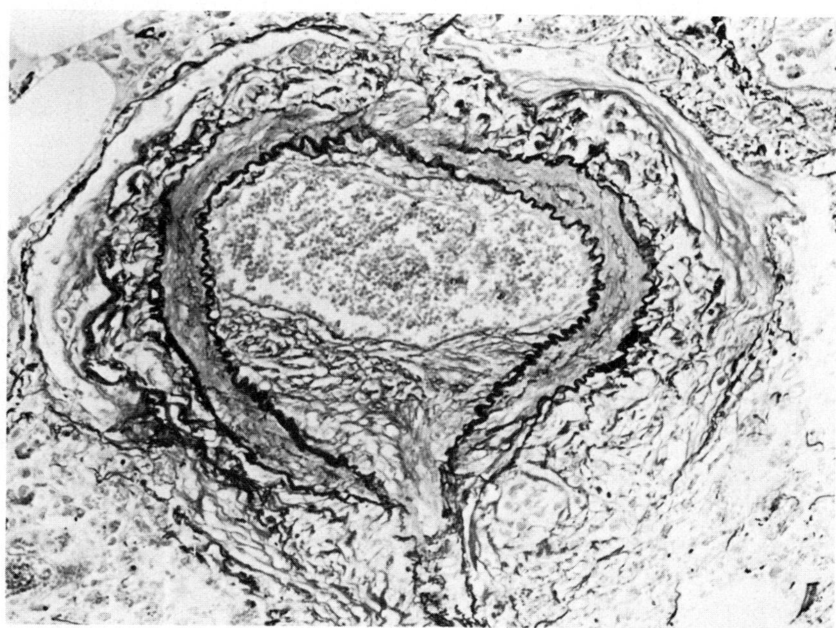

Fig. 28.10 Transverse section of muscular pulmonary artery from the same case of recurrent pulmonary thromboembolism. There is an eccentric pad of intimal fibroelastosis which contrasts sharply with the 'onion-skin' configuration of intimal fibrosis characteristic of primary pulmonary hypertension. (Elastic/Van Gieson, × 150)

verified by the Wagenvoorts[2] occurred in children, the average age being 5·1 years. At this age, the pulmonary hypertension is likely to be present from birth.[22] Thromboembolism is rare in children and this suggests that primary pulmonary hypertension does not have a thromboembolic basis.

SEX

Adult cases of primary pulmonary hypertension are about four times as common in women as in men[2] in contrast to recurrent pulmonary thromboembolism which is only twice as common in women. It has been postulated that non-fatal amniotic fluid embolism to the lung may be involved in the aetiology.[8] It is certainly true that in a minority of cases primary pulmonary hypertension begins in or is aggravated by pregnancy or delivery. It is also true that this relationship can be found in other forms of pulmonary vascular disease.[2] Furthermore, these hypotheses would not explain the occurrence of the disease in men and children.

THROMBOEMBOLISM

Recurrent pulmonary thromboembolism has been considered to be important in the aetiology of primary pulmonary hypertension.[8,35,36] However, after the consideration of the pathology of 156 cases diagnosed clinically the Wagenvoorts[2] concluded that 'the difference in pulmonary vascular pathology between cases of pulmonary hypertension due to thrombosis or thromboembolism on the one hand and cases of vasoconstrictive primary pulmonary hypertension on the other, enable one to distinguish between them, even when the conditions are in advanced stages'. We agree with them that the two conditions should be regarded as distinct diseases.

The vascular lesions in primary pulmonary hypertension are identical with those found in congenital cardiac shunts which are not considered to be embolic in nature.[2] Primary pulmonary hypertension occurs in children in whom thromboembolism is rare. In unequivocal recurrent pulmonary thromboembolism the pathologist is able to see fresh or older thromboemboli in various stages of organization and re-canalization. Such is not the case in primary pulmonary hypertension. The differences in histopathological appearances between the two conditions are shown in Table 28.3. Occasionally organizing thromboemboli are to be found in the terminal portions of the pulmonary arterial tree in cases of primary pulmonary hypertension but they are likely to be secondary to thrombus forming over areas of fibrinoid necrosis. Care must be taken by the pathologist not to confuse intra-arterial septa with angiomatoid or plexiform lesions.

BRONCHOPULMONARY ANASTOMOSES

Such anastomoses were found in the lungs of two of the patients of Wade and Ball.[21] Although they felt that these anastomoses may have been primary, we are inclined to the view that they were almost certainly secondary to the pulmonary vascular occlusion characteristic of primary pulmonary hypertension. Other authors have favoured the idea that bronchopulmonary anastomoses may induce primary pulmonary hypertension.[37–39] Haemodynamically, this seems unlikely since severe pulmonary hypertension does not accompany the development of extensive broncho-pulmonary anastomoses in patients with bronchiectasis.

FAMILIAL PULMONARY HYPERTENSION

Primary pulmonary hypertension is usually acquired in young adult life but there is indisputable evidence that some cases are familial. The familial occurrence of primary pulmonary hypertension was first observed in 1927 by Clarke and his associates[40] in two sisters with right ventricular hypertrophy, one of whom died in congestive cardiac failure. In one family of 186 persons reported by Lange[41] 82 were said to be cyanosed. He personally examined 42 members of the family and found cyanosis in 30 and an accentuated second sound in the pulmonary area in ten. However, no studies by cardiac catheterization were available at that time.

Fleming[32] reported the familial occurrence of primary pulmonary hypertension in one family and this report assumed even greater interest later when the father re-married and the disease appeared in his second family.[42] This distribution of primary pulmonary hypertension is best explained on the basis of an autosomal dominant mode of inheritance. The great variation in age at which symptoms developed in this family suggests that there may be a sub-clinical form of the disease consistent with the longevity of some members of the family. There is no evidence of sex-linking as cases have occurred in both men and women. Autosomal dominance best explains the distribution of cases in other families in which the disease has been proven in more than one generation.[43–46]

Hood and his colleagues[47] suggested that a recessive mode of inheritance best explained the distribution of cases in families in which only one generation was affected.[48,49] Hood *et al.*[47] regarded their three cases of primary pulmonary hypertension occurring in all the female members of one family in one generation as consistent with an autosomal recessive mode of inheritance with incomplete penetrance in the male sibs. However, Thompson and McRae[42] note that the parents were not examined and may have had a mild form of the disease. On this basis the mode of inheritance even in such cases apparently restricted to one generation could be interpreted as autosomal dominance with varying expression. There is some evidence that the incidence of the disease is much more equally distributed between the two sexes when only one generation is affected, and symptoms tend to appear at a younger age.

An alternative view is that familial primary pulmonary hypertension is not due to a single genetic abnormality but, like systemic hypertension, is an expression of multiple genetic and environmental factors.

Familial pulmonary hypertension, however, must not be considered to result from congenital vascular anomalies.[2] The various vascular lesions described as such are either a response to abnormal functional stimuli, as in the case of medial hypertrophy, or secondary to the pulmonary hypertension, as in the case of plexiform lesions. Plexiform lesions which are highly characteristic, though not pathognomonic, of the pathology of primary pulmonary hypertension are acquired rather than congenital in nature. They may be produced experimentally in dogs by the surgical creation of shunts.[50]

'PRIMARY PULMONARY VASCULAR SCLEROSIS'

This condition referred to in older papers on the pathology of the pulmonary circulation corresponds to what we now term primary pulmonary hypertension. The early reported examples are obviously a heterogeneous group and we shall not give reference to these papers but instead refer the reader to the studies of Brenner[51] who included a comprehensive bibliography on the subject.

AUTOIMMUNITY

The concept that primary pulmonary hypertension is an autoimmune disease is based on the fact that its pulmonary vascular pathology is characterized by fibrinoid necrosis and pulmonary arteritis and that the condition is sometimes associated with Raynaud's phenomenon and an accompanying collagen disease such as scleroderma or rheumatoid disease.[21] There appears to be a definite relationship between primary pulmonary hypertension and the collagen diseases and it has been noted in no fewer than 35 reported cases.[2]

DIET

In Chapter 27 reference is made to the development of pulmonary arterial hypertension and associated pulmonary vascular disease in animals fed on a diet of *Crotalaria spectabilis*, *Crotalaria fulva*, or *Senecio jacobaea*. Also discussed is the possibility that the ingestion of the anorexigen aminorex fumarate may have been responsible for a recent epidemic of primary pulmonary hypertension in Western Europe. These facts suggested that some cases of primary pulmonary hypertension in man may be due to dietary or medicinal factors. The possibility is certainly strong enough to indicate the taking of a careful dietary history in cases of primary pulmonary hypertension with special reference to slimming drugs related to amphetamine and to herbal remedies.

Analysis of the Pathological Lesions in Primary Pulmonary Hypertension

As in the same form of hypertensive pulmonary vascular disease associated with congenital cardiac shunts, primary pulmonary hypertension appears to be a progressive condition starting with medial hypertrophy of the muscular pulmonary arteries and muscularization of the pulmonary arterioles. Medial hypertrophy is severe in infants and it is only later that intimal fibrosis and then plexiform lesions develop, increasing in severity and frequency with age.[21] With the development of the proliferative lesions, medial hypertrophy becomes less pronounced but muscularized pulmonary arterioles are still much in evidence in contrast with the state of affairs in recurrent pulmonary thromboembolism. Fibrinoid necrosis is almost certainly an expression of a sudden or a severe rise in pulmonary arterial pressure.

The Stimulus for Vasoconstriction in Primary Pulmonary Hypertension

The stimulus for vasoconstriction in primary pulmonary hypertension is quite unknown. Our ignorance is, moreover, of an even greater depth for, until we understand the factors which determine the control of vascular muscle in the normal pulmonary circuit (Chap. 12) we are hardly likely to appreciate the reason why they have been modified in this disease.

Normally the major trophic stimulus to vascular muscle in the pulmonary circulation appears to be mechanical distension of the vessel wall and in most patients with pulmonary hypertension the initiating lesion is one which would tend by itself to cause some increase in the pulmonary arterial pressures (Chap. 18, p. 274). Such is not the case, however, in primary pulmonary hypertension. Neither is there evidence of any primary occlusive process occurring in the muscular pulmonary arteries or arterioles.

The micro-anatomy of the pulmonary vascular sympathetic (Chap. 12) system is unexplored in normal man, let alone patients with primary pulmonary hypertension. Drugs with α-antagonistic properties have caused a temporary decrease, occasionally of impressive dimensions, in the pulmonary arterial pressure in some patients with primary pulmonary hypertension (Chap. 13, p. 188). The action of such drugs, however, may be largely non-specific. Judging by the effects of drugs on patients with pulmonary hypertension due to congenital heart disease (pp. 279 and 296) one would expect the response to vasodilators to depend on the stage of the disease process in the pulmonary circulation, the later grades of disease rendering the vessels unresponsive. Long-term treatment of patients with primary pulmonary hypertension with sympatholytic drugs or sympathectomy has, in our experience, been unsuccessful.

One is left speculating on the presence of a substance, possibly in the blood stream, which acts in a chemical manner on the muscle fibres in the walls of these vessels. None of those substances which occur normally in the body and which are reviewed in Chapter 13 would appear to have an action powerful enough to qualify for this rôle. The constrictor effects of hypoxia are by far the most obvious under physiological conditions (Chap. 30), and yet prolonged hypoxia does not by itself give rise to the advanced vascular lesions and severe hypertension which occur in primary pulmonary hypertension (Chap. 33). There is, in any case, no reason to believe that hypoxia plays any part in the evolution of this disease, and no evidence of abnormality in the circulating level of any humoral agent.

That the pulmonary circulation may respond uniquely to certain ingested substances is shown by the effects of *Crotalaria spectabilis*, *Crotalaria fulva*, and *Senecio jacobaea* on the rat which are described in Chapter 27. Such a possibility is brought nearer to clinical realities by the suggestive epidemiological evidence concerning the relation between aminorex fumarate and primary pulmonary hypertension discussed in Chapter 27. Even on such epidemiological evidence it would seem likely that the human disease was due not simply to the ingestion of the substance but required the existence of some predisposing factor, since pulmonary hypertension was found in only a small proportion of people taking aminorex fumarate. The higher incidence of the spontaneous disease in females may provide a clue in this respect. Recent observations on the increased susceptibility of the pulmonary arteries of female rats to hypoxia (Chap. 33) and clinical impressions of the deleterious effect of oral contraceptives in patients with pulmonary hypertension associated with congenital heart disease (Chap. 13) likewise suggest that hormonal factors may influence the response of the pulmonary circulation. Since anorexigens (including aminorex) are commonly chemically related to adrenaline, a possible rôle of catecholamines in the spontaneous disease might be suggested. Direct pharmacological evidence of the effects of these substances is, however, not impressive.

PULMONARY VENO-OCCLUSIVE DISEASE

In some cases of unexplained pulmonary hypertension, free from recurrent pulmonary thromboembolism or from any congenital or acquired disease of the heart, the pathology of the pulmonary vasculature and lung parenchyma is quite distinct from that described above. In this rarer form of unexplained pulmonary

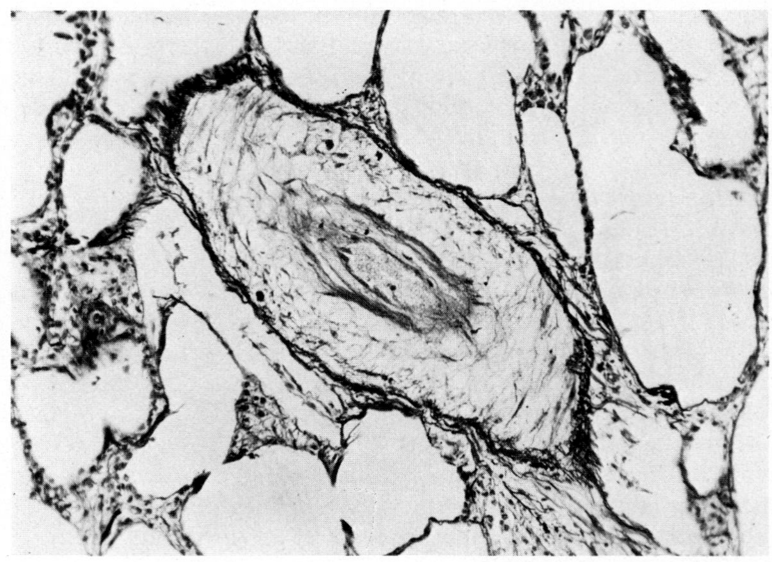

Fig. 28.11 Oblique section of a pulmonary vein in a woman of 45 years with pulmonary veno-occlusive disease. The vein is occluded with loose basophilic intimal fibrous tissue. (Elastic/Van Gieson, × 135)

hypertension the initial pathology appears to occur in the pulmonary veins rather than upon the pulmonary arteries and for this reason the disease is usually called 'pulmonary veno-occlusive disease'[52] (Fig. 28.11).

Intimal proliferation in the small pulmonary veins is commonly found in association with various forms of organic disease of the heart characterized by diminished pulmonary flow and compensatory polycythaemia (Chap. 37), abnormally high pulmonary flow (Chap. 16), or pulmonary venous hypertension (Chap. 22). However, in pulmonary veno-occlusive disease the venous lesions in the lung occur with no predisposing cardiac disease and in particular no obstruction to pulmonary venous flow outside the lungs such as mitral stenosis.[52,53]

In some veins the intimal fibrosis forms eccentrically situated nodules in which occasional elastic fibrils are to be found. Appearances of this type suggest that the lesions may arise as a result of organization of thrombus. This idea is supported by evidence of re-canalization. In some veins this may present as a central channel with a surrounding rim of condensed collagenous tissue. In other veins a colander-like effect is produced, re-canalization having given rise to a number of wide channels separated by fibroelastic septa (Fig. 28.12). Such changes affect all classes of pulmonary veins from the large lobular veins down to the smallest pulmonary post-capillary venules.[52,53] The fibrosis may be severe, especially in the venules, so that many of the affected vessels are totally occluded. The cellular fibrous tissue reaction may extend into the adventitia and immediately adjacent lung parenchyma.

In one case which we studied 95 per cent of the veins included in the sections were involved by the disease process. There is muscularization of the media of small pulmonary veins so that it forms a distinct muscular coat bounded by internal and external laminae. In this way the pulmonary veins come to mimic muscular pulmonary arteries in structure. The few published reports on patients with unexplained pulmonary hypertension who have shown predominant lesions in the pulmonary veins include reference to the oedematous intimal fibrous tissue,[52–57] the organizing thrombi[58] or both.[59,60]

Secondary to the pulmonary venous hypertension which is found in this disease, pulmonary arterial hypertension develops and becomes associated with hypertensive changes in the pulmonary arteries. These include medial hypertrophy of the muscular pulmonary arteries and muscularization of the pulmonary arterioles. Fibrinoid necrosis of the muscular pulmonary arteries also occurs. As in other forms of pulmonary arterial hypertension secondary to pulmonary venous hypertension dilatation lesions, such as plexiform or angiomatoid lesions, do not occur. The elastic pulmonary arteries become atheromatous.

Striking changes occur in the lung parenchyma.[52,53] There is a proliferation of the granular pneumocytes so that the alveolar spaces develop a prominent cellular lining. Groups of granular pneumocytes pass into the alveolar spaces to give an appearance resembling the so-called 'desquamative interstitial pneumonia'.[61] There is striking engorgement of the pulmonary capillary bed, often focal in distribution[54]

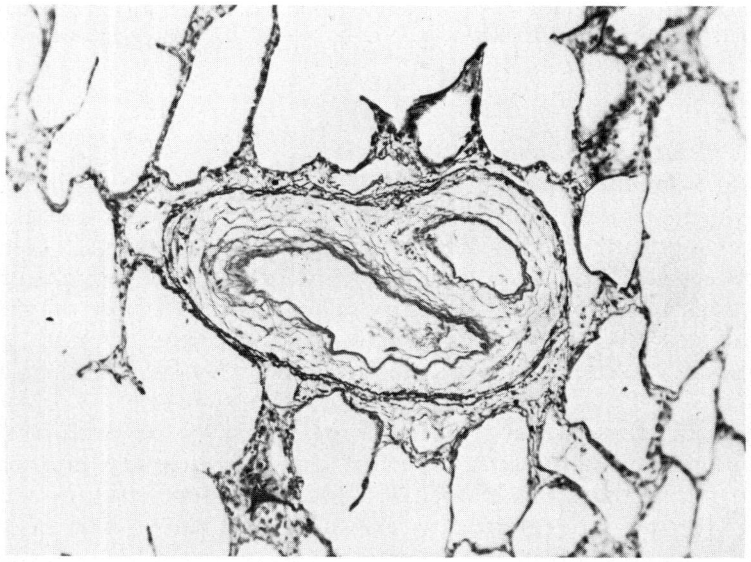

Fig. 28.12 Transverse section of a pulmonary vein from the same case illustrated in Figure 28.11. It shows re-canalization of organized thrombus. (Elastic/Van Gieson, × 125)

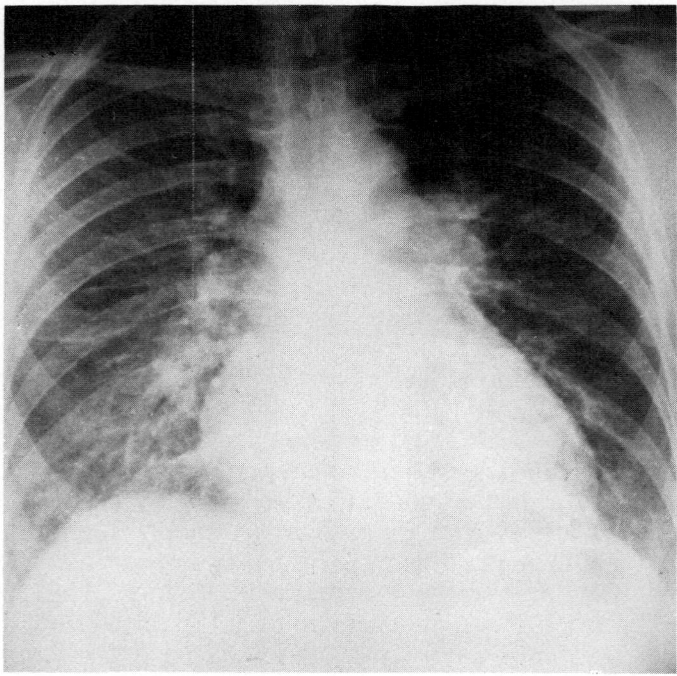

Fig. 28.13 Radiograph of the chest in a woman aged 45 years with pulmonary veno-occlusive disease. It shows cardiomegaly due to right ventricular hypertrophy, dilatation of the pulmonary arteries, and interstitial oedema. There is a small right pleural effusion. Contrast with Figures 28.1 and 28.14.

and diapedesis from these vessels leads to the appearance of haemosiderin-laden macrophages in the alveolar spaces and sometimes to incrustation of elastic laminae by ferric iron. Superimposed on this cellular phase of fibrosing alveolitis a fibrous stage develops in which the alveolar walls show great fibrous thickening. 'Honeycomb lung' does not, however, develop. There is distension of the lymphatic vessels in the connective tissue septa of the lung and around bronchi and pulmonary blood vessels. Small spicules of bone may be found in the alveolar spaces.

In some patients the clinical features of pulmonary veno-occlusive disease are in no way different from those of cases of classical 'primary pulmonary hypertension.'[62] In others there is a history of a preceding febrile illness or respiratory infection.[54,56] Readers are referred to the study of Thadani and his colleagues[62] for a detailed consideration of the results of clinical examinations and laboratory tests in pulmonary veno-occlusive disease, and for a detailed account of the literature on this condition.

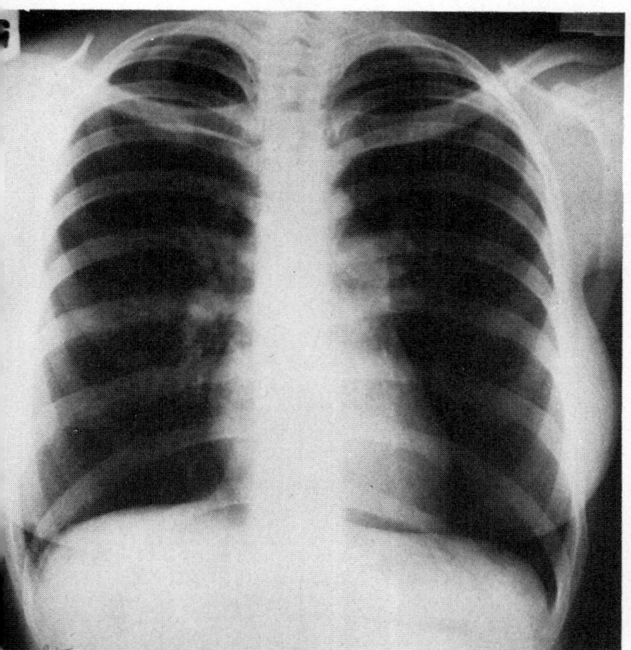

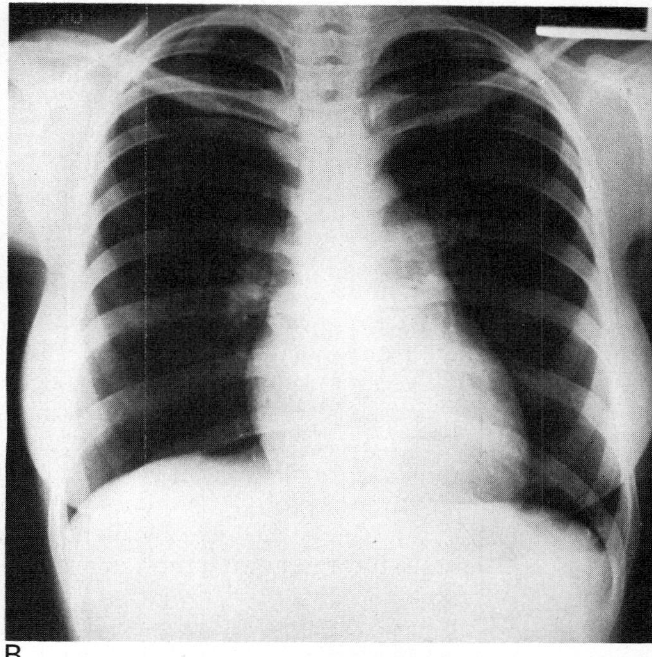

B

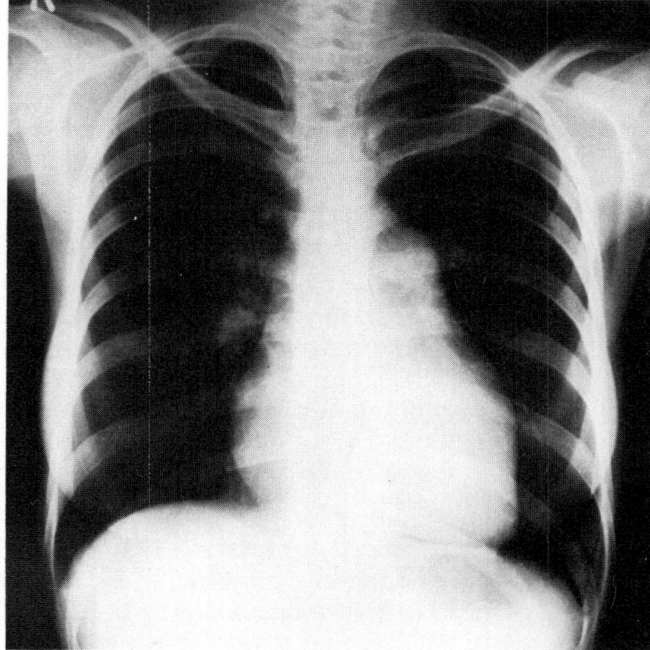

C

Fig. 28.14 Chest radiographs of a patient aged 16 with pulmonary veno-occlusive disease shown at necropsy. Note the progressive enlargement of the heart and of the pulmonary trunk and its main divisions. There is no radiographic evidence of pulmonary venous hypertension. Details of the case are given in the text. A, July 1970; B, October 1970; C, July 1972

Cardiac catheterization reveals a raised pulmonary arterial pressure. The wedge pressure may also be raised but this is not always so. The theoretical reasons for this are considered in Chapter 5 and in Appendix A. An elevated pulmonary wedge pressure was recorded in five of the reported cases.[60,63–66] In only one of these[65] was a simultaneous left atrial pressure recorded and this was found to be normal. However, in another patient direct pulmonary venous pressure measured at operation was also normal.[60] Normal pulmonary wedge pressures were recorded in eight of the reported cases.[6,52,66–70] In one patient[62] the left atrial and pulmonary wedge pressures were normal. Studies of pulmonary function[52] have shown a low arterial saturation and a normal diffusing capacity.

Radiological examination may be of value in distinguishing this disease from primary pulmonary hypertension.[71] Radiographic changes characteristic of pulmonary venous hypertension may occur in varying degrees in pulmonary veno-occlusive disease (Fig. 28.13). They include altered distribution of size of vessels, basal horizontal lines, indistinctness of outline of pulmonary arteries, small accumulations of pleural fluid and even signs of alveolar oedema. These radiological features differ strikingly from those found in classical primary pulmonary hypertension in which the peripheral lung fields are clear (Fig. 28.1). However, in some cases the chest radiograph may give no indication of a raised pulmonary venous pressure (Fig. 28.14).

The patient whose radiograph is shown in Figure 28.14 and whom we reported in association with Thadani and his colleagues[62] exemplifies how difficult it may be to make a correct clinical diagnosis. When first seen in 1970 she was 16 and had been short of breath for three months. The chest radiograph (Fig. 28.14A) showed some dilatation of the pulmonary trunk and its main divisions, the peripheral vessels being normal. During the succeeding few months she became increasingly short of breath to the extent that she was breathless on dressing. The chest radiograph (Fig. 28.14B) shows an increase in the cardiac size and a further dilatation of the pulmonary trunk and its main divisions while the periphery of the lung appears oligaemic. Cardiac catheterization at that time revealed a pulmonary arterial pressure of 96/40 mmHg (mean = 60 mmHg) while the wedge pressure was 6 mmHg. The chest radiograph in 1972 (Fig. 28.14C) shows still further increase in the cardiac size but at no time was there any radiological evidence of pulmonary venous hypertension. Yet necropsy revealed pulmonary veno-occlusive disease.[62]

As with primary pulmonary hypertension, pulmonary veno-occlusive disease occurs not only in adults but also in children and infants of both sexes.[53,65]

Aetiological Factors in Pulmonary Veno-Occlusive Disease

The aetiology of the venous lesions is obscure. Frequently it is possible to elicit the history of an infection. Thus in the case of Brewer and Humphreys[54] there was a history of previous illness resembling influenza and other authors have referred to preceding chest infections.[53,67] In one case, there were raised serological titres for toxoplasmosis,[60] but they were not high enough to be diagnostic. In one case histological examination of lymph nodes was carried out at necropsy but did not show lymphohistiocytic medullary reticulosis, which might be expected if the aetiological agent were toxoplasmosis.[52] Wagenvoort and his colleagues[65] thought that in their case, a 39 days old baby, the disease was acquired *in utero*, as the mother gave a history of upper respiratory infection during the second trimester of pregnancy.

Brown and Harrison[64] commented on increased platelet adhesiveness in their patient and thought it might be of some aetiological significance, but coagulation studies were reported to be normal in the patient described by Rosenthal *et al.*[70] Finally, Corrin and his associates[72] consider the possibility that pulmonary veno-occlusive disease may have an immunological basis. In their case, in a 33-year-old woman, electron microscopy of a lung biopsy specimen showed electron-dense deposits in the capillary basement membranes, and immunoglobin and complement were demonstrated in a corresponding portion by immunofluorescent microscopy. They suggested that immune complexes may have initiated thrombotic occlusion of the small pulmonary veins. It should be noted, however, that their illustrations of electron-dense deposits resemble those found in the pulmonary capillary wall in mitral stenosis and which were considered to be disintegrating extravasated erythrocytes by Kay and Edwards.[73] As noted above, diapedesis of red cells of pulmonary capillaries and venules, with the formation of pulmonary haemosiderosis, is characteristic of pulmonary veno-occlusive disease.

REFERENCES

1. Hatano, S. & Strasser, T. (1975) *Primary Pulmonary Hypertension*. page 14. Geneva: WHO.
2. Wagenvoort, C. A. & Wagenvoort, N. (1970) *Circulation*, **42**, 1163.
3. Romberg, E. (1891) *Deutsch. Arch. Klin. Med.*, **48**, 197.
4. Dresdale, D. T., Schultz, M. & Michtom, R. J. (1951) *Amer. J. Med.*, **11**, 686.
5. Wood, P. (1956) In *Diseases of the Heart and Circulation*. London: Eyre and Spottiswoode.
6. Evans, W., Short, D. S. & Bedford, D. E. (1957) *Brit. Heart J.*, **19**, 93.
7. Heath, D., Whitaker, W. & Brown, J. W. (1957) *Brit. Heart J.*, **19**, 83.
8. Shepherd, J. T., Edwards, J. E., Burchell, H. B., Swan, J. J. C. & Wood, E. H. (1957) *Brit. Heart J.*, **19**, 70.
9. Schafer, H., Blain, J. M., Ceballos, R. & Bing, R. J. (1956) *Ann. Intern. Med.*, **44**, 505.
10. Bouissou, H. (1960) *Arch. Franc. Pediat.*, **17**, 1203.
11. Cawley, L. P. (1957) *Arch. Path.*, **64**, 270.
12. Hartleb, O. & Geiler, G. (1958) *Z. Kreislaufforsch.*, **47**, 1010.
13. Heath, D. & Whitaker, W. (1956) *Circulation*, **14**, 323.
14. Gilmour, J. R. & Evans, W. (1946) *J. Path. Bact.*, **58**, 687.
15. Ahlquist, J. & Burstein, J. (1958) *Acta Med. Scand.*, **160**, 1.
16. Barrett, A. M. & Cole, L. (1946) *Brit. Heart J.*, **8**, 76.
17. Kuida, H., Dammin, G. J., Haynes, F. W., Rapaport, E. & Dexter, L. (1957) *Amer. J. Med.*, **23**, 166.
18. Whitaker, W. & Heath, D. (1959) *Progr. Cardiovasc. Dis.*, **1**, 380.
19. Forbes, I. J. (1958) *J. Path. Bact.*, **76**, 288.
20. Bedford, D. E. (1951) *Proc. Roy. Soc. Med.*, **44**, 597.
21. Wade, G. & Ball, J. (1957) *Quart. J. Med.*, *(NS)*, **26**, 83.
22. Wagenvoort, C. A., Heath, D. & Edwards, J. E. (1964) In *The Pathology of the Pulmonary Vasculature*. Springfield, Ill.: Thomas.
23. Aitchison, J. D. & Richmond, H. G. (1955) *Brit. Heart J.*, **17**, 312.

24. Wagenvoort, C. A. (1959) *J. Path. Bact.*, **78**, 503.
25. Farrar, J. F., Reye, R. D. K. & Stuckey, D. (1961) *Brit. Heart J.*, **23**, 605.
26. Symmers, W. (1952) *J. Clin. Path.*, **5**, 36.
27. Heath, D. & Edwards, J. E. (1960) *Circulation*, **21**, 59.
28. Berthrong, M. & Cochran, T. H. (1955) *Bull. Johns Hopk. Hosp.*, **97**, 69.
29. Cross, K. R. & Kobayashi, C. K. (1947) *Amer. J. Clin. Path.*, **17**, 155.
30. Feuardent, R. (1953) *Presse. Med.*, **61**, 594.
31. Cawley, L. P. & Stofer, B. E. (1957) *Arch. Path.*, **64**, 270.
32. Fleming, J. (1960) *Aust. Ann. Med.*, **9**, 18.
33. Herdenstam, C. G. (1949) *Acta Pediat. (Uppsala)*, 38/special Nr. 284.
34. Goodale, F. & Thomas, W. A. (1954) *Arch. Path.*, **58**, 568.
35. Castleman, B. & Bland, E. F. (1946) *Arch. Path.*, **42**, 581.
36. Barnard, P. J. (1954) *Brit. Heart J.*, **16**, 93.
37. Brinton, W. D. (1950) *Brit. Heart J.*, **12**, 305.
38. Froment, R., Galy, P., Tolot, F., Cahen, P., Gardere, J. & Ugnat, F. A. (1954) *Rev. Lyonn. Med.*, **3**, 255.
39. Arcidiacono, G. (1959) *Arch. Ital. Anat. Istol. Pat.*, **32**, 159.
40. Clarke, R. C., Combs, C. F., Hadfield, G. & Todd, A. T. (1927) *Quart. J. Med.*, **21**, 51.
41. Lange, F. (1948) *Deutsch. Med. Wschr.*, **73**, 322.
42. Thompson, P. & McRae, C. (1970) *Brit. Heart J.*, **32**, 758.
43. Dresdale, D. T., Michtom, R. J. & Schultz, M. (1954) *Bull. New York Acad. Med.*, **30**, 195.
44. Parry, W. R. & Verel, D. (1966) *Brit. Heart J.*, **28**, 193.
45. Rogge, J. D., Mishkin, M. E. & Genovese, P. D. (1966) *Ann. Int. Med.*, **65**, 672.
46. Kingdon, H. S., Cohen, L. S., Roberts, W. C. & Braunwald, E. (1966) *Arch. Int. Med.*, **118**, 422.
47. Hood, W. B., Jn., Spencer, H., Lass, R. W. & Daley, R. (1968) *Brit. Heart J.*, **30**, 336.
48. Van Epps, E. F. (1957) *J. Roentgenol.*, **78**, 471.
49. Coleman, P. N., Edmunds, W. B. & Tregillus, J. (1959) *Brit. Heart J.*, **21**, 81.
50. Heath, D., Donald, D. E. & Edwards, J. E. (1959) *Brit. Heart J.*, **21**, 187.
51. Brenner, O. (1935) *Arch. Intern. Med.*, **56**, 976.
52. Heath, D., Segel, N. & Bishop, J. (1966) *Circulation*, **34**, 242.
53. Heath, D., Scott, O. & Lynch, J. (1971) *Thorax*, **26**, 663.
54. Brewer, D. B. & Humphreys, D. R. (1960) *Brit. Heart J.*, **22**, 445.
55. Mallory, T. B. (1937) *New Engl. J. Med.*, **217**, 1045.
56. Crane, J. T. & Grimes, O. F. (1960) *J. Thorac. Cardiovasc. Surg.*, **40**, 410.
57. Burki, K. (1963) *Arch. Kreislauf-forsch.*, **40**, 35.
58. Höra, J. (1934) *Frankfurt Z. Path.*, **47**, 100.
59. Manzini, C. (1947) *Schweiz. Z. Path.*, **10**, 309.
60. Stovin, P. G. I. & Mitchinson, M. J. (1965) *Thorax*, **20**, 106.
61. Liebow, A. A., Steer, A. & Billingsley, J. G. (1965) *Amer. J. Med.*, **39**, 369.
62. Thadani, U., Burrow, C., Whitaker, W. & Heath, D. (1975) *Quart. J. Med. NS.*, **43**, 133.
63. Grainger, R. G. (1958) *Brit. J. Radiol.*, **31**, 201.
64. Brown, C. H. & Harrison, C. V. (1966) *Lancet*, **ii**, 61.
65. Wagenvoort, C. A., Losekoot, G. & Mulder, E. (1971) *Thorax*, **26**, 429.
66. Scheibel, R. L., Dedeketer, K. L., Gleason, D. F., Pliego, M. & Kieffer, S. A. (1972) *Radiology*, **103**, 47.
67. Tingelstad, J. B., Aterman, K. & Lambert, E. C. (1969) *Amer. J. Dis. Child.*, **117**, 219.
68. Dainauskas, J. R., Hughes, R. L. & English, J. T. (1971) *Amer. Heart J.*, **82**, 817.
69. Braun, A., Greenberg, D., Malik, S. & Jenkins, D. E. (1973) *Arch. Path.*, **95**, 67.
70. Rosenthal, A., Vawter, G. & Wagenvoort, C. A. (1973) *Amer. J. Cardiol.*, **31**, 78.
71. Heath, D. & Oakley, C. (1972) *Brit. Med. J.*, **4**, 773.
72. Corrin, B., Spencer, H., Turner-Warwick, M., Beales, S. J. & Hamblin, J. J. (1974) *Virchows Archiv. A. Path. Anat. Histol.*, **364**, 81.
73. Kay, J. M. & Edwards, F. R. (1973) *J. Path.*, **111**, 239.

29. Portal and Pulmonary Hypertension

When portal hypertension develops as the result of hepatic cirrhosis or portal vein thrombosis, the pulmonary circulation may become involved. This is not surprising since there is a direct anatomical communication between the portal veins and the pulmonary veins. The involvement of the pulmonary circulation may show itself in one of two ways. There may be unsaturation of systemic arterial blood or pulmonary arterial hypertension may develop.

Oxygen Unsaturation of Systemic Arterial Blood

Oxygen unsaturation of the systemic arterial blood in patients with cirrhosis of the liver was recognized as long ago as 1935 (Ref. 1) but its frequency was not appreciated until more recently. Systemic arterial hypoxaemia was found in 17 of 43 patients with hepatic cirrhosis or haemochromatosis in one series[2] and in 12 of 15 patients in another.[3] Various explanations have been proposed to account for this hypoxaemia, such as a 'shift to the right' of the haemoglobin oxygen dissociation curve in such cases.[4] Another suggestion is that it might be explained on a basis of a defect in gas transfer and on over-perfusion of some areas of lung with respect to their ventilation.[5–7]

The most likely explanation is that the systemic arterial hypoxaemia is due to some form of shunt that allows poorly oxygenated venous blood to by-pass the alveolar capillary bed of the lung. The types of shunt which have been proposed are intrapulmonary arteriovenous anastomoses and porta-pulmonary venous anastomoses.

Intrapulmonary Arterio-Venous Shunts

Direct communications between pulmonary arteries and veins have been demonstrated in lungs from cirrhotic patients into which plastic or radio-opaque media have been injected.[5,8–10] Such abnormal vascular channels have usually been found in the pleural region but they have not been studied histologically by serial sections. In one series of thirteen cases of cirrhosis studied at necropsy, the lungs were injected by a micropaque gelatin suspension and examined macroscopically, radiologically, and histologically. In all cases the alveolar septa were abnormally vascular and in six cases vascular structures resembling spider naevi on the skin were seen on the pleural surface. In one case there was immediate reflux of contrast medium from major pulmonary veins after its injection into the pulmonary artery. Thus, although there had been systemic arterial hypoxaemia in eight of the patients forming this series, direct pulmonary arteriovenous communication was established in only one. Other workers have been unable to detect a significant pulmonary arteriovenous shunt in the cirrhotic patients they have investigated.[11]

Porta-Pulmonary Venous Anastomoses

We think it likely that a low systemic arterial oxygen saturation in cirrhosis of the liver is due to the flow of unsaturated blood from the portal veins directly into the pulmonary veins. We have been able to demonstrate that such porta-pulmonary venous anastomoses exist in cirrhotic rats.[12] Hepatic cirrhosis was induced in five rats by continuous administration of phenobarbitone and repeated exposure to carbon tetrachloride vapour. The animals were killed, and barium sulphate suspension was injected into the portal vein by a polythene catheter (Fig. 29.1). By this technique two distinct vascular pathways connecting the portal vein and pulmonary vasculature were found. The portal vein communicated with the peri-oesophageal plexus via the coronary and short gastric veins (Figs 29.1 to 29.3). This plexus anastomosed with a network of mediastinal veins some of which

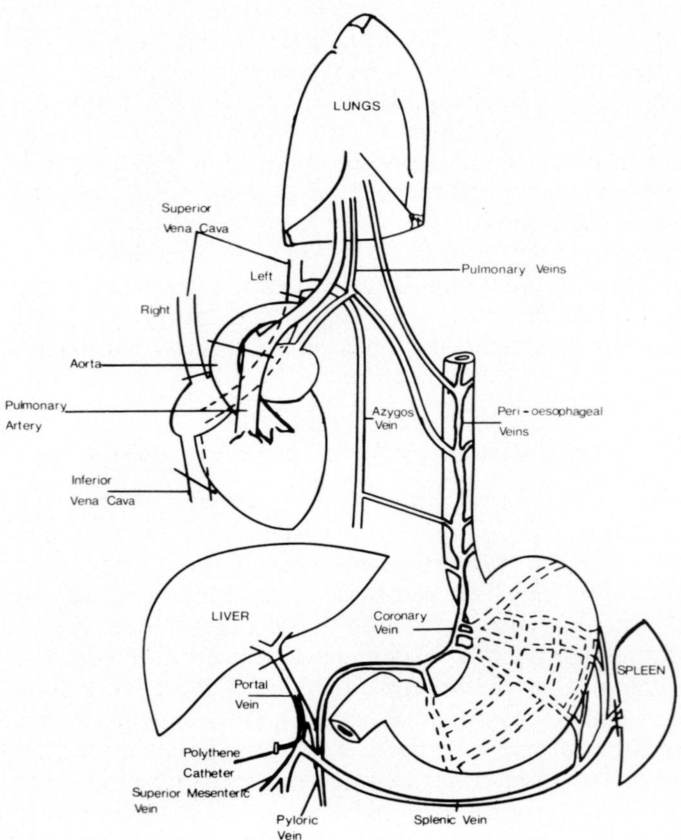

Fig. 29.1 Diagram showing site of injection of barium sulphate suspension into the portal veins of cirrhotic rats as described in the text. The thick black straight lines indicate sites of ligatures.

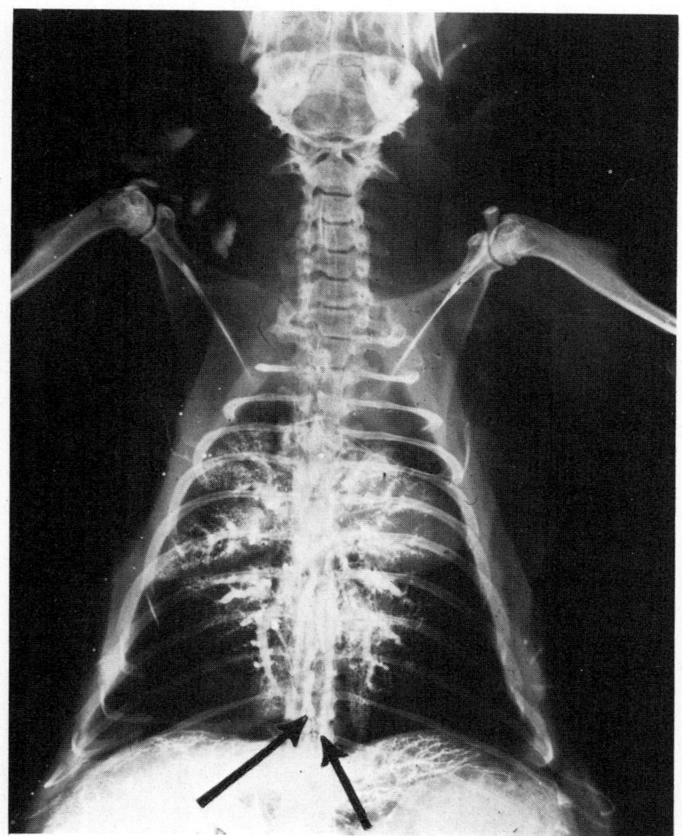

Fig. 29.2 Post-mortem X-radiograph of cirrhotic rat after injection of barium sulphate suspension into portal vein. The peri-oesophageal veins (arrows) and pulmonary veins contain the radio-opaque suspension. (×1·5)

penetrated the pleura and drained directly into the alveolar capillaries (Figs 29.2 to 29.6). Others terminated as tributaries of large extrapulmonary veins (Fig. 29.7).

The porta-pulmonary venous anastomoses could be demonstrated radiologically (Fig. 29.2) and seen with the naked eye (Fig. 29.3). Histologically they consist of thin-walled vessels which pass from the mediastinum to penetrate the pleura and lung where they break into capillary vessels (Figs 29.4 and 29.5). Subsequently these fuse to form larger thin-walled vessels which enter recognizable pulmonary veins (Fig. 29.6). Anastomotic vessels of similar structure enter directly large pulmonary veins immediately recognized by cardiac muscle in their wall (Fig. 29.7).

Calabresi and Abelmann[13] have demonstrated similar porta-pulmonary venous anastomoses in ten cirrhotic human cadavers, although no histological study was carried out.

U

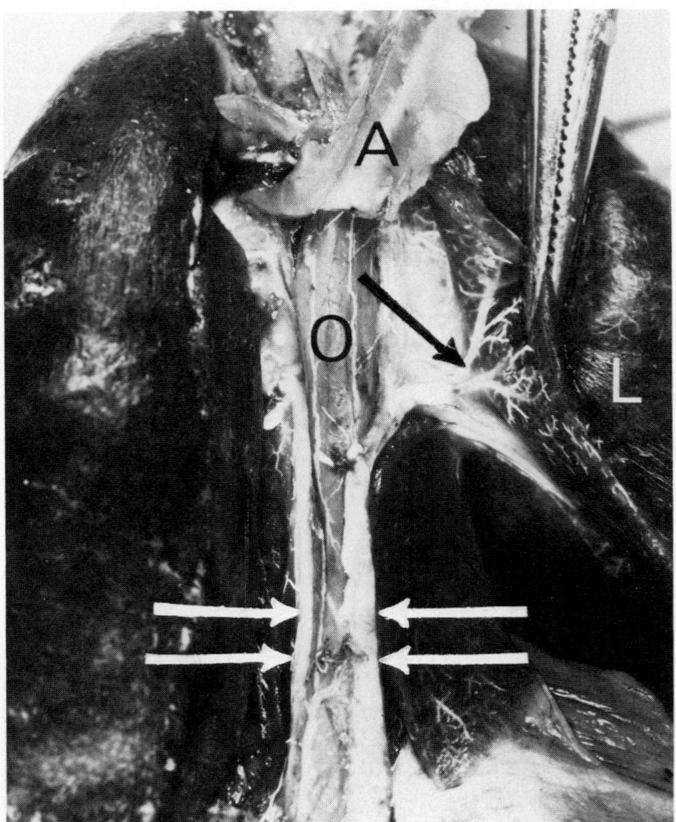

Fig. 29.3 Posterior aspect of thoracic viscera after injection of barium sulphate into portal vein of cirrhotic rat. The aorta (A) is reflected upwards to show the oesophagus (O). The peri-oesophageal veins (double arrows) are distended with barium sulphate and communicate with a network of mediastinal veins (single arrows). The mediastinal veins are shown penetrating the pleura on the medial aspect of the right lung (L). (× 3)

The functional significance of porta-pulmonary venous anastomoses is uncertain. Fritts *et al.*[11] found a systemic arterial saturation of less than 94 per cent in nine of fourteen cases of cirrhosis. They investigated five of these patients with radioactive krypton and demonstrated a porta-pulmonary shunt in all of them. Similar shunts were demonstrated in another series of patients using intrasplenic injections of tritium.[14] On the other hand, Nakamura *et al.*[15] concluded that porta-pulmonary anastomoses did not play an important rôle in the development of systemic arterial hypoxaemia in their patients.

Anatomical and histological demonstration of anastomotic collateral channels does not necessarily prove that such pathways are functional nor does it give information about the rate or direction of possible blood flow. However, it seems likely that, as a result of portal hypertension, unsaturated systemic venous blood will flow along the porta-pulmonary venous anastomoses we have demonstrated into the pulmonary veins. The physiological effects of the two anastomotic pathways we have demonstrated[1 2] are probably different. If the shunt between the peri-oesophageal plexus and major extrapulmonary veins were functional, the effect would be to produce systemic arterial hypoxaemia due to the mixing of de-oxygenated portal venous blood with oxygenated pulmonary venous blood. If the alternative vascular pathway were functional, it would lead to the shunting of portal venous blood from the peri-oesophageal plexus, along the mediastinal veins, through the pleural vessels and thence into the alveolar capillary bed. The combined effects of perfusion by both pulmonary arterial and portal venous blood might give rise to an increased

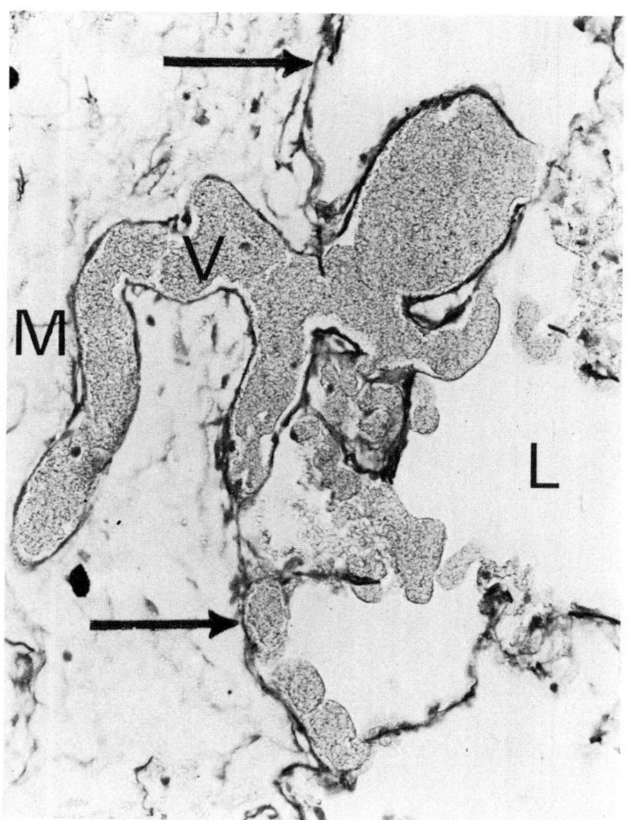

Fig. 29.4 Cirrhotic rat. Mediastinal vein (V) entering lung (L) and breaking up into a sub-pleural plexus of thin-walled vessels distended with barium sulphate. The mediastinum (M) is on the left. The pleura is indicated by arrows. (Elastic/Van Gieson, × 337)

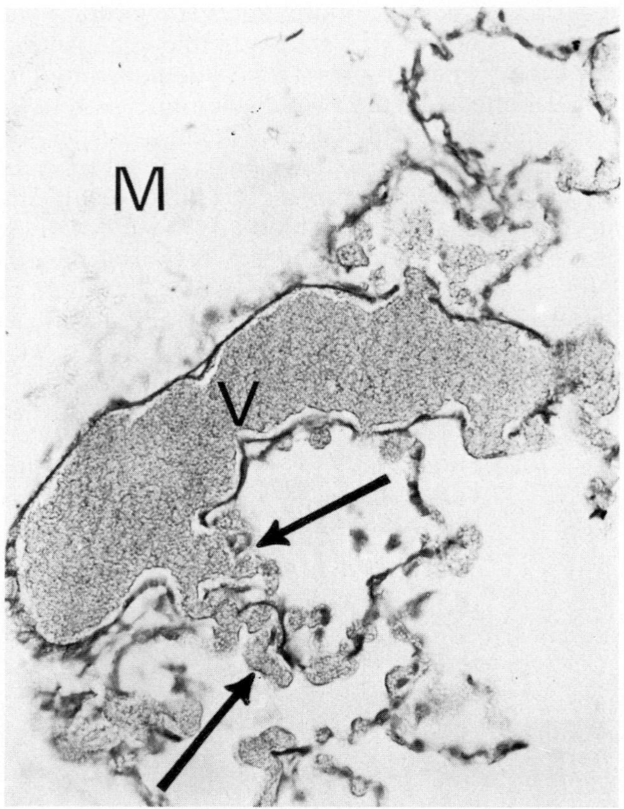

Fig. 29.5 Cirrhotic rat. Part of sub-pleural vascular plexus (V) distended with barium sulphate and draining directly into alveolar capillaries (arrows). Mediastinum (M) is at top left corner. (Elastic/Van Gieson, × 375)

blood flow through the alveolar capillaries. It has been stated that excessive alveolar capillary blood flow can lead to inadequate oxygenation either because flow is too fast for equilibrium to be reacted with the alveolar air, or because in dilated capillaries the central stream is too far away from the alveolar contents.[16] We do not believe this. The alveolar capillary blood flow would have to increase tremendously before there would be a defect of diffusion of sufficient magnitude to cause the low Pa_{O_2} concerned. Streaming in capillaries does not occur because the velocity of flow is too low.

Cirrhosis of the Liver and Pulmonary Hypertension

Pulmonary arterial hypertension is a rare complication of cirrhosis of the liver. In a consecutive series of fifty cases of hepatic cirrhosis studied in the Department of Pathology at Liverpool not one was complicated by right ventricular hypertrophy and hypertensive pulmonary vascular disease. Nevertheless there is no doubt that occasionally a case of cirrhosis of the liver is complicated by pulmonary hypertension for some unknown reason.

Murray, Dawson and Sherlock, for example,[17] described the case of a young man with portal cirrhosis who had a moderate pulmonary hypertension of 44/26 mmHg and an elevated pulmonary vascular resistance of 655 $dyn \cdot s \cdot cm^{-5}$. Kerbel[18] reported the case of a 20-year-old negress with cirrhosis who had a pulmonary arterial pressure of 60 mmHg. Segel and associates[19] described a 43-year-old man who developed severe pulmonary hypertension following hepatic cirrhosis complicating chronic alcoholism. The chest radiograph of a man of 19 years with portal hypertension of unknown aetiology associated with severe pulmonary hypertension is shown in Figure 29.8.

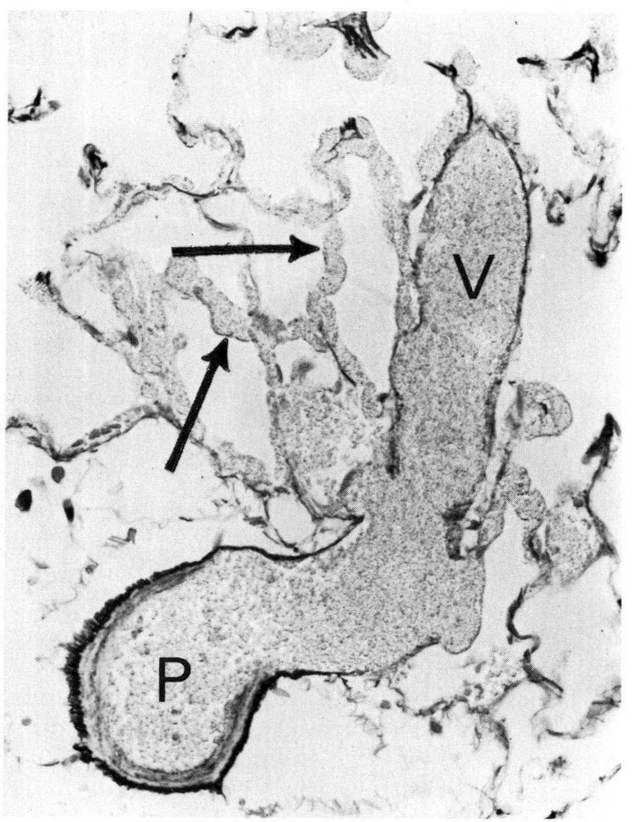

Fig. 29.6 Cirrhotic rat. Alveolar capillaries (arrows) distended with barium sulphate drain into a pulmonary venule (V) and thence into a typical small pulmonary vein (P). (Elastic/Van Gieson, × 375)

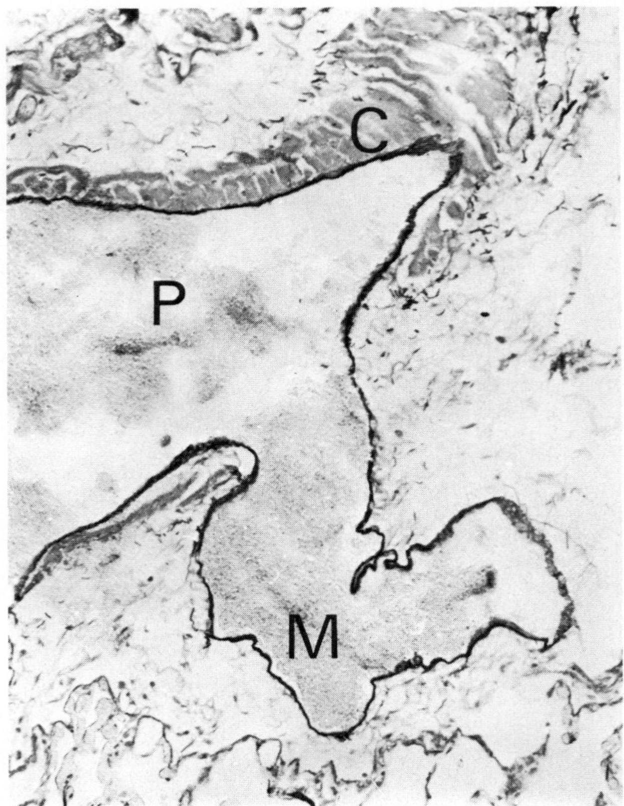

Fig. 29.7 Cirrhotic rat. A thin-walled mediastinal vein (M) drains directly into a major pulmonary vein (P), which has a thick medial coat of cardiac muscle (C). (Elastic/Van Gieson, × 180)

Right ventricular hypertrophy has also been described in female rats in which hepatic cirrhosis was induced by subcutaneous injections of an equal mixture of carbon tetrachloride and mineral oil.[20] Two points of interest that emerge from this animal work are that cardiomegaly developed in only half of the animals and that it was not related to either the degree or the duration of the experimental cirrhosis. This lack of relation between the severity of hepatic cirrhosis and the tendency to develop pulmonary hypertension has also been encountered in human disease.[21] Indeed, in the series of six cases of pulmonary hypertension complicating liver disease reported by Naeye,[22] five were examples of cirrhosis of the liver but the sixth was a case of portal vein thrombosis with cavernous transformation of the portal vein. This suggests that the important predisposing factor is portal hypertension rather than cirrhosis of the liver *per se*. Lunseth[20] was of the opinion that this relationship was affected through porta-pulmonary venous anastomoses similar to those which we have described above. Certainly cardiac hypertrophy may follow in dogs in which shunts between the portal and pulmonary veins have been created surgically.[23]

Findings at Cardiac Catheterization

In one reported case of hepatic cirrhosis complicated by pulmonary hypertension[19] the pulmonary arterial pressure on exercise was 73 mmHg and the pulmonary vascular resistance was 4500 dyn · s · cm^{-5}. The pulmonary wedge pressure was normal. On exercise the cardiac output was increased above the normal range at

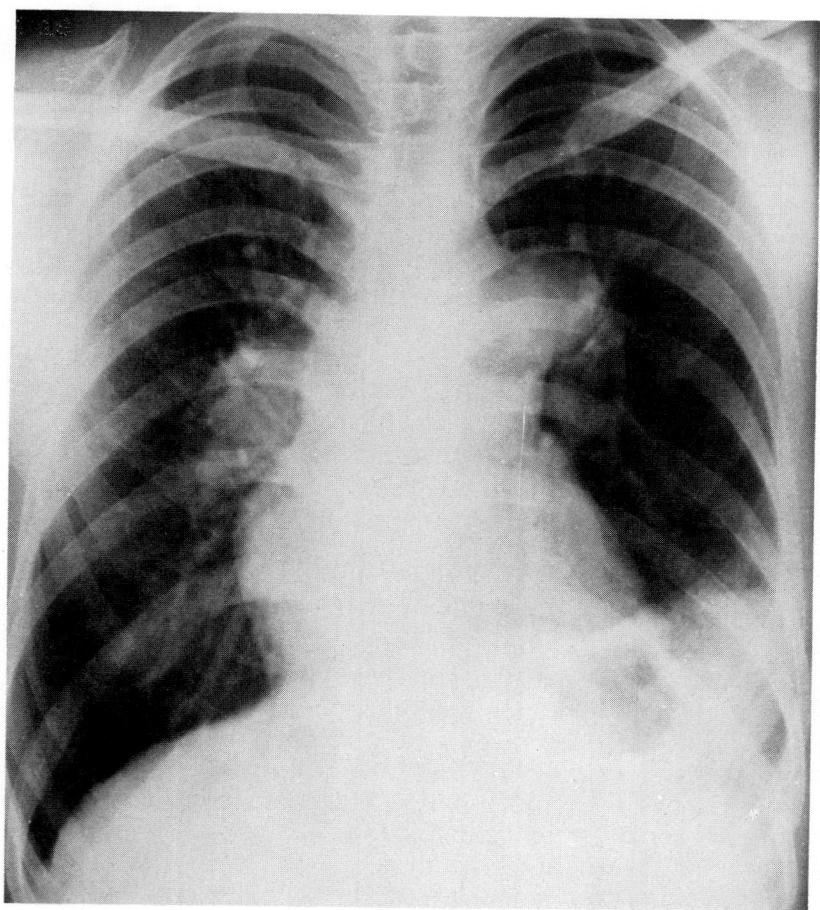

Fig. 29.8 Chest radiograph of a man of 19 years with portal hypertension of unknown aetiology associated with severe pulmonary hypertension. Pulmonary arterial pressure, 110/34 mmHg; pulmonary wedge pressure, 5 mmHg.

$5{\cdot}1\ \text{l}\cdot\text{min}^{-1}/\text{m}^2$ BSA. The plasma volume was increased at $53{\cdot}5\ \text{ml}\cdot\text{kg}^{-1}$. The systemic arterial oxygen saturation was normal at 96·5 per cent.

The slight pulmonary hypertension found in a minority of cases of cirrhosis of the liver has been attributed to such increases in total blood volume.[24,25] As we have seen in Chapter 15, a sustained increase in pulmonary blood flow may lead to pulmonary hypertension but it seems unlikely that the slight changes in blood volume or pulmonary flow found in cases of cirrhosis of the liver are alone reponsible for the severe pulmonary hypertension found in some of them.

The Form of Hypertensive Pulmonary Vascular Disease in Cirrhosis of the Liver

The form of hypertensive pulmonary vascular disease which has been reported in cases of cirrhosis of the liver is identical with that found in pre- and post-tricuspid congenital cardiac shunts and primary pulmonary hypertension. It is characterized by plexiform lesions and necrotizing arteritis.[19,22] Naeye[22] described the pulmonary vascular lesions in six patients, three of whom were female. The age range was 13 to 76 years. As noted above, in five cases there was hepatic cirrhosis while in a girl of 13 years there was no cirrhosis but cavernous transformation of the portal vein. He found that, in five of his six cases, emboli or thrombi were present in the small pulmonary arteries and he believed these to be the cause rather than the effect of the pulmonary hypertension. As discussed at length in Chapter 28, we regard hypertensive pulmonary vascular disease characterized by plexiform lesions as distinct from recurrent pulmonary thromboembolism so that we are not inclined to accept the view that the pulmonary vascular lesions in cirrhosis of the liver are the result of pulmonary thromboembolism. This is not to deny the possibility that pulmonary emboli may exaggerate hypertensive pulmonary vascular disease brought about by some other mechanism.

The Effect of Diet on Liver and Pulmonary Circulation

Above we have considered the possibilities that the pulmonary hypertension complicating cirrhosis of the liver might be haemodynamic or thromboembolic in origin. It is also possible that it may have a dietary basis. It is well known that certain pyrrolizidine alkaloids may affect both the liver and the pulmonary circulation.[26] Fulvine, for example, is now accepted as a major cause of veno-occlusive disease of the liver in the West Indies where it is ingested as a decoction of the plant *Crotalaria fulva* in bush tea. When rats are given fulvine by intraperitoneal injection or by stomach tube, some of them die within three weeks of acute haemorrhagic centrilobular necrosis of the liver. The survivors develop hypertensive pulmonary vascular disease.[26] Experimental results of this kind suggest that ingested materials may in some instances lead to both cirrhosis of the liver and pulmonary vascular disease. Alternatively, it is possible that some metabolite formed in a minority of cases of cirrhosis of the liver passes to the lung to produce hypertensive pulmonary vascular disease. The development of pulmonary hypertension in cirrhosis of the liver and portal vein thrombosis remains a challenging problem.

REFERENCES

1. Snell, A. M. (1935) *Ann. Intern. Med.*, **9**, 690.
2. Blackburn, C. R. B., Read, J., McRae, J., Colebatch, H. J., Playoust, M. R. & Holland, R. A. B. (1960) *Australas. Ann. Med.*, **9**, 204.
3. Bashour, F. A., Miller, W. F. & Chapman, C. B. (1961) *Amer. Heart J.*, **62**, 350.
4. Keys, A. & Snell, A. M. (1938) *J. Clin. Invest.*, **17**, 59.
5. Karlish, A. J., Marshall, R., Reid, L. & Sherlock, S. (1967) *Thorax*, **22**, 555.
6. Cotes, J. E., Field, G. B., Brown, G. J. A. & Read, A. E. (1968) *Lancet*, **i**, 952.
7. Stanley, N. N. (1971) *Thorax*, **26**, 230.
8. Hales, M. R. (1956) *Amer. J. Path.*, **32**, 927.
9. Rydell, R. & Hoffbauer, F. W. (1956) *Amer. J. Med.*, **21**, 450.
10. Berthelot, P., Walker, J. G., Sherlock, S. & Reid, L. (1966) *New Engl. J. Med.*, **274**, 291.
11. Fritts, H. W. Jn., Hardewig, A., Rochester, D. F., Durand, J. & Cournand, A. (1960) *J. Clin. Invest.*, **39**, 1841.
12. Khaliq, S. U., Kay, J. M. & Heath, D. (1972) *J. Path.*, **107**, 167.
13. Calabresi, P. & Abelmann, W. H. (1957) *J. Clin. Invest.*, **36**, 1257.
14. Mellemgaard, K., Winkler, K., Tygstrup, N. & Georg, J. (1963) *J. Clin. Invest.*, **42**, 1399.
15. Nakamura, T., Nakamura, S., Tazawa, T., Abe, S., Aikawa, T. & Tokita, K. (1965) *J. Lab. Clin. Med.*, **65**, 114.
16. Lancet (annotation) (1966) *Lancet*, **i**, 968.
17. Murray, J. F., Dawson, A. M. & Sherlock, S. (1958) *Amer. J. Med.*, **24**, 358.
18. Kerbel, N. C. (1962) *Canad. Med. Ass. J.*, **87**, 1022.
19. Segel, N., Kay, J. M., Bayley, T. J. & Paton, A. (1968) *Brit. Heart J.*, **30**, 575.
20. Lunseth, J. H. (1965) *Arch. Path.*, **79**, 644.
21. Lunseth, J. H., Olmstead, E. G. & Abboud, F. (1958) *AMA Arch. Int. Med.*, **102**, 405.
22. Naeye, R. L. (1960) *Circulation*, **22**, 376.
23. Cohn, R. (1959) *Surgery*, **46**, 887.
24. Segel, N., Bayley, T. J., Paton, A., Dykes, P. W. & Bishop, J. M. (1963) *Clin. Sci.*, **25**, 43.
25. Bayley, T. J., Segel, N. & Bishop, J. M. (1964) *Clin. Sci.*, **26**, 227.
26. Kay, J. M., Heath, D., Smith, P., Bras, G. & Summerell, J. (1971) *Thorax*, **26**, 249.

30. The Influence of Respiratory Gases on the Pulmonary Circulation

The chief function of the pulmonary circulation is to exchange oxygen and carbon dioxide with the atmosphere, and the possibility that these gases might themselves exert some control over the arteries, capillaries or veins of the lung has been one which has interested a large number of investigators over many years. A body of information is now available from human studies which demonstrates that a low alveolar oxygen tension or a high alveolar carbon dioxide tension cause local pulmonary vasoconstriction. Such a mechanism has important implications in physiology and pathology.

THE PHYSIOLOGICAL EFFECTS OF HYPOXIA

Following the original observation by Motley and his colleagues[1] in Cournand's laboratory, a number of investigators has showed that the breathing of gas mixtures low in oxygen causes an increase in the pulmonary arterial pressure in normal man.[2–6] The response is roughly proportional to the degree to which the oxygen saturation of the arterial blood is lowered (Fig. 30.1). In the group of 17 normal

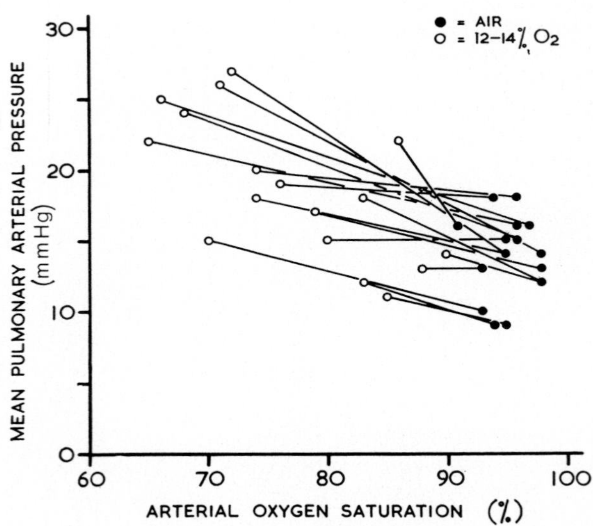

Fig. 30.1 The relation between the mean pulmonary arterial pressure and the systemic arterial oxygen saturation in a group of normal subjects breathing air and 12–14 per cent oxygen. The two observations made on each subject are joined by a line. (Data from Fritts *et al.*[6].)

Table 30.1 The effects of hypoxia on the pulmonary circulation. The figures are the averages of 16 patients with acquired cardiac disease. Statistical analysis is by paired 't' test. Data from Yu *et al.*[9]

	Air	%O_2	*P*
Pulmonary arterial pressure (mmHg)	18	24	$<0{\cdot}001$
Left atrial pressure (mmHg)	9	9	$>0{\cdot}05$
Cardiac output ($1 \cdot min^{-1}/m^2$ BSA)	2·7	3·1	$<0{\cdot}01$
Pulmonary arterial resistance[a] ($dyn \cdot s \cdot cm^{-5}$)	169	257	$<0{\cdot}01$
Pulmonary blood volume (ml)	294	238	$<0{\cdot}01$

[a]See page 135.

subjects shown in Figure 30.1 the mean pulmonary arterial pressure rose from an average of 14 mmHg to 19 mmHg while the arterial oxygen saturation fell from 95 per cent to 77 per cent. The pulmonary arterial pressure rises gradually and reaches its maximum about 15 minutes after starting to breathe the hypoxic gas mixture. After this it tends to fall again.

The wedge pressure is not affected.[3,4,7] If the direct Fick method is used to measure the pulmonary blood flow, care has to be taken to ensure that a steady stage of gaseous exchange has been achieved during the hypoxic period.[2] There is a small increase in the pulmonary blood flow,[3,7,8] but not in proportion to the increase in the difference in pressure across the pulmonary circulation, so that the pulmonary arterial resistance increases.[3,7,8] In a group of six normal subjects, for example, breathing 13 per cent oxygen caused the average pulmonary arterial resistance to increase from 165 to 319 $dyn \cdot s \cdot cm^{-5}$ ($P < 0{\cdot}01$) while the arterial oxygen saturation fell from 98 per cent to 72 per cent.[7]

Such strong evidence that hypoxia causes pulmonary vasoconstriction in normal subjects receives confirmation from studies in patients. The most complete study of the effects of hypoxia on the pulmonary circulation was carried out by Yu and his colleagues[9] on 16 patients with acquired cardiac disease, of whom the majority was rheumatic. The results are summarized in Table 30.1. Hypoxia caused a significant increase in the pulmonary arterial pressure, but had no effect on the left atrial pressure measured directly. The cardiac output was measured by dye-dilution, thus avoiding the problems of unstable respiratory gas exchange. It showed a small but significant increase. The pulmonary arterial resistance increased by approximately 50 per cent. Measurements of the pulmonary blood volume by the technique of injecting indicator successively into the pulmonary artery and left atrium and sampling from a systemic artery (p. 107) showed a decrease of about 20 per cent. A similar decrease in the pulmonary blood volume was found by Oakley and her colleagues[10] although previous measurements of the less specific central blood volume had shown no alteration.[4,6]

Thus, despite earlier doubts, there has accumulated over the years convincing evidence that hypoxia causes pulmonary vasoconstriction in man.

There is now also available from human studies a body of evidence that the vasoconstrictor effect is locally determined. Using the technique of bronchospirometry it is possible to supply one lung alone with a hypoxic mixture. Under these circumstances each lung is subjected to the same inflow and outflow pressures and the distribution of blood flow is an indication of the difference in resistance between the two sides. In earlier experiments the measurement of the blood flow to each lung was carried out by the Fick method for oxygen[11–13] or for carbon dioxide.[14,15] More recently[16–18] it has been measured by the intravenous injection of a solution of ^{85}Kr. This gas is almost entirely eliminated into the alveoli during its first passage through the lung, so that the collection of expired air from each lung and measurement of its radioactivity gives a measure of the division of blood flow between the two lungs. Another method of assessing the distribution of blood flow between the two lungs has been by the intravenous injection of ^{131}I-labelled macroaggregated albumin[19–21] followed by external counting of radioactivity.

There is general agreement that the inhalation of a hypoxic mixture of gases by one lung causes a reduction in the flow of blood to that lung, indicating a vasoconstriction (Fig. 30.2). Figure 30.3 shows average values from an extensive study

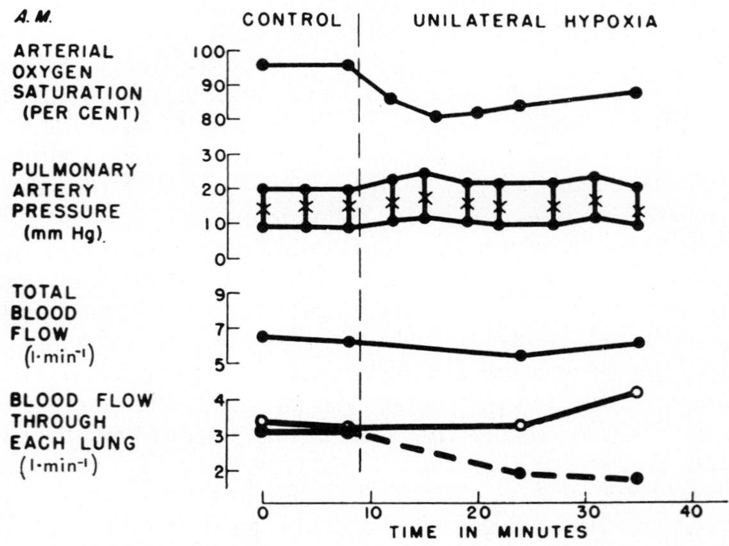

Fig. 30.2 The effects of inducing hypoxia in one lung in a normal subject.[13] One lung, the flow of blood through which is represented by open circles, is supplied with 25 per cent oxygen throughout. The other lung, the flow through which is represented by closed circles, is supplied first with room air (continuous line) and then with 5 per cent oxygen (interrupted line). Hypoxia causes a local diminution in blood flow.

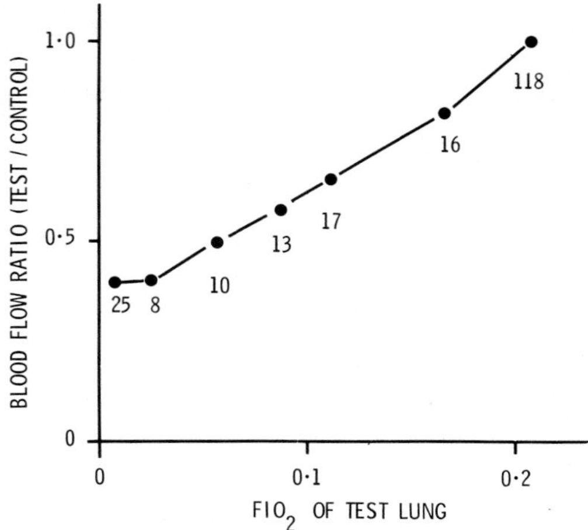

Fig. 30.3 The effects of inducing hypoxia in one lung in man.[18] There is a positive relation between the inspired fractional concentration of oxygen (FI_{O_2}) to the test lung and the ratio of the blood flow (test/control). The points are the means of observations on varying numbers of subjects, given numerically immediately below.

by Durand and his colleagues.[18] It demonstrates that, with a decreasing concentration of oxygen in the inspired air, there is a progressive shift of blood flow away from the hypoxic lung. If one assumes that the vascular resistance of the control lung remains unaffected, it is possible to calculate the percentage change in vascular resistance of the hypoxic lung and relate this to the alveolar PO_2 on that side. Figure 30.4 shows the relation obtained. It indicates that the resistance does not increase in a linear fashion with alveolar oxygen tension. Over a wide range of normal variation in alveolar PO_2 the pulmonary vascular resistance changes very little. From a physiological point of view it may well be of importance that the pulmonary vascular resistance starts to rise rapidly as the value of the normal mixed venous PO_2 is reached (p. 464).

In the upright posture, the breathing of a hypoxic mixture of gases causes a relative increase of the perfusion to the apices of the lungs, as studied by ^{131}I-labelled macroaggregated albumin[21] (p. 99) or by ^{133}Xe (p. 98) and external counting. Presumably this is due to an increased pulmonary arterial pressure (p. 100).

The effects of chronic hypoxia are considered in Chapter 32.

THE PHYSIOLOGICAL EFFECTS OF HYPEROXIA

In normal subjects the breathing of pure oxygen was found to cause a very slight fall in the mean pulmonary arterial pressure (average 1 mmHg) and no change in the cardiac output as measured by the direct Fick method.[22,23] The direct Fick

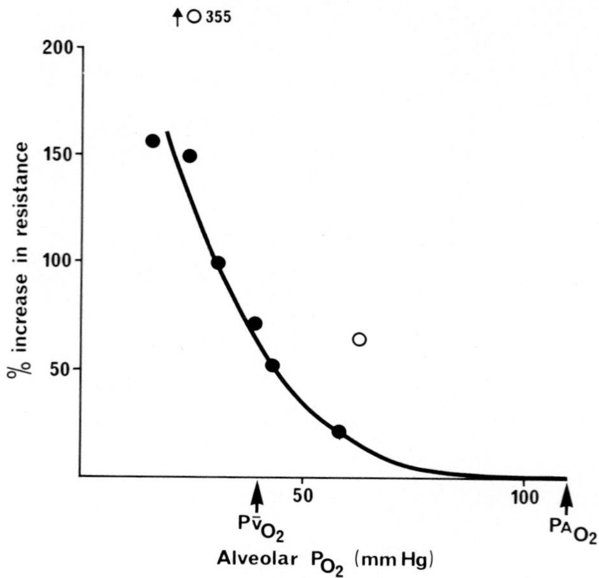

Fig. 30.4 The effects of inducing hypoxia in one lung in man.[18] In this diagram the data shown in Figure 30.3 have been re-calculated in order to plot the pulmonary vascular resistance of the hypoxic lung against its alveolar Po_2. Two points shown by open circles represent the effects of hypoxia plus hypercapnia.

method for oxygen is difficult to apply during the breathing of pure oxygen since the equation for the calculation of the oxygen uptake from the composition of expired air (Appendix B) is no longer applicable. The oxygen uptake has, under these circumstances, to be measured by the slope of the recording of a spirometer drum in a closed circuit.

In patients with mitral stenosis, where the combination of an increased resistance and muscularization of the muscular pulmonary arteries provides a vascular bed more sensitive to vasodilator effects than normal, the breathing of 100 per cent oxygen has been found to cause a distinct fall in pressure in the pulmonary artery.[24–26] In the one study,[26] in which the pulmonary arterial resistance could be measured, it fell from an average of 557 to 388 dyn · s · cm^{-5} ($P < 0{\cdot}05$) during the breathing of 100 per cent oxygen in nine patients. The pulmonary arterial pressure fell from an average of 42 to 34 mmHg. The wedge pressure and cardiac output were unaffected.

The evidence is, therefore, suggestive that oxygen has a dilating effect in the pulmonary circulation and presumably this is at the level of the muscular pulmonary arteries. The dilating effect of pure oxygen is confirmed by studies on patients with pulmonary hypertension and congenital heart disease in which the pulmonary arterial pressure fell while the pulmonary blood flow increased.[27–31] The relation between this effect and the structure of the muscular pulmonary arteries has been shown[29] and is described in Chapter 19, page 296.

Lesser degrees of hyperoxia also have a dilating effect in the pulmonary circulation.[32,33] In eight patients with mitral stenosis[33] the breathing of 47 per cent oxygen was associated with a non-significant decrease in the pulmonary arterial resistance from an average of 344 to 297 dyn · s · cm^{-5}. Pure oxygen caused a greater fall in the pulmonary arterial pressure in patients with mitral stenosis than did 47 per cent oxygen.[33] This graded relation between the concentration of inspired oxygen and its effect is comparable with that which was noted previously between the degree of hypoxia and pulmonary hypertension. In fact there appears to be a continuous (although curvilinear) scale relating inspired oxygen tension to pulmonary vascular resistance which extends from extreme hypoxia to extreme hyperoxia.

In patients with chronic bronchitis and hypoxaemia, the inhalation of high concentrations of oxygen has also been shown to be vasodilatory in the pulmonary circulation (Chap. 34, p. 530).

The effects of prolonged hyperoxia are considered later in this chapter.

THE PHYSIOLOGICAL EFFECTS OF CARBON DIOXIDE

The published results of the inhalation of carbon dioxide by normals and patients with various cardiopulmonary disorders are summarized in Table 30.2. The original studies of Fishman and his colleagues[34] failed to show any change in the pulmonary arterial pressure in normal subjects. An increase in the pulmonary arterial pressure was found in a group of patients with chronic pulmonary disease, but this was accompanied by an increase in the cardiac output and could not be taken as evidence of pulmonary vasoconstriction.[34] Subsequent studies on patients with mitral stenosis or pulmonary disease[35–37] have confirmed the increase in pulmonary arterial pressure. In all these investigations there has been an increase in the cardiac output, but in only one[35] was this measured by a dye-dilution method which avoids the errors inherent in a changing state of respiratory gas-exchange. There is a tendency for an increase in the wedge pressure.[35,36,38,39] In all three studies in which the pulmonary arterial resistance could be calculated[35–37] it was found to be increased, in two of them significantly so.

The subjects of two of these studies included or consisted of patients with chronic bronchitis and emphysema. The curved relation between pressure and flow in the pulmonary circulation of such patients (p. 526) renders difficult the exact interpretation of changes in resistance at different rates of flow. However, the shape of the pressure: flow relation is such that, with an increasing flow, the resistance falls. The existence of an increased resistance with an increased flow is, therefore, indicative of vasoconstriction and will tend to underestimate its magnitude.

Although such results are strongly suggestive of constriction of vascular smooth muscle in patients with mitral stenosis, the mechanical effects of hyperventilation

Table 30.2 Effects of carbon dioxide on the human pulmonary circulation. The figures are the averages of each group of subjects. The paired 't' test has been used throughout where $n > 4$

Ref.	Numbers and types of subjects	FI_{CO_2}	Mean pulmonary arterial pressure mmHg	Wedge pressure mmHg	Cardiac output $l \cdot min^{-1}$ ($/m^2$ BSA)	Pulmonary arterial resistance[a] $dyn \cdot s \cdot cm^{-5}$	Mean systemic arterial pressure mmHg	$\dot{V}_E$ $l \cdot min^{-1}$ ($/m^2$ BSA)	Pa_{CO_2}	Sa_{O_2} % or Pa_{O_2} (mmHg)
5	5 Normals	0	14	—	(3·4)	—	102	(5·6)	37	97
		0·03 or 0·05	14	—	(3·7)	—	112	(14·3)****	43	100****
	10 Bronchitis and emphysema	0	29	—	(2·8)	—	100	(5·8)	45	89
		0·03 or 0·05	33***	—	(3·1)**	—	111****	(11·6)**	52	93
35	10 Mitral valve disease	0	27	17	4·2	185	103	7·8 (n = 19)	39 (n = 8)	97
		0·05	35**	21*	5·0***	240	110	24·8****	43**	97
36	10 Mitral valve disease	0	37	21	3·8	354	99	6·5	40	94
		0·03–0·07	47****	24	4·5***	448*	108***	22·7****	46****	94
	5 Chronic lung disease	0	19	8	6·2	155	107	6·9	49	90
		0·03–0·07	28	7	7·0	259	115	16·9***	56****	87
	5 'Normal'	0	15	7	6·1	108	104	7·1	39	95
		0·03–0·07	18	7	6·7	125	103	19·5**	44****	94
37	11 Bronchitis and emphysema	0	33	—	7·1	361	94	7·2	55	(48)
		0·09–0·10	52	—	8·2	514****	119****	19·5****	78****	(83)****
	5 Pulmonary disease	0	15	—	8·8	96	98	8·1 (n = 4)	38	(77)
		0·09–0·10	30**	—	11·9	214	125**	43·9****	65****	(124)***
	5 Pulmonary disease (HCO_3^- infusion)	0	27	—	9·7	202	—	—	48	—
		0·10	42	—	12·2	310	—	—	76	—
		0·10	43	—	13·2	272	—	—	84[b]*	—

*$P < 0·05$; **$P < 0·02$; ***$P < 0·01$; ****$P < 0·001$.

[a] See page 135.

[b] *($P < 0·05$), refers to the comparison between CO_2 and $CO_2 + NaHCO_3$.

on the pulmonary circulation need to be taken into account in the patients with chronic bronchitis and emphysema (Chap. 34, p. 534).

In eight patients with mitral stenosis given 5 per cent carbon dioxide[35] there was a non-significant increase in the pulmonary blood volume (measured by the double dye-dilution technique, p. 107) from 473 to 536 ml. In normal subjects there was evidence of an increased pulmonary capillary blood volume during the breathing of concentrations of carbon dioxide up to 10 per cent.[40] The latter subjects were in an upright position, so that the increased pulmonary venous and arterial pressures could have increased the perfusion of the apices of the lungs and, thereby, expanded the pulmonary capillary volume.

The inhalation of carbon dioxide (Table 30.2) (see also Refs 41 and 42) is accompanied by an increased systemic arterial pressure, an increased ventilation, an increased arterial P_{CO_2}, a decreased arterial pH and an increased arterial oxygen saturation or P_{O_2}.

Evidence of a local vasoconstrictive action of carbon dioxide has been adduced in man. Hertz[11] originally suggested this from measurements of the oxygen uptake of each lung during bronchospirometry. He found that, in 27 out of 32 studies, when the carbon dioxide absorber was removed from the re-breathing circuit of one lung there was a decrease in the uptake of oxygen by that side. Twining and his colleagues[43] studied the distribution of pulmonary blood flow by the intravenous injection of ^{131}I-macroaggregated albumin during bronchospirometry. In 11 patients 10 per cent CO_2 in O_2 was supplied to one lung while the other lung received 100 per cent O_2. The proportion of the total blood flow going to the lung receiving 10 per cent CO_2 diminished from 46 to 42 per cent on the average ($P < 0{\cdot}01$). This represents an 18 per cent increase in the resistance of the hypercarbic lung. In five cases the end-tidal P_{CO_2} of the hypercarbic lung averaged 58 mmHg as compared with 39 mmHg in the control lung, while the pH calculated for the blood leaving the hypercarbic lung was 7·29. Such an alveolar P_{CO_2} far exceeds the normal mixed venous P_{CO_2} and the relatively modest degree of vasoconstriction may be contrasted with that found with hypoxia.

In the extensive investigation of the effects of unilateral hypoxia by Durand and his colleagues[18] the effects of adding 5 per cent CO_2 to the hypoxic side were also measured. The results are indicated in Figure 30.4. There appears to be a substantial potentiation of the vasoconstrictive effect of hypoxia by an increase in alveolar P_{CO_2} within the physiological range. Such an effect is far in excess of the feeble constrictor effect of hypercarbia alone noted above.[43]

To summarize, the overall evidence seems to favour a vasoconstrictor activity of carbon dioxide in the lung. This function does not, however, appear in itself to be a strong one, certainly not as strong as that exerted by comparable degrees of hypoxia. Increasing the alveolar P_{CO_2} within a physiological range in normal people has produced no measurable effect.[34] The greatest effect has been found in patients with chronic bronchitis given a very high concentration of carbon dioxide[37] with an arterial P_{CO_2} well within the pathological range. Under such circumstances part of the measured effect may be due to the mechanical effects of hyperventilation[44] and some caution is also necessary in the interpretation of calculations of the cardiac output based on oxygen uptake. In addition, there is evidence[18] that an increased alveolar P_{CO_2} may potentiate the local vasoconstrictor effect of hypoxia.

THE PHYSIOLOGICAL EFFECTS OF HYDROGEN ION CONCENTRATION

The published effects of changing the hydrogen ion concentration, $[H^+]$, of the blood are summarized in Table 30.3. The intravenous infusion of sodium bicarbonate[36,45,46] has increased the arterial pH to around 7·5 but had no significant effect on the pulmonary arterial pressure. In normal subjects[45] and a group of patients composed mostly of mitral stenosis[36] no significant increase in the pulmonary blood flow was found. The pulmonary arterial resistance of the latter group[36] showed a non-significant decrease. In a group of patients with chronic pulmonary disease, Enson and his colleagues[46] found a substantial increase in the pulmonary blood flow. This, together with a non-significant fall in the pulmonary arterial pressure suggested vasodilatation. However, in the absence of measurement of the wedge pressure and in view of the curvilinear relation between pressure and flow in these patients (p. 526), this interpretation requires caution.

The intravenous infusion of tris buffer has given similar results (Table 30.3). In a group of normal subjects, there was no significant change in either the pulmonary arterial pressure or the cardiac output[45] and no effect was concluded. On the other hand, in a group of patients with chronic pulmonary disease there was no significant change in the pulmonary arterial pressure but an increase in pulmonary blood flow, the extent of which suggested vasodilatation.[46] The reservations discussed in the previous paragraph apply also to this interpretation. The intravenous infusion of THAM buffer in patients with chronic bronchitis had no effect on either the pulmonary arterial pressure or the pulmonary blood flow.[47]

The results of alkalinizing infusions have, therefore, been equivocal. Studies in which an increased $[H^+]$ of the blood has been caused by means of the intravenous infusion of hydrochloric acid have also failed to provide any consistent effect on the pulmonary circulation in patients with mitral stenosis[36] or chronic bronchitis[48,49] (Table 30.3). It seems likely[50] that the intracellular $[H^+]$ of the smooth muscle of the pulmonary blood vessels does not change greatly in response to such transient acidity of the extracellular fluid. In one study,[49] however, patients with chronic bronchitis were given ammonium chloride by mouth for 5–7 days, resulting in a substantial decrease in arterial pH but no change in the pulmonary arterial resistance (Table 30.3).

The intravenous infusion of hydrochloric acid in patients with chronic bronchitis had no effect on the pulmonary blood volume[48] measured by radiocardiography (p. 109).

Reports of experiments on animals[51] have pointed to a pulmonary vasoconstriction during acidosis and a pulmonary vasodilatation during alkalosis. Such experiments are often able to explore the effects of hydrogen ion concentrations considerably

Table 30.3 Effects of changing the hydrogen ion concentration of the blood on the human pulmonary circulation. The figures are the averages of each group of subjects. Average pH was calculated from the sum of the hydrogen ion concentrations and then expressed as the negative logarithm. The paired 't' test has been used to compare the figures 'before' and 'during' where $n > 4$

Number and type of subject (reference)	Mean pulmonary arterial pressure mmHg		Mean wedge pressure mmHg		Cardiac output $l \cdot min^{-1}$ (/m^2 BSA)		Pulmonary arterial resistance[a] $dyn \cdot s \cdot cm^{-5}$		Arterial pH		Pa_{CO_2} mmHg		Sa_{O_2} %		Pa_{O_2} mmHg		$\dot{V}_E$ $l \cdot min^{-1}$ (/m^2 BSA)	
	Before	During	Before	During	Before	During	Before	During	Before	During	Before	During	Before	During	Before	During	Before	During
Infusion of $NaHCO_3$																		
4 Normals (45)	12	13	—	—	(2·9)	(3·4)	—	—	7·42	7·49	39	43	96	97	—	—	(4·1)	(4·1)
7 Chronic pulmonary disease (46)	34	31	—	—	(2·9)	(3·9)****	—	—	7·40	7·51****	47	55****	86	86	—	—	(5·0)	(5·1)
6 Mostly mitral stenosis (36)	33	31	16	19	4·5	4·6	311	238	7·46	7·53***	37	39	92	92	—	—	8·1	7·5
Infusion of tris																		
5 Normals (45)	12	13	—	—	(3·2)	(3·4)	—	—	7·41	7·49*	36	36	97	96	—	—	(4·2)	(4·6)
5 Chronic pulmonary disease (46)	26	25	—	—	(3·4)	(4·3)*	—	—	7·41	7·50****	44	42	88	73	—	—	(5·3)	(4·7)
Infusion of THAM																		
14 Bronchitis (47)	47	47	—	—	4·5	4·8	—	—	7·41	7·44****	49	52***	—	—	87	78****	9·4	8·4****
Infusion of HCl																		
7 Mostly mitral stenosis (36)	37	38	20	19	3·6	4·2	456	408	7·45	7·41****	37	37	91	93	—	—	6·4	7·1
5 Bronchitis (48)	21	23	5	5	3·1	3·0	420	479	7·43	7·34****	45	46	90	91	—	—	—	—
14 Bronchitis (48)	24	26****	—	—	3·2	3·1	—	—	7·42	7·35****	46	47	89	91***	—	—	(5·6) ($n = 11$)	(7·3)****
11 Bronchitis (49)	27	28	12	13	(2·9)	(3·5)****	233	212*	7·40	7·31****	48	46*	—	—	64 ($n = 10$)	85****	(4·6)	(6·3)****
Ingestion of NH_4Cl																		
9 Bronchitis (49)	27	26	9	8	(2·9)	(3·0)	321	302	7·40	7·33****	49	48	—	—	63	69*	(5·2)	(5·7)**

*$P < 0·05$; **$P < 0·02$; ***$P < 0·01$; ****$P < 0·001$.
[a] See page 135.

more and less than those feasible in human work. In the reports summarized above and in Table 30.3, the systemic arterial pH under experimental conditions ranged from 7·31 during acid infusions to 7·53 during alkaline infusions. Such a range embraces the great majority of patients with heart disease and the effects which would be expected from the clinical application of acid or alkaline infusions.

One great difficulty in interpreting these experiments is the inability of knowing to what extent changes in $[H^+]$ of the blood have given rise to changes in the $[H^+]$ of the cells. Work on a variety of tissues shows that, while changes in extracellular P_{CO_2} will affect the intracellular $[H^+]$ within minutes, changes in extracellular $[H^+]$ with bicarbonate or other buffers will take a matter of hours to alter the $[H^+]$ inside cells.[50] The fact that changing the extracellular $[H^+]$ has had so little effect on the pulmonary circulation does not, therefore, preclude the possibility that the vasomotor action of carbon dioxide is mediated through changes in the intracellular $[H^+]$ of vascular smooth muscle. Indeed, from a chemical point of view this would seem to be the most likely mode of action. Carbon dioxide itself is relatively inert and unlikely to give rise to the conformational changes in enzymic proteins which largely determine the control of their activity. Hydrogen ions, on the other hand, are well known to be active in this respect.

Attempts to Modify the Effects of Hypoxia and Hypercarbia by Changing Hydrogen Ion Concentration

In five patients with chronic bronchitis[37] (Table 30.2) the effects of breathing 10 per cent carbon dioxide were measured with and without an intravenous infusion of sodium bicarbonate. Unfortunately, with so few observations, none of the haemodynamic changes was statistically significant. In addition the simultaneous changes in pressure, flow and P_{CO_2}, together with the curved pressure : flow relation in these patients (p. 526), obscure the interpretation.

Table 30.4 summarizes the results of three investigations in which attempts were made to modify hypoxic pulmonary vasoconstriction by intravenous infusions of tris and bicarbonate and by the ingestion of ammonium chloride for five to seven days. In none of these studies was there any significant modification of the effects of hypoxia.

As has been discussed above, the difficulty with all such studies is to know what is happening to the intracellular $[H^+]$. We shall need to return to this point when considering the possible intra-cellular mechanisms of action of hypoxia and hypercarbia.

LOCATION OF THE VASOCONSTRICTIVE EFFECT OF HYPOXIA

The observation that the wedge pressure is unaffected by hypoxia would reasonably exclude a significant constriction of the pulmonary venous system in man. In animals this seems also to be the case.[52] Bergofsky and Haas[53] varied the

Table 30.4 The effects of hydrogen ion concentration on the influence of hypoxia in man. The figures are the averages of each group of subjects. Average pH was calculated from the sum of the hydrogen ion concentrations and then expressed as the negative logarithm. In none of these studies was there a significant modification of the pulmonary hypertension caused by hypoxia.

Number and type of subject (reference)	$F_{I_{O_2}}$	Special conditions	Mean pulmonary arterial pressure mmHg	Mean wedge pressure mmHg	Cardiac output $l \cdot min^{-1}$ ($/m^2$ BSA)	Pulmonary arterial resistance[a] $dyn \cdot s \cdot cm^{-5}$	Arterial pH	Pa_{CO_2} mmHg	Sa_{O_2} %	Pa_{O_2} mmHg	$\dot{V}_E$ $l \cdot min^{-1}$ ($/m^2$ BSA)
5 Normals	0·21	Control	12	—	(3·2)	—	7·41	38	97	—	(4·2)
(45)	0·12	Control	17	—	(3·5)	—	7·43	36	76	—	(4·9)
	0·21	Tris[b]	13	—	(3·4)	—	7·48	36	96	—	(4·6)
	0·12	Tris[b]	18	—	(3·7)	—	7·52	33	79	—	(4·6)
4 Normals	0·21	Control	12	—	(2·9)	—	7·42	39	96	—	(4·1)
(45)	0·12	Control	17	—	(3·3)	—	7·44	37	80	—	(4·8)
	0·21	NaH CO_3[b]	13	—	(3·4)	—	7·49	43	97	—	(4·1)
	0·12	NaH CO_3[b]	18	—	(3·8)	—	7·52	36	77	—	(4·9)
6 Bronchitis	0·21	Control	23	10	(2·9)	242	7·41	48	—	69	(5·6)
(49)	0·12–0·13	Control	29	11	(3·3)	298	7·45	42	—	42	—
	0·21	NH_4Cl[c]	22	9	(2·8)	260	7·35	47	—	72	(5·9)
	0·12–0·13	NH_4Cl[c]	27	9	(3·1)	323	7·39	42	—	46	—

[a] See page 135.
[b] Administered by i.v. infusion.
[c] Administered orally over 5–7 days.

Po_2 of different sections of the pulmonary circulation of the isolated perfused cat lung by altering the Po_2 of the alveolar gas and the inflowing blood and perfusing in a normal and reversed direction. In this way, they could distinguish between the arterial and venous contributions to the increased resistance caused by hypoxia. They found that the contribution from the pulmonary veins was negligible. The major contribution came from those vessels which equilibrated with alveolar gas and from the pulmonary arteries. Studies of the capillary red cell concentration in rapidly frozen dogs' lungs led Glazier and Murray[54] to the conclusion that the site of hypoxic vasoconstriction was in the pulmonary arteries.

Insight into the chief location of hypoxic pulmonary vasoconstriction is provided by morbid anatomical studies of people living at high altitude (Chap. 32, p. 487). In this population, there is an increase in the muscularization of the pulmonary arterioles and muscular pulmonary arteries. It may be deduced that the arterioles are certainly the site of vasoconstriction, while the muscularization of the muscular pulmonary arteries may be a direct effect of hypoxia or may simply be the result of the pulmonary hypertension caused by arteriolar constriction.

The vasoconstrictor effects of carbon dioxide also seem to occur in the pulmonary arterial tree. Daum and his colleagues[38] report that the increase in the wedge pressure which occurs during the breathing of carbon dioxide is accompanied by an increase in left atrial and right atrial pressure. The unilateral breathing of high concentrations of carbon dioxide had no effect on the wedge pressure of that side, there being a bilateral increase in the wedge pressure if the arterial pH fell substantially. Such observations eliminate the pulmonary veins as a site of vasoconstriction.

THE PHYSIOLOGICAL AND PATHOLOGICAL SIGNIFICANCE OF THE EFFECTS OF HYPOXIA AND HYPERCARBIA

The homeostatic importance of a mechanism by which the blood supply to an under-ventilated part of the lung may be diminished was first pointed out by von Euler and Liljestrand.[55] By this means, an unequal distribution of the ventilation : perfusion ratio with resultant systemic arterial hypoxaemia may be prevented (Chap. 36). Such a local, physiological mechanism has to operate within limits defined by the composition of the mixed venous blood and the inspired air according to the O_2–CO_2 diagram for blood and air combined (Fig. 36.6, p. 575).

It can be seen from the O_2–CO_2 diagram that a movement from a normal ventilation : perfusion ratio of 0·8 in the direction of a progressive diminution in ventilation occurs on the horizontal part of the diagram in which the greatest changes in Po_2 occur. To give an indication of the magnitude of the differences in Po_2 which are involved, we may take, as representative figures of the normal state of affairs, an alveolar Po_2 of 110 mmHg, a mixed venous Po_2 of 40 mmHg and a systemic arterial Po_2 of 100 mmHg. Looking at the relation between the alveolar Po_2 and the degree of pulmonary vasoconstriction, shown in Figure 30.4, it appears that the response of the pulmonary circulation to a diminution in alveolar Po_2 is initially

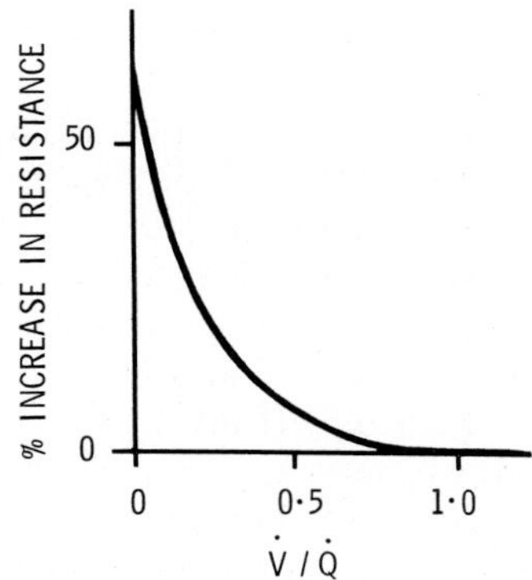

Fig. 30.5 Diagram relating the degree of pulmonary vasoconstriction to the local ventilation:perfusion ratio in a region of normal lung. The diagram has been calculated from the data of Figure 30.4 together with the O_2–CO_2 diagram (Fig. 36.6, p. 575). The vasomotor effects of P_{CO_2} are ignored.

feeble. On the other hand, vasoconstriction becomes rapidly stronger when the alveolar P_{O_2} approximates the normal mixed venous P_{O_2}. Such an arrangement might well be physiologically advantageous, allowing the local blood flow to remain relatively unaffected over a wide normal range of alveolar P_{O_2}, but effectively operating the mechanism of hypoxic vasoconstriction when the local ventilation becomes severely curtailed.

Returning to the O_2–CO_2 diagram (Fig. 36.6, p. 575) it is clear that the effects of hypoventilation on P_{O_2} are strikingly different in magnitude from those related to P_{CO_2}. From the point of normal ventilation:perfusion ratio in the direction of a progressive decrease in ventilation, there is relatively little change in P_{CO_2}. Normally the mixed venous P_{CO_2} is in the region of 45 mmHg while the alveolar and arterial P_{CO_2} is in the region of 40 mmHg. There is, therefore, so small a difference in P_{CO_2} between the mixed venous blood and the alveolar gas that a total lack of regional ventilation can raise the alveolar P_{CO_2} only some 5 mmHg. Judging by the effects of inhaling carbon dioxide in normal people,[5] this is unlikely to have much effect on the local blood vessels. However, against this must be set the possibility, substantiated by the work of Durand's laboratory,[18] that an increased alveolar P_{CO_2} potentiates the vasoconstrictive effect of alveolar hypoxia (p. 459) (Fig. 30.4).

Moving in the opposite direction along the O_2–CO_2 diagram (Fig. 36.6, p. 575) from a state of normal to a state of high ventilation : perfusion ratio gives rise to a rapid decrease in alveolar P_{CO_2} and a much less substantial increase in P_{O_2}. In either case the vasodilatory effects appear to be slight.

Since the O_2–CO_2 diagram carries figures for the ventilation : perfusion ratio (Fig. 36.6, p. 575), it is possible to relate the ventilation:perfusion ratio to the alveolar P_{O_2} under the defined conditions of inspired air and mixed venous blood. The relation between alveolar P_{O_2} and the degree of pulmonary vasoconstriction is given by Figure 30.4 and one may, therefore, derive from the two Figures a single diagram which indicates the relation between the ventilation : perfusion ratio and the degree of pulmonary vasoconstriction. This is shown in Figure 30.5. The curved shape of the O_2–CO_2 diagram (Fig. 36.6, p. 575) and the curved nature of the relation between pulmonary vasoconstriction and alveolar Po_2 (Fig. 30.4) make the relation between the ventilation : perfusion ratio and the degree of pulmonary vasoconstriction a highly curved one, such that constriction develops rapidly only at low levels of ventilation. If the alveolar Pco_2 potentiates the effect of hypoxia this increased sensitivity at low levels of ventilation will be enhanced.

Such considerations apply to the local control of the pulmonary circulation in response to local changes in ventilation. Under these circumstances the changes in alveolar Po_2 and Pco_2 are dictated by the composition of the mixed venous blood and inspired air and, so far, we have discussed the changes which might be anticipated in the presence of a normal mixed venous blood. In the presence of disease, on the other hand, there may be changes in the composition of the mixed venous blood which could, by changing the position of the mixed venous fixed point on the O_2–CO_2 diagram (Fig. 36.6, p. 575), have important effects on the control of pulmonary vasomotor tone. Thus the diminution in mixed venous Po_2 which accompanies cardiac failure could render the pulmonary circulation particularly susceptible to regional hypoventilation. Similarly, the high mixed venous Pco_2 which may accompany chronic obstructive airways disease will extend the operating range of local alveolar Pco_2 beyond the physiological.

The relation between the alveolar Po_2 and the pulmonary arterial resistance of the whole lung has not been explored in the same detail as is available from work

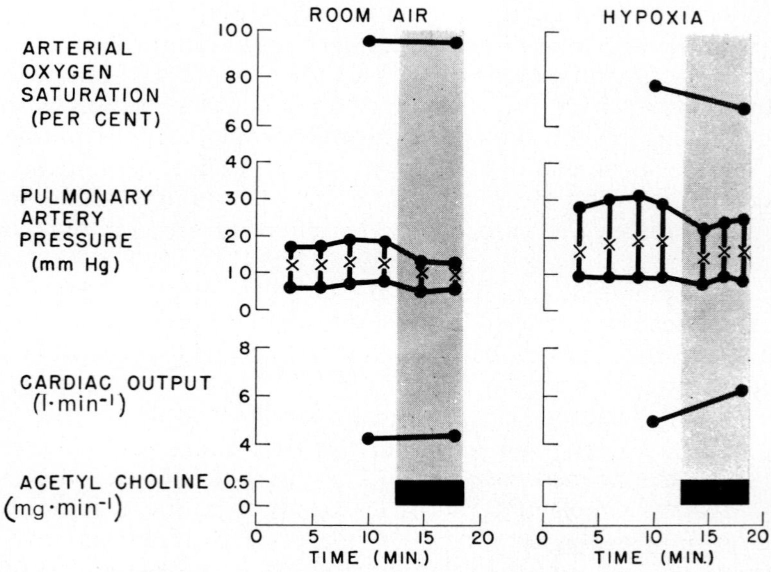

Fig. 30.6 The effects of hypoxia and the infusion of acetylcholine into the pulmonary artery in a patient who had had a total sympathectomy.[8]

with unilateral hypoxia. To some extent it could not be expected since it would be physiologically impossible to examine the effects of an alveolar Po_2 which, throughout both lungs, approached that of the mixed venous blood. Provided that the ventilation:perfusion ratio varies little throughout the lungs, it seems reasonable to suppose that the low levels of alveolar Po_2 which may occur in disease will have a global effect on the pulmonary circulation of the magnitude predicted from Figure 30.4.

In the presence of pulmonary disease, however, there may be a wide variation in the ventilation : perfusion ratio which is imposed by the structural abnormalities of the lung and airways. Under these circumstances, the highly curved nature of the relation between vasoconstriction and ventilation : perfusion ratio (Fig. 30.5) could lead to a considerable vasoconstriction of the under-ventilated areas which is not matched by a comparable vasodilatation in the over-ventilated areas. The result might be a nett vasoconstriction in excess of what would be predicted from the total ventilation:perfusion ratio or from the alveolar Po_2. Such theoretical speculations should, perhaps, not be pushed too far but it may be noted that the matter is complicated by the fact that the regional distribution of the pulmonary vascular resistance is arranged in parallel. In addition, because of the inhomogeneity of the ventilation: perfusion ratio (p. 569), the Po_2 measured in the systemic arterial blood of such patients will be considerably lower than the calculated alveolar Po_2.

MECHANISM OF ACTION OF HYPOXIC PULMONARY VASOCONSTRICTION

This is a subject which has tantalized physiologists for a number of years.[56,57] The action of both hypoxia and hypercarbia in the systemic circulation is a vasodilatory one and, in some strange way, this has been regarded as the normal while the response of the pulmonary circulation is abnormal and needs a special explanation. In the following review we shall have to draw more heavily than usual on experiments carried out on animals.

Humoral or Nervous Influences from Outside the Lung

The facts that hypoxic vasoconstriction can be restricted to one lung and that it can be demonstrated in isolated lungs effectively rule out the dependence of the response on the liberation of a vasoconstrictor substance into the systemic circulation. The same may be said for autonomic reflexes having their origin outside the lungs. Pulmonary hypertension can be evoked in the normal fashion by breathing hypoxic mixtures in patients with extensive sympathectomy[8] (Fig. 30.6). The severance of the nervous plexuses around the main bronchus and pulmonary vessels to a lung does not prevent the occurrence of local constriction during the administration of unilateral hypoxia.[13] Guanethidine, which causes a blockade of post-ganglionic sympathetic fibres, does not diminish the response to hypoxia in

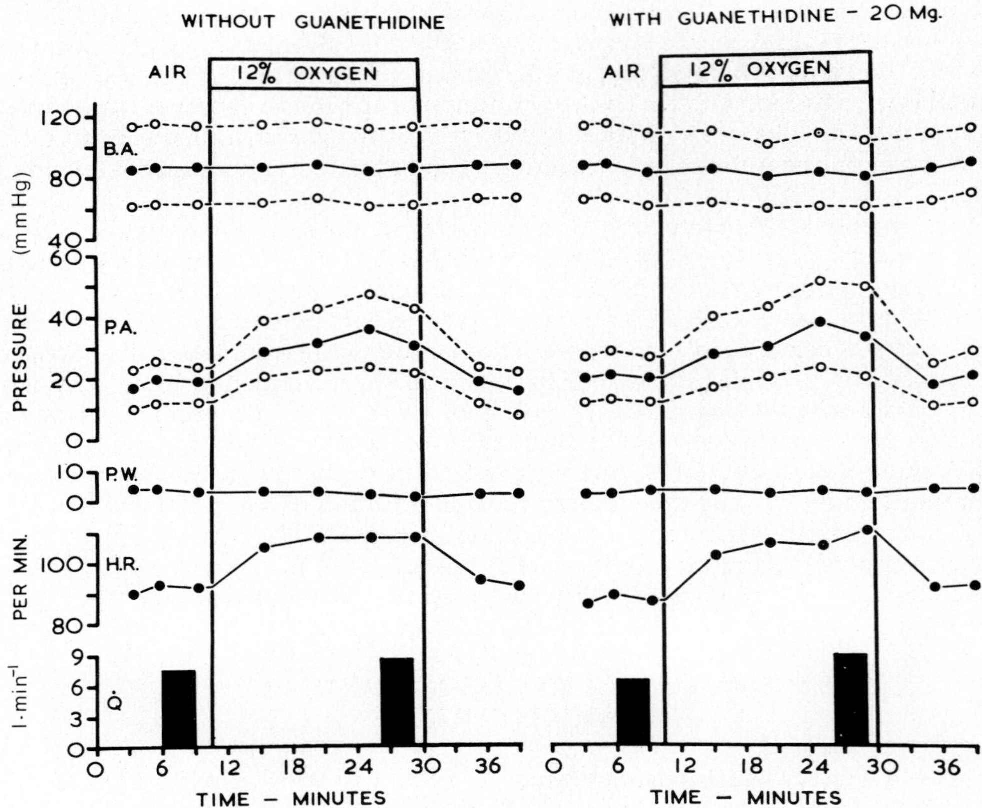

Fig. 30.7 The circulatory effects of hypoxia in a normal subject before and after giving 20 mg guanethidine intravenously.[7] B.A. = brachial arterial pressure. P.A. = pulmonary arterial pressure. P.W. = wedge pressure. H.R. = heart rate. Q = pulmonary blood flow. Systolic and diastolic pressures are represented by discontinuous lines, mean pressures by continuous lines.

normal people[7] (Fig. 30.7). Neither does hexamethonium.[58] There has, however, been one report that sympathectomy and thoracic sympathetic block prevented the development of pulmonary hypertension.[58]

Influence of Pulmonary Mechanics

Changes in alveolar pressure due to changes in compliance or airways resistance appear to play no part in the increased pulmonary vascular resistance due to hypoxia.[57]

Local Release of Vasoconstrictor Substance

A great deal of attention has been given to the possibility that the mechanism may involve the local release of a vasoconstrictor substance. If such is the case, it seems unlikely that the constrictor substance reaches the blood stream in any quantity since there is no transmission of the hypoxic response from one lung to a second lung perfused with the effluent of the first.[59,60]

Since the vasoconstrictor response is so much more sensitive to alveolar Po_2 than to mixed venous Po_2 a primary attack of hypoxia on some tissue component situated between the alveolus and the arterial wall has been widely considered to be likely. Such a possibility received support from the work of Lloyd[61] who showed that hypoxia caused contraction of isolated strips of pulmonary artery only when the adjacent lung tissue was left attached. It has, however, to be noted that the success of these experiments appeared to require the remarkably high concentration of 1 mg procaine/ml. More recent work has demonstrated that isolated strips of pulmonary artery initially relax during hypoxia but develop a contractile response when kept, preferably in a hypoxic environment.[62] Such a contractile response appeared to develop more rapidly if the strips of pulmonary artery were suspended in a fluorochemical with poor properties of solvation or in a humid gaseous environment.[63] In the presence of a humid gaseous environment, even aortic strips developed a contractile response.[63]

Among the components of the perivascular tissue, two have been proposed as likely primary sites for the action of hypoxia—the sympathetic nerve terminals which lie at the medial-adventitial border (p. 174) and mast cells.

Sympathetic Nerve Terminals

No liberation of adrenaline or noradrenaline into the blood could be demonstrated in man during hypoxia.[64,65] The infusion of noradrenaline did not exaggerate the response to hypoxia in man.[64] A number of contradictory results has been published concerning the effects of α- and β-blockade on hypoxic pulmonary vasoconstriction in animals. Where positive results of adrenergic blockade have been obtained they have consisted in an inhibition of the hypoxic effect by α-blockade and an enhancement by β-blockade.[66–72] All these studies were carried out with artificially perfused lungs or lobes, although in one[67] studies on complete animals also gave positive results. The negative results, on the other hand, have come mainly from experiments in which the lungs were being naturally perfused[73–75] although in one[76] a negative result was obtained with an artificially perfused lobe.

The results of depleting the sympathetic nerve terminals with reserpine have also been variable.[64,67,70,74] When it existed, the effect has been to weaken the vasoconstriction of hypoxia.[67,70]

We are unaware of any studies involving those drugs which inhibit the uptake of noradrenaline by sympathetic nerve terminals, the effect of which would be to enhance the hypoxic effect if it involved the release of noradrenaline.

Mast Cells

Mast cells are at present the popular candidate for an intermediary rôle in the response to hypoxia. They are found distributed around the blood vessels of the lung[77] but not confined to this location.[78]

Haas and Bergofsky[77] investigated the effects of 60–90 minutes' exposure to 12·5 per cent oxygen on the perivascular mast cells of rats' lungs. They found no alteration in the numbers of perivascular mast cells but that the degree of granulation of the cells was less ($P < 0{\cdot}05$). (We avoid the term 'degranulation' which presupposes a course of events.) Our own studies have not confirmed these findings in acute hypoxia.[79]

Kay, Waymire and Grover[80] exposed rats to a barometric pressure of 380 mmHg for a period of 20 days and found a distinct increase in the numbers of mast cells in the lungs which was related to right ventricular weight. More recently,[79] we have confirmed this observation and found that the increase in the numbers of mast cells affected those in the alveolar septa and around blood vessels but not those around bronchi. There was no alteration in the degree of granulation.

Mast cells contain a number of vasoactive substances, including 5-hydroxytryptamine and histamine.[81] Of these, the evidence suggests that 5-hydroxytryptamine is not involved in the hypoxic response.[52,69,71,72,82–85]

Some authors have found a release of histamine from animals' lungs during hypoxia;[77,86,87] others have not.[88] As mentioned above (p. 469) no direct transmission of vasoconstriction has been demonstrated when the effluent of a hypoxic lung has been passed through a second lung.

Hypoxia has been shown to cause an *in vitro* release of histamine from peritoneal mast cells in the rat.[77] The treatment of dogs with disodium cromoglycate, which prevents the release of histamine from mast cells, has prevented hypoxic pulmonary vasoconstriction.[89]

Hauge[84] found an inhibition of hypoxic pulmonary vasoconstriction in rats by five different antihistamine drugs. Susmano and Carleton[85] observed such an inhibition with chlorphenyramine but not with two other antihistamine drugs in dogs. Susmano[90] reported a reduction in the effect of hypoxia on the pulmonary arterial pressure in eight humans given chlorphenyramine. There was no measurement of the cardiac output or wedge pressure.

The drug '48/80' releases histamine from tissues. It has been found to cause a diminution in the effect of hypoxia in the rat[71,91] and the cat[92] but not in the calf.[93] In one study[94] '48/80' inhibited the effect of hypoxia in the cat but did not reduce the pulmonary concentration of histamine. On the other hand, Polymyxin B reduced the pulmonary concentration of histamine but had no influence on the effects of hypoxia.[94]

A great difficulty in accepting histamine as the mediator of hypoxic pulmonary vasoconstriction is that its effect on the pulmonary circulation has not universally been shown to be constrictor. Aviado,[57] after an extensive review of the literature, concluded that in the perfused lung histamine caused vasoconstriction, while in the intact lung it caused vasodilatation. This recalls a similar divergency in the effects of sympathetic blockade between perfused and intact lungs (p. 469). The effect of histamine has been reported to be vasodilatory in the lung of the foetal lamb[68] and the neonatal calf[93] both of which are highly sensitive to hypoxia. Shaw[95] found that histamine reversed the pulmonary vasoconstriction caused by hypoxia in the rat and cat. Finally, since our concern is with the human pulmonary circulation, it has to be noted that in man the effects of histamine on the pulmonary circulation are vasodilator (Chap. 13, p. 198).

Prostaglandins

A recent publication suggests that prostaglandins may play a rôle in hypoxic pulmonary vasoconstriction.[96] Investigations in man, however, do not support this suggestion. Pulmonary hypertension due to hypoxia was not affected by the previous administration of aspirin and indomethacin which inhibit prostaglandin synthesis.[97] There was no increase in the concentration of prostaglandins in the pulmonary arterial or systemic arterial blood during hypoxia and no increase in the blood concentration of dihydroketoprostaglandins.[97]

Direct Effect of Hypoxia on Pulmonary Vascular Smooth Muscle

The idea that the response of the peripheral pulmonary arteries to hypoxia required the mediation of some perivascular component rose out of the knowledge that lowering alveolar Po_2 was so much more effective than lowering mixed venous Po_2 in causing vasoconstriction. There is, on the other hand, evidence that the Po_2 of the blood in the arterioles and even the muscular pulmonary arteries is influenced by the composition of the alveolar gas. If a cardiac catheter with a platinum electrode at its tip is wedged in the periphery of the pulmonary arterial tree, it is found to respond within one second when hydrogen is inhaled.[98-100] A similar rapid response to the inhalation of oxygen occurs when the electrode is used polarographically.[98,100] In rapidly frozen cats' lungs, Staub[101] found evidence that the saturation of the haemoglobin in arterial vessels with a diameter less than 200 μm was influenced by the composition of the alveolar gas.

Since the arterioles and possibly the muscular pulmonary arteries seem to be the site of vasoconstriction with hypoxia (p. 462) the fact that their contents and walls are so directly influenced by the composition of the alveolar gas renders the existence of an extravascular intermediary no longer theoretically necessary. We need to explore, therefore, the possibility that hypoxia exerts its effect directly on the arterial smooth muscle cell.

Irrespective of whether hypoxia acts directly on the smooth muscle cell or via an intermediary, its primary intracellular effect is presumably on the activity of the respiratory chain and, thereby, on the rate of phosphorylation of ADP to ATP. The oxygen atom acts as the ultimate acceptor of electrons in the intracellular process of oxidation of hydrogen. It stands at the end of the respiratory chain through which the energy liberated by electron flow is converted into a biologically useful form by the phosphorylation of ADP. Cytochrome oxidase, which is the last link on the respiratory chain, has a remarkably low requirement for oxygen and the supply of oxygen to the respiratory chain does not become rate-limiting for oxidative phosphorylation until the Po_2 reaches 2–3 mmHg. In the cell, the diffusion gradient for oxygen across the cytoplasm has to be added to this limiting condition. However, in a cell of the size found in vascular smooth muscle and in the presence of cytoplasmic myoglobin, this would not add greatly to the minimal effective Po_2 for oxidative phosphorylation. To such a theoretical lack of sensitivity of the intracellular mechanisms immediately dependent on oxygen supply must be added the likelihood that the entire tissue between the alveolus and the interior of the pulmonary arteriole is normally subject to a Po_2 in the region of 100 mmHg. Even if the intracellular Po_2 of the oxygen-sensing cells were that of mixed venous blood (about 40 mmHg) it would be unlikely to have a substantial effect on oxidative phosphorylation, judged by the *in vitro* data available from other tissues. Thus, clearly, somewhere in this anatomical region, a cell is capable of sensing changes in Po_2 to which its immediate intracellular mechanisms of oxidation seem likely to be insensitive. Although, biochemically, such a state of affairs may be unexpected, physiologically it is not so surprising, since the systemic arterial chemoreceptors appear to function under similar circumstances. The blood flow in the carotid body, for instance, is large relative to the oxygen consumption so that the arteriovenous difference in oxygen content is small. From the point of view of the blood it is advantageous to have a receptor sensitive to Po_2 working on the horizontal part of the dissociation curve for haemoglobin (p. 568) where changes in Po_2 are large relative to changes in the content of oxygen.

If the respiratory chain is relatively insensitive to the sort of changes in Po_2 which may be anticipated in the region of the alveolus and its adjacent tissue, the mechanism by which alveolar hypoxia exerts its intracellular effect will need to involve some biochemical system of amplification. Such amplification could occur in the process of production or in the process of utilization of ATP. In the process of production of ATP, amplification could involve high rates of ATP hydrolysis or uncoupling of oxidative phosphorylation. In the process of utilization, amplification might take place at some enzyme activity which is dependent on a high ATP concentration or because of allosteric control by the phosphorylation potential such as occurs in the glycolytic chain at phosphofructokinase. We have no knowledge of the relative dependence on ATP of those enzyme activities in pulmonary arterial smooth muscle which might be involved in the process of contraction. In the myocardium, the ATP concentration at half-maximal activity (Michaelis constant) is about a thousand times higher for the calcium-stimulated ATPase of the sarcolemma and for sarcolemmal sodium : potassium ATPase than it is for myofibrillar ATPase or for various activities of the sarcoplasmic reticulum.[102] In this tissue the two sarcolemmal activities appear normally to be operating near their Michaelis constants under which conditions they would be particularly susceptible to small changes in ATP concentration and a mechanism of amplification would exist. An inhibition of the calcium pump would directly increase the cytoplasmic concentration of calcium ions, while an inhibition of the sodium pump would indirectly have the same effect. Thus it is neither difficult nor unrealistic to imagine mechanisms whereby small decreases in cytoplasmic ATP concentration increase the nett transport of calcium ions across the cell membrane or increase membrane permeability to calcium while remaining sufficient to sustain contractile activity. Should that happen in pulmonary arterial smooth muscle, contraction could follow the direct action of hypoxia on the muscle cells.

In the smooth muscle of taenia coli, contraction could be caused by hypoxia, under which conditions there was a rapid influx of calcium ions but no decrease in calcium loss.[103,104] Hypoxia caused a reversible loss of potassium and gain of sodium by strips of cats' pulmonary arteries but not by strips of pulmonary veins or systemic arteries.[105]

The extracellular ionic composition affects the influence of hypoxia. Depolarization of the smooth muscle of strips of guinea-pigs' pulmonary arteries by solutions high in potassium caused contraction. Solutions with a high concentration of potassium also caused vasoconstriction in isolated lungs[105] and this was reported to increase the effects of hypoxia. This is similar to the observation that the total degree of contraction of pulmonary arterial strips under the influence of noradrenaline was increased during depolarization with high concentrations of extracellular potassium.[106] Such observations are, however, susceptible to a number of interpretations.[107] The intravenous injection of magnesium chloride reduced the effect of hypoxia on the pulmonary circulation in dogs, but had itself no effect on the pulmonary vascular resistance.[108] In this respect it may be noted that the magnesium concentration of the pulmonary artery has been reported to be lower than that in the pulmonary veins or systemic arteries.[109]

Influences from Circulating Blood

Although hypoxic pulmonary vasoconstriction does not appear to be mediated by the release of a humoral agent from a distant organ into the blood stream, there is some evidence that one or more constituent of the blood may be necessary for its operation. Duke and Vane[110] were unable to obtain hypoxic vasoconstriction in isolated perfused cats' lungs when the perfusion circuit was partly made from polyvinylchloride. Normal pulmonary vascular responses were retained for noradrenaline, 5-hydroxytryptamine and prostaglandin $F_{2\alpha}$. Berkov[111] perfused isolated rats' lungs with albumin and electrolyte solution under which conditions no effect of hypoxia occurred unless angiotensin II was present in the perfusate. The quantities of angiotensin II necessary were so small that, in themselves, they had no constrictor effect on the pulmonary circulation. Opposing these reports are the observations by Gorsky and Lloyd[112] that, in an isolated lobe of canine lung, the presence of plasma in the perfusate had only a small and non-specific effect on the responsiveness to hypoxia.

It is of interest at this point to note the observation[113] that patients with alcoholic cirrhosis of the liver fail to develop pulmonary hypertension during hypoxia although there is no proof that the mechanism takes place through alterations in the blood.

PATHOLOGICAL EFFECTS OF HYPEROXIA ON THE PULMONARY CAPILLARY BED

There is now extensive evidence to convince that serious lung disease can occur in patients breathing very high concentrations of oxygen at atmospheric pressure.[114–118] The earliest effects are exudative histological changes of congestion of pulmonary capillaries, intra-alveolar haemorrhages, and fibrinous exudates into the alveoli.[114] Such prominent intra-alveolar exudate of fibrin results in the laying down of 'hyaline membranes' on the walls of alveoli, alveolar ducts, and respiratory bronchioles. Later, the microscopic changes are proliferative in nature, comprising a pronounced hyperplasia of alveolar cells, probably granular pneumocytes, followed by fibroblastic proliferation.[114] As a result of the thickening of the alveolar walls by cellular and fibrous proliferation and by adherent hyaline membranes hypoxaemia develops. Sections may superficially resemble collapsed lung but in that condition reticulin stains show the alveolar septa to be thin whereas in the hyperoxic lung they are thick.[115] The irritant action of oxygen excess on the alveolar walls leads to proliferation of pulmonary capillaries rather in the manner of granulation tissue to form intra-alveolar tufts. Prominent endothelial cells line these capillary tufts.

The histological changes cause hyperoxic lungs to assume a haemorrhagic and beefy appearance. They are deeply congested, inelastic and non-crepitant. Firm in consistence, they retain their shape without collapse. Only small amounts of fluid can be scraped from their surface which may show small pink-grey areas of solidification due to fibrous organization.[114]

Using hyaline membranes and proliferative pneumonitis of the type described above as histological evidence of pulmonary oxygen toxicity, Sevitt[119] recently related the lung changes in 21 patients in the Birmingham Accident Hospital who died after oxygen therapy with the intensity and duration of oxygen administration. He found diffuse pneumonitis inducing hypoxaemia in ten subjects and in nine of them it was associated with the breathing of high concentrations of oxygen (60 to 100 per cent) for at least two days. In at least eight subjects the pneumonitis contributed to death and two others who survived for weeks had extensively fibrosed lungs. The breathing of 40 per cent oxygen for a sufficient time seems to be a threshold for dangerous lung effects.[119] Those breathing oxygen concentrations between 25 and 40 per cent for days developed either sub-clinical focal lung lesions or had no relevant lung changes.

The suggestion that intermittent positive-pressure ventilation is a cause of this serious disturbance of the pulmonary capillary bed has been undermined by experiments in goats[120] and there is now little doubt that the basis for the condition is oxygen toxicity. The potentially lethal effects of this gas were recognized in the last century.[121] Birds, mice, rats and guinea-pigs exposed to 0·7 to 0·8 atmosphere of oxygen died within a few days with grossly congested lungs and changes like pneumonia whereas exposure to 0·4 atmosphere of oxygen for a week was innocuous.

Clinically, there is now widespread recognition of diffuse pneumonitis induced by hyperoxia and characterized by a progressive reduction in pulmonary compliance and vital capacity with the complication of hypoxaemia. Less familiar is the development of focal lesions produced by inspired oxygen concentrations less than or with a duration of exposure shorter than those associated with diffuse changes.[119] Sevitt[119] found that eight of his nine cases with diffuse lung changes had been breathing concentrations above 60 or 80 per cent for at least two days. On the other hand, three of the six subjects with focal changes had been given oxygen concentrations between 25 and 40 per cent for six days or longer. He is of the opinion that his findings are consistent with the lack of ill effects in astronauts of the United States who are said to breathe pure oxygen at one-third of an atmosphere for prolonged periods.

REFERENCES

1. Motley, H. L., Cournand, A., Werkö, L., Himmelstein, A. & Dresdale, D. (1947) *Amer. J. Physiol.*, **150**, 315.
2. Fishman, A. P., McClement, J., Himmelstein, A. & Cournand, A. (1952) *J. Clin. Invest.*, **31**, 770.
3. Westcott, R. N., Fowler, N. O., Scott, R. C., Hauenstein, V. D. & McGuire, J. (1951) *J. Clin. Invest.*, **30**, 957.
4. Doyle, J. T., Wilson, J. S. & Warren, J. V. (1952) *Circulation*, **5**, 263.
5. Fishman, A. P., Fritts, H. W., Jn. & Cournand, A. (1960) *Circulation*, **22**, 204.
6. Fritts, H. W., Jn., Odell, J. E., Harris, P., Braunwald, E. W. & Fishman, A. P. (1960) *Circulation*, **22**, 216.
7. Harris, P., Bishop, J. M. & Segel, N. (1961) *Clin. Sci.*, **21**, 295.
8. Fritts, H. W., Jn., Harris, P., Clauss, R. H., Odell, J. E. & Cournand, A. (1958) *J. Clin. Invest.*, **37**, 99.
9. Yu, P. N., Glick, G., Schreiner, B. F., Jn. & Murphy, G. W. (1963) *Circulation*, **27**, 541.
10. Oakley, C., Glick, G., Luria, M. N., Schreiner, B. F., Jn. & Yu, P. N. (1962) *Circulation*, **26**, 917.
11. Hertz, C. W. (1956) *Klin. Wschr.*, **34**, 472 and 532.
12. Fishman, A. P., Himmelstein, A., Fritts, H. W., Jn. & Cournand, A. (1955) *J. Clin. Invest.*, **34**, 637.
13. Himmelstein, A., Harris, P., Fritts, H. W., Jn. & Cournand, A. (1958) *J. Thorac. Surg.*, **36**, 369.
14. Defares, J. G., Lundin, G., Arborelius, M., Jn., Stromblod, R. & Svanberg, L. (1960) *J. Appl. Physiol.*, **15**, 169.
15. Arborelius, M., Jn., Lundin, G., Svanberg, L. & Defares, J. C. (1960) *J. Appl. Physiol.*, **15**, 595.
16. Arborelius, M., Jn. (1965) *Scand. J. Clin. Lab. Invest.*, **17**, 257.
17. Arborelius, M., Jn. (1969) *J. Appl. Physiol.*, **26**, 101.
18. Durand, J., Leroy-Ladurie, M. & Ranson-Bitker, B. (1970) *Progr. Resp. Res.*, **5**, 156.
19. Lopez-Majano, V., Wagner, H. N., Jn., Twining, R. H., Tow, D. E. & Chernick, V. (1966) *Circulat. Res.*, **18**, 550.
20. Lopez-Majano, V., Wagner, H. N., Jn., Twining, R. H. & Chernick, V. (1968) *Amer. Rev. Resp. Dis.*, **96**, 1190.
21. Lopez-Majano, V. (1970) *Progr. Resp. Res.*, **5**, 188.
22. Barratt-Boyes, B. G. & Wood, E. H. (1957) *J. Appl. Physiol.*, **11**, 129.
23. Barratt-Boyes, B. G. & Wood, E. H. (1958) *J. Lab. Clin. Med.*, **51**, 72.
24. Dressler, S. H., Slonim, A. B., Balchum, O. J., Bronfin, G. J. & Ravin, A. (1952) *J. Clin. Invest.*, **31**, 807.
25. McGregor, M., Bothwell, T. H., Zion, M. M. & Bradlow, B. A. (1953) *Amer. Heart J.*, **46**, 186.
26. Bateman, M., Davidson, L., Donald, K. W. & Harris, P. (1962) *Clin. Sci.*, **22**, 223.
27. Burchell, H. B., Swan, H. J. C. & Wood, E. H. (1953) *Circulation*, **8**, 681.

28. Marshall, H. W., Swan, H. J. C. & Wood, E. H. (1957) *Fed. Proc.*, **16**, 84.
29. Heath, D., Helmholtz, H. F., Jn., Burchell, H. B., Dushane, J. W. & Edwards, J. E. (1958) *Circulation*, **18**, 1155.
30. Shepherd, J. T., Semler, H., Helmholtz, H. F., Jn. & Wood, E. H. (1959) *Circulation*, **20**, 381.
31. Swan, H. J. C., Burchell, H. B. & Wood, E. H. (1959) *Circulation*, **20**, 66.
32. Bishop, J. M., Harris, P., Bateman, M. & Davidson, L. A. G. (1961) *J. Clin. Invest.*, **40**, 105.
33. Bishop, J. M., Harris, P., Bateman, M. & Raine, J. M. (1962) *Clin. Sci.*, **22**, 53.
34. Fishman, A. P., Fritts, H. W., Jn. & Cournand, A. (1960) *Circulation*, **22**, 220.
35. Paul, G., Varnauskas, E., Forsberg, S.-A., Sannerstedt, R. & Widimsky, J. (1964) *Clin. Sci.*, **26**, 111.
36. Rokseth, R. (1966) *Scand. J. Clin. Lab. Invest.*, **18**, Suppl. 90.
37. Kilburn, K. H., Asmundsson, T., Britt, R. C. & Cardon, R. (1969) *Circulation*, **39**, 639.
38. Daum, S., Krofta, K., Jahn, E., Nikodymová, L. & Švorčík, Č. (1970) *Progr. Resp. Res.*, **5**, 166.
39. Tartulier, M., Deyrieux, F., Anterion, H., Tourniaire, A. & Dechamp, C. (1960) *Anesthet. Analg.*, **17**, 78.
40. Rankin, J., McNeill, R. S. & Forster, R. E. (1960) *J. Appl. Physiol.*, **15**, 543.
41. Richardson, D. W., Wasserman, A. J. & Patterson, J. L., Jn. (1961) *J. Clin. Invest.*, **40**, 31.
42. Suutarinen, T. (1966) *Acta Physiol. Scand.*, **67**, Suppl. 266.
43. Twining, R. H., Lopez-Majano, V., Chernick, V., Wagner, H. N., Jn. & Dutton, R. E. (1968) *Bull. Johns Hopk. Hosp.*, **123**, 95.
44. Harris, P., Segel, N., Green, I. & Housley, E. (1968) *Cardiovasc. Res.*, **2**, 84.
45. Bergofsky, E. H., Lehr, D. E. & Fishman, A. P. (1962) *J. Clin. Invest.*, **41**, 1492.
46. Enson, Y., Giuntini, C., Lewis, M. L., Morris, T. Q., Ferrer, M. I. & Harvey, R. M. (1964) *J. Clin. Invest.*, **43**, 1146.
47. Aber, G. M., Bayley, T. J. & Bishop, J. M. (1963) *Clin. Sci.*, **25**, 171.
48. Harvey, R. M., Enson, Y., Betti, R., Lewis, M. L., Rochester, D. F. & Ferrer, M. I. (1967) *Circulation*, **35**, 1019.
49. Housley, E., Clarke, S. W., Hedworth-Whitty, R. B. & Bishop, J. M. (1970) *Cardiovasc. Res.*, **4**, 482.
50. Waddell, W. J. & Bates, R. G. (1969) *Physiol. Rev.*, **49**, 285.
51. Linde, L. M., Simmons, D. H. & Shapiro, B. J. (1968) *Bull. Physiopath. Resp.*, **4**, 7.
52. Bergofsky, E. H. (1974) *Amer. J. Med.*, **57**, 378.
53. Bergofsky, E. H. & Haas, F. (1968) *Bull. Physio-Path. Resp.*, **4**, 91.
54. Glazier, J. B. & Murray, J. F. (1971) *J. Clin. Invest.*, **50**, 2550.
55. Euler, U. S. von & Liljestrand, G. (1946) *Acta Physiol. Scand.*, **12**, 301.
56. Fishman, A. P. (1961) *Physiol. Rev.*, **41**, 214.
57. Aviado, D. M. (1965) *The Lung Circulation*. Pergamon.
58. Judson, W. E., Hollander, W. & Arrowood, J. G. (1954) *J. Clin. Invest.*, **33**, 946.
59. Duke, H. N. (1954) *J. Physiol.*, **125**, 373.
60. Hauge, A. (1969) *Acta Physiol. Scand.*, **76**, 121.
61. Lloyd, T. C., Jn. (1968) *J. Appl. Physiol.*, **25**, 560.
62. Detar, R. & Gellai, M. (1971) *Amer. J. Physiol.*, **221**, 1791.
63. Lloyd, T. C., Jn. (1970) *J. Appl. Physiol.*, **28**, 566.
64. Goldring, R. M., Turino, G. M., Cohen, G., Jameson, A. G., Bass, B. G. & Fishman, A. P. (1962) *J. Clin. Invest.*, **41**, 1211.
65. Flohr, H. (1968) *Bull. Physiopath. Resp.*, **4**, 79.
66. Nisell, O. (1950) *Acta Physiol. Scand.*, **21**, Suppl. 73.
67. Brutsaert, D. (1964) *Arch. Int. Physiol. Biochem.*, **72**, 395.
68. Cassin, S., Dawes, G. S. & Ross, B. B. (1964) *J. Physiol.*, **171**, 80.
69. Lloyd, T. C., Jn. (1964) *J. Appl. Physiol.*, **19**, 1086.
70. Barer, G. R. (1966) *J. Physiol.*, **186**, 97P.
71. Barer, G. R. & McCurrie, J. (1969) *Quart. J. Exper. Physiol.*, **54**, 156.
72. Porcelli, R. J. & Bergofsky, E. H. (1973) *J. Appl. Physiol.*, **34**, 483.

73. Thilenius, O. G., Candiolo, B. M. & Beug, J. L. (1967) *Amer. J. Physiol.*, **213**, 990.
74. Silove, E. D. & Grover, R. F. (1968) *J. Clin. Invest.*, **47**, 274.
75. Malik, A. B. & Kidd, B. S. L. (1973) *Resp. Physiol.*, **19**, 96.
76. Lloyd, T. C., Jn. (1966) *J. Appl. Physiol.*, **21**, 1351.
77. Haas, F. & Bergofsky, E. H. (1972) *J. Clin. Invest.*, **51**, 3154.
78. Williams, A., Heath, D., Smith, P. & Kay, J. M. (1975) Unpublished data.
79. Williams, A., Heath, D., Kay, J. M., Smith, P. & Harris, P. (1976) *Thorax*, submitted for publication.
80. Kay, J. M., Waymire, J. C. & Grover, R. F. (1974) *Amer. J. Physiol.*, **226**, 178.
81. Selye, H. (1965) *The Mast Cells*. Butterworths.
82. Duke, H. N. (1957) *J. Physiol.*, **135**, 45.
83. Brutsaert, D. (1965) *Exper. Med. Surg.*, **23**, 13.
84. Hauge, A. (1968) *Circulat. Res.*, **22**, 371.
85. Susmano, A. & Carleton, R. A. (1971) *J. Appl. Physiol.*, **31**, 531.
86. Aviado, D. M., Samanek, M. & Folle, L. E. (1966) *Arch. Environ. Health*, **12**, 705.
87. Boileau, J. C., Campeau, L. & Biron, P. (1970) *Can. J. Physiol. Pharmacol.*, **48**, 681.
88. Brashear, R. E., Martin, R. R. & Ross, J. C. (1970) *Amer. J. Med. Sci.*, **260**, 21.
89. Grover, R. F. & Kay, J. M. (1972) Personal communication.
90. Susmano, A. (1974) *J. Clin. Invest.*, **53**, 80a.
91. Hauge, A. & Melmon, K. L. (1968) *Circulat. Res.*, **22**, 385.
92. Hauge, A. & Staub, N. C. (1969) *J. Appl. Physiol.*, **26**, 693.
93. Silove, E. D. & Simcha, A. J. (1973) *J. Appl. Physiol.*, **35**, 830.
94. Dawson, C. A., Delano, F. A., Hamilton, L. H. & Stekiel, W. J. (1974) *J. Appl. Physiol.*, **37**, 670.
95. Shaw, J. W. (1971) *J. Physiol.*, **215**, 34P.
96. Said, S. I., Yoshida, T., Kitamura, S. & Vreim, C. (1974) *J. Clin. Invest.*, **53**, 69a.
97. Even, P., Dray, F., Ruff, F., Duroux, P., Santais, M. C. & Sors, H. (1975) In *Lung Metabolism*, ed. Junod, A. & de Haller, R. Academic Press.
98. Jameson, A. G. (1964) *J. Appl. Physiol.*, **19**, 448.
99. Gasteazoro, G., Hirose, T., Stopak, J., Casale, J. & Schaffer, A. I. (1963) *Amer. J. Cardiol.*, **12**, 240.
100. Sobol, B. J., Bottex, G., Emirgil, C. & Gissen, H. (1963) *Circulat. Res.*, **13**, 71.
101. Staub, N. (1961) *Fed. Proc.*, **20**, 107.
102. Harris, P. (1975) *Europ. J. Cardiol.* In press.
103. Bauer, H., Goodford, P. J. & Hütter, J. (1965) *J. Physiol.*, **176**, 163.
104. Goodford, P. J. (1965) *J. Physiol.*, **176**, 180.
105. Bergofsky, E. H. & Holtzman, S. (1967) *Circulat. Res.*, **20**, 506.
106. Bergofsky, E. H. (1968) In *The Pulmonary Circulation and Interstitial Space*, ed. Fishman, A. P. & Hecht, H. H. page 269. University of Chicago Press.
107. Somlyo, A. P. & Somlyo, A. V. (1968) *Pharmacol. Rev.*, **20**, 197.
108. Cropp, G. J. A. (1968) *J. Appl. Physiol.*, **24**, 755.
109. Burch, G. E., Lazzara, R. K. & Yun, T. K. (1965) *Proc. Soc. Exper. Biol. Med.*, **118**, 581.
110. Duke, H. N. & Vane, J. R. (1968) *Lancet*, **ii**, 21.
111. Berkov, S. (1974) *Circulat. Res.*, **35**, 256.
112. Gorsky, B. H. & Lloyd, T. C., Jn. (1967) *J. Appl. Physiol.*, **23**, 683.
113. Daoud, F. S., Reeves, J. T. & Schaefer, J. W. (1972) *J. Clin. Invest.*, **51**, 1076.
114. Nash, G., Blennerhassett, J. B. & Pontoppidan, H. (1967) *New Engl. J. Med.*, **276**, 368.
115. Pratt, P. C. (1965) *Ann. N.Y. Acad. Sci.*, **121**, 809.
116. Cederberg, A., Hellsten, S. & Miörner, G. (1965) *Acta Path. Microbiol. Scand.*, **64**, 450.
117. Soloway, H. B., Castillo, Y. & Martin, A. M. (1968) *Ann. Surg.*, **168**, 937.
118. Burrows, F. G. O. & Edwards, J. M. (1970) *Brit. J. Radiol.*, **43**, 848.
119. Sevitt, S. (1974) *J. Clin. Path.*, **27**, 21.
120. Nash, G., Bowen, J. A. & Langlinais, P. C. (1971) *Arch. Path.*, **91**, 234.
121. Smith, J. L. (1899) *J. Physiol. (London)*, **24**, 19.

31. Chemoreceptors and the Pulmonary Circulation

Glomic tissue is found in the carotid bodies, the glomus jugulare and other sites throughout the body and is generally accepted as subserving a chemoreceptor function. According to Krahl[1] there is a chemoreceptor associated with each branchial arch and its derivatives. Thus, the glomus jugulare represents the second arch, the carotid bodies the third, the aortic glomera the fourth and the aortico pulmonary bodies the fifth arch which fails to persist.[1,2] Each glomus receives its blood and nerve supply from derivatives of its parent branchial arch. The carotid bodies, for example, are supplied by blood from one or other of the carotid arteries near the bifurcation in the neck and are innervated by the glosso-pharyngeal nerve. According to Krahl[1,2] there is a glomus of the sixth branchial arch which might be expected to subserve a chemoreceptor function in association with its vascular system, namely, the pulmonary circulation (Chap. 2). He called this the 'glomus pulmonale'.

The 'Glomus Pulmonale'

Krahl[1,2] described the presence of a nodule of glomic tissue at a fairly constant site just distal and caudal to the bifurcation of the pulmonary trunk. We have been able to confirm this[3] (Figs 31.1 and 31.2) but we do not accept that this is a true 'glomus pulmonale' receiving its blood supply from the pulmonary trunk and acting as a chemoreceptor for the pulmonary circulation. Our studies support the view of Becker[4] that the artery supplying this glomus is one of the intertruncal branches of the coronary arteries passing up between the ascending aorta and pulmonary trunk to supply the nodule of glomic tissue in the bifurcation of the pulmonary trunk. We determined the blood supply of this glomus in a 32 week old stillbirth and a male child aged 3 years by serial sections.[5] We also carried out latex injection studies in rats.[5] In both investigations we were able to confirm the view of Becker that the so-called 'glomus pulmonale' receives a systemic arterial supply via the intertruncal arteries. It is more likely to be one of the coronary group of aortico-pulmonary bodies merely lying in the adventitia of the pulmonary trunk.

Pulmonary Venous Chemoreceptors

Glomic tissue is also found closely applied to the small pulmonary veins and, in contradistinction to the glomus at the bifurcation of the pulmonary trunk, this appears to derive its blood supply from the pulmonary circulation. Such perivenous nodules are small, measuring some $1{\cdot}0 \times 0{\cdot}6$ mm in diameter, and are associated with pulmonary venules about 100 μm in diameter.[6] If such nodules of glomic tissue are sought carefully, they will be found from time to time in routine sections

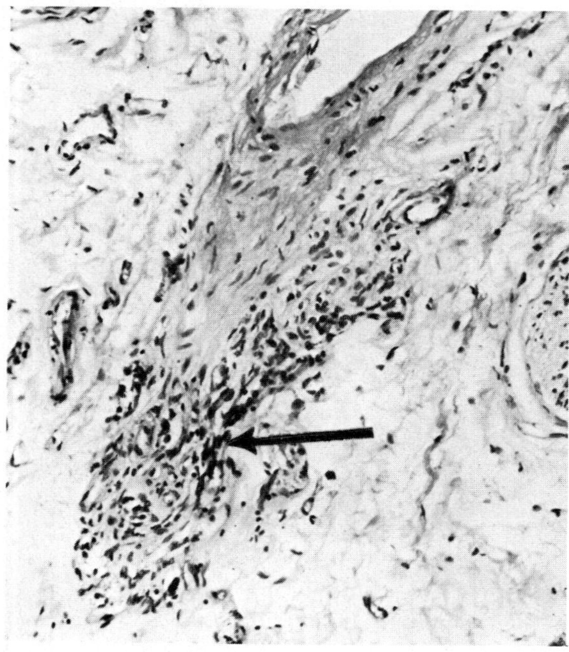

Fig. 31.1 Longitudinal section of a small artery entering the adventitia of the pulmonary trunk of a man aged 56 years, who died of myocardial ischaemia due to coronary occlusion. It terminates in a nodule of glomic tissue (arrow). This nodule has been termed by Krahl the 'glomus pulmonale'. (Haematoxylin & eosin, × 150)

of lungs from necropsy taken for histopathology[6] (Figs 31.3 and 31.4). Multiple nodules of glomic tissue of this type appear to have first been described by Korn and his associates[7] who regarded them as multiple small tumours of chemoreceptor tissue, the chemodectoma. Other authors are not so certain of their nature and accept that they may be neoplastic, hamartomatous or merely hyperplastic.[8] Larger chemodectomas occur as isolated tumours in the lung[9,10]; they have the typical cytological features of glomic cells arranged in characteristic cell clusters or 'Zellballen'. It is of interest to note that such chemodectomas have also been reported as occurring in proximity to pulmonary veins.[10] We are not aware of any work elucidating the functional significance of such pulmonary venous chemoreceptors.

The Carotid Bodies

As well as recognizing the existence of glomic tissue in close association with pulmonary arteries and veins it should be appreciated that glomic tissue monitoring blood in the systemic circulation shows pronounced changes in states of chronic

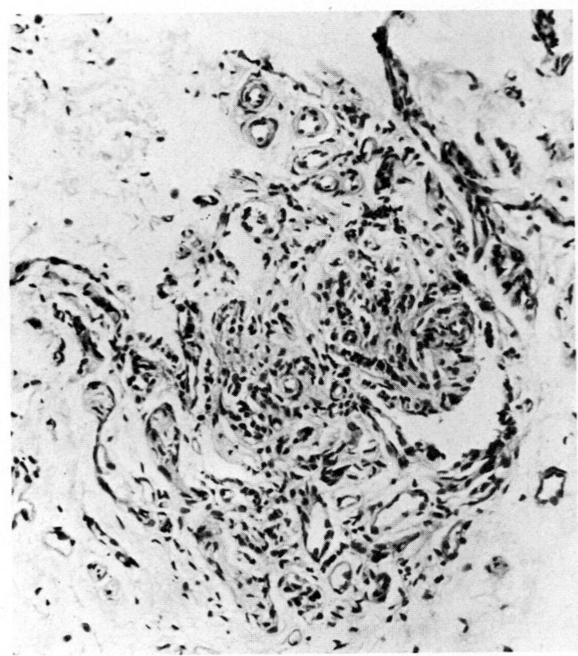

Fig. 31.2 Section of the 'glomus pulmonale' from the same case illustrated in the previous figure at a deeper level where the glomus was separated from its parent artery. It consists of arterioles and capillary blood vessels with closely surrounding glomic cells. (Haematoxylin & eosin, × 150)

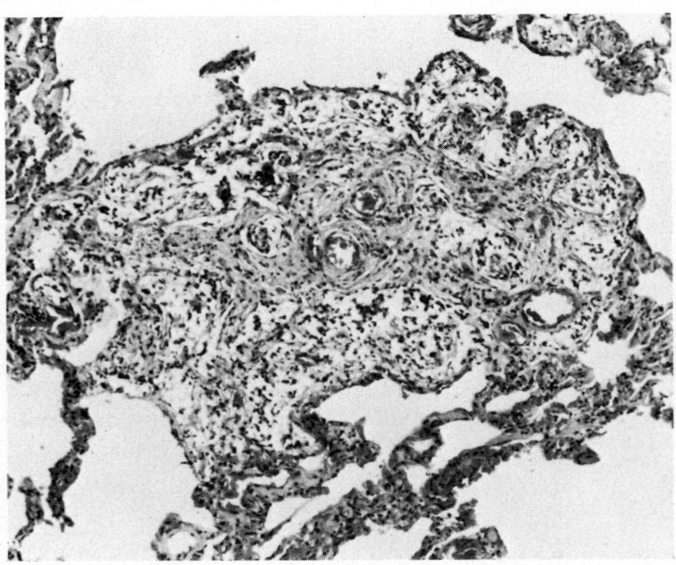

Fig. 31.3 A nodule of chemoreceptor tissue surrounding pulmonary venules in a woman of 67 years dying from a pontine haemorrhage complicating systemic hypertension. The nodule bulges into surrounding alveolar spaces but is interstitial in site, being bounded by pulmonary capillaries. (Haematoxylin & eosin, × 72)

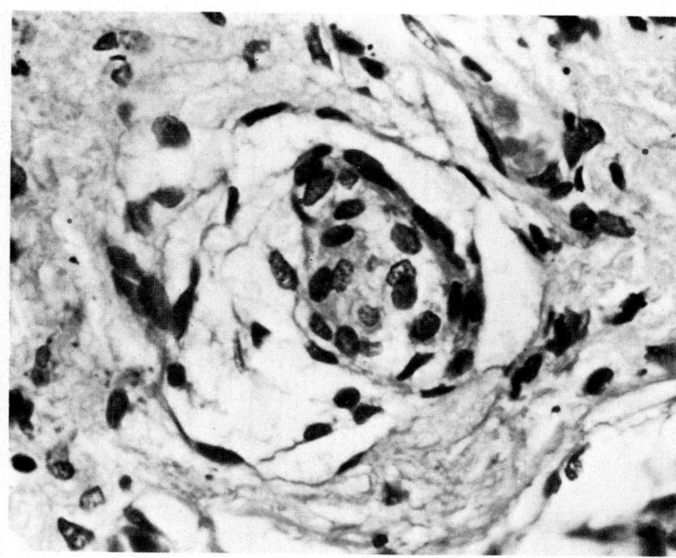

Fig. 31.4 A cluster of chemoreceptor cells from around a pulmonary venule in the same case illustrated in the previous Figure. There is a central syncytium of chief cells with ovoid nuclei, a surrounding clear area, and a limiting layer of flat cells. (Haematoxylin & eosin, × 600)

hypoxia such as we consider in Chapters 32 and 34. The carotid bodies are pedunculated ovoid masses which lie just behind the bifurcation of the common carotid artery on either side of the neck (Fig. 31.5). They are easily accessible for rapid dissection and we now include their examination routinely during necropsy at Liverpool. In one series of cases[11] we found the average weight of the right carotid body was 12·9 mg while that of the left was 11·3 mg.

Under conditions of chronic hypoxia the carotid bodies enlarge. Arias-Stella[12] was the first to report that the carotid bodies of Quechua Indians living in the vicinity of Cerro de Pasco in the Peruvian Andes at an altitude of 14 250 ft above sea level are larger than those of mestizos living on the coastal plain around Lima. The carotid bodies of guinea-pigs, dogs and rabbits born and living at high altitude are larger than representatives of the same species living at sea level.[13]

The carotid bodies enlarge too in states of chronic hypoxia brought about by disease as well as by high altitude. Our studies show that the carotid bodies enlarge in pulmonary emphysema so that their weight increases more than three fold[11,14] (Fig. 31.6). Enlargement of the carotid bodies in this disease is not related to either the type or severity of emphysema but rather to the presence of hypoxia and right ventricular hypertrophy.[11,14] We think it very likely that the carotid bodies are enlarged in cyanotic congenital heart disease but we do not know of any studies of this.

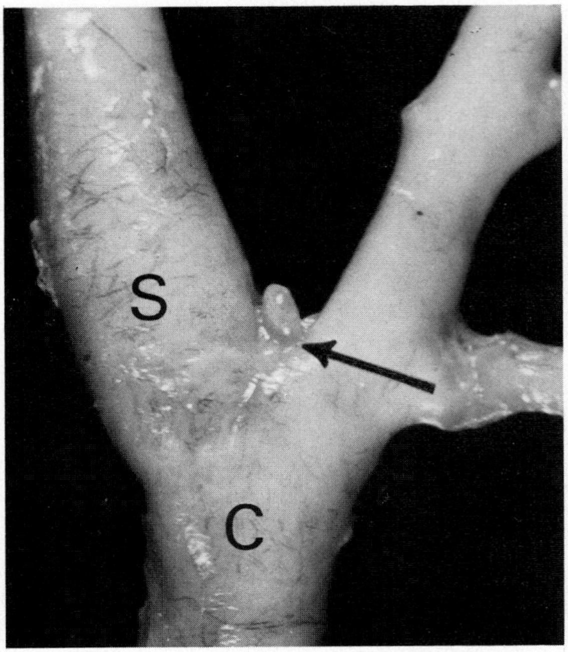

FIG. 31.5

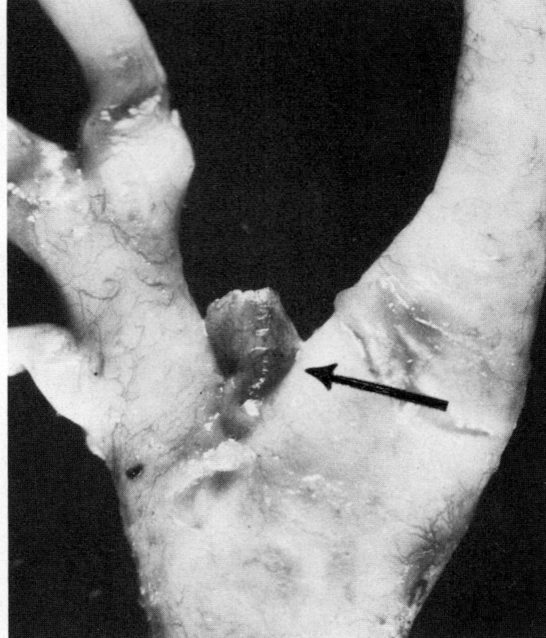

FIG. 31.6

Fig. 31.5 Normal left carotid body weighing 6·9 mg from a man aged 50 years with polycystic disease of the kidneys and a left ventricle of normal weight. The carotid body (arrow) lies at the bifurcation of the common carotid artery, C, and adjacent to the carotid sinus, S. (×3)

Fig. 31.6 Enlarged right carotid body (arrow) weighing 21·9 mg from a man aged 62 years with panacinar emphysema and right ventricular hypertrophy. (×3)

The Histology of Glomic Tissue

When glomic tissue enlarges in states of chronic hypoxia part of the increase in size is due to its vascular engorgement. Part, however, is due to a hyperplasia of some of its constituent cells. There are two types of glomic cell, the chief (type I) cell and the sustentacular (type 2) cell. There are light, dark and pyknotic varients of the chief cell. The light cell is the most abundant and has a pale eosinophilic cytoplasm which contains a variable number of vacuoles. It is some 13 μm in diameter but its outline is ill-defined. The dark cell is of the same size but its cytoplasm stains more deeply with eosin and has a well-defined outline; the chromatin pattern of the nucleus has a denser, more granular pattern. The third form of type 1 cell is the pyknotic cell which has a sharp cytoplasmic outline and an overall diameter of about 10 μm. The cytoplasm is deeply eosinophilic and granular and vacuolation is fairly common. The nucleus is deeply basophilic, apparently structureless and eccentrically situated. Its diameter is about 4 μm. The sustentacular (type 2) cell is elongated and believed to be related to Schwann cells. It has a nucleus, 13 × 4 μm, in which the chromatin is arranged in small clumps to give a pale, dusty appearance. In our studies of the enlargement of carotid bodies at high altitude, we found in guinea-pigs a hyperplasia of the light variety of chief cell.[13] This type of cell is generally regarded as that which fulfils the chemoreceptor function, although it can be shown that the chief cell is separated from blood capillaries by sustentacular cells.[15]

Ultrastructure of Glomic Cells

Without going into detail here on the ultrastructure of chief cells we may note that their cytoplasm contains neurosecretory granules composed of a central osmiophilic core, a clear halo and an outer membrane.[16] It is believed that such granules represent a stored form of catecholamine which is released on stimulation by hypoxia. Certainly in states of chronic hypoxia the central core of the granules becomes smaller and less dense and the halo widens so that the whole is transformed into a microvacuole. This ultrastructural change may be associated with increased secretion of catecholamine but this is not certain since at high altitude and in hypoxia chemoreceptor sensitivity diminishes[17,18] in spite of enlargement of the

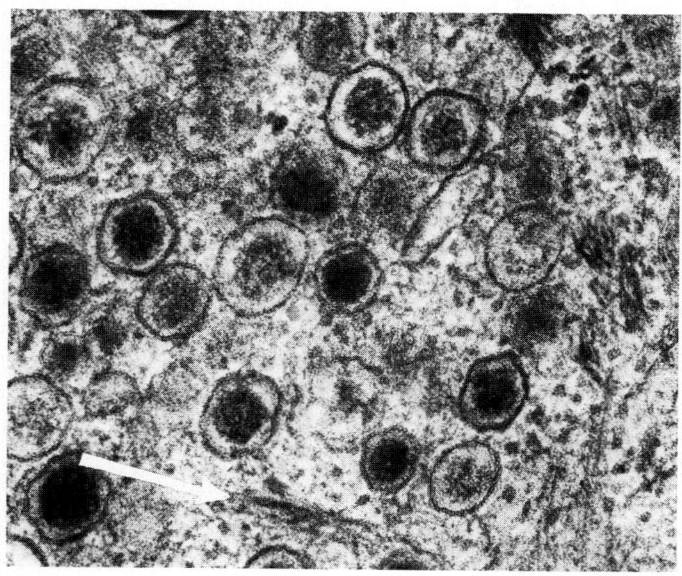

Fig. 31.7 Electron micrograph of part of a bronchial Feyrter cell from a neonatal control Wistar albino rat. Within the cytoplasm are round osmiophilic bodies, the so-called 'catecholamine bodies'. They are composed of a dark central core and a narrow peripheral lighter halo bounded by an outer membrane. Also seen in the cytoplasm are protein microfibrils and free ribosomes which are seen in the background as dots. (× 75 000)

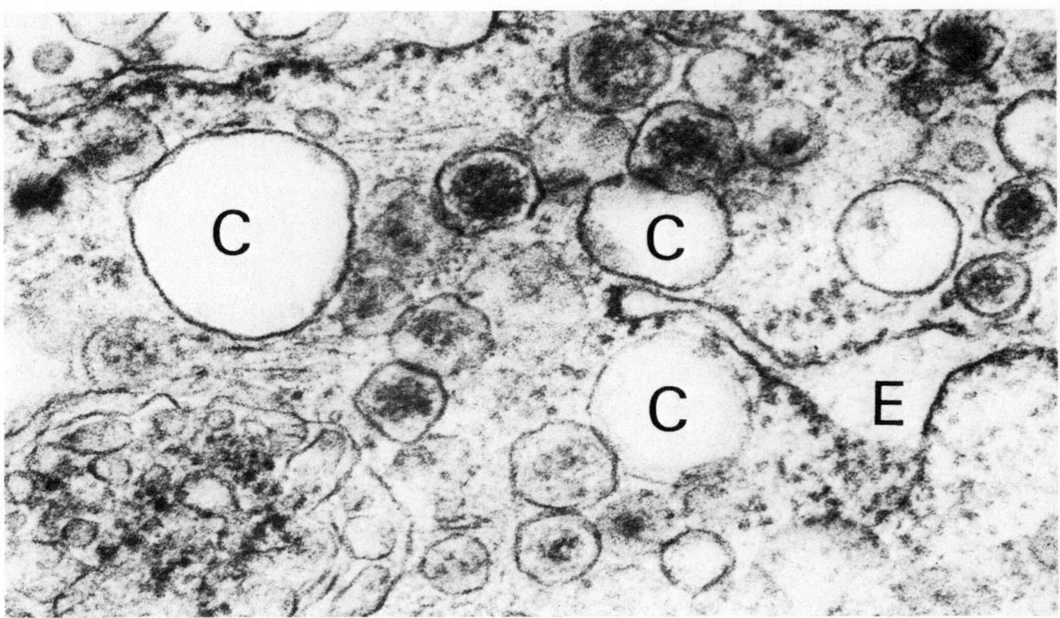

Fig. 31.8 Electron micrograph of part of a bronchial Feyrter cell from a Wistar rat exposed in a hypobaric chamber to a simulated altitude of 18 000 ft (5488 m) above sea level for 20 h. Following this exposure to hypoxia there were changes in the osmiophilic bodies similar to those which occur in the carotid body exposed to hypoxia. In some osmiophilic bodies the central cores were smaller, less dense and eccentric with widening of the surrounding halo to form vesicles. In this area the process has progressed so that the osmiophilic bodies have been replaced by microvacuoles (C) and a wide cisterna of rough endoplasmic reticulum (E). (× 75 000)

glomic tissue. Another possibility that cannot be overlooked is that such ultrastructural changes indicate secretion of a hormone. The chief cell has the electron microscopic features of an APUD cell which is associated with hormone secretion.[19] It is conceivable that hypoxia might stimulate the secretion of an erythropoietic hormone from the carotid bodies[20] although the carotid bodies were not enlarged in a series of cases of anaemia that we studied.[21]

The Carotid Bodies and the Pulmonary Circulation

There is no doubt that in states of chronic hypoxia the carotid bodies show pronounced structural changes at the same time as do the right ventricle and pulmonary vasculature. In one experiment,[22] we subjected rats to hypoxia for five weeks in a decompression chamber and found that all developed right ventricular hypertrophy, hypertrophy of the pulmonary trunk and enlargement of the carotid bodies. When a second group of rats, following a similar period of hypoxia, were allowed to recover in room air for a further period of five weeks, all showed regression of these changes so that the right ventricle, pulmonary trunk and carotid bodies all returned virtually to normal. Such data remind us that in future studies of the effects of hypoxia on the pulmonary circulation an eye should be kept on the behaviour of the carotid bodies.

Feyrter Cells and Neuro-epithelial Bodies

Intercalated within the respiratory mucosa of the intrapulmonary airways of several mammalian species, including man, the rabbit and the rat, are non-ciliated, argyrophilic Feyrter cells. They have ultrastructural features of APUD cells with membrane-bound cytoplasmic bodies identical to those which occur in carotid body chief cells[23] (Fig. 31.7). When exposed to hypoxia these granules show the same changes of microvacuolation that we have noted in the carotid bodies of high altitude guinea pigs[24] (Fig. 31.8). Groups of such argyrophilic cells form intramucosal corpuscles throughout the intrapulmonary airways and are termed neuro-epithelial bodies.[25] They are to be found in infant and adult human lungs and have been described in neonatal and adult rabbits, and in other mammals. The neuro-epithelial bodies are 20 to 40 μm in height and 15 μm in width and are intercalated within the respiratory mucosa. They are composed of non-ciliated, large cells with a clear, slightly eosinophilic and argyrophilic cytoplasm and they extend from the basement membrane to the airway lumen. The function of neuro-epithelial bodies has not yet been established but Lauweryns and Goddeeris[25] believe that they are an intrapulmonary neuroreceptor or chemoreceptor system that is sensitive to hypoxia and which might influence the pulmonary vaso-constrictor response in normal and pathological circumstances.

REFERENCES

1. Krahl, V. E. (1960) *Bull. Sch. Med. Maryland*, **45**, 36.
2. Krahl, V. E. (1962) In *Ciba Foundation Symposium on Pulmonary Structure and Function*, ed. de Reuck, A. V. S. & O'Connor, M. page 53. London: Churchill.
3. Edwards, C. & Heath, D. (1969) *Thorax*, **24**, 209.
4. Becker, A. E. (1966) *M.D. thesis. Laboratory of Pathological Anatomy*. University of Amsterdam.
5. Edwards, C. & Heath, D. (1970) *Cardiovasc. Res.*, **4**, 502.
6. Edwards, C. & Heath, D. (1972) *Brit. J. Dis. Chest*, **66**, 96.
7. Korn, D., Bensch, K., Liebow, A. A. & Castleman, B. (1960) *Amer. J. Path.*, **37**, 641.
8. Spencer, H. (1962) In *Pathology of the Lung*, pages 690–692. Pergamon: London.
9. Hepplestone, A. G. (1958) *J. Path. Bact.*, **75**, 461.
10. Fawcett, F. J. & Husband, E. M. (1967) *J. Clin. Path.*, **20**, 260.
11. Heath, D., Edwards, C. & Harris, P. (1970) *Thorax*, **25**, 129.
12. Arias-Stella, J. (1969) In *The 69th Programme and Abstracts of the American Association of Pathologists and Bacteriologists*, Item 150, San Francisco, Calif.
13. Edwards, C., Heath, D., Harris, P., Castillo, Y., Krüger, H. & Arias-Stella, J. (1971) *J. Path.*, **104**, 231.
14. Edwards, C., Heath, D. & Harris, P. (1971) *J. Path.*, **104**, 1.
15. Grimley, P. M. & Glenner, G. C. (1968) *Circulation*, **37**, 648.
16. Edwards, C., Heath, D. & Harris, P. (1972) *J. Path.*, **107**, 131.
17. Severinghaus, J. W., Bainton, C. R. & Carcelan, A. (1966) *Resp. Physiol.*, **1**, 308.

18. Barer, G. & Jolly, A. (1971) In *Respiratory Control in Chronic Hypoxia*, Programme of Summer Meeting of the Thoracic Society, p. 12.
19. Pearse, A. G. E. (1969) *J. Histochem. Cytochem.*, **17**, 303.
20. Tramezzani, J. H., Morita, E. & Chiocchio, S. R. (1971) *Proc. Natl. Acad. Sci.*, **68**, 52.
21. Winson, M. & Heath, D. (1973) *Arch. Pathol.*, **96**, 58.
22. Heath, D., Edwards, C., Winson, M. & Smith, P. (1973) *Thorax*, **28**, 24.
23. Lauweryns, J. M. & Peuskens, J. C. (1969) *Life Sciences*, **8**, 577.
24. Moosavi, H., Smith, P. & Heath, D. (1973) *Thorax*, **28**, 729.
25. Lauweryns, J. M. & Goddeeris, P. (1975) *Amer. Rev. Resp. Dis.*, **111**, 469.

32. The Pulmonary Circulation at High Altitude

Pulmonary Hypertension at High Altitude

A number of studies have demonstrated the presence of a mild degree of pulmonary arterial hypertension in people who live at high altitude.[1–3] Observations by Peñaloza *et al.*[4], summarized in Table 32.1, showed an average pulmonary arterial pressure of 29 mmHg at rest in the normal population at Morococha, Peru, at an altitude of 4540 m. The pulmonary wedge pressure is unaffected as is the resting pulmonary blood flow. There is thus a mild increase in pulmonary vascular resistance. The atmospheric Po_2 at such an altitude is 90 mmHg and the average oxygen saturation of arterial blood is 78 per cent. Chronic hypoxia stimulates erythropoiesis so that the haematocrit is elevated.

During exercise the pulmonary arterial pressure increases further (Table 32.1) and may reach substantial proportions. Nevertheless, the physical capacity of the indigenous population is normal and capable, for instance, of performing heavy labour in the mines around which mountain communities are often centred. The pulmonary arterial pressure in children within the first few years of life at high altitude is higher again than that in adults (Table 32.2). By the age of five years, however, the pulmonary arterial pressure has fallen to adult proportions appropriate to the altitude.

When highlanders are brought to sea level there is an immediate decrease in the pulmonary arterial pressure which is succeeded by a more gradual decline. After about six weeks the pulmonary arterial pressure has become normal for sea level. This course of events is presumably due first to the release of hypoxic constriction in the pulmonary arterioles and subsequently to a more gradual fall in pulmonary vascular resistance associated perhaps with an involution of vascular muscle (see below). It may be noted that a similar course of events is found during the chronic administration of oxygen to patients with hypoxic chronic bronchitis (Chapter 34).

Muscular Pulmonary Arteries and Pulmonary Arterioles in Highlanders

Arias-Stella and Saldaña[5] studied the terminal portion of the pulmonary arterial tree at necropsy in two groups of otherwise healthy subjects who had died suddenly as a result of an accident or an acute illness. One group of subjects had been born at high altitude in Andean villages of Peru above altitudes of 3440 m and had lived there all their lives. Sixteen of these subjects were infants and 28 were older children or adults in the age range of 6 to 76 years. The second group of subjects had been born and lived at sea level all their lives. These authors studied what they called proximal and distal pulmonary arteries which correspond to what are generally termed muscular pulmonary arteries and

Table 32.1 Pulmonary haemodynamics at rest and during exercise in normal men born and living in Morococha, Peru, at an altitude of 4540 m, and at Lima, Peru, at sea level[4]

	Mean pulmonary arterial pressure mmHg	Mean wedge pressure mmHg	Cardiac index $l \cdot min^{-1}/m^2$ BSA	Oxygen uptake $ml \cdot min^{-1}/m^2$ BSA	Pulmonary arterial resistance $dyn \cdot s \cdot cm^{-5}$	Arterial oxygen saturation %
Morococha (35 subjects)						
Rest	29	5	3·7	159	400	78
Exercise	60	6	7·5	765	430	69
Lima (22 subjects)						
Rest	12	6	4·0	153	160	96
Exercise	18	7	6·8	717	130	95

Table 32.2 Pulmonary haemodynamics at rest in children and adults born and living in Morococha, Peru, at an altitude of 4540 m[2,3]

Age range (years)	Number of subjects	Pulmonary arterial pressure mmHg Systolic	Diastolic	Mean	Wedge pressure mmHg	Pulmonary arterial resistance dyn · s · cm^{-5}
1–5	7	58	32	45	7	—
6–14	25	41	18	28	5	460
18–34	38	41	15	28	5	400

pulmonary arterioles. They found an increase in the number of muscularized pulmonary arterioles to that of parent muscular pulmonary arteries in the high-altitude subjects and an absolute increase in the amount of arterial muscle in the terminal portions of the pulmonary arterial tree (Figs. 32.1 and 32.2). In the older group of high altitude subjects, there was hypertrophy of the media of the muscular pulmonary arteries. Since the chronic hypoxia and pulmonary hypertension is present from birth they suggested that the normal involution of the

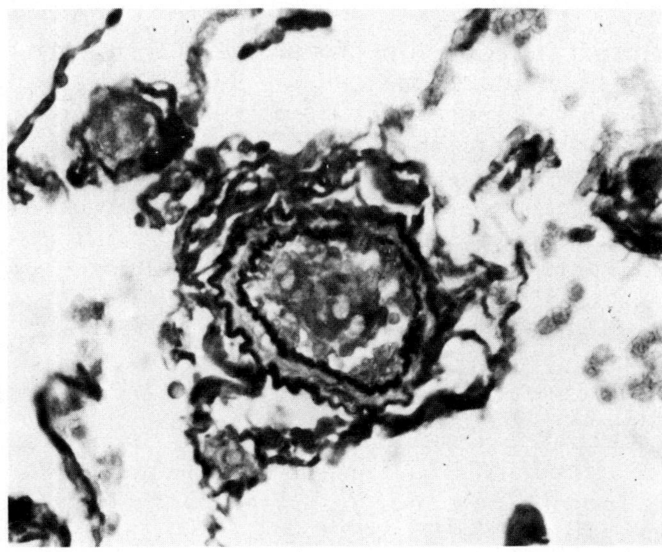

Fig. 32.1 Transverse section of a muscularized pulmonary arteriole from a Quechua Indian who lived in the vicinity of Cerro de Pasco in the Peruvian Andes at an altitude of 14 250 ft above sea level. The arteriole is abnormal with a distinct media of circularly orientated smooth muscle fibres sandwiched between internal and external elastic laminae. There is no intimal fibrosis. (Elastic/Van Gieson, ×375)

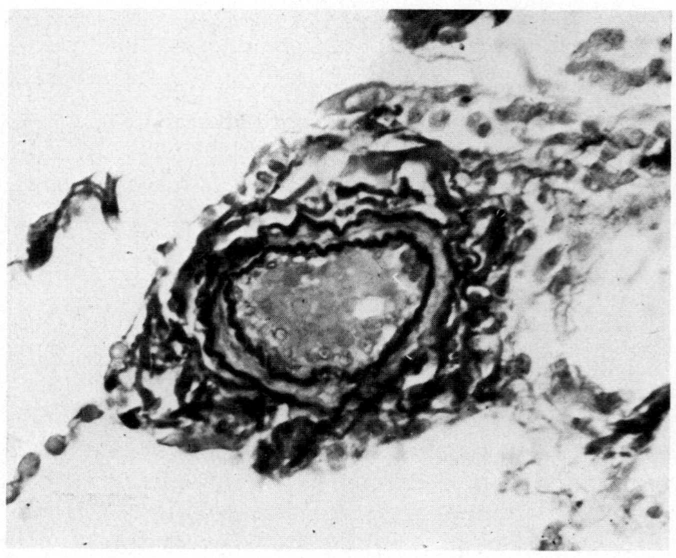

Fig. 32.2 Transverse section of a muscularized pulmonary arteriole from a case of chronic mountain sickness (Monge's disease) from the region of Cerro de Pasco. There is a distinct media of circular muscle bounded by internal and external elastic laminae. (Elastic/Van Gieson, × 375)

muscularized pulmonary arteriole of the foetus (see Chapter 14) to the thin-walled pulmonary arteriole of the adult at sea level (see Chapter 3) never occurs. It seems likely that the muscularized pulmonary arterioles form the organic basis for the increased pulmonary vascular resistance and mild pulmonary hypertension which is characteristic of people living at high altitude. Presumably the hypertrophy of the media of the muscular pulmonary arteries is secondary to the hypertension. The absence of intimal fibrosis in the small pulmonary arterial vessels is consistent with the fact that the pulmonary hypertension of high altitude is reversible (p. 518). This is in keeping with other forms of hypoxic hypertensive vascular disease described in the previous chapter.

Muscular Pulmonary Arteries and Pulmonary Arterioles in Animals

The same muscularization of the pulmonary arterial tree occurs in animals born and living at high altitude. We have found that the pulmonary arterial vessels below 150 μm in diameter show an increased medial thickness in dogs, cats, and cattle living at high altitude (Figs 32.3–32.6; Ref. 6). Among the animals which we studied at a high altitude, the llama was uniquely lacking in such a long term response to chronic hypoxia (Figs 32.7 and 32.8). Such a species-difference may represent an evolutionary adaptation to life in the Altura, the lack of reaction to hypoxia preventing an increase in the pulmonary vascular resistance which limits the cardiovascular performance of other animals. As long ago as 1915 it was reported

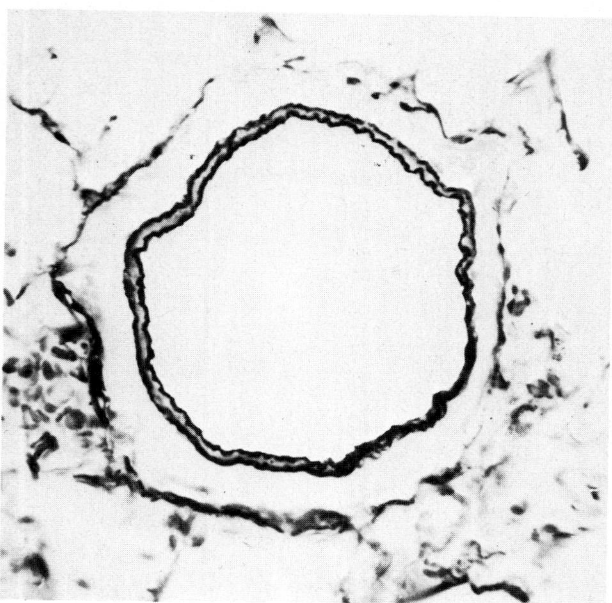

Fig. 32.3 Transverse section of a small pulmonary artery from a dog which was born and lived all its life at low altitude. The media is thin and bounded by internal and external elastic laminae. (Elastic/Van Gieson, × 560)

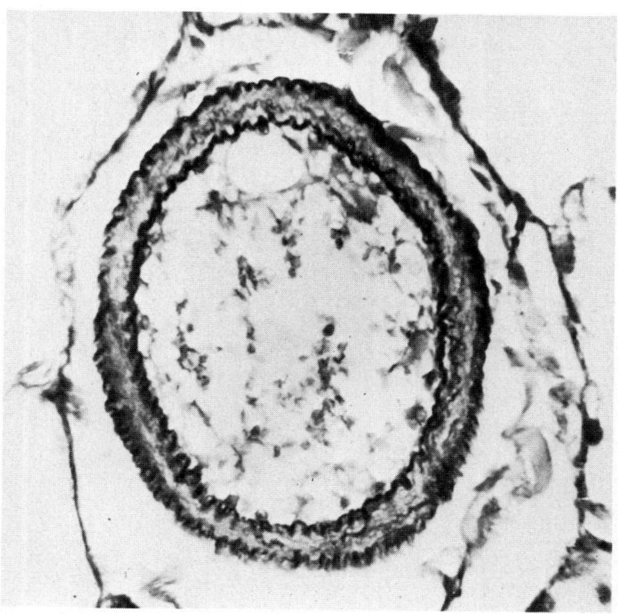

Fig. 32.4 Transverse section of a small pulmonary artery from a dog which was born and lived all its life at Cerro de Pasco in the Peruvian Andes at an altitude of 14 250 ft above sea level. The media is thick and is bounded by crenated internal and external elastic laminae. There is no intimal fibrosis. (Elastic/Van Gieson, × 560)

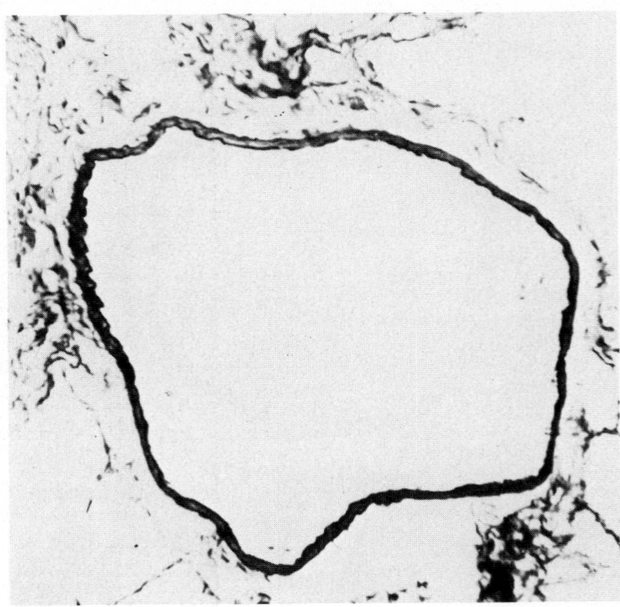

Fig. 32.5 Transverse section of a small pulmonary artery from a cat born and bred at low altitude. The media of circular muscle is thin. (Elastic/Van Gieson)

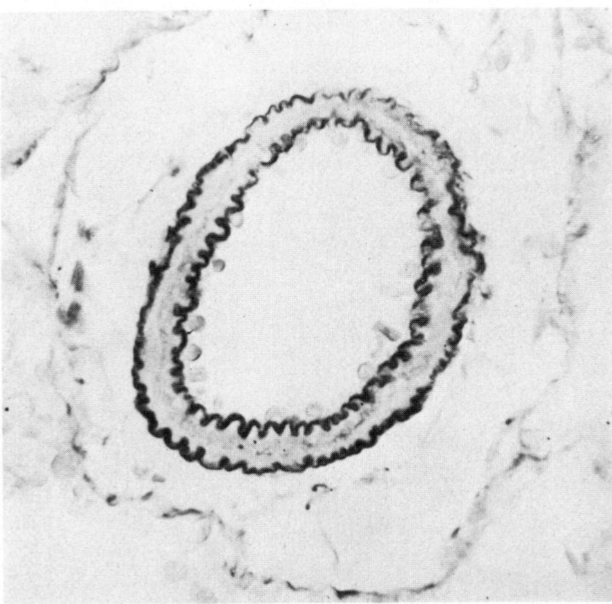

Fig. 32.6 Transverse section of a small pulmonary artery from a cat born and bred at high altitude at Cerro de Pasco. The media is thick and muscular and is bounded by crenated internal and external elastic laminae. (Elastic/Van Gieson)

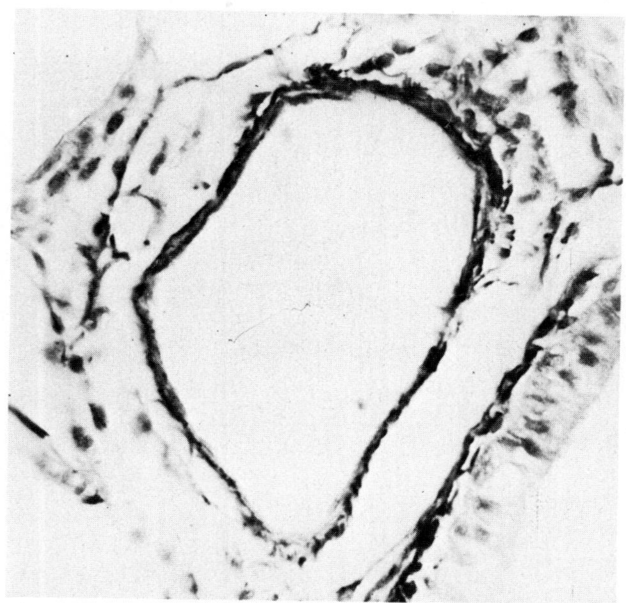

Fig. 32.7 Transverse section of a small pulmonary artery from a llama born and bred in the region of Cerro de Pasco in the Peruvian Andes. The media is thin and bounded by internal and external elastic laminae. There is no intimal fibrosis. (Elastic/Van Gieson, × 560)

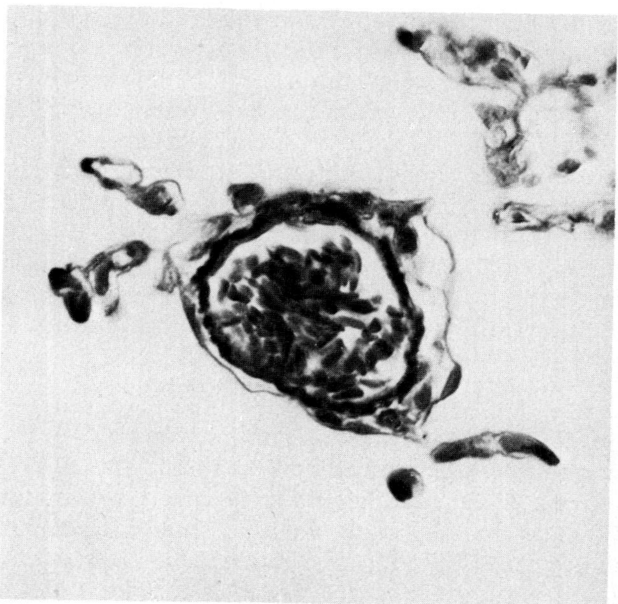

Fig. 32.8 Transverse section of a pulmonary arteriole from a llama born and bred in the region of Cerro de Pasco in the Peruvian Andes. The wall of the arteriole consists of a single elastic lamina. There is no muscular media. (Elastic/Van Gieson, × 760)

Fig. 32.9 Brisket disease, showing dependent oedema in an affected animal grazing at high altitude in the area of Salt Lake City.

that cattle living at high altitude may develop congestive cardiac failure.[7] Since then this syndrome of 'brisket disease' has been shown to be brought about by an increased pulmonary vascular resistance associated with the chronic hypoxia to which such animals are subjected[8,9] (Figs 32.9 and 32.10). A curious feature is that oedema of the brisket has been noted only in the area surrounding Salt Lake City. It does not occur in the Andes. Possibly this distribution is due to a higher content of salt in the diet in this area of Utah. As has been described in the previous chapter rats kept in a hypobaric chamber to simulate very high altitudes may develop similar muscularization of their pulmonary arterioles.[10] However, this does not always take place under such conditions of simulated high altitude and the factors of age and sex may have some bearing on this. Muscularization of the pulmonary arterioles has been reported in young female Wistar albino rats kept at a simulated altitude of 5500 m above sea level for five weeks[10] but not in a group of adult male rats of the same strain kept under identical conditions for a similar period.[11]

Pulmonary Trunk

The constriction of the muscularized pulmonary arterioles induces a mild but persistent pulmonary hypertension and this increases the thickness of the media of the pulmonary trunk[12] and modifies its structure. Experiments on rats kept in a hypobaric chamber to simulate high altitude, show that medial hypertrophy of the pulmonary trunk occurs very rapidly in response to hypoxia. The pulmonary trunk became as thick as the aorta in one group of rats kept at a simulated altitude of 5500 m for five weeks.[11] Regression of such hypertrophy rapidly follows relief from hypoxia. In the experiment referred to above, regression of the thick pulmonary trunk to almost normal thickness occurred within five weeks of being removed from the hypoxic environment.[11] In experiments on rats in a hypobaric chamber, we have been able to show that the hypertrophy of the pulmonary trunk induced by chronic hypoxia is accompanied by right ventricular hypertrophy and enlargement of the carotid body.[11] After a period of relief from such hypoxia the pulmonary trunk, right ventricle and carotid body all revert to normal together.[11]

Before considering the modifications brought about by high altitude on the normal elastic tissue structure of the media of the pulmonary trunk already described in detail in Chapters 3 and 14 and the influence on the time of transition from one form to another we must briefly consider a fourth elastic tissue pattern not referred to in the description of the normal transition of the elastic tissue pattern of the pulmonary trunk at sea level, the 'persistent' type of elastic tissue pattern.

This designation was applied to a type of elastic tissue of the media of the pulmonary trunk which can be observed in the first five years of life.[13] In this, the pulmonary trunk contains such a high content of elastic fibres that at first it resembles the aortic pattern (Fig. 32.11). However, there is a greater degree of fragmentation of elastic tissue fibres. Hence, there is a combination of long, thick fibres reminiscent of the aortic model and markedly fragmented ones. The long fibres are more numerous giving the media a compact appearance. Since these long fibres are characteristic of late foetal life Saldaña and Arias-Stella called the pattern 'persistent'.[13] The presence of a significant number of fragmented fibres distinguishes

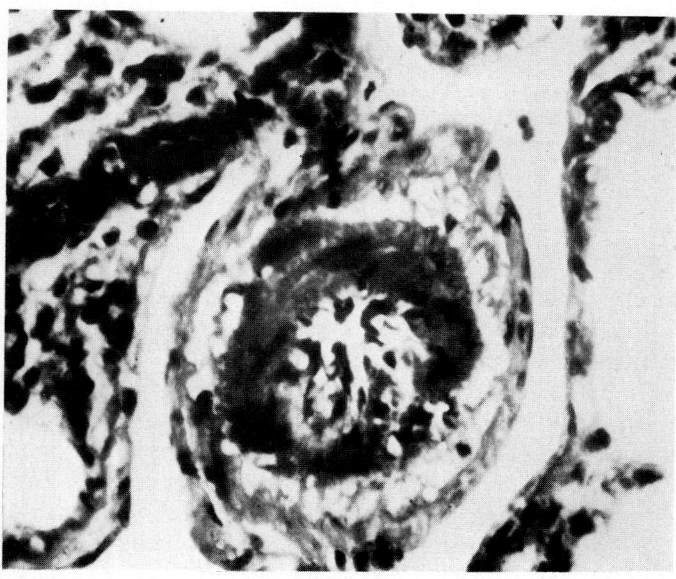

Fig. 32.10 Transverse section of a pulmonary arteriole from a cow with brisket disease. The arteriole is abundantly muscularized.

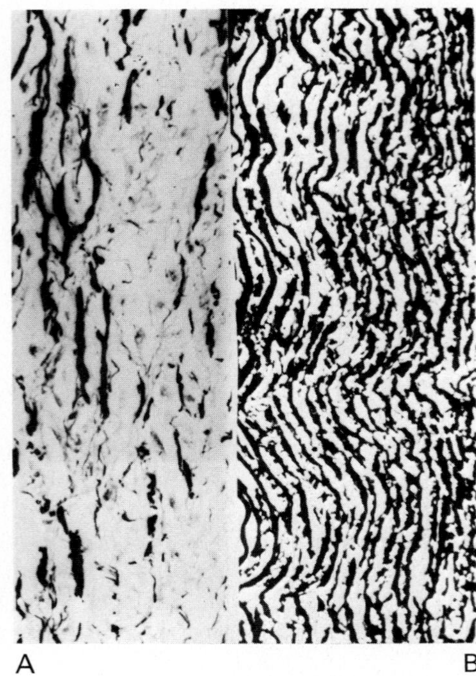

Fig. 32.11 Transverse sections of pulmonary trunk from two Peruvian subjects. A, From an adult mestizo born and bred on the coastal plain around Lima. Note the open network of branched, irregularly-shaped elastic fibrils; this is the adult pulmonary configuration of elastic tissue found in association with acquired pulmonary hypertension. B, From an adult Quechua Indian born and bred in the region of Cerro de Pasco in the Peruvian Andes at an altitude of 14 250 ft above sea level. The elastic tissue is greater in amount and more compactly arranged as roughly parallel fibrils. This is the persistent type of elastic tissue pattern found in association with pulmonary hypertension from birth.

the pattern from the aortic. The presence of numerous long fibres distinguishes it from the transitional pattern described in Chapter 14. The profusion of elastic fibres prevents confusion with the adult pattern of elastic tissue.

In a 'blind' study Saldaña and Arias-Stella[14] determined the type of elastic-tissue pattern of the pulmonary trunk in 267 high-altitude dwellers of all ages who died accidentally or due to non-cardiovascular diseases. A group of dwellers at sea level comprising 283 subjects of comparable ages served as controls. Between 4040 and 4540 m above sea level the aortic pattern of elastic tissue is maintained up to 9-years of age (Fig. 32.12). This elastic tissue configuration evolves only into the 'persistent' pattern of elastic tissue described above, which is seen for the rest of life. According to Saldaña and Arias-Stella[14] the persistent pattern may convert to the adult type much later in life, especially after the age of 60 years. We find it difficult to appreciate the physiological basis for this, since, so far as we are aware, there is no fall in pulmonary arterial pressure in high altitude dwellers at this age.

At altitudes situated between 3440 to 3840 m the aortic pattern is retained up to 3 years (Fig. 32.12). Cases with the transitional pattern are sometimes seen but they appear to evolve rapidly into the persistent form. This type of elastic-tissue pattern is seen mainly in childhood and adolescence and is also present in a majority of young adults. By the age of 55 years, the transition to the adult pattern has been achieved, although once again we do not understand the stimulus for this change in structure in middle age.

These pathways of the evolution of the elastic-tissue pattern differ notably from those seen at sea level and described in Chapter 14. Saldaña and Arias-Stella[14] suggest that they are determined by the existence at high altitudes of a mild degree of pulmonary hypertension from birth. They believe that the differences between the two groups at high altitude are related to the occurrence of greater degrees of pulmonary hypertension at the higher altitudes.

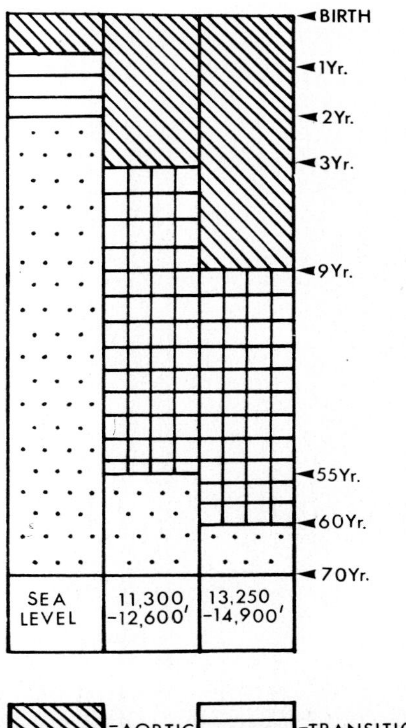

Fig. 32.12 Histogram to illustrate the different patterns of elastic tissue in the media of the pulmonary trunk which occur at different altitudes in the Peruvian Andes. The data on which the diagram is based are derived from studies of Saldaña and Arias-Stella.[14]

Relations Between Histology, Extensibility and Chemical Composition of the Pulmonary Trunk at High Altitude

There is a close relation between these three different aspects of the human pulmonary trunk at high altitude.[15] The content of elastin in the pulmonary trunk increases with age (Chap. 4) but, in those mountain dwellers who have an 'aortic' pattern of elastic tissue in the pulmonary trunk, the content of elastin is higher than would be expected for the age. The content of collagen is normal.

Compared with predicted normal values, the extensibility of the media of such high altitude vessels is found to be diminished (Fig. 32.13). When expressed as a proportion of the predicted normal value, the diminution of extensibility is seen to be maximal at low extensile loads (Fig. 32.14). Such a finding is consistent with the mechanical effects of elastin predominating at shorter degrees of stretch (Chap. 4).

Chronic Mountain Sickness (Monge's Disease)

While in the great majority of the population indigenous to high altitude there is only a mild elevation of pulmonary arterial pressure and no symptoms referable

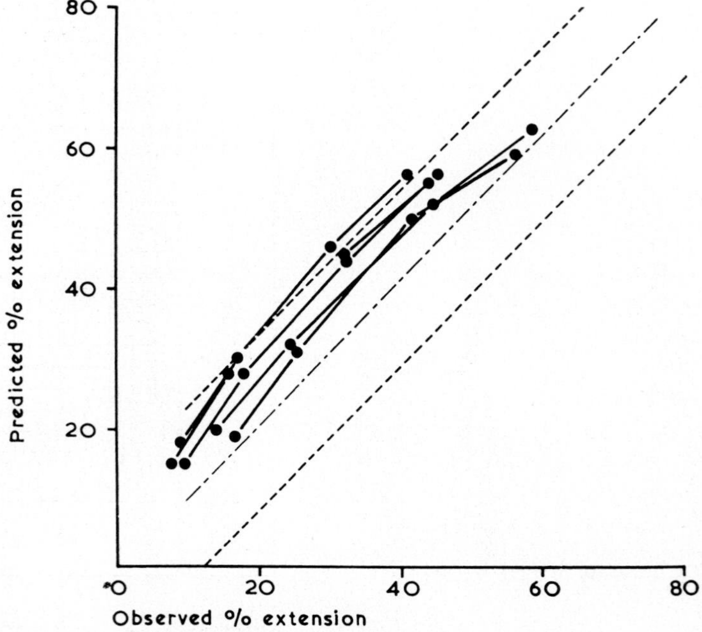

Fig. 32.13 The relation between the observed degree of extension and that predicted[15] in five subjects with an aortic pattern of elastic tissue. The 'normal' regression line[15] is shown, together with lines at a distance of twice the standard error of the estimate. The equations referred to in this legend are derived from studies by Castillo *et al.*[15]

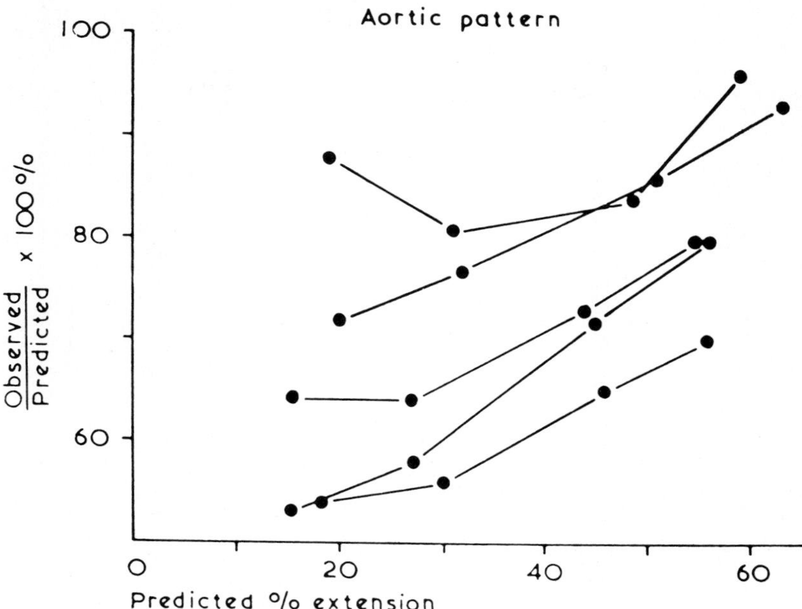

Fig. 32.14 The relation between the degree of extension and the degree of extension expressed as a percentage of that predicted in the high altitude subjects with an aortic pattern of elastic tissue shown in Fig. 32.13.

to pulmonary hypertension, there is a small group of people in whom serious pulmonary hypertension is found (Table 32.3). The condition was first described by Monge[16] in 1928.

As will be seen from Table 32.3, chronic mountain sickness is associated with a lower arterial oxygen saturation than would be normally appropriate for the altitude. There is an impressive rise in the haematocrit. Curiously, dyspnoea is not necessarily a prominent symptom but fatigue, headache, dizziness, paraesthesiae, somnolence and psychiatric disturbances are found more frequently.[17] The only effective treatment for the condition is removal to a lower altitude, when the pulmonary arterial pressure falls, at first abruptly and then more gradually over a period of several weeks. Why this process affects a small proportion of mountain dwellers is not entirely clear, but it would seem to be due to a lower level of alveolar ventilation than normal. People born at high altitude have a diminished ventilatory response to hypoxia[18] while preserving a normal ventilatory response to carbon dioxide. This is surprising both on teleological grounds and because of the increase in size of the carotid bodies which occurs at high altitude[19,20] (Chap. 31). In cats, however, the defect may be released by de-cerebration, which suggests a modification of the central nervous pathways.[21] Patients with chronic mountain sickness have an even lower ventilatory response to hypoxia than normal

Table 32.3 Physiological measurements in normal residents and patients with chronic mountain sickness at Cerro de Pasco, Peru, at an altitude of 4300 m[17]

	Number of subjects	Hb g/100 ml	Arterial oxygen saturation %	Pulmonary arterial pressure mmHg			Wedge pressure mmHg	Cardiac output $l \cdot min^{-1}/m^2$ BSA	Pulmonary arterial resistance $dyn \cdot s \cdot cm^{-5}$
				Systolic	Diastolic	Mean			
Chronic mountain sickness	10	24·8	70	64	33	47	6	4·0	530
Normal residents	12	20·1	81	34	13	23	7	3·8	200

mountain dwellers.[18] It is uncertain whether one needs to seek for some specific neurological lesion in these patients or whether they can be regarded as the 'tail' of a normally distributed group of people with varying degrees of impairment of hypoxic ventilatory drive. An alternative possibility is that these patients are suffering from a mild degree of chronic bronchitis which lowers alveolar ventilation. The observation of a specific loss of ventilatory sensitivity to hypoxia and not hypercapnia is, however, against such a view. Unfortunately, there appears to be no certain morbid anatomical information on this disease, the subject of the only post-mortem to be described being a hunch-back,[22] a condition that on its own is capable of giving rise to hypoxic hypertensive pulmonary vascular disease.

High Altitude Pulmonary Oedema

The occurrence of pulmonary oedema on rapid ascent to high altitude has been known for many years[23] and the clinical features have been well established.[24] It develops most commonly in high altitude natives returning to high altitude after a few weeks at low levels. It may afflict the unacclimatized subject who is exposed to diminished barometric pressure too quickly while engaged in strenuous physical exercise and is thus a hazard for the mountain climber and skier.[25] Younger people are more prone but it is rare in infancy. Cold has been considered by some to be a contributory factor. Cough, dyspnoea, sub-sternal oppression and cyanosis together with pulmonary crepitations are the clinical features. The chest radiograph shows patchy opacities and some enlargement of the larger arterial branches whose outlines become indistinct. Post-mortem histology has shown dilated pulmonary arterial vessels and capillaries, perivascular haemorrhages and oedema and intravascular thromboses in addition to alveolar fluid.[26–28]

When rats are subjected to simulated high altitude in a hypobaric chamber, they show characteristic ultrastructural changes in the pulmonary capillaries.[29] Small oedematous vesicles form as a localized swelling of the fused basement membrane of the alveolar wall and project into the lumens of the capillaries (Fig. 24.7, p. 375). When seen in longitudinal section the vesicles have an elongated shape similar to that of the capillary into which they project. When such a vesicle is cut in transverse section without fortuitously including its pedicle, it appears as a round body and gives the spurious appearance of lying free in the pulmonary capillary (Fig. 24.7, p. 375). The vesicles are covered by a tightly stretched, ultra-thin layer of cytoplasm of the overlying endothelial cell (Fig. 24.6, p. 374) and arise from the oedematous zone around the fused basement membrane by means of a pedicle (Fig. 24.6, p. 374).

Physiologically, there is commonly a considerable elevation of the pulmonary arterial pressure.[30–33] The wedge pressure is normal. The cardiac output is low and the pulmonary arterial resistance considerably increased. In one series of ten cases[33] there was an average mean pulmonary arterial pressure of 42 mmHg and an average mean wedge pressure of 4 mmHg. The average cardiac output was $3{\cdot}1\ 1{\cdot}min^{-1}/m^2$ BSA and the average arterial oxygen saturation 66 per cent.

The inhalation of oxygen causes an impressive fall in the pulmonary arterial pressure and amelioration of symptoms.

The mechanism of high altitude pulmonary oedema has frequently been discussed. Earlier suggestions that it was due to left ventricular failure were negated by the finding of normal levels of pulmonary wedge pressure. It has been suggested that it is due to a leakage of fluid through the walls of small elastic and muscular pulmonary arteries which is brought about by a sudden increase in the intraluminal pressure.[34] Such a considerable increase in pressure is rendered possible in high altitude natives by the increased amount of muscle in the pulmonary arteriolar walls and by the hypertrophy of the right ventricle. This would explain why the illness is most likely to afflict high altitude natives returning after a brief sojourn at low level. The influence of exercise is also consistent with this view since exercise raises the pulmonary arterial pressure even further. Whayne and Severinghaus[35] showed that the breathing of 8 per cent oxygen would cause pulmonary oedema in rats after eight hours at rest but after only ten minutes if the animals were forced to exercise. The oedema fluid in these animals appeared to reach the alveolar walls and alveolar spaces secondarily from its appearance in the perivascular spaces around arterial vessels, and it may be that this is also the mechanism in man.

It is possible that the intracapillary vesicles we describe and illustrate elsewhere (Figs 24.6 and 24.7, p. 374) exert some obstructive effect in the venous portions of the capillaries, elevating capillary pressure and leading to pulmonary oedema.[29] Hypoxic constriction of pulmonary veins is another possibility.[25] Identical endothelial vesicles occur as part of the toxic effects produced on the lung by pyrrolizidine alkaloids contained in *Crotalaria spectabilis*.[36] It has been thought previously that pulmonary oedema due to haemodynamic disturbance such as occurs in mitral stenosis collected only in the broader parts of the interstitial space of the lung containing collagen and reticulin.[37] It is clear that high altitude will give rise to identical oedematous vesicles in the pulmonary capillary bed (Figs 24.6 and 24.7, p. 374).

Influence of Natural Selection

The features which have been described in the pulmonary circulation of man at high altitude may be ascribed either to a process of acclimatization to hypoxia from birth or to the evolution of a specific high altitude strain by natural selection. We favour the former view.[38] In general, the existence of pulmonary hypertension seems to be disadvantageous rather than advantageous, and, from this point of view, it is only in the llama that adaptation by natural selection is likely.

REFERENCES

1. Rotta, A., Caneda, A., Hurtado, A., Velasquez, T. & Chavez, R. (1956) *J. Appl. Physiol.*, **9**, 328.
2. Peñaloza, D., Sime, F., Banchero, N., Gamboa, R., Cruz, J. & Marticorena, E. (1963) *Amer. J. Cardiol.*, **11**, 150.

3. Sime, F., Banchero, N., Peñaloza, D., Gamboa, R., Cruz, J. & Marticorena, E. (1963) *Amer. J. Cardiol.*, **11**, 143.
4. Peñaloza, D., Sime, F., Banchero, N. & Gamboa, R. (1962) *Med. Thorac.*, **19**, 449.
5. Arias-Stella, J. & Saldaña, M. (1963) *Circulation*, **28**, 915.
6. Heath, D., Castillo, Y., Arias-Stella, J. & Harris, P. (1969) *Cardiovasc. Res.*, **3**, 75.
7. Glover, G. H. & Newsom, I. E. (1915) *Colo. Agric. Exp. Station Bull.*, January issue, 204.
8. Hecht, H. H., Lange, R. L., Carnes, W. H., Kuida, H. & Blake, J. T. (1959) *Trans. Ass. Amer. Physcns.*, **72**, 157.
9. Hecht, H. H., Kuida, H., Lange, R. L., Thorne, J. L. & Brown, A. M. (1962) *Amer. J. Med.*, **32**, 171.
10. Abraham, A. S., Kay, J. M., Cole, R. B. & Pincock, A. C. (1971) *Cardiovasc. Res.*, **5**, 95.
11. Heath, D., Edwards, C., Winson, M. & Smith, P. (1973) *Thorax*, **28**, 24.
12. Saldaña, M. & Arias-Stella, J. (1963) *Circulation*, **27**, 1101.
13. Saldaña, M. & Arias-Stella, J. (1963) *Circulation*, **27**, 1086.
14. Saldaña, M. & Arias-Stella, J. (1963) *Circulation*, **27**, 1094.
15. Castillo, Y., Krüger, H., Arias-Stella, J., Hurtado, A., Harris, P. & Heath, D. (1967) *Brit. Heart J.*, **29**, 120.
16. Monge, C. (1928) *An. Fac. de Med.*, UNMSM, Lima.
17. Peñaloza, D. (1969) *Corazon pulmonar cronico por desadaptacion a la altura*, Tesis doctoral. Universidad Peruana Cayetano Heredia.
18. Severinghaus, J. (1972) *Clin. Physiol.*, **2**, 57.
19. Arias-Stella, J. (1969) *Abstracts Amer. Ass. Path. Bact.*
20. Edwards, C., Heath, D., Harris, P., Castillo, Y., Krüger, H. & Arias-Stella, J. (1971) *J. Path.*, **104**, 231.
21. Tenney, S. M., Scotto, P., Ou, L. C., Bartlett, D. & Remmers, J. E. (1971) *High Altitude Physiology*. CIBA Symposium. London: Churchill-Livingstone.
22. Arias-Stella, J. (1971) *High Altitude Physiology*. CIBA Symposium. London: Churchill-Livingstone.
23. Hurtado, A. (1937) ed. Rimac, S. A. Lima.
24. Marticorena, E., Tapia, F. A., Dyer, J., Severino, J., Banchero, N., Gamboa, R., Krüger, H. & Peñaloza, D. (1964) *Dis. Chest.*, **45**, 273.
25. Fred, H. L., Schmidt, A. M., Bates, T. & Hecht, H. H. (1962) *Circulation*, **25**, 929.
26. Menon, N. D. (1965) *New Engl. J. Med.*, **273**, 66.
27. Arias-Stella, J. & Krüger, H. (1963) *Arch. Path.*, **76**, 147.
28. Singh, I., Kapila, C. C., Khanna, P. K., Nanda, R. B. & Rao, B. D. P. (1965) *Lancet*, **i**, 229.
29. Heath, D., Moosavi, H. & Smith, P. (1973) *Thorax*, **28**, 694.
30. Hultgren, H. N., Lopez, C. E., Lundberg, E. & Miller, H. (1964) *Circulation*, **29**, 393.
31. Peñaloza, D. & Sime, F. (1967) *Bull. Physio-Path. Resp.*, 7, 229.
32. Roy, S. B., Guleria, J. S., Khanna, P. K., Manchanda, S. C., Pande, J. N. & Subba, P. S. (1969) *Brit. Heart J.*, **31**, 52.
33. Coudert, J. (1971) *Bull. Physio-Path. Resp.*, 7, 1303.
34. Severinghaus, J. W. (1971) *High Altitude Physiology*. CIBA Symposium. page 61. London: Churchill-Livingstone.
35. Whayne, T. F., Jn. & Severinghaus, J. W. (1968) *J. Appl. Physiol.*, **25**, 729.
36. Kay, J. M., Smith, P. & Heath, D. (1973) *Thorax*, **24**, 511.
37. Kay, J. M. & Edwards, F. R. (1973) *J. Path.*, **111**, 239.
38. Heath, D. & Williams, D. R. (1977). *Man at High Altitude*. Edinburgh: Churchill-Livingstone.

33. The Pulmonary Vasculature in Emphysema

Definition and Classification of Pulmonary Emphysema

Pulmonary emphysema is a permanent enlargement of a part or the whole of the respiratory acini distal to the terminal bronchioles. There are two basic types of emphysema corresponding to a persistent enlargement of the bronchiolar and alveolar portions of the respiratory acinus. The bronchiolar part of the respiratory acinus is the respiratory bronchiole, so-called because alveoli are present in its wall constituting the first site where exchange of respiratory gases may occur in the lung (Fig. 33.1). Persistent enlargement of the respiratory bronchioles (Fig. 33.2) is bronchiolar emphysema (Fig. 33.3). There are two main types of bronchiolar emphysema. One is 'focal dust emphysema' and is almost confined to coal workers, although a minor form does occur in the general population and has been called 'soot emphysema'. The other form is found in the general population and is associated with a history of chronic bronchiolitis commonly due to cigarette smoking; it is called 'centrilobular emphysema' because the abnormal air spaces occur in the centres of secondary lung lobules. Bronchiolar emphysema presents a characteristic appearance of clusters of enlarged respiratory bronchioles with associated carbon pigment and much normal intervening lung tissue (Fig. 33.3). Persistent enlargement of the alveolar ducts, which extend from the respiratory bronchioles to the alveoli, is called alveolar duct emphysema (Fig. 33.4). This is one form of alveolar emphysema. The other is the panacinar form which is more severe involving as its name suggests persistent enlargement of the entire respiratory acinus (Figs 33.5 and

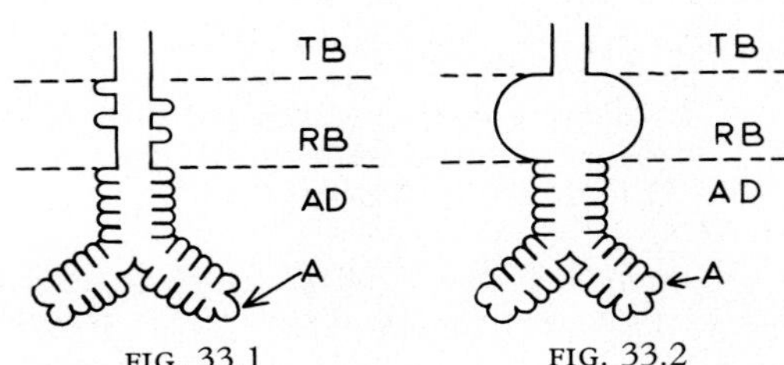

FIG. 33.1 FIG. 33.2

Fig. 33.1 Diagram of a respiratory acinus. Air passes through the terminal bronchioles (TB) to reach the respiratory bronchioles (RB), so-called because alveoli open directly from their walls. Thence, the air passes into alveolar ducts (AD) and alveoli (A). There are thus respiratory and alveolar parts of a respiratory acinus and different forms of emphysema are caused by permanent dilatation of either part. The terminal bronchiole divides into three or four generations of respiratory bronchioles but this is not shown in the diagram.

Fig. 33.2 Diagram to illustrate that in centrilobular emphysema the permanent dilatation distal to the terminal bronchiole first involves the respiratory bronchiole. Abbreviations as in Figure 33.1.

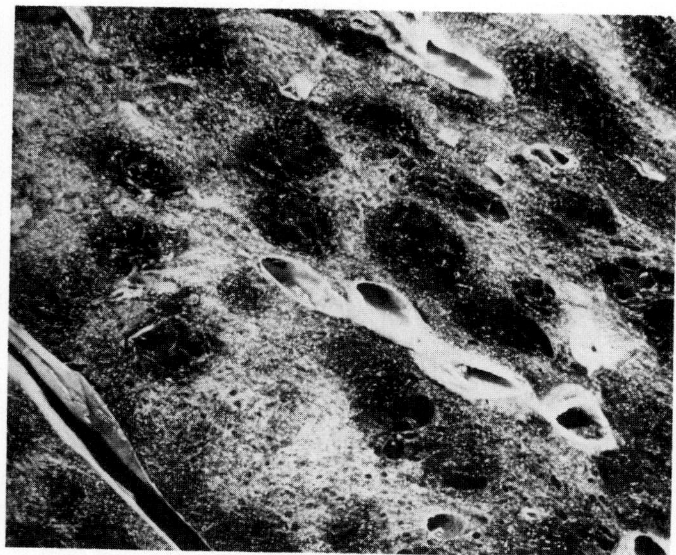

Fig. 33.3 Centrilobular emphysema. The specimen is part of a slice of lung which had been fixed in inflation by the formalin steam method of Weibel and Vidone.[1] The dilated respiratory bronchioles produce localized areas of emphysema associated with carbon pigment and separated by normal lung tissue. (× 2)

33.6). It is often difficult to distinguish confluent centrilobular emphysema from panacinar emphysema. There are localized forms of bullous emphysema in which large air-filled cysts are found on the pleural surfaces of the lungs. This account, however, is mainly concerned with the alveolar and bronchiolar forms of generalized emphysema.

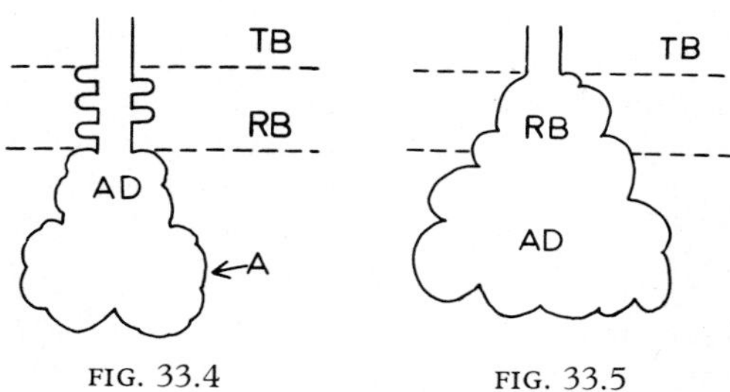

Fig. 33.4 Diagram to illustrate that in alveolar duct emphysema the permanent dilatation distal to the terminal bronchiole first involves the alveolar ducts. Abbreviations as in Figure 33.1.

Fig. 33.5 Diagram to illustrate that in panacinar emphysema the permanent dilatation within the respiratory acinus involves both the alveolar ducts and the respiratory bronchioles. Abbreviations as in Figure 33.1.

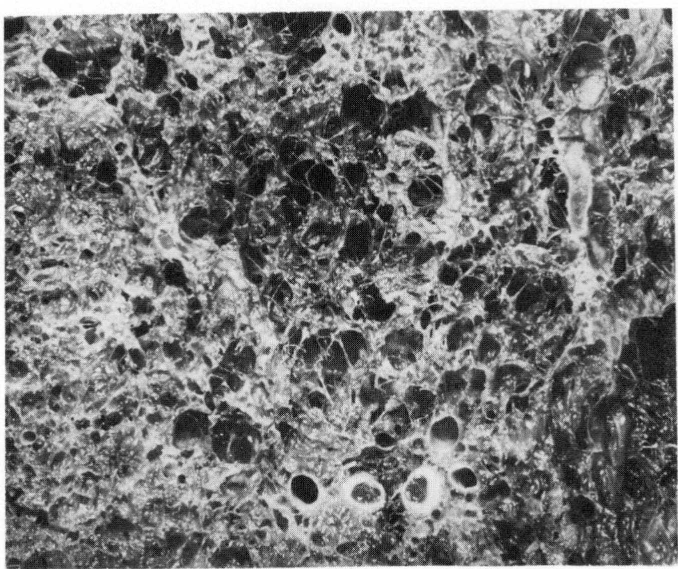

Fig. 33.6 Panacinar emphysema. The specimen is part of a slice of lung which had been fixed in inflation by the formalin steam method of Weibel and Vidone.[1] There are confluent areas of lung destruction so that the appearances contrast sharply with those of centrilobular emphysema shown in Figure 33.3. (×2)

Quantitative Assessment of Severity of Emphysema in Gross Specimens

The usual method of examining the lungs at necropsy by sectioning them in the collapsed state in the post-mortem room is valueless for the study of pulmonary emphysema. The lungs should first be fixed either by distending them with 10 per cent formalin through the trachea or by inflating them with formalin steam (Fig. 33.7).[1,2] The lung is fixed in a state of distension or inflation so that sagittal slices of the lung may be cut allowing one to determine with accuracy the type and distribution of emphysema present. The percentage of lung tissue involved by emphysema may then be determined by 'point counting' (Fig. 33.8).[2,3]

In recent years, morphometric techniques have been introduced to lung microscopy[3–5] which allow one to measure the total number of alveoli in the lung, the total alveolar volume, the mean alveolar volume, the total internal surface area of the lung and the internal surface area of the alveoli. The application of such quantitative techniques to human pulmonary pathology has made it possible to express morphological data numerically and thus to examine how they correlate with other measurements. The three methods employed are the mean linear intercept method, the geometrical method and the method of linear dimensions.[3–5]

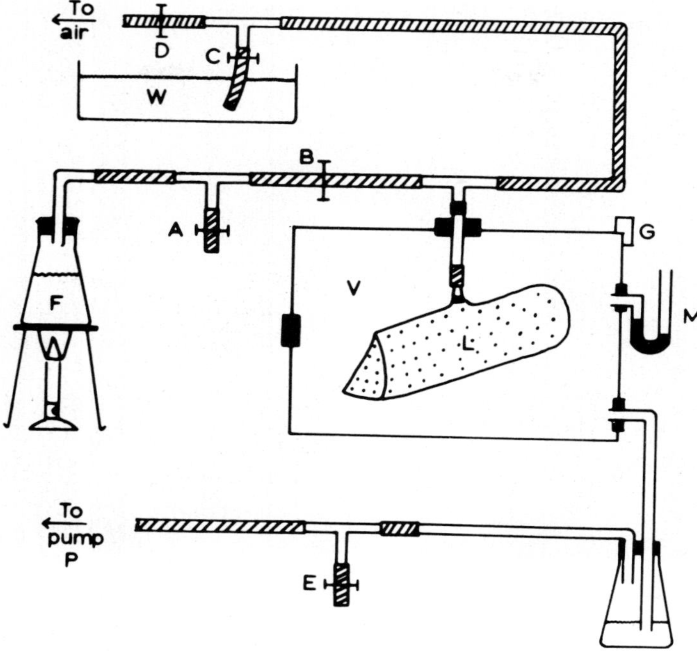

Fig. 33.7 Diagram of the apparatus used by the authors for the fixation of lungs in inflation by formalin steam by the method of Weibel and Vidone.[1] In essence the lung, L, is inflated in a vacuum chamber, V, by a vacuum pump, P. The sub-atmospheric pressure is recorded by a manometer, M. Formalin steam enters the main bronchus of the inflated lung from a flask of boiling formalin, F. A, B, C, D and E are clips used during the procedure. W is a waterbath used to trap excess formalin.

Mean Linear Intercept Method

If a number of lines of known length traverse a series of convex bodies, then the internal surface area of the convex bodies per unit volume is equal to four times the number of intercepts divided by the total length of the traversing lines. If the single traversing line of length t is randomly distributed over a section of lung and intersects alveolar walls m times and if this is repeated c times the 'mean linear intercept' of the randomly placed line, t_{m}, equals ct/m. Thus the internal surface area per unit volume of lung $= 4/t_{\mathrm{m}}$. The total internal surface area of the lung is $4/t_{\mathrm{m}}$ multiplied by the fraction of lung containing air spaces. A correction has to be made in the determination of the internal surface area of a fresh lung for the changes in area due to fixation and processing. The final equation thus becomes

$$S = \frac{4}{t_{\mathrm{m}}} \times V_{\mathrm{p}} \times \lambda \times p^2 \times f^2$$

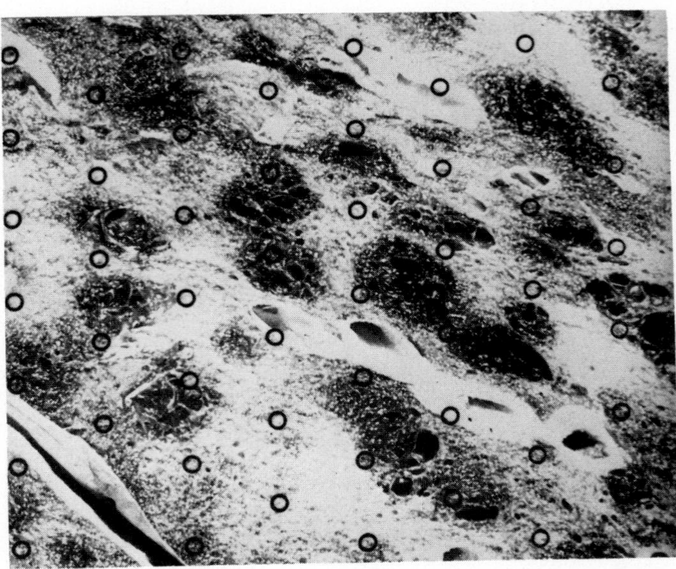

Fig. 33.8 Method of 'point-counting' a lung to determine the percentage of emphysema present. A transparent grid with holes 1 cm apart is placed over a slice of lung fixed in the apparatus shown in Figure 33.7. By determining the state of the lung tissue under each point the percentage of emphysema can be assessed.

where S = internal surface area of fresh lung determined by this method; t_m = mean linear intercept; V_p = volume of processed lung calculated from the fixed lung with the volume processing constant p^3; λ = fraction of lung volume occupied by parenchyma as determined by macroscopic point-counting described earlier in the chapter; p^2 = processing area constant; f^2 = fixation area constant.

Geometrical Method

This method devised by Weibel and Gomez[5] gives an estimate of both the total number of alveoli and the total alveolar surface area. It depends on the fact that the number of transections of given structures found in a unit area of a random section bears a relation to the number of structures present in the unit volume. The relation depends on the density of the structures in the volume and also on the shape of the structures. The number of alveoli per unit volume, n, is then derived from the number of alveoli per unit area, a, and the fraction of lung volume, ρ, occupied by alveoli determined by a microscopical method. These factors are related by the formula

$$n = \frac{a^{3/2}}{\sqrt{\rho} \times \beta}$$

where β is a constant relating the average cross-sectional area of the bodies to their volume, and for human pulmonary alveoli is 1·55. The number of alveoli per unit is determined by the use of a squared graticule in the eyepiece.

The total number of alveoli in the lung N is equivalent to the number of alveoli per unit volume, n, multiplied by the volume of the processed lung V_p and the fraction of the lung occupied by parenchyma determined macroscopically, λ,

$$N = n \times V_p \times \lambda$$

The total internal surface area of the lung may be determined by the formula

$$S = N \times \left[\frac{V \times \lambda \times \rho}{N}\right]^{2/3} \times K$$

where the symbols represent the factors already referred to in the text. K is a constant representing the surface to volume relation of the alveolus and in the human lung equals 4·8.

The Method of Linear Dimensions

This method utilizes measurements made of various dimensions of alveoli in sections so that the mean volume and the mean surface area of the alveoli can be calculated. The total volume of all the alveoli in the lung is determined in two stages. An estimate is first made of the fraction of the total lung volume occupied by parenchyma by macroscopic point-counting on lung slices described above. Subsequently, the fraction of the volume occupied by alveoli may be determined by microscopic point-counting. One can then calculate the total number of alveoli in the lung by dividing the total alveolar volume by the mean alveolar volume. To calculate the total alveolar surface area, the mean alveolar surface area is multiplied by the total number of alveoli.

Internal Surface Area of Normal and Emphysematous Lungs

When the total internal surface areas of normal lungs (*i.e.* for both right and left lungs added together) have been measured by the method of mean linear intercepts[6] the results have ranged from 43 m^2 to 84 m^2. When the results are calculated for a standard lung volume of 6000 ml, the scatter is reduced, the results[3,6–8] lying between 60 m^2 and 88 m^2. The method of mean linear intercepts estimates the whole internal surface area of the lung whereas the geometrical method and the method of linear dimensions estimate the internal surface area of the alveoli only. Hence, the internal surface of the lung estimated by these methods is somewhat smaller, ranging between 43 m^2 and 80 m^2. Standardized to a lung volume of 6000 ml, the mean value for the normal total internal surface area of the lungs is 70 m^2.

In alveolar emphysema the internal surface area of the lungs is reduced. By the method of mean linear intercepts the range has been given as 32–46 m^2 (Ref. 6) and 32–66 m^2 (Ref. 9). By the geometrical method the results are only 67 per cent of these values and by the method of linear dimensions the results are 74 per cent of those obtained by the method of mean linear intercepts.[6] In alveolar emphysema the mean value for the total internal surface area for a standard lung volume of 6000 ml is reduced to 46 m^2. By contrast in bronchiolar emphysema the internal surface area is very little reduced and an analysis of data in the literature gave a mean figure of 61 m^2, a figure some 87 per cent of the normal mean.[6]

The Number of Alveolar Spaces in the Normal Lung and in Emphysema

The mean of our results[6] for the estimation of the total number of alveoli in the human lung is 273×10^6. The mean for the results of Weibel[3] is 292×10^6. By the geometrical method the number of alveoli per ml of lung[6] is found to range from 77×10^3 to 191×10^3. Weibel[3] gives a range of 110×10^3 to 322×10^3, his series including two normal children with small lung volumes and increased numbers of alveoli.

The total numbers of alveoli are considerably reduced in alveolar emphysema,

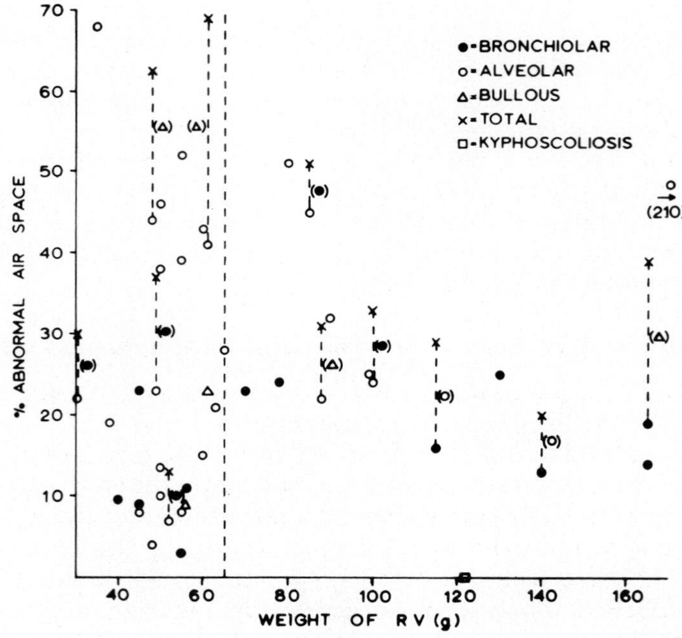

Fig. 33.9 The relation between the weight of the free wall of the right ventricle and the percentage of abnormal air space in the lung as determined by point-counting. The symbols represent the type of emphysema present, the key to the various forms being shown in the right upper corner of the Figure. In some instances only one form of emphysema was present. In others two forms existed together. In such cases, the main type of emphysema present is indicated by the symbol at the base of a vertical interrupted line. This extends upwards to the total percentage of abnormal air space present, the secondary form being indicated in brackets at the side of the interrupted line.

the ranges reported in two studies being 38×10^6 to 64×10^6 (Ref. 6) and 16×10^6 to 130×10^6 (Ref. 9). The mean value for alveolar numbers in alveolar emphysema is 63×10^6. In bronchiolar emphysema the loss of alveolar spaces is less pronounced, the data available in the literature giving a mean value of 215×10^6 (Ref. 6).

Relations Between the Type and Extent of Emphysema and the Weight of the Right Ventricle

The size of the right ventricle after death may be taken as an indication of the level of the pulmonary arterial pressure during life assuming pulmonary stenosis is absent. For this purpose, measurements of ventricular wall thickness are inaccurate and may be misleading. It is, therefore, essential to weigh the right ventricle and the method of Fulton, Hutchinson and Jones[10] is a standard one.

When the weight of the right ventricle is compared with the percentage of lung occupied by emphysema, no general relation between these two measurements is apparent[11] (Fig. 33.9). On the other hand, when the cases are divided into alveolar and bronchiolar varieties, there is a suggestion that right ventricular hypertrophy

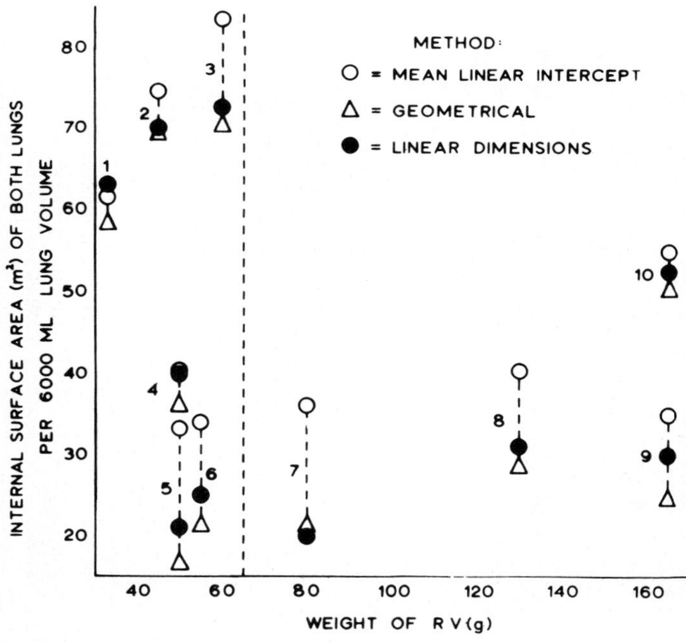

Fig. 33.10 The relation between the weight of the free wall of the right ventricle and the internal surface area (in m^2) of both lungs expressed per 6000 ml of lung volume. The internal surface area was determined by three morphometric methods as shown (see text). Cases 1, 2 and 3 are from patients free from cardiopulmonary disease. Cases 4 to 7 are in patients with panacinar emphysema. Cases 8 and 9 are in cases of mixed centrilobular and panacinar emphysema. Case 10 is in a patient with pure centrilobular emphysema.

is more likely to occur in bronchiolar emphysema. It is certainly true that a much less severe degree of the bronchiolar form of emphysema will produce the same degree of right ventricular hypertrophy as occurs with much more pronounced alveolar emphysema. This is to some extent a reflection of the fact that point-counting the area of lung damaged by multiple small foci of bronchiolar emphysema spuriously minimizes its severity. Thus, right ventricular hypertrophy may occur when as little as 14 per cent of the lung is involved by bronchiolar emphysema, whereas in cases of panacinar emphysema 40 to 70 per cent of the lung often needs to be affected before right ventricular hypertrophy develops. Leopold and Gough[12] found that 41 of their 75 cases of centrilobular (bronchiolar) emphysema had right ventricular hypertrophy, whereas only 9 of their 65 cases of alveolar emphysema had hypertrophy of this chamber. It seems, therefore, that it is the bronchiolar form of emphysema which is the more likely to give rise to serious pulmonary hypertension. This matter is considered again in the following chapter.

Figure 33.10 relates the weight of the right ventricle in the cases of emphysema to the internal surface area standardized to a total lung volume of 6000 ml (Ref. 8). In Figure 33.11 the right ventricular weight in the same ten cases is related to the

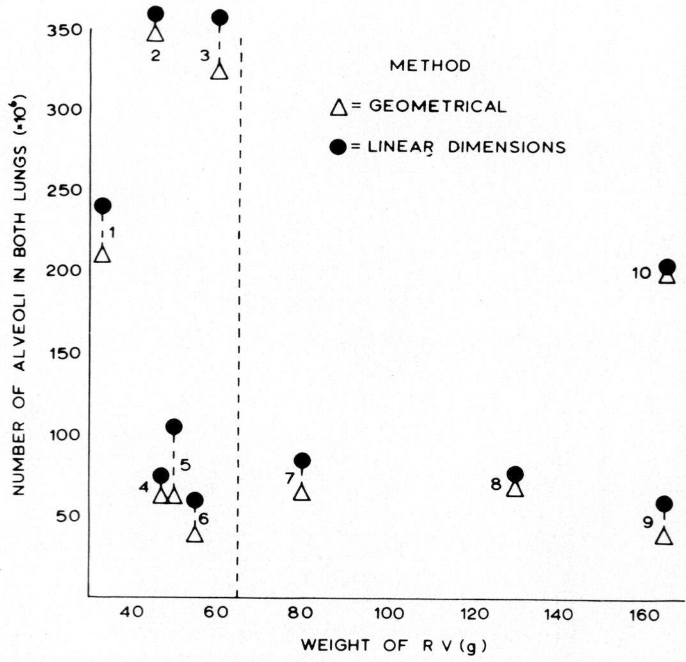

Fig. 33.11 The relation between the weight of the free wall of the right ventricle and the number of alveoli in both lungs ($\times 10^6$) as determined by the geometrical method and the method of linear dimensions (see text). The cases are the same as those referred to in Figure 33.10.

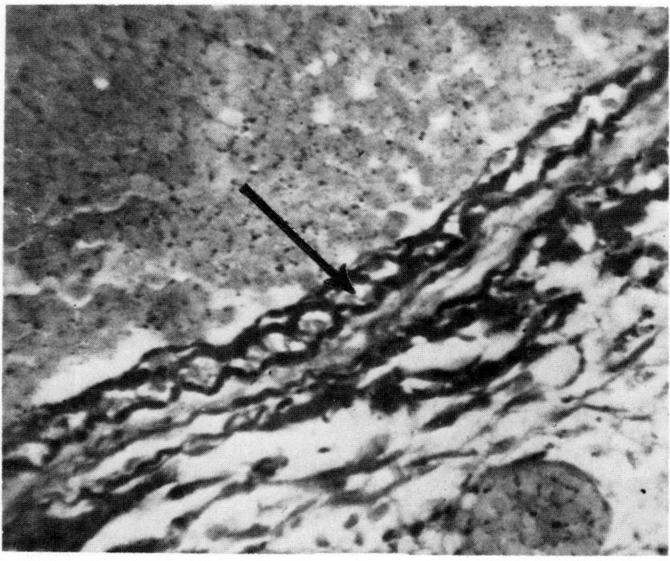

Fig. 33.12 Transverse section of part of a muscular pulmonary artery from a case of centrilobular emphysema. The media of the artery is thin walled and is bounded by internal and external elastic laminae. Fasciculi of longitudinal muscle (arrow) are seen internal to the inner elastic lamina.

number of surviving alveolar spaces per ml of lung. From these figures it is clear that there is no apparent relation between these measures of lung involvement by emphysema and the weight of the right ventricle. If a reduction in total internal surface area is equated with a reduction in pulmonary capillary bed, these findings are inconsistent with the widely held view that right ventricular hypertrophy in emphysema is a result of loss of pulmonary capillary bed. It is clear that we must look elsewhere for a possible organic basis for the development of right ventricular hypertrophy in emphysema and the following section considers the morbid anatomy of the pulmonary arteries in this condition.

The Pulmonary Vasculature in Emphysema

There are four main histological features of the pulmonary vasculature in cases of emphysema: the development of intimal longitudinal muscle, muscularization of the pulmonary arterioles, a lack of significant medial hypertrophy of the muscular pulmonary arteries, and a lack of occlusive lesions.[13]

Longitudinal muscle may develop in the intima of muscular pulmonary arteries and pulmonary arterioles as small fasciculi of longitudinally orientated smooth muscle fibres (Fig. 33.12). This may develop to form a thicker, continuous band of longitudinal muscle in the intima (Fig. 33.13). Intimal elastosis occurs so that the longitudinal muscle fibres become separated from one another by elastic fibrils

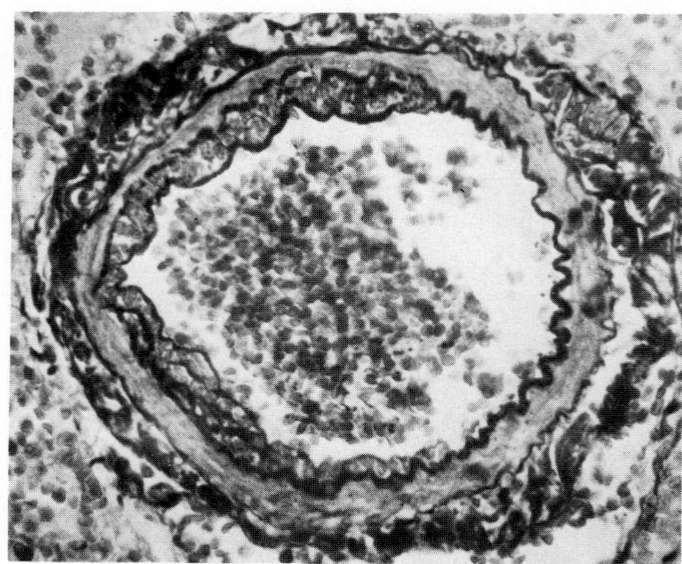

Fig. 33.13 Transverse section of a muscular pulmonary artery from the same case showing a well-developed layer of longitudinal muscle internal to the inner elastic lamina.

(Fig. 33.14). Finally, intimal fibrosis occurs and obliterates the longitudinal muscle so that the observer unaware of the earlier muscular stages of the process might dismiss the intimal change as a non-specific intimal fibrosis (Fig. 33.15). The development of longitudinal muscle is not related to right ventricular hypertrophy and hence to pulmonary hypertension.[13] It occurs in cases of emphysema with and without right ventricular hypertrophy (Fig. 33.16).

Previous studies on the development of longitudinal muscle in pulmonary arteries[14] suggested that it is a reaction to the combined stimulus of pulmonary hypertension and repeated stretching of the arteries. Dunnill[15] considers that the muscular pulmonary arteries in centrilobular emphysema are distorted by the abnormal air sacs in the centres of secondary lung lobules, and that this stretching, associated sometimes with pulmonary arterial hypertension, may be the cause of the development of longitudinal muscle in the pulmonary arteries in this type of emphysema. We have been able to confirm the observation of Liebow[16] that longitudinal muscle occurs in pulmonary arteries distorted and stretched around emphysematous bullae.

In some cases the pulmonary arterioles become muscularized. The normal wall, which consists of a single elastic lamina, is replaced by a distinct media of circular muscle sandwiched between internal and external elastic laminae (Fig. 33.17).[13] There is a close relation between the development of such muscularized pulmonary arterioles and right ventricular hypertrophy in emphysema. This suggests that, in

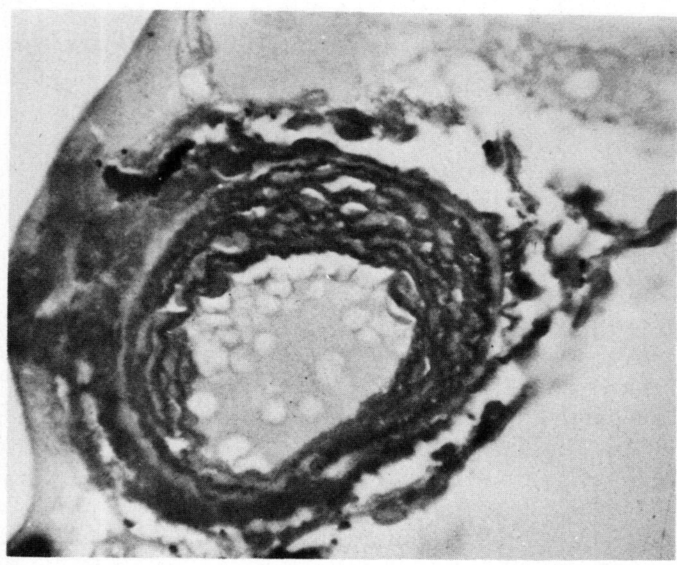

Fig. 33.14 Transverse section of a small muscular pulmonary artery in a case of emphysema showing a layer of longitudinal muscle in the intima, the individual fibres being separated from one another by elastic fibrils.

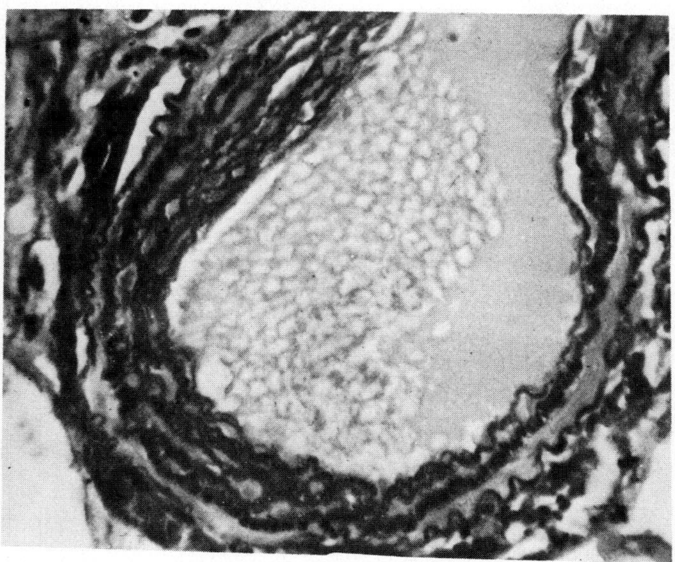

Fig. 33.15 Transverse section of a muscular pulmonary artery from a case of emphysema showing intimal fibroelastosis with only traces of longitudinal muscle remaining to indicate the true pathogenesis of the intimal proliferation.

emphysema, muscularized pulmonary arterioles form the basis for an increased pulmonary vascular resistance. It has been suggested[15] that the distortion of small muscular pulmonary arteries around dilated respiratory bronchioles in bronchiolar emphysema may bring about an inreased pulmonary vascular resistance but this seems less likely. Muscularized pulmonary arterioles are found more commonly in the bronchiolar form of emphysema implying that pulmonary hypertension is more common in this condition, and this is consistent with the frequency of right ventricular hypertrophy in bronchiolar emphysema discussed above.

In contrast to the muscularization of the arterioles, the muscular pulmonary arteries show little tendency to undergo hypertrophy in emphysema[13] even in the presence of right ventricular hypertrophy. These vessels do not show the pronounced medial hypertrophy that characterizes the pulmonary vascular disease associated with congenital cardiac shunts (Chap. 16), left atrial hypertension (Chap. 22), or primary pulmonary hypertension (Chap. 28). Other workers have also commented upon this anomalous finding in emphysema.[12,15,17] It may be a reflection of the fact that the degree of pulmonary hypertension found in the majority of cases of emphysema is less severe than that in mitral stenosis or congenital cardiac shunts[18] (Chap. 34). Furthermore, the pulmonary hypertension of emphysema, unlike that

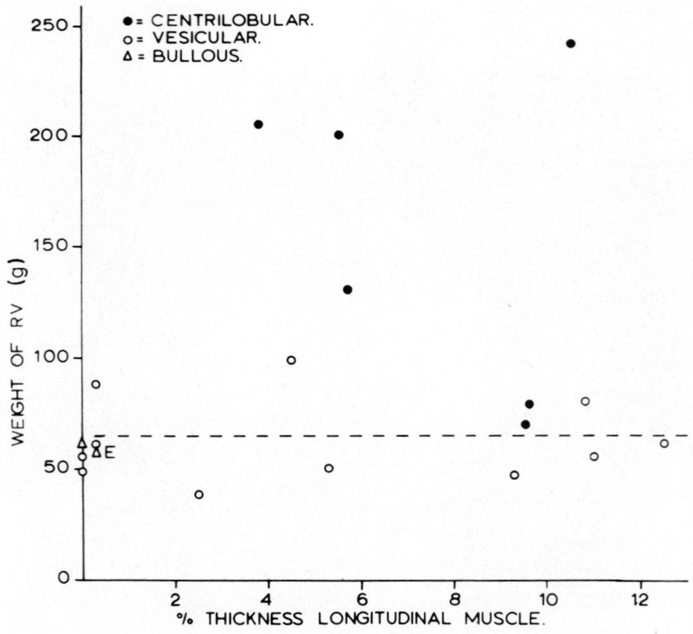

Fig. 33.16 The relation between the thickness of intimal longitudinal muscle in muscular pulmonary arteries, expressed as a percentage of the external diameter of the vessel, and the weight of the free wall of the right ventricle in cases of centrilobular, vesicular (alveolar), and bullous emphysema.

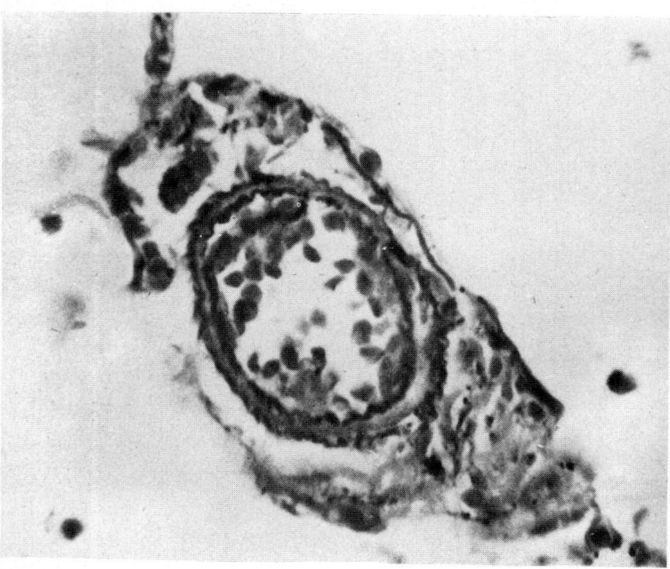

Fig. 33.17 Transverse section of an abnormal muscularized pulmonary arteriole from a case of centrilobular emphysema complicated by right ventricular hypertrophy. There is a distinct media of circular muscle sandwiched between internal and external elastic laminae.

in acquired and congenital heart disease, tends to be periodic rather than sustained, an elevation of the pulmonary arterial pressure occurring during attacks of respiratory infection and fluid retention.[18]

An important finding is the absence of severe occlusion of the pulmonary vasculature due to intimal fibrosis (Fig. 33.18). Such intimal fibrosis as is found is fine in structure contrasting with the coarse fibroelastosis that characterizes the pulmonary vascular disease of congenital cardiac shunts (Chap. 16). Intimal fibrosis of this mild degree is probably of little or no significance in bringing about an increased pulmonary vascular resistance in emphysema.

Hypoxic Hypertensive Pulmonary Vascular Disease

Muscularization of the terminal portions of the pulmonary arterial tree seems to occur in all states of chronic hypoxia irrespective of its aetiology.[19] Thus it has been found in centrilobular and panacinar emphysema, in normal Quechua Indians born and living at high altitude in the Peruvian Andes (Chap. 32, p. 487), in sufferers from Monge's disease (so-called 'chronic mountain sickness'), the Pickwickian syndrome, and kyphoscoliosis. These conditions are all characterized by hypercarbia as well as hypoxia except for the normal people living at high altitude who have hypocarbia. The fact that these mountain dwellers also show muscularization of the terminal portions of the pulmonary arterial tree suggests that this histological

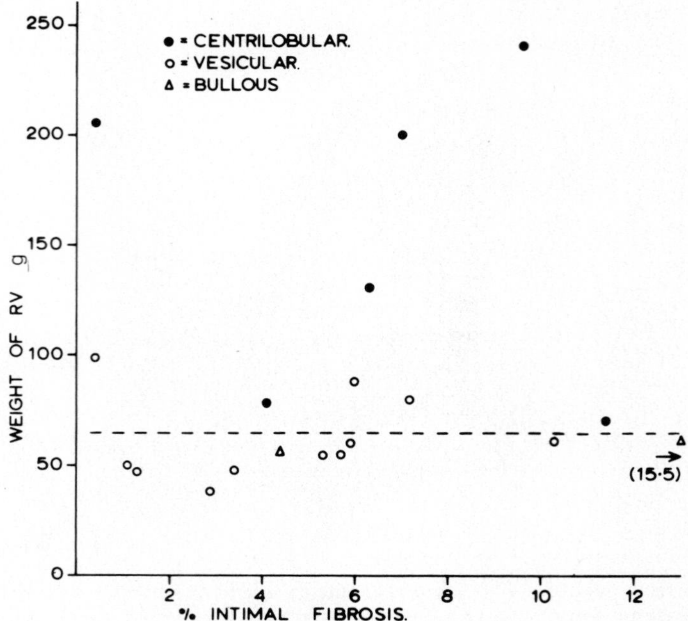

Fig. 33.18 The relation between the thickness of a layer of intimal fibrosis in muscular pulmonary arteries, and the weight of the free wall of the right ventricle in cases of centrilobular, vesicular (alveolar), and bullous emphysema. The intimal fibrosis is expressed as a percentage of the internal diameter of the vessel measured between diametrically opposite points on the internal elastic lamina.

change is to be associated with the stimulus of chronic hypoxia. This association has led us to introduce the concept of 'hypoxic hypertensive pulmonary vascular disease' having the histological features described in detail above.[19] It may well be that hypoxia acts directly on the affected pulmonary blood vessels because pulmonary arterioles can be shown to be related to those segments of the bronchial tree where they could come into immediate contact with alveolar air[19] and it is known that the alveolar gas composition influences the composition of the blood in vessels as large as muscular pulmonary arteries.[20]

THE REVERSIBILITY OF HYPOXIC HYPERTENSIVE PULMONARY VASCULAR DISEASE

In states of chronic hypoxia, the changes in the pulmonary vasculature are largely muscular without occlusive intimal fibrosis. Histological appearances of this type suggest that hypoxic hypertensive pulmonary vascular disease is readily reversible and in fact there is ample experimental evidence in animals to support this view.[21,22] Furthermore, there is clinical evidence to suggest that hypoxic pulmonary hypertension in man is readily reversible (Chap. 32).

In one experiment[21] rats were confined to a decompression chamber for 33 days and maintained at a pressure of 380 mmHg simulating an altitude of 5500 m.

This period of hypoxia was followed by 37 days of recovery at atmospheric pressure (760 mmHg). On the fifth day of the experiment and every seventh day subsequently, two test rats and two untreated control rats were subjected to right heart cannulation for the measurement of intracardiac pressures. The animals were then killed and a quantitative pathological examination of the heart and pulmonary blood vessels was carried out. During the hypoxic phase of the experiment, there was a progressive rise in the right ventricular mean pressure in the test rats. This was accompanied by a progressive increase in right ventricular weight and muscularization of the pulmonary arterioles. Half the test rats showed medial thickening of their smaller muscular pulmonary arteries. The organic basis of the increased pulmonary vascular resistance was considered to be the abnormal muscularization of the smaller pulmonary arterial blood vessels. During the recovery phase of the experiment, the test rats showed a progressive reduction in right ventricular mean pressure with concomitant regression of the right ventricular hypertrophy and pulmonary vascular disease.

In another study[22] it was shown that rats exposed to chronic hypoxia without relief for five weeks by exposing them to a barometric pressure of 380 mmHg develop right ventricular hypertrophy, medial hypertrophy of the pulmonary trunk and enlargement of the carotid bodies. When rats after such a period of chronic hypoxia are allowed to recover in room air for a further period of five weeks the right ventricle, the thickness of the pulmonary trunk and the volume of the carotid bodies all return virtually to normal.[22]

OTHER PULMONARY VASCULAR LESIONS IN EMPHYSEMA

Unusually a severe and sustained pulmonary hypertension may occur in patients with emphysema. Under these circumstances more pronounced medial hypertrophy and intimal fibrosis occurs in the muscular pulmonary arteries. Even fibrinoid necrosis in the muscular pulmonary arteries has been reported in a case of chronic bronchitis and emphysema[23] but this is very rare.

Pulmonary thrombosis may occur in the pulmonary vasculature in emphysema. According to McLean[24] pulmonary thrombi form and are covered by endothelium, phagocytosed by macrophages, and replaced by basophilic intercellular substance showing a loose, fibrillar pattern. Capillary blood vessels, many of them derived from the vasa vasorum, which are tributaries of the bronchial arteries (Chap. 39), penetrate the arterial media and enter the fibrous tissue, frequently re-canalizing it. The intimal fibrous tissue, which may or may not be symmetrical, according to the configuration of the thrombus organized (Chap. 37), becomes acellular and finally its origin from thrombus is unrecognizable. There is some splitting of the internal elastic lamina with some intimal elastosis but these changes are not so pronounced as in the form of hypertensive pulmonary vascular disease complicating congenital cardiac anomalies. Pronounced fibrous change tends to occur in arteries adjacent to ectatic bronchioles where the surrounding lung parenchyma is organized following previous inflammation. In such areas the arteries may become totally obliterated and recognized only by the remnants of elastic tissue in their walls. Pulmonary veins in the area show similar intimal fibrosis but the significance of this must be assessed carefully before ascribing it to emphysema for in the lungs of most normal subjects intimal fibrosis occurs as a normal age change (Chap. 3).

Bronchial Vascular Lesions and Bronchopulmonary Anastomoses in Emphysema

The bronchial vasculature is often normal in emphysema, but when the disease is severe there may be intimal proliferation in those bronchial arteries adjacent to ectatic bronchi which show evidence of previous inflammation. According to Cudkowicz and Armstrong[25] many bronchial arteries in emphysema may be narrowed or even obliterated following medial hypertrophy and intimal fibrosis while blocked visceral pleural branches may occasionally be re-vascularized and re-canalized by means of parietal visceral pleural vessels. It is difficult to be certain that such changes in the bronchial arteries are of pathological significance. Normal bronchial arteries are very thick-walled and appear almost occluded (Chap. 38). Age changes in them have not been studied and may account for the appearances described. Nevertheless, sepsis in adjacent bronchioles may play some part as it appears to do in the production of similar changes in the pulmonary arteries in emphysema. It has been suggested[25] that occlusive lesions of the bronchial arteries can cause ischaemic changes in the structures supplied by them. For instance, the walls of the small bronchi become fibrous with a loss of cartilage and mucous glands. However, it is difficult to be sure that such changes are due to occlusion of the bronchial arteries. They might equally well be the effect of chronic inflammation.

Bronchopulmonary anastomoses have been described in emphysema[25,26] and the degree of their development is apparently proportional to the severity of the pulmonary disease. Enlarged bronchial arteries anastomose with fibrotic pulmonary arteries near damaged bronchi. The anastomotic channels seen rarely exceed 100 μm in diameter and are usually simple channels through the media.[25] Tortuous anastomotic channels, lying within the almost obliterated lumen of a branch of a pulmonary artery may also be found and traced peripherally into a recognizable bronchial artery. Such anastomoses are not dilated pre-existing channels, but appear to be formed by the re-canalization of thrombosed pulmonary arteries by bronchial vasa vasorum. Bronchopulmonary venous anastomoses have also been described in emphysema.

REFERENCES

1. Weibel, E. R. & Vidone, R. A. (1961) *Amer. Rev. Resp. Dis.*, **84**, 856.
2. Dunnill, M. S. (1962) *Thorax*, **17**, 320.
3. Weibel, E. R. (1963) *Morphometry of the Human Lung*. Berlin: Springer.
4. Hasleton, P. S. (1972) *J. Anat.*, **112**, 391.
5. Weibel, E. R. & Gomez, D. M. (1962) *J. Appl. Physiol.*, **17**, 343.
6. Heath, D., Brewer, D. & Hicken, P. (1968) *Cor Pulmonale in Emphysema*. Springfield, Ill.: Thomas.
7. Duguid, J. B., Young, A., Cauna, D. & Lambert, M. W. (1964) *J. Path. Bact.*, **88**, 405.
8. Hicken, P., Brewer, D. & Heath, D. (1966) *J. Path. Bact.*, **92**, 529.
9. Dunnill, M. S. (1965) *Med. Thorac.*, **22**, 261.

10. Fulton, R. M., Hutchinson, E. C. & Morgan Jones, A. (1952) *Brit. Heart J.*, **14**, 413.
11. Hicken, P., Heath, D. & Brewer, D. B. (1966) *J. Path. Bact.*, **92**, 519.
12. Leopold, J. G. & Gough, J. (1957) *Thorax*, **12**, 219.
13. Hicken, P., Heath, D., Brewer, D. B. & Whitaker, W. (1965) *J. Path. Bact.*, **90**, 107.
14. Heath, D. (1963) *J. Path. Bact.*, **85**, 407.
15. Dunnill, M. S. (1961) *J. Clin. Path.*, **14**, 246.
16. Liebow, A. A. (1964) In *Aging of the Lung*, ed. Cander, L. & Moyer, J. H. page 99. New York.
17. Cameron, A. H. (1956) *Thorax*, **11**, 105.
18. Whitaker, W. (1954) *Quart. J. Med., (NS).*, **23**, 57.
19. Hasleton, P. S., Heath, D. & Brewer, D. B. (1968) *J. Path. Bact.*, **95**, 431.
20. Duling, B. R. & Berne, R. M. (1970) *Circulat. Res.*, **27**, 669.
21. Abraham, A. S., Kay, J. M., Cole, R. B. & Pincock, A. C. (1971) *Cardiovasc. Res.*, **5**, 95.
22. Heath, D., Edwards, C., Winson, M. & Smith, P. (1973) *Thorax*, **28**, 24.
23. Dunnill, M. S. (1960) *Brit. J. Dis. Chest*, **54**, 355.
24. McLean, K. H. (1958) *Aust. Ann. Med.*, **7**, 69.
25. Cudkowicz, L. & Armstrong, J. B. (1953) *Thorax*, **8**, 46.
26. Marchand, P., Gilroy, J. C. & Wilson, V. H. (1950) *Thorax*, **5**, 207.

34. Pulmonary Haemodynamics in Chronic Bronchitis and Emphysema

In the preceding chapter we have discussed evidence which shows that right ventricular hypertrophy and morphological changes in the pulmonary arterial tree consistent with pulmonary hypertension are more related to the type of emphysema than to its extent. In the present chapter we shall attempt to consider physiological and clinical observations in the light of such morphological information.

The Diagnosis of Emphysema

The clinical diagnosis of emphysema, resting on the classical triad of the shape of the chest, the diminution of normal areas of dullness to percussion and the decrease in breath sounds, is notoriously unreliable. Radiology is a little more helpful, giving perhaps a less equivocal indication of an increase in the size of the lungs from an increased antero-posterior diameter and flattening of the diaphragms. Relatively large regions of lung affected with emphysema can be distinguished from normal regions by their increased translucency due to the disappearance of vascular shadows. The great limitation of radiology is that it quite fails to demonstrate the widespread small lesions of centrilobular emphysema which the morbid anatomical evidence shows to be of such importance.

Measurements of total lung capacity or residual volume by physiological methods are no more helpful. Methods which rely on the dilution of inhaled foreign gases may fail to demonstrate emphysematous regions with very little ventilation. Even the measurement of total gas volume by whole-body plethysmography reveals such a wide scatter of normal values that the values in emphysema are not clearly distinguished. While, with these reservations, the methods may show an increase in total lung volume in a patient with panacinar emphysema, they are totally unable to identify centrilobular emphysema which, even in a fatal case, may occupy only 14 per cent of the lung (p. 512).

Obstruction of Airways

For the clinician and for the physiologist, panacinar and centrilobular emphysema form the bulk of a group of patients whose main functional abnormality is an increased airways resistance, and for which the term 'chronic obstructive lung disease' is commonly used. Thus, while the pathologist has been preoccupied with the parenchyma, the clinician has been preoccupied with the bronchial tree. So striking is this difference in viewpoint that the visiting Martian might well be excused the belief that they were studying different diseases.

The increased resistance to the respiratory flow of air implies a narrowing of airways which may arise from causes intrinsic or extrinsic to their walls. Intrinsic causes comprise bronchospasm, thickening of the bronchial mucosa, fibrosis of the wall and occlusion of the lumen with an excess of mucus, all of which may be associated with chronic inflammation. The extrinsic mechanism whereby the resistance of the airways is increased is due to a compression of them during expiration. The increase in intrathoracic pressure, which causes the expiratory flow of air through the airways, also acts on their walls, tending to make them collapse.[1] This is opposed in the larger airways by the presence of cartilage and in the smaller intrapulmonary branches by the tethering of the pulmonary parenchyma. Destruction of the parenchyma by emphysema may thus leave the intrapulmonary airways unsupported and allow them to be more easily compressed during expiration.

An intrinsic narrowing in the bronchial tree may reduce or increase this effect according to its position. At one anatomical extreme, a narrowing of the bronchioles will enhance the compression of airways during expiration since it will increase the alveolar pressure surrounding the bronchi. At the opposite extreme, a narrowing at the larynx will reduce the expiratory compression of airways by increasing their intraluminal pressure.[2] Patients often unconsciously make use of the latter mechanism by breathing against a partly closed glottis or against pursed lips.

Studies on human lungs at necropsy[3] have shown that airways with a calibre of less than 2 mm normally contribute only about 25 per cent of the total airways resistance. In subjects with centrilobular or panacinar emphysema there was an increase in the total airways resistance to which the small airways now contributed as much as 90 per cent. By means of catheters situated in the segmental and main-stem bronchus it could be shown that in patients with chronic obstructive lung disease there were two levels of resistance in the airways.[4] One was situated in the small airways and was relatively fixed. The other was situated in the larger airways and became greatly increased during expiration. Similar conclusions were drawn from bronchography.[5] It will be recalled from the previous discussion that an increased resistance at the level of small airways will be expected particularly to cause collapse of the larger airways during expiration.

Such observations suggest that, as far as an increased airways resistance is concerned, it is the abnormality of the small bronchi and bronchioles which is primary, the expiratory collapse of the larger airways being secondary. Since, however, as we have noted, the small airways normally contribute little to the total airways resistance, the earlier stages of the disease will be missed by conventional tests of respiratory function.[6] Methods of demonstrating disease of small airways by the distribution of ventilation and perfusion,[7] the presence of frequency-dependent compliance,[8] a reduction in the maximum mid-expiratory flow rate[9] or an increase in the 'closing volume'[10] have, therefore, been of particular interest. In patients with chronic bronchitis who had normal routine respiratory function tests the presence of frequency-dependent compliance[8] and an abnormal distribution of ventilation and perfusion[7] has been demonstrated. It is noteworthy that the presence of frequency-dependent compliance[11] a reduction in the maximum mid-expiratory flow rate[9] and an increase in the 'closing volume'[10] has been shown in otherwise-normal cigarette smokers. An increase in the 'closing volume' probably points to lesions in airways less than 1 mm in diameter.[12] The specific association between cigarette smoking and centrilobular emphysema has been shown to be remarkably strong.[13]

Disease of the Airways in Emphysema

An increased resistance to air flow has been demonstrated in airways with a calibre less than 2 mm in lungs with either centrilobular or panacinar emphysema.[3] Leopold and Gough[14] made a careful study of the small airways by serial sections. They found that centrilobular emphysema is specifically associated with inflammation and often narrowing of the bronchiole which supplies the lesion. With panacinar emphysema the bronchioles were rarely affected. Evidence of chronic inflammation in main, lobar and segmental bronchi was present in all cases of centrilobular emphysema and in the majority of cases with panacinar emphysema.

Clinical Groupings of Patients with Chronic Bronchitis and Emphysema

The group of patients with what is sometimes referred to as 'chronic non-specific lung disease'[15] has long defied classification. Some of them may be regarded as having chronic bronchitis because of a chronic cough productive of mucoid sputum. In others there is radiological evidence of emphysema. Most will have an increased resistance to the expiratory flow of air. Other aspects which vary greatly from patient to patient are disturbances of respiratory gas exchange, the occurrence of episodes of acute respiratory failure with oedema and the existence of pulmonary arterial hypertension.

Although the criteria at present available have not allowed any satisfactory classification, clinicians have been able to distinguish from the heterogenous population two types in which the above variables are assembled in particular patterns which may suggest a pathological distinction.[16–19] These two types may be referred to as 'bronchitic' and 'emphysematous'. In their relatively pure form, they represent about one half of the total number of patients[20] so that there are many intermediate cases. Both types have an increased expiratory airways resistance.

The 'emphysematous' type is characterized by a thin body-build and progressive dyspnoea in middle age. The chest radiograph reveals evidence of emphysema and there is an increase in the total lung capacity. Despite an impressive dyspnoea the arterial P_{CO_2} is normal and P_{O_2} not greatly reduced. Polycythaemia does not occur. Measurements of the pulmonary diffusing capacity are reduced, although the physiological meaning of this is not clear (p. 647). Episodes of acute respiratory failure and oedema are unusual and the cardiac size normal.

Patients of the 'bronchitic' type present with many years of productive cough. They tend to be of stocky build. The chest radiograph shows no evidence of emphysema but cardiac enlargement is common. The total lung capacity is not increased and emphysema not prominent at routine necropsy. In these patients

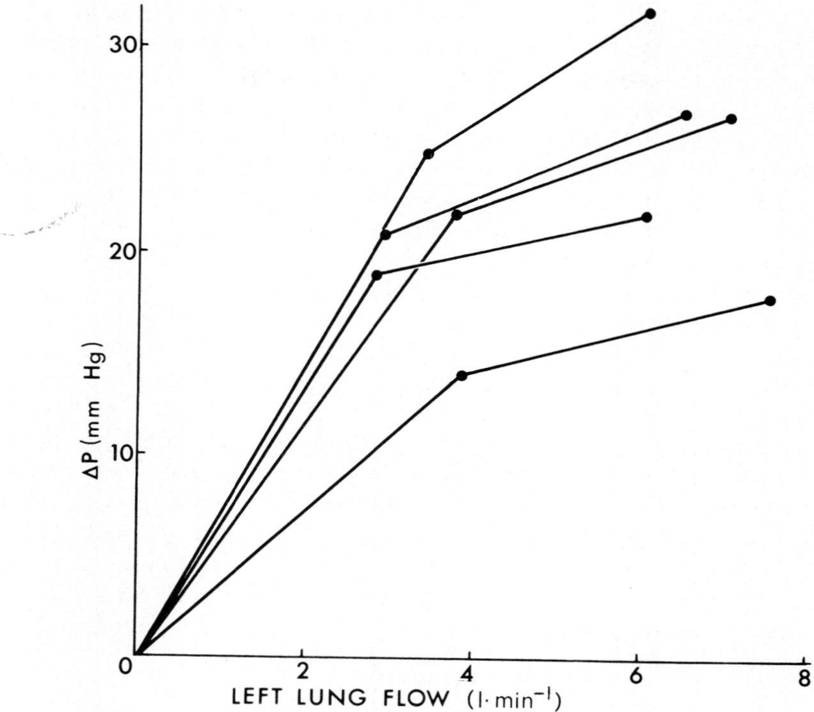

Fig. 34.1 The relation between pressure and flow in the pulmonary circulation of five patients with chronic bronchitis and emphysema.[34] The technique of occluding the right pulmonary artery is the same as that in Figure 9.13, page 130. ΔP = mean pulmonary arterial pressure minus wedge pressure.

there is a serious disturbance of respiratory gas exchange with an increased arterial P_{CO_2}, a decreased arterial P_{O_2} and polycythaemia. The pulmonary diffusing capacity is, however, normal. These patients are particularly prone to attacks of acute respiratory failure with oedema.

There is a temptation to identify the 'bronchitic' type with centrilobular emphysema and the 'emphysematous' type with panacinar emphysema. However, in the one study[20] in which an attempt was made to relate the clinical grouping with morbid anatomy, no such clear-cut association was found.

Pulmonary Haemodynamics in the Absence of Acute Respiratory Failure

In those studies where the 'bronchitic' and 'emphysematous' types have been studied separately[21,22] the pulmonary arterial pressure has been found to be raised in the 'bronchitic' patients and near normal in the 'emphysematous' patients at rest. In a recent series[22] the average mean pulmonary arterial pressure at rest was 28 mmHg in 'bronchitic' patients and 16 mmHg in 'emphysematous' patients.

Since the original report by Herles and his colleagues,[23] the occurrence of an abnormally high wedge pressure in a proportion of patients has frequently been confirmed.[24–30] Although there has been some controversy concerning the resting cardiac output it seems, on the whole, that this does not differ greatly from normal[31] and no difference has been demonstrated between the 'bronchitic' and 'emphysematous' types.[21,22] The pulmonary arterial resistance may be normal or may show a mild or moderate increase.[25–30,32,33]

We have studied the relation between pressure and flow in the pulmonary circulation in patients with chronic bronchitis and emphysema,[34] using the technique of occluding the right branch of the pulmonary artery with a balloon on the end of a cardiac catheter (p. 129). The relation differs strikingly from the normal (Fig. 34.1). The initial part of the relation is steeper than normal (*cf.* Fig. 9.13, p. 130) indicating an increased resistance. Unlike normal subjects or patients with mitral stenosis (Fig. 23.4, p. 357) the relation is curvilinear, such that the arterio-venous difference in pressure (ΔP) does not increase proportionately with flow. Thus, with an increasing flow there is a decrease in resistance. This implies that those vessels which are the chief sites of resistance are narrower than normal at a normal flow but distend readily when the flow increases. Such a combination might be due to vasoconstriction or to compression from outside the vessel wall. Later in the chapter we discuss evidence which supports the second explanation.

The Effects of Exercise

Table 34.1 summarizes the effects of exercise in a number of studies which have included simultaneous measurements of the pulmonary arterial and wedge pressures and the cardiac output. The pulmonary arterial pressure increases. The wedge pressure also increases and this seems to be more pronounced in the more severely affected groups of patients. The response of the cardiac output to exercise has been normal in these and several other studies. This appears to be so even in the presence of systemic oedema. Exercise is usually associated with some degree of decrease in the arterial oxygen saturation or P_{O_2}. This does not necessarily imply a decreased alveolar P_{O_2} since the saturation of the mixed venous blood decreases, which increases the effect of the physiological shunt (p. 466). The arterial P_{CO_2} tends to rise.

The effects of exercise on the pulmonary arterial resistance have been variable and, for the most part, small. The reason for this becomes apparent when the curvilinearity of the pressure : flow relation is taken into account.[34] Figure 34.2 shows the relation between pressure and flow studied by the unilateral occlusion technique (p. 129) in a patient with chronic bronchitis and emphysema at rest and during exercise. The difference from the effects of exercise in normal subjects (Fig. 11.5, p. 160) and patients with mitral stenosis (Fig. 23.5, p. 358) is striking. The observations during exercise no longer occur on the resting pressure : flow line or an extension of it. Instead the arterio-venous difference in pressure has become

Table 34.1 The effects of exercise and acute respiratory failure with oedema in patients with chronic bronchitis and emphysema. The figures are averages

Ref.	Relation to systemic oedema	Number of cases	Mean pulmonary arterial pressure mmHg		Wedge pressure mmHg		Cardiac output $l \cdot min^{-1}$ (/m^2 BSA)		Pulmonary arterial resistance[a] $dyn \cdot s \cdot cm^{-5}$ ($\times m^2$ BSA)		Sa_{O_2} %		Pa_{CO_2} mmHg	
			Rest	Exercise	Rest	Exercise	Rest	Exercise	Rest	Exercise	Rest	Exercise	Rest	Exercise
81	Never oedema	20	28	47	9	16	(3·3)	(4·7)	300	300	83	78	—	—
28	Recent oedema and polycythaemia	15	47	77	11	17	(3·3)	(4·9)	514	636	81	68	57	64
33	Previous oedema	17	28	46	12	20	(3·7)	(5·1)	230	251	—	—	50	55
32	Previous acute respiratory failure in 3	12	19	31	8	13	(3·2)	(5·3)	(276)	(304)	94	95	43	46
25	Without oedema	14	25	34	9	11	(3·0)	(4·0)	256	269				
	With oedema	8	29	43	10	13	(2·7)	(3·6)	397	474				
82	Without oedema	20	20	30	10	15	(3·2)	(5·2)	(250)	(231)				
27	Never oedema	43	21	31	9	14	(3·1)	(5·2)	(264)	(233)				
	Previous oedema	29	29	42	10	15	(3·2)	(6·2)	(297)	(265)				
	In oedema	15	33	39	12	16	(3·7)	(5·7)	(454)	(315)				
83	Never oedema	26	17	28	8	11	(3·3)	(6·0)	140	140	92	91	41	43
	Previous oedema	14	22	37	9	16	(3·5)	(5·7)	190	182	91	88	42	46
	In oedema	10	27	50	11	19	(3·5)	(5·5)	207	241	87	82	46	56
30	No recent oedema	74	23	—	7	—	(3·7)	—	207	—	87	—	41[b]	—
	Recovery from oedema	18	34	—	10	—	(3·7)	—	352	—	82	—	45[c]	—
	In oedema	29	41	—	13	—	(3·4)	—	417	—	78	—	51[d]	—
29	Previous oedema	6	29	—	14	—	(2·7)	—	254	—	—	—	51	—
	Never oedema	6	43	—	13	—	(3·0)	—	503	—	—	—	57	—

[a] See page 135.
[b] $n = 43$
[c] $n = 7$
[d] $n = 14$

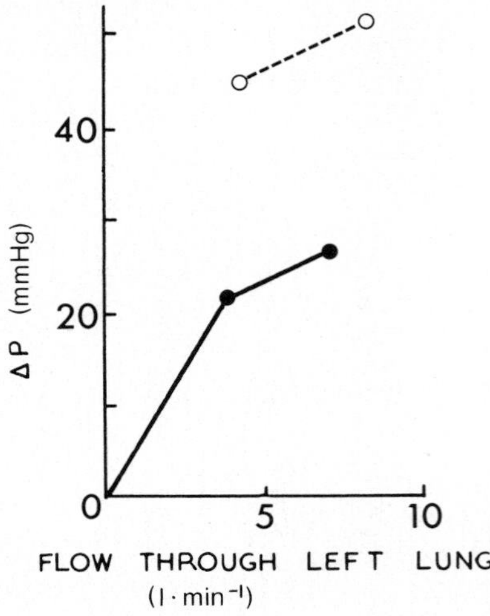

Fig. 34.2 The effect of exercise on the relation between pressure and flow in the pulmonary circulation in a patient with chronic bronchitis and emphysema.[34] Technique as in Figure 9.13, page 130.

inappropriately high for the magnitude of the flow, which means that the resistance is inappropriately high for the level of flow. This implies that the vessels which are the site of resistance are inappropriately narrow for the magnitude of the flow. The mechanism of such a narrowing is discussed below, where it is argued that changes in the alveolar pressure may play an important rôle.

Although the resistance during exercise is inappropriately high for the level of flow, in absolute terms it may be unchanged (without occlusion in Fig. 34.2) or even lower (with occlusion in Fig. 34.2) than the resting level at naturally occurring blood flow. While, therefore, the rectilinearity of the pressure : flow relation in normal people and patients with mitral stenosis permits the interpretation of changes in resistance in terms of changes in the compliance of the resistance vessels, this cannot apply to patients with chronic bronchitis and emphysema in whom the pressure : flow relation is curvilinear. This caveat also embraces the interpretation of changes in resistance due to the effects of drugs in such patients (Chap. 13, p. 184; Chap. 30, pp. 457, 460, 462).

The Effects of Acute Respiratory Failure

Acute respiratory infections and respiratory failure, to which patients of the 'bronchitic' type are particularly prone, have substantial effects on the pulmonary circulation.[30,35–40] Table 34.1 presents data from a number of publications in which measurements of both the pulmonary arterial and wedge pressures as well as the cardiac output have been made. The pulmonary arterial pressure rises substantially. The wedge pressure also increases[30,40] and Herles and his colleagues[30] record two patients with a wedge pressure of 25 mmHg. The cardiac output changes little.[31] There is an increase in the pulmonary arterial resistance.

The pathophysiological events which accompany attacks of acute respiratory failure in these patients are complex.[41] There is an increased airways resistance due to the acute inflammation. This exacerbates the abnormality of respiratory gas exchange so that the arterial Po_2 is commonly as low as 30–40 mmHg with an arterial Pco_2 of 60–70 mmHg and an acidosis. Renal blood flow diminishes[37,42–46] and the kidneys retain water and electrolytes excessively. Thus there is an increased extracellular fluid volume with oedema, and some increase in the plasma volume.[37,47,48] In addition, the existence of a prolonged hypoxia gives rise to polycythaemia[49–51] which contributes to the increased blood volume and is associated with an increased viscosity of the blood.[28]

Although these patients are oedematous and have a raised systemic venous pressure and cardiac size,[52] the term 'cardiac failure' seems hardly appropriate to describe a condition in which the cardiac output is normal. The term seems even less apt in the light of the normal response of the cardiac output to exercise. It may be argued that a raised right atrial pressure in the presence of a normal cardiac output bespeaks failure of the right ventricle. This, however, ignores the substantial increase in the pulmonary arterial pressure which accompanies the episode of acute respiratory failure and which, by increasing the right ventricular afterload, renders impossible a simple analysis in terms of Starling's Law. The cold, sweaty skin of congestive cardiac failure, due to cutaneous vasoconstriction, is not found in these patients who have warm hands and a full pulse. This may also be taken to suggest that the condition is not akin to congestive cardiac failure, but may equally be explained by the vasodilatory effect of retained carbon dioxide. An increase in the extracellular fluid volume from any cause can produce a condition which clinically simulates congestive failure. In the presence of cardiac disease this appears to be caused by the effects of a low cardiac output on renal function which leads to a retention of water and electrolytes. In bronchitic and emphysematous patients with acute respiratory failure it seems likely that a similar retention of water and electrolytes occurs, not from any diminution in the cardiac output, but from the direct or indirect biochemical effects of an impaired exchange of respiratory gases.

In seeking to explain the mechanism whereby patients with bronchitis and emphysema develop pulmonary hypertension, we have to consider a number of factors. First, there are the direct effects of the alveolar gases on the pulmonary circulation. In addition, there may be a contribution to the pulmonary arterial pressure due to the expansion of the blood volume. An increased viscosity of the blood due to polycythaemia may affect the pulmonary vascular resistance. There may be destruction of the pulmonary capillary bed. Finally, the presence of an increased airways resistance may have mechanical effects on the calibre of the pulmonary blood vessels and on the intrathoracic pressure.

The Rôle of Hypoxia

The evidence that alveolar hypoxia is a powerful pulmonary vasoconstrictor is presented in Chapter 30, while in Chapter 32 the pulmonary hypertension of chronic hypoxia is discussed. There is also evidence for a pulmonary vasoconstrictive

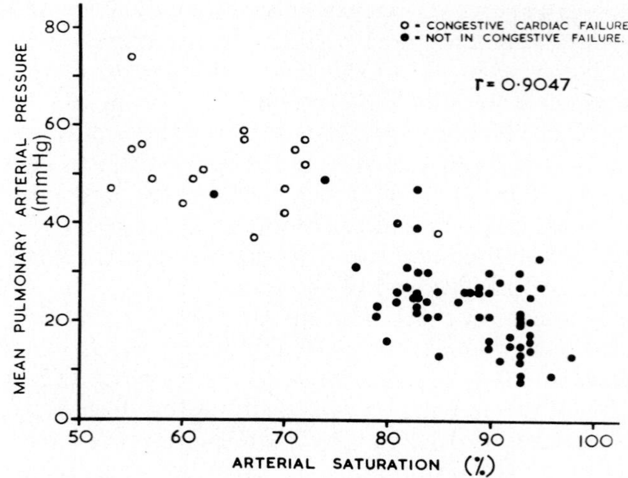

Fig. 34.3 The relation between the mean pulmonary arterial pressure and the arterial oxygen saturation in patients with chronic bronchitis and emphysema reported in the literature.[35,36,39,53,87]

action of carbon dioxide (Chap. 30, p. 457) which seems to be enhanced in the presence of hypoxia (p. 459). In a condition where there is widespread airways obstruction and alveolar dilatation leading to alveolar underventilation, it would be reasonable to expect the changes in the alveolar gas to have an effect on the pulmonary vasculature.

Several authors have noted a negative correlation between the arterial oxygen saturation and the pulmonary arterial pressure[28,33,35,45,53,54] (Fig. 34.3). While this is not proof of causation it is necessary to the thesis of a causative rôle for hypoxia. A positive correlation has also been shown between the arterial P_{CO_2} and the pulmonary arterial pressure[28,33,35,45,53] and between the arterial hydrogen ion concentration and the pulmonary arterial pressure.[54]

Perhaps the strongest evidence for the rôle of hypoxia comes from the specific histological changes which are found in the pulmonary circulation in these patients (Chap. 33) and which occur in a number of diverse conditions among which the common factor is alveolar hypoxia.

Reports of the effects of breathing high concentrations of oxygen have been confirmatory but only partly so. Table 34.2 summarizes studies on patients in a quiescent phase in whom simultaneous measurements of the pulmonary arterial and wedge pressures were made together with the cardiac output. There is a slight fall in the pulmonary arterial pressure with no effect on the wedge pressure. The cardiac output tends to diminish. The result is a slight tendency to a fall in the pulmonary arterial resistance, but not a return to normal despite the fact that the arterial oxygen saturation has become normal. In patients with acute respiratory failure the breathing of high concentrations of oxygen was also reported to have little effect on the pulmonary arterial pressure.[38,39] In daily studies during the first five days of recovery from acute respiratory failure, Abraham and his colleagues[40] found that the breathing of 28 per cent oxygen caused a small fall in the pulmonary arterial pressure which diminished as the pressure fell with progressive recovery. In the acute stage, they recorded an average fall in the pulmonary arterial pressure from 48 to 43 mmHg in eight patients when breathing 28 per cent oxygen. Acetylcholine caused a similar fall in the pulmonary arterial pressure, suggesting that the vasoconstrictive element had been relieved by oxygen.

Supposing that the pulmonary hypertension of chronic bronchitis is entirely due to chronic hypoxia, two factors may operate to prevent the acute inhalation of oxygen returning the pulmonary arterial pressure to normal. As is shown in Table 34.2, the inhalation of oxygen causes an increase in the arterial $P\text{CO}_2$ in these patients and this and its associated acidosis may have a vasoconstrictor influence in the lungs. In addition, experience with mountain dwellers has shown that the acute breathing of oxygen causes only a partial removal of hypoxic pulmonary hypertension; some six weeks' residence at low altitude is necessary before the pulmonary arterial pressure returns completely to normal (Chap. 32, p. 487). Thus the muscular hypertrophy of the pulmonary arterioles may in itself reduce their calibre and one would need to wait until this had regressed before the pulmonary arterial resistance became normal. The prolonged administration of about 30 per cent oxygen for periods of four to eight weeks in patients with chronic bronchitis and emphysema caused an average fall in the mean pulmonary arterial pressure from 43 to 32 mmHg in six patients. Although this decrease in the pulmonary arterial

Table 34.2 The effects of breathing high concentrations of oxygen on the pulmonary circulation of patients with chronic bronchitis and emphysema. Figures for statistical probability are those given in the original texts except for reference 85.

Ref.	Number of cases	$F\text{I}_{\text{O}_2}$	Pulmonary arterial pressure mmHg	Wedge pressure mmHg	Cardiac output $\text{l} \cdot \text{min}^{-1}$ ($/\text{m}^2$ BSA)	Pulmonary arterial resistance[a] $\text{dyn} \cdot \text{s} \cdot \text{cm}^{-5}$	Sa_{O_2} %	Pa_{O_2} mmHg	Pa_{CO_2} mmHg
84	21	0·21	25	5	5·6	286	80	—	48
		1·00	20***	4	4·8*	267	99	—	61***
81	20	0·21	29	8	(3·4)	341	85	—	—
		0·66	27	7	(3·8)	275	95	—	—
85	8	0·21	42	10	5·7	286	—	57	48
		1·00	39*	10	4·8***	267	—	540	61***
33	16	0·21	28	12	(3·7)	230	—	61	50
		0·80	25*	12	(3·5)	193*	—	456	55*

*$P < 0{\cdot}05$; **$P < 0{\cdot}02$; ***$P < 0{\cdot}01$.

[a] See page 135.

pressure was greater than that produced by the acute inhalation of oxygen, it still left a degree of pulmonary hypertension.

Thus, both in the acute and chronic administration of oxygen, the relative lack of response of the pulmonary arterial pressure suggests that factors other than simple hypoxic pulmonary hypertension may be operating. Such factors include the influence of an increased blood volume, an increased blood viscosity due to polycythaemia and the mechanical effects of an increased airways resistance.

The Rôle of Blood Volume

The retention of water by the kidneys during the phase of acute respiratory failure may be expected to expand the blood volume and thus increase the 'static' pressure throughout the circulation.[55] Radiologically, there is an enlargement of both the heart and the pulmonary arteries.[56,57] Experiments on normal subjects have shown that various intravenous infusions will cause an increase in both the pulmonary arterial and wedge pressures with no alteration in the pulmonary arterial resistance (Chap. 11, p. 162). A similar effect has been found to occur in patients with chronic bronchitis and emphysema.[58] The results are summarized in Table 34.3. The infusion of 800–1000 ml of albumin solution caused an increase in the mean pulmonary arterial pressure and the wedge pressure. There was an increase in the cardiac output while the pulmonary arterial resistance showed a non-significant fall. The breathing of 14–15 per cent oxygen caused an increased pulmonary arterial pressure associated with an increased pulmonary arterial resistance before the infusion of albumin. After the infusion the effect of hypoxia was

Table 34.3 The separate and combined effects of hypoxia and the infusion of 800–1000 ml of albumin solution in patients with chronic bronchitis and emphysema. Data from Abraham *et al.*[29] Mean values for 12 subjects

Condition	Mean pulmonary arterial pressure mmHg	Wedge pressure mmHg	Cardiac output $l \cdot min^{-1}/m^2$ BSA	Pulmonary arterial resistance[c] $dyn \cdot s \cdot cm^{-5}$	Pa_{O_2} mmHg
Before infusion					
air	36	14	2·8	367	64
hypoxia	44[a]	14	3·1[a]	462[a]	40
After infusion					
air	42[b]	17[b]	3·7[b]	334	66
hypoxia	46[a]	17	4·0	349	44

[a] $P < 0·05$ air *vs.* hypoxia.
[b] $P < 0·05$ for effect of infusion.
[c] See page 135.

Table 34.4 The effects of repeated venesection in patients with chronic bronchitis and emphysema complicated by polycythaemia. Data from Segel and Bishop.[28] Mean values of 15 patients

	Before venesections	After venesections	P
Mean pulmonary arterial pressure (mmHg)	47	43	$<0{\cdot}02$
Wedge pressure (mmHg)	11	11	
Cardiac output ($l \cdot min^{-1}/m^2$ BSA)	3·3	3·5	
Pulmonary arterial resistance[a] ($dyn \cdot s \cdot cm^{-5}$)	514	442	$<0{\cdot}01$
Packed cell volume (%)	60	44	$<0{\cdot}001$
Blood viscosity (centipoises)	5·7	2·6	$<0{\cdot}001$
Pa_{O_2} (mmHg)	52	53	
Pa_{CO_2} (mmHg)	57	57	

[a] See page 135.

substantially less. The results may be explained by a raised transmural pressure preventing the opposing constrictor action of hypoxia.

Considering these figures in relation to the conditions obtaining during acute respiratory failure in bronchitic and emphysematous patients, two points emerge. First, the figures help explain how, in the presence of a raised left atrial pressure consequent on an increased blood volume, the relief of hypoxia can be expected only partially to reduce the pulmonary arterial pressure. Second, it is of interest that the combination of an increased blood volume and hypoxia fails to simulate completely the physiopathology of acute respiratory failure in these patients, since the pulmonary arterial resistance has not increased. This suggests that other factors are operating under clinical conditions.

The Rôle of Blood Viscosity

Viscosity is an element to the Poiseuille equation (p. 119) and, while the viscous properties of circulating blood are anomalous (p. 131), they may still be expected to affect the resistance in the pulmonary circulation. The polycythaemia which develops in a number of patients with chronic bronchitis and emphysema could, therefore, by increasing the blood viscosity, increase the resistance to flow through the lungs. Segel and Bishop[28] have investigated this possibility in patients with severe bronchitis and emphysema by studying the effects of reducing the polycythaemia with repeated venesection. Their results are summarized in Table 34.4. Repeated venesection effectively reduced both the packed cell volume and the viscosity of the blood. There was a fall in the pulmonary arterial pressure. The wedge pressure and cardiac output did not change and the pulmonary arterial resistance decreased significantly although to nowhere near normal. The arterial partial pressures of oxygen and carbon dioxide were unaffected. The blood volume diminished, which would be expected to favour an increased pulmonary arterial resistance. The results, therefore, indicate that, in these patients with severe

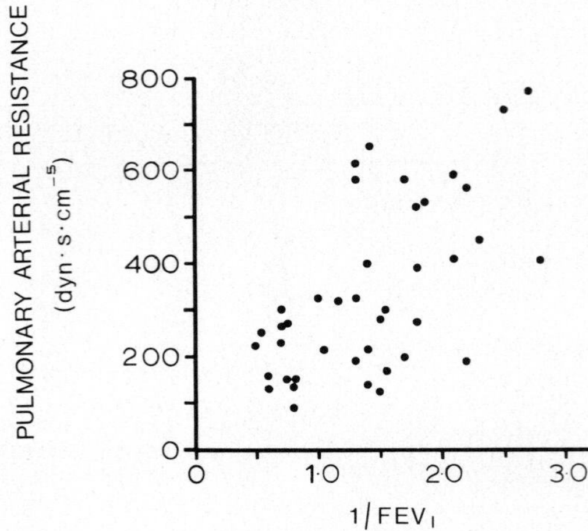

Fig. 34.4 Relation between the reciprocal of the FEV_1 and the mean pulmonary arterial pressure in patients with chronic bronchitis and emphysema.[59] $r = +0{\cdot}615$; $P < 0{\cdot}01$.

pulmonary disease, the development of polycythaemia and an increased viscosity of the blood contributes to the increased pulmonary arterial resistance.

The Mechanical Rôle of an Increased Airways Resistance

That the pulmonary arterial pressure in patients with chronic bronchitis and emphysema correlates negatively with the systemic arterial oxygen saturation and positively with the systemic arterial P_{CO_2} and hydrogen ion concentration is well documented (p. 530). All these factors—hypoxia, hypercarbia and acidosis—are in turn related to the impared exchange of respiratory gases in which an abnormal airways resistance plays an important rôle. It is hardly surprising, therefore, that there is a reciprocal relation between the FEV_1 and the pulmonary arterial pressure in these patients[59] (Fig. 34.4). In addition there is evidence that the increased airways resistance may have a direct mechanical influence on pulmonary haemodynamics by its effect on the alveolar pressure. The possible influence of the alveolar pressure on the pulmonary circulation has already been touched on earlier in the chapter (pp. 526 and 528). In order to investigate this matter we measured the effects of increasing the alveolar pressure on the pressure:flow relation in the normal pulmonary circulation.[59] The increase in alveolar pressure was achieved by raising the gas pressure at the mouth. Figure 34.5 illustrates the effects. At a normal mouth pressure the relation between pressure and flow is rectilinear. When the mouth pressure is maintained at 9 mmHg more than atmospheric the initial part of the pressure:flow relation becomes steeper, indicating an increased resistance. The relation, however, is now a curved one such that the arterio-venous difference in pressure does not increase proportionately with the blood flow. The

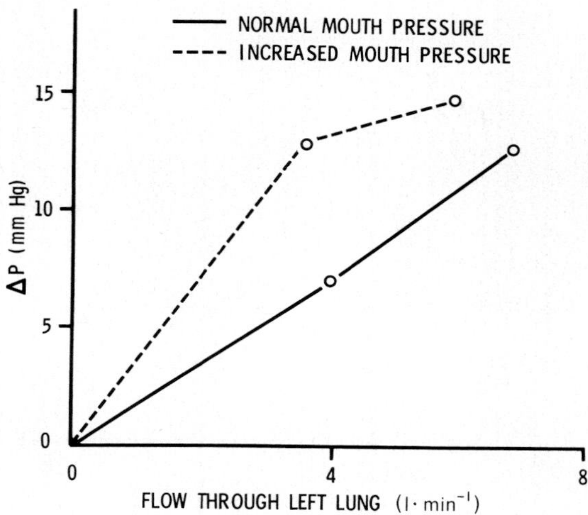

Fig. 34.5 The effects of increasing the mouth pressure on the relation between pressure and flow in the normal pulmonary circulation.[59] Technique as in Figure 9.13, page 130.

curved shape suggests that the vessels which are the site of resistance are not only narrower but also more distensible during positive pressure breathing. It is difficult to conceive such a combination of changes except in terms of compression from outside the wall of the vessels. Normally, in the recumbent position, they are in a state of nearly maximal distension, having reached the inextensible portion of length–tension relation to their walls (pp. 129 and 162). The external compression both narrows their lumen, increasing their resistance, and at the same time allows them to expand more readily when, with an increased flow, their intra-luminal pressure is raised. The smaller vessels within the lungs would seem to be particularly liable to be affected by this mechanism since the alveolar pressure will be higher than the pressure elsewhere in the chest because of the forces of elastic recoil of the lungs.

It needs to be noted at this point that, under these conditions, the wedge pressure follows the left atrial pressure.[59] The 'sluice' or 'waterfall' mechanism (p. 100) may apply regionally in the lung because of the influence of hydrostatic pressure, and may apply to the whole lung when removed from the body. When the lungs are within the body, however, the elevation of pulmonary venous pressure which accompanies a sudden increase in alveolar pressure will prevent this mechanism having a general application throughout the lung (p. 168).

The results of increasing the alveolar pressure on the pressure:flow relation of the normal lung bear a striking resemblance to the relation found during natural breathing in patients with chronic bronchitis and emphysema (*cf.* Figs 34.1 and 34.4). In addition, increasing the pressure at the mouth had the effect of raising the wedge pressure, although not to the same extent as the pulmonary arterial pressure. Presumably this is part of the increase in general 'static' pressure which will

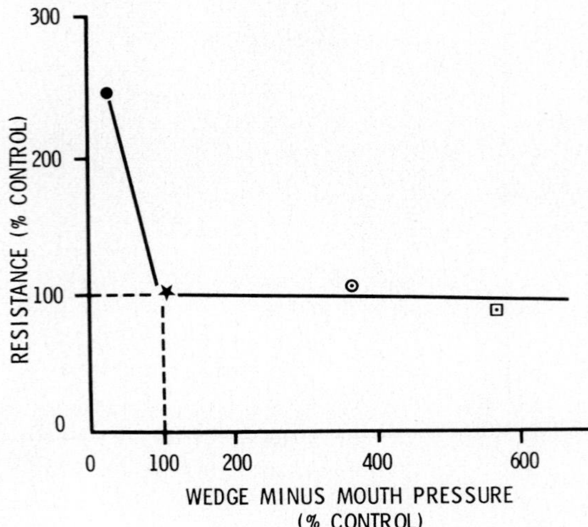

Fig. 34.6 The relation between transmural pressure and resistance in the human pulmonary circulation. The transmural pressure has been estimated by subtracting the alveolar pressure from the wedge pressure. ●, Observations[59] during pressure breathing; ⊙, observations after the intravenous infusion of dextran;[62] ⊡, observations after the intravenous infusion of dextran.[63]

accompany the squeezing of the heart and blood vessels in the thorax.[55,60] A similar mechanism may also contribute to the increased wedge pressure found in patients with chronic bronchitis and emphysema.

In patients with chronic bronchitis and emphysema the airways resistance is particularly increased during expiration (p. 523). This, together with the prolongation of expiration commonly observed in such patients, could have the effect of increasing the time-averaged pressure in the alveoli, and the few published observations on the mean intra-pleural pressure show it to be raised.[61]

In addition, an abnormally wide ventilatory swing in alveolar pressure, such as occurs in these patients, may have the effect of compressing the pulmonary blood vessels. This is because, while, as we have seen above, the pulmonary resistance vessels appear to be compressible, they do not seem to be comparably distensible. For instance, the rapid expansion of the blood volume (p. 162) or the compression of the systemic circulation (p. 162) raise the pulmonary arterial and wedge pressures but do not substantially decrease the pulmonary arterial resistance.

Figure 34.6 shows the percentage change in the pulmonary arterial resistance during pressure breathing and the percentage change in pulmonary arterial resistance found by Fleming and Bloom[62] and by Giuntini *et al.*[63] when the transmural pressure had been increased by intravenous infusions. The change in resistance is plotted against the change in transmural pressure as indicated roughly by the wedge pressure minus the alveolar pressure. When the transmural pressure is raised, there is no change in the resistance. But, when the transmural pressure is lowered, there is a sharp increase in resistance.

Thus, when there is an increased airways resistance, the lower alveolar pressure during inspiration will not greatly distend the pulmonary blood vessels, but the higher alveolar pressure during expiration will compress them. In this way, the average pulmonary vascular resistance throughout the respiratory cycle will be increased although the mean alveolar pressure may be unchanged. The mechanism is indicated diagrammatically in Figure 34.7.

It can be shown by similar arguments that an increased amplitude of the respiratory swing in intrathoracic pressure may well have the effect of increasing the mean left atrial and pulmonary venous pressure.

In order to investigate such mechanical effects of an increased airways resistance, we have compared the haemodynamic effects of hyperventilation in patients with chronic bronchitis and emphysema and in normal subjects.[59] Hyperventilation was voluntary but 6 per cent carbon dioxide was added to the inspired air. The findings are summarized in Table 34.5 and Figure 34.8 and 34.9. Hyperventilation caused an increase in both the pulmonary arterial and wedge pressure in the patients. The pulmonary arterial resistance increased significantly (Fig. 34.8). Since the cardiac output was not affected the increased resistance may with greater confidence be interpreted in terms of a change in the calibre of resistance vessels in the presence of a curved pressure: flow relation. By contrast (Fig. 34.9; Table 34.5) hyperventilation had no effect on the pulmonary circulation in normal subjects.

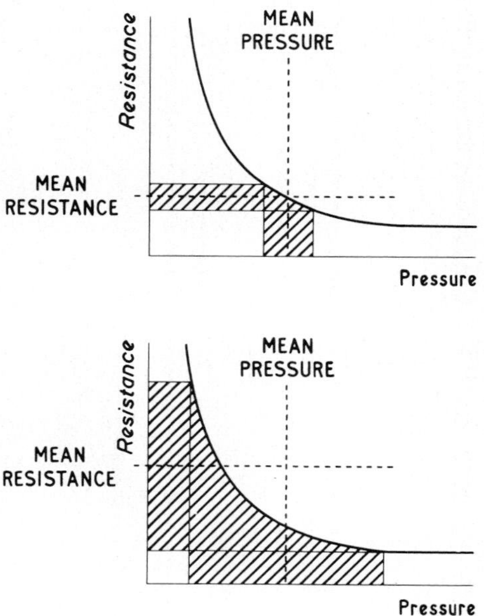

Fig. 34.7 Diagram, based on Figure 34.6, to indicate how, because of the curved relation between resistance and transmural pressure, an increased respiratory swing in alveolar pressure may increase the mean pulmonary arterial resistance in the absence of change in mean alveolar pressure.

Table 34.5 The effects of voluntary hyperventilation on the human pulmonary circulation. The figures are averages of each group of subjects. The paired 't' test has been used when $n > 4$

Ref.	Numbers and type of subjects	FI_{CO_2}	Condition	Mean pulmonary arterial pressure mmHg	Wedge pressure mmHg	Cardiac output $l \cdot min^{-1}$ (/m² BSA)	Pulmonary arterial resistance[a] $dyn \cdot s \cdot cm^{-5}$ (× m² BSA)	$\dot{V}_E$ $l \cdot min^{-1}$ (/m² BSA)	Pa_{CO_2} mmHg	Sa_{O_2} %
59	6 Normals	0	Control	18	8	6·2	145	9·5	38	—
		0·06	Hyperventilation	19	8	6·2	154	33·2****	47****	—
59	6 Bronchitis and emphysema	0	Control	28	9	3·9	457	8·2	51	—
		0·06	Hyperventilation	43****	18****	3·8	607**	20·8****	59	—
64	4 Mitral valve disease	0	Control	33	20	4·5	157	9·6	38	98
		0	Hyperventilation	29	19	4·7	173	18·4	26	98
		0·05	Hyperventilation	46	27	5·6	272	32·0	43	99
86	7 Mitral valve disease	0	Control	29	20	5·0	137	7·2	39	93
		Adjusted	Hyperventilation	28	18*	5·0	154	21·3***	39	94
86	12 Mitral valve disease	0	Control	30	18	4·5	237	6·6	40	95
		0	Hyperventilation	25***	19	5·9***	84***	15·6****	29****	97
32	12 Bronchitis and emphysema	0	Control	19	8	(3·2)	(276)	(5·5)	43	94
		Adjusted	Hyperventilation	22	10	(3·5)	(288)	(12·8)[b]	47	96

*P < 0·05; ** P < 0·02; *** P < 0·01; **** P < 0·001.

[a] See page 135.

[b] P < 0·05 given in original publication.

The hyperventilation in these studies was insufficient to prevent some increase in systemic arterial P_{CO_2}. There is evidence (p. 457) that hypercarbia may give rise to pulmonary vasoconstriction and it is not possible to eliminate this as a cause of the increased pulmonary arterial resistance. The effects on the normal and bronchitic lung were, in our studies, strikingly different for a comparable increase in arterial P_{CO_2}. On the other hand, the absolute level of P_{CO_2} was higher in the bronchitic patients and there is no reason to assume that the relation between P_{CO_2} and its vasoconstrictor response should be linear. Rokseth's data[86] (Table 30.2, p. 458) show that, during hypercarbic hyperventilation, the proportional increase in the pulmonary arterial resistance was greater in the patients with chronic bronchitis and emphysema (60 per cent) than in the patients with disease of the mitral valve (26 per cent) or in patients with normal pulmonary haemodynamics (16 per cent) for a comparable increase in arterial P_{CO_2}. However, these differences may also be explained by the differences in the absolute level of P_{CO_2}.

The results of other investigations on the effects of voluntary hyperventilation are also shown in Table 34.5. Rokseth[86] studied the effects of maintaining the arterial P_{CO_2} by adding carbon dioxide to the inspired air during hyperventilation.

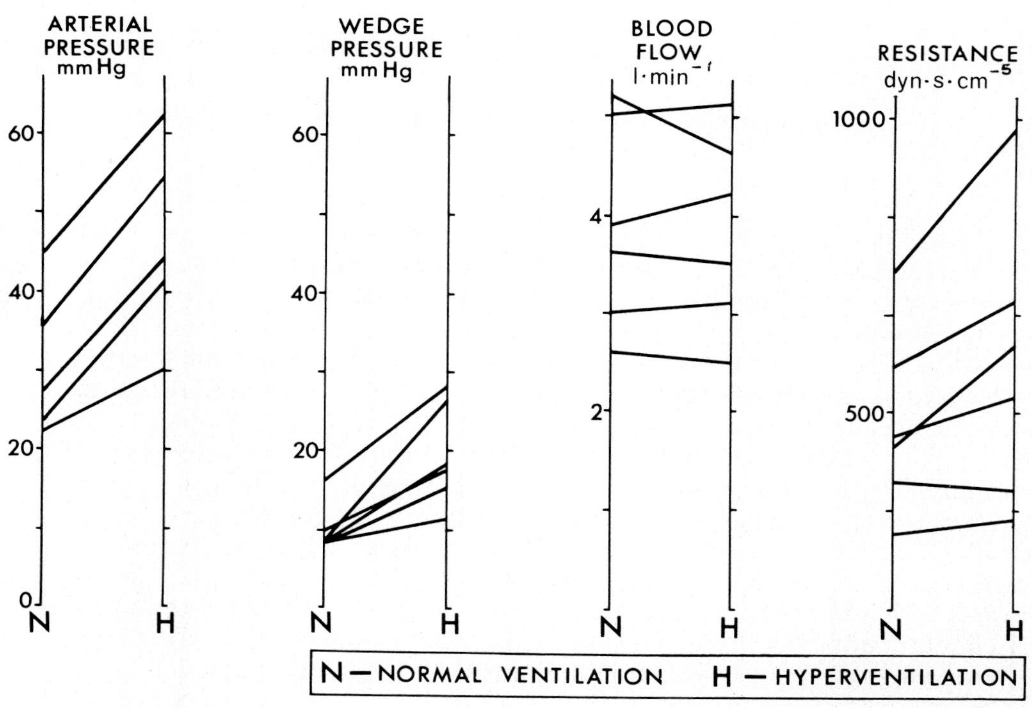

Fig. 34.8 The effects of voluntary hyperventilation on pulmonary haemodynamics in patients with chronic bronchitis and emphysema.[59]

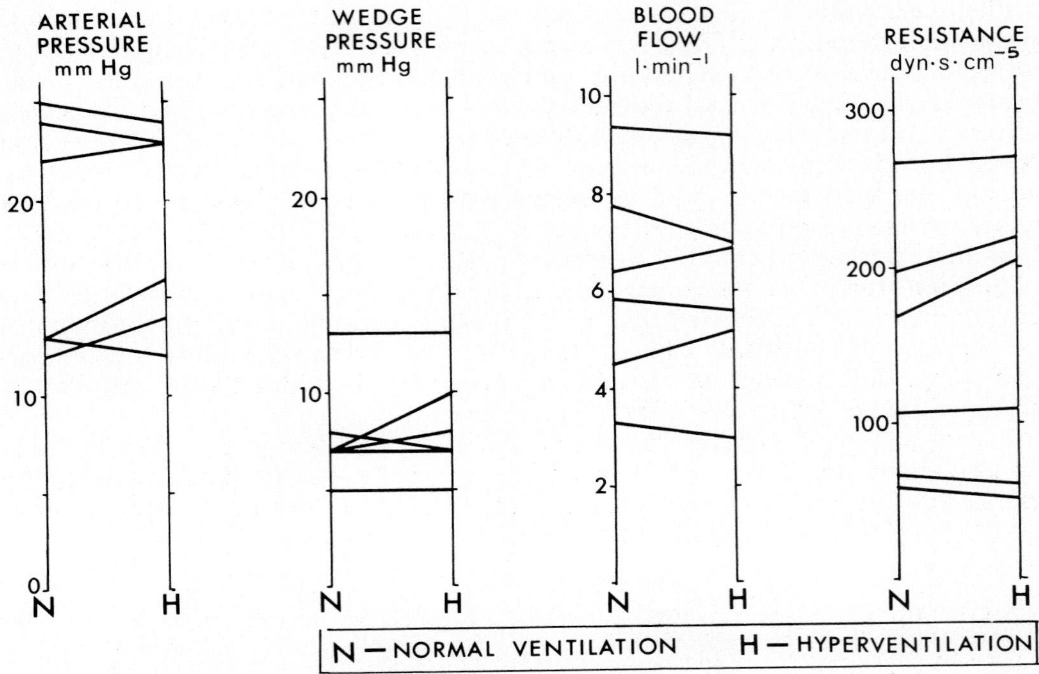

Fig. 34.9 The effects of voluntary hyperventilation on pulmonary haemodynamics in normal subjects.[59]

The majority of the patients had mitral valvar disease and we have shown only the data pertaining to that homogeneous group, patients with other diseases contributing too few numbers for separate presentation. Isocarbic ventilation was associated with no change in the pulmonary arterial resistance, but hypocarbic ventilation was associated with a decreased resistance. In these studies, an increase in the cardiac output contributed importantly to the decrease in the pulmonary arterial resistance under hypocarbic conditions. Paul and his colleagues[64] found no effect of hypocarbic ventilation on the cardiac output or the pulmonary arterial resistance in a smaller group of patients with mitral valve disease (Table 34.5). Lockhart and his colleagues,[32] in a group of patients with bronchitis and emphysema, failed to find an increased pulmonary arterial resistance during voluntary hyperventilation (Table 34.5). The patients, however, represented a mild form of the disease, with a normal arterial P_{CO_2} and an average FEV_1 of 2·7 l compared with 0·9 l in our study.[59]

Some support for the mechanical influence of the airways resistance on the pulmonary circulation in chronic bronchitis during hyperventilation comes from observations that the amplitude of the respiratory swing in pulmonary arterial pressure during exercise correlates with the mean pulmonary arterial pressure.[65]

Such a correlation, however, must include the effects on the wedge pressure as well as the effects on the pulmonary arterial resistance.

The increase in the wedge pressure in patients with chronic bronchitis and emphysema during hyperventilation is best explained by the mechanical effects of the increased airways resistance. Pulmonary veno-constriction plays no part. During the breathing of high concentrations of carbon dioxide the increase in wedge pressure has been shown to be accompanied by an increase in both the left and right atrial pressures[66] and in the oesophageal pressure.[26]

Destruction of Blood Vessels

Morphometry has shown that there is no correlation between right ventricular hypertrophy and the total alveolar surface area (p. 511). If the size of the capillary bed is equated with the alveolar surface area it follows that destruction of the capillary bed is not an important determining factor in the development of pulmonary hypertension. On the other hand, regional impairment of pulmonary blood flow has been found to correspond with the paucity of blood vessels shown on angiography and tomography.[67]

Multifactorial Nature of Pulmonary Hypertension in Chronic Bronchitis and Emphysema

All of the factors which have just been discussed would seem to play a part in the production of pulmonary hypertension in these patients. Alveolar hypoxia has a direct constrictor effect to which hypercarbia may contribute. The anatomical changes in the pulmonary arterioles secondary to chronic hypoxia may themselves increase resistance. Polycythaemia increases resistance by its effect on the viscosity of the blood. The retention of water by the kidneys expands the blood volume and raises the 'static' pressure throughout the pulmonary circulation. When the airways resistance is severely increased or when its effects are magnified by hyperventilation the changes in the alveolar and intra-thoracic pressure may increase both the left atrial pressure and the pulmonary arterial resistance.

Physio-Pathological Relations

The particular association between centrilobular emphysema and pulmonary hypertension has been discussed in the preceding chapter (p. 512). Right ventricular hypertrophy may occur when as little as 14 per cent of the lung is involved by centrilobular emphysema, whereas in cases of panacinar emphysema 40 to 70 per cent of the lung often needs to be affected before right ventricular hypertrophy develops.

It seems likely that the critical anatomical position of the bronchiolar lesion on the gas pathway causes it to have a more profound effect on the exchange of respiratory gases. A glance at Figure 33.2 (p. 504) shows that the dead space constituted by the lesion is interposed on the pathway between the bronchiole and the alveoli. If this occurs throughout the lung, each inspired breath will have to pass through the bronchiolar dead space before it can reach the alveoli. If we take a total lung capacity of 5 to 6 l, 14 per cent represents a volume in the region of 700 to 800 ml. To this must be added the normal anatomical dead space. Since the average tidal volume is in the region of 500 ml, it follows that the air taken in at each breath gets lost in the dead space without effectively reaching the alveoli. The ultimate transfer of gas to the capillaries has, therefore, to be accompanied by diffusion over considerably larger distances than normal.

By contrast, large regions of panacinar emphysema often co-exist with normal lung. Under these circumstances the normal or increased ventilation of normal lung can effectively remove carbon dioxide, while destruction of the capillary bed in the emphysematous areas together with local hypoxic vasoconstriction will help restore the equality of ventilation : perfusion ratios and thus maintain the systemic arterial Po_2.

Another factor which could contribute to the effects of centrilobular emphysema on the pulmonary circulation may be the more severe involvement of the small airways in this form of emphysema (p. 524).

The Distribution of Pulmonary Blood Flow

Radiological examination of the lungs in the presence of emphysema may be carried out by the plain radiograph[56,68] or by tomography[69] or by angiography.[70,71] Localized regions of emphysema have an increased translucency on the plain radiograph due to a diminution in the capillary bed and small vessels. The pulmonary trunk in the 'emphysematous' type of patient often appears more prominent than normal. This does not necessarily signify a dilatation and is more often due to the clockwise rotation of the heart which accompanies its rather vertical position. Typically, the pulmonary arterial tree shows an abnormally abrupt diminution in calibre at about the third or fourth division. This does not correspond with any histological change (Chap. 33) which suggests that it may be due to a lack of tethering of the smaller intrapulmonary vessels or to compression by an increased alveolar pressure. The peripheral arteries tend to run a straighter course than normal except where they curve round an emphysematous bulla. There appear to be fewer smaller arterial branches than normal. Patients of the 'bronchitic' type have no characteristic abnormality of the pulmonary arterial tree. In the presence of pulmonary hypertension and particularly in the presence of systemic oedema, the heart is enlarged and there is some dilatation of the entire pulmonary arterial tree.

The demonstration of the distribution of the pulmonary blood flow by the intravenous injection of ^{131}I-labelled macroaggregated albumin and the external counting of radioactivity (p. 99) has given evidence of regions of poor perfusion.[72–76] The 'bronchitic' and 'emphysematous' types are not distinguished by the scintigrams.[72,76] How reproducible are the results is disputed.[72,75] Scintigraphy is a more sensitive indicator of differences in regional perfusion than is the plain radiograph.[73] Opinions vary concerning the correlation between scintigraphy and pulmonary angiography,[72,74–76] but, as Schrijen and Jezek[76] point out, the two procedures are not measuring the same thing.

Regions of decreased perfusion may also be demonstrated by the intravenous injection of ^{133}Xe and external monitoring of radioactivity.[67] Using this technique, the regional blood flow could be shown to be low in those areas where the ventilation was poor.[67] Despite this, patients with chronic bronchitis and emphysema have a notable lack of homogeneity of ventilation : perfusion ratios giving rise to hypoxaemia and increasing the total ventilation necessary to prevent hypercarbia. This is considered in greater detail in Chapter 36.

The Absence of Arterio-Venous Shunts

Fritts and his colleagues[77] studied the presence of arterio-venous shunts in the lungs by injecting a mixed solution of ^{85}Kr and Evans' blue dye intravenously and sampling from a systemic artery. The dye traverses the pulmonary circulation irrespective of the presence or absence of ventilation. On the other hand 95 per cent of krypton is lost during the first circulation through a ventilated alveolus. Shunts, such as Thebesian and bronchial, which carry venous blood originating from sites other than the pulmonary artery will not be measured by this method. Calculations from the dilution curves of the two tracers failed to demonstrate the presence of an abnormal pulmonary arterio-venous shunt in patients with emphysema. (See also Chap. 36, p. 581.)

The absence of abnormal pulmonary arterio-venous shunts has been confirmed using ^{99m}Tc-labelled microspheres made from human serum albumin. The microspheres, with a diameter of 10–32 μm, were too large to pass through the pulmonary capillaries. Measurement of the residual radioactivity over the head after the intravenous injection of bound and unbound technecium allowed an estimate of the presence of pulmonary arterio-venous shunts. The average shunt was 1·1 per cent in normals and 0·6 per cent in patients with chronic bronchitis and emphysema.[78]

Pulmonary Haemodynamics in Asthma

From the two publications of Helander and his colleagues[79,80] Table 34.6 summarizes the data from 17 patients in whom measurements of the pulmonary arterial and wedge pressures and the cardiac output were made before and during an asthmatic attack. In eight of the patients, the attack was induced by the inhalation of a histamine spray. In nine, the attack occurred spontaneously or was induced by the inhalation of a specific allergen. There are interesting differences between the haemodynamic effects in the two groups. After the inhalation of histamine, the pulmonary arterial pressure increases significantly and there is a tendency for the wedge pressure to rise. The cardiac output is unaffected. The pulmonary arterial resistance increases significantly. In the presence of a constant pulmonary blood flow this must represent a change in the compliance characteristics of the resistance vessels. The effects are the opposite of those obtained during the infusion of histamine into the circulation (p. 198) which causes a decreased pulmonary arterial resistance and an increased pulmonary blood flow and no asthma. If, as seems likely, the direct effect of histamine on the pulmonary circulation is

Table 34.6 The effects of asthma on the human pulmonary circulation. Data from Helander *et al.*[79,80] We have selected those cases where measurements of pulmonary arterial pressure, pulmonary wedge pressure and cardiac output are available throughout the study and have not duplicated cases which appear to be the same in both publications. Statistical analysis by paired 't' test

	Spontaneous attack or specific allergen (9 cases)		Inhalation of histamine (8 cases)	
	Before	During	Before	During
Mean pulmonary arterial pressure (mmHg)	17	22**	17	29***
Wedge pressure (mmHg)	8	11	7	10
Cardiac output ($l \cdot min^{-1}$)	5·7	6·9**	5·8	6·2
Pulmonary arterial resistance[a] ($dyn \cdot s \cdot cm^{-5}$)	144	137	161	243***
Arterial oxygen saturation (%)	94	88***	95	91
Arterial P_{CO_2} (mmHg)	39	43**	40	43
Amplitude of respiratory variation in intravascular presence (mmHg)	14	31****	10	28****

**$P < 0{\cdot}02$; ***$P < 0{\cdot}01$; ****$P < 0{\cdot}001$.
[a] See page 135.

vasodilatory, the increased pulmonary arterial resistance following the inhalation of histamine is secondary to its action on the airways. The mechanism may be explained by the effects of an increased alveolar pressure compressing the resistance vessels (p. 534) and increasing the left atrial pressure (p. 535).

During a spontaneous attack of asthma or during an attack induced by a specific allergen, there is also an increase in the pulmonary arterial pressure, although not of such a great magnitude. The wedge pressure tends to rise. The important differences in this group are the significant increase which occurs in the cardiac output and the constancy of the pulmonary arterial resistance. In other respects the two groups are similar. The changes in the blood gases and the amplitude of the respiratory swing in intravascular pressure are virtually the same. If the bronchospasm following the inhalation of histamine is thought to lead to the compression of pulmonary blood vessels, it has to be explained why a similar bronchospasm in the second group does not have the same effect. Perhaps the answer lies in the curved relation between pressure and flow which develops in the pulmonary circulation when the alveolar pressure is raised (p. 534). Under these circumstances, the increase in the pulmonary blood flow renders it impossible to interpret the changes in pulmonary arterial resistance in terms of changes in the compliance characteristics of resistance vessels (p. 528).

REFERENCES

1. Dayman, H. (1951) *J. Clin. Invest.*, **30**, 1175.
2. Rodbard, S. (1953) *Amer. J. Med.*, **15**, 356.
3. Hogg, J. C., Macklem, P. T. & Thurlbeck, W. M. (1968) *New Engl. J. Med.*, **278**, 1355.

4. Macklem, P. T., Fraser, R. G. & Brown, W. C. (1965) *J. Clin. Invest.*, **44**, 897.
5. Fraser, R. G. (1961) *J. Canad. Ass. Radiol.*, **12**, 102.
6. Macklem, P. T. (1972) *Amer. J. Med.*, **52**, 721.
7. Anthonisen, N. R., Bass, H., Oriol, A., Place, R. E. G. & Bates, D. V. (1968) *Clin. Sci.*, **35**, 495.
8. Woolcock, A. J., Vincent, N. J. & Macklem, P. T. (1969) *J. Clin. Invest.*, **48**, 1097.
9. McFadden, E. R., Jn. & Linden, D. A. (1972) *Amer. J. Med.*, **52**, 725.
10. McCarthy, D. S., Spencer, R., Greene, R. & Milic-Emili, J. (1972) *Amer. J. Med.*, **52**, 747.
11. Ingram, R. H., Jn. & O'Cain, C. F. (1971) *Bull. Physio-Path. Resp.*, 7, 195.
12. Hughes, J. M. B., Rosenzweig, D. Y. & Kivitz, P. B. (1970) *J. Appl. Physiol.*, **29**, 340.
13. Anderson, A. E., Jn., Hernandez, J. A., Holmes, W. L. & Foraker, A. G. (1966) *Arch. Environ. Health*, **12**, 569.
14. Leopold, J. G. & Gough, J. (1957) *Thorax*, **12**, 219.
15. CIBA Guest Symposium (1959) *Thorax*, **14**, 286.
16. Ogilvie, C. (1959) *Thorax*, **14**, 113.
17. Mitchell, R. S., Vincent, T. N., Ryan, S. & Filley, F. G. (1964) *Amer. J. Med. Sci.*, **247**, 513.
18. Burrows, B., Niden, A. H., Fletcher, C. M. & Jones, N. L. (1964) *Amer. Rev. Resp. Dis.*, **90**, 14.
19. Nash, E. S., Briscoe, W. A. & Cournand, A. (1965) *Med. Thorac.*, **22**, 305.
20. Burrows, B., Fletcher, C. M., Heard, B. E., Jones, N. L. & Wootliff, J. S. (1966) *Lancet*, **i**, 830.
21. Weitzenblum, E., Roeslin, N., Hirth, C. & Oudet, P. (1970) *Respiration*, **27**, 493.
22. Moyses, B., Weitzenblum, E., Methlin, G. & Oudet, P. (1974) *Bull. Physio-Path. Resp.*, **10**, 811.
23. Herles, F., Daum, S. & Bednář, B. (1960) *Proceedings of IIIrd European Congress of Cardiology*, page 491.
24. Evans, T. O., Van der Reis, L. & Selzer, A. (1963) *Amer. Heart J.*, **66**, 741.
25. Williams, J. F. & Behnke, R. H. (1964) *Ann. Intern. Med.*, **60**, 824.
26. Lim, T. P. K. & Brownlee, W. E. (1968) *Dis. Chest.*, **53**, 113.
27. Lockhart, A., Tzareva, M., Nader, F., LeBlanc, P., Schrijen, F. & Sadoul, P. (1969) *Clin. Sci.*, **37**, 503.
28. Segel, N. & Bishop, J. M. (1966) *J. Clin. Invest.*, **45**, 1555.
29. Abraham, A. S., Hedworth-Whitty, R. B. & Bishop, J. M. (1967) *Clin. Sci.*, **33**, 371.
30. Herles, F., Ježek, V. & Daum, S. (1968) *Brit. Heart J.*, **30**, 654.
31. Wade, O. L. & Bishop, J. M. (1962) *Cardiac Output and Regional Blood Flow.* Blackwell
32. Lockhart, A., Nader, F., Tzareva, M. & Schrijen, F. (1970) *Europ. J. Clin. Invest.*, **1**, 69.
33. Horsfield, K., Segel, N. & Bishop, J. M. (1968) *Clin. Sci.*, **34**, 473.
34. Harris, P., Segel, N. & Bishop, J. M. (1968a) *Cardiovasc. Res.*, **2**, 73.
35. Harvey, R. M., Ferrer, M. I., Richards, D. W., Jn. & Cournand, A. (1951) *Amer. J. Med.*, **10**, 719.
36. Fowler, N. O., Westcott, R. N., Scott, R. C. & Hess, E. (1952) *Circulation*, **6**, 888.
37. Lewis, C. S., Samuels, A. J., Daines, M. C. & Hecht, H. (1952) *Circulation*, **6**, 874.
38. Mounsey, J. P. D., Ritzmann, L. W., Silverstone, N. J., Briscoe, W. A. & McLemore, G. A. (1952) *Brit. Heart J.*, **14**, 153.
39. Whitaker, W. (1954) *Quart. J. Med.*, **23**, 57.
40. Abraham, A. S., Cole, R. B., Green, I. D., Hedworth-Whitty, R. B., Clarke, S. W. & Bishop, J. M. (1969) *Circulat. Res.*, **24**, 51.
41. Stuart-Harris, C. H. & Hanley, T. (1957) *Chronic Bronchitis, Emphysema and Cor Pulmonale.* Bristol: Wright.
42. Davis, C. E. & Kilpatrick, J. A. (1951) *Clin. Sci.*, **10**, 53.
43. Fishman, A. P., Maxwell, M. H., Crowder, C. H. & Morales, P. (1951) *Circulation*, **3**, 703.
44. Stuart-Harris, C. H., MacKinnon, J., Hammond, J. D. S. & Smith, W. D. (1956) *Quart. J. Med.*, **25**, NS., 389.
45. Aber, G. M., Bayley, T. J. & Bishop, J. M. (1963) *Clin. Sci.*, **25**, 159.
46. Aber, G. M. & Bishop, J. M. (1965) *Clin. Sci.*, **28**, 511.
47. Taquini, A. C., Fasciolo, J. C., Suarez, J. R. E. & Chiodi, H. (1949) *Arch. Intern. Med.*, **82**, 534.
48. Samet, P., Fritts, H. W., Jn., Fishman, A. P. & Cournand, A. (1957) *Medicine*, **36**, 211.

49. Grant, J. L., MacDonald, A., Edwards, J. B., Stacey, R. R. & Stueck, G. H., Jn. (1958) *J. Clin. Invest.*, **37**, 1166.
50. Shaw, D. B. & Simpson, T. (1961) *Quart. J. Med.*, **30**, 135.
51. Vanier, T., Dulfano, M. J., Wu, C. & Desforges, J. F. (1963) *New Engl. J. Med.*, **269**, 169.
52. Platts, M., Hammond, J. & Stuart-Harris, C. (1960) *Quart. J. Med.*, **29**, 559.
53. Yu, P. N., Lovejoy, F. W., Joos, H. A., Nye, R. E. & McCann, W. S. (1953) *J. Clin. Invest.*, **32**, 130.
54. Enson, Y., Giuntini, C., Lewis, M. L., Morris, T. Q., Ferrer, M. I. & Harvey, R. M. (1964) *J. Clin. Invest.*, **43**, 1146.
55. Starr, I. (1940) *Amer. J. Med. Sci.*, **199**, 40.
56. Simon, G. (1964) *Clin. Radiol.*, **15**, 293.
57. Heard, B. E. (1969) *Pathology of Chronic Bronchitis and Emphysema*. Churchill.
58. Abraham, A. S., Hedworth-Whitty, R. B. & Bishop, J. M. (1967) *Clin. Sci.*, **33**, 371.
59. Harris, P., Segel, N., Green, I. & Housley, E. (1968b) *Cardiovasc. Res.*, **2**, 84.
60. Fenn, W. O., Otis, A. B., Rahn, H., Chadwick, L. E. & Hegnauer, A. H. (1947) *Amer. J. Physiol.*, **151**, 258.
61. Christie, R. V. (1934) *J. Clin. Invest.*, **13**, 295.
62. Fleming, J. W. & Bloom, W. L. (1957) *J. Clin. Invest.*, **36**, 1233.
63. Giuntini, C., Maseri, A. & Bianchi, R. (1966) *J. Clin. Invest.*, **45**, 1770.
64. Paul, G., Varnauskas, E., Forsberg, S.-Å., Sannerstedt, R. & Widimsky, J. (1964) *Clin. Sci.*, **26**, 111.
65. Weitzenblum, E., El Gharbi, T., Vandevenne, A., Bleger, A., Hirth, C. & Oudet, P. (1972) *Bull. Physio-Path. Resp.*, **8**, 49.
66. Daum, S., Krofta, K., Jahn, E., Nikoodýmová, L. & Švorčík, Č. (1970) *Prog. Resp. Res.*, **5**, 166.
67. Bentivoglio, L. G., Beercl, F., Stewart, P. B., Bryan, A. C., Ball, W. C., Jn. & Bates, D. V. (1963) *Amer. Rev. Resp. Dis.*, **88**, 315.
68. Laws, J. W. & Heard, B. E. (1962) *Brit. J. Radiol.*, **35**, 750.
69. Fraser, R. G. & Bates, D. V. (1959) *Amer. J. Roentgenol.*, **82**, 39.
70. Scarrow, G. D. (1966) *Clin. Radiol.*, **17**, 54.
71. Jacobson, G., Turner, A. F., Balchum, O. J. & Jung, R. (1967) *Amer. J. Roentgenal.*, **100**, 374.
72. Bryant, L. R., Cohn, J. E., O'Neill, R. P., Danielson, G. K. & Greenlaw, R. H. (1968) *Amer. Rev. Resp. Dis.*, **97**, 832.
73. Lopez-Majano, V., Tow, D. E. & Wagner, H. N. (1966) *J. Amer. Med. Ass.*, **197**, 81.
74. Samad, I. A., Wood, D., Danders, D. E., Suero, J. T. & Woolf, C. R. (1968) *Dis. Chest*, **53**, 571.
75. Beerel, F. R., Vance, J. W., Cordasco, E. M., Wende, R. W. & Toffolo, R. R. (1969) *Arch. Intern. Med.*, **124**, 8.
76. Schrijen, F. & Ježek, V. (1971) *Bull. Physio-Path. Resp.*, **7**, 627.
77. Fritts, H. W., Jn., Hardewig, A., Rochester, D. F., Durand, J. & Cournand, A. (1960) *J. Clin. Invest.*, **39**, 1841.
78. Strauss, H. W., Hurley, P. J., Rhodes, B. A. & Wagner, H. N. (1969) *J. Lab. Clin. Med.*, **74**, 597.
79. Helander, E., Lindell, S.-E., Söderholm, B. & Westling, H. (1962) *Acta Allerg.*, **17**, 112.
80. Helander, E., Lindell, S.-E., Lindholm, B., Söderholm, B. & Westling, H. (1967) *Scand. J. Resp. Dis.*, **48**, 45.
81. Kitchin, A. H., Lowther, C. P. & Matthews, M. B. (1961) *Clin. Sci.*, **21**, 93.
82. Romero Colomer, P. & Schrijen, F. (1974) *Bull. Physio-Path. Resp.*, **10**, 301.
83. Ježek, V., Schrijen, F. & Sadoul, P. (1973) *Cardiology*, **58**, 20.
84. Wilson, R. H., Hoseth, W. & Dempsey, M. E. (1955) *Ann. Intern. Med.*, **42**, 629.
85. Aber, G. M., Harris, A. M. & Bishop, J. M. (1964) *Clin. Sci.*, **26**, 133.
86. Rokseth, R. (1966) *Scand. J. Clin. Lab. Invest.*, **18**, Suppl. 90.

35. Pulmonary Embolism

THE LUNG AS A FILTER

The pulmonary capillary bed is an effective filter of particulate matter in the blood and the patient histopathologist will find all manner of fragments impacted in the terminal portions of the pulmonary arterial tree. Most of this chapter will be concerned with thromboembolism, the commonest and most important clinical form, but we shall first review the origins and effects of other embolic fragments.

The various types of tissue and cell embolism to the lung have been considered in detail by Wagenvoort, Heath and Edwards.[1] One of the commonest is bone marrow embolism[2] which may follow accidents with bone fractures and operations such as those in which cleavage of the sternum has been performed for correction of cardiac anomalies.[1] It may also follow spontaneous fracture due to tumour metastasis or multiple myeloma. However, not infrequently no predisposing cause can be found. The fragments of marrow remain recognizable for several days before organization.

Sometimes large nuclear masses are found impacted in the pulmonary capillaries. These were first described by Aschoff[3] as megakaryocytes which had passed as emboli to the lungs, and there have been studies which confirm this view.[4,5] The megakaryocytes pass in the venous blood from the bone marrow to the lung where they break up to form platelets.[5] Sharnoff and Kim[4] found pulmonary megakaryocytes in all but three of 355 consecutive necropsies. They found pulmonary megakaryocytes to be especially common after surgical operations, in infectious disease, anaemia and pulmonary thromboembolism.

Fragments of adipose tissue or isolated fat cells may impact in the small pulmonary arteries following trauma or operation.[1] Embolism of lipid-laden macrophages to the pulmonary capillaries may arise from atheromatous plaques in the elastic pulmonary arteries in patients with congenital heart disease with pulmonary hypertension.[1] Other tissues described as forming emboli to the lung include liver, muscle and brain.[1,6] Hairs[7] are sometimes found.

Fat embolism is very common following accidents with bone fracture or contusion of adipose tissue. The crushing of bone marrow or adipose tissue liberates fat which enters systemic veins and the pulmonary arterial tree. The fat enters pulmonary capillaries and small muscular pulmonary arteries. It may be detected as oily patches in the blood and is readily demonstrated by the usual stains for neutral fat. Sevitt[8] thought pulmonary fat embolism to be very common but a rare cause of significant symptoms. Large fat emboli, however, have been held responsible for sudden death.[9] Small fat emboli may be found in the lung in the absence of trauma.

Amniotic Fluid

This is a clinical and pathological entity which may occur in women during, or shortly after, childbirth. It is characterized by a sudden onset of dyspnoea and cyanosis with the rapid development of shock. The condition is often fatal and death may occur during childbirth or up to several days afterwards. Attention was brought to the condition by Steiner and Lushbaugh[10] and many other workers.[1] During labour, amniotic fluid enters veins and passes to the pulmonary circulation. Partial detachment of the placenta, rupture of the myometrium or cervical tears may allow amniotic fluid to enter the maternal veins and powerful, spastic uterine contractions are a predisposing factor.[1] Various constituents of the amniotic fluid may be found histologically in the pulmonary capillaries or arterioles. They include vernix, epithelial squames, and lanugo hair from the foetal skin, meconium, bile pigment and mucin from the foetal intestine and trophoblast cells.[1] Chorionic villi are seen rarely. While these various constituents are sometimes readily apparent, on other occasions they may be very difficult to find and require the use of special stains. A combination of phloxine and alcian-green is said to be valuable for this.[11] The possibility has been raised that non-fatal amniotic fluid embolism is a cause of primary pulmonary hypertension.[12]

While amniotic fluid embolism to the lungs is rare and serious, small fragments of trophoblasts are frequently found in the lungs of pregnant women and they rarely give rise to symptoms. The trophoblastic tissue appears as large syncytial multi-nucleated masses. Trophoblastic embolism may be fatal and in such cases it appears to initiate thrombosis in the pulmonary arterial tree.[1] Trophoblastic embolism may be severe in cases of hydatidiform mole and give rise to pulmonary infarction.

Tumour

Neoplastic cells may infiltrate through systemic veins or the thoracic duct to enter the blood stream and thus get trapped in the lungs like other emboli. Most tumour emboli degenerate but some will grow and invade the pulmonary blood vessel in which they are situated to invade the surrounding lung and give rise to a haematogenous metastasis. The tumour emboli may lead to overlying thrombosis in the pulmonary arteries. Occasionally, tumour emboli in the pulmonary arterial tree may reveal their presence by the haemodynamic abnormalities they produce. We studied a woman of 35 years who developed pulmonary arterial hypertension due to impaction of multiple embolic fragments of a myxoma of the right atrium into her pulmonary arterial tree.[13]

Air and Gas

Wagenvoort and associates[1] give a comprehensive list of conditions in which air embolism to the pulmonary circulation may occur. They include caisson disease, rapid ascent to high altitude by airmen, and fractures of the skull. Air embolism may be produced in various surgical and diagnostic procedures such as intravenous injections or infusions, abortions, pneumoencephalography, and the induction of a pneumothorax.[1] Chronic pulmonary gas embolism in rabbits will give rise to cellular intimal proliferation of the pulmonary arteries.[14] While the introduction of small quantities of air into the pulmonary circulation does not give rise to symptoms, the introduction of large quantities may be fatal, although this may not be until after some hours. The air turns into a frothy mass inside the pulmonary artery and will not easily pass the pulmonary capillary bed. The pathologist will need to open the pulmonary artery under water to detect air embolism to the lung. Other material than gas may occasionally be introduced from outside the body, such as the cotton-wool fibres which have been found following cardiac catheterization or intravenous injection,[15] foreign material injected intravenously by drug addicts,[16] mercury used in sampling syringes,[17] intravenous needles and tubing and a wide variety of foreign bodies.[18]

THROMBOEMBOLISM

Site of Origin of Thrombus

Marshall[19] and Gray[20] have well summarized the literature, extending over more than a century since the time of Virchow, on the site of origin and incidence of thromboembolism. By far the commonest sites of origin of thrombi are the deep veins of the legs, especially in the calf. More recent *in vivo* studies using intravenous injections of fibrinogen labelled with ^{131}I have confirmed this.[21] Frequently, several thrombi are found which have arisen independently in different parts of the veins of the legs. Extension of the thrombus occurs in the direction of the flow of blood.

Factors Affecting the Incidence of Thromboembolism

Although thromboembolism is rare in children, opinion is divided as to whether age affects its incidence in adults. Similarly, there is no unanimous evidence that it affects one sex more than the other. There is some evidence that the incidence of thromboembolism increases in cold weather. An unexpectedly low prevalence of blood group O has been found in patients having anticoagulant therapy for thromboembolism.[22] Obesity appears to be a predisposing factor. Among diseases in which thromboembolism is particularly likely to occur, congestive heart failure is the most important and there appears to be a specific association with malignant disease, especially that of the pancreas. It is generally believed that immobilization is an important local factor.

Prevalence and Distribution of Pulmonary Thromboembolism

There is no doubt that pulmonary thromboembolism is very common indeed. In a specially conducted and painstaking post-mortem investigation of 263 right lungs, Morrell and Dunnill[23] found pulmonary emboli in no fewer than 51·7 per cent of the subjects studied. Even so, they thought it likely that the method of study they used did not detect all the cases. The prevalence of pulmonary embolism in the left lungs of the same cases studied routinely by the service pathologist was 11·8 per cent. They found a significant association between recent and old emboli, indicating the recurrent nature of the disease. Thus, fresh emboli were found in 58·8 per cent of the cases, organizing emboli in 38·3 per cent, fibrous bands and webs indicative of organized emboli in 33·8 per cent, and intimal fibrosis indicating long-standing organized thromboembolus in 39·7 per cent.

A substantially higher prevalence of thromboemboli in the right lung than the left was found by Lenègre and Néel,[24] an observation which is not explicable in terms of the relative blood flow to each side. In this study no significant difference emerged between the upper and lower lobes (counting the right middle with the right upper). Such a lack of distinction between the upper and lower lobes is not surprising. The patient may be in any posture when the embolus arrives in the lung; the gradient of blood flow per alveolus from the top to the bottom of the lung in the upright position becomes distinctive only in a relatively inspiratory position[25] (Chap. 7, p. 101); and the position of the major fissure of each lung is, in any case, directed obliquely.

Fate of Pulmonary Thromboemboli

The lungs have an incredible capacity to dispose of thromboemboli. Several hundred millilitres of fresh blood clot may be injected intravenously into dogs over a period of months with no rise in pulmonary arterial pressure.[19] In dogs, even large fresh thrombi are absorbed by the lungs within six weeks,[26–28] small ones more rapidly.[28] Thrombi which have aged for two or three weeks before being liberated into the pulmonary circulation are, however, removed more slowly.[29,30] In patients studied by scintigraphy, the removal of emboli to lobar arteries takes up to four weeks.[31] Two main groups of processes are concerned with the disposal of pulmonary thromboemboli—chemical and cellular.

Chemical disposal consists of fibrinolysis and predominates in the disposal of small thrombi. Lung tissue has a high content of fibrinolysins[32,33] which readily escape into the blood stream during pulmonary surgery.[34–37] Fibrinolysins have been shown to be present in the intima of pulmonary arteries and absent in the intima of systemic arteries.[38] However, fibrinolysis seems to be less active in man than in many other species.[39]

Cellular processes of organization and re-canalization seem likely to be more important in the disposal of larger and older thromboemboli. In this respect thromboemboli are treated like a foreign material such as filter paper.[40] In experimental animals it seems to take several days before fibroblasts and capillaries grow into the embolus.[28,41] The thromboemboli are gradually reduced by organization and re-canalization to patches of intimal fibrosis.[40,42–49] The intimal fibroelastosis which results from organization of thrombus may prove to be very difficult to distinguish from that brought about by a raised pulmonary arterial pressure. Of course, in cases of recurrent pulmonary thromboembolism, intimal fibrosis may arise by both mechanisms in the same patient. A detailed account of the histological changes leading to organization and re-canalization of thrombus in elastic and muscular pulmonary arteries is given later in this chapter (p. 560).

Rarely, pulmonary thromboembolism may initiate massive thrombosis in the main pulmonary arteries.[50] The thrombus becomes organized and attached to one of the main pulmonary arteries or straddles the bifurcation. Fresh thrombus is added, leading to obliteration of the pulmonary circulation. Unusual murmurs may be heard.

Effects of Pulmonary Thromboemboli

The clinical effects of pulmonary thromboemboli have recently been reviewed by Pitney.[51] They may be divided into three main groups, which will be considered in the remaining sections of this chapter. If the blockage of the pulmonary arterial tree is sudden and extensive, death may quickly follow owing to the inability of the right ventricle to maintain the circulation. In certain patients occlusion of pulmonary arterial branches gives rise to pulmonary infarction. In the third and rarest group of patients, multiple small thromboemboli lodge in the smaller branches of the pulmonary arterial tree over a period of time and give rise to severe pulmonary hypertension.

MASSIVE ACUTE PULMONARY THROMBOEMBOLISM

Massive pulmonary embolism is a classical clinical emergency with which every doctor is familiar. The moment of catastrophe is associated with the arrival of a large thromboembolus which lodges at the bifurcation of the pulmonary trunk or in one or both of its primary branches. The results are primarily dependent on the mechanical effects of an obstruction of the pulmonary arterial blood flow.

Haemodynamic Effects of Massive Embolism

In a normal person, the sudden occlusion of the right or left primary branches of the pulmonary trunk by means of a balloon gives rise to no symptoms (Chap. 9, p. 129). The difference in mean pressure between the pulmonary artery and left atrium approximately doubles,[52] the left atrial pressure remaining unchanged and the pulmonary arterial pressure increasing by about 5 mmHg. The cardiac output and heart rate remain unchanged.[52] There is no alteration in the respiratory frequency, total ventilatory minute volume, oxygen uptake and respiratory quotient, or the systemic arterial saturation.[52] In animals about 75 per cent of the pulmonary arterial tree can be obstructed without causing death.[53]

Thus, in the normal human lung, rather more than half the pulmonary arterial bed has to be occluded before the clinical syndrome of acute massive embolism will appear. On the other hand, in the presence of pre-existing pulmonary hypertension, occlusion of one primary branch of the pulmonary trunk will have more important haemodynamic effects. In four patients with mitral stenosis,[52] for instance, occlusion of the right pulmonary artery caused the mean pulmonary arterial

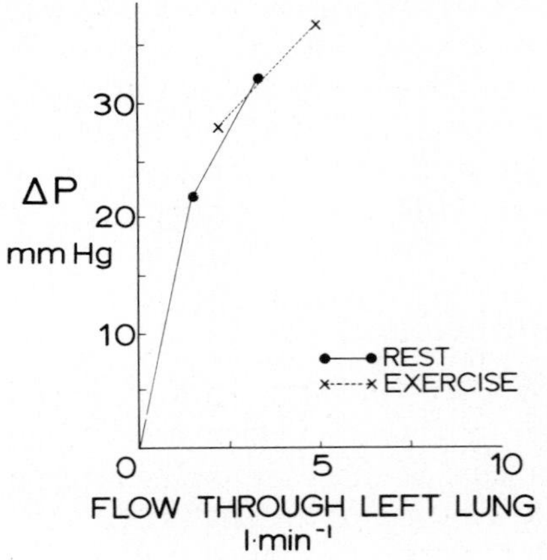

Fig. 35.1 Effects of occlusion of the right pulmonary artery with a balloon in a patient with pulmonary hypertension due to multiple pulmonary thromboemboli. Measurements are shown at rest and during exercise. ΔP = difference between the mean pulmonary arterial pressure and the mean wedge pressure.

pressure to increase from an average of 28 to 36 mmHg (Chap. 23, p. 356). The wedge pressure remained at 22 mmHg. The cardiac output was unchanged, as was the oxygen uptake, but the total ventilation increased from an average of 8·0 to 10·3 l min^{-1}. Figure 35.1 shows the effects of obstructing the right pulmonary artery in a patient with pre-existing thromboembolic pulmonary hypertension. The pulmonary arterial pressure increases to a greater extent than normal, as does the rise induced by exercise.

The presence of pre-existing pulmonary hypertension either from cardiac disease or from previous embolization has an important bearing on the haemodynamic effects of massive pulmonary embolism in patients. Of the 23 patients studied in the acute phase of massive embolism by Miller and Sutton[54] only two had pre-existing cardio-respiratory disease (previous myocardial infarction and mild mitral stenosis). The average value for the mean pulmonary arterial pressure in these 23 patients was 27 mmHg. Similarly, of the 18 patients studied by Hirsh *et al.*,[55] one had rheumatic heart disease and two myocardial infarction, the average mean pulmonary arterial pressure being 29 mmHg for all patients. By contrast, the majority of patients studied by Sasahara and his colleagues[56-58] were known to have pre-existing cardiopulmonary disease and figures of over 40 mmHg for the mean pulmonary arterial pressure were common. Thus, in patients with previous cardiac disease and especially those in whom previous pulmonary embolization has occurred, considerable pulmonary hypertension may exist; in the absence of previous pulmonary hypertension only a modest increase in the pulmonary arterial pressure will be found.

All these clinical studies showed increased right atrial or right ventricular end-diastolic pressures together with a low cardiac output. There seems little doubt that the important haemodynamic consequence of massive pulmonary embolism is an inability of the right ventricle to maintain the cardiac output in the presence of an acutely increased load. If there has been no previous pulmonary hypertension, the right ventricle will fail at only a mild or moderate degree of pulmonary hypertension. If pulmonary hypertension has existed for some time previously, the right ventricle will have had time to become hypertrophied to the extent necessary to maintain a viable cardiac output in the presence of an increased pulmonary vascular resistance. Faced with a sudden further increase in load at the moment of massive embolism, the hypertrophied right ventricle may well be able to maintain a pulmonary arterial pressure considerably higher than normal but not high enough to provide an adequate cardiac output. The different haemodynamic effects of a gradual and a sudden increase in right ventricular load are determined by the time available in the former instance for an increased rate of myocardial protein synthesis to produce right ventricular hypertrophy and an increased capacity for energy production and mechanical activity. It seems likely that the acute increase in mechanical load imposed on the right ventricle by massive pulmonary embolism creates demands which outstrip both the mechanical capacity of the contractile proteins and the metabolic capacity of the myocardium to supply high energy phosphate groups.

There has been a great deal of discussion whether the increased pulmonary vascular resistance which occurs in pulmonary embolism is due simply to the mechanical effects of arterial blockage or whether there is, in addition, an element of spasm of the pulmonary arterial tree. A particular theoretical case has been made out for the effects on the pulmonary circulation of serotonin liberated from thromboemboli. The subject has been reviewed by Marshall[19] to whom the evidence that such effects are important is not persuasive. We take a similar view. The human pulmonary circulation, unlike that of the dog or cat, appears to be unresponsive to serotonin[59] (Chap. 13, p. 198). Leland and Sasahara[56] have shown that the infusion of acetylcholine or the inhalation of oxygen will cause some decrease in the pulmonary arterial pressure in patients with massive pulmonary embolism but such effects, difficult to analyse quantitatively, are not necessarily indicative of an abnormal increase in vascular tone.

Respiratory Gas Exchange in Pulmonary Embolism

Pulmonary embolization interferes with gas exchange in the lungs in a number of ways. The increased total ventilation would tend, if other factors were equal, to reduce the arterial P_{CO_2}. On the other hand, the presence of an unperfused or under-perfused portion of the lung creates an increased physiological dead space. The air expired from this portion of the lung will contain little if any carbon dioxide whereas in the normally or over-perfused portion of the lung equilibration of P_{CO_2} between capillary blood and alveolar gas will occur. Thus, the mixed alveolar air coming from both portions will have a lower P_{CO_2} than the arterial blood. In normal people, the air emitted at the end of a normal expiration corresponds closely to mixed alveolar air and the difference between end-expired P_{CO_2} and arterial P_{CO_2} has been used to demonstrate the presence of embolization.[60,61] Not all workers, however, have found significant differences in patients with pulmonary emboli[62] and the test has not become generally used. The use of end-tidal sampling in patients with chronic bronchitis or emphysema is rendered uninterpretable by the lack of mixing and sequential emptying of air in the lungs.

Some workers have found evidence that occlusion of large pulmonary arteries[63] or embolization of small ones[64] may cause a regional decrease in compliance and an increase in airways resistance, both of which effects will tend to reduce the ventilation to the affected area and maintain ventilation:perfusion homeostasis.

Some decrease in arterial oxygen saturation is usual in patients with embolism. Leland and Sasahara[56] report values of 46–80 mmHg for the Pa_{O_2} in patients with acute embolism. Breathing 100 per cent oxygen raised the arterial Po_2 only to 240–555 mmHg which suggests the presence of anatomical right-left shunting rather than a diffusion defect or inhomogeneity of ventilation:perfusion ratios (Chap. 36, p. 578). In some patients such a shunt could be occurring through a patent foramen ovale. If it is occurring in the lung, the shunt implies the presence of effectively non-ventilating areas in the perfused portion of the lungs. Such areas could be due to co-existing pulmonary disease. They might also include areas of pulmonary oedema due to over-perfusion.[65] The existence of a low mixed venous oxygen content due to a low cardiac output will magnify the effects of shunts on the arterial Po_2.

Clinical Features of Massive Pulmonary Embolism

The clinical features, first described in the classical paper of McGinn and White,[66] have been recently reviewed.[19,20,67] 'Collapse' due to the sudden inadequacy of cardiac output is more often than not the most prominent symptom and the reduced cerebral perfusion may lead to a loss of consciousness. Dyspnoea and hyperventilation are usually prominent, orthopnoea being usually notably absent. A common and ill-explained symptom is the presence of severe pain behind the sternum indistinguishable from angina. It is possibly due to the combination of an acute increase in work and impaired perfusion of the right ventricular myocardium.

The patient's skin is pale and moist, indicative of a decreased cutaneous perfusion. Peripheral cyanosis is usual and central cyanosis may be observed. There is sinus tachycardia and the systemic blood pressure commonly is low, the degree of systemic hypotension being proportional to the gravity of the prognosis. The jugular venous pressure may be raised. In the heart, a third or fourth sound is commonly heard at the left sternal edge. There may be an abnormally wide splitting of the second sound,[68] the pulmonary component of which is not, however, usually louder than normal.[67] Evidence of venous thrombosis will be searched for, especially in the legs.

Of the routine investigations, the electrocardiogram is often normal. A number of electrocardiographic signs may, however, be associated with massive acute embolism (Fig. 35.2). The mean frontal QRS axis may shift to the right with the development of an S wave in lead I, and a Q wave and inversion of the T wave in lead III. In the precordial leads there may be inversion of the T waves as far to the left as V_3 or V_4. Right bundle branch block or incomplete right bundle

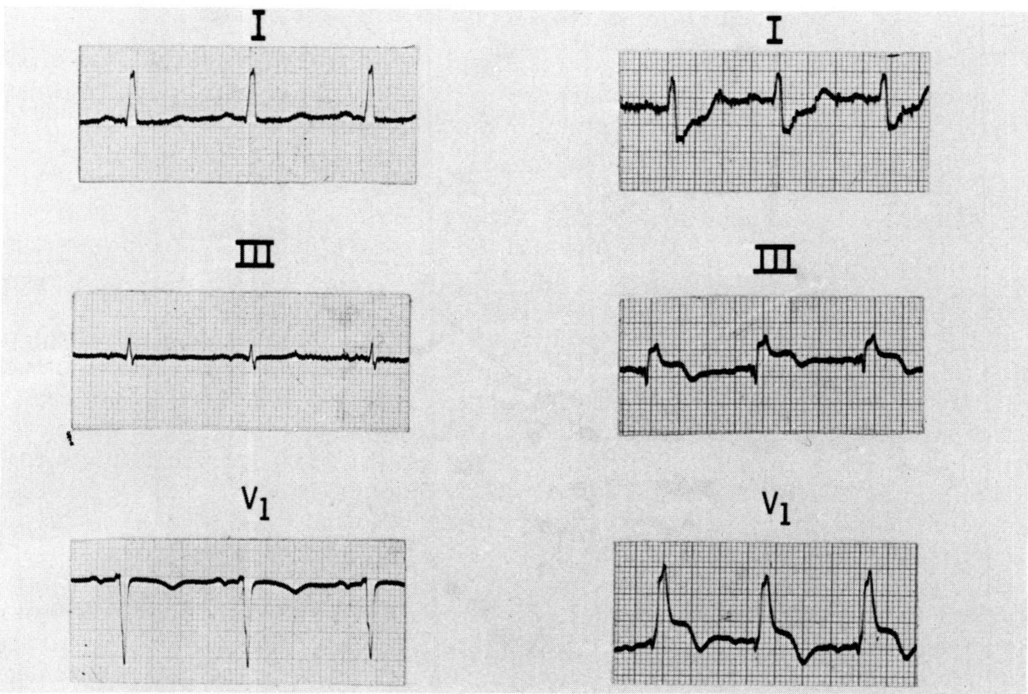

Fig. 35.2 Electrocardiograms before and after an acute massive pulmonary thromboembolism. They show the development of an S_1 and Q_3 with inversion of T_3 and a right bundle branch block.

branch block may occur. The common existence of other cardiopulmonary diseases often confuses the picture. The plain chest radiograph may be normal or may also show evidence of pre-existing cardiopulmonary diseases. The classical sign is of an increased translucency of the affected lung.

More direct evidence of pulmonary thromboembolism and its location is given by pulmonary arteriography[54,69–72] and scintigraphy[73–76] (Chap. 7, p. 99). Of the two, pulmonary arteriography is anatomically the more precise, although with a somewhat greater risk. Scintigraphy suffers from the disadvantage of the length of time taken for scanning if only one crystal is available. Multiple detectors or the gamma camera obviate this disadvantage.

The immediate prognosis of massive pulmonary embolism is grave, two-thirds of the patients dying within the first hour.[77] In experimental animals, respiration usually stops some time before the heart beat[19] and we have also observed this clinically. Should the patient survive the first few hours, the immediate risk declines rapidly[20] the main risk being the incidence of further emboli. The ultimate outcome may be complete recovery or there may be a varying degree of residual pulmonary hypertension due to permanent obstruction.[78]

Treatment of Massive Thromboembolism

It seems unlikely that medical treatment and supportive measures will do much to reduce the immediate mechanical danger of thromboembolism for which surgical removal is a logical procedure. The difficulty is that immediate embolectomy with or without bypass carries a mortality not different from that of the disease. Cross and Mowlem[79] reviewed the experience of a number of surgical centres and reported that the immediate mortality for embolectomy even with bypass was 57 per cent with 11 per cent of late deaths. However, surgical techniques may have improved and Turnier *et al.*[80] report an operative mortality of 29 per cent while Miller[81] reports a figure of 23 per cent.

Since further embolization is an immediate threat to life or, if the patient survives, makes permanent pulmonary hypertension more likely, a major aim of treatment must be to prevent recurrence. To this end ligation of the inferior cava[82] or the formation of a vena caval filter[83] has been recommened. This also is the main reason for anticoagulant therapy. There is some evidence that heparin may in addition reduce bronchoconstriction in thromboembolism[84,85] but the presence of bronchoconstriction is not usually important clinically and may even favour homeostasis of ventilation: perfusion.

Specific intravenous thrombolytic therapy with urokinase or streptokinase is now possible and reports of its use in patients with acute massive pulmonary thromboembolism are encouraging.[55,86] Recently Tibbutt and his colleagues[87] have carried out a controlled clinical trial of streptokinase and heparin. Using pulmonary arteriography, they found a significantly greater degree of thrombolysis after treatment with streptokinase and there was a significantly greater reduction in pulmonary arterial pressure.

PULMONARY INFARCTION

Morbid Anatomy

The lesion at necropsy is dark red and solid, being raised above the surface of the surrounding collapsed lung. It always involves a visceral pleural surface,[88] the affected area of which is covered with fibrin. The long axis of the lesion is parallel to the pleural surface (or, if it involves two adjacent surfaces, to the one most affected).[88] The margin which is directed towards the interior of the lung is irregularly convex.[88]

Histologically the area of 'red infarction' is seen to be stuffed with blood. A recent pulmonary infarct may heal by resorption of this blood leaving the structure of the lung intact.[89] Frequently, however, the lung tissue in the infarcted area becomes necrotic, the infarct being separated from the rest of the lung by a haemorrhagic zone of pulmonary tissue which is not necrotic. After a week, organization begins at the periphery of the infarct with ultimate scarring of the whole area.

Infection of an infarction may occur from organisms carried via the airways or in the embolus giving rise to abscess formation or cavitation. An infective agent within the lumen of a pulmonary artery spreads easily through the wall and may cause extensive inflammation of the arterial wall and the adjacent lung tissue.[1]

Pathogenesis

The pathogenesis of pulmonary infarction has, since its first description by Laennec, proved something of an enigma. Although clinically it is associated with pulmonary arterial occlusion it is difficult to produce experimentally in animals and ischaemia rarely produces a red infarction in other organs. Marshall[19] has reviewed the extensive literature on the experimental production of pulmonary infarction. Pulmonary arterial occlusion alone fails to produce it. The presence or absence of the bronchial arterial supply makes no difference to the development of infarction. The important requirements, in addition to pulmonary arterial occlusion, are an increased pulmonary venous pressure, a diminished local ventilation due to binding of the chest, pleural effusion or bronchial obstruction, pulmonary oedema or pulmonary infection.

In human disease, pulmonary embolism is probably only rarely followed by infarction.[90] In contrast to the distribution of emboli (p. 550) the distribution of pulmonary infarctions shows a distinct predilection for the lower lobes and, in his review, Marshall[19] quotes figures of from 10 to 30 per cent of infarctions occurring in the upper lobes. Since such patients are usually nursed sitting up, the venous pressure is likely to be higher at the base of the lung. In addition, the lung bases are more prone to be affected by infection, bronchial occlusion and pleural effusion, all factors known experimentally to favour infarction. The incidence of infarction is notable in patients with cardiac disease.

Clinical Features

The classical symptoms are pleuritic pain and haemoptysis, possibly with dyspnoea. Not all or any of the symptoms may be present. The classical physical signs, if present, are a diminished movement, dulness, pleural friction and crepitations. There is often a mild fever. Radiologically, the infarcted area casts a shadow which has no specific shape except in so far as it involves one or more visceral pleural surface.[88] The diaphragm on the affected side is often high and less mobile than normal and pleural effusion may be present. Healing may leave a linear shadow.

Among other laboratory investigations, there is typically a leucocytosis and an increase in the erythrocyte sedimentation rate.

RECURRENT PULMONARY THROMBOEMBOLISM

In this rare form of pulmonary thromboembolic disease, emboli lodge repeatedly in the pulmonary arterial tree over a period of time which may extend for several years. Infarction is not usually a feature and the emboli are not massive enough suddenly to embarrass the right ventricle. Instead there is a gradual occlusion of the pulmonary arterial bed with a progressive increase in the pulmonary vascular resistance. Time is available to the right ventricle to undergo hypertrophy and severe pulmonary hypertension develops.

Changes in Structure in the Pulmonary Circulation

Elastic pulmonary arteries Pulmonary emboli, which are compatible with the survival of the patient and the gradual development of congestive cardiac failure over a period of months or years, may be large enough to impact in elastic vessels as big as tertiary branches of the main pulmonary arteries. Here, after organization and re-canalization, as described below, they may form a lattice work of tough, fibrous trabeculae which form an obstruction so tight as not to yield under considerable pressure.[91] These are readily seen by the naked eye at necropsy. Organized, ante-mortem thrombus will frequently form in the interstices of this fibrous meshwork. The obstruction to flow is associated with the development of medial hypertrophy, intimal fibrous plaques and atherosclerosis proximal to the occlusion. Beyond the meshwork, the elastic arteries appear to have a thin atrophic media and the intima is free from atheroma. However, this apparent atrophy is

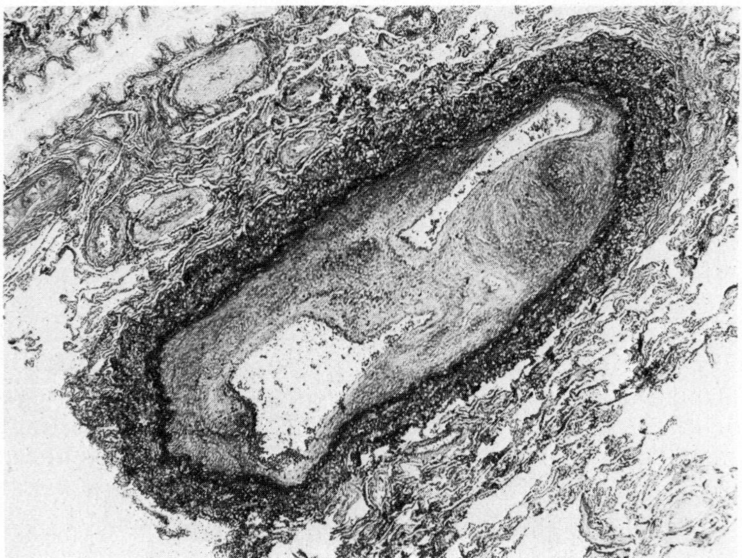

Fig. 35.3 Transverse section of an elastic pulmonary artery from a case of recurrent pulmonary thromboembolism and congestive cardiac failure in a young woman of twenty seven years. At necropsy a considerable quantity of ante-mortem thrombus was found attached to the endocardium of the right ventricle. The elastic artery is almost totally obliterated by organized thrombus which has been re-canalized. The appearances suggest that the re-canalization is of old-standing for there is smooth muscle in the walls of the new vascular channels. The impression given is of two muscular pulmonary arteries within an almost occluded elastic pulmonary artery. (Elastic/Van Gieson, × 35)

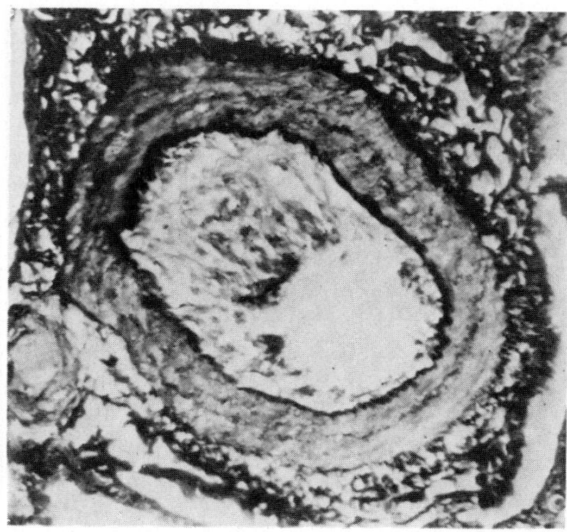

Fig. 35.4 Transverse section of a muscular pulmonary artery from the same case as in Figure 35.3. The media shows considerable hypertrophy. Organizing thrombus partly occludes the lumen. (Elastic/Van Gieson, × 150)

often an optical illusion brought about by comparison with the abnormally thick arteries seen proximal to the point of occlusion, for on direct measurement the media, even beyond the meshwork, is often thicker than normal.[91] These differences in the thickness of the media of the elastic pulmonary artery either side of the point of occlusion are so striking as to be easily visible at necropsy.

Histologically, the lattices consist of fibrous tissue in which there are numerous vascular spaces lined at first with endothelium. There is much elastic tissue in the walls of the small vascular channels within the lumen. Many of the intra-luminal vessels show extensive intimal fibrous proliferation. After several months smooth muscle may form in their walls so that the re-canalized emboli give the appearance of newly-formed muscular pulmonary arteries embedded in fibroelastic tissue in the lumen of an elastic pulmonary artery (Fig. 35.3). Similar appearances are found in the uterine arteries in sub-involution of the uterus and are illustrated by Novak.[92] Proximal to these obstructions the large elastic pulmonary arteries show severe intimal fibrous proliferation.

Muscular pulmonary arteries Recurrent pulmonary thromboembolism leading to pulmonary arterial hypertension and congestive cardiac failure is usually extensive; it is very rare to find emboli involving only one lobe or even one lung.[93] Most of the lesions seen are organized, which suggests that the interval between initial embolism and the patient's death, though variable, is most frequently a matter of months or even years. In spite of this extensive occlusion by organized emboli, infarction is not a prominent feature of the syndrome, although small infarcts are seen.

It is likely, from analogy with observations on the lungs of animals exposed to experimental thromboembolism, that the pulmonary emboli become partly covered by adherent neutrophil polymorphs within a few hours of impaction.[45] After an initial shrinkage of the thrombus to leave an eccentric channel,[42] it is likely that there is early organization in the following three or four days[94] (Fig. 35.4). Granulation tissue grows into those parts of the embolus in contact with the intima of the artery, and macrophages, lymphocytes and plasma cells may be found among its capillary vessels and fibroblasts. Finally, the embolus is completely organized, the thrombus being replaced by fibrous tissue. The internal elastic lamina may split and fragment. With the passage of time, the fibrous tissue, totally or partially occluding the lumen of the artery, becomes less cellular and shrinks. Elastic tissue hyperplasia occurs so that fragmented elastic fibrils are seen between the collagen fibres. In some cases the organized emboli may shrink progressively to end months later as a mere thickening of the intima by fibroelastic tissue. Recanalization of an organized embolus may occur and lead to the colander-like appearance which is commonly seen in congenital heart disease with pulmonary stenosis and described in Chapter 37. Some of the lesions are identical with those of thrombosis occurring *in situ*. With the onset of pulmonary arterial hypertension small muscular arterial vessels less than 100 μm in diameter are found in the lung as in other forms of hypertensive pulmonary vascular disease. These small arterial vessels have a muscular media with distinct internal and external elastic laminae (Fig. 35.5).

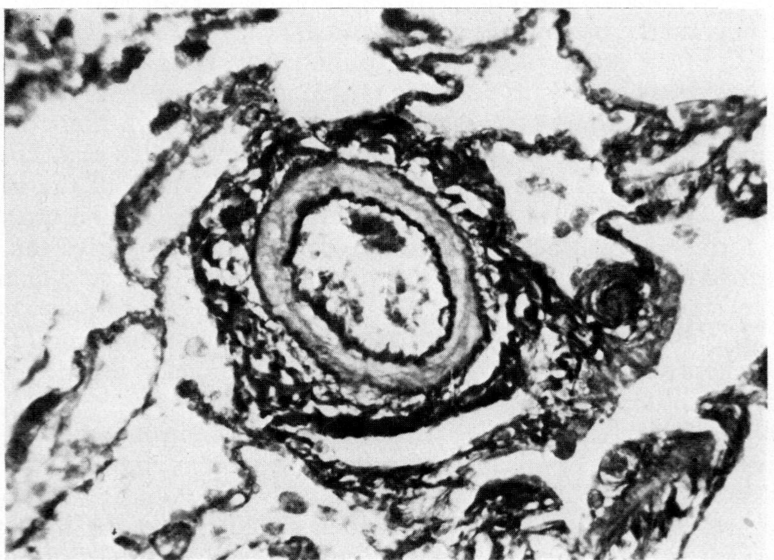

Fig. 35.5 Transverse section of an arterial vessel less than 100 μm in diameter from the same case as in Figure 35.3. There is a muscular media with distinct internal and external elastic laminae. (Elastic/Van Gieson, × 250)

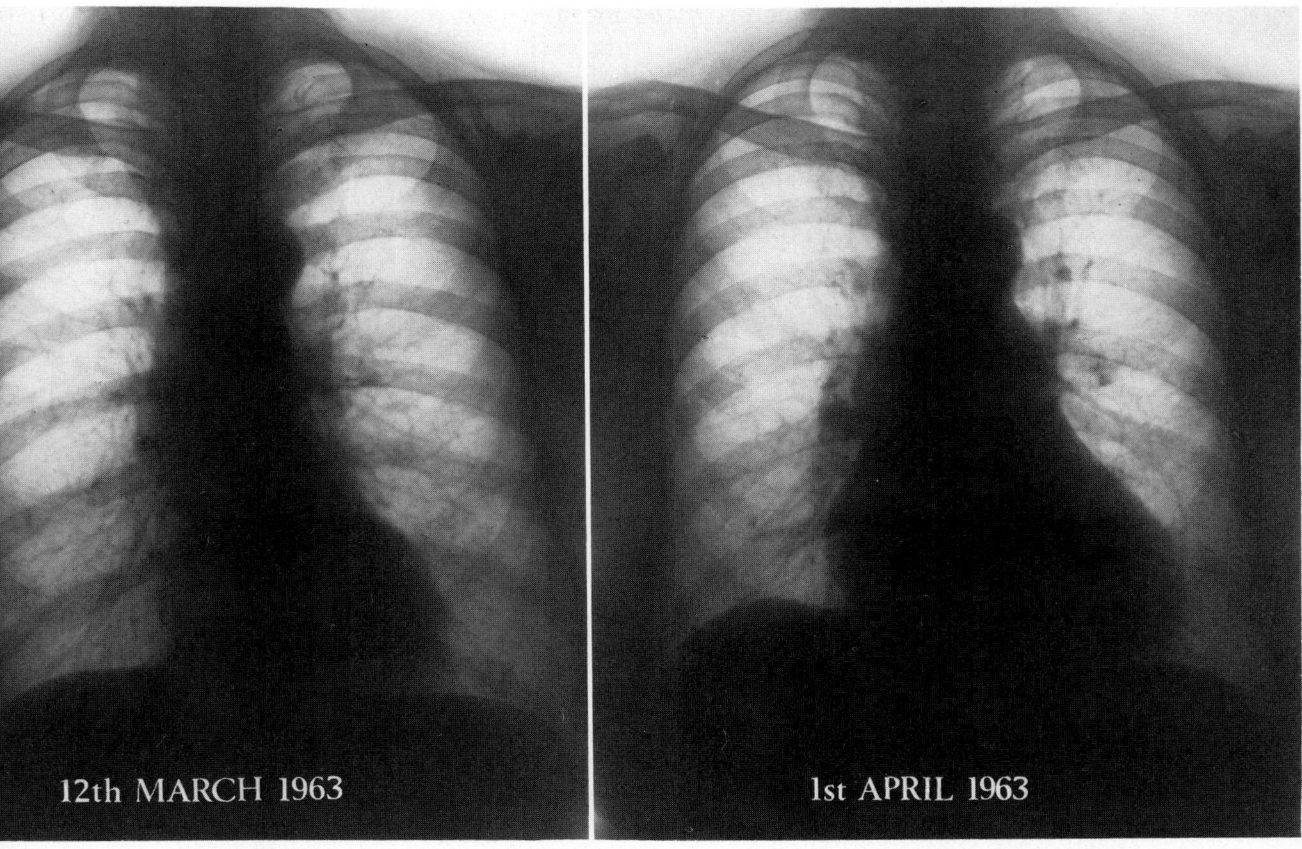

Fig. 35.6 Chest radiographs showing the effects of the rapid development of recurrent pulmonary thromboembolic disease following abdominal surgery. The symptoms were solely an increasing shortness of breath. The first film was taken the day before operation. By comparison, the second film shows cardiac enlargement and enlargement of the pulmonary trunk and its main divisions. The pulmonary peripheral vessels appear normal and there is no sign of infarction.

It will be seen that wide ranges of appearance may be found in the course of organization of pulmonary emboli, and, if the widespread obliteration of the pulmonary vascular bed by this process should become associated with pulmonary hypertension, to this range of histological appearance will be added increased medial thickness. Hence the histological appearances of grades 1 to 3 hypertensive pulmonary vascular disease will be closely mimicked. However, in spite of this wide spectrum of changes in structure, dilatation lesions are not found. This does not support the view expressed by some authors[95] that the changes in structure in the small pulmonary arteries in congenital heart disease are primarily thromboembolic in nature.

The similarity in appearance produced by organized pulmonary emboli on the one hand and primary thrombosis occurring over an already diseased pulmonary artery may make it very difficult for the pathologist to differentiate between classical 'primary pulmonary hypertension' and recurrent pulmonary thromboembolism. This differential diagnosis is considered in detail in Chapter 28, p. 427. It has assumed considerable interest and importance in the diagnosis of some of the cases occurring in the recent epidemic of cases of primary pulmonary hypertension in Western Europe linked with the ingestion of certain types of anorexigen.

Clinical Features[93,96–100]

Unlike massive pulmonary embolism, this is a disease of insidious onset with a history ranging from a few weeks (Fig. 35.6) to years. The predominating symptom is usually an increasing shortness of breath. Goodwin,[100] from extensive personal experience, recognizes two main clinical groups. In one group the origin of venous thrombi is usually evident, there are pulmonary infarctions and episodes of syncope are referable to further embolism. The other group is characterized by fatigue and syncope on effort and progressive cardiac failure.

Hyperventilation is usually obvious at rest and always during exercise. Cyanosis may be evident. The cardiovascular physical signs are those of pulmonary hypertension and chronic right ventricular overload. The jugular '*a*' wave may be prominent or the venous pulse may indicate the presence of a functional tricuspid incompetence. The systolic thrust of a hypertrophied right ventricle may be felt to the left of the sternum. The pulmonary component of the second sound is increased and there may be an ejection systolic murmur over the outflow tract of the right ventricle.

The electrocardiogram indicates a varying degree of right ventricular and right atrial hypertrophy. The chest radiograph may show the development of cardiac enlargement (Figs 35.6 and 35.7). There may be evidence of infarction. As the disease progresses the pulmonary trunk and its main branches enlarge (Figs 35.6 and 35.7). The peripheral pulmonary arterial branches may seem entirely normal or there may be an increased translucency of the periphery.

At cardiac catheterization, the major haemodynamic abnormality is an elevated pulmonary arterial pressure, the mean level of which may be as high as 60–70 mmHg.[96,97,99] The wedge pressure is normal. The diffusing capacity of the lungs is diminished (p. 647).

Both pulmonary arteriography and scintigraphy[101] may be helpful in establishing the diagnosis. Their relative values are discussed by McIntyre and Sasahara.[102] Arteriography is probably better at showing occlusion of the larger vessels. Scintigraphy appears to have an advantage where there is multiple occlusion of smaller vessels.

The prognosis for these patients is bad. A certain number, however, appear to respond to anticoagulant therapy which should always be tried.

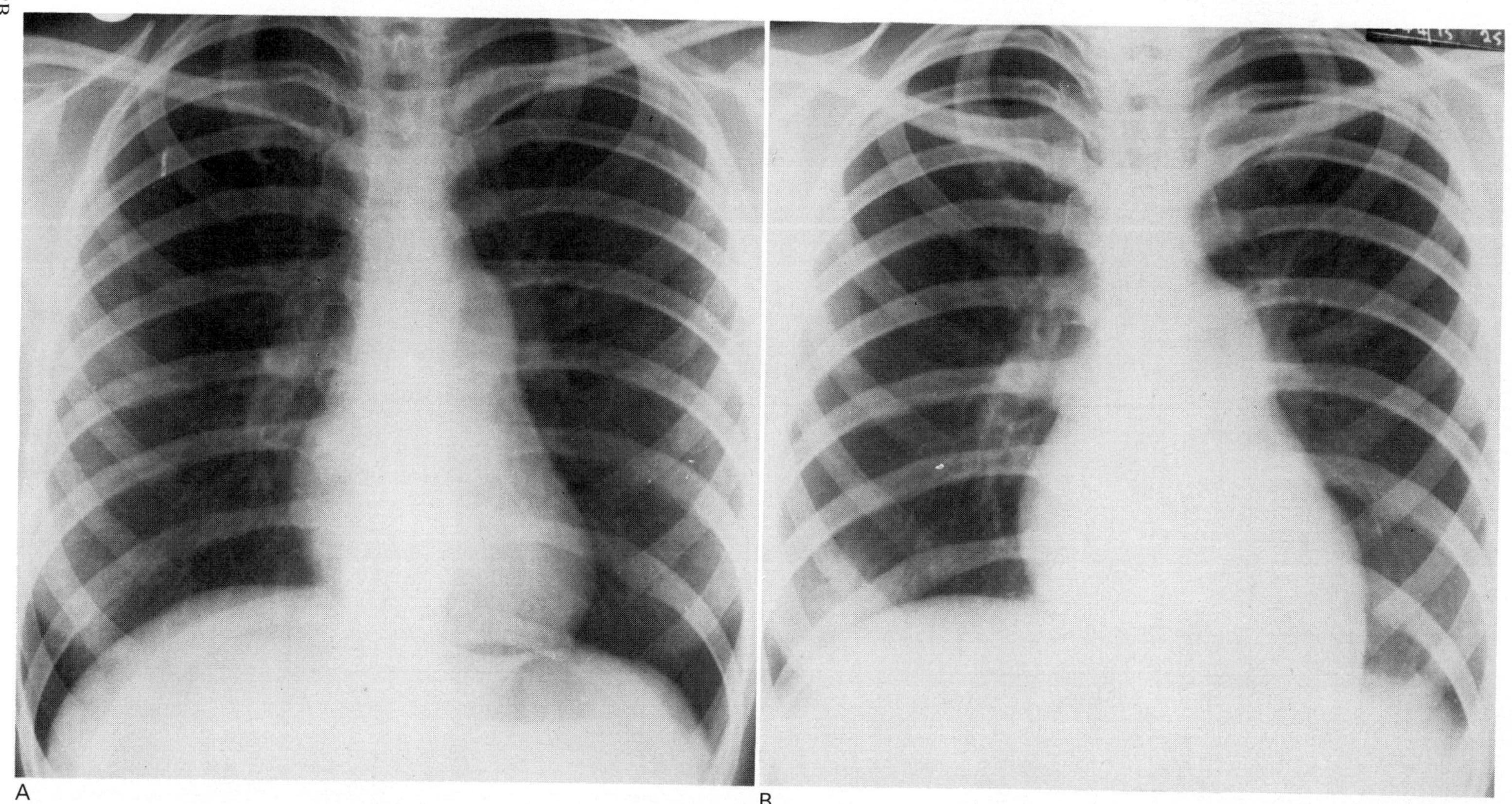

Fig. 35.7 Chest radiographs of a girl aged 19 years with pulmonary hypertension due to recurrent thromboembolism. A, November, 1974. There is enlargement of the pulmonary trunk and the major pulmonary arteries. The peripheral vessels are normal. B, February, 1975. The enlargement of the pulmonary trunk and the main branches has increased. The peripheral pulmonary vessels remain small. The cardiac size has increased. During this period of time the patient became progressively dyspnoeic and cyanosed despite treatment with anticoagulant. The diagnosis was confirmed at necropsy. No site of origin of thrombi was obvious clinically and only the heart and lungs were available for post-mortem examination.

Pathogenesis of Recurrent Pulmonary Thromboembolism

Although in some patients a source of venous thrombi may be evident, in the majority this is not so. As has been discussed above, there is evidence that the production of small thromboemboli is a normal phenomenon and the suggestion has been made[19,100] that chronic pulmonary embolism is caused not by the production of an excessive number of thromboemboli but by the intrinsic inability of the pulmonary circulation to deal with them. So far, no evidence has been found of inadequate fibrinolytic activity in the blood of these patients. The abnormality, if it exists, may, however, lie in the pulmonary vascular endothelium.

REFERENCES

1. Wagenvoort, C. A., Heath, D. & Edwards, J. E. (1964) In *The Pathology of the Pulmonary Vasculature*, page 296. Springfield, Ill.: Thomas.
2. Rappaport, H., Raum, M. & Horrell, J. B. (1951) *Amer. J. Path.*, **27**, 407.
3. Aschoff, L. (1893) *Virchow Arch. Path. Anat.*, **134**, 11.
4. Sharnoff, J. G. & Kim, E. S. (1958) *Arch. Path.*, **66**, 176.
5. Sharnoff, J. G. & Kim, E. S. (1958) *Arch. Path.*, **66**, 340.
6. McMillan, J. B. (1956) *Amer. J. Path.*, **32**, 405.
7. Brüning, E. J. (1960) *Z. Kreisl.*, **49**, 631.
8. Sevitt, S. (1960) *Lancet*, **ii**, 825.
9. Robb-Smith, A. H. T. (1941) *Lancet*, **i**, 135.
10. Steiner, P. E. & Lushbaugh, C. C. (1941) *J.A.M.A.*, **117**, 1245 & 1340.
11. Attwood, H. D. (1958) *J. Path. Bact.*, **76**, 211.
12. Shepherd, J. T., Edwards, J. E., Burchell, H. B., Swan, H. J. C. & Wood, E. H. (1957) *Brit. Heart J.*, **19**, 70.
13. Heath, D. & MacKinnon, J. (1964) *Amer. Heart J.*, **68**, 227.
14. Barnard, P. J. (1957) *Arch. Path.*, **63**, 322.
15. Heath, D. & MacKinnon, J. (1962) *Brit. Heart J.*, **24**, 518.
16. Wendt, V. E., Puro, H. E., Shapiro, J., Mathews, W. & Wolf, P. L. (1964) *J. Amer. Med. Ass.*, **188**, 755.
17. Buxton, J. T., Hewitt, J. C., Gadsden, R. H. & Bradham, G. B. (1965) *J. Amer. Med. Ass.*, **193**, 573.
18. Barrett, N. R. (1950) *Brit. J. Surg.*, **37**, 416.
19. Marshall, R. (1965) *Pulmonary Embolism.* Springfield, Ill.: Thomas.
20. Gray, F. D., Jn. (1966) *Pulmonary Embolism.* Henry Kimpton.
21. Kakkar, V. V., Nicolaides, A. N., Renney, J. T. G., Friend, J. R. & Clarke, M. B. (1970) *Lancet*, **i**, 540.
22. Jick, H. & Shone, D. (1969) *Lancet*, **i**, 539.
23. Morrell, M. T. & Dunnill, M. S. (1968) *Brit. J. Surg.*, **55**, 347.
24. Lenègre, J. & Néel, J. (1950) Referred to by Marshall, R. (1965) *Pulmonary Embolism.* Springfield, Ill.: Thomas.
25. Anthonisen, N. R. & Milic-Emili, J. (1966) *J. Appl. Physiol.*, **21**, 760.
26. Allison, P. R., Dunnill, M. S. & Marshall, R. (1960) *Thorax*, **15**, 273.
27. Hume, M., Glenn, W. W. L. & Grillo, T. (1960) *Ann. Surg.*, **151**, 507.
28. Wessler, S., Freiman, D. G., Ballon, J. D., Katz, J. H., Wolff, R. & Wolf, E. (1961) *Amer. J. Path.*, **38**, 89.
29. Freiman, D. G., Wessler, S. & Lertzman, M. (1961) *Amer. J. Path.*, **39**, 95.
30. Marshall, R., Sabiston, D. C., Allison, P. R., Bosman, A. R. & Dunnill, M. S. (1963) *Thorax*, **18**, 1.

31. Poe, N. D., Swanson, L. A., Dove, E. K. & Taplin, G. V. (1967) *Amer. Heart J.*, **73**, 582.
32. Lewis, J. H. & Ferguson, J. H. (1950) *J. Clin. Invest.*, **29**, 1059.
33. MacLeod, M., Stalker, A. L. & Ogston, D. (1962) *Lancet*, **i**, 191.
34. Lincoln, A. F., Moorman, J. A. & Schultz, R. L. (1957) *Surg. Gyn. Obst.*, **105**, 541.
35. Soulier, J. P., Mathey, J., Lebollock, A. G., Daumet, P. & Fayet, H. (1952) *Rev. Hématol.*, **7**, 30.
36. Marchal, G., Samama, M., Mirabel, J. & Vaysse, J. (1960) *Sem. Hôp.*, **36**, 1994.
37. Walker, W. & LaForet, E. G. (1956) *J. Thorac. Surg.*, **32**, 548.
38. Todd, A. S. (1958) *J. Path. Bact.*, **78**, 281.
39. Niewiarowski, S. & Latallo, Z. (1959) *Thromb. Diath. Haem.*, **3**, 404.
40. Wartman, W. B., Hudson, B. & Jennings, R. B. (1951) *Circulation*, **4**, 756.
41. Wartman, W. B., Jennings, R. B. & Hudson, B. (1951) *Circulation*, **4**, 747.
42. Harrison, C. V. (1948) *J. Path. Bact.*, **60**, 289.
43. Harrison, C. V. (1951) *J. Path. Bact.*, **63**, 195.
44. Heard, B. E. (1952) *J. Path. Bact.*, **64**, 13.
45. Barnard, P. J. (1953) *J. Path. Bact.*, **65**, 129.
46. Jaques, W. E. & Hyman, A. L. (1957) *Arch. Path.*, **64**, 487.
47. Scebat, L., Cloarec, M., Renais, J. & Lancret, P. (1959) *Arch. Mal. Coeur*, **1**, 112.
48. Gore, I., Tanaka, K., Nakashima, T. & Larkey, B. J. (1962) *Amer. J. Path.*, **41**, 77.
49. Hand, R. A. & Chandler, A. B. (1962) *Amer. J. Path.*, **40**, 469.
50. Magidson, O. & Jacobson, G. (1955) *Brit. Heart J.*, **17**, 207.
51. Pitney, W. R. (1972) *Clinical Aspects of Thromboembolism.* Churchill-Livingstone.
52. Harris, P., Segel, N. & Bishop, J. M. (1968) *Cardiovasc. Res.*, **2**, 73.
53. Haggart, G. E. & Walker, A. M. (1923) *Arch. Surg.*, **6**, 764.
54. Miller, G. A. H. & Sutton, G. C. (1970) *Brit. Heart J.*, **32**, 518.
55. Hirsh, J., Hale, G. S., McDonald, I. G., McCarthy, R. A. & Pitt, A. (1968) *Brit. Med. J.*, **4**, 729.
56. Leland, O. S., Jn. & Sasahara, A. A. (1965) In *Pulmonary Embolic Disease*, ed. Sasahara, A. A. & Stein, M. D. page 110. Grune & Stratton.
57. Sasahara, A. A., Sidd, J. J., Tremblay, G. & Leland, O. S., Jn. (1966) *Progr. Cardiovasc. Dis.*, **9**, 259.
58. Sasahara, A. A., Cannilla, J. E., Morse, R. L., Sidd, J. J. & Tremblay, G. M. (1967) *Amer. J. Cardiol.*, **20**, 10.
59. Harris, P., Fritts, H. W., Jn. & Cournand, A. (1960) *Circulation*, **21**, 1134.
60. Robin, E. D., Julian, D. G., Travis, D. M. & Crump, C. H. (1959) *New Engl. J. Med.*, **260**, 586.
61. Robin, E. D., Fakner, C. E., Bromberg, P. A., Croteau, J. R. & Travis, D. M. (1960) *New Engl. J. Med.*, **262**, 283.
62. Colp, C. R. & Williams, M. H. (1962) *Amer. Rev. Resp. Dis.*, **85**, 799.
63. Severinghaus, J. W., Swenson, E. W., Finley, T. N., Lategola, M. T. & Williams, J. (1961) *J. Appl. Physiol.*, **16**, 53.
64. Nadel, J. A., Colebatch, H. J. H. and Olsen, C. R. (1964) *J. Appl. Physiol.*, **19**, 387.
65. Swenson, E. W., Llamas, R. & Ring, G. C. (1965) In *Pulmonary Embolic Disease*, ed. Sasahara, A. A. & Stein, M. page 170. Grune & Stratton.
66. McGinn, S. & White, P. D. (1935) *J. Amer. Med. Ass.*, **104**, 1473.
67. Sutton, G. C., Honey, M. & Gibson, R. V. (1969) *Lancet*, **i**, 271.
68. Cobbs, B. W., Logue, R. B. & Dorney, E. R. (1966) *Amer. Heart J.*, **71**, 843.
69. Sasahara, A. A., Stein, M., Simon, M. & Littman, D. (1964) *New Engl. J. Med.*, **270**, 1075.
70. Sautter, R. D. (1965) *J. Amer. Med. Ass.*, **194**, 336.
71. Scannell, J. G. (1967) *Progr. Cardiovasc. Dis.*, **9**, 488.
72. Simon, M. & Sasahara, A. A. (1965) In *Pulmonary Embolic Disease*, ed. Sasahara, A. A. & Stein, M. page 214. Grune & Stratton.
73. Sasahara, A. A., Belko, J. S. & Simpson, R. G. (1967) *Radiology*, **88**, 363.

74. Wagner, H. N., Jn., Sabiston, D. C., McAfee, J. G., Tow, D. E. & Stern, H. S. (1969) *New Engl. J. Med.*, **271**, 377.
75. Lopez-Majano, V. (1970) *Progr. Resp. Res.*, **5**, 290.
76. Bischoff-Delaloye, A., Hedinger, W. & Delaloye, B. (1971) *J. Nucl. Biol. Med.*, **15**, 13.
77. Gorham, L. W. (1961) *Arch. Int. Med.*, **108**, 8.
78. Symbas, P. N., Jacobs, W. F. & Schlant, R. C. (1971) *Amer. J. Cardiol.*, **28**, 342.
79. Cross, F. S. & Mowlem, A. (1967) *Circulation*, Suppl. 2, **35**, 86.
80. Turnier, E., Kerth, W. J. & Gerbode, F. (1973) *Amer. J. Surg.*, **125**, 611.
81. Miller, G. A. H. (1972) *Brit. J. Surg.*, **59**, 837.
82. Storey, W. S., Jacobs, J. K. & Collins, H. A. (1963) *Surg. Gyn. Obst.*, **116**, 292.
83. DeWeese, M. S. & Hunter, D. C. (1963) *Arch. Surg.*, **86**, 852.
84. Gurewich, V., Thomas, D., Stein, M. & Wessler, S. (1963) *Circulation*, **28**, 339.
85. Thomas, D., Stein, M., Tanabe, G., Rege, V. & Wessler, S. (1964) *Amer. J. Physiol.*, **206**, 1207.
86. Miller, G. A. H., Sutton, G. C., Kerr, I. H., Gibson, R. V. & Honey, M. (1971) *Brit. Med. J.*, **2**, 681.
87. Tibbutt, D. A., Davies, J. A., Anderson, J. A., Fletcher, E. W. L., Hamill, J., Holt, J. M., Lea Thomas, M., Lee, G. de J., Miller, G. A. H., Sharp, A. A. & Sutton, G. C. (1974) *Brit. Med. J.*, **1**, 343.
88. Hampton, A. D. & Castleman, B. (1940) *Amer. J. Roentgenol.*, **43**, 305.
89. Giese, W. (1960) *Die Atemorgane.* In *Lehrbuch der Speziellen Pathologischen Anatomie*, ed. Kaufmann, 2nd ed. Vol. II. Berlin: De Gruyter.
90. Smith, G. T., Dexter, L. & Dammin, G. J. (1965) In *Pulmonary Embolic Disease.* ed. Sasahara, A. A. & Stein, M. page 120. Grune & Stratton.
91. Castleman, B. & Bland, E. F. (1946) *Arch. Path.*, **42**, 581.
92. Novak, E. (1947) *Gynecological and Obstetrical Pathology.* 2nd ed. P.184. Philadelphia: Saunders.
93. Owen, W. R., Thomas, W. A., Castleman, B. & Bland, E. F. (1953) *New Engl. J. Med.*, **249**, 919.
94. Barnard, P. J. (1954) *Brit. Heart J.*, **16**, 93.
95. O'Neal, R. M. & Thomas, W. A. (1955) *Circulation*, **12**, 370.
96. Ehrner, L., Garlind, T. & Linderholm, H. (1959) *Acta Med. Scand.*, **164**, 270.
97. Wilcken, D. E. L., Mackenzie, K. M. & Goodwin, J. F. (1960) *Lancet*, **ii**, 781.
98. Wood, P. (1956) *Diseases of Heart and Circulation.* 2nd ed.Eyre & Spottiswoode.
99. Goodwin, J. F., Harrison, C. V. & Wilcken, D. E. L. (1963) *Brit. Med. J.*, **1**, 701, 777.
100. Goodwin, J. F. (1965) In *Pulmonary Embolic Disease.* ed. Sasahara, A. A. & Stein, M. page 239. Grune & Stratton.
101. Secker-Walker, R. H. & Siegel, B. A. (1973) *Radiol. Clin. N. Amer.*, **11**, 215.
102. McIntyre, K. M. & Sasahara, A. A. (1971) *J. Nucl. Med.*, **12**, 732.

36. The Relation Between Ventilation and Perfusion

Anatomical Shunt and Anatomical Dead-Space

Under normal circumstances nearly all the venous blood returning from the various parts of the body flows through the alveolar capillaries where it exchanges gases with the air. A small fraction of venous blood, however, passes directly into the systemic arterial stream from bronchial veins, Thebesian veins, or through pulmonary vessels which do not perfuse alveoli. In the presence of certain congenital abnormalities of the heart and lungs, the magnitude of this 'anatomical' right-to-left shunt is considerably increased.

The ventilation of the lungs may be considered in similar terms. Although most of the inspired air passes into the alveoli, a certain portion fails to reach so deeply into the lung and is breathed out in the next expiration without having taken part in the gaseous exchange with the blood stream. This latter portion of the inspired air serves only to ventilate the anatomical dead-space and is analogous to the anatomical shunt of blood. Thus the arterial blood consists of alveolar capillary blood diluted with a certain volume of venous blood shunted directly through the anatomical shunt, and the expired air consists of alveolar air diluted with a certain volume of inspired air 'shunted' directly through the dead-space.

From the point of view of the exchange of gases in the lungs, the important part of the total cardiac output is the pulmonary capillary blood flow and the important part of the total ventilation is the alveolar ventilation. The pulmonary capillary blood flow ($\dot{Q}_C$) is normally about 6 l min^{-1} at rest. The alveolar ventilation ($\dot{V}_A$) is somewhat less, the ratio of alveolar ventilation to capillary blood flow ($\dot{V}_A/\dot{Q}_C$) being normally about 4 : 5 at rest. This ratio, which will be referred to as the 'ventilation : perfusion ratio', has an important influence on the exchange of respiratory gases. This is not only true of the lungs as a whole, but also in the more complex situation which occurs when there is a variation in the ratio between various parts of the lungs. In this chapter, the effects of changes in the *total* ventilation : perfusion ratio will first be considered, and then the effects of a lack of uniformity of the ratio *within* the lungs.

Variations in Total Alveolar Ventilation

At rest, the quantity of oxygen consumed by the tissues of the body each minute is 220–260 ml (STPD). The quantity of carbon dioxide liberated each minute by the tissues is usually about four-fifths of this amount, depending on the value of the respiratory exchange ratio (R). Over a prolonged period the quantities of gases exchanged in the tissues must equal those exchanged in the lungs.

Even if the ventilation of the alveoli becomes abnormally low, this basic rate of exchange of gases must still continue. Carbon dioxide continues to pour into the

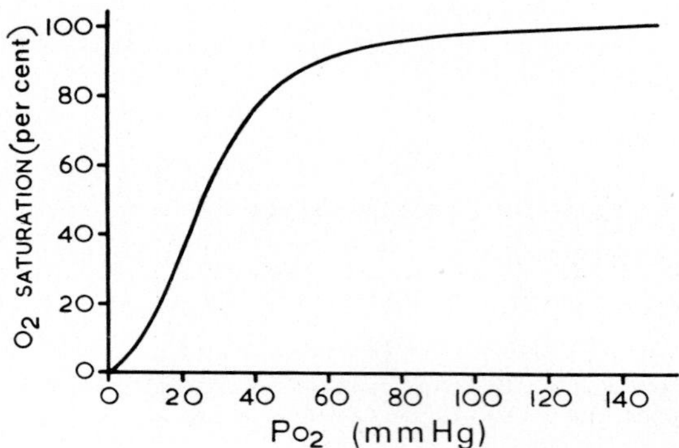

Fig. 36.1 The oxygen dissociation curve of blood.

alveoli and oxygen continues to be taken up from them at the same rate as before, so that there develops a surfeit of carbon dioxide in the alveoli while oxygen becomes scarce. In this way the alveolar Pco_2 rises and the alveolar Po_2 falls. If there is complete equilibrium between the alveolar air and the blood in the capillaries, these changes in Pco_2 and Po_2 will also be present in the blood as it leaves the alveoli. The rise in Pco_2 causes an increase in the content of carbon dioxide in the blood. A slight lowering of Po_2 in the blood has little effect on the content of oxygen because of the flatness of the oxygen dissociation curve at this point (Fig. 36.1). With a further decrease in Po_2, however, the steep part of the dissociation curve may be reached and a considerable fall in the content of oxygen and the oxygen saturation can then occur.

Hence the net result of a substantial lowering of alveolar ventilation is an increase in the carbon dioxide content and a decrease in the oxygen saturation of the end-capillary blood. These changes are also largely reflected in the arterial blood.

The reverse is not entirely true. An increase in the total alveolar ventilation will lower the Pco_2 and raise the Po_2 in the alveoli while similar alterations will occur in the partial pressures of these gases in the capillary blood. However, although the lowered carbon dioxide tension in the blood causes a lowered carbon dioxide content, the increase in oxygen tension can cause very little rise in the oxygen content or saturation because it occurs on the flat part of the oxygen dissociation curve (Fig. 36.1). In other words, the haemoglobin in the blood leaving the pulmonary capillaries is already 97–98 per cent saturated with oxygen even under normal conditions and over-ventilation can do very little to increase this.

Variations in Total Perfusion

The effects of variations in the rate of perfusion of the pulmonary capillaries are more simply described. The basic rate of exchange of carbon dioxide and oxygen in the lungs must be maintained. Hence increasing the total rate of perfusion will simply narrow the arterio-venous difference of oxygen and carbon dioxide, while decreasing the rate of perfusion will widen these differences. A glance at the Fick equation will show how this must be so:

$$10 \times \dot{Q}c = \frac{\dot{V}O_2}{Cc'_{O_2} - C\bar{v}_{O_2}} = \frac{\dot{V}CO_2}{C\bar{v}_{CO_2} - Cc'_{CO_2}}$$

where the suffix 'c'' refers to end-capillary blood.

If $\dot{V}O_2$ and $\dot{V}CO_2$ are kept constant, then $\dot{Q}c$ will vary inversely as $(Cc'_{O_2} - C\bar{v}_{O_2})$ and $(C\bar{v}_{CO_2} - Cc'_{CO_2})$. In fact, since the contents of oxygen and carbon dioxide of end-capillary blood are kept reasonably constant, the alterations in the arterio-venous differences of these gases are effected simply by alterations in the composition of the mixed venous blood.

Unevenness of Ventilation : Perfusion Within the Lungs

Even in a normal lung, the ratio of ventilation to perfusion varies slightly from alveolus to alveolus and from area to area (p. 582). In some diseases, and classically in emphysema, this variation throughout the lungs becomes of considerable magnitude and interferes with the exchange of respiratory gases. Sometimes the primary fault in distribution is a ventilatory one, such as the partial or complete obstruction of a bronchus, local infection or fibrosis, pressure by tumour or pleural fluid, paralysis of the diaphragm, or local immobility of the chest wall from strapping or injury. At other times the primary fault is a circulatory one such as in pulmonary haemangiomata or embolization or thrombosis in the branches of the pulmonary artery (Chap. 35). When a long-standing under-ventilation of a part of the lungs occurs, the circulation to that part may become reduced, thus restoring the ventilation : perfusion ratio. This happens, for instance, in the case of segmental collapse and in pneumothorax. The reason for such an adaptation may be a mechanical one or it may be that local hypoxia causes local pulmonary vaso-constriction (Chap. 30, p. 454). We know of no study of the appearances of the pulmonary vessels under these conditions.

The effect of a lack of uniformity of ventilation : perfusion on the composition of the arterial blood is the same as the effect of a right-left shunt. There is a fall in arterial oxygen tension and content and a very slight rise in carbon dioxide tension and content. The passage of blood through a poorly ventilated alveolus is, in fact, a form of a shunt, for the difference between the perfusion of an ill-ventilated alveolus and the perfusion of an unventilated alveolus becomes ultimately one of degree. Thus the magnitude of the inhomogeneity of ventilation : perfusion may be expressed from the point of view of the blood phase as an increase in the volume of right-left shunt.

Similar considerations can be applied to the gas phase. The ventilation of poorly perfused portions of the lung causes, in effect, an increase in the volume of dead-space ventilation, for the difference between the ventilation of an ill-perfused alveolus and the ventilation of an unperfused alveolus becomes ultimately one of degree.

Hence an inhomogeneity of ventilation : perfusion may be expressed from the point of view of the gas phase as an increase in the volume of dead-space ventilation.

There are, therefore, two forms of shunt which tend to reduce the oxygenation of the arterial blood. The first is an anatomical shunt of venous blood from bronchial and Thebesian veins or through pulmonary vessels which have no contact with alveoli. The second is the effective shunt caused by uneven ventilation : perfusion. The addition of the two represents the 'physiological shunt' or 'venous admixture'. Similarly, there are two forms of dead-space ventilation: the ventilation of the anatomical dead-space and an additional effective dead-space ventilation due to uneven ventilation : perfusion. The addition of the two represents the 'physiological dead-space'.

In Table 36.1 the effects of uneven ventilation : perfusion on the blood gases are shown by means of an arithmetical example. The lungs have been divided into two portions. In one, the ventilation : perfusion ratio is high. In the other, it is low. If the compositions of the mixed venous blood and the inspired air are known, the alveolar Po_2 and Pco_2 can be derived from the $O_2 - CO_2$ diagram (p. 575). As would be expected, the portion with a high ventilation : perfusion ratio has a high alveolar Po_2 and a low alveolar Pco_2 while the portion with a low ventilation : perfusion ratio has a low alveolar Po_2 and a high alveolar Pco_2. Since, in each portion, complete equilibration is assumed to occur between the alveolar air and the end-capillary blood, the partial pressures of the gases in the end-capillary blood follow exactly those in the alveolar air. Hence the oxygen content of the blood leaving the portion with a low ventilation : perfusion ratio is lower than that leaving the portion with a high ratio.

The mixed alveolar Po_2 is weighted heavily by the contribution of gas from the portion with a high ventilation : perfusion ratio which is nearly twice the contribution from the portion with a low ratio. Thus the mixed alveolar Po_2 comes to lie closer to the alveolar Po_2 of the portion with a high ratio. On the other hand, the mixed end-capillary Po_2 is weighted by the contribution of blood from the portion with the low ventilation : perfusion ratio and comes to lie closer to the alveolar Po_2 of this portion. The result of this lack of uniformity of the ventilation : perfusion ratio is, therefore, to make the mixed end-capillary Po_2 lower than the mixed alveolar Po_2. In the example given in Table 36.1, the difference in Po_2 between mixed alveolar air (PA_{O_2}) and mixed end-capillary blood (Pc'_{O_2}), amounts to 25 mmHg. On the other hand the difference in Pco_2 (*i.e.* $PA_{CO_2} - Pc'_{CO_2}$) is only 3 mmHg.

Part of the difference in Po_2 is due to the influence of the shape of the oxygen dissociation curve. Although the blood leaving the portion with a low ventilation : perfusion ratio has a low content of oxygen, the oxygen content of the blood leaving the portion with a high ventilation : perfusion ratio is not raised to the opposite extent above normal. This is because, as in the case of total alveolar over-ventilation (p. 568) the elevation of the Po_2 in the portion with the high ventilation : perfusion ratio occurs on the plateau of the oxygen dissociation curve (Fig. 36.1). Thus the shape of the oxygen dissociation curve has the effect of magnifying the anoxaemia caused by a lack of uniformity of the ventilation : perfusion ratio.

Table 36.1 Theoretical example to show the effect of uneven ventilation : perfusion. The lung has been imagined to be composed of two portions—one with a high ventilation : perfusion ratio, and one with a low ratio. The third column shows the composite values for the entire lung. The irregularity of the ventilation: perfusion ratio has given rise to an A—a difference in oxygen tension of 25 mmHg

$\dot{V}$A = alveolar ventilation
$\dot{Q}$C = pulmonary capillary blood flow
R = respiratory exchange ratio
Suffix A = alveolar
Suffix c′ = end-capillary

	High $\dot{V}/\dot{Q}$ portion	Low $\dot{V}/\dot{Q}$ portion	Total
$\dot{V}$A (ml/min)	3086	1600	4686
$\dot{Q}$C (ml/min)	2000	4000	6000
$\dot{V}$A/$\dot{Q}$C	1·54	0·40	0·78
R	1·30	0·55	0·80
PA_{O_2} (mmHg)	118	74	103
PA_{CO_2} (mmHg)	36	44	39
Cc'_{O_2} (vol. per cent)	20·1	18·8	19·2
Cc'_{CO_2} (vol. per cent)	47	51	50
Pc'_{O_2} (mmHg)	118	74	78
Pc'_{CO_2} (mmHg)	36	44	42

THE MATHEMATICAL ANALYSIS OF THE EFFECTS OF UNEVEN VENTILATION : PERFUSION

The following sections treat in a more precise manner the abnormalities which have just been described in general terms. Our understanding of these matters is largely dependent on the work of Riley and Cournand[1,2] and of Fenn and Rahn,[3,4] and the exposition which follows is based on the graphical analysis with which those authors have so brilliantly illuminated the problem. In this analysis, the partial pressures of oxygen and carbon dioxide are represented on a diagram, the '$O_2 - CO_2$ diagram'. This will be shown first for air, then for blood, and finally for both blood and air together.

The $O_2 - CO_2$ Diagram for Air

The relation between PO_2 and PCO_2 in mixed expired air can be shown (Appendix C) to be:

$$PE_{O_2} = PI_{O_2} - \frac{PE_{CO_2}}{R} + \frac{PE_{CO_2}FI_{O_2}(1-R)}{R} \qquad \text{(i)}$$

Similarly, the relation between Po_2 and Pco_2 in alveolar air can be shown (Appendix C) to be:

$$P_{A_{O_2}} = P_{I_{O_2}} - \frac{P_{A_{CO_2}}}{R} + \frac{P_{A_{CO_2}} F_{I_{O_2}}(1-R)}{R} \qquad \text{(ii)}$$

In practice, the composition of the inspired air is known and the respiratory exchange ratio, R, can be calculated from the analysis of mixed expired air. This leaves the alveolar Po_2 and Pco_2 as the two unknown quantities in equation (ii). To solve this it is usual to assume that the arterial Pco_2 approximates alveolar Pco_2.

Since equations (i) and (ii) have exactly the same form, a composite equation can be written which will hold good for alveolar air or any degree of admixture of alveolar air with dead-space air:

$$P_{X_{O_2}} = P_{I_{O_2}} - \frac{P_{X_{CO_2}}}{R} + \frac{P_{X_{CO_2}} F_{I_{O_2}}(1-R)}{R} \qquad \text{(iii)}$$

In this case 'X' refers to any mixture of alveolar and dead-space air, and it will be remembered that the dead-space air has the composition of inspired air. If the composition of the inspired air, the barometric pressure and the respiratory exchange ratio are held constant, the relation between the Po_2 and Pco_2 of any mixture of respiratory gases will be seen from equation (iii) to be rectilinear. This is the basis of the $O_2 - CO_2$ diagram for air which is shown in Figure 36.2. The axes are Pco_2 and Po_2. From the point representing the composition of inspired air a number of straight 'R-lines' diverge. Each line represents the relation between Po_2 and Pco_2 in any mixture of respiratory gases for a given value of the respiratory exchange ratio.

The $O_2 - CO_2$ Diagram for Blood

According to the Fick equation:

$$\text{Pulmonary capillary blood flow } (\dot{Q}c) = \frac{\dot{V}o_2}{10^\star(Cc'_{O_2} - C\bar{v}_{O_2})} = \frac{\dot{V}co_2}{10^\star(C\bar{v}_{CO_2} - Cc'_{CO_2})}$$

$$\therefore R = \frac{\dot{V}co_2}{\dot{V}o_2} = \frac{C\bar{v}_{CO_2} - Cc'_{CO_2}}{Cc'_{O_2} - C\bar{v}_{O_2}} \qquad \text{(iv)}$$

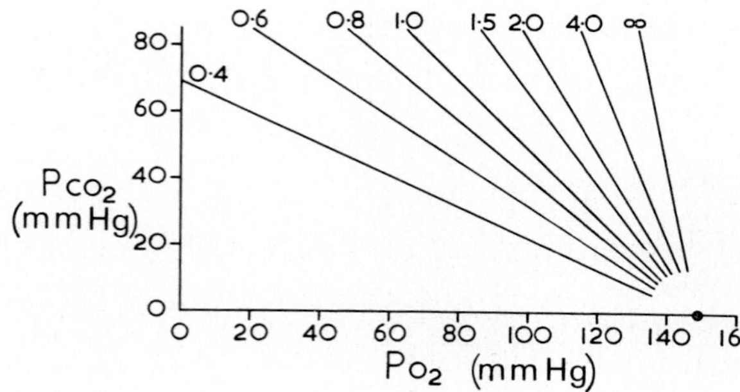

Fig. 36.2 The $O_2 - CO_2$ diagram for air. The value for R is given at the top of each line.

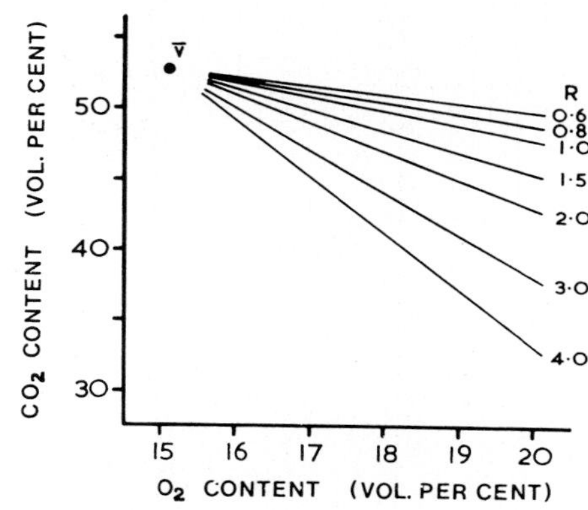

Fig. 36.3 The O_2-CO_2 diagram for blood expressed in terms of content of gas.

Similarly,

$$\text{Total cardiac output } (\dot{Q}) = \frac{\dot{V}O_2}{10^\star(Ca_{O_2} - C\bar{v}_{O_2})} = \frac{\dot{V}CO_2}{10^\star(C\bar{v}_{CO_2} - Ca_{CO_2})}$$

and

$$R = \frac{C\bar{v}_{CO_2} - Ca_{CO_2}}{Ca_{O_2} - C\bar{v}_{O_2}} \qquad \text{(v)}$$

Since equations (iv) and (v) have the same form, a composite equation can be written which will hold good for end-capillary blood or for any degree of admixture of this blood with mixed venous blood:

$$R = \frac{C\bar{v}_{CO_2} - Cx_{CO_2}}{Cx_{O_2} - C\bar{v}_{O_2}} \qquad \text{(vi)}$$

If both the respiratory exchange ratio and the composition of mixed venous blood remain fixed, then the relation between Co_2 and Cco_2 in any mixture of blood leaving the lungs will be seen from equation (vi) to be rectilinear. In Figure 36.3 the axes are Cco_2 and Co_2. From the point representing the composition of mixed venous blood ($\bar{v}$) a number of straight 'R-lines' can, therefore, be drawn. Each line represents the relation between the oxygen and carbon dioxide content in any mixture of mixed venous and pulmonary capillary blood for a given value of R.

The values for the content of oxygen and carbon dioxide in blood can be translated into the corresponding partial pressures of those gases by means of their known dissociation curves. The procedure is complicated by the fact that the dissociation curve for each gas is also influenced by the partial pressure of the other gas, but it can readily be carried out by means of Dill's nomogram.[4,5] The resulting

⋆ The correction figure of 10 is necessitated by the fact that $\dot{Q}$ is measured in l/min and $C\bar{v}$ and Cc' are measured in ml/100 ml.

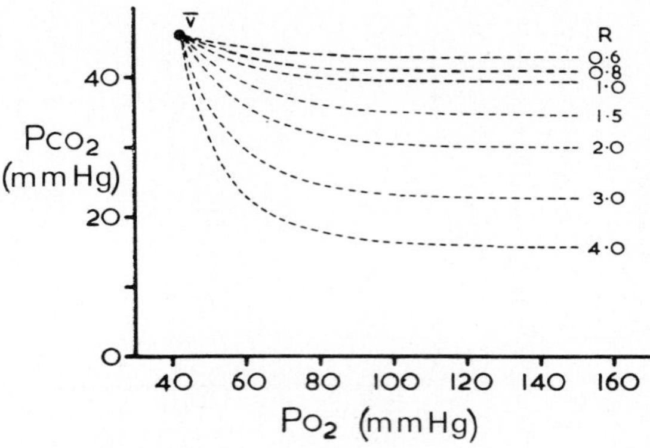

Fig. 36.4 The $O_2 - CO_2$ diagram for blood.

'R-lines' for blood plotted in terms of partial pressure have a curved shape (Fig. 36.4).

The $O_2 - CO_2$ Diagram for Blood and Air Combined

Since the axes in Figures 36.2 and 36.4 are the same, it is possible to represent both blood and air simultaneously on the same $O_2 - CO_2$ diagram. In Figure 36.5, for instance, the R = 0·8 line for gas has been drawn from a point (I) representing the composition of normal inspired air, and the R = 0·8 line for blood has been drawn from a point (v̄) representing the composition of mixed venous blood.

In the steady state, the respiratory exchange ratio for air must be the same as that for blood. If an alveolus has a value of R = 0·8, then the composition of its alveolar air must be represented by a point on the R = 0·8 line for air, while the composition of the blood leaving it must similarly be represented by a point on the R = 0·8 line for blood. If there is complete equilibration between the alveolar air and the end-capillary blood (*i.e.* if there is no diffusion barrier) then these two points are identical and must lie at the intersection of the two R-lines. This point is called the *ideal* point.

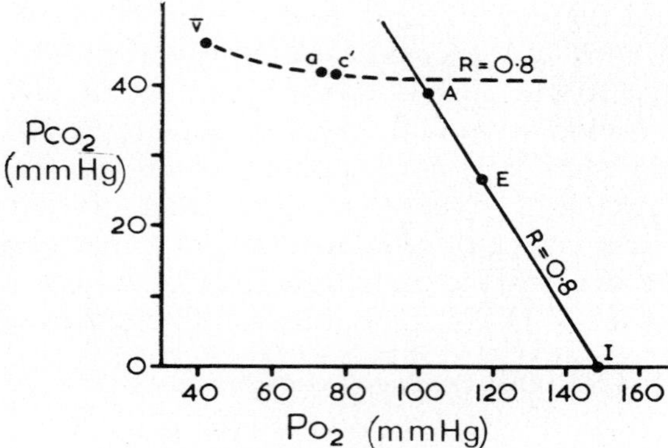

Fig. 36.5 The $O_2 - CO_2$ diagram for blood and air combined showing lines for a respiratory exchange ratio of 0·8.

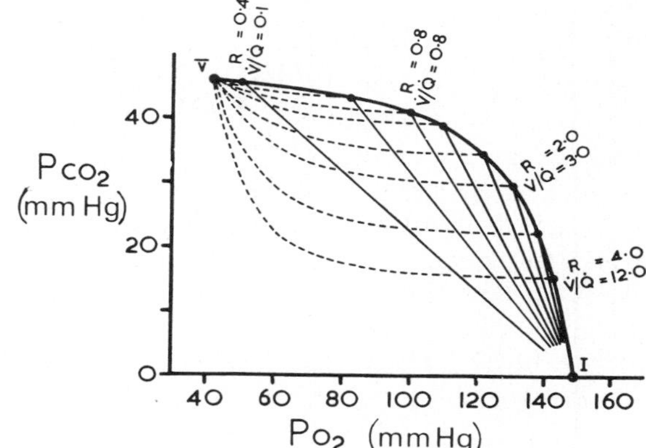

Fig. 36.6 The $O_2 - CO_2$ diagram for blood and air combined. The thick curved line joins all *ideal* points between the composition of mixed venous blood ($\bar{v}$) and the composition of inspired air (I).

In Figure 36.6 a number of R-lines for air and for blood have been drawn from one point representing inspired air and another point representing mixed venous blood. One may imagine this graph as describing a myriad of individual alveoli each exchanging oxygen and carbon dioxide in a ratio slightly different from its neighbour but each being supplied with the same mixed venous blood and inspired air. Where the blood and the gas line for a certain value of R intersect represents the *ideal* point for an alveolus which is exchanging oxygen and carbon dioxide in this particular ratio. In Figure 36.6 a thick curved line joins all these *ideal* points. It extends from the point ($\bar{v}$) representing the composition of mixed venous blood to the point (I) representing the composition of inspired air. One may represent on it the air and blood leaving any single alveolus of a lung supplied with this mixed venous blood and this inspired air, providing that complete equilibration has occurred across the alveolar membrane.

Owing to the nature of its construction, the *ideal* line carries a scale of values for R. It will be noticed that in Figure 36.6 it is also marked with values for the ventilation : perfusion ratio. The logic of this may to some extent be apparent intuitively. Thus, as the ventilation : perfusion ratio becomes very small, the composition of the *ideal* point must approach that of the mixed venous blood. Conversely, as the ratio becomes very high, the composition of the *ideal* point must approach that of the inspired air. The exact relation between the respiratory exchange ratio and the ventilation : perfusion ratio is given in Appendix C.

From a physiological point of view it is the ventilation : perfusion ratio in any alveolus which determines its respiratory exchange ratio and not the reverse. Thus those alveoli with a high ventilation : perfusion ratio will have a high value for R, and those alveoli with a low ventilation : perfusion ratio will have a low value for R.

The Effects of Uneven Ventilation : Perfusion

The *ideal* points on the $O_2 - CO_2$ diagram have so far been discussed in terms of individual alveoli. Each alveolus has its own ventilation : perfusion ratio and its own respiratory exchange ratio. In the absence of a diffusion barrier, the partial pressures of oxygen and carbon dioxide of the air in each alveolus are the same as those of the blood leaving it and may be represented at the *ideal* point where the R-line for air intersects with that for blood. Where the whole lung is concerned this is not so, because the lack of uniformity of ventilation : perfusion within the lung causes the composition of mixed alveolar air and of mixed end-capillary blood to shift away from their *ideal* values.

This is illustrated in Figure 36.5 which represents, on the $O_2 - CO_2$ diagram, the values for mixed alveolar air (A) and mixed end-capillary blood (c′) calculated from the example of inhomogeneous ventilation : perfusion given in Table 36.1. The total respiratory exchange ratio for the whole lung is 0·8 and this must apply equally to air and blood. Thus the composition of mixed alveolar air and mixed end-capillary blood must lie on the R = 0·8 line but each point has shifted away from the *ideal* point where the R-lines intersect.

The mixed alveolar air comes to have a higher Po_2 and lower Pco_2 than at the *ideal* point. This is because the alveoli with a high ventilation : perfusion ratio, high Po_2 and low Pco_2 contribute a greater volume of air to the mixed alveolar air than do those alveoli with a low ventilation : perfusion ratio, low Po_2 and high Pco_2. The mixed end-capillary blood has a lower oxygen tension and a higher carbon dioxide tension than at the *ideal* point. This is also partly because the alveoli with a low ventilation : perfusion ratio, low Po_2 and high Pco_2 contribute a greater volume of blood to the mixed end-capillary blood than do those alveoli with a high ventilation : perfusion ratio, high Po_2 and low Pco_2. However, in the case of blood, the shift away from the *ideal* point is increased still further by the unequal effects of the shape of the oxygen dissociation curve.

The composition of arterial blood (a) and mixed expired air (E) may also be represented in Figure 36.5. Each of these points lies further away from the *ideal* point along the appropriate R-line. In the case of blood, this further shift away from the *ideal* point is due to the anatomical shunt. In the case of expired air, the further shift is due to the ventilation of the anatomical dead-space. Normally the anatomical shunt consists of the flow of venous blood which joins the systemic arterial stream from bronchial and Thebesian veins and from pulmonary vessels which have no contact with alveoli.

The Assessment of Physiological Shunt and Dead-Space Ventilation

The concept of physiological shunt incorporates both the anatomical and distributional components into one hypothetical shunt and the arterial blood is regarded as consisting of two streams, one (the physiological shunt) having no contact with air and the other (alveolar capillary flow) equilibrating with 'ideal' alveolar air. Thus,

$$\text{Total pulmonary flow} = \text{physiological shunt} + \text{capillary flow}$$

$$\text{Total flow } (\dot{Q}t)^{\star} = \dot{V}o_2/(Ca_{O_2} - C\bar{v}_{O_2})$$

$$\text{Capillary flow } (\dot{Q}c) = \dot{V}o_2/(Cc^{i}_{O_2} - C\bar{v}_{O_2})$$

* See page 79.

where $Cc^{i}_{O_2}$ is the content of oxygen in 'ideal' alveolar capillary blood.

$$(\text{Physiological shunt})/(\text{Total flow}) = 1 - \dot{Q}c/\dot{Q}t$$
$$= (Cc^{i}_{O_2} - Ca_{O_2})/(Cc^{i}_{O_2} - C\bar{v}_{O_2})$$

Similarly the concept of physiological dead space comprises an anatomical and a distributional component and the expired air is regarded as consisting of two streams, one (the physiological dead space ventilation) having no contact with blood and the other (alveolar ventilation) having the composition of 'ideal' alveolar air. Reference to Figure 36.5 will show that, while the effects of the physiological shunt are mainly on P_{O_2}, those of dead-space ventilation affect P_{CO_2} more than P_{O_2}. It is, therefore, usual to calculate dead-space ventilation using carbon dioxide rather than oxygen. The formula, which is derived in Appendix N, is:

$$(\text{Dead-space ventilation})/(\text{Total ventilation}) = (P_{A_{CO_2}} - P_{E_{CO_2}})/P_{A_{CO_2}}$$

Both the calculation of physiological shunt and the calculation of dead-space ventilation require a knowledge of the composition of 'ideal' alveolar air. In practice, for this purpose, the arterial P_{CO_2} is used as approximating to 'ideal' alveolar P_{CO_2}. In order to calculate the 'ideal' alveolar P_{O_2} for the derivation of the physiological shunt, the value for arterial P_{CO_2} is substituted for alveolar P_{CO_2} in the alveolar air equation (eq. ii, p. 572). The existence of an inhomogeneity of ventilation: perfusion inevitably causes a difference between mixed alveolar and mixed capillary P_{CO_2}[6]. This difference will increase with an increasing inhomogeneity so that the use of arterial P_{CO_2} to represent 'ideal' P_{CO_2} becomes less realistic. Owing to the shape of the 'ideal' line for blood and air combined (Fig. 36.6), the assumption that the arterial P_{CO_2} approximates the 'ideal' P_{CO_2} is more secure in the presence of a predominating shunt than it is in the presence of a predominating dead-space ventilation.

The A—a Difference in P_{O_2}

The extent to which arterial P_{O_2} differs from 'ideal' alveolar P_{O_2} is known as the A − a difference. Raine and Bishop[7] found the A − a difference to average 6 mmHg in normals under the age of 40 years and 17 mmHg in normals over that age.

The two processes which determine the size of the A − a difference are the physiological shunt and the diffusion barrier of the lungs. Up to the present, we have for the sake of simplicity of presentation ignored the existence of a diffusion barrier. A certain difference between the oxygen tension of alveolar air and that of capillary blood must exist in order that the gas may pass across the alveolar–capillary membrane (Chap. 42). This difference is large at the mixed venous end of the pulmonary capillary where it is normally in the region of 60 mmHg. As the blood passes along the alveolar capillary it acquires more oxygen. Thus its P_{O_2} increases until, by the time it reaches the end of the capillary, the P_{O_2} of the blood is very close to that of the alveolar air. There is, however, still a slight difference between alveolar and end-capillary P_{O_2} even in normal people, and this forms part

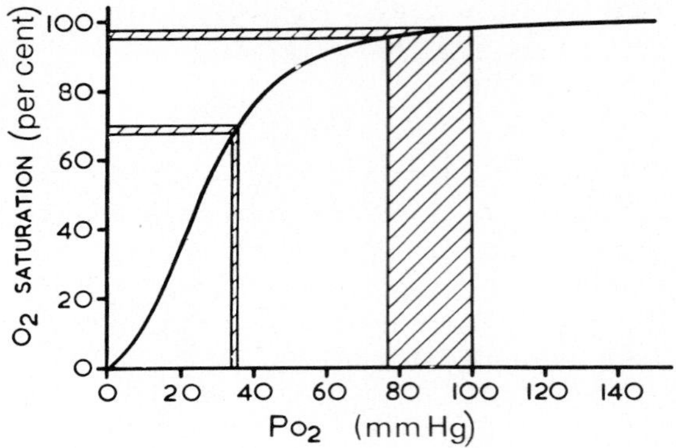

Fig. 36.7 Diagram to show how the effect of the physiological shunt on arterial PO_2 is much less under hypoxic conditions. The curved line is the oxygen dissociation curve for blood, as in Figure 36.1. The hatched areas show how the same difference in saturation has a variable influence on the PO_2.

of the total A − a difference in oxygen tension. In normal people, it amounts only to 1 mmHg or less. In patients with 'alveolar–capillary block', on the other hand (Chap. 42), the diffusion barrier accounts for most of the A − a difference which becomes increased.

The effects of diffusion and of the physiological shunt on the A − a difference may be separated by varying the composition of the inspired gas.[8,9] A hypoxic gas-mixture causes the A − a oxygen difference due to diffusion to be magnified, while inspired gas-mixtures containing more oxygen than room air cause the A − a difference due to diffusion to disappear (Chap. 42, p. 641). The effect of varying the oxygen percentage of the inspired air on the A − a oxygen difference due to the physiological shunt is the opposite. When a patient breathes air containing a high percentage of oxygen, the oxygen content and tension of the 'ideal' blood lie on the plateau of the oxygen dissociation curve. Hence the admixture of venous blood will cause a substantial fall in arterial PO_2 (Fig. 36.7). When the patient breathes a low-oxygen mixture, the oxygen tension and content of the 'ideal' blood can be brought to a position on the steep part of the dissociation curve. Under these circumstances the admixture of the same quantity of venous blood will cause only a negligible fall in arterial PO_2 (Fig. 36.7). Thus the A—a difference in PO_2 due to the physiological shunt diminishes while breathing low oxygen mixtures. This is used in the method devised by Riley and Cournand to distinguish between and measure separately the effects of impaired diffusion and uneven ventilation : perfusion[1,9] (Chap. 42, p. 641).

In the absence of a knowledge of the composition of mixed end-capillary blood, it is not possible to determine what portion of the total shunt is contributed by the distribution component and what portion by the anatomical component (p. 577). If 100 per cent oxygen is breathed, however, the distribution component of the physiological shunt virtually disappears. This is because, however poorly ventilated an alveolus, the oxygen that is taken up by its capillaries can only be replaced by pure oxygen from the bronchi, and thus no fall in its oxygen tension is possible. Hence the alveolar PO_2 varies only with the more limited variations in the local alveolar P_{CO_2}. At the same time, the A—a difference due to the anatomical component is magnified by the fact that the arterial and end-capillary blood is fully saturated and the relation between the content and partial pressure of oxygen depends only on its solubility.

In normal man, the A – a difference does not exceed 40 mmHg while breathing pure oxygen and the anatomical component of the physiological shunt is about 2 per cent of the total cardiac output. This leaves an approximately equal shunt normally due to the distribution component.

At first sight the anatomical component might seem a less nebulous quantity than the distribution component. The estimation of the anatomical component, however, is itself dependent on the assumption that the venous blood mixing with the arterial stream has the same composition as mixed venous blood. Neither of these two components, therefore, measures any strictly material quantity.

Application of Methods of Analysis of Uneven Ventilation : Perfusion

The analysis of the A – a difference for oxygen discussed above has proved of great value in elucidating disturbances of ventilation and perfusion. In emphysema, for instance, where the disturbances are found at their greatest, the physiological shunt estimated by this method was found to range between 10 and 46 per cent of the total cardiac output.[10]

In essence, the application of the concept of 'ideal' alveolar gas assumes the existence of one equilibrating unit or 'alveolus' together with a shunt of mixed venous blood and a 'shunt' of inspired air. Briscoe[11–14] has analysed the lung in terms of two compartments. The basis for the division into two compartments is the shape of the wash-out or wash-in curve for nitrogen during or after the breathing of pure oxygen. If the lung behaved as a single wash-out chamber, the concentration of nitrogen in the expired gas would fall exponentially during the breathing of oxygen. In patients with emphysema, the plot of the logarithm of the concentration of nitrogen against time is not linear and may be described by two exponents. One represents a well-ventilated space and the other a poorly-ventilated space. Using measurements of the arterial oxygen saturation and the oxygen uptake together with a series of graphical analyses, figures can be derived for the magnitude of the blood flow through each space. The results of such an analysis in ten emphysematous patients are summarized in Table 36.2.[14] The poorly-ventilated space occupies two thirds of the lung. Its ventilation per unit volume is only one twenty-fifth of that of the well-ventilated space. The distribution of blood flow is approximately the same to each space while the ventilation : perfusion ratio is ten times higher in the well-ventilated space.

It would be wrong to ascribe any anatomical meaning to the two spaces. They are abstractions, just as the one 'ideal' space is an abstraction, serving simply as a model which aids our understanding of the degree of unevenness of ventilation and perfusion. In reality, as discussed above, the lung must consist of a population of alveoli each with an individual ventilation : perfusion ratio and respiratory exchange ratio. Such a population can best be described as a continuous distribution.

Table 36.2 Two-compartment analysis of ventilation and perfusion in patients with emphysema. Data from Briscoe *et al.*[14] The figures are the averages of ten patients

	Poorly-ventilated space	Well-ventilated space
Per cent of functional residual capacity	66	34
Ventilation/min/unit lung volume	0·19	5·0
Ventilation : perfusion ratio	0·23	2·24
Per cent of total blood flow	52	48
End-capillary oxygen saturation (per cent)	76	98

One attempt to describe the lung in this fashion has used the change in arterial oxygen saturation during a nitrogen wash-out.[15,16] The theoretical basis of the method has, however, been questioned.[17]

The technique of Wagner and his colleagues from West's laboratory is a remarkable advance in this direction.[18–20] The technique is based not on the respiratory gases but on a mixture of biologically inert foreign gases of differing solubility. The mixture is infused intravenously and the arterial and expired concentrations measured during steady state conditions, together with the cardiac output and ventilation. A trial-and-error system using a series of computer subroutines then allows the description of the distribution of ventilation : perfusion ratios with respect either to ventilation or perfusion. The programme allows for anatomical dead-space and anatomical shunt and 48 compartments with varying ventilation : perfusion ratios which permits a continuous distribution curve to be drawn.[18] In normal young subjects there is a narrow log-normal distribution of ventilation : perfusion ratios with respect to ventilation and to perfusion. The 95 per cent limits of the distribution are from a ventilation : perfusion ratio of 0·3 to one of 2·1. In older subjects a 'tail' of low ventilation : perfusion ratios develops on the distribution with respect to perfusion.[19] The change from supine to the erect posture separates the two distributions (with respect to flow and ventilation) and shifts the distribution with respect to ventilation in the direction of high ventilation : perfusion ratios.[19] The breathing of oxygen causes the appearance of an anatomical shunt, thought to be due to the closure of alveoli. In a patient with emphysema the width of the distribution was greatly increased.[21]

The alveolar–arterial difference in nitrogen tension has been used as an indication of ventilation : perfusion inequalities.[22,23] The alveolar P_{N_2} varies with the ventilation : perfusion ratio, being higher when the ratio is low. This gives rise to an alveolar–arterial difference in P_{N_2} which increases with an increasing in-homogeneity of ventilation : perfusion. Nitrogen passes freely across the alveolar–capillary 'membrane', so that there is no diffusion component to the A—a difference. In addition, the P_{N_2} of arterial and mixed venous blood is the same since there is no metabolism of the gas in the tissues. Thus the A—a difference for nitrogen is not influenced by an anatomical shunt and is due purely to inequalities of the ventilation : perfusion ratio. The urinary P_{N_2} is the same as that in the blood, which obviates the need for a blood sample. Using this method, Klocke and Rahn[23] found an average A – a difference of 3 mmHg in normals and 22 mmHg in patients with emphysema.

A different method of assessing inequalities of ventilation : perfusion depends on the recording of the change in respiratory exchange ratio during a single expiration by means of a mass spectrometer.[24] Alveoli with a high ventilation : perfusion ratio tend to empty earlier during expiration than those with a low ratio and the analysis of the change in respiratory exchange ratio gives an indication of ventilation : perfusion inhomogeneity.

Different methods measure different components of the physiological shunt. As discussed above, the A—a difference in P_{N_2} is due to the distribution component (ventilation : perfusion inequalities). On the other hand the A—a difference in P_{O_2} while breathing pure oxygen indicates the anatomical component (p. 578). The method of Fritts,[25] analysing the arterial concentration of dye and ^{85}Kr injected simultaneously into the right heart, measures that portion of the anatomical component which occurs in the lungs (Chap. 34, p. 543). Davidson and his colleagues[26] made measurements of the total anatomical shunt from the A—a difference in P_{O_2} during oxygen breathing and measurements of the intrapulmonary portion of the anatomical shunt by a method based on that of Fritts. They found that the A—a difference in P_{O_2} averaged 47 mmHg in a group of normals and 84 mmHg in a group of patients with emphysema. The total anatomical shunt was in the region of 3 per cent of the cardiac output in normals and 5 per cent in emphysematous patients but the difference could be ascribed to chance. The intrapulmonary portion of the anatomical shunt was in the region of 1 per cent of the cardiac output in normals and 3 per cent in emphysematous patients, the difference again being ascribable to chance.

Inhomogeneity of the ventilation : perfusion ratio can play an important part in the exchange of respiratory gases in many diseases other than emphysema. This applies to many primary diseases of the pulmonary parenchyma as well as to those diseases where the abnormality of the distribution arises primarily from the vascular side such as pulmonary embolism (Chap. 35, p. 553), mitral stenosis (Chap. 23, p. 359), left ventricular failure[27] and shock.[28] Expressed in the terms used in this chapter, it is the anatomical component of the physiological shunt which is increased in patients with cyanotic congenital heart disease or with pulmonary haemangiomata. An anatomical shunt may also occur in the lungs in patients with hereditary telangiectasia[25] and in some patients with cirrhosis of the liver there appears to be a shunt of blood directly from the portal venous system into the pulmonary veins[25] (Chap. 29).

Regional Distribution of Ventilation : Perfusion Ratios

The physiological methods which have just been discussed have treated the lung as a whole, even if their analysis has involved the use of quasi-anatomical conceptual models. The use of external monitoring of radioactivity allows a geographical exploration of ventilation : perfusion inequalities through the lung. The methods available are, however, relatively crude since the external counters receive signals from large regions of lung which must, in disease, often comprise territories with widely varying ventilation : perfusion ratios.

Measurements of the regional distribution of the pulmonary blood flow using radioactive gases and recording radioactivity at the surface of the chest are discussed in Chapter 7. The original method[29], using the inhalation of $C^{15}O_2$ (p. 97) expressed the ratio of regional flow to regional alveolar volume (Appendix G). In the more commonly used method[30] (p. 98) an intravenous injection of ^{133}Xe is given from which the distribution of radioactivity is given unrelated to the volume of alveolar gas under the counter. In order to equate the regional flow to regional alveolar volume a separate measurement of the distribution of radioactivity has to be made after the equilibration of alveolar gases by rebreathing (eq. i, p. 98).

The regional distribution of ventilation may be measured in a similar fashion following the inhalation of a radioactive gas. For this purpose, the distribution of radioactivity may be measured after a single inspiration.[29,30] In this case, the regional ventilation has to be related to the regional volume of alveolar gas, either by assessment from the anteroposterior measurement of the chest[29] or by measuring the distribution of radioactivity after equilibration by re-breathing.[30] Alternatively, the ratio of regional ventilation to alveolar volume may be calculated from wash-in[31] or wash-out[32] curves of radioactivity.

If both the regional ventilation ($\dot{V}r$) and the regional blood flow ($\dot{Q}r$) are derived in relation to regional alveolar volume, the regional ventilation : perfusion ratio ($\dot{V}r/\dot{Q}r$) is obtained by simple division.

In normal young adults in the seated position, there is a progressive increase in ventilation per alveolar volume from the apex to the base.[29,30,32,33] This is due to the greater compliance of the bases under those circumstances.[34] Hanging in the vertical position causes the apices to expand more than the bases and the apices are thus existing at a less compliant portion of their pressure: volume curve. The ventilatory gradient disappears on lying down.[33]

In the upright position there is also a progressive increase in regional blood flow per alveolar volume from the apex to the base[29,30,32,33] (Chap. 7, p. 100). The gradient for flow exceeds that for ventilation so that, in the normal young subject in the upright posture, the ventilation : perfusion ratio decreases from the apex to the base of the lung. Whether old age has any effect on the distribution of ventilation and perfusion is disputed.[35,36] Computations from observed regional ventilation : perfusion ratios show that the distribution of the ratio down the lung will account for the major portion of the A – a difference in oxygen tension in normal men.[29]

A considerable regional inhomogeneity of ventilation is found in patients with chronic bronchitis and emphysema.[31] The regional blood flow usually decreases where ventilation is low and corresponds to avascular, emphysematous areas demonstrated radiologically.[31] There appears to be some distinction between 'bronchitic' and 'emphysematous' patients. 'Bronchitic' patients show a particular decrease in ventilation and perfusion at the lung bases.[32,37,38] 'Emphysematous' patients have been found to have a decrease in ventilation and perfusion more severely affecting the upper zones[38] or occurring throughout the lung.[32]

The re-distribution of blood flow in patients with mitral stenosis is described in Chapter 23, page 359. There is a reduction of the blood supply to the lung bases and an increase to the apices. The distribution of ventilation, on the other hand, is normal[39] so that there is an exaggerated gradient of the ventilation : perfusion ratio from the apex to the base.

REFERENCES

1. Riley, R. L. & Cournand, A. (1949) *J. Appl. Physiol.*, **1**, 825.
2. Riley, R. L. & Cournand, A. (1951) *J. Appl. Physiol.*, **4**, 77.
3. Fenn, W. O., Rahn, H. & Otis, A. B. (1946) *Amer. J. Physiol.*, **4**, 102.
4. Rahn, H. E. & Fenn, W. O. (1955) In *A Graphical Analysis of the Respiration Gas Exchange.* Washington: American Physiological Society.
5. Dill, D. B., Edwards, H. T. & Consolazio, W. V. (1937) *J. Biol. Chem.*, **118**, 635.
6. Evans, J. W., Wagner, P. D. & West, J. B. (1974) *J. Appl. Physiol.*, **36**, 533.
7. Raine, J. M. & Bishop, J. M. (1963) *J. Appl. Physiol.*, **18**, 284.
8. Lilenthal, J. L., Jn., Riley, R. L., Proemmel, D. D. & Franke, R. E. (1946) *Amer. J. Physiol.*, **157**, 199.
9. Riley, R. L., Cournand, A. & Donald, K. W. (1951) *J. Appl. Physiol.*, **4**, 102.
10. Donald, K. W., Renzetti, A., Riley, R. L. & Cournand, A. (1952) *J. Appl. Physiol.*, **4**, 497.
11. Briscoe, W. A. & Cournand, A. (1959) *J. Appl. Physiol.*, **14**, 284.
12. Briscoe, W. A. (1959) *J. Appl. Physiol.*, **14**, 291.
13. Briscoe, W. A. (1959) *J. Appl. Physiol.*, **14**, 299.
14. Briscoe, W. A., Cree, E. M., Filler, J., Houssay, H. E. J. & Cournand, A. (1960) *J. Appl. Physiol.*, **15**, 785.
15. Lenfant, C. & Okubo, T. (1968) *J. Appl. Physiol.*, **24**, 668.
16. Okubo, T. & Lenfant, C. (1968) *J. Appl. Physiol.*, **24**, 658.
17. Peslin, R., Dawson, S. & Mead, J. (1971) *J. Appl. Physiol.*, **30**, 462.
18. Wagner, P. D., Saltzman, H. A. & West, J. B. (1974a) *J. Appl. Physiol.*, **36**, 588.
19. Wagner, P. D., Laravuso, R. B., Uhl, R. R. & West, J. B. (1974b) *J. Clin. Invest.*, **54**, 54.
20. West, J. B. (1974) *Anesthesiology*, **41**, 124.
21. West, J. B. (1975) *Bull. Physio-Path. Resp.*, **11**, 155P.
22. Canfield, R. E. & Rahn, H. (1957) *J. Appl. Physiol.*, **10**, 165.
23. Klocke, F. J. & Rahn, H. (1961) *J. Clin. Invest.*, **40**, 286.
24. West, J. B., Fowler, R. T., Hugh-Jones, P. & O'Donnell, T. V. (1957) *Clin. Sci.*, **16**, 529.
25. Fritts, H. W., Jn., Hardewig, A., Rochester, D. F., Durand, J. & Cournand, A. (1960) *J. Clin. Invest.*, **39**, 1841.
26. Davidson, F. F., Glazier, J. B. & Murray, J. F. (1972) *Amer. J. Med.*, **52**, 754.
27. Valencia, A. & Burgess, J. H. (1969) *Circulation*, **40**, 641.
28. Ayres, S. M., Mueller, H., Giannelli, S., Jn., Fleming, P. & Grace, W. J. (1970) *Amer. J. Cardiol.*, **26**, 588.
29. West, J. B. & Dollery, C. T. (1960) *J. Appl. Physiol.*, **15**, 405.
30. Ball, W. C., Stewart, P. B., Newsham, L. G. S. & Bates, D. V. (1962) *J. Clin. Invest.*, **41**, 519.
31. Bentivoglio, L. G., Beerel, F., Stewart, P. B., Bryan, A. C., Ball, W. C., Jn. & Bates, D. V. (1963) *Amer. Rev. Resp. Dis.*, **88**, 315.
32. Moyses, B., Weitzenblum, E., Methlin, G. & Oudet, P. (1974) *Bull. Physio-Path. Resp.*, **10**, 811.
33. Bryan, A. C., Bentivoglio, L. G., Beerel, F., MacLeish, H., Zidulka, A. & Bates, D. V. (1974) *J. Appl. Physiol.*, **19**, 395.

34. Milic-Emili, J., Henderson, J. A. M., Dolovich, M. B., Trop, D. & Kaneko, K. (1966) *J. Appl. Physiol.*, **21**, 749.
35. Holland, J., Milic-Emili, J., Macklem, P. T. & Bates, D. V. (1968) *J. Clin. Invest.*, **47**, 81.
36. Kronenberg, R. S., Drage, C. W., Ponto, R. A. & Williams, L. E. (1973) *Amer. Rev. Resp. Dis.*, **108**, 576.
37. Anthonisen, N. R., Bass, H., Oriol, A., Place, R. E. G. & Bates, D. V. (1968) *Clin. Sci.*, **35**, 495.
38. Gaziano, D., Seaton, A. & Ogilvie, C. (1970) *Brit. Med. J.*, **2**, 330.
39. Dawson, A., Kaneko, K. & McGregor, M. (1965) *J. Clin. Invest.*, **44**, 999.

37. The Structure of the Pulmonary Blood Vessels in Pulmonary Stenosis

Pulmonary stenosis may be at the valve or in the infundibulum. If it occurs as an isolated abnormality, it is much more frequently of the valvar type. When the stenosis is the only congenital cardiac anomaly, the pulmonary blood flow is the same as the systemic blood flow unless there are abnormal communications between the bronchial and pulmonary circulations (Chap. 39). The mean pressure in the pulmonary artery, under these circumstances, is normal or slightly less than normal.[1] The pulse pressure may, however, be so greatly diminished as to be imperceptible.

When pulmonary stenosis is associated with a defect of the atrial or ventricular septum, the magnitude of the pulmonary blood flow and the pressure in the pulmonary artery varies greatly from case to case and may be reduced, normal or increased. In the combination of pulmonary stenosis and ventricular septal defect, the direction of the shunt depends on the relative magnitude of the systemic vascular resistance and of the resistance of the pulmonary stenosis plus the pulmonary vascular resistance. Thus, if the pulmonary stenosis is severe, the shunt will be from right to left and the pulmonary blood flow and pulmonary arterial pressure will be low. If the stenosis is mild, the shunt will be from left to right and the pulmonary blood flow will be increased. If, at the same time, the ventricular septal defect is a large one, the increase in pulmonary blood flow may even be associated with pulmonary arterial hypertension.[2]

When pulmonary stenosis is associated with an atrial septal defect, the direction of the shunt is dependent on the relative distensibilities of the two ventricles during diastole (p. 319). With a mild pulmonary stenosis, the shunt is from left to right since the wall of the right ventricle is thinner than that of the left ventricle. In this case the pulmonary blood flow is increased. If the pulmonary stenosis is very severe, however, the right ventricle may hypertrophy sufficiently to make it less distensible than the left ventricle so that the shunt is from right to left and the pulmonary blood flow diminished.

Thus, while such terms as Fallot's tetrad have a precise anatomical meaning, they give no adequate description of the functional state of the circulation. In patients with pulmonary stenosis, the structural abnormalities which develop in the pulmonary circulation depend largely on the magnitude of the pulmonary blood flow and the pressure in the pulmonary artery.[1] For this reason, these patients will be considered in three functional groups according to whether they have a diminished, a normal, or an elevated flow of blood through the lungs. In each group we shall be concerned with the changes in the structure of the small pulmonary arteries and veins, and with the pattern of the elastic tissue in the media of the pulmonary trunk.

Diminished Pulmonary Blood Flow

Pulmonary Trunk

The thickness of the media of the normal adult pulmonary trunk is 0·4 to 0·7 of that of the adult aortic media.[3] If the pulmonary arterial pressure and pulmonary blood flow are abnormally low, the media of the pulmonary trunk is thin. The elastic fibrils of the media are either very thin and sparse or the elastic tissue is clumped together to form irregularly-shaped isolated masses (Fig. 37.1).[3,4] The pulmonary trunk beyond a valvular or an infundibular stenosis frequently shows pronounced dilatation. Presumably this dilatation is due to the turbulence of the blood which vibrates the wall of the vessel beyond the stenosis and makes it more distensible.[5,6]

Thrombotic Lesions

A decreased flow of blood through the pulmonary circulation predisposes to the formation of thrombi in the small pulmonary arteries and veins.[7] Pulmonary thrombosis occurs much more commonly when the flow of blood through the lungs is less than about $2{\cdot}5\ \mathrm{l \cdot min^{-1}/m^2}$ BSA, which is approximately the lower limit of the range of normality.[1] Pulmonary thrombosis is very uncommon in the first decade of life and then usually occurs only when there is very severe pulmonary stenosis[1] which has reduced the pulmonary blood flow to less than $2{\cdot}0\ \mathrm{l \cdot min^{-1}/m^2}$ BSA.

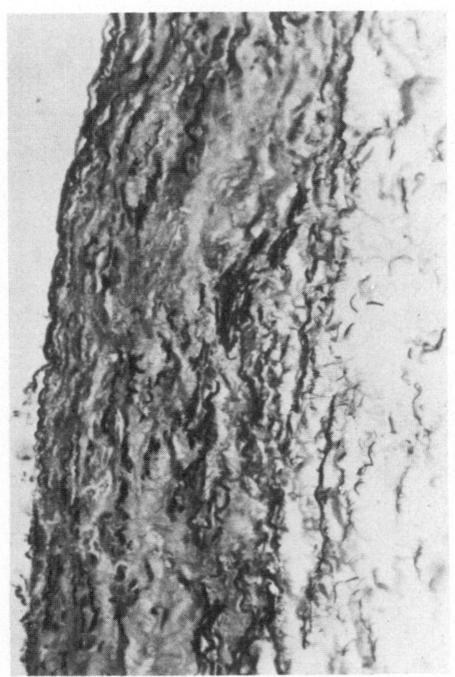

Fig. 37.1 Transverse section of pulmonary trunk from a case of Fallot's tetrad with abnormally low pulmonary arterial pulse pressure and flow occurring in an adult. The media is thin and its elastic tissue is clumped together in irregularly-shaped masses. (Elastic/Van Gieson)

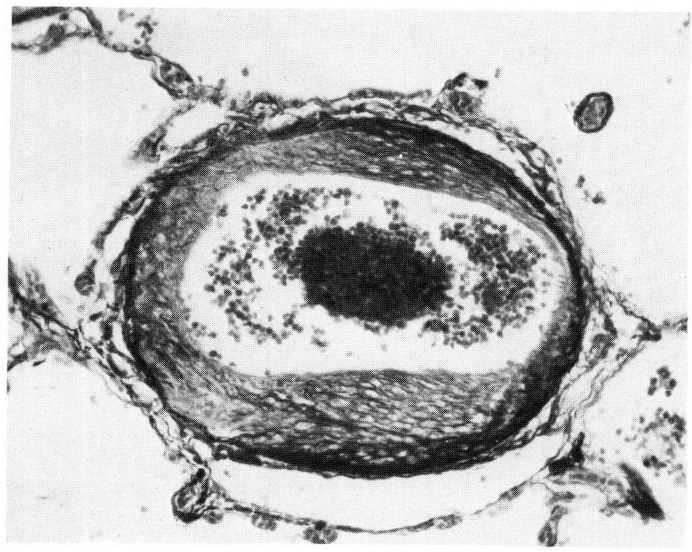

Fig. 37.2 Transverse section of a pulmonary vein from a man of twenty-seven years with cor triloculare biatriatum and pulmonary stenosis. There is irregular, concentric intimal thickening in which the fibrous tissue shows a lattice-like arrangement. (Elastic/Van Gieson, × 250)

In the second decade of life thrombosis is much commoner. It is possible that the size of the congenitally abnormal pulmonary valve tends to remain fixed while the body grows. It may even diminish on account of progressive fibrosis of the infundibulum. This would lead to a progressive diminution of the ratio of pulmonary flow to systemic flow.

The right-to-left shunts associated with severe pulmonary stenosis and septal defects cause anoxaemia. This in turn gives rise to polycythaemia which predisposes to thrombosis. This added factor in the production of pulmonary thrombi assumes great importance if the haemoglobin level exceeds 20 g per cent.[1]

Age itself is a third factor involved in the incidence of thrombotic lesions for it determines the duration of the preceding factors of diminished pulmonary blood flow and polycythaemia.

The Appearance and Distribution of the Thrombotic Lesions

The appearance and distribution of the thrombotic lesions found in the small pulmonary vessels in different types of cyanotic congenital heart disease without pulmonary hypertension have been studied in adolescents and adults.[8] The lesions may assume one of the following forms:

Concentric lesions In these (Fig. 37.2) there is a layer of collagen of variable thickness involving the whole circumference of the vessel. Elastosis is commonly associated with the collagen fibres which tend to be coarse. In some cases the

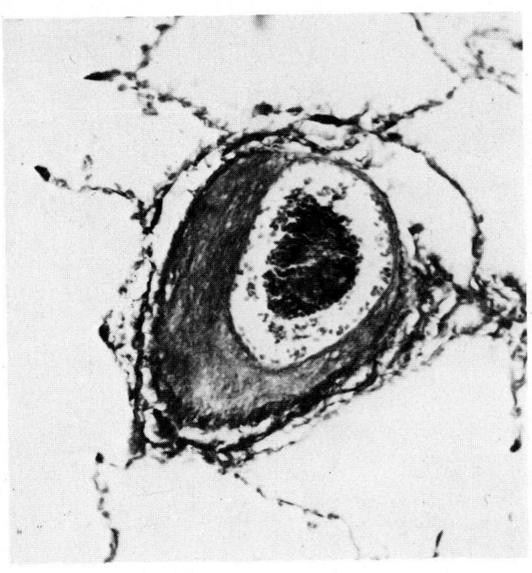

Fig. 37.3 Transverse section of a pulmonary vein from a man of thirty-six years with Fallot's tetrad, showing an eccentric thrombotic lesion in which there is crescentic intimal fibrous thickening. (Elastic/Van Gieson, × 150)

fibrous tissue has a lattice-like arrangement. In others the collagen is acellular and hyaline. Fibrin is rarely seen.

Eccentric lesions are of two types. (a) In the crescentic form (Fig. 37.3) there is an intimal fibrosis identical in character with that described in the concentric lesion. It differs, however, in that it involves part, usually more than half, of the vessel wall to produce a crescentic shape. Occasionally the intimal thickening occurs at two or more separate points around the vessel circumference. (b) The nodular form comprises one or more separate thrombi, covered with endothelium, which project into the lumen (Fig. 37.4). There is frequently much fibrin and active organization. This type, together with the lesions of true and simulated recanalization, to be described below, is probably formed more rapidly than the concentric and crescentic lesions and may progress to the latter forms by organization.

Lesions due to, or simulating, recanalization (a) Two or more small channels lined with endothelium occur in the original vascular lumen which has otherwise been occluded by fibrous tissue. Each channel is completely surrounded by fibrous tissue and thereby separated from the elastica of the original vessel. This type is regarded as true recanalization of clot (Figs 37.5 and 37.6).

(b) Irregular bands of fibrous tissue cross the vascular lumen, dividing it into two or more smaller channels which are lined with endothelium and are situated in the periphery (Figs 37.7 and 37.8). While this may indicate true recanalization, it might equally well be regarded as due to separate thrombi which fuse together and divide the lumen into a number of channels.[8]

In the majority of adult and adolescent patients with cyanotic congenital heart disease without pulmonary hypertension, who have an abnormally low pulmonary

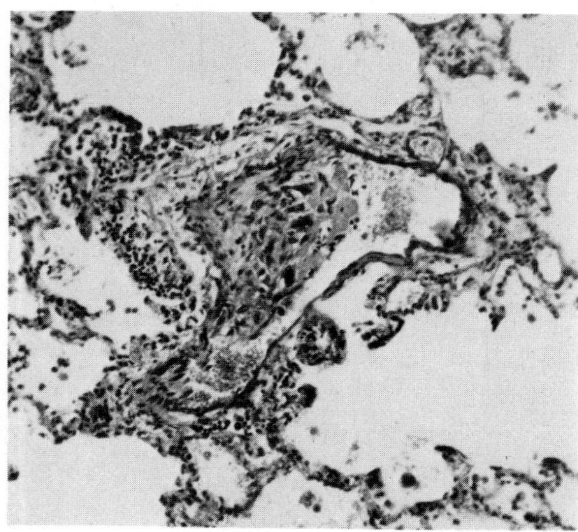

Fig. 37.4 Transverse section of a pulmonary vein from a boy of seven years with tricuspid atresia. An eccentric nodular thrombotic lesion is present. (Elastic/Van Gieson, × 150)

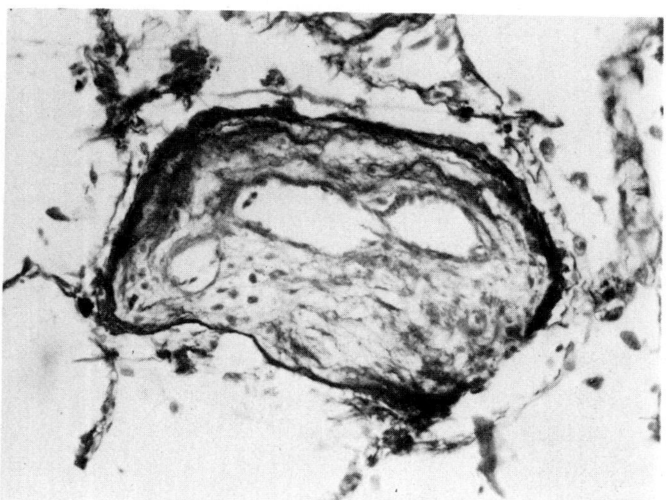

Fig. 37.5 Transverse section of a pulmonary vein from the same case illustrated in Figure 37.3. The lumen is completely occluded by organized thrombus apart from three central channels. No normal intima is seen and the appearances are probably produced by true recanalization. (Elastic/Van Gieson, × 250)

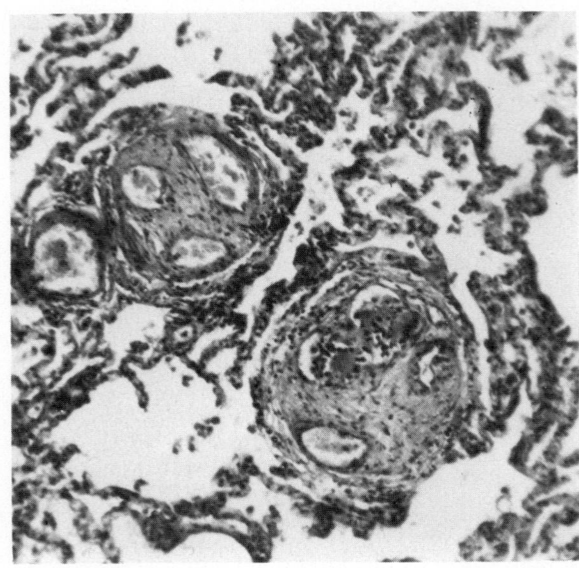

Fig. 37.6 Transverse section of two pulmonary veins from a boy of seven years with tricuspid atresia showing recanalization of thrombi. (Elastic/Van Gieson, × 150)

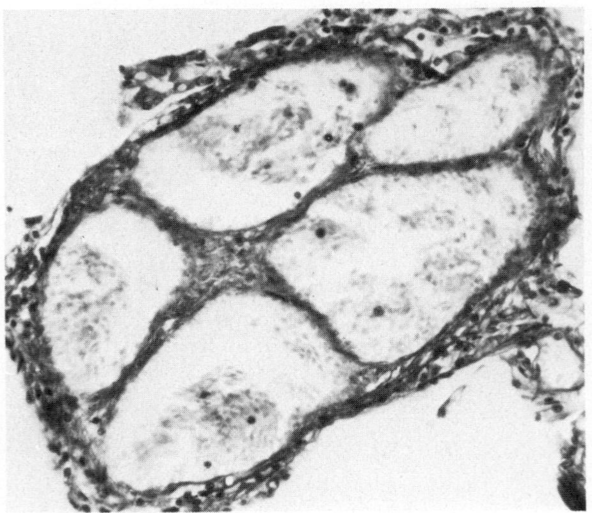

Fig. 37.7 Transverse section of a pulmonary vein from a boy of fourteen years with transposition of the great vessels with pulmonary stenosis. Thin fibrous septa divide the lumen into multiple channels. (Elastic/Van Gieson, × 250)

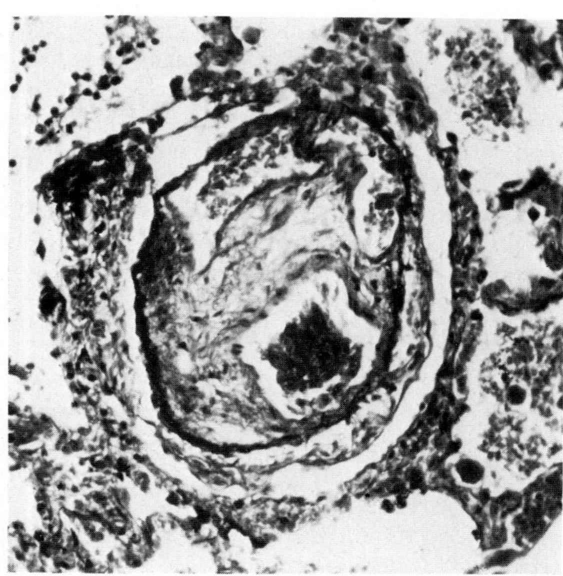

Fig. 37.8 Transverse section of a small pulmonary vein from the same case shown in Figure 37.7. Fibrous septa divide the lumen into several channels. (Elastic/Van Gieson, × 250)

blood flow with severe polycythaemia, thrombotic lesions are found in about 70 per cent of the small pulmonary vessels.[8] Such lesions are found in all classes of vessel but the highest incidence is in the small veins and arteries. They are found less commonly in the arterioles and venules which are below 100 μm in diameter.

The eccentric and concentric lesions described above occur with equal frequency. The lesions simulating recanalization on the other hand are uncommon. They are seen most frequently in veins, and in personally studied cases have accounted for up to 10 per cent of the different types of thrombotic lesion seen. In an exceptional case of tricuspid atresia studied by one of us in association with Dr. P. V. Best[8] such lesions were seen in 35 per cent of the veins, suggesting that the condition favouring their formation is an unusually diminished pulmonary blood flow.

The similarity noted between the histological characteristics of the intimal thickening normally found with advancing age[9] (p. 34) and the concentric and crescentic thrombotic lesions suggests that they may have a common pathogenesis and that intimal change due to age may be the result of thrombosis occurring much more slowly and to a lesser degree than in the present cases. A similar conclusion has been reached following a study of intimal thickening and organization of mural thrombi in systemic veins.[10] However, recanalization is not seen as one of the changes in the pulmonary vascular tree due to increasing age.

A high incidence of severe thrombotic lesions, especially those which could be ascribed to recanalization in small pulmonary blood vessels, is of importance in obstructing the pulmonary vascular tree in those very cases where pulmonary blood flow is already diminished.[8] However, these remarks apply only when the vascular obstruction is severe. The success of anastomotic operations in most cases of cyanotic congenital heart disease and the existence of organized thrombi in many of the pulmonary vessels in such patients who have survived to old age indicate the benign nature of the common thrombotic lesions. On the other hand, extreme vascular obstruction, as occurs in tricuspid atresia, may prevent a successful outcome if a Blalock-Taussig operation is performed to increase the pulmonary blood flow[11] for the numerous organized thrombi, while leaving vessels adequate to accommodate a low blood flow, have obliterated the vascular channels to such a degree that they are incapable of carrying the increased flow.

Medial Atrophy

Wagenvoort and his associates[12] examined lung biopsy specimens from 44 patients with pulmonary stenosis and from 117 patients with Fallot's tetrad. They confirm the presence of intimal fibrosis in the small pulmonary blood vessels which they agree seems to arise from organization of thrombi. They find such intimal lesions to be commoner in Fallot's tetrad than in pulmonary stenosis. These workers also found medial atrophy and luminal dilatation of the muscular pulmonary arteries in both isolated pulmonary stenosis and in Fallot's tetrad. We agree that in these conditions the media of the muscular pulmonary artery is thin (Figs 37.9 and 37.10).

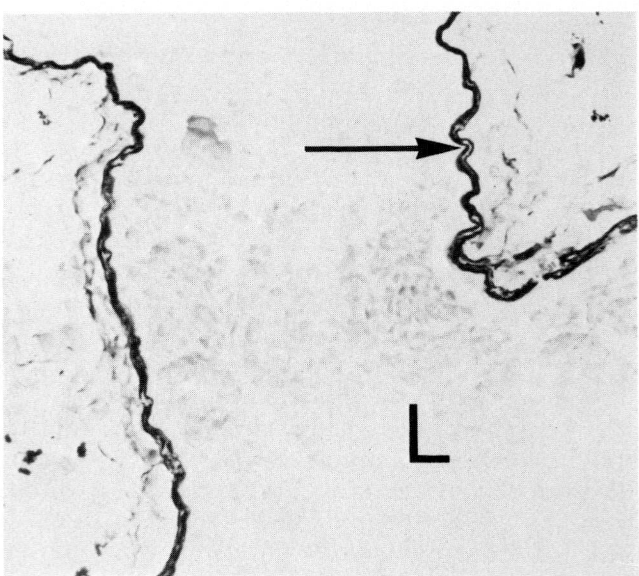

Fig. 37.9 Longitudinal section of a muscular pulmonary artery from a boy aged seven years with tricuspid atresia. The lumen of the parent vessel is indicated as L. The media of the artery (arrow) is very thin and atrophic. (Elastic/Van Gieson, × 600)

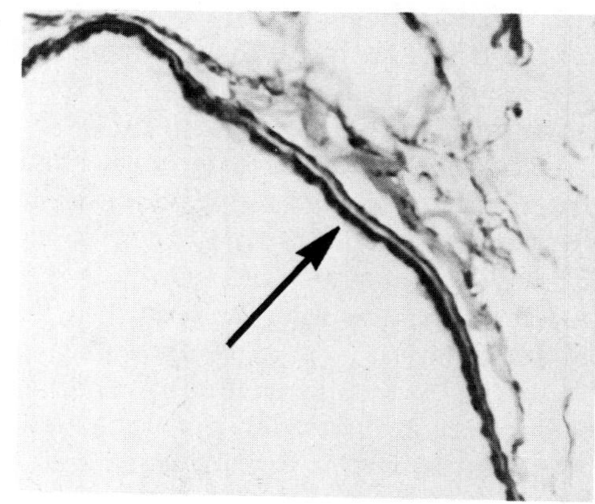

Fig. 37.10 An arc of a muscular pulmonary artery from the same case as in Figure 37.9 showing the atrophic media sandwiched between internal and external elastic laminae (arrow). (Elastic/Van Gieson, × 600)

The difficulty arises in the fact that these vessels normally have a very thin media, as we have seen earlier, so the unequivocal demonstration of medial atrophy in them is not easy. Nevertheless while recognizing these difficulties Wagenvoort *et al.* were able to assure themselves that this process had occurred in their cases.[12] As we note above in pulmonary stenosis the mean pulmonary arterial pressure is normal or slightly less than normal, but the pulse pressure is often much diminished. Wagenvoort and his co-workers[12] believe that this haemodynamic abnormality is a likely causative factor in thinning of the media of the pulmonary arteries in pulmonary stenosis. As we have described above, there is frequently medial atrophy and dilatation of the pulmonary trunk in pulmonary stenosis and this can be much more easily demonstrated by the morbid anatomist (Fig. 37.1).

A Normal Pulmonary Blood Flow

The major pulmonary arteries are of normal thickness and the pattern of the elastic tissue in the pulmonary trunk is normal.[3] In such patients, whether children or adults, pulmonary thrombosis is virtually absent.[1] The media of the small muscular pulmonary arteries is of normal thickness.

An Increased Pulmonary Blood Flow

When pulmonary stenosis is associated with a high pulmonary blood flow and pulmonary hypertension, the media of the pulmonary trunk is thicker than normal and the ratio of the thickness of the media of the pulmonary trunk to that of the aorta may be as high as 0·9 (Ref. 3). The pulmonary hypertension in patients with pulmonary stenosis and a large post-tricuspid shunt appears to exist from birth, for the elastic tissue in the pulmonary trunk retains its foetal pattern (Chap. 17,

Fig. 17.19). The patients in this sub-group have neither of the two main factors predisposing to pulmonary thrombi and these lesions do not occur. Instead the muscular pulmonary arteries may remain thick-walled from birth to give rise to an early stage of hypertensive pulmonary vascular disease.[1]

Occasionally pulmonary hypertension of a more severe degree develops in patients with Fallot's tetrad in whom an anastomosis between the systemic and pulmonary circulation has been constructed, as in a Pott's or Blalock's operation. Under these circumstances, grade 4 hypertensive pulmonary vascular disease with dilatation lesions may develop.[13] It is of great interest that severe vascular changes of this type may co-exist with the thrombotic lesions characteristic of pulmonary hypotension described in this chapter.[13] Wagenvoort *et al.* believe that muscular pulmonary arteries largely occluded by lesions produced by or simulating re-canalization of clot may be immune to the effects of pulmonary hypertension.[13]

REFERENCES

1. Heath, D., Dushane, J. W., Wood, E. H. & Edwards, J. E. (1958) *Thorax*, **13**, 213.
2. Broadbent, J. C., Wood, E. H. & Burchell, H. B. (1953) *Proc. Mayo Clin.*, **28**, 101.
3. Heath, D., Dushane, J. W., Wood, E. H. & Edwards, J. E. (1959) *J. Path. Bact.*, **77**, 443.
4. Temesvari, A. & Fodor, I. (1956) *Z. KreislForsch.*, **45**, 161.
5. Roach, M. R. (1963) *Circulat. Res.*, **13**, 537.
6. Roach, M. R. (1963) *Amer. J. Cardiol.*, **12**, 802.
7. Rich, A. R. (1948) *Johns Hopk. Hosp. Bull.*, **82**, 389.
8. Best, P. V. & Heath, D. (1958) *J. Path. Bact.*, **75**, 281.
9. Brenner, O. (1935) *Arch. Intern. Med.*, **56**, 211.
10. Scott, G. B. D. (1956) *J. Path. Bact.*, **72**, 543.
11. Brown, J. W., Heath, D., Morris, T. L. & Whitaker, W. (1956) *Brit. Heart J.*, **18**, 499.
12. Wagenvoort, C. A., Nauta, J., Van der Schaar, P. J., Weeda, H. W. H. & Wagenvoort, N. (1967) *Circulation*, **36**, 924.
13. Wagenvoort, C. A., Dushane, J. W. & Edwards, J. E. (1960) *Proc. Mayo Clin.*, **35**, 186.

38. The Course and Structure of the Bronchial Vasculature

THE ANATOMY OF THE BRONCHIAL CIRCULATION

The course of the bronchial arteries may be demonstrated by the injection into them of a radio-opaque medium such as a mixture of equal amounts of bismuth-oxychloride cream and 50 per cent gelatin in water. This mixture, when injected into the aorta at necropsy under a pressure equivalent to the mean systolic blood pressure recorded in life, at a temperature of between 25° and 35°C, flows evenly into the bronchial circulation filling vessels greater than 60 μm in diameter.[1] Antero-posterior and lateral radiographs of the lung may be taken to demonstrate the course of the bronchial arteries as soon as the medium has cooled and hardened to prevent leakage from vessels. A mixture of bismuth oxychloride and sodium iodide is another radio-opaque medium that does not penetrate capillaries.[2]

The bronchial arteries arise from the inferior aspect of the arch and descending portion of the aorta at about the level of the fifth dorsal vertebra, the commonest site of origin being the antero-lateral aspect of the aorta one inch distal to the left subclavian artery.[2] They arise from the aorta either separately or on a common trunk. Occasionally they are branches of the intercostal[2] or internal mammary arteries.[3] As many as three bronchial arteries have been noted to enter the hilum of the lung on one or other side.[1] Usually one of these arteries is larger than the others. The small branches which accompany it usually arise about a centimetre distal to the major artery, but they may be given off from the aorta anywhere above the diaphragm. When there is more than one bronchial artery, the upper, normally placed, major vessel supplies the greater portion of the lung, the remainder supplying the posterior and medial aspects of the lower lobe.[2] The lower the origin of the small additional bronchial arteries, the smaller the area of lung they supply. The bronchial arteries do not leave the aorta at right angles to its axis but form an acute angle upwards with it and during systole the elongation and dilatation of the aorta is said to accentuate this angulation.[2]

Passing laterally from the aorta, the bronchial arteries cross the oesophagus anteriorly and posteriorly; the left branches are usually behind. In the course to the hilum of the lung, branches are sent to the mediastinum, oesophagus, hilar lymph nodes and vagi. On reaching the hilum an annulus is formed around the main bronchus and from this two distinct sets of branches arise. These have been called the 'visceral pleural' and 'true bronchial' arteries.[1]

Visceral Pleural Bronchial Arteries

These vessels are distributed characteristically in two main areas. Hilar branches radiate directly from the annulus at the hilum to supply the medial visceral (mediastinal) pleura; a branch from these vessels may supply the apical pleura.

According to Cudkowicz and Armstrong[1] lateral branches supply the anterior, lateral and interlobar visceral pleura. However, Verloop[4] has suggested that only the narrow zone of anterior and lateral pleura bordering on the mediastinal pleura is supplied by these arteries, the remainder of it being supplied by subpleural pulmonary arteries which form a stellate pattern in the pleura. Visceral pleural bronchial arteries are distinguished radiographically from true bronchial arteries by their superficial position and independent course from the bronchial tree and their large calibre at peripheral sites where the true bronchial arteries usually disappear (Chap. 39, p. 611). Numerous bronchial arterioles, derived from the bronchial pleural arteries, pass along the interlobular septa to reach the interstitial tissue of the alveoli and supply it with systemic arterial blood.[1]

'True' (Intrapulmonary) Bronchial Arteries

The main bronchial artery arises from the annulus described above, enters the lung closely applied to the main bronchus and continues along its posterior aspect, sending branches to each segmental bronchus. The bronchial arteries then wind around the lateral margins of the bronchi to reach an anterior position. Their characteristic course is spiral in contrast to the rectilinear one of the pulmonary arteries.[5] The bronchial arteries pass for a considerable distance into the lung before coming into contact with lung parenchyma, lying between the fibrous covering of the bronchi and the invaginated pleura which fuses with the outer bronchial coat at the origin of the segmental bronchi.

The true bronchial arteries follow the course of the bronchial tree. They are closely adherent to the bronchial walls and bifurcate with the bronchi, there being two bronchial arteries with each bronchus, one along each side of its wall. The classification of bronchi adopted by the Thoracic Society[6] can, therefore, be used to describe the main divisions of the bronchial arteries.

The pulmonary arteries are true end-arteries but the intrapulmonary bronchial arteries branch and anastomose repeatedly around the bronchi forming peribronchial and intramural networks like the arcades of the mesenteric arteries.[5] On account of this anatomical arrangement it is practically impossible to cut off the systemic arterial supply of a bronchus; the ligation of one bronchial artery is rapidly followed by the growth of collaterals. In both large and small bronchi, the peribronchial network referred to above comprises three or four bronchial arteries with communicating branches. These pass through gaps in the cartilage to the perichondrium and thence to the submucosa where another network is formed.

Branches to Other Structures

Branches of the bronchial arteries pass to the peribronchial lymph nodes and supply the capsule while smaller branches enter the stroma, lying in the septa between the lymphoid follicles.[1] Such branches arise from the bronchial arteries supplying the bronchus in approximation to which the lymph node lies. Bronchial arteries are found in the adventitia of the elastic and larger muscular pulmonary arteries as vasa vasorum. They are also seen in the perineurium and between the fibres of the vagus nerves.

Bronchial Veins

It was believed formerly that bronchial veins were found only at the hilum of the lung[3] but studies[2] suggest that bronchial veins may be of either the deep 'true' bronchial or pleurohilar type.

The deep bronchial veins begin as tiny radicles in the walls of the terminal bronchioles and finally form large trunks which are larger than the main bronchial arteries. There is one main deep bronchial vein to each lung. The bronchial veins communicate freely with the pulmonary veins throughout their course, and drain into the left atrium either directly or indirectly via the pulmonary veins.

The pleurohilar veins form a dense sub-pleural network which passes towards the mediastinum along the anterior and posterior surfaces of the lung. They drain into one or more veins which run beneath the pleura at the junction of lung and mediastinum. The right pleurohilar veins drain into the azygos vein and thence into the superior vena cava. The left pleurohilar veins drain into the hemiazygos, superior intercostal and left innominate veins. Thus the true bronchial veins drain into the pulmonary venous system while the pleurohilar veins drain into the systemic venous system. There is free communication between these two systems of veins in the lung. This point may be of some importance in cases of mitral stenosis, as discussed in the next chapter.

HISTOLOGICAL STRUCTURE OF THE BRONCHIAL ARTERIES

Immediately after arising from the aorta the bronchial arteries have the characteristic structure of systemic arteries and consist of ten to twenty layers of smooth muscle fibres between a thick internal and a very thin external elastic lamina (Fig. 38.1). A single endothelial lining is seen internal to this media. When the artery enters the bronchial wall, it often shows internal to the normal layer of circularly-orientated smooth muscle fibres a thick layer largely composed of elastic fibrils probably derived from splitting of the internal elastic lamina. Between these elastic fibrils are a few longitudinal muscle fibres (Fig. 38.2). In other bronchial arteries a very thick layer of longitudinal muscle is seen internal to the coat of circular muscle (Fig. 38.3). In some small bronchial arteries and bronchial arterioles this layer of longitudinal muscle fibres may become very well-developed with virtual loss of the circular muscle coat (Fig. 38.4). Other bronchial arterioles have the structure of a typical systemic artery, with a comparatively thick media of circularly-arranged smooth muscle situated between internal and external elastic laminae (Figs 38.5 and 38.6). Bronchial capillary vessels have the same structure as those in other parts of the systemic or pulmonary circulations. The wall is thin and appears to consist of a single elastic lamina (Figs 38.5 and 38.6).

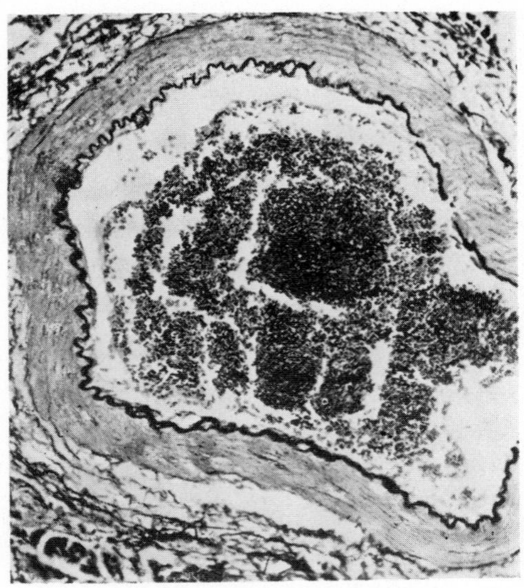

Fig. 38.1 Transverse section of a large bronchial artery, showing a thick muscular media of circularly arranged muscle. The internal elastic lamina is thick but the external lamina is very thin. (Elastic/Van Gieson, ×125)

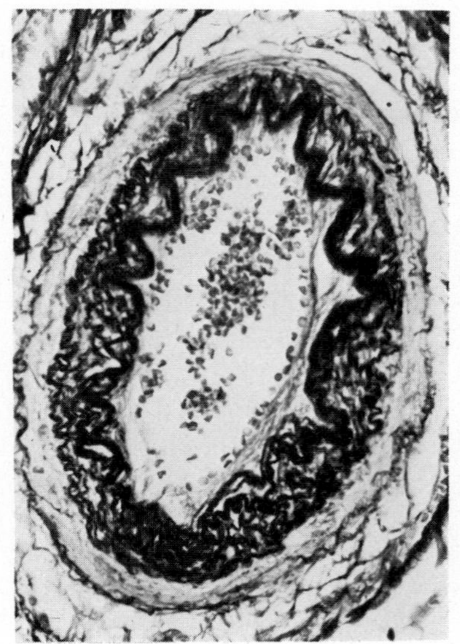

Fig. 38.2 Transverse section of a bronchial artery in the wall of a bronchus. The layer of circular muscle is thinner than in Figure 38.1. Internal to it is a layer largely composed of elastic fibrils which may have been derived from splitting of the internal elastic lamina. Between these elastic fibrils are a few longitudinal muscle fibres. (Elastic/Van Gieson, ×215)

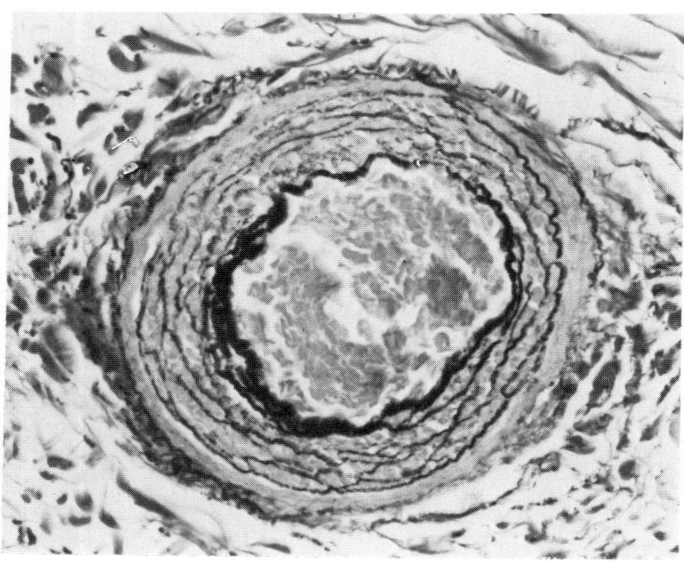

Fig. 38.3 Transverse section of another bronchial artery in the wall of a bronchus. In this vessel there is an outer layer of circularly-orientated smooth muscle and a very thick layer of longitudinal muscle internal to it. (Elastic/Van Gieson, × 375)

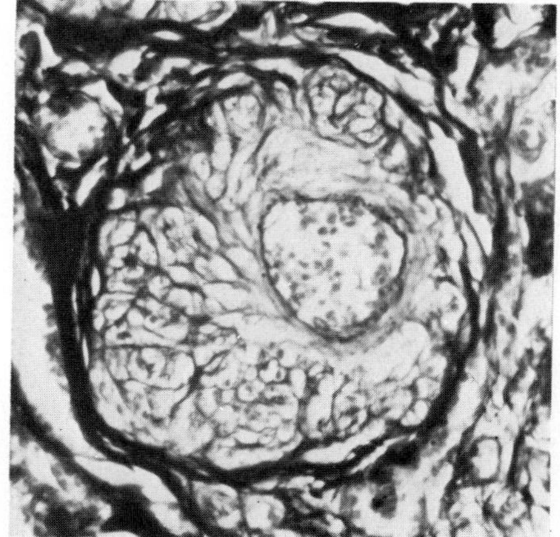

Fig. 38.4 Transverse section of a bronchial arteriole in which there is practically no circular muscle. There is, however, a thick layer of longitudinally arranged muscle. The lumen is eccentric. (Elastic/Van Gieson, × 250)

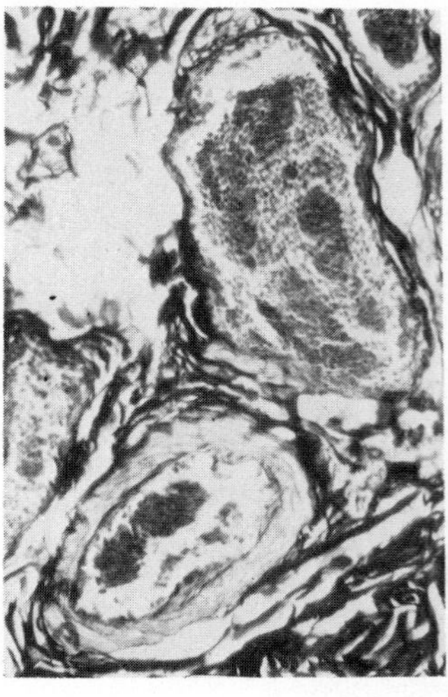

Fig. 38.5 Oblique section of a bronchial arteriole and a bronchial capillary vessel. The arteriole (below) has the structure of a typical systemic artery, with a well-defined media of circularly-arranged smooth muscle between internal and external elastic laminae. The capillary vessel (above) has a thin wall composed of an elastic lamina. (Elastic/Van Gieson, × 150)

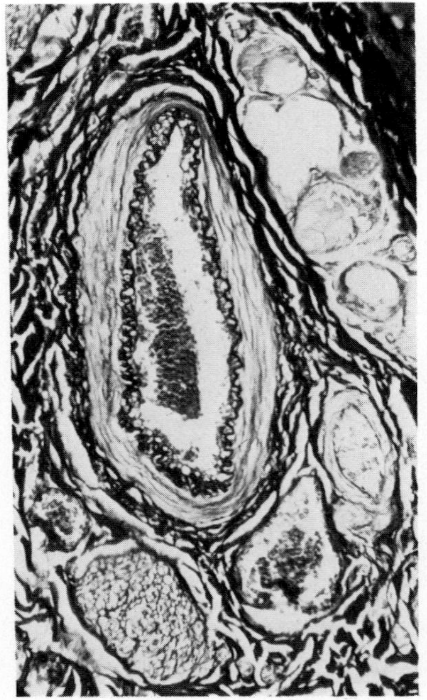

Fig. 38.6 Transverse section of a bronchial wall showing a large bronchial artery whose wall is composed largely of circularly-oriented smooth muscle. The internal elastic lamina is thick. In the lower right corner are a bronchial arteriole and a bronchial capillary vessel similar to those illustrated in Figure 38.5. A group of mucous glands is seen to the upper right. A nerve is seen in the lower left of the figure. (Elastic/Van Gieson, × 150)

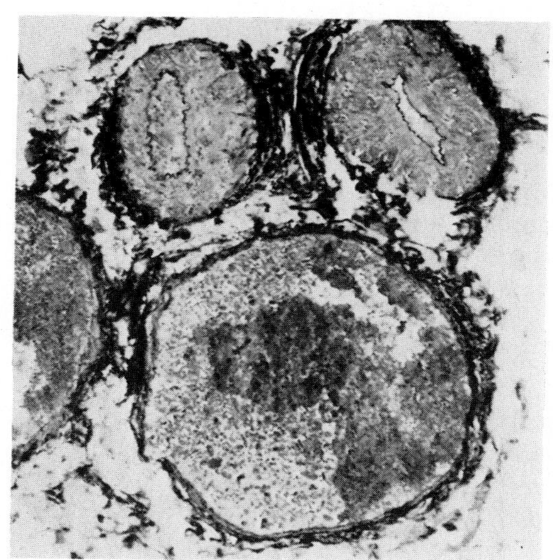

Fig. 38.7 Transverse sections of two thick-walled bronchial arteries and a thin-walled bronchial vein (vasa vasorum) in the wall of the pulmonary trunk. (Elastic/Van Gieson, × 95)

The bronchial arteries which form the vasa vasorum of the pulmonary trunk and major elastic pulmonary arteries are very thick-walled and muscular (Fig. 38.7). The bronchial veins which accompany them form a striking contrast in being very thin-walled (Fig. 38.7).

Modified Bronchial Arteries ('Sperrarterien')

In the normal lung some bronchial arteries have been described as having a thick, well-formed musculo-elastic zone adjacent to the intima. These vessels are said to have an enormously thickened media which appears as massive muscular knots due to the spiral course of the dense muscle around the periphery of the media.[4] This peculiar structure may be maintained over short or long segments of the vessel before returning to the normal structure of the bronchial artery. Thin-walled lateral branches may arise from such segments. Bronchial arteries in the pleura may show a similar structure. 'Sperrarterien' have been considered to be abnormal sclerosed bronchial arteries.[7]

REFERENCES

1. Cudkowicz, L. & Armstrong, J. B. (1951) *Thorax*, **6**, 343.
2. Marchand, P., Gilroy, J. C. & Wilson, V. H. (1950) *Thorax*, **5**, 207.
3. Miller, W. S. (1947) *The Lung*. 2nd ed. Thomas: Springfield, Ill.
4. Verloop, M. C. (1948) *Acta Anat.*, **5**, 171.
5. Liebow, A., Hales, M. R. & Lindskog, G. E. (1949) *Amer. J. Path.*, **25**, 211.
6. Thoracic Society, (1950) *Thorax*, **5**, 222.
7. McLean, K. (1958) *Aust. Ann. Med.*, **7**, 69.

39. The Form of Bronchopulmonary Anastomoses

Bronchopulmonary anastomoses occur in the normal lung but they are much commoner and more prominent in certain diseases.

In the Normal Adult Lung

Bronchopulmonary arterial anastomoses have been demonstrated in serial sections of normal lungs[1–5] but they are rare in subjects free of cardiopulmonary or certain forms of haematological disease. They may be considered to be branches of bronchial arteries since like them they have longitudinal muscle within the intima. They are tortuous and of small calibre and run only a short course[5] of less than 300 μm. Before entering the pulmonary artery, the anastomotic vessel undergoes a change in structure so that it first becomes transitional in appearance between a bronchial and pulmonary artery and then assumes the structure of its pulmonary component. Wagenvoort and his colleagues[5] illustrate the structure of such a bronchopulmonary anastomosis in serial sections. It seems unlikely that such narrow tortuous vessels are of haemodynamic significance in the pulmonary circulation of a normal adult. Rarely bronchopulmonary anastomoses in the normal lung are straight and wide. Naturally bronchopulmonary anastomoses occur in the area of distribution of the bronchial arteries—the hilum, bronchial walls and that part of the pleura supplied by them.

In the Normal Foetal and Newborn Lung

The original common pulmonary vascular plexus provides an excellent opportunity for the formation of different types of vascular communication[4,5] and so it is not surprising that bronchopulmonary arterial anastomoses have been found often in the lungs of foetuses, newborns and young children.[4] Weibel suggests that some of these anastomoses may be lost with further development of the lungs but Wagenvoort *et al.*[5] point out that their sparsity in the adult lung may merely mean that their number has not kept pace with the growth of the pulmonary vascular tree. The structure of the neonatal bronchopulmonary anastomosis is like that of the adult except that no longitudinal muscle is found in the intima. This is not surprising, since at this age bronchial arteries are devoid of longitudinal muscle. The external elastic lamina of the anastomotic vessel may be thick, a feature more reminiscent of a pulmonary than a bronchial artery. Bronchopulmonary anastomoses in the perinatal period are often straight and wide and this seems consistent with their having a greater functional significance at this age than later on.

The Stimuli for Anastomosis Formation in Disease

There appear to be two main stimuli for the production of bronchopulmonary arterial anastomoses in disease. These are a diminished pulmonary blood flow and the formation of new tissue within the lung.

Widespread thrombosis within the small pulmonary blood vessels frequently occurs in cyanotic congenital heart disease such as Fallot's tetrad, tricuspid atresia or pulmonary atresia and in certain forms of haematological disease such as sickle-cell anaemia. These conditions are characteristically associated with extensive bronchopulmonary arterial anastomoses.[6,7] The connexions appear to be stimulated by the peripheral occlusive lesions in the pulmonary arteries, but they can occur in the absence of such occlusion and are then presumably stimulated simply by the reduced blood flow.[8] Ligation of a main branch of a pulmonary artery will cause them to develop in dogs.[9] There is physiological evidence that this also occurs in man[10] and Figure 39.1 shows the development of bronchial arteries following pulmonary arterial thrombosis in the human. In dogs, the bronchial collateral supply is obvious within a week of ligation and is maximal at three months, by which time the bronchial arteries are ten times their normal size. It is also possible that occlusion of the pulmonary arteries by intimal fibroelastosis may evoke such anastomoses since they have been observed in patients with pulmonary hypertension.

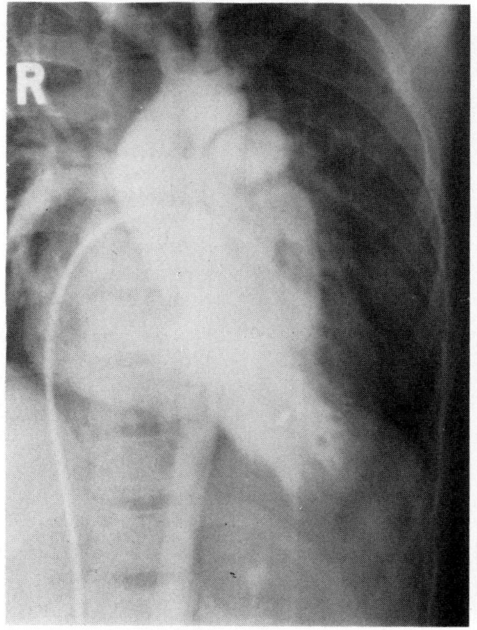

A

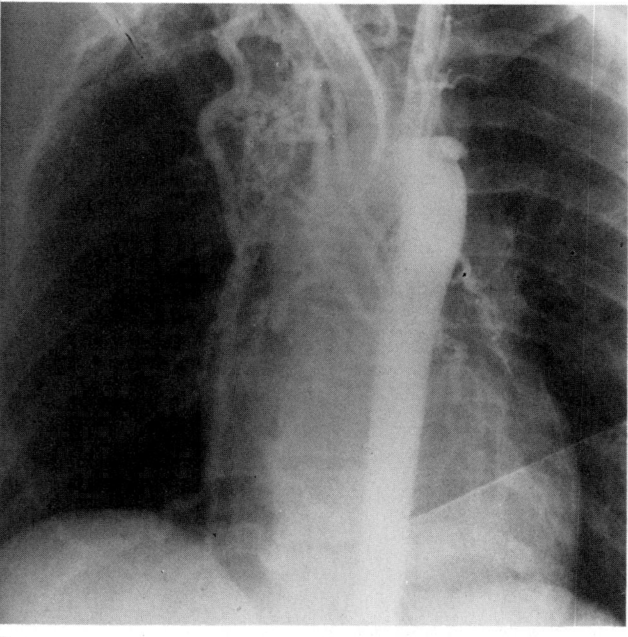

B

Fig. 39.1 Angiograms from a patient with tricuspid atresia taken before and after the development of thrombosis of the right pulmonary artery following a Glenn operation. A. The first angiogram shows a normal right pulmonary artery. B. The second shows many bronchial arteries entering the right lung from the aorta.

The development of inflammatory or neoplastic tissue appears to be more important in stimulating the formation of the bronchopulmonary arterial anastomoses which have been reported in such diseases as bronchiectasis, lung abscess, pulmonary tuberculosis[11] and bronchial carcinoma.[12] Just as we noted above that the pulmonary vascular plexus in the foetus offered opportunity for the formation of different types of vascular communication, so the formation of numerous small thin-walled vessels in granulation tissue seems to provide the same facility. In bronchiectasis, Liebow and his associates[6] believe that the bronchopulmonary anastomoses are formed by the joint invasion of granulation tissue by capillaries from both the pulmonary and bronchial circulation.

The Nature of the Bronchopulmonary Arterial Anastomoses in Disease

Several forms of arterial anastomosis have been described. Injection studies have demonstrated the existence of such anastomoses in bronchiectasis (Fig. 39.2). They occur in relation to, and distal to, the large bronchiectatic sacs which begin in the third and fourth order of branching.[13] Before communicating with one another, the bronchial and pulmonary arteries form helices, those of the systemic vessels being tighter, wider and more numerous. The anastomotic vessel arches over the pulmonary artery and then joins it[13] (Fig. 39.2). Similar large anastomoses

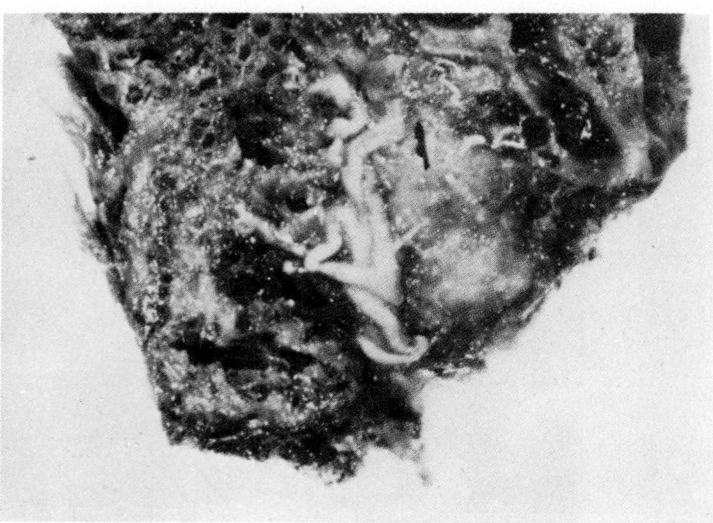

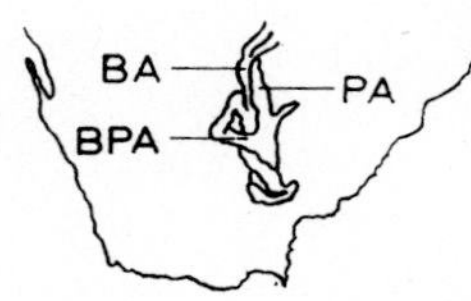

Fig. 39.2 Large proximal arterial bronchopulmonary anastomosis, from a case of bronchiectasis, displayed by injection of 'Micropaque' and subsequent dissection. Line diagram to aid identification of the components of the anastomosis: BA, Bronchial artery; BPA, bronchopulmonary anastomosis; PA, pulmonary artery. (×2·5)

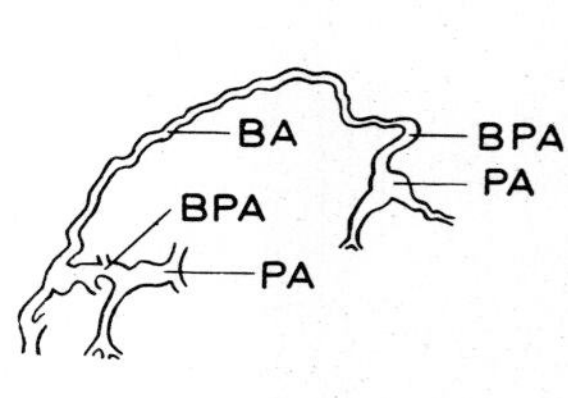

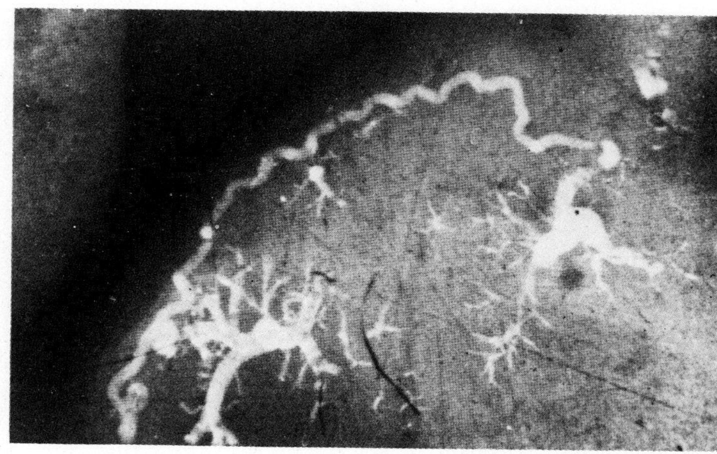

Fig. 39.3 Pleural arterial bronchopulmonary anastomoses, from a case of cor triatriatum, demonstrated by injection of a radio-opaque medium and subsequent radiography as described in the text. Abbreviations as in Figure 39.2. (× 4)

between a pulmonary artery, at a level of third to sixth generation bronchi, and a closely adjacent bronchial artery were noted by Turner-Warwick.[8] Numerous anastomoses occur around a single bronchus. The bronchial artery is the same size as, or slightly smaller than, the vessel it joins. How these communications arise is not known. They may be enlargements of pre-existing anastomoses such as we describe above; this could explain the fact that such connexions can occur in areas remote from disease. On the other hand, they may be newly formed channels, acquired directly as a result of the disease. For example, as stated above, bronchiectasis may be preceded by organizing pneumonia in which the capillaries of granulation tissue may be derived from both systems and join.[13]

Turner-Warwick[8] found bronchopulmonary anastomoses between peripheral branches of the pulmonary arteries and systemic arteries in the subpleural region on the mediastinal surface of the lungs (Figs 39.3 and 39.4). In addition there were connexions within the lung between longitudinal bronchial arteries lying in relation to one bronchus and a lateral branch of a pulmonary artery lying in relation to another bronchus (Fig. 39.5). Such connexions were present both in patients with congenital heart disease and in those with acquired diseases of the lung. She found that in bronchiectasis, bronchial carcinoma and interstitial pulmonary fibrosis, in areas of abnormal bronchial arterial proliferation, there were many abnormal, minute end-to-end anastomoses both sub-pleurally and within the lung. Often these were bizarre in form and could be readily differentiated from the larger anastomoses described above.

Another quite distinct form of bronchopulmonary arterial anastomosis appears to arise from the vasa vasorum of the large, elastic pulmonary arteries.[14] These

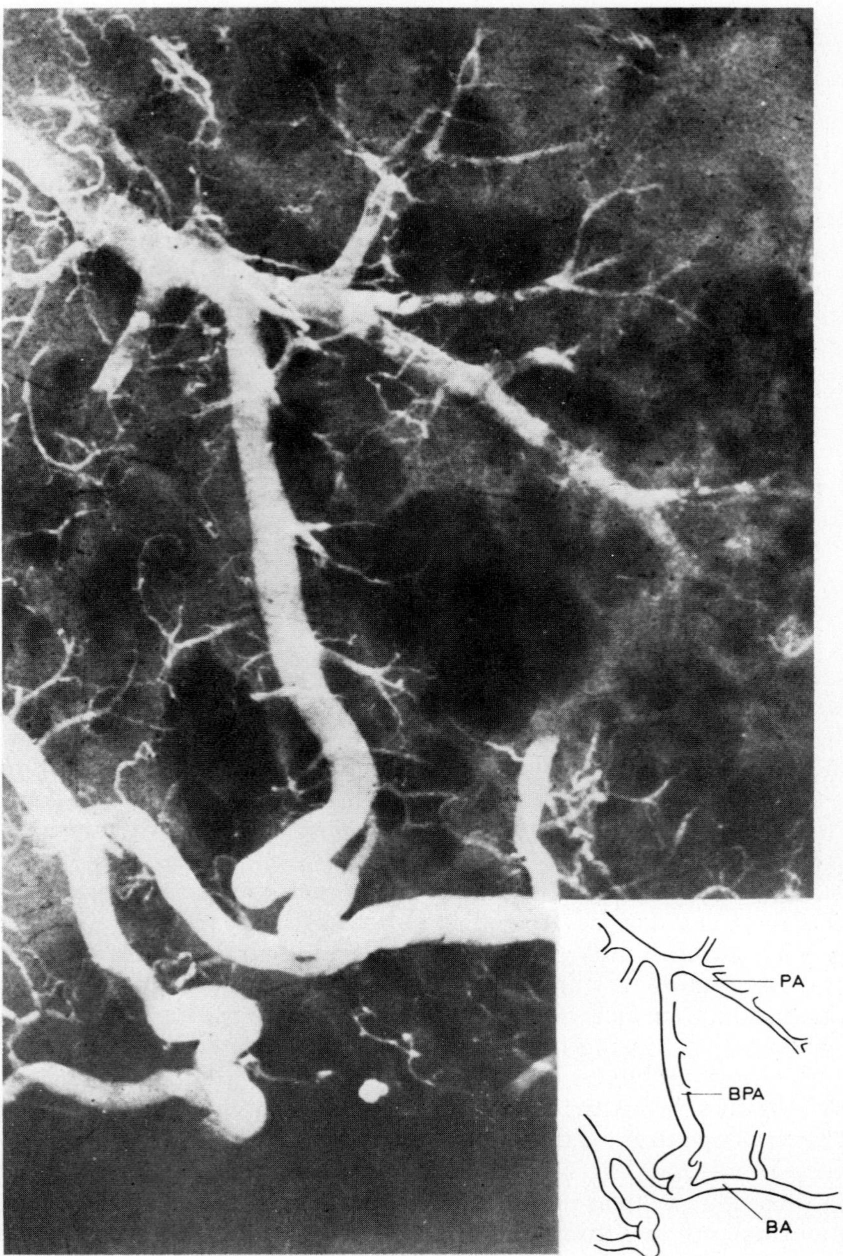

Fig. 39.4 Pleural arterial bronchopulmonary anastomosis, from a case of interstitial pulmonary fibrosis with acquired pulmonary hypertension, demonstrated by injection of a radio-opaque medium and subsequent radiography as described in the text. Abbreviations as in Figure 39.2. (× 9)

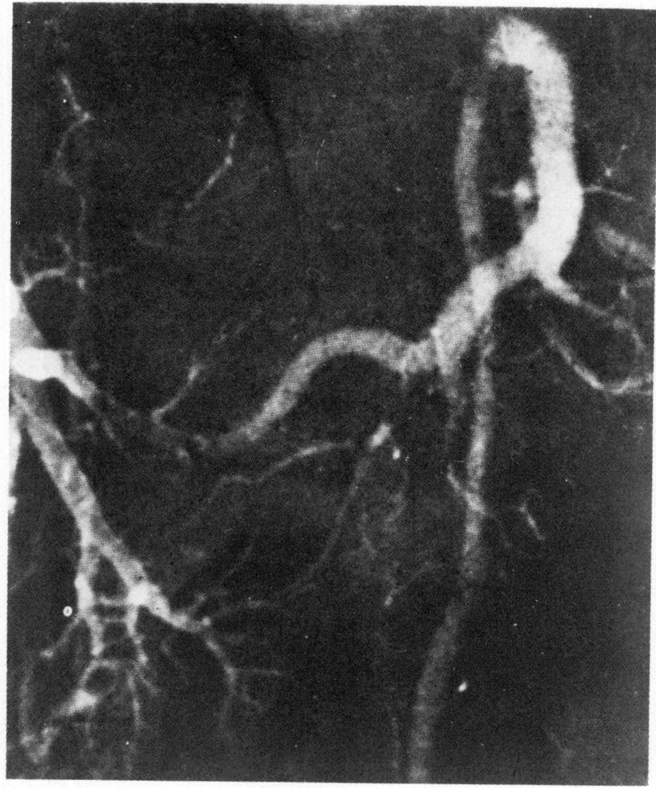

Fig. 39.5 Arterial bronchopulmonary anastomosis, from a case of cor triatriatum, demonstrated by injection of a radio-opaque medium and subsequent radiography as described in the text. The bronchial artery is the vessel running perpendicular to the right of the picture. The pulmonary artery is seen running obliquely downwards to the left of the picture. The anastomotic vessel is seen connecting these two arteries. (× 9)

components of the bronchial circulation are normally situated in the adventitia (Chap. 38, Fig. 38.7). When a pulmonary artery becomes occluded, the vasa vasorum tend to proliferate, dilate and penetrate the intima, recanalizing the original lumen. The distribution of the bronchial arteries remains normal. Bronchopulmonary anastomoses of this type have been described in transposition of the great vessels with ventricular septal defect,[15] chronic bronchitis and emphysema,[16] and pulmonary tuberculosis.[17] There is enlargement of the bronchial arteries in the tuberculous areas and also an increase in their numbers as compared to normal areas of lung. Dilatation of bronchial arteries is particularly prominent near miliary tubercles. Tuberculous cavities have only a systemic arterial supply.

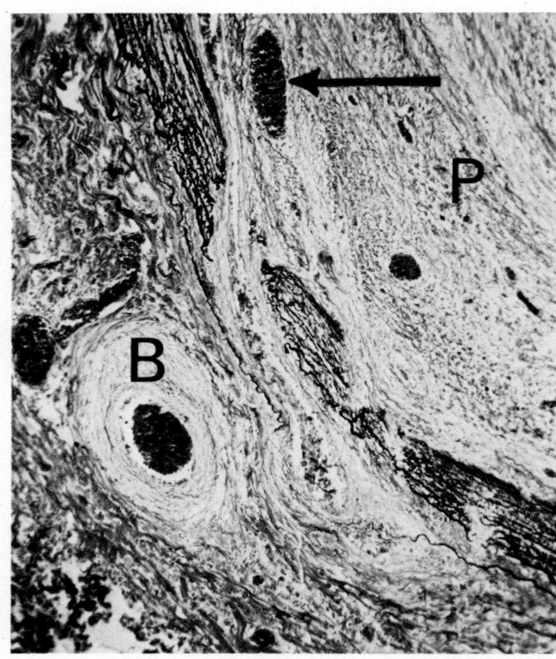

Fig. 39.6 Bronchopulmonary anastomosis from a negro male aged 28 years with sickle-cell anaemia. He collapsed and died in the street and at necropsy was found to have widespread pulmonary arterial thrombosis. In the upper right of the picture is a thrombosed elastic pulmonary artery, P. Within the organized thrombus are recanalization channels (arrow). One of these has broken through the media of the artery to effect communication with one of its vasa vasorum, B, which is derived from a bronchial artery. (Elastic/Van Gieson, × 115)

Widespread thrombosis in the pulmonary arterial tree and the development of bronchopulmonary anastomoses sometimes complicate sickle-cell anaemia.[7] Wintrobe[18] notes that unsaturation of systemic arterial blood is comparatively frequent in sickle-cell anaemia and suggests that this is due principally to intrapulmonary shunting of blood. Our studies show that these intrapulmonary shunts are of the type just described where vasa vasorum in the walls of elastic pulmonary arteries dilate and penetrate the media to recanalize the occluded pulmonary artery[7] (Figs 39.6 and 39.7).

Some communications between the systemic and pulmonary arterial systems are of developmental origin. This is obviously so with a patent ductus arteriosus. Pulmonary arteries may arise directly from a common truncus arteriosus. In the condition of 'hemitruncus arteriosus'[19] one lung is supplied by a large vessel arising from the ascending aorta. A similar developmental origin of a systemic arterial supply to the lungs may occur in some patients with pulmonary atresia.[20–22]

In this abnormality there is a complete congenital disconnexion between the right ventricle and the arterial supply to the lungs.[23] The pulmonary arterial tree may preserve its normal development distal to an atresia at the pulmonary valve or the pulmonary trunk and its main branches may be absent in varying patterns.[23] Within the lungs, the disposition of the peripheral pulmonary arterial tree is normal. The degree of central pulmonary arterial development appears to influence the type of systemic arterial supply to the lung.[20] Jefferson, Rees and Somerville[20] demonstrated with aortography that, when the pulmonary trunk or its main branches were present, the systemic arterial supply to the lungs consisted of small vessels with a widespread origin from the aorta and its branches. Such vessels are similar to those which may arise in adult life following an occlusion of the pulmonary artery and Jefferson and his colleagues[20] suggest that they may often arise after birth, as the ductus arteriosus becomes closed. In contrast, where the pulmonary

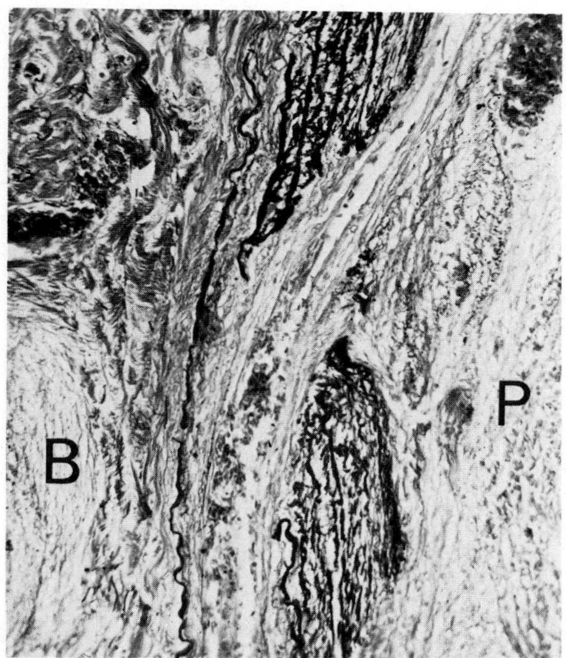

Fig. 39.7 A view at higher magnification of the thin-walled vessel effecting communication between the thin-walled recanalization channels in the thrombosed pulmonary artery, P and the vasa vasorum, B. Note the ragged edges of the media where it is traversed by the anastomotic vessel. This appearance contrasts sharply with the well-formed bronchopulmonary anastomoses which have the structure of arteries which are found in the normal foetal and adult lung. (Elastic/Van Gieson, ×230)

trunk and/or its main central branches are absent, the systemic arterial supply to the lungs is different, consisting of one to five vessels 3–20 mm wide (Figs 39.8 and 39.9). They rise usually from below the isthmus of the aorta but occasionally from the aortic arch or one of its branches.[20–22,24] It seems likely that such vessels have an embryological origin and represent a persistence of the primitive intersegmental branches of the dorsal aortae which supply the lung bud. Large systemic arteries of this type run directly into the hilum and continue with a normal intrapulmonary branching pattern. Often, however, there is a stenosis at the point of junction.[20,22] (Fig. 39.9). Jefferson and his colleagues[20] found that, in the absence of such stenoses, the pulmonary arterial tree of the portion of the lung supplied by the systemic branches showed the changes of hypertensive pulmonary vascular disease.

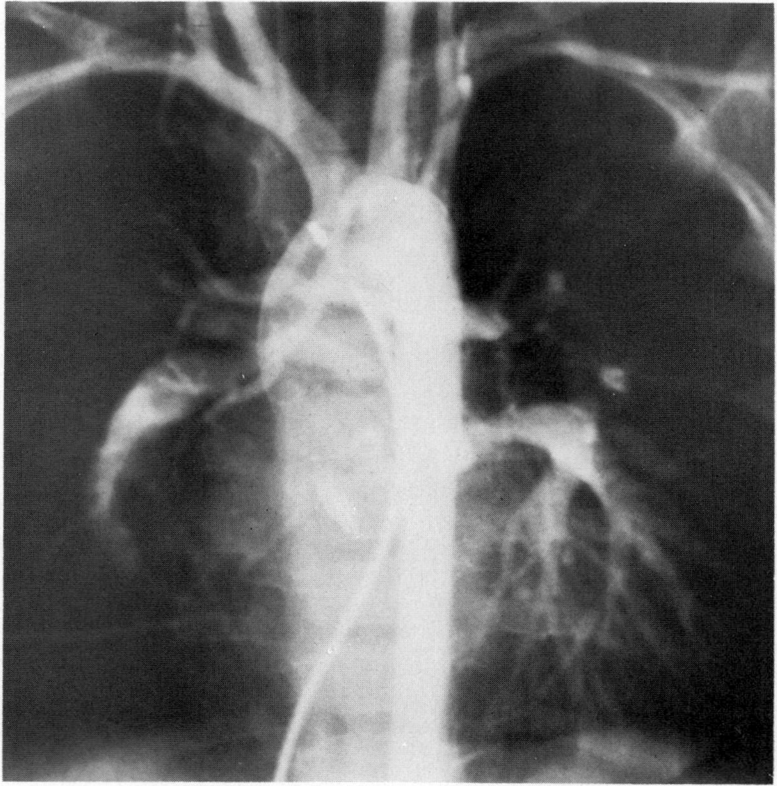

Fig. 39.8 Aortogram from a patient with pulmonary atresia with absent pulmonary trunk. A number of large vessels run from the aorta to supply the lungs. The distribution within the lungs corresponds to the normal anatomy of the pulmonary arterial tree. Stenoses are apparent near the origin of the vessels supplying the left lower lobe and right lower lobe.

Radiological Signs of Enlarged Bronchial Arteries

The characteristic appearances of enlarged bronchial and mediastinal collateral arteries on the plain radiograph have been described by Campbell and Gardner.[25] Absence or diminution in the size of the shadows of the right and left pulmonary arteries or that cast by the pulmonary trunk are a pointer to the presence of an alternative supply of blood to the lung. The enlarged collateral arteries from the systemic circulation cast shadows high in the mediastinum and in the region of the hilum. They have a nodular appearance and their branches are distributed in an abnormal fashion in the lung fields.

The mediastinal shadows are best seen in the left anterior oblique position below the aortic arch, from which the bronchial arteries descend.[25] In the antero-posterior position they are most obvious high up on the right as a diffuse mottled mass, and spreading much higher than the normal position of the right pulmonary artery.

On angiocardiographic examination the bronchial arteries fill with contrast medium later than the ascending aorta and arise from the undersurface of the arch or from the descending aorta. They fill the 'aortic window' to some extent before they spread widely around the hilum of the lung and are best seen in the lateral and left oblique positions.[25] When large systemic arterial communications occur in association with absence of the pulmonary trunk or its main branches, they take their origin from the descending aorta or from the aortic arch or one of its branches. They are best demonstrated by selective angiography.[20,22]

Post-Mortem Demonstration of Arterial Anastomoses

Bronchopulmonary arterial anastomoses may be demonstrated by histological examination of serial sections. They may also be studied by the injection of radio-opaque media into the pulmonary or bronchial vascular tree.[26] In the injection studies of Turner-Warwick,[8] illustrations of which she has been so kind as to allow us to use (Figs 39.2–39.5), the bronchial arteries were injected indirectly through the left carotid artery using 80 per cent 'Micropaque' in 15 per cent gelatin at a pressure of 120 mmHg at 40°C for 25 minutes. Following this the lungs were distended and fixed with 10 per cent formalin. Sagittal slices of lung, 0·5-cm thick, were cut and examined radiographically. The radiographic demonstration of bronchopulmonary anastomoses is open to serious errors in interpretation. The study of shadows does not yield the precise information on the structure of the anastomotic vessels that can be gathered from the histological examination of serial sections.

Capillary Bronchopulmonary Anastomoses

We have seen anastomoses between the bronchial and pulmonary circulations at capillary level in a case of ventricular septal defect with pulmonary hypertension.[27] Throughout the lung there were abnormal angiomatoid vascular spaces lying in trabeculae of dense fibrous tissue around pulmonary arteries and veins, and bronchi. The walls of these vascular spaces often had no elastic tissue but much was seen in

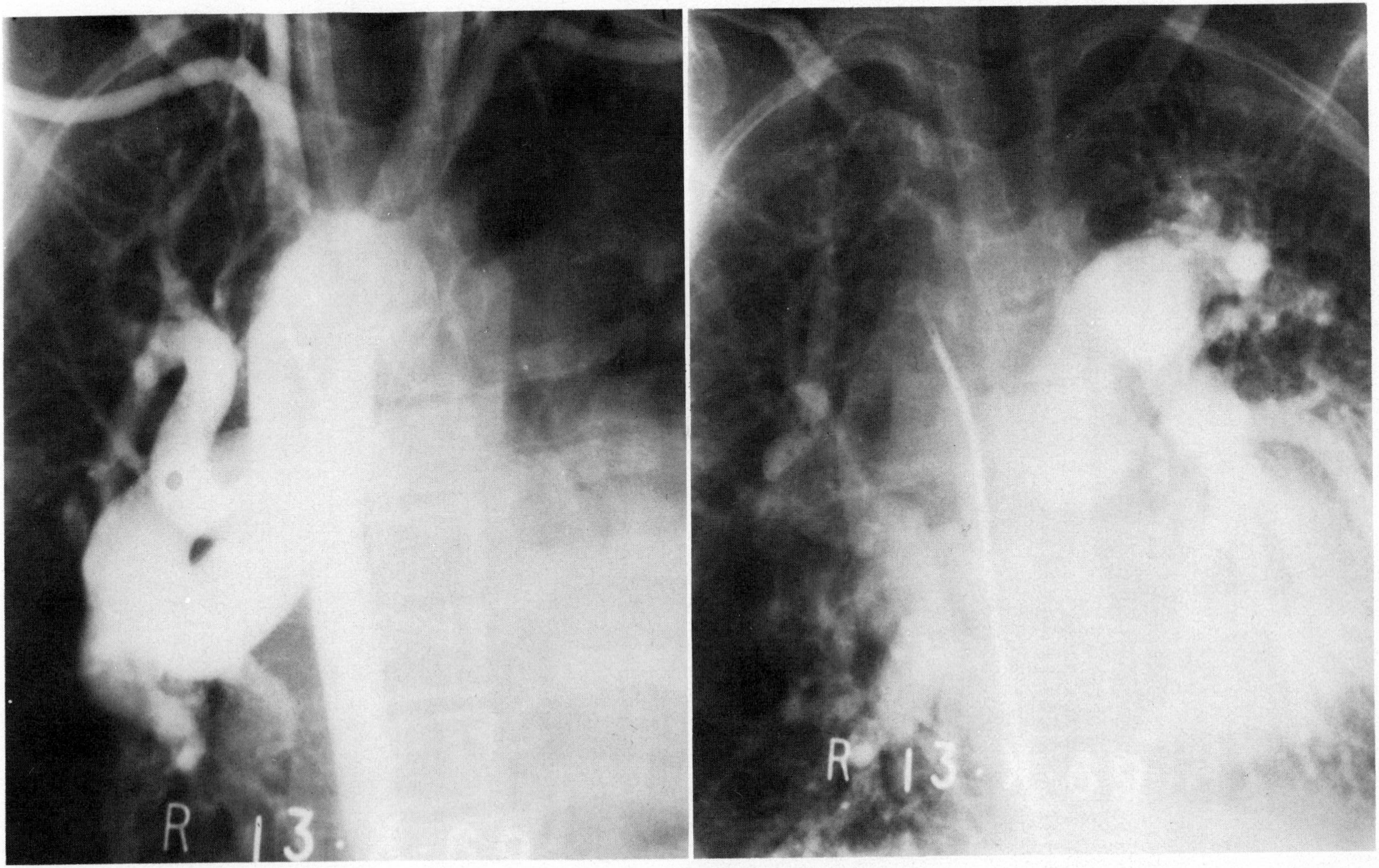

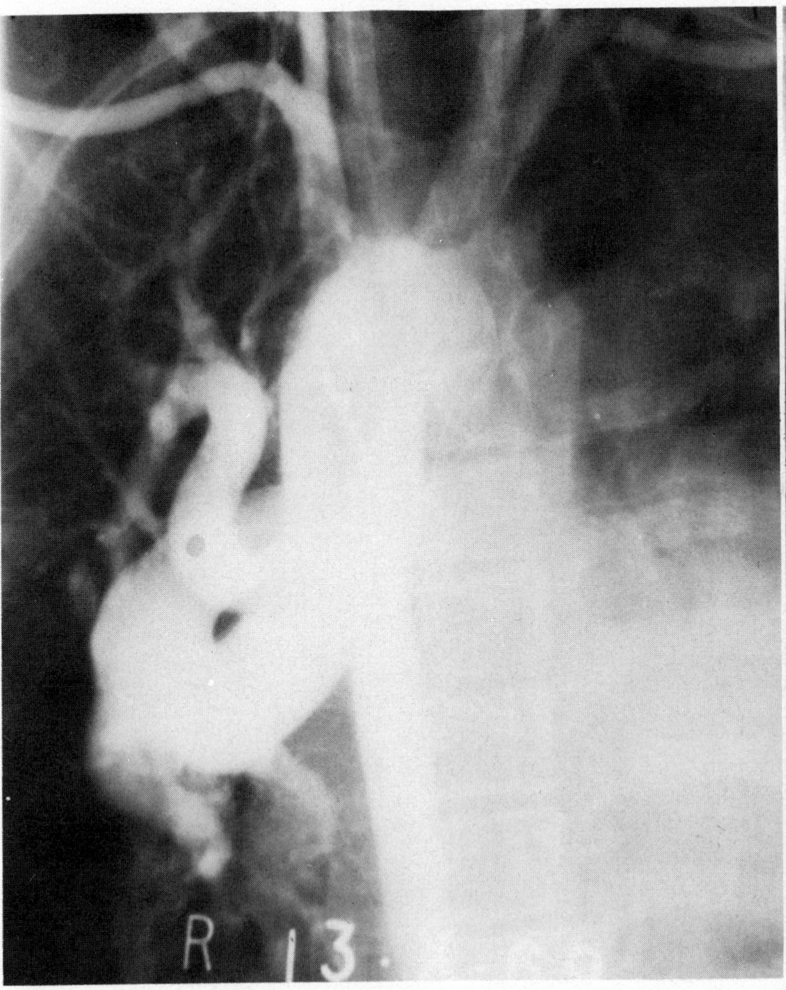
R 13
A
R 13
B

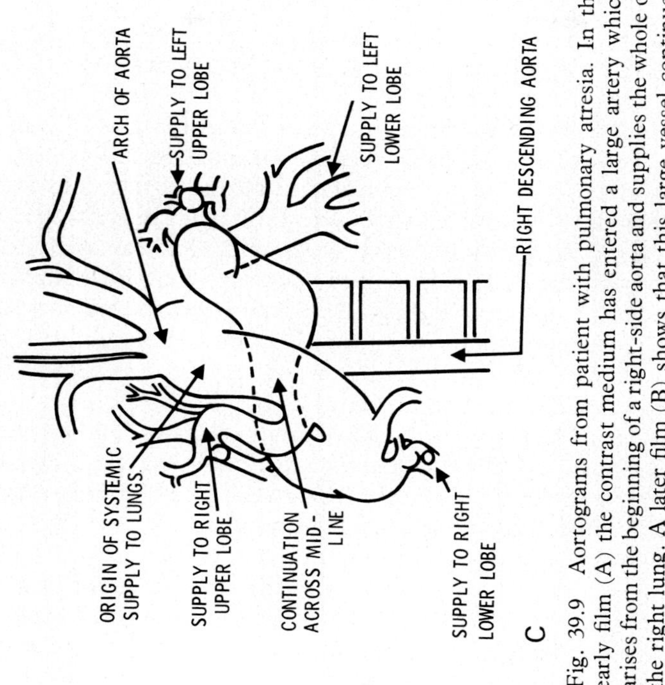

Fig. 39.9 Aortograms from patient with pulmonary atresia. In the early film (A) the contrast medium has entered a large artery which arises from the beginning of a right-side aorta and supplies the whole of the right lung. A later film (B) shows that this large vessel continues across the mid-line to supply the whole of the left lung. The pulmonary trunk is missing but the central portion of the systemic supply to the lungs resembles the normal bifurcation into right and left branches. Figure C shows a reconstruction of the two films.

the dense collagen separating them. Occasionally these thin-walled vessels communicated with a pulmonary artery or with one of the dilated and prominent thin-walled bronchial vessels in the wall of a bronchus. In most cases the vascular spaces in the lung were so numerous and complex as to make it impossible to detect communications of this type. Small branches of elastic pulmonary arteries which were largely occluded by fibrous intimal thickening also passed through dense collagen and elastic fibres to communicate with dilated thin-walled vessels in the walls of bronchi. These dilated vascular spaces were found in bronchi and bronchioles lying immediately beneath the bronchial mucosa or outside the muscle coat. In several instances abnormal, thin-walled bronchial vessels joined to form para-bronchial vessels which could be traced in serial sections to their junction with a pulmonary vein. In other areas, communications between a pulmonary artery and vein by groups of thin-walled vessels appeared likely but could not be conclusively demonstrated. The tortuous vascular channels in the lung of two patients with primary pulmonary hypertension described by Wade and Ball[28] as broncho-pulmonary anastomoses were also thin-walled. These vessels, up to 200 μm in diameter, connected bronchial arteries with muscular pulmonary arteries, about 250 μm in diameter, distal to an obstructed segment in the pulmonary vessel. Their walls consisted of a normal intima supported by a thick elastic lamina and only traces of muscle.

Venous Bronchopulmonary Anastomoses

Pulmonary veins are not 'end vessels' in the same sense as the pulmonary arteries.[6] As we have seen in Chapter 38, the bronchial veins communicate freely at the hilum of the lung with mediastinal plexuses that drain into the azygos system of veins and hence into the superior vena cava and right side of the heart. The bronchial veins beyond the second order of branching of bronchi also communicate freely with the pulmonary veins and drain into the left atrium. This potential bronchopulmonary venous shunt is available for the passage of blood in either direction in the lung. It has been suggested, for instance, that in the pulmonary venous hypertension of mitral stenosis there may be widening of these numerous venous anastomoses allowing blood to flow from the pulmonary veins to the pleurohilar branches of the bronchial venous system and hence into the superior vena cava and right atrium.[11] Liebow *et al.*[6] observed that in severe emphysema there may be dilatation of the bronchial veins along the bronchi as peripheral as the sixth order branches. They suggested that this expansion allows blood to flow in either direction. With the onset of congestive cardiac failure and elevation of the pressure in the right atrium the pressure in the small bronchial veins might exceed that in the pulmonary veins. Hence an extra-pulmonary right-to-left shunt could develop with the passage of hypoxic blood into the left side of the heart. This concept appears to be unproven. In a few unpublished observations on patients with chronic bronchitis we have attempted to raise the pressure in the azygos system by occluding the superior vena cava with a balloon attached to a catheter. In no case did this give rise to a fall in systemic arterial Po_2 suggesting that no significant right–left shunt occurred through the bronchial venous system.

Some patients with cirrhosis of the liver develop an accentuation of normal communications that exist between the portal and pulmonary veins via the mediastinal venous plexi.[29] The relation between the portal and pulmonary venous systems is considered in detail in Chapter 29.

Bronchopulmonary venous anastomoses develop not only as a result of a dilatation of pre-existing communications, as in the examples quoted above, but also by the development of new vessels. It has been shown experimentally[30] that, when the pulmonary veins of one lung are ligated, new transpleural veins may develop from capillaries of the granulation tissue in the obliterated pleural space. These transpleural vessels join with the end of pulmonary veins in the lung giving rise to bronchopulmonary venous anastomoses. A recirculation of blood occurs, the flow being from the right ventricle via the pulmonary arteries to the pulmonary veins and thence into the transpleural veins, the superior vena cava and the right chambers of the heart.

REFERENCES

1. Von Hayek, H. (1940) *Z. Anat. Entwicklungsgesch.*, **110**, 42.
2. Von Hayek, H. (1942) *Anat. Anz.*, **93**, 155.
3. Verloop, M. C. (1948) *Acta Anat.*, **5**, 171.
4. Weibel, E. (1959) *Z. Zellforsch.*, **50**, 653.

5. Wagenvoort, C. A., Heath, D. & Edwards, J. E. (1964) *The Pathology of the Pulmonary Vasculature.* Springfield, Ill.: Thomas.
6. Liebow, A. A., Hales, M. R. & Bloomer, W. E. (1959) *Pulmonary Circulation*, ed. Adams, W. R. & Veith, I. page 79. New York: Grune & Stratton.
7. Heath, D. & Thompson, I. McK. (1969) *Thorax*, **24**, 232.
8. Turner-Warwick, M. (1961) *Bronchial Artery Patterns in Lung and Heart Disease.* Ph.D. thesis. University of London.
9. Cockett, F. B. & Vass, C. C. N. (1951) *Thorax*, **6**, 268.
10. Fishman, A. P., Turino, G. M., Brandfonbrener, M. & Himmelstein, A. (1958) *J. Clin. Invest.*, **37**, 1071.
11. Marchand, P., Gilroy, J. C. & Wilson, V. H. (1950) *Thorax*, **5**, 207.
12. Cudkowicz, L. & Armstrong, J. B. (1952) *Thorax*, **8**, 152.
13. Liebow, A. A., Hales, M. R. & Lindskog, G. E. (1949) *Amer. J. Path.*, **25**, 211.
14. Cudkowicz, L. & Armstrong, J. B. (1951) *Thorax*, **6**, 343.
15. Cudkowicz, L. & Armstrong, J. B. (1952) *Brit. Heart J.*, **14**, 374.
16. Cudkowicz, L. & Armstrong, J. B. (1953) *Thorax*, **8**, 46.
17. Cudkowicz, L. (1952) *Thorax*, 7, 270.
18. Wintrobe, M. M. (1961) *Clinical Hematology*, 5th ed. page 673. Philadelphia: Lea & Febiger.
19. Jefferson, K. & Rees, S. (1973) *Clinical Cardiac Radiology*. London: Butterworths.
20. Jefferson, K., Rees, S. & Somerville, J. (1972) *Brit. Heart J.*, **34**, 418.
21. Stuckey, D., Bowdler, J. D. & Reye, R. D. K. (1968) *Brit. Heart J.*, **30**, 258.
22. Macartney, F., Deverall, P. & Scott, O. (1973) *Brit. Heart J.*, **35**, 28.
23. Somerville, J. (1970) *Brit. Heart J.*, **32**, 641.
24. Tynan, M. J. & Gleeson, J. A. (1966) *Brit. Heart J.*, **28**, 573.
25. Campbell, M. & Gardner, F. (1950) *Brit. Heart J.*, **12**, 183.
26. Cudkowicz, L. (1968) *The Human Bronchial Circulation in Health and Disease.* Baltimore: Williams & Wilkins.
27. Brewer, D. B. & Heath, D. (1959) *J. Path. Bact.*, **77**, 141.
28. Wade, G. & Ball, J. (1957) *Quart. J. Med. N.S.*, **26**, 83.
29. Calabresi, P. & Abelmann, W. H. (1957) *J. Clin. Invest.*, **36**, 1257.
30. Hurwitz, A., Calabresi, M., Cooke, R. W. & Liebow, A. A. (1954) *Amer. J. Path.*, **30**, 1085.

40. Measurement and Functional Significance of the Bronchial Collateral Circulation

Not all the supply of blood through the bronchial arteries passes to the lungs, since a certain quantity drains into the azygos and hemiazygos systems. That portion which is directed through the lungs might be called the bronchial collateral circulation to the lungs but it should not be confused with the flow of blood through dilated arterial vessels which by-passes the obstructive lesions of grade 4 hypertensive pulmonary vascular disease (Chap. 16) and which has been referred to there as the 'pulmonary collateral circulation' (Fig. 16.19, p. 257). Nor is it only the bronchial arteries which in disease supply blood into the pulmonary circulation through anastomoses, since the intercostal, internal mammary and mediastinal arteries or vessels of possibly a more primitive developmental origin also contribute to the additional blood supply from the systemic circulation. In this chapter the systemic component of the blood to the lungs will be called the '*collateral circulation*'.

The Influence of the Collateral Circulation on the Estimation of the Pulmonary Blood Flow

The presence of a collateral circulation in the lungs gives rise to an inaccuracy in the estimation of the pulmonary blood flow by the conventional Fick method.[1] The nature and degree of the inaccuracy depends on the composition of the blood flowing through the anastomoses. Figure 40.1 indicates the pathways through which oxygen enters and leaves the pulmonary blood volume. There are three sources of

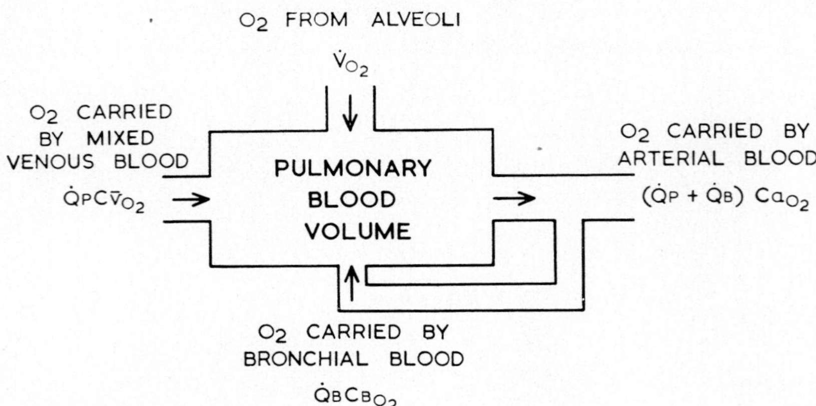

Fig. 40.1 Diagram to show the pathways through which the oxygen enters and leaves the pulmonary blood volume.

entry of oxygen into the pulmonary blood volume: from the air, from the mixed venous blood carried in the pulmonary artery, and from the collateral circulation. The rate of uptake of oxygen from the air is $\dot{V}O_2$ (Fig. 40.1). The rate of entry of oxygen through the pulmonary artery is $\dot{Q}P C\bar{v}_{O_2}$ where $\dot{Q}P$ is the rate of flow of blood into the main pulmonary artery and $C\bar{v}_{O_2}$ is the oxygen content of mixed venous blood. Similarly, the rate of entry of oxygen via the collateral circulation is $\dot{Q}B CB_{O_2}$ where $\dot{Q}B$ is the collateral flow and CB_{O_2} is the oxygen content of the blood entering the pulmonary blood volume from the collateral circulation (Fig. 40.1). The left atrium represents the only pathway through which oxygen may leave the pulmonary blood volume and the rate of exit of oxygen is $(\dot{Q}P+\dot{Q}B)Ca_{O_2}$ where Ca_{O_2} is the oxygen content of systemic arterial blood (Fig. 40.1).

Since over any long period of time the rate of entry of oxygen into the pulmonary blood volume must equal the rate of exit:

$$\dot{V}O_2 + \dot{Q}P C\bar{v}_{O_2} + \dot{Q}B CB_{O_2} = (\dot{Q}P + \dot{Q}B)Ca_{O_2}$$

Solving for $\dot{V}O_2$:

$$\dot{V}O_2 = \dot{Q}P(Ca_{O_2} - C\bar{v}_{O_2}) + \dot{Q}B(Ca_{O_2} - CB_{O_2})$$

Dividing both sides by $(Ca_{O_2} - C\bar{v}_{O_2})$:

$$\frac{\dot{V}O_2}{Ca_{O_2} - C\bar{v}_{O_2}} = \dot{Q}P + \dot{Q}B\left(\frac{Ca_{O_2} - CB_{O_2}}{Ca_{O_2} - C\bar{v}_{O_2}}\right)$$

or, in other words, the pulmonary blood flow as measured by the Fick method is equal to:

$$\dot{Q}P + \dot{Q}B\left(\frac{Ca_{O_2} - CB_{O_2}}{Ca_{O_2} - C\bar{v}_{O_2}}\right) \qquad \text{(i)}$$

The equation indicates that the Fick calculation represents the sum of two components:

(*a*) The flow through the main pulmonary artery ($\dot{Q}P$);

(*b*) An additional quantity which may or may not equal the flow $\dot{Q}B$ entering the pulmonary vessels from the collateral anastomoses.

This second component will equal the collateral flow ($\dot{Q}B$) when the oxygen content of the blood passing through the anastomoses (CB_{O_2}) is equal to that of mixed venous blood ($C\bar{v}_{O_2}$). It will be larger than the collateral flow when the oxygen content of the blood passing through the anastomoses is less than that of mixed venous blood. It will be smaller than the collateral flow when the oxygen content of the blood passing through the anastomoses lies between that of arterial (Ca_{O_2}) and that of mixed venous blood. It will be zero when the oxygen content of the blood passing through the anastomoses is equal to that of arterial blood.

The estimation of the pulmonary blood flow by the dye-dilution technique is also influenced by the presence of a collateral circulation in the lungs. When a dye is injected into the pulmonary artery and sampled from a systemic artery, the estimated pulmonary blood flow will include the flow of collateral circulation to the lungs irrespective of the oxygen saturation of the blood passing through the anastomoses. This situation has been used in the measurement of the collateral circulation[1] and will be discussed in greater detail later in the chapter.

Measurement of the Collateral Circulation by the Fick Principle

These methods are dependent on the calculation of the exchange of respiratory gases across the alveoli. They are, therefore, only concerned with the flow through pre-capillary anastomoses in the lung. The simplest case is when there is no flow of mixed venous blood through the pulmonary artery to the lungs, such as occurs in patients with pulmonary atresia, some forms of tricuspid atresia,[2] and persistent truncus arteriosus. In such patients the pre-capillary collateral flow constitutes the entire circulation through the alveoli and carries unsaturated blood from the systemic arterial tree. The oxygen content of the pre-capillary blood in the lungs is, therefore, the same as that in the systemic artery (Ca_{O_2}). The oxygen uptake by the lungs ($\dot{V}O_2$) can be measured in the usual way. All that remains to complete the Fick equation is the oxygen content of the pulmonary venous blood ($C\text{PV}_{O_2}$). This cannot be measured directly, but, if the patient breathes 25 per cent oxygen, it may be assumed to equal approximately that of blood which is 98 per cent saturated. Thus the flow of blood through the alveoli may be estimated and this is equal to the collateral circulation.

$$\text{Pre-capillary collateral circulation} = \frac{\dot{V}O_2}{C\text{PV}_{O_2} - Ca_{O_2}}$$

Using this calculation, the average pre-capillary collateral flow was found to be $3{\cdot}2\ \text{l} \cdot \text{min}^{-1}$ in four patients with congenital atresia of the main pulmonary artery who were at rest.[3]

The first use of this type of calculation was to estimate the collateral flow which develops in a dog's lung when the pulmonary artery to that lung is ligated.[4] By means of a bronchospirometry tube, the pathological lung was supplied with pure oxygen, and the other lung with air. The rate of uptake of oxygen by the pathological lung ($\dot{V}O_2$) was given by the slope of the spirometer tracing. The oxygen content of the collateral supply to this lung was taken to be the same as a systemic arterial sample (Ca_{O_2}) and the oxygen content of the blood leaving the lung ($C\text{PV}_{O_2}$) was assumed to be the same as that of an arterial sample taken when both lungs breathed 100 per cent oxygen. This technique has been used to measure the collateral supply to the affected lung of a patient with congenital absence of the right pulmonary artery and the rate of flow was estimated[5] to be $950\ \text{ml min}^{-1}$.

There has been a similar study of two patients with acquired occlusion of one pulmonary artery.[3] The affected lung was in this case supplied with 25 per cent oxygen and the pulmonary venous oxygen content was estimated to be equivalent to the oxygen capacity minus 0·6 ml/100 ml. The normal lung was supplied with 12 per cent oxygen in order to cause a lowering of the systemic arterial oxygen saturation and thus widen the arterio-venous difference across the capillaries of the affected lung. In one of these patients who had had a pulmonary artery ligated 10 years previously the estimated collateral flow through the affected side was 860 $ml \cdot min^{-1}$. In the other patient the pulmonary artery had been occluded by a tumour for about six months and no collateral flow could be demonstrated.

A further extension of the method was applied to patients with unilateral pulmonary lesions in whom the pulmonary arteries were patent.[3] The collateral flow through the affected lung of these patients could be measured if the pulmonary artery supplying this lung were temporarily occluded by means of a balloon attached to a cardiac catheter. Under these circumstances, the total flow of blood through the affected lung could again be equated to the collateral supply. In three patients with carcinoma of the bronchus no collateral flow could be demonstrated. In two patients with bronchiectasis and one patient with idiopathic clubbing, the collateral flow through the one lung ranged between 315 and 382 $ml \cdot min^{-1}$.

The temporary occlusion of one branch of the pulmonary artery avoided the problem of assessing collateral flow in a situation where the normal channels were open for the flow of mixed venous blood through the lungs. Bing *et al.*[6,7] made an early attempt to solve this problem in patients with Fallot's tetrad and a collateral supply to both lungs. The principle of their method was to make separate estimates of the flow of blood through the main pulmonary artery and the flow of blood through the pulmonary capillaries. The difference between these two quantities represented the pre-capillary collateral flow. The method was based on the Fick principle, but carbon dioxide was used as the tracer gas and not oxygen. The carbon dioxide content of mixed venous blood ($C\bar{v}_{CO_2}$) was measured by direct sampling through a cardiac catheter. The carbon dioxide content of pulmonary venous blood ($C_{PV_{CO_2}}$) was derived by measuring the end-expiratory ('alveolar') P_{CO_2} and applying this to the carbon dioxide dissociation curve for blood. The output of carbon dioxide by the lungs ($\dot{V}_{CO_2}$) was measured by the collection and analysis of expired air. The flow of blood to the lungs via the main pulmonary artery was then calculated from the Fick formula*

$$\frac{\dot{V}_{CO_2}}{(C\bar{v}_{CO_2} - C_{PV_{CO_2}})}$$

The flow of blood through the pulmonary capillaries was calculated from a similar formula in which the same values for $\dot{V}_{CO_2}$ and $C_{PV_{CO_2}}$ were used. The carbon dioxide content of the blood entering the pulmonary capillaries ($C_{N_{CO_2}}$) was, however, inserted instead of the value ($C\bar{v}_{CO_2}$) for the mixed venous blood. For this

* It will be remembered from page 616 that the Fick formula may be inaccurate in the presence of a collateral circulation to the lungs. By analogy to equation (i) on page 617, the flow which was measured was:

$$\frac{\dot{V}_{CO_2}}{C\bar{v}_{CO_2} - C_{PV_{CO_2}}} = \dot{Q}_P + \dot{Q}_B\left(\frac{C_{B_{CO_2}} - C_{PV_{CO_2}}}{C\bar{v}_{CO_2} - C_{PV_{CO_2}}}\right)$$

Since, in these patients with right-to-left shunts, $C_{B_{CO_2}}$ would be greater than $C_{PV_{CO_2}}$, the flow measured by this equation also included a portion of the collateral flow.

purpose, air was re-breathed in a bag until it had equilibrated with the blood entering the pulmonary capillaries. From the P_{CO_2} of this air and the carbon dioxide dissociation curve of blood, $C_{N_{CO_2}}$ could be calculated. The pulmonary capillary blood flow was then given by the formula:

$$\frac{\dot{V}_{CO_2}}{(C_{N_{CO_2}} - C_{PV_{CO_2}})}$$

Using these formulae in a series of 38 patients with Fallot's tetrad, Bing *et al.*[6,7] made estimates of the collateral flow varying from zero to 2·8 $l \cdot min^{-1}/m^2$ BSA and averaging 0·9 $l \cdot min^{-1}/m^2$ BSA.

Measurement of the Collateral Circulation by Dye-Dilution[1,8,9]

This method has been used to measure the collateral pulmonary circulation in patients with acquired disease of the lungs. It is not applicable to patients who also have an intracardiac shunt. The technique consists in injecting an indicator dye into the right atrium and recording dilution curves simultaneously in blood withdrawn from the pulmonary artery and the brachial artery (Fig. 40.2). The curve from the pulmonary artery is used to calculate the output of the right ventricle[10]

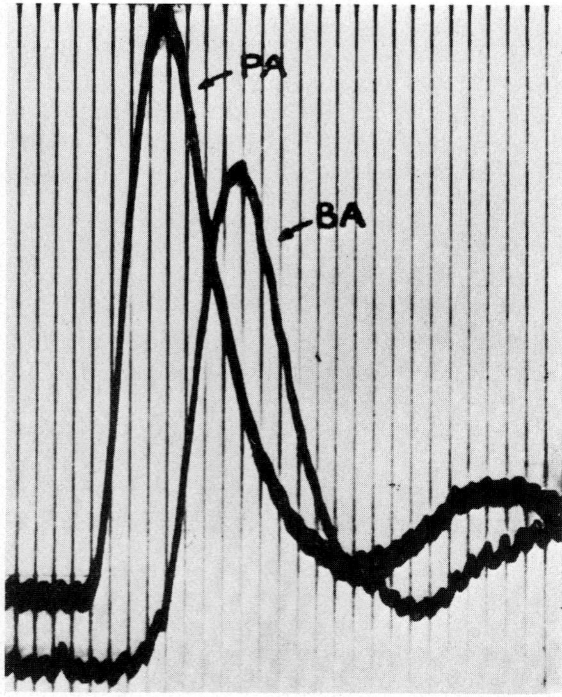

Fig. 40.2 Dye-dilution curves recorded in the pulmonary artery (PA) and brachial artery (BA) after the injection of T-1824 into the right atrium of a normal subject.[10]

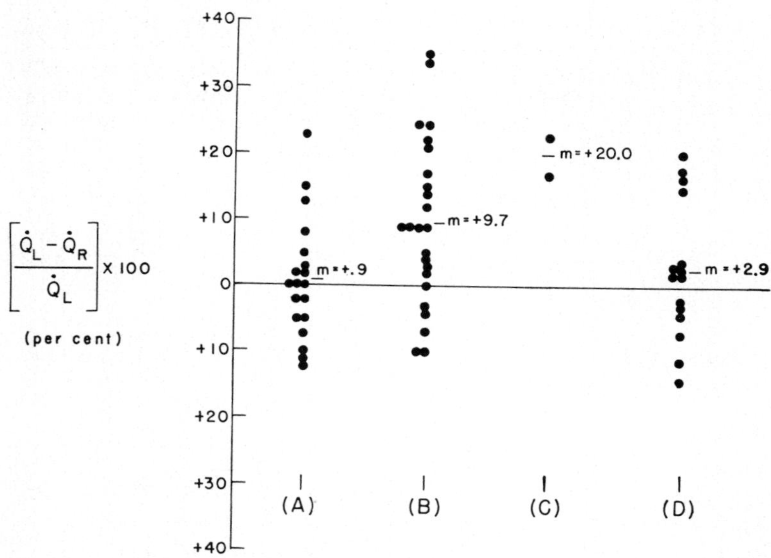

Fig. 40.3 Measurements of the volume of flow through the bronchial circulation in: (A) normal subjects; (B) patients with bronchiectasis; (C) a patient with ligation of the left pulmonary artery; and (D) patients with pulmonary tuberculosis. $\dot{Q}_L$ = the output of the left ventricle; $\dot{Q}_R$ = the output of the right ventricle; $\dot{Q}_L - \dot{Q}_R$ represents the bronchial blood flow which is here expressed as a percentage of the left ventricular output.[1]

and the curve from the brachial artery is used to calculate the output from the left ventricle. The amount by which the output of the left ventricle exceeds that of the right ventricle represents the flow of blood through the collateral anastomoses into the lung. The method depends on the assumption that the recirculation of dye through the collateral circulation is insufficiently fast to influence the downslope of the brachial arterial curve. Such contamination with recirculated dye, however, would have the effect of diminishing the calculated collateral flow and would not exaggerate this quantity. The measurement is independent of the site of the anastomoses in the pulmonary circulation and of the composition of the blood passing through them.

The inaccuracies of the method make it unsuitable for the estimation of collateral flow in any individual patient unless this is very large. In a group of ten normal subjects, however, the average value for the estimated collateral flow was 0·9 per cent of the left ventricular output, a figure which agrees with the direct measurements of bronchial arterial flow in animals.[11] In 11 patients with bronchiectasis the average value for the estimated collateral flow was 9·7 per cent of the left ventricular output and in six patients with pulmonary tuberculosis it was 2·9 per cent. A figure of 20 per cent was obtained in a patient who had undergone ligation of the left pulmonary artery nine months previously (Fig. 40.3). Table 40.1 gives the results

Table 40.1 The cardiac output measured by the Fick method ($\dot{Q}_F$) together with the right ventricular output ($\dot{Q}_R$) and left ventricular output ($\dot{Q}_L$) measured by dye-dilution in a patient with unilateral bronchiectasis before and after pneumonectomy. $\dot{Q}_L - \dot{Q}_R$ represents the bronchial blood flow which is here expressed as a percentage of the left ventricular output.

	$\dot{Q}_F$	$\dot{Q}_R$	$\dot{Q}_L$	$\left[\frac{\dot{Q}_L - \dot{Q}_R}{\dot{Q}_L}\right] \times 100$
Before pneumonectomy	6·1	5·7	8·6	+34
	6·1	5·5	8·4	+34
After pneumonectomy	5·4	4·9	5·9	+17

obtained in a patient with unilateral bronchiectasis before and after pneumonectomy. In this patient the collateral flow diminished from 34 to 17 per cent of the left ventricular output after the operation.

It will be remembered from page 617 that in the presence of a collateral circulation the pulmonary blood flow measured by the Fick method will equal the right ventricular output if the composition of the blood passing through the anastomoses is the same as that of systemic arterial blood. If the composition of the anastomotic blood is the same as that of mixed venous blood, the flow measured by the Fick method will be equal to the output of the left ventricle. A comparison of the values obtained by the Fick method with those obtained by the dye-dilution method will, therefore, give an indirect indication of the composition of the blood passing through the anastomoses. Figure 40.4 shows that in normal subjects the Fick measurement

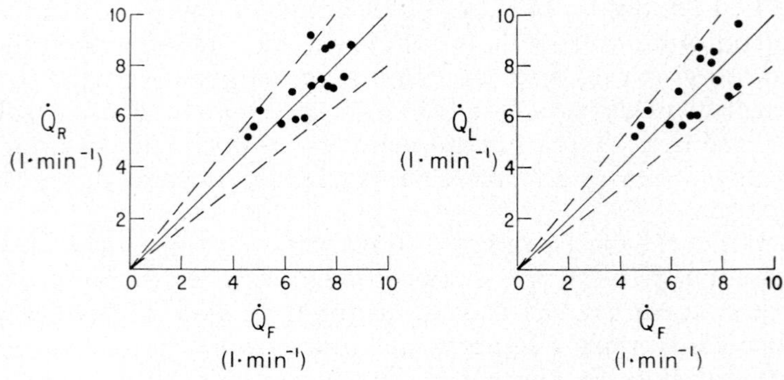

Fig. 40.4 A comparison of the cardiac output estimated by the Fick method ($\dot{Q}_F$) with that of the right ventricle ($\dot{Q}_R$) and the left ventricle ($\dot{Q}_L$) estimated by dye-dilution in normal subjects. The diagonal line represents perfect agreement. The interrupted lines represent a difference of ±20 per cent. $\dot{Q}_F$ does not differ systematically from either $\dot{Q}_R$ or $\dot{Q}_L$.

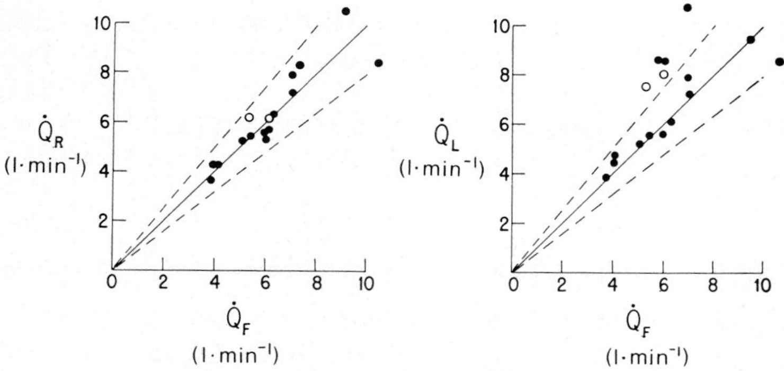

Fig. 40.5 A comparison of the cardiac output estimated by the Fick method ($\dot{Q}_F$) with that of the right ventricle ($\dot{Q}_R$) and left ventricle ($\dot{Q}_L$) in patients with bronchiectasis and in one patient (open circles) with ligation of one pulmonary artery. The diagonal line represents perfect agreement. The interrupted lines represent a difference of ± 20 per cent. $\dot{Q}_F$ agrees with $\dot{Q}_R$, but appears to be systematically lower than $\dot{Q}_L$.

coincides with the output of both right and left ventricles. In Figure 40.5 it will be seen that the Fick measurement in patients with bronchiectasis agrees more closely with the right ventricular output. This suggests that the blood passing through the anastomoses is arterial in nature, a finding which is consistent with the anatomical nature of the anastomoses in these patients (p. 604).

Effects of the Collateral Circulation on the Exchange of Respiratory Gases

The influence which the collateral circulation has on the exchange of respiratory gases depends on the site of entry of the anastomotic vessels, the composition of the blood passing through them and the relation between ventilation and perfusion. For instance, in patients with congenital cyanotic heart disease who have pre-capillary systemic–pulmonary anastomoses, the blood passing through the collateral circulation will exchange both oxygen and carbon dioxide with the alveolar gas. Most of such patients have a diminished or absent flow of blood through the pulmonary artery owing to the anatomical cardiac abnormality and thus the collateral circulation has an important or even vital respiratory function which is physiologically identical with the effects of a surgically induced systemic–pulmonary communication.

On the other hand, the pre-capillary collateral anastomoses which accompany bronchiectasis (p. 604) will have little respiratory function because the blood passing through them will be systemic arterial blood which has already undergone equilibration with alveolar gas. Any respiratory exchange which may occur will arise from regional differences in the ventilation : perfusion ratio.

Blood from the bronchial circulation will also enter the pulmonary circulation by the normal passage from the bronchial venules into the pulmonary venules. It is presumed that the blood in the bronchial veins is less saturated than is systemic arterial blood and this post-capillary shunt is thought to be responsible for part of the difference which exists between the alveolar and arterial partial pressure of oxygen (A—a difference, Chap. 36, p. 567).

Haemodynamic Effects of the Collateral Circulation

Where there are large, free developmental communications between the systemic arterial and pulmonary arterial systems, the pulmonary arterial pressure in the relevant portion of the lung will be the same as that in the systemic arteries. Under these circumstances, the affected part of the lung will be liable to develop the changes of hypertensive pulmonary vascular disease. Such communications occur in association with pulmonary atresia, truncus arteriosus or hemitruncus and unilateral absence of a pulmonary artery. Should there be a stenosis at the origin of the communicating vessel the changes of hypertensive pulmonary vascular disease may not occur.[12]

Substantial pre-capillary communications from the bronchial arteries in patients with bronchiectasis often occur in scarred areas of the lung where the pulmonary capillary bed has been obliterated and replaced by granulation tissue derived from the bronchial arteries. In these circumstances there may be a reversal of flow in the affected branch of the pulmonary artery,[13] so that blood withdrawn from the catheter may be arterial even when the end of the catheter is lying in a large vessel.[14] Angiocardiography has demonstrated such a reversal of flow in pulmonary arteries of patients with total bronchiectasis of one lung.[15] Under these conditions, the pressure obtained in the wedged position may be higher than that in the pulmonary artery and show a systolic pulsation.[14] The increased pulmonary blood flow resulting from the collateral circulation in bronchiectasis may contribute to an increased pulmonary arterial pressure. However, since the measured volume of bronchial blood flow seldom exceeds one-third of the left ventricular output, it would not be expected to have any noticeable effect if the pulmonary circulation were otherwise normal.

REFERENCES

1. Fritts, H. W., Jn., Harris, P., Chidsey, C. A., Clauss, R. H. & Cournand, A. (1961) *Circulation*, **23**, 390.
2. Brown, J. W., Heath, D., Morris, T. L. & Whitaker, W. (1956) *Brit. Heart J.*, **18**, 499.
3. Fishman, A. P., Turino, G. M., Brandfonbrener, M. & Himmelstein, A. (1958) *J. Clin. Invest.*, **37**, 1071.
4. Bloomer, W. E., Harrison, W., Lindskog, G. E. & Liebow, A. A. (1949) *Amer. J. Physiol.*, **157**, 317.
5. Madoff, I. M., Gaensler, E. A. & Strieder, J. W. (1952) *New Engl. J. Med.*, **247**, 149.
6. Bing, R. J., Vandam, L. D. & Gray, F. D., Jn. (1947) *Bull. Johns Hopk. Hosp.*, **80**, 107.
7. Bing, R. J., Vandam, L. D. & Gray, F. D., Jn. (1947) *Bull. Johns Hopk. Hosp.*, **80**, 121.
8. Cudkowicz, L., Calabresi, M., Nims, R. G. & Gray, F., Jn. (1959) *Amer. Heart J.*, **58**, 743.

9. Cudkowicz, L. (1968) In *The Human Bronchial Circulation in Health and Disease*. Baltimore: Williams & Wilkins.
10. Fritts, H. W., Jn., Harris, P., Chidsey, C. A., III, Clauss, R. A. & Cournand, A. (1957) *J. Appl. Physiol.*, **11**, 362.
11. Bruner, H. D. & Schmidt, C. F. (1947) *Amer. J. Physiol.*, **148**, 648.
12. Jefferson, K., Rees, S. & Somerville, J. (1972) *Brit. Heart J.*, **34**, 418.
13. Liebow, A. A., Hales, M. R. & Bloomer, W. E. (1959) In *Pulmonary Circulation*, ed. Adams, W. R. & Veith, I. P.86. New York: Grune & Stratton.
14. Roosenburg, J. G. & Deenstra, H. (1954) *Dis. Chest*, **26**, 664.
15. Liebow, A. A., Hales, M. R., Harrison, W., Bloomer, W. E. & Lindskog, G. E. (1950) *Yale J. Biol. Med.*, **22**, 637.

41. The Pulmonary Vasculature in Fibrosis of the Lung

Fibrosis of the lung may be massive or interstitial. In massive pulmonary fibrosis, usually the result of pneumoconiosis, large confluent areas of lung parenchyma are replaced by fibrous tissue. Interstitial pulmonary fibrosis affects individual alveolar walls (Figs 41.1 and 41.2). Both forms are associated with pulmonary vascular disease but interstitial fibrosis in the lung also adversely affects the diffusion of oxygen into the blood.

INTERSTITIAL FIBROSIS

It has become clear in recent years that interstitial pulmonary fibrosis, now usually referred to as fibrosing alveolitis, follows an early cellular phase which has been considered by some authors to be a separate disease entity 'desquamative interstitial pneumonia'. With chronicity the interstitial fibrosis may evolve into 'honeycomb lung' (Fig. 41.3) which is associated with pronounced changes in the

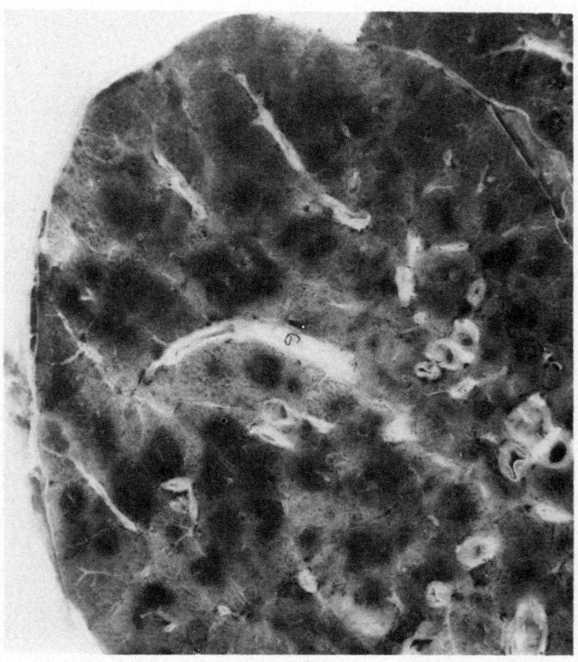

Fig. 41.1 A slice of lung, natural size, from a man of 61 years with chronic myeloid leukaemia who was treated with busulphan ('Myleran'). There is interstitial pulmonary fibrosis, the cut surface of the lung showing pale areas of fibrosis which are situated mainly in the peripheral areas of secondary lung lobules.

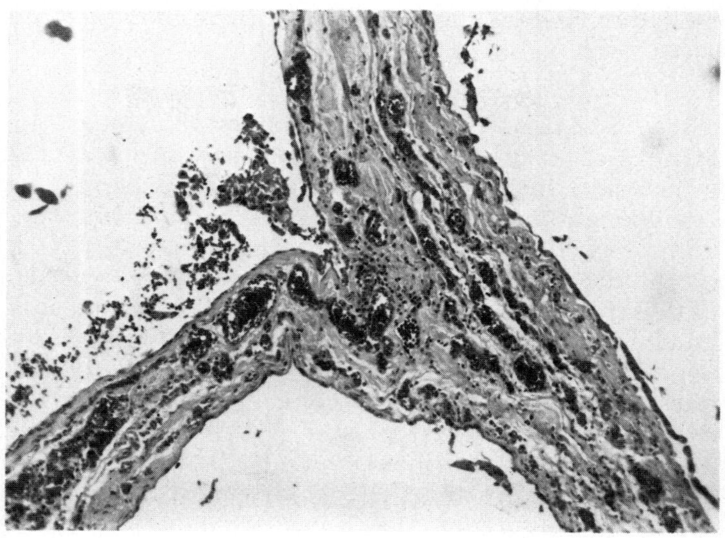

Fig. 41.2 Interstitial pulmonary fibrosis. There is gross fibrous thickening of the alveolar wall. This excess of fibrous tissue around the pulmonary capillaries impairs the diffusion of oxygen from the alveoli. The wall is lined by flat alveolar epithelium (Haematoxylin & eosin, × 110)

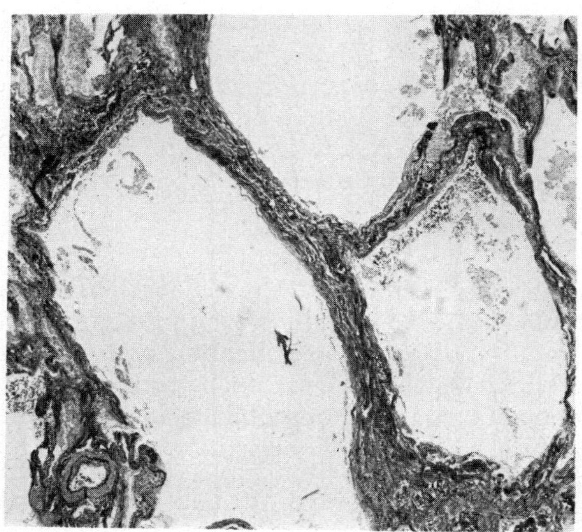

Fig. 41.3 Honeycomb lung. The lung parenchyma is transformed into cysts, the walls of which are composed of fibroelastic tissue. In the lower left hand of the figure is a thick-walled small muscular pulmonary artery. (Elastic/Van Gieson, × 24)

pulmonary vasculature. First we may briefly consider the relation of these three pathological states.

DESQUAMATIVE INTERSTITIAL PNEUMONIA

In 1965 Liebow, Steer and Billingsley[1] described the clinical, radiological and pathological features of what they regarded as a new form of pneumonia which they called 'desquamative interstitial pneumonia'. Scadding and Hinson,[2] however, regarded this condition as merely the early cellular phase of fibrosing alveolitis and we agree with this view. In this early stage, large numbers of cells appear in the alveolar spaces. At the same time, granular pneumocytes (see Chap. 3) become prominent in the alveolar walls. The intra-alveolar cells present a strikingly uniform appearance throughout the lung. They stain positively by the periodic-acid Schiff reaction and contain a brown pigment that is not haemosiderin. We have studied the nature of these intra-alveolar cells by means of electron microscopy and found that both macrophages and granular pneumocytes are present.[3] Small lymphoid follicles are found but necrosis, fibrinous exudate in the alveolar spaces and hyaline membranes are not. At this early stage there is a characteristic but not pathognomonic radiographic appearance of 'ground-glass' opacification at the lung bases especially at their peripheries. Even at this phase of the disease focal areas of fibrous thickening of the alveolar walls can be found but the pulmonary arterial tree is unaffected.

FIBROSING ALVEOLITIS

Later fibrous tissue is laid down in the interstitium of the lung so that the alveolar walls become thick and fibrous (Fig. 41.2). This is the fully developed mural stage of fibrosing alveolitis. Lymphocytes, plasma cells, eosinophils and mast cells may be found in association with the thickened alveolar walls.[4] In fibrosing alveolitis induced by busulphan ('Myleran') (Fig. 41.1), a drug used in the treatment of chronic myeloid leukaemia, there is associated intra-alveolar fibrosis. This follows organization of disintegrated groups of granular (type 2) pneumocytes (see p. 34) which liberate their lamellar bodies.[4] Similar disintegration of intra-alveolar cells and subsequent organization occurs in rats to which *Crotalaria spectabilis* seeds (Chap. 27) have been administered.[5]

HONEYCOMB LUNG

Fibrosing alveolitis is sometimes followed by the development of a cystic condition called 'honeycomb lung' (Fig. 41.3). Cysts varying in diameter from 1 to 10 mm are brought about by dilatation of bronchioles. Heppleston[6] studied the condition by microdissection and serial histological sections and came to the conclusion that obliteration or dilatation of respiratory bronchioles was the basis of its development. He believed that unaffected adjacent bronchioles underwent a compensatory dilatation forming cystic cavities near consolidated and fibrotic areas. Progressive enlargement of the cysts was due to secondary valvular destruction of the bronchioles that communicated with them. By means of tri-dimensional photographic reconstruction of the lesions found in honeycomb lung Pimentel[7] found that the cystic change was usually due to pronounced changes in the lobular bronchioles caused by the obliteration or rigidity of alveolar ducts and the corresponding alveoli and even by localization of interstitial fibrosis in the bronchiolar wall. He found that the whole lobular bronchiolar system was involved but that the terminal and respiratory bronchioles bore the brunt of the pathology. The changes were those of diffuse, saccular or cystic bronchiolectasis. The bronchioles showed disruption or obliteration, changes in direction and mode of division, amputations, and anastomoses between bronchioles and cysts belonging to anatomically independent airways. There was some evidence that the cysts developed as a result of multiple valvular arrangements which let the air in but do not let it out.

There are many causes of honeycomb lung.[7] These include sarcoidosis, berylliosis, asbestosis, cadmium-poisoning, eosinophilic granuloma of the lung, Letterer-Siwe disease, Hand-Schuller-Christian disease, scleroderma, rheumatoid disease, Hamman-Rich syndrome, the specific granulomata including tuberculosis (especially after treatment with streptomycin), X-irradiation fibrosis, busulphan lung and tuberous sclerosis. With the gradual onset of fibrosing alveolitis and honeycomb lung there is a simultaneous development of pulmonary vascular disease. This is quite different in form and functional significance from the hypoxic hypertensive pulmonary vascular disease that complicates emphysema and states of chronic hypoxia as described in Chapters 32 and 33.

Pulmonary Vascular Disease in Honeycomb Lung

In a histological study of the small pulmonary arteries in seven cases of interstitial pulmonary fibrosis and honeycomb lung, we found a pattern of pulmonary vascular disease characteristic of honeycomb lung but independent of the primary lung disease.[8] This was characterized by an initial stage of muscularization (Fig. 41.4) and a secondary stage of fibrous atrophy and ablation. The muscular stage consists of the development of a thick media of circular muscle and the formation of longitudinal muscle in the intima (Fig. 41.4) in both muscular pulmonary arteries and pulmonary arterioles. The fibrous stage is distinguished by pronounced intimal fibroelastosis and recanalization of thrombus. There is fibrous atrophy of the media and finally fibrous ablation of affected vessels. In some instances there is a plexus of thin-walled vessels which may be the histological counterpart of pulmonary systemic anastomoses demonstrated radiographically in this condition.

The early stage of muscularization is almost certainly associated with the development of pulmonary hypertension. The longitudinal muscle forms probably as a result of three factors: repeated longitudinal stretch, distortion of the pulmonary arteries around the cystic spaces, and the association of chronic hypoxia.

The second stage of fibrous atrophy and ablation of pulmonary arteries is likely to be associated with a change in the pulmonary vascular resistance from a labile reversible type to one that is irreversible and has a fixed organic basis.[8] This view is based on analogy with similar vascular lesions in congenital cardiac shunts (Chap. 16). The fibrous atrophy of the media probably explains the absence of correlation between medial thickness and right ventricular weight.[8] Naeye[9] has reported almost identical changes in the pulmonary vasculature in cases of

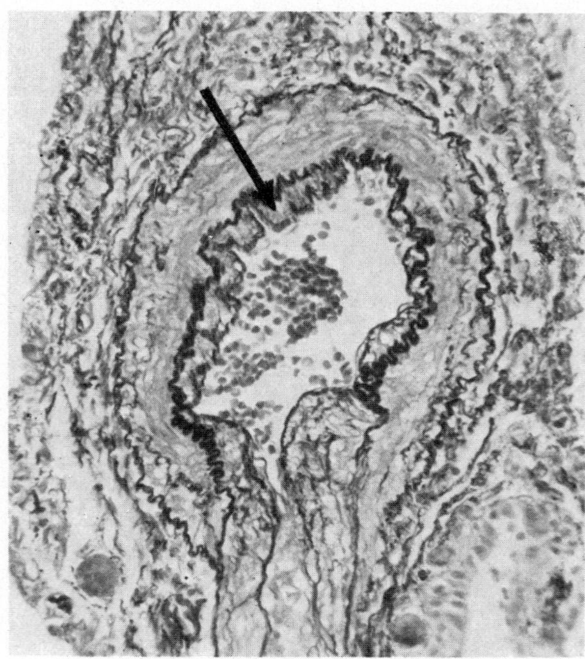

Fig. 41.4 Transverse section of a small muscular pulmonary artery from a case of honeycomb lung showing hypertrophy of the original media of circular muscle. There is also the development of fasciculi of longitudinal muscle in the intima (arrow). (Elastic/Van Gieson, × 250)

scleroderma, which give rise to interstitial pulmonary fibrosis and honeycomb lung. He describes intimal fibroelastosis, atrophy of the underlying media and longitudinal muscle in the intima.[9] While he regards these changes as characteristic of scleroderma we think it more likely that they characterize interstitial pulmonary fibrosis and honeycomb lung.

In one case, in which cyst formation was confined to a sharply defined sub-pleural band, we were able to compare the structure of the pulmonary arteries in those areas directly involved by the honeycomb change and in the comparatively normal intervening areas.[8] We found intimal fibroelastosis to be confined to the arteries in the affected lung whereas muscularization of pulmonary arterioles was found throughout normal and affected areas. In addition medial hypertrophy of muscular pulmonary arteries was greater in the cystic areas. Such findings suggest that intimal changes are associated directly with honeycomb change in the surrounding lung. In contrast, muscularization of pulmonary arterioles results from pulmonary hypertension brought about by the honeycomb change, and this exerts its effects throughout the entire pulmonary arterial tree.[8]

In some cases of honeycomb lung of several years duration with pronounced pulmonary vascular changes of the type described above, there is no development of right ventricular hypertrophy. This may be related to the formation of numerous thin-walled dilated vessels that may allow the blood flow to by-pass the occluded terminal radicles of the pulmonary arterial tree. We have seen such vessels in histological sections[8] and plexuses of such vessels about 50 μm in diameter have been demonstrated radiographically in cases of interstitial pulmonary fibrosis.[10] Turner-Warwick showed these vascular plexuses to consist of newly formed anastomotic channels connecting muscular pulmonary arterioles and systemic blood vessels. Her injection studies also revealed large isolated sub-pleural pulmonary systemic anastomoses up to 1·5 mm in diameter and she thought these had arisen from dilatation of pre-existing anastomoses brought about by pulmonary hypertension. Similar pulmonary systemic anastomoses have been demonstrated radiographically by Livingstone *et al.*[11]

There is also physiological evidence for intrapulmonary veno-arterial shunts in lungs from cases of scleroderma showing interstitial fibrosis.[12] Two possible functions for these complex pre-capillary anastomoses in the lung are to allow blood to by-pass occluded terminal radicles of the pulmonary arterial tree and to allow a collateral supply of blood to enter the affected honeycomb areas of lung from the systemic circulation.

It is clear that the form of pulmonary vascular disease that complicates honeycomb lung (that is cystic dilatation of the *terminal* bronchioles), is very different from hypoxic hypertensive pulmonary vascular disease complicating centrilobular emphysema (that is dilatation of the *respiratory* bronchioles). The pulmonary vascular disease of fibrosing alveolitis and honeycomb lung is characterized by intimal fibrosis and eventual fibrous ablation of pulmonary arteries whereas hypoxic hypertensive pulmonary vascular disease is characterized by a lack of intimal fibrosis and muscularization of the terminal portions of the pulmonary arterial tree, microanatomical features that are associated with reversibility of pulmonary hypertension (see Chap. 33).

Alveolar–Capillary Block

Patients with interstitial fibrosis of the lung commonly develop characteristic defects of respiratory function which have been termed 'alveolar–capillary block' and which will be considered in detail in the next chapter. Until recently it was considered likely that the impairment of diffusion in interstitial fibrosis of the lung was due in part to the increased distance that the oxygen has to travel across the thickened alveolar–capillary wall and in part to the reduction in blood–gas interface[13]. These alveolar walls may indeed be thickened by a wide variety of tissues, including collagen, elastic, extensions of bronchiolar epithelium, granular pneumocytes, and the formation of hyaline membranes. Sometimes in honeycomb lung there is an associated hyperplasia of smooth muscle fibres, the so-called 'leiomyomatosis'. Leiomyomatosis is seen in an exuberant form in the lungs of cats infested with the lung worm *Aelurostrongylus abstrusus*. However, it has become clear that the defects of respiratory function in fibrosing alveolitis are due in much greater measure to disturbances of ventilation: perfusion ratios, as will be described in the following chapter.

Hamman–Rich Syndrome

In 1944 Hamman and Rich[14] described an acute form of diffuse interstitial fibrosis of the lung of unknown aetiology which often followed an illness resembling bronchopneumonia. The histopathology is characterized by oedema and haemorrhage. No bacteria are present and only a few leucocytes are found, eosinophils being prominent among them. Necrosis of alveolar and bronchiolar epithelium is typical. Hence the inflammatory reaction is quite distinct from that usually associated with pyogenic bacteria. This disease produces severe thickening of the alveolar capillary membrane by means of enlargement of alveolar epithelial cells, by formation of a hyaline membrane lining the alveoli, by oedema and fibrin deposit in the alveolar walls and by extensive, diffuse and progressive interstitial proliferation of fibrous tissue throughout all lobes of both lungs with focal organization of intra-alveolar haemorrhage.[14]

MASSIVE FIBROSIS

In some diseases massive pulmonary fibrosis occurs rather than the fibrous thickening of individual alveolar walls as just described. Widespread disturbances of the pulmonary circulation occur when there is such gross fibrosis in the lung as in massive pneumoconiosis due to the long-continued inhalation of coal dust, silica, or industrial dusts containing iron, talc or gypsum. In general, the capillaries are destroyed and replaced by fibrous tissue, the muscular pulmonary arteries are occluded or even destroyed by fibrous tissue (Figs 41.5 and 41.6) and the large, elastic pulmonary arteries become obstructed at the point where they enter massive areas of fibrosis but are patent and dilated proximal to these. Hence the right ventricle is forced to maintain its output against an increased peripheral vascular resistance in the lung.

Pulmonary Capillaries

In all the pneumoconioses there is great proliferation of fibroblasts in the alveolar walls with the destruction and replacement of the pulmonary capillaries. Characteristically, in coal-workers' pneumoconiosis, there are fibrotic masses in addition. The presence and state of the capillaries in these depend upon the type of massive lesion concerned.[15] In the fibro-anthracotic type of Policard *et al.*,[16] characterized by coal-dust pigment distributed through loosely-arranged collagen, Wells[15] found many large capillary channels about 500 μm in diameter lined by only a thin endothelium abutting directly on the fibrous tissue. In the fibro-hyaline type of lesion,[16] in which less numerous dust cells are embedded in tightly packed, hyaline collagen fibres, there are only occasional small vessels with walls thicker than those found in the fibro-anthracotic masses.[15] In the irregular processes at the edges of the massive fibrotic lesions there is a relative vascular abundance with vessels up to 150 μm in diameter.

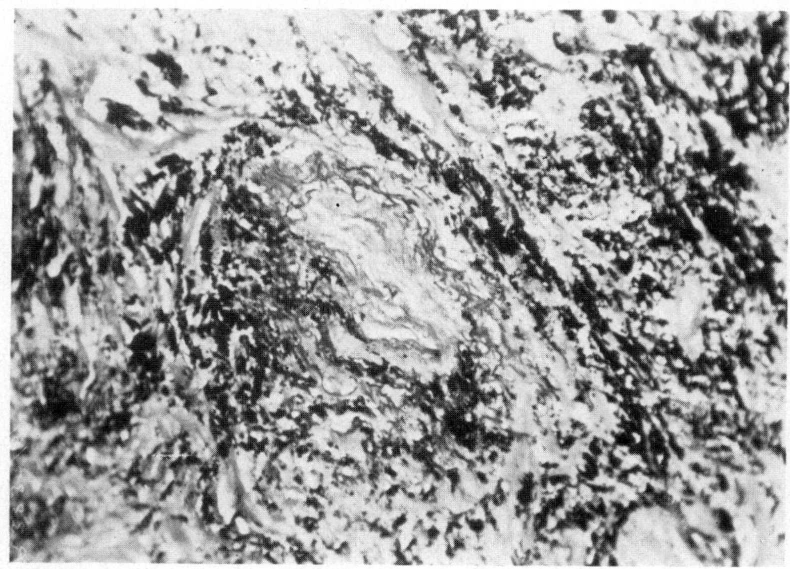

Fig. 41.5 Silicosis. Transverse section of a muscular pulmonary artery in the region of a silicotic nodule. The vessel has been engulfed by fibroanthracotic tissue which has grown in from the adventitia and led to fibrous occlusion of the lumen. The remains of the internal elastic lamina mark the position of the vessel. (Elastic/Van Gieson, × 150)

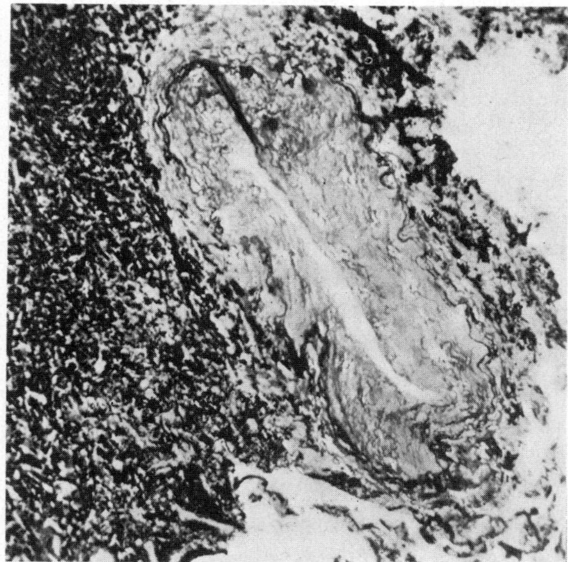

Fig. 41.6 Silicosis. Oblique section of a muscular pulmonary artery in apposition to a fibroanthracotic nodule. There is gross intimal fibrosis so that the lumen is almost obliterated. The media is disrupted by fibrous tissue growing in from around the vessel. (Elastic/Van Gieson, × 85)

Muscular Pulmonary Arteries and Pulmonary Veins

The small pulmonary arteries and veins show occlusive, cellular intimal fibrosis. There is often stenosis or distortion of these vessels by medial fibrosis. Eventually the lumen may be replaced by capillary-like channels and the whole vessel is overrun by dust-bearing tissue so that only elastic stains reveal the presence of the remains of blood vessels. Vascular damage is disproportionately great in the presence of superimposed infection, especially tuberculosis, and this is particularly true if quartz has been inhaled. In many of the occupational chest diseases, specific dust particles or fibres, asbestos bodies and dust-cells may be demonstrated in the outer part of the media and in the perivascular lymphatics.[15,17] In coal-workers' pneumoconiosis, the accumulation of dust cells in such sites may interfere with the nutrition of the media for there is often a loss of muscle and elastic tissue with replacement by collagen.[15]

Elastic Pulmonary Arteries

The large pulmonary arteries frequently show dilatation which extends into the intrapulmonary branches. When there are fibrous masses, many of the larger pulmonary arteries in the lung are engulfed in them and obliterated. Even patent vessels skirting around the edges of such fibrotic lesions are distorted and frequently deficient in smaller branches.[15] Atheroma is common in these elastic arteries and occasionally ulceration of the intima occurs in vessels near fibrous masses or hard lymph nodes. The media of the larger pulmonary arteries shows fibrosis which may end in cicatricial stenosis or aneurysmal dilatation and rupture.[17] There is often a great affinity of the media for basic dyes and intense metachromasia with toluidine blue.[15] Thrombosis is common in the large pulmonary arteries of patients with massive pneumoconiosis.[15] In some instances the histological appearances reveal two or three distinct episodes of thrombosis but in others there has clearly been a prolonged single episode.

REFERENCES

1. Liebow, A. A., Steer, A. & Billingsley, J. G. (1965) *Amer. J. Med.*, **39**, 369.
2. Scadding, J. G. & Hinson, K. F. W. (1967) *Thorax*, **22**, 291.
3. Brewer, D. B., Heath, D. & Asquith, P. (1969) *J. Path.*, **97**, 317.
4. Littler, W. A., Kay, J. M., Hasleton, P. S. & Heath, D. (1969) *Thorax*, **24**, 639.
5. Kay, J. M., Smith, P. & Heath, D. (1969) *Thorax*, **24**, 511.
6. Heppleston, A. G. (1956) *Thorax*, **11**, 77.
7. Pimentel, J. C. (1967) *Thorax*, **22**, 444.
8. Heath, D., Gillund, T. D., Kay, J. M. & Hawkins, C. F. (1968) *J. Path. Bact.*, **95**, 423.
9. Naeye, R. L. (1963) *Dis. Chest.*, **44**, 374.
10. Turner-Warwick, M. (1963) *Thorax*, **18**, 225.
11. Livingstone, J. L., Lewis, J. G., Reid, L. & Jefferson, K. E. (1964) *Quart. J. Med.*, N.S. **33**, 71.
12. Conner, P. K. & Bashour, F. A. (1961) *Amer. Heart J.*, **61**, 494.
13. Arnott, W. M. (1955) *Brit. Med. J.*, **ii**, 279.
14. Hamman, L. & Rich, A. R. (1944) *Bull. Johns Hopk. Hosp.*, **74**, 177.
15. Wells, A. L. (1954) *J. Path. Bact.*, **68**, 573.
16. Policard, A., Croizier, L. & Martin, A. (1939) *Ann. Anat. Path.*, **16**, 97.
17. Schepers, G. W. H. (1955) *Arch. Industr. Health*, **12**, 7.

42. Diffusion

The exchange of oxygen and carbon dioxide between air and blood in the lungs is carried out across a total alveolar surface which is estimated to be approximately 70 square metres (p. 509). The surface area of the pulmonary capillaries is presumably of a similar order. It is now generally accepted that the transfer of gases takes place entirely by the simple physical processes of diffusion and solution, although for many years the existence of active secretion of oxygen by the alveolar cells was a matter of controversy.

The Nature of Diffusion

The diffusion of a substance through a space is due entirely to the random motion of its molecules which cause it to move from a point of high concentration to a point of low concentration. The rate of diffusion is thus proportional to the concentration gradient (dC/dx). Even with the same concentration gradient, different substances diffuse at different rates and this variation in diffusivity is characterized in physics by the coefficient of diffusion (k). Thus, according to Fick's law, the mass of substance diffusing across unit area in unit time is equal to the coefficient of diffusion multiplied by the concentration gradient ($k \cdot dC/dx$). Since the process of diffusion is dependent on the random motion of molecules, gases with smaller molecules diffuse more rapidly than those with larger ones. The coefficient of diffusion of a gas in fact varies inversely as the square root of its molecular weight. For example, the coefficient for carbon dioxide is $\sqrt{32/44} = 0{\cdot}85$ times that for oxygen.

In considering the diffusion of respiratory gases in the lungs, we are mainly concerned with changes in partial pressure rather than changes in concentration. In a gas phase, the partial pressure of a gas is strictly related to its concentration. But, when gases become dissolved in liquids, their concentration is equal to their partial pressure (P) multiplied by their solubility (α) (*i.e.* $C = P\alpha$). Carbon dioxide, for instance, is twenty times as soluble in saline as is oxygen. At the same partial pressure its concentration will, therefore, be twenty times that of oxygen, and, for the same partial pressure gradient, the concentration gradient for carbon dioxide in solution is twenty times as steep as it is for oxygen ($dC/dx = \alpha\, dP/dx$). Hence, if we are measuring the diffusibility of gases in liquids by their movement along a partial pressure gradient instead of along a concentration gradient, carbon dioxide is much more diffusible than oxygen.

The Diffusion Barrier in the Lungs

The diffusion barrier in the lungs is a compromise between the anatomical necessity to separate blood and air and the physiological necessity to bring them together. It may be considered in three anatomical zones: the gas in the alveolus, the 'alveolar–capillary membrane', and the blood in the capillary.

The diffusion of gases within the alveolus is usually thought to be so fast relative to the distances involved that this does not impose any significant impediment to their passage.[1]

Presumably diffusion occurs chiefly across the thin side of the pulmonary capillary which does not rest on the supporting framework of connective tissue (Chap. 24, p. 370, Fig. 24.4). If this is so, the 'alveolar–capillary membrane' consists of the ultrathin cytoplasmic extensions of membranous (type 1) pneumocytes, the fused basement membrane of these pneumocytes and the endothelial cells of the pulmonary capillaries and the endothelial cells themselves. To this must be added the thin, watery layer containing surfactant which lines the alveolar epithelium. Physiologically, it is convenient to include the plasma in the capillary as part of this 'membrane', since both plasma and tissue constitute a mechanical barrier to diffusion. The resistance imposed by this barrier may be measured separately (p. 639).

The resistance to the passage of gases between the plasma and the red cells is dependent not only on the processes of diffusion across the red cell membrane and within its cytoplasm but also on the chemical reactions which take place inside the cell.

Of the two respiratory gases, carbon dioxide is so highly 'diffusible' that even in those diseases where the diffusing capacity of the lungs is decreased it can readily pass from the capillaries to the alveoli. The retention of carbon dioxide in disease is due almost entirely to a deficiency of ventilation. A decrease in the diffusing capacity of the lungs will, on the other hand, impair the transport of oxygen from air to blood and give rise to hypoxaemia.

The Diffusing Capacity of the Lungs

The diffusing capacity of the lungs for a particular gas (D_L) is defined as the number of millilitres of the gas (at STPD) which can pass per minute from the alveoli into the blood stream when the difference in partial pressure between the gas and the blood phase is 1 mmHg.

$$D_L = \frac{\text{ml of gas diffusing per minute}}{\text{alveolar tension (mmHg)—mean capillary tension (mmHg)}}$$

Two points may be noted about this definition. In the first place it is expressed in terms of the partial pressure gradient and not of the concentration gradient. This means that D_L for a particular gas is related not only to its coefficient of diffusion (k) but to its solubility (α). Thus D_L for carbon dioxide would be greater than D_L for oxygen.

The second point to be noted about the definition of D_L is that it ignores any measurement of the surface over which the gas is absorbed. It is inevitable that this should be so, since the surface is not susceptible to measurement. The result, however, is that the value of D_L is to some extent proportional to the size of the lungs. To allow for this, D_L is often expressed in terms of the body surface area.

It will be seen that the measurement of the diffusing capacity for a particular gas depends on a knowledge of its total rate of exchange across the alveolar membrane together with its partial pressure in the alveoli and in the capillary blood. The quantity of oxygen or carbon dioxide entering or leaving the body per minute is easily measured (Appendix B) but the difference in the partial pressure of these gases between the alveoli and capillary blood is considerably more difficult to estimate. In the case of carbon dioxide, this difference is so minute that for practical purposes it is regarded as non-existent (Chap. 36, p. 577). Hence it is impossible to measure the diffusing capacity for carbon dioxide. The diffusing capacity for oxygen (D_{LO_2}) may, however, be measured, and is described later in this chapter.

It is relatively easy to estimate the partial pressure of oxygen in the alveoli (P_{AO_2}) by means of the alveolar air equation (Appendix C) but the estimation of the mean partial pressure of oxygen in the pulmonary capillaries is more complex (p. 641). For this reason it is technically simpler to measure the diffusing capacity for carbon monoxide (D_{LCO}). The affinity of haemoglobin for carbon monoxide is so great that, when a patient is breathing a low concentration of this gas, the partial pressure inside the red cells may be assumed to be zero. In this way, the estimation of (D_{LCO}) requires only the measurement of the quantity of carbon monoxide absorbed each minute ($\dot{V}CO$) and its partial pressure in the alveoli (P_{ACO}).

The Diffusing Capacity for Carbon Monoxide (D_{LCO})

The methods which are available may be divided into two types according to whether the subject breathes a low concentration of carbon monoxide continuously for a period of minutes (steady-state methods) or whether he takes a single deep breath of a mixture containing carbon monoxide (breath-holding methods). In both cases, the alveolar concentration of carbon monoxide and its rate of uptake are determined from an analysis of the expired air.

Steady-State Methods for Estimating the Diffusing Capacity for Carbon Monoxide

In these methods the uptake of carbon monoxide is calculated in a similar way to the uptake of oxygen (Appendix B) from a knowledge of the composition of inspired and expired air and the volume of expired air. A number of methods have been used to estimate the alveolar partial pressure of carbon monoxide. In the Filley method[2] a modification of the alveolar air equation is used which depends on the assumption that arterial P_{CO_2} represents alveolar P_{CO_2}. The formula, which is derived in Appendix O, is

$$P_{ACO} = P_{ICO} - (P_{ACO_2}/P_{ECO_2})(P_{ICO} - P_{ECO})$$

The assumption that arterial P_{CO_2} represents alveolar P_{CO_2} becomes weakest in the presence of a large dead-space ventilation, when an a − A difference for carbon dioxide may develop and the arterial P_{CO_2} will exceed the mean alveolar P_{CO_2} (Chap. 36, p. 577). Under these circumstances, as may be seen from the equation, the use of arterial P_{CO_2} will give an erroneously high figure for the diffusing capacity.

Average figures of 17 (Ref. 2), 24 (Ref. 3) and 21 (Ref. 4) ml/min/mmHg have been reported in normal subjects at rest.

The method of Bates *et al.*[5] uses end-tidal sampling as representative of alveolar air. This also will be sensitive to the magnitude of the dead-space ventilation relative to alveolar ventilation since, at a normal tidal volume, the end-expired sample may be contaminated with dead-space gas. Other methods depend on the assumption of a value for the dead-space or its separate measurement by methods which involve the same assumption as those discussed above.

Breath-Holding Methods for Estimating DL_{CO}

The most widely used method of this type is that devised by Forster and his colleagues.[6] The basis for the method was described earlier in this century by Krogh.[7] If a subject takes a deep breath of air containing a small concentration of carbon monoxide and holds it, the concentration of carbon monoxide in the alveoli should, theoretically, decline in an exponential fashion according to the equation:

$$FA_t = FA_o \cdot \exp[-DL \cdot t \cdot (PB - 47)/VA] \qquad \text{(i)}$$

where: FA_o and FA_t are the fractional concentrations of carbon monoxide in the alveoli at the beginning and after a time t min; PB is the barometric pressure; 47 mmHg is the vapour pressure of water at 37°C; DL is the diffusing capacity; and VA is the alveolar volume. This equation is derived in Appendix P. In the original techniques the subject expired a certain amount after breathing in the mixture and an 'alveolar' sample of expired air was taken. Then, after waiting a measured number of seconds, a further expiration was made and a second 'alveolar' sample of air obtained. The concentration of carbon monoxide in the two alveolar samples together with an assessment of the alveolar volume were used to solve equation (i) for DL.

There are errors attached to the use of two alveolar samples taken at different degrees of expiration, since differently ventilated alveoli contribute to the expired air in varying proportions throughout expiration. This is particularly so in patients with emphysema. To avoid this difficulty, Forster *et al.*[8] used a mixture of gases containing helium, carbon monoxide, oxygen and nitrogen. The principle is the same as that used in the measurement of the pulmonary capillary blood flow (Chap. 6, p. 87) and pulmonary parenchymal volume (Chap. 24, p. 378). The helium is not absorbed and the initial as well as final alveolar concentrations of carbon monoxide may be calculated from a single 'alveolar' end-expired sample using the formula:

$$\text{Initial } FA_{CO} = \frac{\text{Final } FA_{He}}{FI_{He}} \times FI_{CO}$$

where: FA and FI are the alveolar and inspired fractional concentrations of a gas; and the suffices CO and He represent carbon monoxide and helium, respectively.

In fact the rate of decline in the alveolar concentration of carbon monoxide was found by this method not to be quite exponential[8] and this was thought to be due to a variation in the diffusing capacity throughout the lung (p. 643). However, in practice,[6] the use of varying times of breath-holding has not led to any great variation in the estimated DL_{CO}.

Although in theory the alveolar space from which the carbon monoxide has been taken up should be calculable from the helium concentration in the 'alveolar' sample, in practice this has not been found to be satisfactory. The alveolar volume has, therefore, to be measured separately, usually by a helium-dilution method. This points to a weakness of the method. The clearance rate of carbon monoxide is measured only in that portion of the lung which contributes expired air at the moment of sampling and this is assumed to be representative of the whole alveolar space. Such an assumption seems reasonable in normals but becomes untenable in patients with emphysema.

The average value for DL_{CO} by this method in groups of normal adults has been estimated at 25 (Ref. 6), 28 (Ref. 9), 26 (Ref. 10) and 35 (Ref. 3) ml/min/mmHg.

The Diffusing Capacity of the Alveolar–Capillary 'Membrane' (DM) and the Volume of Blood in the Pulmonary Capillaries (Vc)*

Roughton and Forster[11,12] have shown how the diffusion of carbon monoxide from the alveolus to the surface of the red cell and the entry of the gas into the red cell may be separately measured.

The total pulmonary diffusing capacity for carbon monoxide (DL_{CO}) decreases when high concentrations of oxygen are breathed.[13,14] This is because, in the presence of a high oxygen tension, haemoglobin does not accept carbon monoxide so readily and the rate of entry of carbon monoxide from the plasma into the red cells (θ) is diminished.[11,12] The variable quantity θ is the rate of uptake (ml/min) of carbon monoxide by 1 ml of blood for each 1 mmHg carbon monoxide tension. If Vc is the volume of blood in the pulmonary capillaries, then θVc is the total rate at which carbon monoxide is taken up by the red cells in the capillaries per 1 mmHg carbon monoxide tension in the plasma.

DL is the rate of passage of carbon monoxide divided by the partial-pressure gradient. The resistance to this passage of gas would be the pressure gradient divided by the rate of flow. Thus the resistance to the diffusion of carbon monoxide is 1/DL. This resistance is composed of two contributory resistances. The first is the resistance offered by the alveolar–capillary membrane (1/DM). The second is the resistance to the passage of carbon monoxide across the red cell membrane and into its interior (1/θVc). Since these two component resistances are arranged in series then

$$\frac{1}{D\text{L}} = \frac{1}{D\text{M}} + \frac{1}{\theta \text{Vc}}$$

Of the four quantities composing this equation, DL may be measured and θ may be calculated from a knowledge of the mean capillary oxygen tension.[15] In order

* It will be noted that the symbol Vc, signifying a volume of blood, does not conform to the conventions listed on page xiii. It is retained here, however, in view of its widely accepted use.

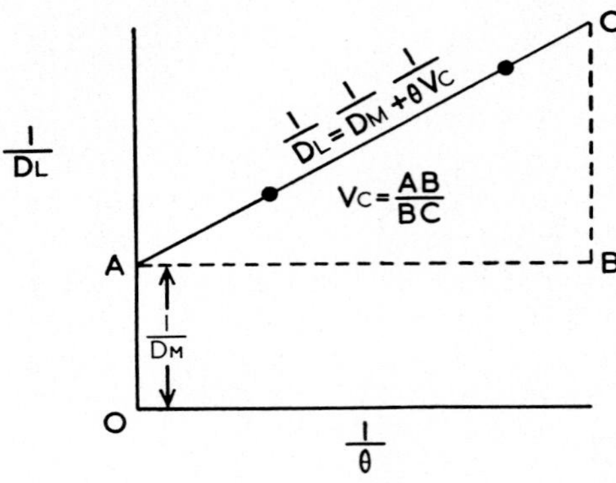

Fig. 42.1 Diagram to show the relation between DL, DM, Vc, and θ.

to determine DM and Vc, measurements of DL are made at two or more different oxygen tensions. The equation may then be solved graphically by plotting 1/DL against $1/\theta$ (Fig. 42.1). The intercept of the line with the 1/DL axis measures 1/DM, and the slope of the line measures 1/Vc. Since DM is measured by extrapolation of a line it is subject to more inaccuracy than Vc.[16,17]

In a group of eight normal adults studied in this way while sitting[18] the average value for DL was 32, and that for DM was 64 ml/min/mmHg. The average volume of blood in the pulmonary capillaries (Vc) was 97 ml. In another group of 19 seated normal adults[19] the average value for DL was 28 and that for DM was 98 ml/min/mmHg, while the average value for Vc was 65 ml. Since the value for DM is two to three times that for DL, the alveolar–capillary membrane only comprises one-third to one-half of the total resistance to diffusion. Evidence has been adduced that the uptake of carbon monoxide by the lung is pulsatile[20] due probably to changes in the pulmonary capillary volume with the heart beat.

The fact that the diffusing capacity is dependent on the capillary blood volume and haemoglobin concentration as well as on diffusion has led some authorities to prefer the term 'transfer factor'. We have, however, retained the original term 'diffusing capacity' since it is still more generally used.

The Diffusing Capacity for Oxygen (DL_{O_2})

In disease, it is the exchange of oxygen which is impaired by defective diffusion and ideally it would be preferable to measure the diffusing capacity of the lungs for this physiological gas rather than for carbon monoxide. In practice, however, the measurement of DL_{O_2} is so much more difficult than that of DL_{CO} that nowadays it is rarely carried out.

The use of carbon monoxide to measure diffusing capacity has the great practical advantage that the partial pressure of the gas in the capillaries is so small that it may be ignored. In the case of oxygen, the partial pressure of the gas in the capillary blood may not be ignored and its measurement presents several problems.

In the first place, the partial pressure of oxygen in the capillary blood is continually increasing as it passes from the arterial to the venous side so that it is necessary to estimate the mean level of P_{O_2} in the capillaries. This may be carried out by the Bohr integration procedure[21] provided that the oxygen saturation and partial pressure can be measured in the blood at the point where it enters the capillaries and the point where it leaves them.

Although the composition of the blood entering the lungs may readily be measured, we have no means of sampling it directly as it leaves the pulmonary capillaries. Our nearest approach to such a sample is systemic arterial blood, but the oxygen tension of this blood is lower than that of pulmonary end-capillary blood because of the presence of venous admixture (Chap. 36). In fact the A − a difference in oxygen tension may be due either to the limited diffusing capacity of the lungs or to venous admixture.

In the method devised by Riley and Cournand[21–23] these two processes may be distinguished by varying the composition of the inspired gas. While breathing room air, the alveolar P_{O_2}, is about 100 mmHg and the mixed venous P_{O_2} is about 40 mmHg. This large pressure gradient at the beginning of the capillary causes oxygen to pass rapidly into the capillary blood. Thus, by the time the blood reaches the end of the capillary (about three-quarters of a second later) its P_{O_2} is normally only a fraction of a millimetre of mercury lower than the alveolar P_{O_2}.

If the subject is made to breathe a hypoxic gas-mixture, the alveolar P_{O_2} will fall. This will cause a fall in the arterial P_{O_2} and a less extensive fall in arterial saturation owing to the fact that, on the haemoglobin dissociation curve, the point for arterial blood lies on the horizontal portion (Fig. 36.7, p. 578). If the cardiac output does not change,* there will be a corresponding fall in the oxygen content of the mixed venous blood. In this case, however, the fall occurs on the steep portion of the dissociation curve (Fig. 36.7) and thus the decrease in mixed venous P_{O_2} is much less extensive. In this way, the oxygen pressure gradient at the beginning of the pulmonary capillary is less under hypoxia than when breathing room air. The transfer of oxygen from the alveolus is, therefore, slower and the P_{O_2} of the blood leaving the pulmonary capillary is still measurably lower than the alveolar P_{O_2}.

Hence the effect of hypoxia is to increase that part of the A—a difference which is due to diffusion. At the same time, hypoxia diminishes the effect of venous admixture on the arterial oxygen tension. This is because, if the oxygen tension and content of pulmonary capillary blood are brought to a position on the steep portion of the haemoglobin dissociation curve, the admixture of venous blood causes only a small fall in arterial P_{O_2}. Thus the A—a difference becomes mainly due to diffusion and the arterial P_{O_2} lies close to the end-capillary P_{O_2}. Unfortunately the effects of venous admixture are not entirely eliminated under hypoxia and the estimation of the true end-capillary P_{O_2} necessitates a laborious trial and error procedure.[15]

Having established the mean oxygen tension of capillary blood ($P\bar{c}_{O_2}$), the

* If, as is often the case (Chap. 30), the cardiac output increases, the effects described in this paragraph will be magnified.

diffusing capacity for oxygen (DL_{O_2}) may be estimated from a knowledge of the oxygen uptake ($\dot{V}O_2$) and the alveolar oxygen tension (PA_{O_2}).

$$DL_{O_2} = \frac{\dot{V}O_2}{PA_{O_2} - P\bar{c}_{O_2}} \text{ml /min/mmHg}$$

Technically, the central difficulty of the method is to achieve a difference between the oxygen tension in the alveoli and that in the end-capillary blood which is of sufficient magnitude to be outside the range of the analytical error of the measurements. In normal people at rest, even hypoxia often fails to achieve this and it is for this reason that the upper limits of the normal resting range of values for DL_{O_2} have never been clearly defined. The lower limit of the normal range is in the region of 15 ml O_2 min/mmHg.

The Representation of an Impaired Diffusing Capacity on the $O_2 - CO_2$ Diagram

The effects of an impaired diffusing capacity may now be represented on the $O_2 - CO_2$ diagram described in Chapter 36 (p. 574). In Figure 42.2, the points representing the composition of alveolar air (A) and end-capillary blood (c′) lie on their respective R-lines. The end-capillary point has shifted away from the ideal point (where the R-lines intersect) in the direction of the mixed venous point ($\bar{v}$), just as it does in the presence of an inequality of the distribution of the ventilation : perfusion ratio. The alveolar point has also shifted away from the ideal point, but in a direction away from the inspired air point (I). This is the opposite to what occurs in the presence of an inequality of the distribution of the ventilation : perfusion ratio (*cf.* Fig. 36.5, p. 574). The alveolar and end-capillary points thus come to lie nearly on the same horizontal line so that, while they have a different PO_2, their PCO_2 is almost identical. This follows from the very high 'diffusibility' of carbon dioxide compared with that of oxygen.

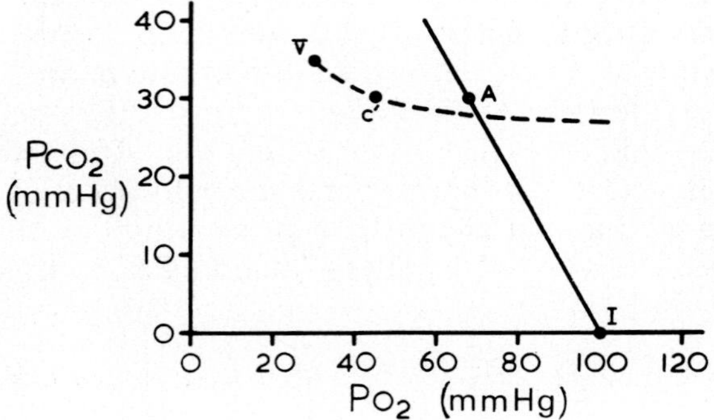

Fig. 42.2 The representation of an impaired diffusing capacity on the $O_2 - CO_2$ diagram. $\bar{v}$, mixed venous blood; c′, end capillary blood; A, alveolar gas; I, inspired gas. The continuous line represents the R = 0·8 line for gas. The discontinuous line represents the R = 0·8 line for blood. It will be noted that the inspired gas is hypoxic.

Comparison of Different Methods for Estimating the Diffusing Capacity

In comparing the diffusing capacity for oxygen with that for carbon monoxide a small correction has to be made for their different coefficients of diffusion and solubility (p. 635). In fact both their molecular weights and their solubilities are similar and the rate of diffusion of carbon monoxide is 0·83 that of oxygen. In a group of eight normal subjects[4] in which paired observations of the diffusing capacity for oxygen and carbon monoxide (Filley method) were carried out the average value was 25·6 ml/min/mmHg for $D_{L_{O_2}}$ and 20·6 ml/min/mmHg for $D_{L_{CO}}$ which corresponds well with the difference in diffusivity. Others have found a similar consistency.[24,25] The breath holding method for $D_{L_{CO}}$ has been found to give higher figures than the Bates method at rest[26] but the two methods are consistent during exercise. The reason for this probably lies in the effects of ventilation in the steady state method (p. 644) since the breath holding and steady state methods gave roughly the same result during voluntary hyperventilation.[26]

Regional Inhomogeneity of Diffusion

Inhomogeneity of diffusion occurs in relation to alveolar volume, to ventilation or to perfusion.

Dollery and his colleagues[27] recorded by external counting the clearance rate of $C^{15}O$ in various regions of the lung after a single inhalation of the tracer. In the upright position the clearance rate was twice as much at the level of the fourth intercostal space as it was at the level of the second. During exercise this difference disappeared. The difference can be ascribed to the lack of filling of capillaries at the apices of the lungs in the upright posture. It is independent of ventilation and represents an inhomogeneity of diffusing capacity relative to alveolar volume. Another form of inhomogeneity which has been shown to exist is in the ratio of diffusing capacity to alveolar capillary blood flow.[28,29]

Such regional differences may lead to errors of some magnitude in the estimation of the diffusing capacity. Inhomogeneities of D_L, D_M or V_c relative to ventilation or perfusion will give rise to an underestimation of each of these quantities.[29,30] An inhomogeneity of ventilation: perfusion ratios will also, in itself, give rise to errors.[30]

PHYSIOLOGICAL VARIATIONS IN THE DIFFUSING CAPACITY

Age

The diffusing capacity for oxygen[31] and for carbon monoxide[32-34] decreases slightly with age. It is not possible to say whether this represents a diminution in the pulmonary capillary volume or whether it arises from errors due to an increasing inhomogeneity of ventilation and perfusion.

Posture

DL_{CO} increases on lying down.[6,9,19,35] This appears to be due to an increased capillary volume.[9,19] In four normal adults, the average value for Vc was 59 ml sitting and 86 ml lying. The average value for DM was 99 sitting and 77 lying.[19] In eight subjects, tilting from the horizontal to an angle of 45° caused the average value for Vc to fall from 135 to 110 ml while DM remained unchanged.[9] Since the measurement of DM seems less reliable than that of Vc[19] the results can best be interpreted in terms of the changes in pulmonary capillary volume which would be expected to accompany the different postures.

Lung Volume

The DL_{CO} by the breath holding method increases with an increasing alveolar volume in the same individual[36,37] and is related to alveolar volume among different individuals.[33] No such increase in DL_{CO} is found by steady state methods.[3,37,38] Since, in the breath holding method, the clearance rate for carbon monoxide is multiplied by a separate measurement of the alveolar volume (p. 639), one suspects that the relation to alveolar volume may be strongly influenced by the mathematical relation. On the other hand, it is reasonable to expect the mass of the lung to influence the magnitude of DL and the steady state DL_{CO} has been shown to decrease roughly a half after pneumonectomy.[39]

Ventilation

The Filley method for DL_{CO} is highly sensitive to the level of ventilation and nearly doubles during hyperventilation[3,40] whether the arterial P_{CO_2} is maintained or not.[40] A similar increase with hyperventilation has been reported for the Bates method.[26] In this investigation it was shown that hyperventilation achieved by increasing the tidal volume and maintaining the rate caused an increase in DL_{CO}, while hyperventilation achieved by increasing the respiratory frequency and maintaining the tidal volume had no effect. Voluntary hyperventilation had no effect on the exercise DL_{CO} by the Bates method.[39] This last observation is not contradictory to the previous, since, during exercise, a certain degree of hyperventilation would already have occurred. The breath holding method for DL_{CO} is not affected by previous voluntary hyperventilation.[6]

The Valsalva manoeuvre decreases the breath holding DL_{CO} while the opposite, Mueller, manoeuvre increases it.[41] Such changes would be expected to follow a decrease and increase respectively in the capillary blood volume. Vc was measured during the Valsalva and tended to decrease.

Respiratory Gases

In measuring the diffusing capacity for oxygen, it is assumed that this capacity remains unchanged in the presence of hypoxia. The diffusing capacity for carbon monoxide is known to vary with the level of the alveolar oxygen tension. In the calculation of Vc and DM, however, this variation is assumed to take place entirely in the rate of entry of carbon monoxide into the red cells (θ), while the values for Vc and DM are regarded as constant. Thus it will be seen that the measurements of DL_{O_2}, Vc and DM are based on the supposition that a change in the alveolar oxygen tension has no effect on the pulmonary capillaries.

Since variations in the alveolar oxygen tension are known to cause alterations in the pulmonary blood flow and the pulmonary arterial pressure (Chap. 30), it seems hardly likely that this supposition is true. The measurement of DL_{O_2} at three different levels of alveolar oxygen tension gave good agreement.[22] Other observations, however, have suggested that under relatively severely hypoxic conditions both DL_{O_2}[42,43] and DM[1] may be increased.

The breathing of high concentrations of carbon dioxide was found to cause an increase in DL_{CO} measured by the breath holding method[44] and in the one subject in whom Vc was measured this was found to have increased.

Pulmonary Blood Flow

Variations in the pulmonary blood flow have little effect on the diffusing capacity. Increasing the flow by means of drugs did not change DL_{CO} measured either by the steady-state or the breath holding technique.[3] In another investigation, the steady state diffusing capacity was measured in each lung separately while the right main pulmonary artery was obstructed to a variable extent with a balloon.[40] An increase in the blood flow through one lung of up to 230 per cent had no appreciable effect on DL_{CO}. Only when the blood flow decreased to less than 50 per cent of normal did a decrease in DL_{CO} become apparent. In both these studies, the subjects were in the supine position so that the inequalities of perfusion associated with the upright posture were not involved.

Mechanical Alterations in the Pulmonary Blood Volume

The inflation of an anti-gravity suit has been used as a method of inducing an increase in the pulmonary blood volume (Chap. 11, p. 162). Some workers[19] have been unable to show that this caused any change in DL_{CO}. Others have found that DL_{CO} increases[3,45] irrespective of the subject's posture. The infusion of albumin solution[3] has also caused an elevation of DL_{CO}.

The effect of noradrenaline (p. 185) is to increase the pulmonary vascular pressures while the effect of ganglion-blocking drugs (p. 191) is the reverse. Noradrenaline caused an increase in Vc in people who were tilted 45° with their head up, but had no effect on Vc while they were horizontal.[46] The ganglion-blocking agent trimethapan caused a decrease in Vc irrespective of the position of the subject.[46] Neither of these drugs had any notable effect on DM.

Exercise

The diffusing capacity of the lungs is increased during exercise whichever technique of measurement is used[3,4,19,26,31,41,42,47–49] but beyond this simple statement lie several unanswered questions. As has been discussed above, the increase in DL_{CO} is not due to the increase in blood flow.[3,40] With the steady-state methods, hyperventilation itself can cause an increase in DL_{CO} comparable with that which occurs on exercise,[26,40] but this does not account for the increase in DL_{CO} which is found during exercise with the breath holding technique.[3] There is an increase in Vc.[41,50] On the other hand the methods for producing an artificial congestion of the lungs which have been reviewed above do not lead to such an increase in diffusing capacity as does exercise. Thus, it seems that the dilatation of the capillaries which occurs during exercise is not entirely explicable simply in terms of an increase in the distending pressure. Perhaps they are caused to dilate by some chemical alteration in the blood. Consistent with this suggestion is the observation that changes in DL_{CO} lag behind changes in capillary blood flow at the beginning and end of exercise.[41] DM also increases during exercise. Some workers[19] have found that it increases more than Vc but others have found the reverse.[41] Earlier studies[31,42] demonstrated that beyond an oxygen uptake of about 1 litre per minute the diffusing capacity for oxygen remained unchanged. Later studies with graded exercise[4] failed to confirm this for either DL_{O_2} or DL_{CO}.

THE DIFFUSING CAPACITY IN DISEASE

Diffuse Interstitial Pulmonary Fibrosis

Austrian *et al.*[51] were the first to demonstrate the practical importance of the diffusing capacity in disease. They found that the diffusing capacity for oxygen was especially diminished in a group of diseases characterized by a widespread increase in the thickness of the alveolar–capillary membrane. Since then a large number of reports has shown a diminution in the diffusing capacity for oxygen and carbon monoxide[52] in the various forms of interstitial fibrosis described in Chapter 41. The increased distance interposed between the alveolar gas and the capillary blood could be seen as a cause of the impaired diffusing capacity and the term 'alveolar–capillary block' was originally used to describe the physiological derangement common to these diseases. The simplicity of the original concept now requires some modification. The separate measurement of DM and Vc has shown that both these quantities are decreased[18,39] so that, as well as the increased resistance imposed by the interstitial fibrosis, a diminution in the pulmonary capillary volume contributes to the decreased diffusing capacity. In the most severely affected patient studied by McNeill *et al.*[18] DM was approximately 10 per cent of normal while Vc was approximately 25 per cent of normal. In addition the development of 'honeycomb' lung (Chap. 41) in many of these patients gives rise to inequalities of ventilation : perfusion and abnormal anatomical shunts.[53,54]

The prominent symptom of these patients is dyspnoea, especially on effort. To begin with, there is no cyanosis at rest, but the arterial oxygen saturation falls during exercise. Ultimately, arterial unsaturation is present even while resting.

Owing to the hyperventilation, the arterial PCO_2 is usually low. Cyanosis should disappear when breathing oxygen and patients obtain a great relief from and often become dependent on oxygen therapy.

Emphysema

Although measurements of the diffusing capacity by various methods have given low values in patients with severe emphysema,[52] the interpretation of the results in the presence of a great inequality of ventilation and capillary flow and volume is difficult.[1,30] Both the diffusing capacity for oxygen and the Filley method for carbon monoxide depend on the use of arterial PCO_2 to represent 'ideal' alveolar PCO_2 and the assumptions which underlie this break down in the presence of such large ventilation: perfusion inequalities as may occur in emphysema. Equally, the use of end-tidal PCO_2 in the Bates method become untenable in the presence of emphysema where the wide variation in ventilatory time-constants renders unrepresentative the alveolar contribution at end-expiration. The breath-holding technique for carbon monoxide is no less questionable, since it samples a rapidly ventilated portion of the lung which must be unrepresentative. The diffusing capacity tends to be decreased in the 'emphysematous' rather than the 'chronic bronchitis' type of patient (Chap. 34, p. 524).

Cardiovascular Diseases

The diffusing capacity and its components Vc and DM are affected in varying directions and degrees by cardiovascular disease involving the pulmonary circulation. We shall consider first the effects of an isolated increase in the pulmonary arterial resistance, then the effects of a sustained increase in the pulmonary blood flow and, finally, the effects of an increased pulmonary venous pressure.

Patients with primary pulmonary hypertension may be taken to represent an isolated increase in the pulmonary arterial resistance. The condition is associated with a reduction in DL_{CO} which may become severe.[18,55–57] Three papers[18,55,56] report a diminution in DM and three[18,56,57] a diminution in Vc. The findings in thromboembolic pulmonary hypertension have been similar[56,58]; DL_{CO} is reduced together with DM and Vc. It is uncertain to what extent an inhomogeneity of the ventilation: perfusion ratio interferes with the measurement in both these conditions. Since the wedge pressure is not abnormally low it seems unlikely that there is an abnormal decrease in the size of West's zone 3 at the base of the lung (p. 100). Possibly there is a focal reduction of the alveolar capillary bed where an obstructive lesion occurs in the supplying muscular pulmonary artery. Such an effect would be expected to occur particularly in the territory of zone 2 (p. 100).

DL_{CO} and Vc are both increased in the presence of congenital left-to-right shunts.[10,56,59,60] The values have been shown to return to normal after operation.[56,60] It is reported that the values also decrease in the presence of an increased pulmonary vascular resistance.[61] It seems, therefore, that an increase in the pulmonary capillary volume develops under conditions of long-standing increase in the pulmonary blood flow. Presumably these effects are mediated by small increases in pressure on the arterial side of the capillary bed which diminish the territory of zone 1 (p. 100) and, over a long period, may dilate capillaries. As discussed above (p. 645) the magnitude of the pulmonary blood flow itself is not a determining factor for the diffusing capacity. The effects of an increasing pulmonary arterial resistance are to be expected in view of the findings in patients with an isolated increase in resistance discussed above. Standing somewhat against the above observations is the report[62] of normal DL_{CO}, DM and Vc in patients with an increased pulmonary blood flow due to hyperthyroidism.

The effects of a chronic increase in the pulmonary venous pressure are more complex and determined by opposing influences of distending pressure, arterial resistance and changes in the alveolar–capillary membrane. Many authors have found that DL_{CO} tends to diminish in mitral stenosis or incompetence and that the diminution is most evident in the more severely affected cases. The literature is reviewed by Yu.[56] We shall consider only those large series of cases in which separate measurements of DM and Vc have been made and in which haemodynamic measurements are also available.[56,57,63] DL_{CO} and DM are normal in patients with mild disease but become progressively diminished with increasing haemodynamic disturbance. The expectation of an impressive increase in the pulmonary capillary blood volume in the earlier stages has not greatly been substantiated by the generality of results. The values for Vc reported by McCredie[63] in the milder forms of the disease are within his normal range. The values for Vc reported by Yu[56] in less severely affected patients correspond to his normal figures for the recumbent posture but are a little higher than those for the sitting posture (Table 23.2, p. 361). In the severer forms of the disease Vc becomes abnormally low.[56,57,63] McCredie[63] showed negative correlations between the pulmonary arterial pressure, wedge pressure and pulmonary arterial resistance on the one hand and the pulmonary capillary blood volume on the other.

The effect of the disease on the diffusing capacity is a composite of the opposing effects of a raised pulmonary venous pressure and an increased pulmonary vascular resistance on Vc together with the increased thickness of the alveolar–capillary 'membrane' which diminishes DM. In the early stages the slight tendency to an increased Vc is presumably due to the raised pulmonary venous pressure which causes a filling of the capillaries of the apices of the lungs similar to what happens in the recumbent posture. Thereafter the increasing pulmonary vascular resistance, as in primary disease of the pulmonary arteries, tends to decrease Vc. The effects of non-uniformity in the lungs, discussed above, need, however, to be taken into account in the interpretation of these data.[29,30]

Anaemia and Polycythaemia

The factor, θ, is the rate of uptake of carbon monoxide by 1 ml of blood (p. 639). It depends, therefore, on the concentration of haemoglobin. Thus, in the presence of anaemia, the value for θ will be low and, in the presence of polycythaemia, it will be high. The diffusing capacity for carbon monoxide is low in anaemic patients.[16] This is due to the low value of θ, since, when the appropriate value for θ is used, D_M and V_C are normal. Treatment of the anaemia with transfusion brings the diffusing capacity back to normal.

Polycythaemia increases the diffusing capacity which returns to normal or below normal following treatment.[17] V_C, corrected for haemoglobin concentration, is less than normal and not affected by treatment in these patients.[17] Burgess and Bishop[17] suggest that the reduction in V_C may be due to thrombosis in small pulmonary arteries.

REFERENCES

1. Forster, R. E. (1957) *Physiol. Rev.*, **37**, 391.
2. Filley, G. F., Macintosh, D. J. & Wright, G. W. (1954) *J. Clin. Invest.*, **33**, 530.
3. Ross, J. C., Frayser, R. & Hickman, J. B. (1959) *J. Clin. Invest.*, **38**, 916.
4. Turino, G. M., Bergofsky, E. H., Goldring, R. M. & Fishman, A. P. (1963) *J. Appl. Physiol.*, **18**, 447.
5. Bates, D. V., Boucot, N. G. & Donner, A. E. (1955) *J. Physiol.*, **129**, 237.
6. Ogilvie, C. M., Forster, R. E., Blakemore, W. S. & Morton, J. W. (1957) *J. Clin. Invest.*, **36**, 1.
7. Krogh, M. (1915) *J. Physiol.*, **49**, 271.
8. Forster, R. E., Fowler, W. S. & Bates, D. V. (1954) *J. Clin. Invest.*, **33**, 1135.
9. Lewis, B. M., McElroy, W. T., Hayford-Welsing, E. J. & Samberg, L. C. (1960) *J. Clin. Invest.*, **39**, 1345.
10. Auchinloss, J. H., Gilbert, R. & Eich, R. H. (1959) *Circulation*, **19**, 232.
11. Roughton, F. J. W. (1945) *Amer. J. Physiol.*, **143**, 621.
12. Roughton, F. J. W. & Forster, R. E. (1957) *J. Appl. Physiol.*, **11**, 290.
13. Forbes, W. H., Sargent, F. & Roughton, F. J. W. (1945) *Amer. J. Physiol.*, **143**, 594.
14. Forster, R. E., Roughton, F. J. W., Cander, L., Briscoe, W. A. & Kreuzer, F. (1957) *J. Appl. Physiol.*, **11**, 277.
15. Roughton, F. J. W., Forster, R. E. & Cander, L. (1957) *J. Appl. Physiol.*, **11**, 269.
16. Rankin, J., McNeill, R. S. & Forster, R. E. (1961) *J. Clin. Invest.*, **40**, 1323.
17. Burgess, J. H. & Bishop, J. M. (1963) *J. Clin. Invest.*, **42**, 997.
18. McNeill, R. S., Rankin, J. & Forster, R. E. (1958) *Clin. Sci.*, **17**, 465.
19. Lewis, B. M., Lin, T. H., Noe, F. E. & Komisaruk, R. (1958) *J. Clin. Invest.*, **37**, 1061.
20. Menkes, H. A., Sera, K., Rogers, R. M., Hyde, R. W., Forster, R. E., II & Dubois, A. (1970) *J. Clin. Invest.*, **49**, 335.
21. Riley, R. L. & Cournand, A. (1951) *J. Appl. Physiol.*, **4**, 77.
22. Riley, R. L., Cournand, A. & Donald, K. W. (1951) *J. Appl. Physiol.*, **4**, 102.
23. Donald, K. W., Renzetti, A., Riley, R. L. & Cournand, A. (1951) *J. Appl. Physiol.*, **4**, 497.
24. Forster, R. E., Cohn, J. E., Briscoe, W. A., Blakemore, W. A. & Riley, R. L. (1955) *J. Clin. Invest.*, **34**, 1417.
25. Marks, A. D., Cugell, D. W., Cadigan, J. B. & Gaensler, E. A. (1957) *Amer. J. Med.*, **22**, 51.
26. Apthorp, G. H. & Marshall, R. (1961) *J. Clin. Invest.*, **40**, 1775.
27. Dollery, C. T., Dyson, N. A. & Sinclair, J. D. (1960) *J. Appl. Physiol.*, **15**, 411.
28. Hyde, R. W., Marin, M. G., Rynes, R. I., Karreman, G. & Forster, R. E. (1971) *J. Appl. Physiol.*, **31**, 605.
29. Johnson, R. L., Jn. & Miller, J. M. (1968) *J. Appl. Physiol.*, **25**, 1.
30. Read, J., Read, D. J. C. & Pain, M. C. F. (1965) *Clin. Sci.*, **29**, 107.
31. Cohn, J. E., Carroll, D. G., Armstrong, B. W., Shepard, R. H. & Riley, R. L. (1954) *J. Appl. Physiol.*, **6**, 588.
32. Donevan, R. E., Palmer, W. H., Varvis, C. J. & Bates, D. V. (1959) *J. Appl. Physiol.*, **14**, 483.
33. Barrows, B., Kasik, J. E., Niden, A. H. & Barclay, W. R. (1961) *Amer. Rev. Resp. Dis.*, **84**, 789.

34. McGrath, M. & Thomson, M. L. (1959) *J. Physiol.*, **146**, 572.
35. Bates, D. V. & Pearce, J. F. (1956) *J. Physiol.*, **132**, 232.
36. Cadigan, J. B., Marks, A., Ellicott, M. F., Jones, R. H. & Gaensler, E. A. (1961) *J. Clin. Invest.*, **40**, 1495.
37. Mittman, C. & Burrows, B. (1959) *J. Appl. Physiol.*, **14**, 496.
38. MacNamara, J., Prime, F. J. & Sinclair, J. D. (1960) *Lancet*, **i**, 404.
39. Bates, D. V., Varvis, C. J., Donevan, R. E. & Christie, R. V. (1960) *J. Clin. Invest.*, **39**, 1401.
40. Turino, G. M., Brandfonbrener, M. & Fishman, A. P. (1959) *J. Clin. Invest.*, **38**, 1186.
41. Johnson, R. L., Jn., Spicer, W. S., Bishop, J. M. & Forster, R. E. (1960) *J. Appl. Physiol.*, **15**, 893.
42. Riley, R. L., Shepard, R. H., Cohn, J. E., Carroll, D. G. & Armstrong, B. W. (1954) *J. Appl. Physiol.*, **6**, 573.
43. Bartels, H., Beer, R., Fleischer, E., Hoffheinz, H. J., Krall, J., Rodewald, G., Wenner, J. & Witt, I. (1955) *Pflüg. Arch. ges. Physiol.*, **261**, 99.
44. Rankin, J., McNeill, R. S. & Forster, R. E. (1960) *J. Appl. Physiol.*, **15**, 543.
45. Ross, J. C., Lord, T. H. & Ley, G. D. (1960) *J. Appl. Physiol.*, **15**, 843.
46. Lewis, B. M., McElroy, W. T., Hayford-Welsing, E. J. & Samberg, L. C. (1960) *J. Clin. Invest.*, **39**, 1345.
47. Cotes, J. E., Snidel, D. P. & Shepard, R. H. (1960) *J. Appl. Physiol.*, **15**, 372.
48. Linderholm, H. (1959) *Acta Med. Scand.*, **163**, 61.
49. Cadigan, J. B., Marks, A., Ellicott, M. F., Jones, R. H. & Gaensler, E. A. (1961) *J. Clin. Invest.*, **40**, 1495.
50. Lewis, B. M., Forster, R. E. & Beckman, E. L. (1958) *J. Appl. Physiol.*, **12**, 57.
51. Austrian, R., McClement, J. H., Renzetti, A. D., Jn., Donald, K. W., Riley, R. L. & Cournand, A. (1951) *Amer. J. Med.*, **11**, 667.
52. Bates, D. V., Macklem, P. T. & Christie, R. V. (1971) In *Respiratory Function in Disease*. Saunders.
53. Finley, T. N., Swenson, E. W. & Comroe, J. H., Jn. (1962) *J. Clin. Invest.*, **41**, 618.
54. Arndt, H., King, T. K. C. & Briscoe, W. A. (1970) *J. Clin. Invest.*, **49**, 408.
55. McCredie, R. M. (1966) *Circulation*, **33**, 854.
56. Yu, P. N. (1969) In *Pulmonary Blood Volume in Health and Disease*. Lea & Febiger.
57. Burgess, J. H. (1974) *Circulation*, **49**, 541.
58. Nikodymova, L., Daum, S., Stiksa, J. & Widimsky, J. (1968) *Respiration*, **25**, 51.
59. Bedell, G. N. (1961) *J. Lab. Clin. Med.*, **57**, 269.
60. Bucci, G. & Cook, C. D. (1961) *J. Clin. Invest.*, **40**, 1431.
61. Rankin, J. & Callies, Q. C. (1958) *Circulation*, **18**, 768.
62. Stein, M., Kimbel, P. & Johnson, R. L. (1961) *J. Clin. Invest.*, **40**, 348.
63. McCredie, R. M. (1964) *J. Clin. Invest.*, **43**, 2279.

Appendix A

The Wedge Pressure in Pulmonary Veno-occlusive Disease

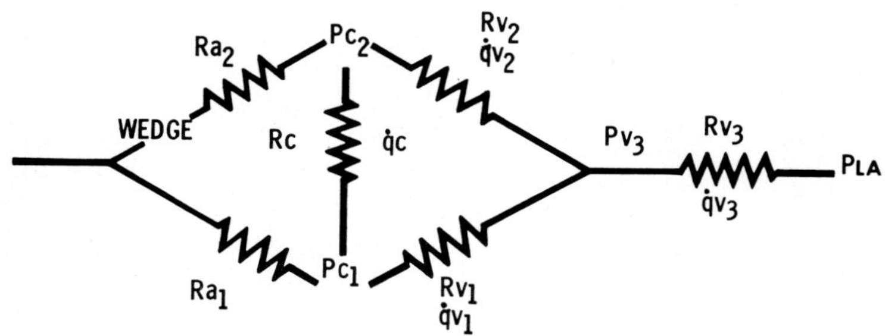

Consider (Fig. A.1) a catheter wedged into one branch (a_2) of a terminal bifurcation of a muscular pulmonary artery supplying two adjacent capillary beds (c_1 and c_2). The pressure registered by the catheter is Pc_2. The pressure in the unwedged capillary bed is Pc_1. The two capillary beds drain through separate small venous systems having resistances Rv_1 and Rv_2 and carrying flows $\dot{q}v_1$ and $\dot{q}v_2$. The small venous systems eventually join to form a large common vein the proximal pressure in which is Pv_3. Suppose a resistance in this common vein of Rv_3 and a flow through it of $\dot{q}v_3$. The terminal venous pressure is equated to left atrial pressure, PLA. Blood may flow ($\dot{q}c$) from the unwedged capillary bed to the wedged capillary bed through a capillary resistance, Rc.

First it is clear that, if the resistances of the small veins (Rv_1 and Rv_2) are negligible, the wedge pressure will equal Pv_3 and this will differ from left atrial pressure by a quantity determined by the flow ($\dot{q}v_3$) and resistance (Rv_3) of the large vein. Thus, if pulmonary veno-occlusive disease affects only large veins, the wedge pressure will give a reasonable estimate of the capillary pressure existing during normal flow.

In the presence of small venous obstructions (significant magnitude of Rv_1 and Rv_2) the situation is not so simple. We may write:

$$\dot{q}c = (Pc_1 - Pc_2)/Rc \qquad \text{(i)}$$

$$\dot{q}v_2 = (Pc_2 - Pv_3)/Rv_2 \qquad \text{(ii)}$$

$$\dot{q}v_1 = (Pc_1 - Pv_3)/Rv_1 \qquad \text{(iii)}$$

$$\dot{q}c = \dot{q}v_2 \qquad \text{(iv)}$$

Substituting (i) and (ii) in (iv) we have:

$$(Pc_1 - Pc_2)/Rc = (Pc_2 - Pv_3)/Rv_2 \qquad \text{(v)}$$

From (iii) we have:

$$Pc_1 = \dot{q}v_1 \cdot Rv_1 + Pv_3$$

Substituting for Pc_1 in (v) we have:

$$(\dot{q}v_1 \cdot Rv_1 + Pv_3 - Pc_2)/Rc = (Pc_2 - Pv_3)/Rv_2$$

Rearranging we find that:

$$Pc_2 = Pv_3 + \dot{q}v_1 \cdot Rv_1 \cdot Rv_2/(Rc + Rv_2)$$

Examining this equation, it is apparent that what the wedge pressure measures is largely dependent on the magnitude of the resistance (Rc) between the two capillary beds. If Rc is infinite (*i.e.* no communication between the adjacent beds)

$$Pc_2 = Pv_3$$

In this case, the wedge pressure measures the venous pressure beyond the obstructions to the small veins. Thus, if there is no obstruction to large veins the wedge pressure will give approximately the left atrial pressure and not the pulmonary capillary pressure existing during life.

If, on the other hand, Rc is zero (*i.e.* free communication between the two adjacent capillary beds)

$$Pc_2 = Pc_1$$

Under these circumstances the wedge pressure will come closer to the capillary pressure existing under normal conditions of flow. It may not do so entirely because the total flow may be limited by the arterial resistance Ra, which would tend to reduce the magnitude of Pv_1.

Thus, the wedge pressure may never quite give the magnitude of the pulmonary capillary pressure existing under conditions of normal flow if there is widespread narrowing of small venules.

Appendix B

The Measurement of the Uptake of Oxygen by the Pulmonary Capillaries

The volume of oxygen entering the lungs each minute from the air is:

$$826\,\dot{V}_I\,F_{I_{O_2}}\ \text{ml (STPD)}$$

where $\dot{V}_I$ is the inspired gas volume ($l \cdot min^{-1}$ at BTPS) and $F_{I_{O_2}}$ is the fractional concentration of oxygen in the inspired gas. The correction factor, 826, is necessitated by the change from $l \cdot min^{-1}$ at BTPS to $ml \cdot min^{-1}$ at STPD.

The volume of oxygen leaving the lungs each minute via the expired gas is:

$$826\,\dot{V}_E\,F_{E_{O_2}}\ \text{ml (STPD)}$$

where $\dot{V}_E$ is the expired gas volume ($l \cdot min^{-1}$ at BTPS) and $F_{E_{O_2}}$ is the fractional concentration of oxygen in the expired gas.

The volume of oxygen taken up by the pulmonary capillaries each minute ($\dot{V}_{O_2}$ $ml \cdot min^{-1}$ at STPD) will be equal to the difference between the inspired and expired volumes of oxygen provided that: (a) no oxygen is absorbed by the walls of the respiratory passages into systemic capillaries, and (b) the volume of oxygen held in the lungs remains constant. Thus:

$$826\,\dot{V}_I\,F_{I_{O_2}} = 826\,\dot{V}_E\,F_{E_{O_2}} + \dot{V}_{O_2}$$

and

$$\dot{V}_{O_2} = 826\,(\dot{V}_I\,F_{I_{O_2}} - \dot{V}_E\,F_{E_{O_2}}) \qquad \text{(i)}$$

If it is also assumed that the volume of nitrogen inspired is equal to that which is expired, the measurement of the volume of inspired gas may be dispensed with. Thus:

$$\dot{V}_I\,F_{I_{N_2}} = \dot{V}_E\,F_{E_{N_2}}$$

where $F_{I_{N_2}}$ and $F_{E_{N_2}}$ are the fractional concentrations of nitrogen in the inspired and expired gases respectively. Hence:

$$\dot{V}_I = \frac{F_{E_{N_2}}}{F_{I_{N_2}}}\dot{V}_E \qquad \text{(ii)}$$

Substituting (ii) in (i):

$$\dot{V}_{O_2} = 826\,\dot{V}_E\left(\frac{F_{E_{N_2}}}{F_{I_{N_2}}}F_{I_{O_2}} - F_{E_{O_2}}\right) \qquad \text{(iii)}$$

Similarly

$$\dot{V}_{CO_2} = 826\,\dot{V}_E\left(F_{E_{CO_2}} - \frac{F_{E_{N_2}}}{F_{I_{N_2}}}F_{I_{CO_2}}\right) \qquad \text{(iv)}$$

Appendix C

The Alveolar Air Equation and the Calculation of Alveolar P_{O_2}

From equation (iii) in Appendix B:

$$\dot{V}_{O_2} = 826\,\dot{V}_E\left(\frac{F_{E_{N_2}}}{F_{I_{N_2}}}F_{I_{O_2}} - F_{E_{O_2}}\right) \qquad \text{(iii)}$$

The expired air ($\dot{V}_E$) may be considered as if it were composed of two portions: a portion ($\dot{V}_A$) due to gas which has come from the alveoli and a portion ($\dot{V}_D$) due to gas which has passed only into and out of the physiological dead-space (Chap. 36). Thus:

$$F_{E_{O_2}} = \frac{\dot{V}_D\,F_{I_{O_2}} + \dot{V}_A\,F_{A_{O_2}}}{\dot{V}_E} \qquad \text{(v)}$$

where $F_{A_{O_2}}$ is the fractional concentration of oxygen in alveolar air.

Similarly:

$$F_{E_{N_2}} = \frac{\dot{V}_D\,F_{I_{N_2}} + \dot{V}_A\,F_{A_{N_2}}}{\dot{V}_E} \qquad \text{(vi)}$$

where $F_{A_{N_2}}$ is the fractional concentration of nitrogen in alveolar air.

Substituting (v) and (vi) in (iii):

$$\dot{V}_{O_2} = 826\,\dot{V}_E\left[\frac{(\dot{V}_D\,F_{I_{N_2}} + \dot{V}_A\,F_{A_{N_2}})}{\dot{V}_E}\frac{F_{I_{O_2}}}{F_{I_{N_2}}} - \frac{(\dot{V}_D\,F_{I_{O_2}} + \dot{V}_A\,F_{A_{O_2}})}{\dot{V}_E}\right]$$

$$= 826\,\dot{V}_A\left[\frac{F_{A_{N_2}}}{F_{I_{N_2}}}F_{I_{O_2}} - F_{A_{O_2}}\right] \qquad \text{(vii)}$$

Similarly:

$$\dot{V}_{CO_2} = 826\,\dot{V}_A\left[F_{A_{CO_2}} - \frac{F_{A_{N_2}}}{F_{I_{N_2}}}F_{I_{CO_2}}\right] \qquad \text{(viii)}$$

The respiratory quotient of gaseous exchange in the alveoli (R) is equal to $\dot{V}_{CO_2}$ divided by $\dot{V}_{O_2}$:

$$R = \frac{\dot{V}_{CO_2}}{\dot{V}_{O_2}} \qquad \text{(ix)}$$

Substituting (vii) and (viii) in (ix):

$$R = \frac{\left(F_{A_{CO_2}} - \dfrac{F_{A_{N_2}}}{F_{I_{N_2}}} F_{I_{CO_2}}\right)}{\left(\dfrac{F_{A_{N_2}}}{F_{I_{N_2}}} F_{I_{O_2}} - F_{A_{O_2}}\right)}$$

$$= \frac{F_{A_{CO_2}} F_{I_{N_2}} - F_{A_{N_2}} F_{I_{CO_2}}}{F_{A_{N_2}} F_{I_{O_2}} - F_{A_{O_2}} F_{I_{N_2}}}$$

Now

$$F_{I_{N_2}} = 1 - F_{I_{CO_2}} - F_{I_{O_2}}$$

and

$$F_{A_{N_2}} = 1 - F_{A_{CO_2}} - F_{A_{O_2}}$$

Thus:

$$R = \frac{F_{A_{CO_2}}(1 - F_{I_{CO_2}} - F_{I_{O_2}}) - F_{I_{CO_2}}(1 - F_{A_{CO_2}} - F_{A_{O_2}})}{F_{I_{O_2}}(1 - F_{A_{CO_2}} - F_{A_{O_2}}) - F_{A_{O_2}}(1 - F_{I_{CO_2}} - F_{I_{O_2}})}$$

$$= \frac{F_{A_{CO_2}}(1 - F_{I_{O_2}}) - F_{I_{CO_2}}(1 - F_{A_{O_2}})}{F_{I_{O_2}}(1 - F_{A_{CO_2}}) - F_{A_{O_2}}(1 - F_{I_{CO_2}})} \qquad \text{(x)}$$

If, as is usual, $F_{I_{CO_2}}$ is zero:

$$R = \frac{F_{A_{CO_2}}(1 - F_{I_{O_2}})}{F_{I_{O_2}}(1 - F_{A_{CO_2}}) - F_{A_{O_2}}} \qquad \text{(xi)}$$

Now

$$F_{A_{O_2}} = \frac{P_{A_{O_2}}}{P_B - 47} \quad \text{and} \quad F_{A_{CO_2}} = \frac{P_{A_{CO_2}}}{P_B - 47}$$

Thus

$$R = \frac{\dfrac{P_{A_{CO_2}}}{P_B - 47}(1 - F_{I_{O_2}})}{F_{I_{O_2}}\left(1 - \dfrac{P_{A_{CO_2}}}{P_B - 47}\right) - \dfrac{P_{A_{O_2}}}{P_B - 47}}$$

Whence, by re-arrangement:

$$P_{A_{O_2}} = F_{I_{O_2}}(P_B - 47) - P_{A_{CO_2}}\left(F_{I_{O_2}} + \frac{1 - F_{I_{O_2}}}{R}\right)$$

$$= P_{I_{O_2}} - P_{A_{CO_2}}\left(F_{I_{O_2}} + \frac{1 - F_{I_{O_2}}}{R}\right)$$

$$P_{A_{O_2}} = P_{I_{O_2}} - \frac{P_{A_{CO_2}}}{R} + \frac{P_{A_{CO_2}} F_{I_{O_2}}(1 - R)}{R} \qquad \text{(xii)}$$

This is the usual form of the alveolar air equation. The third term of equation (xii) is a very small quantity, usually amounting to about 2 mmHg. Thus an approximate and convenient form of the equation is:

$$P_{A_{O_2}} \simeq P_{I_{O_2}} - \frac{P_{A_{CO_2}}}{R} \qquad \text{(xiii)}$$

It will be noted that equations (vii) and (viii) have exactly the same form as equations (iii) and (iv) of the preceding Appendix, the only difference being that alveolar values are substituted for expired air. If equations (iii) and (iv) are treated along the same lines as followed (vii) and (viii), it may be shown that:

$$R = \frac{F_{E_{CO_2}}(1 - F_{I_{O_2}}) - F_{I_{CO_2}}(1 - F_{E_{O_2}})}{F_{I_{O_2}}(1 - F_{E_{CO_2}}) - F_{E_{O_2}}(1 - F_{I_{CO_2}})} \qquad \text{(xiv)}$$

and

$$P_{E_{O_2}} = P_{I_{O_2}} - \frac{P_{E_{CO_2}}}{R} + \frac{P_{E_{CO_2}} F_{I_{O_2}}(1 - R)}{R} \qquad \text{(xv)}$$

The similarity between equations (xv) and (xii) is of importance in the construction of the $O_2 - CO_2$ diagram (Chap. 36, p. 571).

The Relation between the Ventilation: Perfusion Ratio and the Respiratory Exchange Ratio

When there is no carbon dioxide in the inspired gas, equation (viii) becomes:

$$\dot{V}_{CO_2} = 826\, \dot{V}_A\, F_{A_{CO_2}}$$

Now

$$P_{A_{CO_2}} = (P_B - 47)\, F_{A_{CO_2}}$$

$$= 713\, F_{A_{CO_2}} \qquad \text{(Assuming } P_B = 760\text{)}$$

Hence

$$\dot{V}_{CO_2} = \frac{\dot{V}_A\, P_{A_{CO_2}}}{0{\cdot}863} \qquad \text{(xvi)}$$

Also

$$\dot{V}_{CO_2} = R\dot{V}_{O_2} \qquad \text{(Equation ix)}$$

Thus, substituting in (xvi):

$$\dot{V}_{O_2} = \frac{\dot{V}_A\, P_{A_{CO_2}}}{0{\cdot}863\, R} \qquad \text{(xvii)}$$

From the Fick equation:

$$\dot{V}_{O_2} = 10\, \dot{Q}c\, (Cc'_{O_2} - C\bar{v}_{O_2}) \qquad \text{(p. 79).} \qquad \text{(xviii)}$$

Thus, from (xvii) and (xviii):

$$\frac{\dot{V}_A \, P_{A_{CO_2}}}{0{\cdot}863\,R} = 10\,\dot{Q}c\,(Cc'_{O_2} - Cv_{O_2})$$

and

$$\frac{\dot{V}_A}{\dot{Q}c} = \frac{8{\cdot}63\,R\,(Cc'_{O_2} - C\bar{v}_{O_2})}{P_{A_{CO_2}}}$$

Appendix D

The Validity of the Fick Method in the Presence of Pulsatile Flow

The Fick method attempts to measure the average flow of blood through the 'central' blood volume. Flow through this volume is pulsatile, but not uniformly so either in amplitude or phase, and this is accompanied by rhythmic changes (both active and passive) in the volume of the component chambers and vessels (Chap. 6, p. 81). The uptake of oxygen is also changing from instant to instant.

In the following analysis we shall consider the total volume of oxygen passing into and out of the central blood volume during the period over which the measurement is made. This period is of such length that the total volumes of oxygen and of blood which have entered the central blood volume during the course of the measurement may be assumed to be equal to those which have left it. On the other hand, these assumptions will not hold good for any small length of time within this total period.

To examine the simplest instance, it is assumed that the period of measurement is divided into two halves (t/2). The oxygen uptake, the rate of flow of blood into and out of the central volume and the oxygen content of the mixed venous and arterial blood are assumed to differ between the two halves but to remain constant within each half.

The mixed venous oxygen content and the rate of flow of blood into the 'central' blood volume in each half period are Cv_1, $\dot{Q}v_1$ and Cv_2, $\dot{Q}v_2$ respectively. The corresponding symbols on the arterial side are Ca_1, $\dot{Q}a_1$ and Ca_2, $\dot{Q}a_2$. The rates of uptake of oxygen by the pulmonary capillaries are $\dot{V}_1$ and $\dot{V}_2$.

Then, since over the entire period of time the quantity of oxygen entering the central blood volume equals that which leaves it:

$$\left(\frac{t}{2}\right)\dot{V}_1 + \left(\frac{t}{2}\right)\dot{V}_2 = \left(\frac{t}{2}\right)\dot{Q}a_1\,Ca_1 - \left(\frac{t}{2}\right)\dot{Q}v_1\,Cv_1 + \left(\frac{t}{2}\right)\dot{Q}a_2\,Ca_2 - \left(\frac{t}{2}\right)\dot{Q}v_2\,Cv_2$$

or,

$$\dot{V}_1 + \dot{V}_2 = \dot{Q}a_1\,Ca_1 - \dot{Q}v_1\,Cv_1 + \dot{Q}a_2\,Ca_2 - \dot{Q}v_2\,Cv_2 \qquad \text{(i)}$$

The volume of blood entering the 'central' volume over the entire period of time is also equal to that which leaves it. Hence:

$$\left(\frac{t}{2}\right)\dot{Q}v_1 + \left(\frac{t}{2}\right)\dot{Q}v_2 = \left(\frac{t}{2}\right)\dot{Q}a_1 + \left(\frac{t}{2}\right)\dot{Q}a_2$$

or,

$$\dot{Q}v_1 + \dot{Q}v_2 = \dot{Q}a_1 + \dot{Q}a_2 = 2\bar{\dot{Q}} \qquad \text{(ii)}$$

where $\bar{\dot{Q}}$ is the mean flow through any cross-section of the circulation.

The output measured by the Fick method is:

$$\dot{Q}_{FICK} = \frac{\frac{1}{2}(\dot{V}_1 + \dot{V}_2)}{\frac{1}{2}(Ca_1 + Ca_2) - \frac{1}{2}(Cv_1 + Cv_2)}$$

$$= \frac{\dot{V}_1 + \dot{V}_2}{(Ca_1 + Ca_2) - (Cv_1 + Cv_2)} \qquad \text{(iii)}$$

It can be shown by substitution that (iii) will be a true measure of average flow only if the flow is constant or if the oxygen contents of mixed venous and arterial blood are constant.

If flow is constant at $\dot{Q}$, then from (i):

$$\dot{V}_1 + \dot{V}_2 = \dot{Q}[(Ca_1 + Ca_2) - (Cv_1 + Cv_2)]$$

and

$$\dot{Q} = \frac{\dot{V}_1 + \dot{V}_2}{(Ca_1 + Ca_2) - (Cv_1 + Cv_2)}$$

which is the same as (iii). Similarly, if the oxygen contents of mixed venous and arterial blood are constant at Cv and Ca respectively, then from (i):

$$\dot{V}_1 + \dot{V}_2 = Ca(\dot{Q}a_1 + \dot{Q}a_2) - Cv(\dot{Q}v_1 + \dot{Q}v_2)$$

$$= 2\bar{\dot{Q}}(Ca - Cv)$$

and

$$\dot{Q} = \frac{\dot{V}_1 + \dot{V}_2}{2Ca - 2Cv}$$

which is again the same as (iii).

Appendix E

The Validity of the Dye-Dilution Method in the Presence of Pulsatile Flow

Let the total quantity of injected dye be I. Then equation (i) of Appendix D may be expressed in terms of the concentration of dye as follows:

$$I = \left(\frac{t}{2}\right)\dot{Q}a_1\ Ca_1 - \left(\frac{t}{2}\right)\dot{Q}v_1 \times 0 + \left(\frac{t}{2}\right)\dot{Q}a_2\ Ca_2 - \left(\frac{t}{2}\right)\dot{Q}v_2 \times 0$$

$$= \left(\frac{t}{2}\right)\dot{Q}a_1\ Ca_1 + \left(\frac{t}{2}\right)\dot{Q}a_2\ Ca_2$$

Dividing both sides by $\frac{t}{2}(\dot{Q}a_1 + \dot{Q}a_2)$:

$$\frac{I}{\frac{t}{2}(\dot{Q}a_1 + \dot{Q}a_2)} = \frac{\dot{Q}a_1\ Ca_1 + \dot{Q}a_2\ Ca_2}{\dot{Q}a_1 + \dot{Q}a_2}$$

$$= \overline{C}$$

where $\overline{C}$ is the mean concentration of dye in arterial blood. Thus,

$$\frac{\dot{Q}a_1 + \dot{Q}a_2}{2} = \frac{I}{\overline{C}t} = \text{Mean blood flow,}$$

which is the formula used to calculate flow. Hence the theoretical limitations to the Fick method discussed in Appendix D do not apply to the dye-dilution method.

Appendix F

The Derivation of Poiseuille's Equation

The unit of viscosity is the poise. In a fluid of viscosity 1 poise the force required to move a square centimetre surface parallel to a similar surface 1 cm apart at a velocity of 1 cm · s^{-1} is 1 dyne.

We shall consider a liquid of viscosity η poises flowing in a stream-line fashion at $\dot{Q}$ ml · s^{-1} through a rigid cylindrical tube of radius r cm and length l cm. The difference in pressure along the tube is ΔP dyn · cm^{-2}. The velocity of movement of the liquid increases the nearer the axial stream is approached (p. 91) and the stream may be considered as a series of infinitely thin concentric cylinders, each one of which moves forward with a slightly greater velocity than its outside neighbour.

Let v cm · s^{-1} be the velocity of such a cylinder of liquid with a radius of x cm and length l cm. A cylinder of liquid just outside this cylinder has a radius of $(x+dx)$ cm and a velocity of $(v-dv)$ cm · s^{-1}. Then the tangential stress per unit area due to viscosity is equal to:

$$-\eta\frac{dv}{dx}$$

The minus sign indicates that the force is in the opposite direction to the velocity.

Since the surface area of the inner cylinder is $2\pi xl$, the total tangential stress due to viscosity is:

$$-2\pi x\, l\eta\frac{dv}{dx}$$

But this viscous force must equal the difference in mechanical thrust at each end of the liquid cylinder. The difference in mechanical thrust is equal to the difference in pressure multiplied by the cross-sectional area of the cylinder ($\pi x^2 \Delta P$)

Thus

$$\pi x^2 \Delta P = -2\pi x\, l\eta\frac{dv}{dx}$$

Therefore

$$-l\eta\, dv = \frac{\Delta P}{2}x\, dx$$

Integrating both sides:

$$-l\eta\int dv = \frac{\Delta P}{2}\int x\, dx$$

Therefore

$$-l\eta v = \frac{\Delta P}{4}\cdot x^2 + C$$

When $x = r, \quad v = o$

Therefore

$$C = -\frac{\Delta P}{4} \cdot r^2$$

Therefore

$$l\eta v = \frac{\Delta P}{4}(r^2 - x^2)$$

or

$$v = \frac{\Delta P}{4 l\eta}(r^2 - x^2)$$

Now the cross-section of the ring of fluid of thickness dx is $2\pi x\, dx$ in area. Therefore the volume of flow through this ring of fluid is

$$\begin{aligned} d\dot{Q} &= v\, 2\pi x\, dx \\ &= \frac{\Delta P}{4 l\eta}(r^2 - x^2)\, 2\pi x\, dx \\ &= \frac{\Delta P \pi x (r^2 - x^2)\, dx}{2 l\eta} \end{aligned}$$

Thus the total volume of flow through the whole cross-sectional area of the tube is:

$$\begin{aligned} \dot{Q} &= \frac{\pi \Delta P}{2 l\eta} \int_o^r x(r^2 - x^2)\, dx \\ &= \frac{\pi \Delta P}{2 l\eta}\left[r^2 \int_o^r x\, dx - \int_o^r x^3\, dx \right] \\ &= \frac{\pi \Delta P}{2 l\eta}\left[\frac{r^4}{2} - \frac{r^4}{4} \right] \\ &= \frac{\Delta P r^4}{8 l\eta} \end{aligned}$$

Therefore

$$\Delta P = \frac{8\, \eta l \dot{Q}}{\pi r^4}$$

Appendix G

Derivation of Formula for Disappearance of $C^{15}O_2$ from the Lung used in the Measurement of Regional Blood Flow

The concentration of $C^{15}O_2$ in blood is given by:

$$k \cdot P_{C^{15}O_2}$$

where k is a constant describing a linear portion of the dissociation curve. The quantity of $C^{15}O_2$ removed by flowing blood from a region of lung in a small period of time dt is:

$$dV = -\dot{Q}_C \cdot k \cdot P_{C^{15}O_2} \cdot dt \qquad \text{(i)}$$

where $\dot{Q}_C$ is the capillary flow to the region. The regional fractional concentration of $C^{15}O_2$ is V/V_A if V is the quantity of $C^{15}O_2$ and V_A is the alveolar gas volume being studied. Then the alveolar $P_{C^{15}O_2}$ for the region is given by:

$$\frac{V(P_B - 47)}{V_A} \qquad \text{(ii)}$$

where P_B is the barometric pressure and 47 mmHg is the water vapour pressure at 37°C.

Substituting (ii) in (i) and re-arranging we have:

$$\frac{dV}{dt} + \frac{\dot{Q}_C}{V_A} \cdot k(P_B - 47)V = 0$$

the solution to which is:

$$V(t) = V(o) \exp\left[-\frac{\dot{Q}_C}{V_A} \cdot k(P_B - 47)t\right]$$

in which $V(t)$ and $V(o)$ are the quantities of $C^{15}O_2$ at times t and zero. (The solution given may be demonstrated along the lines used in Appendix P, p. 684). It follows that:

$$\frac{\dot{Q}_C}{V_A} = \frac{\log_e [V(o)/V(t)]}{k(P_B - 47)t}$$

which is the ratio of capillary blood flow to alveolar gas volume.

Appendix H

Measurement of Blood Volume in a Branching System

Figure H.1 considers an almost instantaneous injection of dye M over a minute period of time Δt. $\dot{Q}$ = flow. Then the concentration of dye in the bolus, $C = M/\dot{Q}\Delta t$. Suppose this bolus moves forward without any further dispersion to the end of the tube in time t. Then it will displace a column of liquid equal to $\dot{Q}t$. And $\dot{Q}t$ equals the volume of liquid in the tube.

Now consider a more complicated model such as that shown in Figure H.2. Here there are two pathways of different cross-sectional area and length. Suppose again that mass M of dye is injected in time Δt. Then the concentration of dye in the initial bolus, C, equals $M/\dot{Q}\Delta t$.

At the moment when the bolus meets the division of the tube, part of it passes down one pathway and part of it down the other. The concentration (C) in the bolus remains unchanged. If $\dot{q}_1$ and $\dot{q}_2$ represent the flow down each pathway and m_1 and m_2 represent the mass of dye which enters each respective pathway, then

$$C = \frac{m_1}{\dot{q}_1\Delta t} = \frac{m_2}{\dot{q}_2\Delta t} = \frac{M}{\dot{Q}\Delta t}$$

Whence it follows that the mass of dye is distributed between the two pathways in proportion to the flow through them. If h_1 and h_2 represent the fraction of total flow passing down the two pathways, then

$$\dot{q}_1 = h_1\dot{Q}$$

and

$$\dot{q}_2 = h_2\dot{Q}$$

But also

$$m_1 = h_1 M$$

and

$$m_2 = h_2 M$$

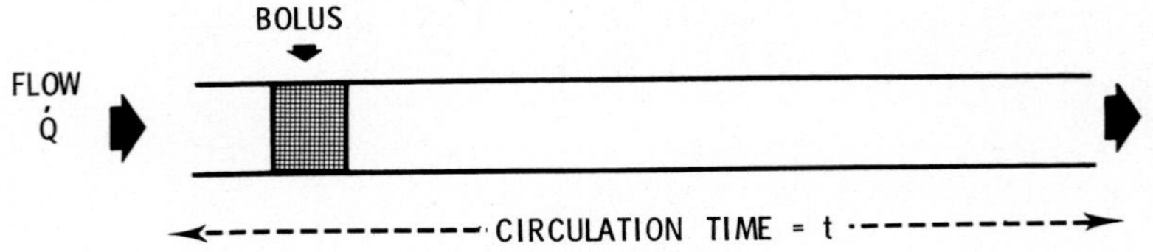

Fig. H.1 Diagram to show passage of a bolus of dye down an unbranched vessel. The symbols are explained in the text.

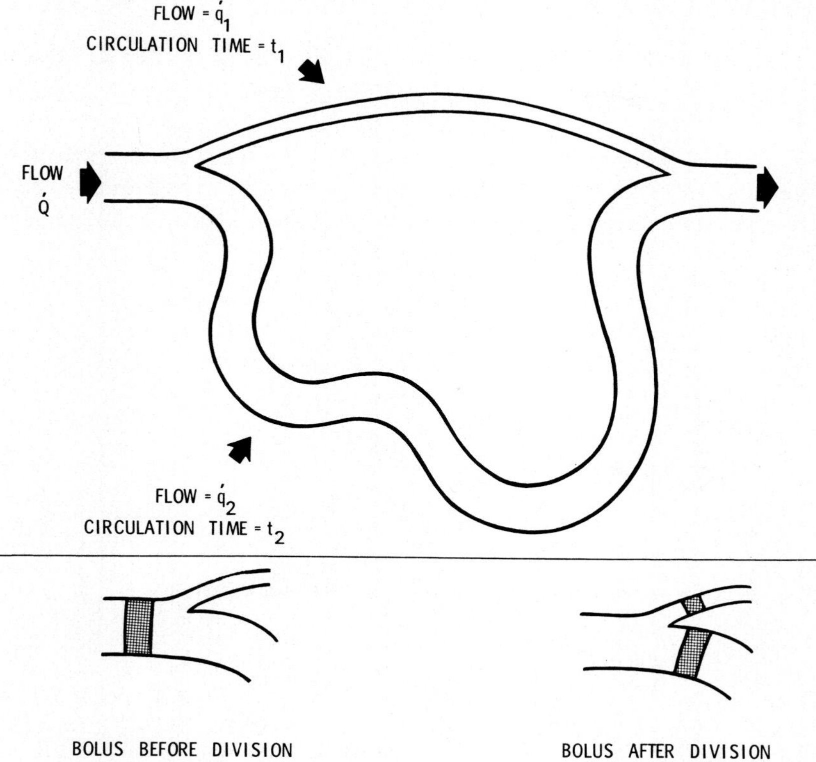

Fig. H.2 Diagram to show passage of a bolus of dye down two unequal divisions of a blood vessel.

From previous considerations the volume of liquid in the short pathway (v_1), equals q_1t_1 when t_1 is the time taken for the bolus to reach the exit. Similarly

$$v_2 = q_2t_2$$

Thus the total volume of the system (V)

$$\begin{aligned}
&= v_1 + v_2 \\
&= \dot{q}_1t_1 + \dot{q}_2t_2 \\
&= \dot{Q}h_1t_1 + \dot{Q}h_2t_2 \\
&= \dot{Q}(h_1t_1 + h_2t_2) \\
&= \dot{Q}\left(\frac{m_1t_1}{M} + \frac{m_2t_2}{M}\right) \\
&= \dot{Q}\bar{t}
\end{aligned}$$

when $\bar{t}$ is the mean circulation time as defined on p. 106.

Appendix I

Derivation of Left Ventricular Dye-Curve used in the Calculation of Mean Pulmonary Transit Time*

The primary model consists of a right ventricular chamber emptying directly into a left ventricular chamber without an intervening pulmonary circulation (Fig. I.1). An instantaneous injection of dye is introduced into the right ventricle.

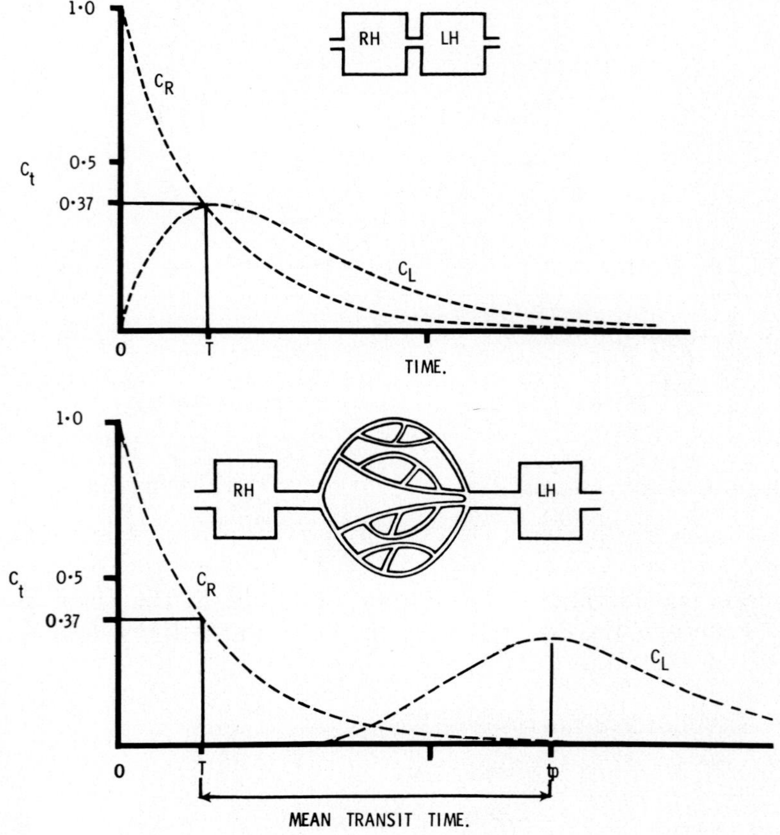

Fig. I.1 Modified from Giuntini, C. (1971) *Bull. Physio-Path. Resp.*, 7, 1125.

The model shown in the upper diagram consists of a left ventricle emerging immediately from a right ventricle with no intervening pulmonary circulation. The ventricles have equal volumes. An instantaneous injection of indicator is made into the right ventricle. The subsequent dilution curve in the right ventricle is exponential (C_R). The dilution curve in the left ventricle (C_L) reaches a maximum at the turnover time of each ventricle (T).

In the lower diagram the two ventricles are separated by the pulmonary circulation. The mean circulation time in the pulmonary circulation is now derived from the time of maximal concentration in the left ventricle (t_P) minus the turnover time in the right ventricle (T).

*Chapter 8, p. 109

$C_{(R,t)}$ and $C_{(L,t)}$ = concentrations of dye in the right and left ventricles at time t.
$V_{(R)}$ and $V_{(L)}$ = volumes of right and left ventricles.
$\dot{Q}$ = flow of blood.

The concentration of dye in the right ventricle follows an exponential wash-out curve which may be derived in a similar way to that used in Appendix P:

$$C_{(R,t)} = C_{(R,0)}\, e^{-\dot{Q}t/V_{(R)}} \tag{i}$$

$$dC_{(L)} = \frac{\dot{Q}C_{(R)}\,dt - \dot{Q}C_{(L)}\,dt}{V_{(L)}}$$

$$= \frac{\dot{Q}}{V_{(L)}}(C_{(R)}\,dt - C_{(L)}\,dt)$$

Substituting for $C_{(R)}$ from (i):

$$dC_{(L)} = \frac{\dot{Q}}{V_{(L)}} \cdot C_{(R,0)} \cdot e^{-\dot{Q}t/V_{(R)}} \cdot dt - \frac{\dot{Q}}{V_{(L)}} \cdot C_{(L)}\,dt.$$

If $V_{(L)} = V_{(R)} = V$, then by re-arranging:

$$\frac{dC_{(L)}}{dt} \cdot e^{\dot{Q}t/V} + \frac{\dot{Q}}{V} e^{\dot{Q}t/V} \cdot C_{(L)} = \frac{\dot{Q}}{V} \cdot C_{(R,0)}$$

$$\frac{dC_{(L)}}{dt} \cdot e^{\dot{Q}t/V} + C_{(L)} \cdot \frac{d(e^{\dot{Q}t/V})}{dt} = \frac{\dot{Q}C_{(R,0)}}{V}$$

$$\frac{d(C_{(L)}e^{\dot{Q}t/V})}{dt} = \frac{\dot{Q}C_{(R,0)}}{V}$$

$$C_{(L,t)}e^{\dot{Q}t/V} = \int \frac{\dot{Q}C_{(R,0)}}{V}\,dt$$

$$= \frac{\dot{Q}C_{(R,0)}t}{V} + K \qquad \text{(integration constant)}$$

When t = 0, $C_{(L)} = 0$ and K = 0. Thus,

$$C_{(L,t)} = \frac{\dot{Q}t\,C_{(R,0)}\,e^{-\dot{Q}t/V}}{V} \tag{ii}$$

$$\frac{dC_{(L)}}{dt} = \frac{\dot{Q}}{V} \cdot C_{(R,0)} \cdot e^{-\dot{Q}t/V} \cdot (1 - \dot{Q}t/V)$$

When the concentration of dye is at its peak, $dC_{(L)}/dt = 0$. Thus

$$1 - \frac{\dot{Q}t}{V} = 0$$

and

$$t = \frac{V}{\dot{Q}} = T, \qquad \text{the turnover time} \tag{iii}$$

Thus $C_{(L)}$ reaches a maximum at the turnover time of each ventricle.

Appendix J

The Relation Between the Distensibility of a Vessel and the Extensibility of its Wall

Where, as in the walls of arteries, there is a curved relation between tension and length, it is impossible to describe the extensibility by one coefficient. Any index of the proportion in which length varies with a changing tension will itself be dependent on the degree of stretch.

Several indices might be used, although none is entirely satisfactory. The simplest index would be

$$\frac{\text{Change in length } (dl \text{ cm})}{\text{Change in tension } (dT \text{ dyn} \cdot \text{cm}^{-1})}$$

but this has little meaning without a knowledge of the absolute length of the substance (*e.g.* arterial circumference) to which the index applies.

Classically, the coefficient should be the relation between the tension and the total degree of stretch (Δl) expressed as a fraction of the unstretched length (l_0):

$$\frac{\Delta l}{l_0} \cdot \frac{1}{T}$$ (p. 43)

However, except at the unstretched length itself, this coefficient gives no indication of the immediate way in which length is varying with tension at a particular point on the length–tension diagram.

A third possibility is to relate the change in tension with the change in length expressed as a fraction of the existing absolute length:

$$\frac{dl}{l\,dt}$$

This provides a figure which is not dependent on absolute length and one which is immediately appropriate to a particular point on the length–tension diagram. On the other hand, it gives no indication of the degree of change from the unstretched length. For our present purpose, this last coefficient of extensibility is the most convenient and will be designated ε.

Similar considerations apply to the curved relation between volume and pressure in a vessel, and the most convenient coefficient of distensibility for the present purpose is:

$$B = \frac{dQ}{Q\,dP}$$

where Q is volume (ml) and P is pressure (dyn · cm^{-2}).

Consider a cylindrical blood vessel of variable radius r and constant length h. The volume of blood inside the vessel is:

$$Q = \pi r^2 h$$

and

$$\frac{dQ}{dr} = 2\pi rh \qquad \text{(i)}$$

Then

$$\varepsilon = \frac{2\pi\, dr}{2\pi r\, dT}$$

and

$$\frac{dr}{dT} = \varepsilon r \qquad \text{(ii)}$$

From (i) and (ii):

$$\begin{aligned} \frac{dQ}{dT} &= \frac{dQ}{dr} \cdot \frac{dr}{dT} \\ &= 2\pi r^2 h\varepsilon \\ &= 2Q\varepsilon \qquad \text{(iii)} \end{aligned}$$

From Laplace's Law:

$$T = Pr$$

where P is the pressure inside the vessel (p. 52)
Differentiating:

$$dT = r\,dP + P\,dr$$

$$\therefore\ dP = \frac{dT - P\,dr}{r}$$

and

$$\begin{aligned} \frac{dP}{dT} &= \frac{1 - P\dfrac{dr}{dT}}{r} \\ &= \frac{1 - P\varepsilon r}{r} \qquad \text{(iv)} \end{aligned}$$

By definition:

$$\begin{aligned} B &= \frac{dQ}{Q\,dP} \\ &= \frac{1}{Q} \cdot \frac{dQ}{dT} \cdot \frac{dT}{dP} \end{aligned}$$

Thus, from (iii) and (iv):

$$B = \frac{1}{Q} \cdot 2Q\varepsilon \cdot \frac{r}{1 - P\varepsilon r}$$

$$\therefore \; B = \frac{2}{\dfrac{1}{\varepsilon r} - P}$$

Appendix K

Derivation of Hydraulic Impedance

As has been discussed in Chapter 10, the concept of impedance is essentially a geometric one which describes the relation between the pressure modulus (P), the flow modulus ($\dot{Q}$) and the phase angle difference $(\varphi - \psi)$ in the shape of a triangle (Fig. 10.3, p. 141). The mathematical description of such a geometrical relation involves the use of the quantity

$$i = \sqrt{-1}$$

on the properties of which it is necessary briefly to digress.

Since there is no known number which, when squared, will give a negative quantity, the quantity, i, is referred to as an 'imaginary' quantity. It is, however, susceptible to the usual laws of algebra so that $i^2 = -1$, $i^3 = -i$, $i^4 = +1$, $i^5 = i$ and so on. Figure K.1 shows an ordinate of imaginary numbers crossing an abscissa of real numbers at zero. Notice that $+1 \times i = i$ so that multiplying a real number by i has the effect of turning the axis through 90°. Similarly $i \times i = -1$, which has turned the axis through a further 90°; and $-1 \times i = -i$, which has turned the axis through a further 90°; and $-i \times i = +1$, which has returned us to the starting point.

Thus if we want to describe two quantities x and y which are set at right angles to each other as in Figure K.2 we can write the function

$$x + yi$$

The expression does not imply that the quantities are capable of being simply added to each other. Neither does it imply that the length of the hypotenuse, $\overline{OG}$, is equal to $x + yi$ since, from Pythagoras' theorem, it is evidently equal to $\sqrt{x^2 + y^2}$. The expression should be read as meaning 'x with y set at right angles in an anti-clockwise direction', which defines the hypotenuse OG in direction as well as length. Such an expression, which contains both real and imaginary components, is called a 'complex quantity'. It is a way of defining mathematically a line in space.

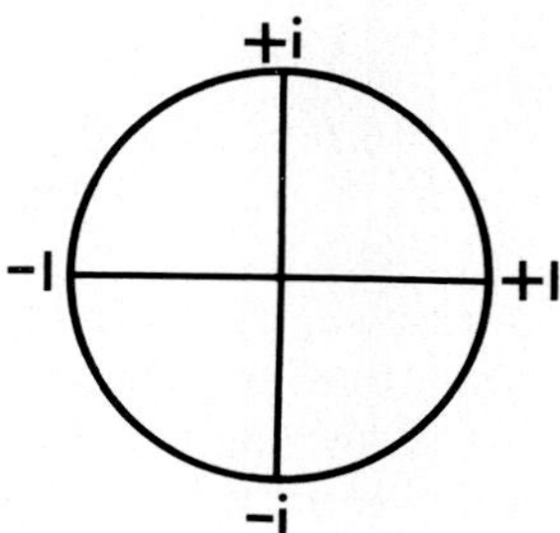

Fig. K.1 Relation between real and imaginary axes. See text.

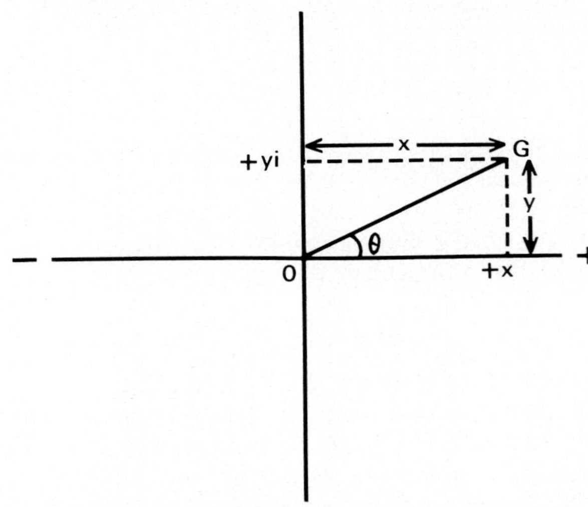

Fig. K.2 Geometrical representation of $x+yi$.

Multiplication of such a complex quantity by i can be carried out in the usual manner so that,

$$(x+yi)i = xi-y$$

This is represented as line OH in Figure K.3. Notice that, once more, the process of multiplication has caused the line representing the complex quantity to move through a right angle in an anti-clockwise direction from OG to OH.

If in Figure K.2 the angle between OG and the real axis is denoted θ, it follows that

$$x = \text{OG} \cos \theta$$

and

$$y = \text{OG} \sin \theta$$

so that

$$x+yi = \text{OG} (\cos \theta + i \sin \theta)$$

If we apply this formula to Figure 5.1, p. 58 we can describe the arm OG by

$$r(\cos \theta + i \sin \theta)$$

where r is the radius of the circle. This new expression is also a complex quantity in which $r \cos \theta$ is the real part and $ir \sin \theta$ is the imaginary part. It is the real part which describes the motion of a projection of OG on the abscissa.

The movement of G round the circumference depends on a continual increase in the magnitude of θ. This angle will increase at the rate of ω, the angular velocity expressed in radians sec^{-1}. Thus, after time t, θ will have increased by ωt radians. In addition, θ is contributed to by a constant factor which represents the phase angle. If, as before, the phase angle for pressure is represented by φ and the phase angle for flow is represented by ψ then

$$\theta = \omega t + \varphi \qquad \text{for pressure}$$

and

$$\theta = \omega t + \psi \qquad \text{for flow}$$

As will be recalled from Figure 10.3, p. 141, the radius of the circle represents the amplitudes of pressure (P) or flow ($\dot{Q}$) so that

$$\text{pressure arm} = P[\cos(\omega t + \varphi) + i \sin(\omega t + \varphi)]$$

$$\text{flow arm} = \dot{Q}[\cos(\omega t + \psi) + i \sin(\omega t + \psi)]$$

Impedance will be given by:

$$Z = \frac{\text{pressure arm}}{\text{flow arm}} = \frac{P}{\dot{Q}} \frac{[\cos(\omega t + \varphi) + i \sin(\omega t + \varphi)]}{[\cos(\omega t + \psi) + i \sin(\omega t + \psi)]}$$

Now it can be shown by Maclaurin's theorem that

$$\cos x + i \sin x = \exp(ix)$$

So that,

$$Z = \frac{P}{\dot{Q}} \cdot \frac{\exp[i(\omega t + \varphi)]}{\exp[i(\omega t + \psi)]}$$

$$Z = \frac{P}{\dot{Q}} \exp[i(\varphi - \psi)] \qquad \text{(i)}$$

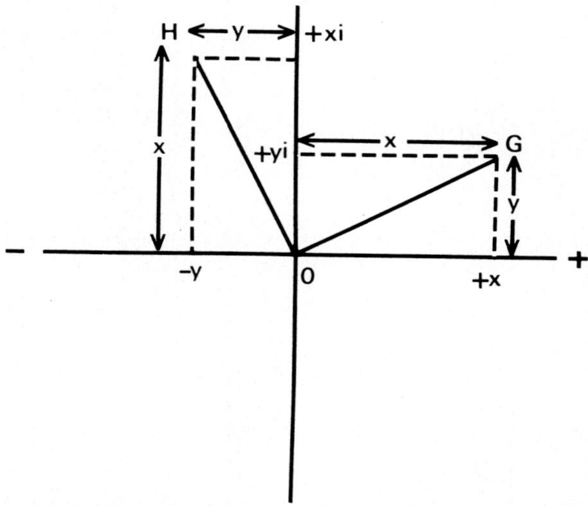

Fig. K.3 Effect of multiplying $x + yi$ by i is to move OG to OH.

and

$$Z = \frac{P}{\dot{Q}} [\cos (\varphi - \psi) + i \sin (\varphi + \psi)] \qquad \text{(ii)}$$

It will be noticed that the term ωt has disappeared from the final expression.

The expression of impedance is, as would be expected, also a complex quantity. The real part is

$$\frac{P}{\dot{Q}} \cos (\varphi - \psi)$$

while the imaginary part is

$$\frac{P}{\dot{Q}}\, i \sin (\varphi - \psi)$$

If there is no phase angle between pressure and flow $\sin (\varphi - \psi)$ becomes zero and $\cos (\varphi - \psi)$ becomes unity, so that

$$Z = \frac{P}{\dot{Q}}$$

It will be recalled, however, that the existence of a phase angle is due to the presence of a reactance. If there is no reactance, the system functions as a pure resistance and $P/\dot{Q}$ is the conventional formula for resistance (provided that the magnitude of the venous pressure is ignored).

In the case of a purely capacitative reactance, the flow wave precedes the pressure wave by 90°, so that $\varphi - \psi$ becomes $-90°$ while $\sin (\varphi - \psi)$ becomes -1 and $\cos (\varphi - \psi)$ becomes zero. Thus

$$Z = -\frac{P}{\dot{Q}}\, i$$

Similarly, in the case of a purely inertial reactance

$$Z = \frac{P}{\dot{Q}}\, i$$

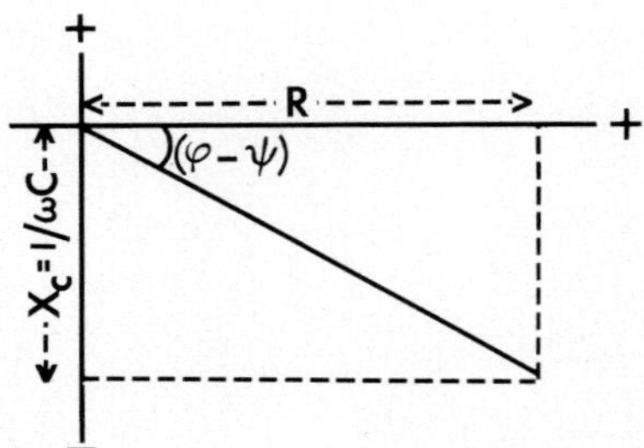

Fig. K.4 Geometrical representation of a combination of resistance (R) and capacitative reactance (X_C).

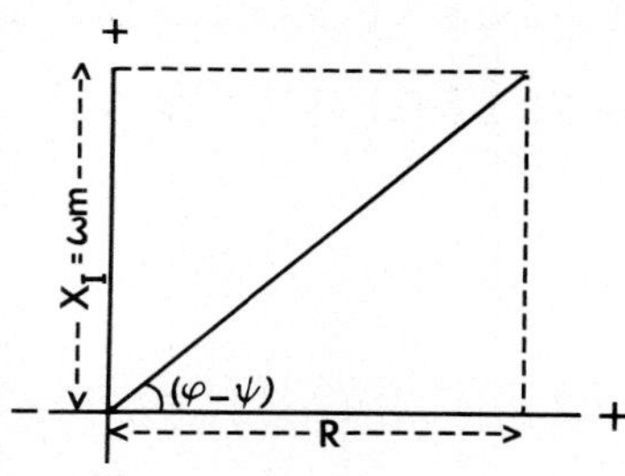

Fig. K.5 Geometrical representation of a combination of resistance (R) and inertial reactance (X_I).

It will be seen, therefore, that the real part of impedance describes its resistance component while the imaginary part describes its reactance component. So that we may write:

$$Z = R + iX$$

where X is the reactance. Figure K.4 shows a combination of resistance and capacitative reactance. Resistance and reactance are placed at right angles. Since

$$X_C = 1/\omega C \quad \text{(p. 139)}$$

$$Z = R + 1/i\omega C$$

Figure K.5 shows a similar combination of resistance and inertial reactance. Since

$$X_I = \omega m \quad \text{(p. 140)}$$

$$Z = R + i\omega m$$

When both capacitative and inertial reactances exist together (Fig. K.6) they have to be added albegraically, so that

$$X = X_I - X_C$$

and

$$Z = R + i(\omega m - 1/\omega C)$$

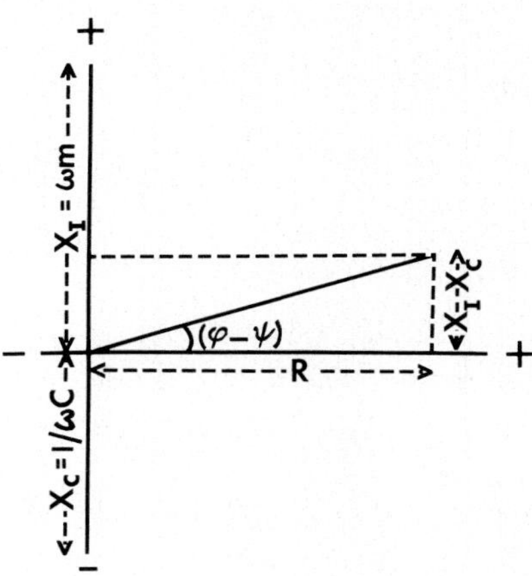

Fig. K.6 Geometrical representation of a combination of resistance (R) inertial reactance (X_I) and capacitative reactance (X_C).

Appendix L

Effects of Damping and Reflection on Impedance

Damping

The viscosity of the blood and the visco-elastic properties of the walls of blood vessels cause damping of the propagating waves. There is an attenuation of the amplitude of the wave and a change in the phase angle.

Consider a homogeneous tube which extends indefinitely and along which a sinusoidal pressure wave is propagated. Then the magnitude of the pressure at time, t, and distance, x, from the origin will be given by:

$$\mathrm{p}(t, x) = \mathrm{P}[\cos(\omega t + \varphi) + i \sin(\omega t + \varphi)] \quad \text{(i)}$$

$$= \mathrm{P} \exp [i(\omega t + \varphi)] \quad \text{(ii)}$$

where P is the modulus of pressure, ω is the angular velocity and φ is the phase angle at the commencement (see App. K, p. 673). Damping will affect the magnitude of the modulus, P, and the angle $(\omega t + \varphi)$. The modulus, P, will be reduced exponentially along the tube, so that P becomes:

$$\mathrm{P} \exp(-k_1 x) \quad \text{(iii)}$$

The angle $(\omega t + \varphi)$ will be decreased as the wave passes along the tube so that it becomes:

$$(\omega t + \varphi) - k_2 x \quad \text{(iv)}$$

where k_2 is the rate of change of angle with distance. Thus

$$k_2 = \frac{d(\omega t + \varphi)}{dx}$$

But

$$\frac{\mathrm{d}(\omega t + \varphi)}{dx} = \frac{d(\omega t + \varphi)}{dt} \cdot \frac{dt}{dx}$$

$$= \frac{\omega}{v}$$

where v is the forward velocity of the wave. Combining (iii) and (iv) in (i) gives:

$$\mathrm{p}(t, x) = \mathrm{P} \exp(-k_1 x) [\cos(\omega t + \varphi - k_2 x) + i \sin(\omega t + \varphi - k_2 x)]$$

$$= \mathrm{P} \exp [i(\omega t + \varphi - k_2 x) - k_1 x]$$

$$= \mathrm{P} \exp [i(\omega t + \varphi) - (k_1 + i k_2) x]$$

The complex quantity $(k_1 + ik_2)$ may be represented as a single 'propagation' constant, W, in which case:

$$\mathrm{p}(t, x) = \mathrm{P} \exp [i(\omega t + \varphi) - \mathrm{W}x] \qquad \text{(v)}$$

Reflections

Up to now we have considered a vessel of indefinite length and consistent physical properties. When a discontinuity occurs, as in branching, some of the forward-propagating wave ('incident' wave) will be reflected backwards. If $\mathrm{P_a}$ is the amplitude of the incident wave, $\mathrm{P_b}$ the amplitude of the reflected wave and $\mathrm{P_c}$ the amplitude of that portion which is transmitted onwards, then, if we ignore dissipation:

$$\mathrm{P_a} = \mathrm{P_b} + \mathrm{P_c}$$

$$\text{Reflection coefficient (S)} = \mathrm{P_b/P_a}$$

$$\text{Transmission coefficient (H)} = \mathrm{P_c/P_a}$$

Imagine a discontinuity occurring at a distance G down a vessel with otherwise constant wall characteristics, then, from (v), the pressure due to the incident wave at time t and position G:

$$\mathrm{p_a}(t, \mathrm{G}) = \mathrm{P_a} \exp [i(\omega t + \varphi) - \mathrm{WG}]$$

The pressure due to the reflected wave at G will be:

$$\mathrm{p_b}(t, \mathrm{G}) = \mathrm{SP_a} \exp [i(\omega t + \varphi) - \mathrm{WG}]$$

The pressure due to the reflected wave at a distance, x, down the tube from its origin will be:

$$\mathrm{p_b}(t, x) = \mathrm{SP_a} \exp [i(\omega t + \varphi) - \mathrm{WG} - \mathrm{W}(\mathrm{G} - x)]$$

The total pressure at x will be:

$$\begin{aligned} \mathrm{p}(t, x) &= \mathrm{p_a}(t, x) + \mathrm{p_b}(t, x) \\ &= \mathrm{P_a} \exp [i(\omega t + \varphi) - \mathrm{W}x] + \mathrm{SP_a} \exp [i(\omega t + \varphi) - \mathrm{WG} - \mathrm{W}(\mathrm{G} - x)] \\ &= \mathrm{P_a} \exp [i(\omega t + \varphi) - \mathrm{W}x]\{1 + \mathrm{S} \exp [-2\mathrm{W}(\mathrm{G} - x)]\} \qquad \text{(vi)} \end{aligned}$$

Since the total pressure at x and time t is

$$\begin{aligned} \mathrm{p}(t, x) &= \mathrm{p_a}(t, x) \left\{1 + \frac{\mathrm{p_b}(t, x)}{\mathrm{p_a}(t, x)}\right\} \\ &= \mathrm{p_a}(t, x)[1 + \mathrm{S}(x)] \end{aligned}$$

it follows from (vi) that

$$\mathrm{S}(x) = \mathrm{S} \exp [-2\mathrm{W}(\mathrm{G} - x)]$$

and

$$\mathrm{p}(t, x) = \mathrm{P_a} \exp [i(\omega t + \varphi) - \mathrm{W}x][1 + \mathrm{S}(x)]$$

The flow wave at x may be described in similar terms:

$$\dot{q}(t, x) = \dot{Q}_a \exp [i(\omega t + \psi) - Wx][1 - S(x)]$$

Hence the impedance at x is:

$$Z(x) = \frac{P_a}{\dot{Q}_a} \exp [i(\varphi - \psi)] \cdot \frac{1 + S(x)}{1 - S(x)} \qquad \text{(vii)}$$

If there were no discontinuity at G and no reflections in the system, then

$$S(x) = 0$$

and

$$Z = \frac{P_a}{\dot{Q}_a} \exp [i(\varphi - \psi)]$$

This value for impedance is that given in Appendix K, equation (i). It is independent of x, the distance along the axis of the vessel, and is called the 'characteristic impedance' of the vessel, Z_0. Thus we may write, from (vii):

$$Z(x) = Z_0 \frac{1 + S(x)}{1 - S(x)}$$

Similarly the impedance at the point of discontinuity,

$$Z(G) = Z_0 \frac{1 + S(G)}{1 - S(G)}$$

and

$$S(G) = \frac{1 - Z_0/Z(G)}{1 + Z_0/Z(G)}$$

The nature of the reflection coefficient, therefore, depends on the relation between the characteristic impedance, Z_0, and the impedance at the discontinuity, Z(G). In the case of a closed termination to the vessel, Z(G) becomes infinite and S(G) = 1. In the case of a wide-open termination to the vessel, Z(G) becomes zero and S(G) = −1. Since

$$p(G) = p_a(G)[1 + S(G)]$$

and

$$\dot{q}(G) = \dot{q}_a(G)[1 - S(G)]$$

a closed termination means that $p(G) = 2p_a(G)$ and $\dot{q}(G) = 0$. Similarly an open termination means that $p(G) = 0$ and $\dot{q}(G) = 2\dot{q}_a(G)$.

Appendix M
Estimation of Interstitial Space by Indicator Dilution

Consider a volume (V_i) of interstitial space labelled at $t = 0$ with a mass (m) of indicator to produce a concentration (C_{i_0}) (Fig. M.1). The subsequent release of indicator into the capillary represents a frequency function with a mean time $\bar{t}$. According to the conventional calculation $\dot{Q}\bar{t}$ measures V_i, where $\dot{Q}$ is the flow through the capillary.

Let

$$D = \text{diffusion factor}$$

i.e. the mass of dye passing in unit time from V_i into the capillary per unit difference in concentrations C_i and C_c (the concentration in the capillary). This takes into account the diffusion constant, molecular size, permeabilities of the different structures and geometry of the system. D has the dimensions of volume/time.

We shall suppose that instantaneous mixing occurs within the capillary space and V_i:

$$dm = (C_{i_t} - C_{c_t})D\,dt \qquad \text{(i)}$$

$$C_{c_t} = \frac{dm}{\dot{Q}\,dt} \qquad \text{(ii)}$$

Substituting for C_{c_t} from (ii) into (i):

$$\frac{dm}{dt} = \left(C_{i_t} - \frac{1}{\dot{Q}} \cdot \frac{dm}{dt}\right)D$$

$$= C_{i_t}D - \frac{D}{\dot{Q}} \cdot \frac{dm}{dt}$$

$$\frac{dm}{dt} = \frac{C_{i_t}D}{1 + \dfrac{D}{\dot{Q}}} = \left(\frac{\dot{Q}D}{\dot{Q}+D}\right)C_{i_t} = kC_{i_t} \qquad \text{(iii)}$$

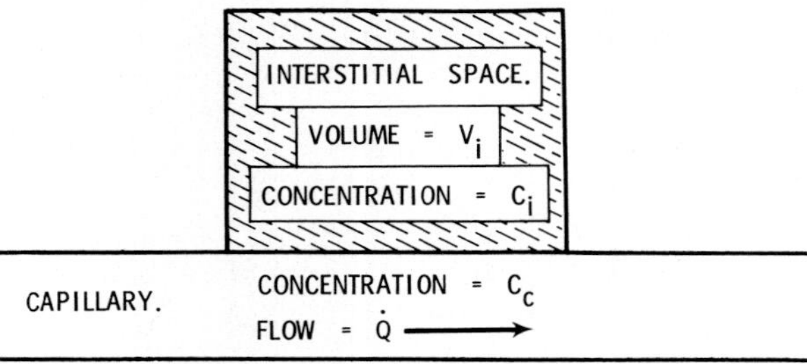

$$C_{i_{t/n}} = \frac{C_{i_0}V_i - kC_{i_0}t/n}{V_i} = C_{i_0}\left(1 - \frac{k}{V_i}\cdot\frac{t}{n}\right)$$

$$C_{i_{2t/n}} = \frac{C_{i_{t/n}}V_i - kC_{i_{t/n}}t/n}{V_i} = C_{i_{t/n}}\left(1 - \frac{k}{V_i}\cdot\frac{t}{n}\right)$$

$$= C_{i_0}\left(1 - \frac{k}{V_i}\cdot\frac{t}{n}\right)^2$$

$$\therefore\ C_{i_{nt/n}} = C_{i_t} = C_{i_0}\left(1 - \frac{k}{V_i}\cdot\frac{t}{n}\right)^n = C_{i_0}\, e^{-(k/V_i)t} \qquad \text{(iv)}$$

when n becomes infinite.

Substituting for C_{i_t} from (iv) into (iii):

$$\frac{dm}{dt} = kC_{i_0}\, e^{-(k/V_i)t}$$

$$t\, dm = kC_{i_0} t\, e^{-(k/V_i)t}\, dt$$

$$\int_0^\infty t\, dm = kC_{i_0}\int_0^\infty t\, e^{-(k/V_i)t}\, dt \qquad \text{(v)}$$

$$\int u\cdot\frac{dv}{dt}\cdot dt = uv - \int v\cdot\frac{du}{dt}\cdot dt$$

Let $u = t$ and $\frac{dv}{dt} = e^{-(k/V_i)t}$

Then

$$\frac{du}{dt} = 1$$

and

$$v = \int e^{-(k/V_i)t}\, dt = -\frac{V_i}{k}\cdot e^{-(k/V_i)t} + K_1$$

where K_1 is a constant of integration. Thus

$$\int t\, e^{-(k/V_i)t}\, dt = t\left(-\frac{V_i}{k}e^{-(k/V_i)t} + K_1\right) - \int\left(-\frac{V_i}{k}e^{-(k/V_i)t} + K_1\right)dt$$

$$\therefore\ \int t\, e^{-(k/V_i)t}\, dt = t\left(-\frac{V_i}{k}e^{-(k/V_i)t} + K_1\right) - \left(\frac{V_i}{k}\right)^2 e^{-(k/V_i)t} - K_1 t + K_2$$

$$= -t \cdot \frac{V_i}{k} \cdot e^{-(k/V_i)t} - \left(\frac{V_i}{k}\right)^2 e^{-(k/V_i)t} + K_2$$

$$\int_0^\infty t\, e^{-(k/V_i)t}\, dt = \left(\frac{V_i}{k}\right)^2 \qquad \text{(vi)}$$

Substituting (vi) into (v):

$$\int_0^\infty t\, dm = kC_{i_0}\left(\frac{V_i}{k}\right)^2 = \frac{C_{i_0}V_i^2}{k}$$

$$\bar{t} = \frac{1}{m}\int_0^\infty t\, dm = \frac{C_{i_0}V_i^2}{mk}$$

But

$$m = C_{i_0}V_i$$

$$\therefore \bar{t} = \frac{V_i}{k} = \left(\frac{\dot{Q}+D}{\dot{Q}D}\right)V_i$$

$$\therefore \dot{Q}\bar{t} = \left(\frac{\dot{Q}+D}{D}\right)\cdot V_i$$

$$\therefore \dot{Q}\bar{t} = \left(1 + \frac{\dot{Q}}{D}\right)\cdot V_i$$

It follows that $\dot{Q}\bar{t}$ approaches V_i as D becomes very large relative to $\dot{Q}$. Thus, $\dot{Q}\bar{t}$ gives a realistic estimate of V_i only when rates of diffusion are extremely high relative to flow. Otherwise $\dot{Q}\bar{t}$ will over-estimate V_i.

Of course, in the lung, as D becomes low, the magnitude V_i itself decreases since little indicator will have crossed the capillary wall from the blood to the tissue space. Thus, the method tends to over-estimate the smaller values of V_i.

Appendix N

Calculation of the Physiological Dead-Space

Expired air consists of a mixture of 'ideal' alveolar and dead-space air. The quantity of a particular gas, X, in the expired air is equal to its fractional concentration, F_{E_X}, multiplied by the volume of expired air, V_E. Thus the rate of expiration of X is $\dot{V}_E F_{E_X}$. This consists of a contribution from alveolar ventilation, $\dot{V}_A F_{A_X}$, and a contribution from dead-space ventilation, $\dot{V}_D F_{D_X}$. The concentration of X in the dead space, F_{D_X} is the same as the inspired concentration, F_{I_X}. Thus

$$\dot{V}_E F_{E_X} = \dot{V}_A F_{A_X} + \dot{V}_D F_{I_X}$$

Since $\dot{V}_E = \dot{V}_A + \dot{V}_D$, we may write

$$\dot{V}_E F_{E_X} = (\dot{V}_E - \dot{V}_D) F_{A_X} + \dot{V}_D F_{I_X}$$

$$\dot{V}_D (F_{A_X} - F_{I_X}) = \dot{V}_E (F_{A_X} - F_{E_X})$$

$$\dot{V}_D / \dot{V}_E = (F_{A_X} - F_{E_X}) / (F_{A_X} - F_{I_X})$$

At the same atmospheric pressure and temperature the fractional concentration of X in the gas phase is proportional to its partial pressure. Thus we may write

$$\dot{V}_D / \dot{V}_E = (P_{A_X} - P_{E_X}) / (P_{A_X} - P_{I_X}) \qquad \text{(i)}$$

In the case of carbon dioxide, its inspired concentration is usually zero and the arterial P_{CO_2} is assumed to approximate the 'ideal' alveolar P_{CO_2}. Thus

$$\dot{V}_D / \dot{V}_E = (Pa_{CO_2} - P_{E_{CO_2}}) / Pa_{CO_2} \qquad \text{(ii)}$$

from which the physiological dead space ventilation may be calculated.

Since the ventilation each minute is equal to the tidal volume (V_T) multiplied by the frequency, we may also write

$$V_D / V_T = (Pa_{CO_2} - P_{E_{CO_2}}) / Pa_{CO_2} \qquad \text{(iii)}$$

from which the physiological dead space (V_D) may be calculated.

Appendix O

Calculation of the Alveolar Carbon Monoxide Tension ($P_{A_{CO}}$)

This calculation is required for the steady state methods of measuring the diffusing capacity of the lung (p. 637).

Substituting CO for X in equation (i) of Appendix N, we may write

$$\dot{V}_D/\dot{V}_E = (P_{A_{CO}} - P_{E_{CO}})/(P_{A_{CO}} - P_{I_{CO}}) \qquad \text{(i)}$$

Substituting CO_2 for X in the same equation we may write

$$\dot{V}_D/\dot{V}_E = (P_{A_{CO_2}} - P_{E_{CO_2}})/P_{A_{CO_2}} \qquad \text{(ii)}$$

Equating (i) and (ii):

$$(P_{A_{CO}} - P_{E_{CO}})/(P_{A_{CO}} - P_{I_{CO}}) = (P_{A_{CO_2}} - P_{E_{CO_2}})/P_{A_{CO_2}}$$

Re-arranging we have:

$$P_{A_{CO}} = P_{I_{CO}} - (P_{A_{CO_2}}/P_{E_{CO_2}})(P_{I_{CO}} - P_{E_{CO}})$$

The two unknown quantities are $P_{A_{CO}}$ and $P_{A_{CO_2}}$. In practice $P_{A_{CO_2}}$ is replaced by arterial P_{CO_2} (Filley method) or by end-tidal P_{CO_2} (Bates method).

Appendix P

The Uptake of Carbon Monoxide from the Alveoli in the Breath-Holding Method for Measuring $D_{L_{CO}}$

We shall consider an initial fractional concentration F_{A_O} of carbon monoxide in an alveolar volume V_A at a barometric pressure P_B. The vapour pressure of water at 37°C is 47 mmHg. The diffusing capacity of the lungs for carbon monoxide is D_L.

After a very small interval of time, t/n, the fractional concentration of carbon monoxide in the alveoli has fallen to $F_{A_{t/n}}$ since a quantity of carbon monoxide

$$\left[F_{A_O}(P_B - 47)D_L \frac{t}{n}\right]$$

has diffused out of the alveoli. Thus:

$$F_{A_{t/n}} = \frac{F_{A_O}V_A - F_{A_O}(P_B - 47)D_L \frac{t}{n}}{V_A}$$

$$= F_{A_O}\left[1 - \frac{(P_B - 47)D_L}{V_A} \cdot \frac{t}{n}\right]$$

Similarly, the alveolar concentration of carbon monoxide after a further period of time, t/n, is:

$$F_{A_{2t/n}} = F_{A_{t/n}}\left[1 - \frac{(P_B - 47)D_L}{V_A} \cdot \frac{t}{n}\right]$$

$$= F_{A_O}\left[1 - \frac{(P_B - 47)D_L}{V_A} \cdot \frac{t}{n}\right]^2$$

At the end of time, *t*, the alveolar concentration of carbon monoxide is:

$$F_{A_{nt/n}} = F_{A_t} = F_{A_O}\left[1 - \frac{(P_B - 47)D_L}{V_A} \cdot \frac{t}{n}\right]^n$$

Now, when n becomes infinite,

$$\left(1 + \frac{a}{n}\right)^n = \exp(a)$$

Hence,

$$F_{A_t} = F_{A_O} \cdot \exp\left[-(P_B - 47)D_L \cdot t/V_A\right]$$

Index

Page numbers in bold type refer to illustrations or tables. Throughout, HPVD = hypertensive pulmonary vascular disease

C

E

F

H

L

M

Q

R